HISTORIÆ NATURALIS CLASSICA

EDIDERUNT

J. CRAMER ET H. K. SWANN

TOMUS XXVII

THE FLOWERING PLANTS
OF AFRICA

BY

FR. THONNER

REPRINT 1962

BY J. CRAMER · WEINHEIM

WHELDON & WESLEY, LTD AND HAFNER PUBLISHING CO.
CODICOTE, HERTS.   NEW YORK, N.Y.

THE FLOWERING PLANTS
OF AFRICA

BY

FR. THONNER

REPRINT 1962

BY J. CRAMER · WEINHEIM

WHELDON & WESLEY, LTD AND HAFNER PUBLISHING CO.
CODICOTE, HERTS.   NEW YORK, N.Y.

PRINTED IN GERMANY

THE

FLOWERING PLANTS OF AFRICA

THE
FLOWERING PLANTS
OF AFRICA

AN ANALYTICAL KEY TO THE GENERA
OF AFRICAN PHANEROGAMS

BY

FR. THONNER

WITH 150 PLATES AND A MAP

DULAU & CO., LTD.
37 SOHO SQUARE, LONDON
1915

PREFACE

THE flora of Africa being now comparatively well known, the author of the present work considered the time opportune to present to the public an analytical key for determining in an easy way the generic name of every phanerogamous plant growing wild, whether indigenous or naturalized, or cultivated upon a large scale within the geographical limits of Africa including the islands.

The names and limits of the genera and families adopted in this work are those accepted in ENGLER & PRANTL'S " Die natürlichen Pflanzenfamilien," the most recent work containing the description of all genera of flowering plants, and its supplement " Genera Siphonogamarum " by DALLA TORRE & HARMS.

As the present work is intended for the use not only of botanists, but also of colonists and travellers in Africa, who take an interest in botany, I have used, wherever it was possible, as distinctive characters, those which are visible to the naked eye in a plant in flower, being careful, however, not to deviate too much from the natural system.

Besides the diagnostic characters of the genera, I have also indicated the approximative number of the species described to the end of the year 1910, their geographical distribution, their uses, and their more important synonyms.

As to the terms used in indicating the geographical distribution of African plants, " North Africa " (including North-west- and North-east Africa) means all northern extratropical Africa, " South Africa " (including South-west- and South-east Africa) southern extratropical Africa, " tropical Africa " Africa within the tropics, including all islands, whereas the continent of Africa within the tropics including only the small islands in the proximity of the coast, is designated by " Central Africa."

The present work was originally published in German under the title " Die Blütenpflanzen Africas " (Berlin, R. Friedländer & Sohn, 1908). A new edition being desirable, I have preferred the English language, and I am indebted to Dr. A. B. RENDLE, of the British Museum, for revising my translation.

The plates were drawn by the Vienna artist JOSEPH FLEISCHMANN from herbarium specimens kindly lent from the collections of the Hofmuseum at Vienna and the Jardin botanique de l'Etat at Brussels by their respective keepers Dr. A. ZAHLBRUCKNER and Dr. E. DE WILDEMAN. Drawings already published have been used for a few plates only; these are duly indicated.

FRANZ THONNER.

VIENNA (AUSTRIA), September 1913.

LIST OF PRINCIPAL WORKS CONSULTED

A. ENGLER & K. PRANTL, Die natürlichen Pflanzenfamilien (Leipzig, 1889—1908).
C G. DE DALLA TORRE & H. HARMS, Genera Siphonogamarum (Leipzig, 1900—1907).
A. ENGLER, Syllabus der Pflanzenfamilien, 6. ed. (Berlin, 1909).
— Das Pflanzenreich (Leipzig, 1900—1910).
— Monographien afrikanischer Pflanzenfamilien und -gattungen (Leipzig, 1898—1904).
— Die Vegetation Afrikas (Berlin, 1908—1910).
G. BENTHAM & J. D. HOOKER, Genera plantarum (London ,1862—1883).
J. D. HOOKER & B. D. JACKSON, Index Kewensis plantarum phanerogamarum (Oxford 1895—1908).
A. DE CANDOLLE, Prodromus systematis naturalis regni vegetabilis (Paris 1824—1873).
C. S. KUNTH, Enumeratio plantarum (Stuttgart, 1833—1850).
G. WALPERS, Repertorium botanices systematicae (Leipzig, 1842—1847).
— Annales botanices systematicae (Leipzig, 1848—1868).
A. & C. DE CANDOLLE, Monographiae phanerogamarum (Paris, 1878—1896).
H. BAILLON, Histoire des plantes (Paris, 1867—1895).
TH. DURAND & H. SCHINZ, Conspectus florae Africae (Bruxelles, 1895—1898).

R. DELILE, Flore d'Egypte (Paris, 1810).
E. BOISSIER, Flora orientalis (Basel, 1867—1888).
P. ASCHERSON & G. SCHWEINFURTH, Illustrations de la flore d'Egypte (Le Caire, 1887).
E. SICKENBERGER, Contributions à la flore d'Egypte (Le Caire, 1901).
E. DURAND & G. BARRATTE, Florae Libycae prodromus (Genève, 1910).
J. A. BATTANDIER & TRABUT, Flore de l'Algérie (Alger, 1888—1910).
— Flore de l'Algérie et de la Tunisie (Alger, 1902).
W. TRELEASE, Botanical observations on the Azores (St. Louis, 1897).
R. T. LOWE, A manual flora of Madeira (London, 1868).
PH. BARKER-WEBB & S. BERTHELOT, Phytographia Canariensis (Paris, 1836—1840).
J. PITARD & L. PROUST, Les îles Canaries (Paris, 1908).

D. OLIVER & W. T. THISELTON-DYER, Flora of tropical Africa (London, 1868-1910).
J. MILDBREAD, Wissenschaftliche Ergebnisse der deutschen Central-Africa-Expedition ; Botanik (Berlin, 1910).
A. ENGLER, Die Pflanzenwelt Ostafrikas (Berlin, 1895).
A. RICHARD, Tentamen florae Abyssinicae (Paris, 1847).
R. PIROTTA, Flora della colonia Eritrea (Roma, 1903—1908).
J. A. GRANT & D. OLIVER, The botany of the Speke and Grant expedition. (London, 1872—1875).
W. PETERS, Naturwissenschaftliche Reise nach Mozambik (Berlin, 1862—1864).
TH. SIM, Forest flora and forest resources of Portuguese East Africa (Aberdeen, 1909).
J. B. BALFOUR, Botany of Socotra (Edinburgh, 1888).
H. FORBES, The natural history of Socotra and Abdelkuri (Liverpool, 1903).
F. VIERHAPPER, Beitrage zur Kenntniss der Flora Südarabiens und der Inseln Socotra, Semha und Abdelkuri (Wien, 1907).
J. A. SCHMIDT, Beiträge zur Flora der kapverdischen Inseln (Heidelberg, 1852).
J. A. GUILLEMIN, S. PERROTET, & A. RICHARD, Florae Senegambiae tentamen (Paris, 1830—1833).
J. PALISOT BEAUVOIS, Flore d'Oware et de Benin (Paris 1804).
W. J. HOOKER, Niger flora (London, 1849).

H. POBEGUIN, Essai sur la flore de la Guinée française (Paris, 1906).

TH. DURAND & E. DE WILDEMAN, Matériaux pour la flore du Congo (Bruxelles, 1897—1901).

E. DE WILDEMAN & TH. DURAND, Contributions à la flore du Congo (Bruxelles, 1900).

— — Reliquiae Dewevreanae (Bruxelles, 1901).

— — Illustrations de la flore du Congo (Bruxelles, 1898—1904).

— — Plantae Thonnerianae Congolenses (Bruxelles, 1900).

E. DE WILDEMAN, Etudes sur la flore du Katanga (Bruxelles 1902—1903).

— Etudes sur la flore du Bas- et du Moyen-Congo (Bruxelles, 1903—1910).

— Mission E. Laurent (Bruxelles 1905—1907).

— Notice sur des plantes utiles ou interessantes de la flore du Congo (Bruxelles 1903—1906).

— Plantae novae horti Thenensis (Bruxelles, 1904—1910).

— Companie du Kasai (Bruxelles, 1909).

TH. & H. DURAND, Sylloge florae Congolanae (Bruxelles, 1909).

W. P. HIERN, Catalogue of the African plants collected by Welwitsch (London, 1896—1901).

O. WARBURG, Die Kunene-Sambesi-Expedition (Berlin, 1903).

J. C. MELLIS, St. Helena (London, 1875).

A. GRANDIDIER & DRAKE DEL CASTILLO, Histoire naturelle de Madagascar (Paris, 1886—1902).

P. BARON, Compendium des plantes malgaches (Paris, 1901—1906).

J. PALACKY, Catalogus plantarum Madagascariensium (Prag, 1906).

J. G. BAKER, Flora of Mauritius and the Seychelles (London, 1877).

J. B. BALFOUR, Flora of the Island of Rodriguez (London, 1879).

J. DE CORDEMOY, Flore de l'île de la Réunion (Paris, 1895).

A. VOELTZKOW, Die von Aldabra bis jetzt bekannte Flora und Fauna (Frankfurt, 1902).

W. HARVEY, The genera of South-African plants, 2. ed. (Capetown, 1868).

W. HARVEY, O. W. SONDER & W. THISELTON-DYER, Flora Capensis (London, 1859—1910).

W. HARVEY, Thesaurus Capensis (Dublin, 1859—1863).

H. BOLUS & A. H. WOLLEY-DOD, A list of the flowering plants of the Cape peninsula (Capetown, 1903).

TH. SIM, The forests and forest flora of the Colony of the Cape of Good Hope (Aberdeen, 1907).

J. M. WOOD, Handbook to the flora of Natal (Durban, 1907).

— Natal plants (Durban, 1898—1910).

H. SCHINZ, Beiträge zur Kenntniss der afrikanischen Flora (Genève, 1892—1908).

— Die Pflanzenwelt Deutsch-Südwestafrikas. (Genève, 1896—1900).

A. ZAHLBRUCKNER, Plantae Pentherianae (Wien, 1900—1905).

CHALLENGER Report on the scientific results of the voyage of H.M.S. "Challenger (London, 1885).

H. SCHENK, Vergleichende Darstellung der Pflanzengeographie der subantarktischen Inseln (Jena, 1905).

LINNEAN SOCIETY, Journal. Botany. (London, 1857—1910).

KEW GARDENS, Bulletin of miscellaneous information. (London, 1892—1910)

W. CURTIS, The Botanical Magazine (London, 1793—1910).

W. J. & J. D. HOOKER, Icones plantarum (London 1837—1910).

B. SEEMANN & J. BRITTEN, The Journal of Botany (London 1853—1910).

A. ENGLER, Botanische Jahrbücher für Systematik, Pflanzengeschichte und Pflanzengeographie (Leipzig, 1881—1910).

— Notizblatt des königl. botanischen Gartens und Museums zu Berlin (Leipzig, 1897—1910).

K. SCHUMANN & F. FEDDE, Just's botanischer Jahresbericht (Leipzig, 1873—1910).

F. FEDDE, Repertorium novarum specierum regni vegetabilis (Berlin, 1906—1910).

BOTANISCHES CENTRALBLATT (Leiden, 1880—1910).
SOCIÉTÉ BOTANIQUE DE FRANCE, Bulletin (Paris, 1854—1910).
SOCIÉTÉ LINNÉENNE DE PARIS, Bulletin (Paris, 1889—1899).
MUSÉUM D'HISTOIRE NATURELLE, Bulletin (Paris, 1895—1910).
G. BEAUVERD, Bulletin de l'herbier Boissier, 2me série (Genéve, 1901—1908).
R. PIROTTA, Annuario del istituto botanico di Roma (Milano, 1885—1908).
— Annali di Botanica (Roma, 1904—1910).
SOCIEDADE BROTERIANA, Boletim (Coimbra, 1883—1910).

J. LINDLEY & TH. MOORE, The treasury of botany (London, 1884).
J. C. WILLIS, A manual and dictionary of the flowering plants and ferns, 3. ed. (Cambridge, 1908).
J WIESNER, Die Rohstoffe des Pflanzenreichs, 2. Aufl. (Leipzig, 1900).
G. DRAGENDORFF, Die Heilpflanzen (Stuttgart, 1898).
L. LEWIN, Lehrbuch der Toxikologie, 2. Aufl. (Wien, 1897).
F. MACMILLAN, A handbook of tropical gardening and planting (Colombo, 1910).
M. WOODROW, Gardening in the tropics (Paisley, 1910).
A. VOSS, Vilmorin's Blumengärtnerei (Berlin, 1896).
A. MOLONEY, Sketch of the forestry of West Africa (London, 1887).
J. H. HOLLAND, The useful plants of Nigeria (London, 1908).
R. SADEBECK, Die Kulturgewächse der deutschen Kolonien (Jena, 1899).
J. L. DE LANESSAN, Les plantes utiles des colonies françaises (Paris, 1886).
G. NIEDERLEIN, Ressources végétales des colonies françaises (Paris, 1902).
A. SEBIRE, Les plantes utiles du Senegal (Paris, 1899).
A. CHEVALIER, Les végétaux utiles de l'Afrique tropicale française (Paris, 1905—1910).
E. HECKEL, Les plantes utiles de Madagascar (Paris, 1910).
L. CUOCO, Fauna e flora medica ed industriale della colonia Eritrea (Napoli, 1897).
C. DE FICALHO, Plantas uteis da Africa portugueza (Lisboa, 1884).

B. D. JACKSON, A glossary of botanic terms, 2. ed. (London, 1905).

TABLE OF CONTENTS

KEY TO THE FAMILIES

KEY TO THE GENERA

LIST OF PLATES

MAP

KEY TO THE FAMILIES

EMBRYOPHYTA SIPHONOGAMA
(PHANEROGAMAE)

1. Ovules naked, borne on a floral axis without carpels, or on open carpels without a stigma.   Perianth simple or none.   Flowers unisexual.   Stem woody.   [Subdivision **GYMNOSPERMAE.**] 2
   Ovules encased in the ovary formed by stigma-bearing carpels and nearly always closed to the top, rarely (*Resedaceae*) open above.   [Subdivision **ANGIOSPERMAE**] 5

2. Leaves pinnately compound or dissected, forming a crown at the top of the stem.   Stem simple or scantily branched towards the top.   Juice mucilaginous.   Perianth none.   Stamens with numerous pollen-sacs.   Embryo with 2 more or less connate cotyledons.   [Class CYCADALES.]
   1. Cycadaceae.
   Leaves undivided, scattered along the branches of the stem, rarely (*Gnetaceae*) leaves 2, arising from the top of an undivided turnip-shaped stem and sometimes splitting lengthwise.   Stamens with 1—9 pollen-sacs.   Embryo with 2—15 free cotyledons. 3

3. Perianth present.   Juice not resinous.   Leaves not-needle-shaped.   Shrubs.   [Class GNETALES.] . . . . **4. Gnetaceae.**
   Perianth absent.   Juice resinous, rarely scarcely so, but then leaves needle-shaped.   Leaves needle- or scale-shaped.   [Class CONIFERAE.] . 4

4. Seeds overtopping the fleshy or rudimentary carpels and surrounded by a fleshy aril.   Carpels with 1 ovule. . . . . . . **2. Taxaceae.**
   Seeds concealed between the carpels, without an aril.   Carpels usually with 2 or more ovules. . . . . **3. Pinaceae.**

5. (1.) Embryo with a single cotyledon, rarely undivided.   Vascular bundles scattered in the stem.   Leaves usually parallel-veined (net-veined in many *Araceae Dioscoreaceae* and *Taccaceae* and a few *Hydrocharitaceae Liliaceae* and *Orchidaceae*), generally narrow entire and sessile with a dilated base.   Flowers usually 3-merous.   [Class MONOCOTYLEDONEAE.] 6
   Embryo with 2 cotyledons, rarely with only one well-developed cotyledon or undivided.   Vascular bundles of the stem nearly always disposed in a cylinder.   Leaves usually net-veined, rarely sessile with a dilated base and a narrow entire blade.   Flowers usually 4- or 5-merous.   [Class DICOTYLEDONEAE.] 52

A

6. Perianth wanting or rudimentary, that is, reduced to small, hypogynous, free or partially-united scales, rarely (*Potamogetonaceae*) replaced by sepaloid appendages of the connective 7

Perianth well developed, calyx- or corolla-like or consisting of calyx and corolla, rarely (*Eriocaulaceae* and *Restionaceae*) wanting in the female flowers . . . . : 15

7. Flowers in the axils of membranous or more or less dry bracts (glumes) in spikelets consisting of one or several flowers and one or several empty glumes and nearly always arranged in spikes, racemes, panicles, or heads. Land-, marsh-, or freshwater-plants. Carpel solitary, with a single basal or laterally attached ovule. 8

Flowers in spadices with a fleshy rachis and surrounded by one or several spathes, more rarely solitary or in glomerules, heads, or spikes ; in the latter case (*Potamogetonaceae*) saltwater plants. 9

8. Embryo enclosed in the lower part of the albumen. Seed and ovule attached at the base, free from the pericarp and the wall of the ovary. Style 1, with 1—3 stigmas. Anthers usually affixed at the base. Sheaths of the cauline and inner radical leaves closed all round, usually without a ligule. Stem usually triangular solid and without nodes.

17. Cyperaceae.

Embryo outside the albumen, at its base. Seed and ovule attached laterally, but often near the base, usually adnate to the pericarp or the wall of the ovary. Style 1, with 1—6 stigmas, or styles 2. Anthers usually affixed at the back. Sheaths of the leaves nearly always split on one side and ending in a ligule. Stem usually cylindrical and hollow between the nodes.

16. Gramineae.

9. Plants without differentiation into stem and leaves, consisting of small floating leaf- or granule-like shoots. Flowers 2—3 together in cavities of the shoots. . . . . **20. Lemnaceae.**

Plants differentiated into stem and leaves. 10

10. Flowers solitary or in glomerules in the axils of the leaves. Carpel solitary.

Naias, **9. Naiadaceae.**

Flowers in spikes, spadices, or heads, rarely (*Potamogetonaceae*) solitary or in glomerules, but then several separate carpels. 11

11. Male flowers in panicles, female in heads or spadices. Flowers dioecious. Leaves narrow, usually serrate or prickly. Stem usually woody.

Pandanus, **6. Pandanaceae.**

Male or all flowers solitary or in spikes, heads, or cymes. 12

12. Flowers in globose heads. . . . . *Sparganium,* **7. Sparganiaceae.**

Flowers solitary or in spikes, spadices, or cymes. 13

13. Ovaries several, separate, rarely ovary solitary, and then marine plants, very rarely freshwater-plants with hermaphrodite flowers. If flowers in spadices or spikes, then hermaphrodite or polygamous with 1 or several one-ovuled ovaries. . . . . **8. Potamogetonaceae.**

Ovary solitary. Land-, marsh-, or freshwater-plants ; the latter with unisexual flowers. Flowers in spadices, unisexual, rarely hermaphrodite, but then with a several-ovuled ovary. 14

14. Flowers monoecious ; male inflorescence, at least when young, separated from the female by a deciduous spathe. Flowers usually surrounded by hairs. Ovule 1, pendulous. Seed-coat not fleshy.

Typha, **5. Typhaceae.**

Flowers hermaphrodite or unisexual ; if monoecious, then male inflorescence in uninterrupted connexion with the female, or separated from it by an empty interval or by barren flowers, but not by a spathe. Seed-coat fleshy. . . . . **19. Araceae.**

15. (6.) Ovary superior. 16
Ovary inferior or half-inferior. 37

16. Carpel solitary or carpels connate and forming a single entire or slightly lobed ovary. 17
Carpels several, separate or cohering only at the base. 33

17. Perianth calyx-like, sometimes slightly coloured, but firmly membranous or leathery, or differentiated by size or coalescence into an inner and an outer whorl of segments, all of which are sepaloid. . . . 18
Perianth corolla-like or consisting of outer sepaloid and inner petaloid segments. 25

18. Leaves folded in the bud, subsequently splitting into pinnately or palmately disposed segments, rarely only 2-cleft. Stem woody, but sometimes very short. Flowers in spadices or panicles with spathes. **18. Palmae.**
Leaves undivided, rarely divided, but then not folded and springing from a herbaceous stem. 19

19. Flowers in spadices with a spathe forming sometimes a continuation of the stem. . . . . **19. Araceae.**
Flowers not in spadices. 20

20. Stamen 1. Ovule 1, erect. Stigmas several. Flowers solitary or in glomerules in the axils of the leaves. . . . *Naias*, **9. Naiadaceae.**
Stamens 2—6. 21

21. Anthers turned outwards. Ovary with 1 ascending ovule in each cell and with several sessile stigmas. Flowers hermaphrodite. Seeds exalbuminous. . . . . . . *Triglochin*, **11. Scheuchzeriaceae.**
Anthers turned inwards. Seeds albuminous. 22

22. Anthers 1-celled. Flowers unisexual, in spikelets usually arranged in spikes or panicles. Perianth dry. Stamens 2—3. Ovary with 1 pendulous ovule in each cell. . . . . **22. Restionaceae.**
Anthers 2-celled. If flowers unisexual and in spikelets, then perianth not dry. 23

23. Flowers monoecious, in heads surrounded by an involucre. Ovary with 1 pendulous ovule in each cell. . . . . . . **25. Eriocaulaceae.**
Flowers hermaphrodite, polygamous, or dioecious. 24

24. Style 1 with 3 long and thin stigmas. Perianth dry. Leaves linear.

31. Juncaceae.

Style 1 with 3 thick or short stigmas or with a single stigma, or styles 3. Perianth usually herbaceous. . . . . **32. Liliaceae.**

25. (17.) Perianth corolla-like. Usually ovules inverted and embryo or its radicle placed next to the hilum, more rarely ovules straight and embryo or its radicle remote from the hilum, and then albumen fleshy or cartilaginous. 26

Perianth differentiated into calyx and corolla. Ovules straight. Embryo small, remote from the hilum. Albumen more or less mealy . . 31

26. Seeds with mealy albumen. 27

Seeds with fleshy or cartilaginous albumen. 29

27. Ovules 2 or more in each ovary-cell. Seeds with a large embryo enclosed in the albumen. . . . . **29. Pontederiaceae.**

Ovule 1 in each ovary-cell. Seeds with a small embryo appressed to the albumen. Perianth white or yellow. 28

28. Perianth-segments free or nearly so. Anthers opening lengthwise. Stigmas 3. Fruit a berry. Stem climbing. Leaves scattered, ending in tendrils. Flowers in panicles. . . *Flagellaria*, **21. Flagellariaceae.**

Perianth-segments united below into a tube. Anthers opening by apical pores. Stigma 1. Fruit a capsule. Stem erect. Leaves all radical. Flowers in heads. . . . . . *Maschalocephalus*, **26. Rapateaceae.**

29. Stamens 3. Ovule 1 in each ovary-cell. Perianth yellow.

33. Haemodoraceae.

Stamens 6 or more, rarely 3, but then ovules 2 or more in each ovary-cell. 30

30. Anthers opening at the apex. Stamens affixed to the perianth. Ovary adnate to the perianth at the base. Ovules numerous in each cell. Perianth blue. Leaves linear or lanceolate. *Walleria*, **34. Amaryllidaceae.**

Anthers opening lengthwise, rarely at the apex, but then stamens (at least some of them) and ovary free from the perianth. . . **32. Liliaceae.**

31. (25.) Ovary 2—3-celled. Fertile stamens 2—6. . **28. Commelinaceae.**

Ovary 1-celled, sometimes with incomplete partitions. Ovules numerous. Fertile stamens 3. Flowers in heads, short spikes, or umbels. . . 32

32. Sepals 3, subequal. Anthers opening by a terminal lid. Staminodes none. Stigma 1. Leaves scattered. Flowers in umbels.

Mayaca, **23. Mayacaceae.**

Sepals 3, very unequal, or 2. Anthers opening by longitudinal slits. Staminodes 3. Stigmas 3. Leaves all radical. Flowers in heads or spikes.

Xyris, **24. Xyridaceae.**

33. (16.) Leaves divided. Woody plants. Seeds albuminous. **18. Palmae.**

Leaves undivided. Herbaceous plants. 34

34. Plants without green colour, growing upon mould. Leaves reduced to scales. Perianth of 6 petaloid segments. Seeds albuminous.

Sciaphila, **15. Triuridaceae.**

Plants of green colour, growing in the water. Leaves well developed. Perianth of 6 segments differentiated into sepals and petals, or of 1—3 segments. Seeds exalbuminous. 35

35. Perianth consisting of 1—3 coloured segments.

Aponogeton, **10. Aponogetonaceae.**

Perianth consisting of 6 segments more or less distinctly differentiated into sepals and petals, rarely in the female flowers only of 3 greenish segments. 36

36. Ovules numerous, covering the whole inner surface of the carpels.

13. Butomaceae.

Ovules 1—2, rarely more, and then all inserted at the upper suture of the carpels. . . . . **12. Alismataceae.**

37. (15.) Stamen 1. Flowers irregular. 38

Stamens 2—18. Flowers usually regular. 41

38. Staminodes small or wanting. Ovary 1-celled with numerous ovules. Style adnate to the filament. Seeds exalbuminous. Leaves usually with longitudinal nervation. . . . . . . **44. Orchidaceae.**

Staminodes, at least some of them, petal-like. Ovary 1-celled with a single ovule or more frequently 3-celled. Seeds albuminous. Leaves with pinnate nervation. 39

39. Anthers 2-celled. Sepals united below. Flowers symmetrical.

40. Zingiberaceae.

Anthers 1-celled. Sepals free. Flowers asymmetrical. . . . 40

40. Ovules several or many in each ovary-cell. Seeds with straight embryo. Leaf-stalk not thickened. . . . . . *Canna*, **41. Cannaceae.**

Ovules solitary in each cell. Seeds with curved embryo. Leaf-stalk thickened towards the apex or throughout its whole length.

42. Marantaceae.

41. Stamens 2—4, usually 3. 42

Stamens 5—18, usually 6. 45

42. Perianth-segments sepal-like or the outer sepal-, the inner petal-like. Ovary 1-celled, sometimes incompletely 6-celled. Seeds exalbuminous. Water plants. . . . . **14. Hydrocharitaceae.**

Perianth-segments petal-like. Ovary usually 3-celled. Seeds albuminous. Land- or marsh-plants. 43

43. Stamens opposite the outer perianth-segments. Anthers opening outwards or laterally. . . . . **38. Iridaceae.**

Stamens alternating with the outer or with all perianth-segments. Anthers opening inwards or laterally. 44

44. Leaves well developed, green. Inner perianth-segments about equalling the outer. Anthers opening lengthwise. Stigmas 3, linear, or stigma single. . . . . **33. Haemodoraceae.**

Leaves scale-like, not green, rarely well-developed and green, but then inner perianth-segments much smaller than the outer or wanting, anthers provided with an enlarged connective and opening transversely, and stigmas 3, short and thick. . . . . . . **43. Burmanniaceae.**

45. Ovary incompletely 6—15-celled with 6—15 stigmas, more rarely completely 1-celled with 3 stigmas. Perianth consisting of calyx and corolla, more

rarely only of 3 petal-like segments.   Water-plants with submerged or floating leaves. . . . . **14. Hydrocharitaceae.**
Ovary 3-celled, rarely 1-celled, but then stigmas 6.   Perianth usually of 6 petaloid segments.   Land-plants. 46

46. Ovary 1-celled.   Style umbrella-shaped, 6-lobed.   *Tacca*, **36. Taccaceae.**
Ovary 3-celled 47

47. Ovules in each ovary-cell 2, one above the other.   Flowers unisexual, regular. Stem climbing. . . . . **37. Dioscoreaceae.**
Ovules in each ovary-cell 1, 2 side by side, or more.   Flowers hermaphrodite, rarely unisexual but irregular. 48

48. Perianth distinctly differentiated into calyx and corolla.   Leaves toothed. Inflorescence spadix-like. . . . . . *Ananas*, **27. Bromeliaceae.**
Perianth more or less corolla-like. 49

49. Flowers distinctly irregular, in fascicles usually arranged in spikes or racemes. Stamens 5, rarely 6.   Seeds with more or less mealy albumen.   Leaves with pinnate nervation.   Tall plants. . . . . . **39. Musaceae.**
Flowers regular or nearly so.   Stamens 6 or more.   Seeds with fleshy or cartilaginous albumen.   Leaves nearly always with longitudinal nervation. 50

50. Flowers solitary, terminal.   No bulb or tuber ; usually a short woody trunk. Placentas much projecting, thickened, shield-shaped.
Barbacenia, **35. Velloziaceae.**
Flowers in umbels, spikes, racemes, or panicles, more rarely solitary, but then underground stem a bulb or a tuber.   Placentas not much projecting and thickened. 51

51. Ovary half-inferior, with 2 basal ovules in each cell.   Anthers opening at the apex.   Seeds with a large embryo adjoining the albumen.   Flowers in racemes or panicles. . . . . *Cyanastrum*, **30. Cyanastraceae.**
Ovary inferior, rarely half-inferior, but then with more than two ovules in each cell.   Seeds with a small embryo enclosed in the albumen.
34. Amaryllidaceae.

52. (5.) Perianth wanting or simple or consisting of a calyx and a choripetalous corolla ; petals, if present, free, more rarely cohering at the apex or in the middle, but free at the base.   [Subclass Archichlamydeae.] . 53
Perianth consisting of a calyx and a sympetalous corolla ; petals more or less united, at least at the base.   [Subclass Metachlamydeae or Sympetalae.] 551

53. Perianth wanting or simple, that is, consisting of similar segments, more rarely of 2—7 somewhat dissimilar ones without a distinct differentiation into sepals and petals.   [Apetalae.] 54
Perianth differentiated into calyx and corolla, more rarely consisting of 8 or more slightly dissimilar segments not distinctly separated into sepals and petals.   [Choripetalae.] 188

54. Perianth absent in the hermaphrodite and female flowers, but sometimes replaced by bracteoles.   Ovary naked.. 55

Perianth present in the hermaphrodite and female flowers 69
55. Ovary completely 1-celled. 56
Ovary 2—4-celled, at least in its lower half. 65
56. Ovule solitary, rarely (*Balanophoraceae*) ovules 3. 57
Ovules numerous, rarely (*Casuarinaceae*) 2. 63
57. Ovule basal or attached by a basal funicle. 58
Ovule apical or adnate to the wall of the ovary. 62
58. Ovule straight. 59
Ovule incurved or inverted. 61
59. Flowers in fascicles, the male with a perianth. Stamens 1—5. Stigma 1.
Fruit dry. Seed albuminous. . . . . . . **54. Urticaceae.**
Flowers in spikes, the male without a perianth, but sometimes with 2—6
bracteoles. Stamens 2—12. Fruit succulent. 60
60. Flowers unisexual. Stigmas 2, thread-like. Fruit a drupe. Seed exalbuminous. Trees, shrubs, or undershrubs. Leaves without stipules.
Myrica, **48. Myricaceae.**
Flowers hermaphrodite or polygamous, more rarely unisexual, but then
leaves stipulate. Fruit a berry. Seed with copious albumen.
46. Piperaceae.
61. Ovule incurved. Stigmas 2—5. Seed with curved embryo. Flowers
usually in glomerule-, or spike-like cymes. . **67. Chenopodiaceae.**
Ovule inverted. Stigmas 1—2. Seed with straight embryo. Flowers
usually in heads. . . . . **226. Compositae.**
62. Leaves well-developed, stipulate. Green plants. Ovule solitary, free.
53. Moraceae.
Leaves scale-like. Coloured (not green) herbaceous plants.
. 62. Balanophoraceae.
63. (56.) Ovules 2, ascending, straight. Male flowers with a 2-parted perianth.
Stamen 1. Fruit a nut. Trees or shrubs. Leaves whorled, scale-like.
Male flowers in spikes, female in heads. *Casuarina*, **45. Casuarinaceae.**
Ovules numerous, inverted. Male flowers without a perianth, but sometimes with a disc. Fruit a capsule. Leaves well developed. Flowers
in spikes or catkins. 64
64. Flowers with a disc sometimes replaced by scales. Stamens 2 or more.
Trees or shrubs. Leaves alternate, entire toothed or lobed, stipulate.
47. Salicaceae.
Flowers without a disc. Stamen 1 (or stamens 2 with united filaments.)
Aquatic herbs. . . . . . *Hydrostachys*, **94. Hydrostachyaceae.**
65. (55.) Ovary 2-celled at the base, with 1 ovule in each incomplete cell. Styles
2. Stamens 4. Trees or shrubs. Flowers in spikes or catkins.
50. Betulaceae.
Ovary completely 2—4-celled. 66
66. Ovules solitary in each ovary-cell. 67
Ovules 2 or more in each ovary-cell. Shrubs or trees. Leaves opposite.
Male flowers without a perianth. 68

67. Ovary 2—3-celled. Ovules with a double coat. .   **122. Euphorbiaceae.**
Ovary 4-celled. Ovules with a single coat. Styles 2. Stamen 1. Male
flowers without a perianth. Fruit a drupe. Herbs. Leaves opposite.
Callitriche, **123. Callitrichaceae.**

68. Ovary 2-celled with 2 ovules in each cell. Style 1, with 2 stigmas. Stamens 2. Fruit a nut. Leaves pinnate, exstipulate.
Fraxinus, **197. Oleaceae.**

Ovary 3—4-celled with numerous ovules in each cell. Styles 3—4. Stamens
3—8. Fruit a capsule or a schizocarp. Leaves undivided, stipulate.
Myrothamnus, **99. Myrothamnaceae.**

69. (54.) Ovary superior or nearly so. 70
Ovary inferior to half-inferior. 153

70. Ovary 1, entire or lobed. 71
Ovaries 2 or more, distinct or united at the base only. 146

71. Ovary 1-celled, sometimes incompletely chambered. 72
Ovary completely or almost completely 2- or more-celled. 118

72. Ovule 1. 73
Ovules 2 or more. 103

73. Ovule erect or ascending or attached by a basal funicle. 74
Ovule pendulous or descending. 94

74. Ovule straight. 75
Ovule incurved or inverted. 80

75. Style 1 or none ; stigma solitary or stigmas 2 or more, contiguous at the
base. Stamens 1—12. 76
Styles 2—4, free or united at the base ; stigmas not contiguous at the base.
Stamens 4—50. 79

76. Flowers hermaphrodite or polygamous. Stigma sessile, 2-lobed. Seed
with fleshy albumen. Shrubs or trees. Leaves without stipules.
Exocarpus, **56. Santalaceae.**
Flowers unisexual, rarely polygamous, but then herbs and stigma penicillate. 77

77. Leaves exstipulate. Stamens 2—12. Stigmas 2. Seed without albumen.
Myrica, **48. Myricaceae.**
Leaves stipulate, rarely exstipulate, but then stigma 1. Stamens 1—5. 78

78. Stamens straight in bud. Juice milky. Trees. . . . **53. Moraceae.**
Stamens incurved in bud. Juice not milky. . . . . **54. Urticaceae.**

79. Leaves simple, entire toothed lobed or cleft, with a stem-clasping sheath
at the base. Seed with copious mealy albumen. **66. Polygonaceae.**
Leaves compound, exstipulate. Stamens 5. Seed without albumen.
Pistacia, **127. Anacardiaceae.**

80. (74.) Ovule incurved. Embryo distinctly curved ; albumen usually
mealy. 81
Ovule inverted. Embryo straight or nearly so ; albumen usually fleshy
or wanting. 87

81. Perianth-segments 6, petal-like, free.   Stamens 8—10.   Style 3—4-cleft.
    Flowers dioecious.   Spiny trees.   .   .   *Didierea*, **134. Sapindaceae.**
    Perianth-segments 1—5.   82
82. Perianth with valvate and folded aestivation, lobed, enlarged in fruit.
    Stamens hypogynous, united at the base.   .   .   .   **69. Nyctaginaceae.**
    Perianth with imbricate or open aestivation, rarely with valvate not folded
    aestivation ; in the latter case deeply divided.   83
83. Stamens 1—10, perigynous, rarely (*Queria*) 10, hypogynous.   Stipules
    present, rarely absent, and then leaves opposite and styles 2—3.

    75. Caryophyllaceae.

    Stamens 1—5, hypogynous or nearly so, rarely distinctly perigynous, but
    then stipules wanting and leaves alternate or style 1.   84
84. Stamens as many as the perianth-segments or one less (3—5), alternating
    with them, hypogynous.   Flowers hermaphrodite.   85
    Stamens as many as the perianth-segments or one less, but opposite to them,
    or considerably fewer, or in greater number.   Leaves without sti-
    pules.   86
85. Flowers in cymes, 5-merous.   Perianth membranous.   Embryo hooked.
    Leaves whorled, usually stipulate.   .   .   *Adenogramma*, **72. Aizoaceae.**
    Flowers in spikes or racemes, with bracteoles.   Perianth herbaceous.
    Embryo nearly ring-shaped.   Leaves alternate, usually exstipulate.

    71. Phytolaccaceae.
86. Perianth more or less scarious or papery.   Seed albuminous ; embryo
    ring- or horseshoe-shaped.   Flowers with bracteoles.   **68. Amarantaceae.**
    Perianth more or less herbaceous or membranous.   Stigmas 2—5.

    67. Chenopodiaceae.
87. (80.) Leaves stipulate.   88
    Leaves exstipulate.   89
88. Leaves opposite, undivided.   Stamens 2—5.   Seed albuminous.

    75. Caryophyllaceae.

    Leaves alternate.   Seed exalbuminous.   .   .   .   .   .   **103. Rosaceae.**
89. Stem herbaceous.   Flowers in heads, unisexual.   Stamens as many as
    and alternate with the perianth-segments.   Stigmas 2 in the female
    flowers.   Seed exalbuminous.   .   .   .   .   .   **226. Compositae.**
    Stem woody.   Stigma 1.   90
90. Perianth with imbricate aestivation.   Stamens numerous, free or nearly
    so.   Seed exalbuminous.   .   .   .   *Calophyllum*, **149. Guttiferae.**
    Perianth with valvate aestivation.   91
91. Stamens attached to the perianth, as many as its segments, 4, rarely 5 ;
    filaments free.   Seed exalbuminous.   92
    Stamens free from the perianth, as many as its segments or more often in
    greater number ; filaments more or less united.   Seed albuminous.   93
92. Stamens opposite the perianth-segments.   Flowers in spikes or heads.

    55. Proteaceae.

Stamens alternate with the perianth-segments. Flowers solitary or in
fascicles. . . . . *Elaeagnus*, **172. Elaeagnaceae.**

93. Stamens 5—15 ; filaments united at the base only. Anthers opening
laterally. Perianth 5-toothed. Style slender. Seed without an aril ;
embryo large. . . . . *Pisonia*, **69. Nyctaginaceae.**
Stamens very numerous or with the filaments united throughout their
length. Anthers opening outwards. Perianth 2—4-, rarely 5-lobed.
Seed with an aril ; embryo small. · . . . . . **82. Myristicaceae.**

94. (73.) Ovule straight. 95
Ovule incurved or inverted. 96

95. Perianth 4-parted. Stamens 4. Seed without albumen. Shrubs or trees.
Flowers in spikes or heads. . . . . **55. Proteaceae.**
Perianth 9—12-parted. Stamens 12—16. Seed with a thin albumen.
Herbs. Flowers solitary or in pairs in the axils of the leaves.
Ceratophyllum, **77. Ceratophyllaceae.**

96. Leaves stipulate. 97
Leaves exstipulate. 100

97. Leaves compound, but sometimes with one leaflet only. Ovary tightly
enclosed by the perianth. Seed exalbuminous. Herbs, undershrubs,
or shrubs. . . . . **103. Rosaceae.**
Leaves simple, but sometimes (*Moraceae*) dissected. 98

98. Anthers 3—4-celled. Seed albuminous. *Macaranga*, **122. Euphorbiaceae.**
Anthers 2-celled. Seed usually exalbuminous. 99

99. Flowers solitary or in fascicles. Stamens straight in the bud. Shrubs
or trees. Juice not milky. . . . . **52. Ulmaceae.**
Flowers in spikes, racemes, panicles, or heads, or inserted upon a dilated
and often concave receptacle, rarely in fascicles, but then stamens bent
inwards in the bud. Shrubs or trees with a milky juice or herbs.
53. Moraceae.

100. Anthers opening by valves. Perianth-segments 4 or 6. Seed without
albumen. Trees or shrubs. . . . . **84. Lauraceae.**
Anthers opening by longitudinal slits. 101

101. Stamens numerous. Flowers unisexual. Seed with copious fleshy albumen. Trees or shrubs. . . . . **83. Monimiaceae.**
Stamens 8-10. 102

102. Style simple. Seed with a straight embryo and a fleshy albumen or without albumen. . . . . **171. Thymelaeaceae.**
Styles 2. Seed with a curved embryo and mealy albumen. Flowers in
panicles. . . . . *Galenia*, **72. Aizoaceae.**

103. (72.) Ovules basal or inserted upon a central placenta. 104
Ovules parietal or suspended from the apex of the cell. . . . 108

104. Perianth of 2—3 minute scales. Ovules numerous, inserted upon a central
placenta. Water-plants. . . . . . . **93. Podostemonaceae.**
Perianth of 4—5 segments. 105

105. Flowers unisexual or polygamous, 4-merous. Ovules 2. Stigma 1.

Seeds without albumen ; embryo straight.   Shrubs.   Leaves alternate.
Empleurum, **115.   Rutaceae.**
Flowers hermaphrodite.   Seeds with mealy albumen ; embryo more or
less curved.   Usually herbs.   106

106. Leaves alternate.   Stamens 5.   .   .   .   .   .   .   **68.   Amarantaceae.**
Leaves opposite or whorled.   107

107. Stigma 1, rarely stigmas 2, and then ovules 2—4.   Stamens 5 or more,
perigynous.   .   .   .   .   **72.   Aizoaceae.**
Stigmas 3—5, more rarely 2, but then ovules numerous or stamens 1—3.
75.   Caryophyllaceae.

108. (103.) Ovules 2, suspended side by side from the apex of the cell or from
a central placenta.   Fruit drupaceous, usually one-seeded.   .   .   109
Ovules 2, one above the other, or more than 2, affixed to one or more
parietal placentas.   112

109. Stamens as many as, and alternate with the perianth-segments.   Leaves
exstipulate.   .   .   .   .   **132.   Icacinaceae.**
Stamens as many as, and opposite the perianth-segments, or in greater
number.   110

110. Flowers hermaphrodite.   Leaves exstipulate.   .   .   .   **59.   Olacaceae.**
Flowers unisexual.   Leaves stipulate.   111

111. Stamens very numerous.   Perianth 4—5-parted.   Flowers fascicled.
Guya, **159.   Flacourtiaceae.**
Stamens 2—8, rarely more, but then perianth 6—8-parted.
122.   Euphorbiaceae.

112. Ovules 2 or more, attached to a single placenta.   Stamens more or less
perigynous.   Fruit a legume.   Leaves compound or reduced to the
dilated foot-stalk, usually stipulate.   .   .   .   .   **105.   Leguminosae.**
Ovules 3 or more, attached to 2 or more placentas, rarely to a single one,
but then fruit a berry and leaves simple and undivided.   .   .   .   113

113. Style simple, or a sessile stigma.   114
Styles, style-branches, or sessile stigmas 2 or more.   116

114. Perianth-segments imbricate in bud.   Stamens 10 or more.   Ovary
sessile.   Seeds albuminous.   .   .   .   .   .   .   **159.   Flacourtiaceae.**
Perianth-segments valvate in bud, more rarely imbricate, but then ovary
stalked.   Seeds exalbuminous.   115

115. Stamens more or less perigynous.   Ovary sessile or short-stalked.
Perianth-segments valvate in bud.   Leaves exstipulate.   Seeds with
straight embryo.   .   .   .   .   **173.   Lythraceae.**
Stamens hypogynous, more rarely perigynous, but then ovary long-
stalked and leaves stipulate.   Seeds with curved embryo.
87.   Capparidaceae.

116. Ovary at first open at the apex.   Styles or sessile stigmas 3, free.   Stamens
10—30.   Perianth 5—6-cleft about halfway down.   Seeds exalbuminous ; embryo curved.   .   .   .   .   .   *Ochradenus*, **89.   Resedaceae.**

Ovary closed. Stamens 4 or more ; if 10 or more, then perianth deeply
      divided. 117
117. Stamens as many as perianth-segments, 4—6, surrounded by a corona.
      Styles 3, free or united at the base. . . .   **161. Passifloraceae.**
      Stamens more than perianth-segments, 6—40. Shrubs or trees.
                                              159. Flacourtiaceae.
118. (71.) Ovules solitary in each ovary-cell. 119
      Ovules 2 or more in each ovary-cell. 129
119. Ovules erect or ascending. 120
      Ovules pendulous or descending. 124
120. Style 1, with 1—3 stigmas. Stamens inserted within the disc or at its
      edge. Flowers polygamous or unisexual. Seeds albuminous. Leaves
      pinnate, exstipulate. . . . .   **134. Sapindaceae.**
      Styles 2—10, free or united below. Seeds albuminous, rarely exalbumin-
      ous, but then leaves stipulate. Leaves undivided or lobed. . . 121
121. Perianth-segments 3 or 6. Stamens 3. Flowers unisexual or polygamous.
      Dwarf shrubs. . . . .   **125. Empetraceae.**
      Perianth-segments 4—5. Stamens 4 or more. 122
122. Seeds with straight embryo. Fruit drupaceous. Styles 2—4, united
      below. Stamens 4—5, perigynous. Perianth valvate in bud. Shrubs.
      Leaves stipulate, alternate. . . . . . .   **137. Rhamnaceae.**
      Seeds with curved embryo and mealy albumen. Fruit dry, rarely baccate.
      Herbs or undershrubs, rarely shrubs, but then leaves exstipulate. 123
123. Flowers solitary or in cymes. Herbs or undershrubs. . **72. Aizoaceae.**
      Flowers in spikes or racemes. . . . . . .   **71. Phytolaccaceae.**
124. Stamens hypogynous. 125
      Stamens perigynous. 127
125. Flowers hermaphrodite. Perianth-segments 4. Stamens 2, 4, or 6.
      Ovary-cells 2. Seeds exalbuminous ; embryo curved. Herbs. Leaves
      exstipulate. . . . .   *Lepidium,* **88. Cruciferae.**
      Flowers unisexual, rarely hermaphrodite, but then perianth-segments 5,
      ovary-cells 5, and leaves stipulate. 126
126. Flowers unisexual. Leaves simple or palmately compound. Ovary
      usually 3-celled. . . . .   **122. Euphorbiaceae.**
      Flowers hermaphrodite, rarely unisexual, but then leaves pinnate and
      ovary surrounded by large scales. Ovary 5-celled. Leaves compound,
      stipulate. . . . .   **113. Zygophyllaceae.**
127. Flowers unisexual or polygamous. Perianth of the male flowers consisting
      of calyx and corolla, that of the female and hermaphrodite flowers
      simple, valvate in bud. Stamens 5. Styles 2. Fruit capsular.
      Embryo straight. Leaves stipulate.
                              Trichocladus, **101. Hamamelidaceae.**
      Flowers hermaphrodite. Perianth simple. Leaves exstipulate. . . 128
128. Style and stigma simple. Embryo straight. Shrubs. Leaves alternate.
                                              171. Thymelaeaceae.

Styles or stigmas 2—5. Embryo curved. . . . . . **72. Aizoaceae.**

129. (118.) Flowers unisexual or polygamous. 130
Flowers hermaphrodite. 136

130. Stamens 2. Ovary 2-celled with 2 ovules in each cell. Style 1, with 2 stigmas. Perianth 4-partite. Flowers polygamous. Leaves opposite, pinnate, exstipulate. Trees. . . . . *Fraxinus*, **197. Oleaceae.**
Stamens 3 or more, rarely 2, but then flowers unisexual. Leaves simple or digitate, rarely pinnate, but then alternate. 131

131. Leaves with a pitcher-shaped appendage. Style absent ; stigma 4-partite. Ovary 4-celled with numerous ovules in each cell.

Nepenthes, **91. Nepenthaceae.**

Leaves without pitchers. Style present. 132

132. Style 1, with 2—6 stigmas. Seeds exalbuminous. Leaves alternate, without stipules. . . . . **134. Sapindaceae.**
Styles 2 or more, free at the base, towards the apex, or throughout. 133

133. Perianth-segments valvate in bud, united below. Filaments united.

144. Sterculiaceae.

Perianth-segments imbricate or open in bud, rarely valvate, but then free and filaments also free. 134

134. Ovules with ventral raphe, 2 in a cell. Fruit usually opening septicidally and loculicidally. Leaves usually stipulate. **122. Euphorbiaceae.**
Ovules with dorsal raphe. Shrubs or trees. 135

135. Flowers monoecious. Stamens 4—6. Ovary 3-celled with 2 ovules in each cell. Fruit a loculicidal capsule. Leaves opposite, without stipules. . . . . **124. Buxaceae.**
Flowers dioecious or polygamous. Stamens 10 or more. Fruit a berry or a drupe. Leaves alternate. . . . . . **159. Flacourtiaceae.**

136. (129.) Perianth-segments free or nearly so. Stamens hypogynous or nearly so. 137
Perianth-segments evidently united. Stamens usually perigynous. . 142

137. Stem herbaceous or woody at the base only. 138
Stem woody throughout its length. 140

138. Perianth-segments 2—3. Stamens 1—4. Water-plants.

93. Podostemonaceae.

Perianth-segments 4—5. Land-plants. Seeds with curved embryo. 139

139. Perianth-segments 4. Stamens 1—6. Ovary-cells 2. Style 1. Seeds exalbuminous. Leaves exstipulate. . . . . . **88. Cruciferae.**
Perianth-segments 5. Ovary-cells 3—7. Styles 3—7. Seeds albuminous. Leaves stipulate. . . . . **72. Aizoaceae.**

140. Ovary long-stalked. Perianth-segments 2—4, valvate or imbricate in bud ; in the latter case stamens 4—8. Seeds exalbuminous ; embryo curved. . . . . **87. Capparidaceae.**
Ovary sessile or short-stalked. Stamens 10 or more. Seeds albuminous ; embryo straight. 141

141. Perianth-segments 5, valvate in bud. *Grewia*. **141. Tiliaceae.**

Perianth-segments 3—8, imbricate or open in bud. **159. Flacourtiaceae.**

142. (136.) Styles or sessile stigmas 2—5. Seeds albuminous ; embryo curved.
72. Aizoaceae.

Style 1 or a sessile stigma. Seeds exalbuminous or with a straight embryo. 143

143. Stigmas or stigma-lobes 1—2. Ovules numerous in each ovary-cell. 144
Stigmas or stigma-lobes 4. Ovules 2—4 in each ovary-cell. Flowers 4-merous. Leaves opposite, stipulate. 145

144. Stamens 1—16. Ovary sessile or short-stalked. Embryo straight.
Leaves without stipules. . . . . . . **173. Lythraceae.**
Stamens very numerous. Ovary long-stalked. Embryo curved. Leaves alternate, with small stipules. . . *Maerua*, **87. Capparidaceae.**

145. Perianth with valvate aestivation. Stamens 4. Ovules ascending, at least the lower ones. Seeds exalbuminous. . . **169. Penaeaceae.**
Perianth with imbricate aestivation. Stamens 8. Ovules pendulous.
Seeds albuminous. . . . . *Geissoloma*, **168. Geissolomataceae.**

146. (70.) Ovules solitary in each carpel. 147
Ovules 2 or more in each carpel. 152

147. Ovules erect, incurved. Perianth regular, 4—5-parted. Seeds with a curved embryo and mealy albumen. Leaves undivided, without stipules. 148
Ovules pendulous or affixed laterally, rarely erect, but then perianth irregular and strap-shaped or surrounded by an epicalyx. . . 149

148. Flowers in spikes or racemes. Fruit succulent, baccate.
Phytolacca, **71. Phytolaccaceae.**
Flowers in cymes. Fruit dry. . . . . **72. Aizoaceae.**

149. Perianth-segments free or nearly so. Stamens hypogynous. . 150
Perianth-segments obviously united, at least in the female flowers. Stamens usually perigynous. 151

150. Flowers unisexual. Stamens as many as perianth-segments. Fruits fleshy, drupaceous. . . . . **80. Menispermaceae.**
Flowers hermaphrodite or polygamous. Stamens usually more than perianth-segments. Fruits usually dry. . . **78. Ranunculaceae.**

151. Leaves undivided, exstipulate. Shrubs or trees. Flowers unisexual.
Stamens 10 or more. Seeds with copious albumen.
83. Monimiaceae.
Leaves more or less deeply divided or compound, stipulate. Seeds without albumen. . . . . **103. Rosaceae.**

152. Perianth of 6 free segments, imbricate in bud. Stamens numerous, free. Herbs. Leaves floating, peltate, exstipulate.
Brasenia, **76. Nymphaeaceae.**
Perianth 4—8-lobed, valvate in bud. Stamens 4 or more, united at the base. Trees. Leaves stipulate. . . . . . **144. Sterculiaceae.**

153. (69.) Ovary 1-celled. 154
Ovary, at least after fertilisation, completely or almost completely 2- or more-celled. 177

154. Ovule 1. 155
Ovules 2 or more. 167
155. Ovule erect, ascending, attached by an erect funicle, or adnate to the
ovary-wall. 156
Ovule pendulous or descending. 162
156. Ovule adnate to the ovary-wall. Style simple ; stigma entire. Stamens
as many as and opposite the perianth-segments. Perianth valvate
in bud. Leaves without stipules. Shrubs growing upon trees.

61. Loranthaceae.

Ovary free from the ovary-wall. Trees or shrubs growing on the ground,
or herbaceous plants. 157
157. Ovule straight. Embryo straight. Flowers unisexual. Stamens as
many as and opposite the perianth-segments or more. . . . 158
Ovule incurved or inverted. Embryo curved, more rarely straight, but
then stamens as many as and alternating with the perianth-segments. 159
158. Stamens 1—5. Leaves simple or digitate, stipulate. **54. Urticaceae.**
Stamens numerous. Stigmas 2. Trees. Leaves pinnate, exstipulate.

Juglans, **49. Juglandaceae.**

159. Ovule inverted. Stamens as many as and alternating with the. perianth-
segments. Seeds exalbuminous ; embryo straight. **226. Compositae.**
Ovule incurved. Stamens as many as and opposite the perianth-segments
or more. Seeds albuminous ; embryo curved. Herbs. . . 160
160. Flowers unisexual. Perianth-segments 2—4, valvate in bud. Stamens
10—30. Stigma 1. Fruit drupaceous.

Cynocrambe, **70. Cynocrambaceae.**

Flowers hermaphrodite. Perianth-segments 5, imbricate in bud. Stamens 5. Stigmas 2—5. Fruit opening by a lid or bursting irregularly. 161
161. Style short, with long stigmas. Leaves alternate, exstipulate. Flowers
in spike- or panicle-like inflorescences. . *Beta,* **67. Chenopodiaceae.**
Style long, with 2 short stigmas. Leaves opposite, linear, stipulate.
Flowers in heads. . . . . *Sclerocephalus,* **75. Caryophyllaceae.**
162. (155.) Ovule straight. Style simple. Stamen 1. Flowers polygamous.
Reddish-brown herbs, parasitic upon roots. Leaves reduced to scales.

Cynomorium, **184. Cynomoriaceae.**

Ovule incurved or inverted. Green plants. Leaves well developed. 163
163. Flowers unisexual or polygamous. Stamens as many as and opposite the
perianth-segments or fewer. 164
Flowers hermaphrodite. Stamens as many as and alternate with the
perianth-segments or more. Leaves exstipulate. 166
164. Anthers opening by longitudinal slits. Flowers unisexual. Leaves stipulate. . . . . **53. Moraceae.**
Anthers opening by valves. Leaves exstipulate. 165
165. Flowers unisexual. Leaves penninerved. *Hypodaphnis,* **84. Lauraceae.**
Flowers polygamous. Leaves palminerved.

Gyrocarpus, **85. Hernandiaceae.**

166. Stamens 2. Styles 2. Embryo straight. Leaves radical.

Gunnera, **183. Halorrhagaceae.**

Stamens 3—5. Styles 4, or a single style. Embryo curved. Leaves alternate. . . . . **72. Aizoaceae.**

167. (154.) Ovules 2—5. 168
Ovules numerous. 174

168. Ovules adnate to the ovary-wall. Stamens 2—6. Shrubs parasitic on the stem of trees. . . . . **61. Loranthaceae.**

Ovules free from the ovary-wall. Plants growing on the ground or parasitic upon roots. 169

169. Ovules suspended from the apex of the ovary-cell. Stamens 8—10, rarely 4—5. Seeds exalbuminous. Shrubs or trees. Flowers in spikes, racemes, or heads. . . . . **179. Combretaceae.**

Ovules inserted on a central, sometimes subparietal, placenta. Seeds albuminous. 170

170. Styles 4. Ovules 4. Stamens 4. Perianth of the male flowers consisting of calyx and corolla. Herbs or undershrubs.

Laurembergia, **183. Halorrhagaceae.**

Style 1. Perianth of all flowers simple. 171

171. Stigma 6—10-lobed. Stamens 5. Albumen ruminate. Shrubs or trees.

Octoknema, **60. Octoknemataceae.**

Stigma entire or 2—5-lobed. 172

172. Stamens 8, twice as many as the perianth-segments. Embryo with inferior radicle. Shrubs. Leaves opposite.

Grubbia, **58. Grubbiaceae.**

Stamens 2—6, as many as, or fewer than, the perianth-segments. Embryo with superior radicle or undivided. 173

173. Stem and leaves or scales green. Embryo with 2 cotyledons.

56. Santalaceae.

Stem and leaves not green; stem herbaceous; leaves scale-like. Flowers unisexual, in spikes or heads. Embryo without cotyledons.

62. Balanophoraceae.

174. (167.) Placentas apical. Style wanting. Stamens 3—4, united. Flowers hermaphrodite. Stem herbaceous, not green, bearing neither leaves nor scales. . . . . *Hydnora*, **65. Hydnoraceae.**

Placentas parietal. Style present. Stem bearing leaves or scales. 175

175. Filaments united, 8 or more. Style 1. Embryo without cotyledons. Herbs. Leaves scale-like, not green. Flowers unisexual.

64. Rafflesiaceae.

Filaments free. Embryo with 2 cotyledons. Shrubs or trees. Leaves well developed. 176

176. Flowers unisexual. Perianth 4—5-parted. Stamens 4—5. Style 1.

Grevea, **96. Saxifragaceae.**

Flowers hermaphrodite. Perianth 7—8-parted. Stamens numerous. Styles 2—3. . . . . *Bembicia*, **159. Flacourtiaceae.**

177. (153.) Ovules solitary in each ovary-cell. 178
    Ovules 2 or more in each ovary-cell. 183

178. Ovules erect or ascending. 179
    Ovules pendulous or descending. 180

179. Leaves opposite or whorled. Perianth corolla-like. Ovary-cells and
    styles 2. Embryo curved. . . . . **219. Rubiaceae.**
    Leaves alternate. Perianth calyx-like. Embryo straight.

                                         137. Rhamnaceae.

180. Perianth wanting in the male flowers. Stamens 4. Ovary almost com-
    pletely 2-celled. Seeds exalbuminous. Shrubs. Leaves stipulate.
                              Corylus, **50. Betulaceae.**
    Perianth present in all flowers. Seeds albuminous. Herbs or under-
    shrubs, rarely shrubs or trees,· but then, as usually, leaves exstipu-
    late. 181

181. Flowers in umbels or heads, rarely in whorls, and then leaves stipulate.
    Perianth-segments 5, alternating with as many stamens. Ovary-cells
    and styles 2. Seeds with horny albumen ; embryo small.
                                    186. Umbelliferae.
    Flowers solitary or in axillary fascicles or in spikes. Leaves exstipulate.
    Perianth-segments 4, rarely 3 or 5. Seeds with fleshy or mealy albumen.
    Herbs or undershrubs. 182

182. Flowers hermaphrodite. Seeds with a curved embryo and mealy albumen.
    Leaves undivided. . . . . *Tetragonia*, **72. Aizoaceae.**
    Flowers unisexual or polygamous. · Stamens 2, 4, or 8. Seeds with a
    straight embryo and fleshy albumen. Leaves, at least the lower ones,
    deeply divided. . . . . *Myriophyllum*, **183. Halorrhagaceae.**

183. (177.) Ovules 2 in each ovary-cell. Styles 3—6. Perianth-segments
    more or less united. Flowers unisexual, spicate. Leaves stipulate.
    Trees or shrubs. . . . . **51. Fagaceae.**
    Ovules numerous in each ovary-cell, rarely (*Lecythidaceae*) 2—6, but then
    style 1 and flowers hermaphrodite. 184

184. Perianth-segments obviously united below. Seeds albuminous. Leaves
    without stipules. 185
    Perianth-segments free or nearly so. Seeds exalbuminous. . . . 186

185. Flowers unisexual, in terminal spikes racemes or panicles. Perianth
    regular. Fruit a berry. Embryo without cotyledons. Herbs. Leaves
    scale-like, not green. . . . . . *Cytinus*, **64. Rafflesiaceae.**
    Flowers hermaphrodite, solitary or fascicled in the axils of the leaves.
    Perianth irregular. Stamens adnate to the style. Fruit a capsule.
    Embryo with 2 cotyledons. Leaves well developed, green.
                     Aristolochia, **63. Aristolochiaceae.**

186. Flowers unisexual, in cymes. Perianth irregular. Stamens numerous.
    Styles 2—6, free or united at the base. Leaves stipulate.
                         Begonia, **165. Begoniaceae.**

                                                              B

Flowers hermaphrodite, solitary or in racemes or heads. Perianth
   regular. Style 1, undivided. 187
187. Stamens 3—6. Leaves stipulate. Herbs.
                            Ludwigia, **182. Oenotheraceae.**
   Stamens numerous. Leaves exstipulate. Trees or shrubs.
                                  176. Lecythidaceae.
188. (53.) Ovary superior or nearly so. 189
   Ovary inferior to half-inferior. 481
189. Ovary 1, entire or lobed. 190
   Ovaries 2 or more, separate or united at the base only. . . . 451
190. Ovary 1-celled, sometimes with incomplete partitions or containing one
   or more empty rudimentary cells besides the fertile one. . . . 191
   Ovary completely or almost completely 2- or more-celled, the partitions
   sometimes not quite reaching the apex ; or one cell only fertile, the others
   empty but well developed. 273
191. Ovule 1. 192
   Ovules 2 or more. 214
192. Ovule erect or ascending or attached by a basal funicle. . . . 193
   Ovule pendulous or descending. 205
193. Leaves stipulate. Sepals 5. 194
   Leaves exstipulate. 198
194. Stigma 1, entire. 195
   Stigma 1, five-lobed, or stigmas 2—3. Stamens 1—5, more or less distinctly perigynous. Flowers regular. Leaves undivided. . . 197
195. Flowers regular. Corolla with imbricate or contorted aestivation. Stamens 4—5, hypogynous. Shrubs or trees. Leaves opposite, undivided.
                            Dovera, **131. Salvadoraceae.**
   Flowers irregular, rarely regular, but then leaves alternate and corolla
   with valvate aestivation or stamens more than 5. Stamens more or
   less distinctly perigynous. 196
196. Style basal or nearly so. . . . . **103. Rosaceae.**
   Style terminal or nearly so. Stamens 9—10. . . **105. Leguminosae.**
197. Stigma 5-lobed. Calyx valvate in bud. Seeds exalbuminous. Shrubs
   or trees. . . . . *Maesopsis*, **137. Rhamnaceae.**
   Stigmas 2—3. Seeds albuminous. . . . . **75. Caryophyllaceae.**
198. Sepals 2, free or nearly so. 199
   Sepals 3—7, free or more or less united, or an entire calyx. . . 201
199. Flowers unisexual. Stamens 8—10. Style 3—4-cleft. Trees. Leaves
   undivided. . . . . *Didierea*, **134. Sapindaceae.**
   Flowers hermaphrodite. Stamens 2—7. Herbs or shrubs. . . 200
200. Corolla regular. Stamens 4—7, free or nearly so. Style 3-parted
   Embryo large, curved. Shrubs. Leaves undivided.
                            Portulacaria, **73. Portulacaceae.**

Corolla irregular. Stamens 2, three-cleft (or 6, united in 2 bundles). Style simple. Embryo small. Herbs. Leaves dissected. **86. Papaveraceae.**

201. Stamens numerous. Style 1. Corolla with imbricate or contorted aestivation. Leaves opposite. Shrubs or trees.

Calophyllum, **149. Guttiferae.**

Stamens 1—10, rarely more, but then styles 3 or corolla with valvate aestivation. 202

202. Stamens as many as the petals, 4, opposite and adnate to them. Stigma 1. Calyx entire or toothed. Petals 4, valvate. Shrubs or trees.

55. Prrteaceae.

Stamens as many as and alternate with the petals or fewer or more numerous. 203

203. Stigmas or stigma-lobes 1—2. Stamens 2, 4, or 6. Sepals 4. Petals 4. Flowers hermaphrodite. Seeds with curved embryo. Herbs or under-shrubs, rarely shrubs. . . . . **88. Cruciferae.**

Stigmas or stigma-lobes 3, rarely only 1, but then fertile stamens 1, 5, 8, or more. Shrubs or trees. 204

204. Flowers in axillary clusters, hermaphrodite. Sepals and petals valvate in bud. Petals hooded. Stamens 8—10, with 4-celled anthers (or 16—20 united in pairs). Style and stigma simple.

Hua, **144. Sterculiaceae.**

Flowers in panicles. Petals not hooded. Stamens neither with 4-celled anthers nor united in pairs. . . . . . **127. Anacardiaceae.**

205. (192.) Leaves stipulate. Stamens 9—10. 206

Leaves exstipulate, rarely (*Polygalaceae*) stipulate, but then stamens 8. 207

206. Flowers irregular. Stamens more or less perigynous. Style simple.

105. Leguminosae.

Flowers regular. Stamens hypogynous. Styles 3—4, free or partly united. Trees, shrubs, or undershrubs.

Erythroxylon, **112. Erythroxylaceae.**

207. Flowers distinctly irregular, hermaphrodite. Stamens 8; filaments united; anthers opening by a pore. Style 1. Shrubs or trees. Leaves undivided. . . . . *Securidaca*, **120. Polygalaceae.**

Flowers regular or nearly so, rarely distinctly irregular, but then unisexual or with 10 stamens. Anthers opening by longitudinal slits. . . 208

208. Flowers unisexual. Stamens as many as and opposite the petals or more. Leaves simple or digitate. . . . **80. Menispermaceae.**

Flowers hermaphrodite or polygamous, rarely (*Anacardiaceae*) unisexual, but then stamens alternating with the petals or leaves pinnate. . 209

209. Stamens distinctly perigynous, 4 ,8, or 10. Style simple; stigma entire. Leaves undivided. Shrubs. . . . . . **171. Thymelaeaceae.**

Stamens hypogynous or nearly so, rarely (*Anacardiaceae*) distinctly perigynous, but then stigma lobed and leaves pinnate. . . . 210

210. Stamens as many as and opposite the petals, 4—5. Calyx little developed, entire or obscurely toothed. Shrubs. Leaves undivided.
57. Opiliaceae.

Stamens as many as and alternate with the petals or more. Calyx distinctly developed. 211

211. Stamens 6. Sepals 4. Petals 4. Embryo curved. Herbs or under-shrubs, rarely shrubs. Leaves simple. . . . . **88. Cruciferae.**

Stamens 4 or more, rarely 6, but then sepals 3 and petals 3. Shrubs or trees. 212

212. Stamens numerous; filaments united. Style thread-shaped. Corolla with imbricate or contorted aestivation. Leaves opposite, undivided. Shrubs. . . . . *Endodesmia*, **149. Guttiferae.**

Stamens 4—20; if more than 10, then style short and thick, corolla with valvate aestivation, and leaves pinnate. 213

213. Ovule with ventral raphe. Stamens 10. Leaves with 1—3 transparently dotted leaflets. . . . . *Eriander*, **115. Rutaceae.**

Ovule with dorsal raphe. . . . . **127. Anacardiaceae.**

214. (191.) Ovules 2. 215

Ovules 3 or more. 231

215. Ovules or their funicle erect or ascending. 216

Ovules or their funicle pendulous or descending. 224

216. Ovules attached one above the other, rarely side by side; in the latter case flowers irregular, stamens 9—10, and style terminal or nearly so. Leaves usually stipulate. 217

Ovules attached one opposite the other or side by side. Flowers regular, more rarely irregular, but then stamens 6 or style basal. Leaves usually exstipulate. 218

217. Flowers regular. Calyx 5-lobed, valvate in bud. Stamens 5, opposite the petals, hypogynous. Leaves undivided.
Waltheria, **144. Sterculiaceae.**

Flowers irregular, more rarely regular, but then, as usually, stamens perigynous or more than 5. Leaves usually compound.
105. Leguminosae.

218. Ovules straight. Stamens 5 or 10, more or less distinctly perigynous. Leaves compound. Shrubs or trees. . . . . **104. Connaraceae.**

Ovules incurved or inverted. Leaves simple, undivided or dissected; in the latter case herbs. 219

219. Styles 2, free or united below. Stamens 2—5, hypogynous or nearly so. Leaves opposite. Herbs or undershrubs. . **75. Caryophyllaceae.**

Style 1, with a single stigma. Leaves alternate, rarely opposite, but then shrubs or trees. 220

220. Style basal. Stamens perigynous. Leaves alternate. Shrubs or trees. Seeds exalbuminous. . . . . **103. Rosaceae.**

Style terminal or nearly so. Stamens hypogynous, rarely perigynous, but then leaves opposite. 221

221. Stamens 5, perigynous. Sepals united below. Leaves opposite. Shrubs or trees. . . . . . . *Pleurostylia,* **129. Celastraceae.**

Stamens 6, hypogynous. Sepals free. Leaves alternate. . . . 222

222. Flowers irregular. Sepals 2. Petals 4. Fruit a 2-seeded nut. Herbs. Leaves dissected. . . . . *Sarcocapnos,* **86. Papaveraceae.**

Flowers regular. Sepals 3—6. Leaves undivided. 223

223. Perianth of 4 sepals and 4 petals. Anthers opening by longitudinal slits. Style distinctly developed. Fruit a 1-seeded nut. Under-shrubs. Flowers white. . . . *Dipterygium,* **87. Capparidaceae.**

Perianth of 3—6 sepals, 3 petals, and 6 honey-scales. Anthers opening by valves. Style none. Fruit a berry. Shrubs. Flowers yellow.
Berberis, **79. Berberidaceae.**

224. (215.) Ovules suspended from a free central placenta. Stamens 4—10. Shrubs or trees. Leaves undivided, exstipulate. **59. Olacaceae.**

Ovules attached to the wall of the ovary, usually near the apex. . . 225

225. Ovules one above the other, rarely side by side ; in the latter case flowers irregular with 9—10 stamens. Leaves usually compound and stipulate.
105. Leguminosae.

Ovules side by side or one opposite the other. Flowers regular, rarely somewhat irregular, but then stamens 3—6. 226

226. Ovules attached laterally. Stamens 3—5. Flowers usually unisexual. Embryo large. Leaves exstipulate, usually compound. **115. Rutaceae.**

Ovules attached by the apex, rarely laterally, but then stamens more than 5. Flowers usually hermaphrodite. Leaves simple. 227

227. Stamens 4—5. Shrubs or trees. Leaves exstipulate.
132. Icacinaceae.

Stamens 6 or more. 228

228. Stamens 6. Style 1. Sepals 4. Petals 4. Embryo curved. Leaves exstipulate. . . . . **88. Cruciferae.**

Stamens 10 or more. Leaves undivided, stipulate. Shrubs or trees. 229

229. Stamens 10, hypogynous. Styles or stigmas 3—4. Sepals 5. Petals 5.
Erythroxylon, **112. Erythroxylaceae.**

Stamens 12 or more. 230

230. Style 1, with a single stigma. Stamens 12—20, perigynous. Sepals 5—12. Petals 5—12. Seeds with scanty albumen or without any.
103. Rosaceae.

Styles 2—6 or style 1 with 2 stigmas ; in the latter case stamens more then 20. Seeds with copious albumen. . . **159. Flacourtiaceae.**

231. (214.) Ovules basal or attached to a central placenta. 232

Ovules attached to one or more parietal placentas. 244

232. Ovules basal. 233
Ovules attached to a central placenta. 239
233. Style or sessile stigma 1, entire. 234
Styles, stigmas, or stigma-lobes 2—6. 236
234. Stamens 10. Calyx closed in bud, subsequently 2—3-parted. Flowers
solitary or in pairs. . . . . **196. Styracaceae.**
Stamens 5—6. Calyx with 3—9 imbricate segments. 235
235. Flowers 5-merous, in cymes. Stamens perigynous. Anthers opening
by longitudinal slits. Style present. Leaves opposite.
Pleurostylia, **129. Celastraceae.**
Flowers 6-merous, in racemes. Stamens hypogynous. Anthers opening
by valves. Style wanting. Leaves alternate or all radical.
79. Berberidaceae.
236. Stamens very numerous. Anthers linear. Style 2-cleft. Trees. Leaves
alternate, stipulate. . . . . *Lophira*, **147. Ochnaceae.**
Stamens 1—20 ; if more than 10, then styles 5. 237
237. Leaves and flowers clothed with glandular hairs ; the former alternate.
Stamens 10—20. Styles 5, free. Ovules upon a long funicle. Seeds
albuminous, with a minute embryo. Undershrubs.
Drosophyllum, **92. Droseraceae.**
Leaves and flowers without glandular hairs. Stamens 1—10. Seeds
with a large or rather large embryo. 238
238. Leaves alternate. Disc present. Ovules upon a short funicle. Seeds
exalbuminous. . . . . **153. Tamaricaceae.**
Leaves opposite. Seeds albuminous ; embryo usually curved.
75. Caryophyllaceae.
239. (232.) Ovules pendulous. Style 1. Fertile stamens 3—6.
59. Olacaceae.
Ovules ascending or horizontal. 240
240. Stamens as many as and opposite the petals. Style simple ; stigma
entire or obscurely lobed. 241
Stamens as many as and alternate with the petals or fewer or more numerous. 242
241. Stamens 3. Leaves opposite. Herbs. *Pelletiera*, **191. Primulaceae.**
Stamens 4—7. Leaves alternate. Shrubs or trees. **190. Myrsinaceae.**
242. Calyx with valvate aestivation. Petals perigynous. Style simple with
an entire or 2-lobed stigma. Seeds exalbuminous ; embryo straight.
173. Lythraceae.
Calyx with imbricate aestivation. Petals hypogynous or nearly so.
Style simple with a 3-lobed stigma or with several stigmas, or styles
2 or more. Seeds albuminous ; embryo usually curved. . . . 243
243. Sepals 2. Stamens 8—30. Stigmas or stigma-lobes 3. Leaves alternate.
73. Portulacaceae.
Sepals 4—5. Stamens 1—10. Leaves opposite. **75. Caryophyllaceae.**

244. (231.) Ovules attached to a single placenta. 245
Ovules attached to two or more placentas. 248

245. Sepals evidently united, rarely free or nearly so, and then petals 5 or
leaves stipulate. Stamens usually perigynous. Stigma 1. Leaves
usually compound. . . . . **105. Leguminosae.**
Sepals free or nearly so. Petals 2—4. Stamens hypogynous. Leaves
exstipulate, simple, but often dissected. Herbs or undershrubs. 246

246. Flowers distinctly irregular. Sepals 5. Petals 2—4. Stamens numer-
ous. Fruit opening at one side. Embryo straight.
Delphinium, **78. Ranunculaceae.**
Flowers regular or nearly so. Sepals 4 or 8. Petals 4. Stamens 4 or 6.
Fruit opening in two valves or remaining closed. Embryo more or
less curved. 247

247. Stamens 4. Anthers opening by valves. Stigma 1. Albumen abundant
Leaves dissected. . . . . . *Epimedium*, **79. Berberidaceae.**
Stamens 6. Anthers opening by longitudinal slits. Albumen scanty or
wanting. . . . . **88. Cruciferae.**

248. (244.) Style 1, undivided, with a single stigma or with 2 or more stigmas
contiguous at the base, or 1 sessile stigma. 249
Styles 2—6, free or more or less united with separated stigmas (not contiguous at the base), or 2—6 free sessile stigmas. 266

249. Fertile stamens as many as petals or fewer, 2—10. 250
Fertile stamens more than petals. 257

250. Fertile stamens 10. Filaments united. Anthers opening outwards.
Stigmas 5. Sepals 3. Trees. . *Warburgia*, **157. Winteranaceae.**
Fertile stamens 2—6. 251

251. Fertile stamens 2—4. Flowers hermaphrodite. Seeds exalbuminous,
with curved embryo. . . . . **87. Capparidaceae.**
Fertile stamens 5, rarely (*Passifloraceae*) 4 or 6, but then flowers unisexual.
Seeds rarely exalbuminous, and then with straight embryo. . . 252

252. Fertile stamens opposite the petals. Shrubs or trees. 253
Fertile stamens alternate with the petals. Leaves simple. Seeds albuminous. 254

253. Flowers irregular. Petals perigynous. Anthers opening by a single
slit. Placentas 3. Seeds exalbuminous. Leaves pinnate.
Moringa, **90. Moringaceae.**
Flowers regular. Anthers opening by 2 slits. Seeds albuminous.
Leaves simple, undivided. . . . . . . **159. Flacourtiaceae.**

254. Sepals united below. Petals perigynous, sometimes nearly hypogynous,
and then, as usual, staminodes or a corona interposed between the petals
and the stamens. Flowers regular. . . . . **161. Passifloraceae.**
Sepals free or nearly so. Petals hypogynous or nearly so ; in the latter
case neither staminodes nor a corona within them. 255

255. Staminodes present, sometimes petal-like. Placentas 3. Flowers regular. Herbs or undershrubs. Leaves stipulate.   **. 147. Ochnaceae.**
     Staminodes wanting. 256

256. Leaves stipulate, rarely exstipulate and then stem herbaceous or suffruticose. Placentas 3. . . . . **158. Violaceae.**
     Leaves exstipulate. Stem woody. Flowers regular. Placentas 2, rarely 3—5. . . . . *Pittosporum*, **97. Pittosporaceae.**

257. (249.) Sepals and petals together 6 (2 sepals and 4 petals), rarely 9 (3 sepals and 6 petals). Stamens 6 or many. Stem herbaceous. Leaves more or less deeply divided. . . . . . . **86. Papaveraceae.**
     Sepals and petals together 7, 8, 10, or more, rarely 9, but then stem woody and leaves undivided. 258

258. Sepals and petals together 9 ; sepals 3, small ; petals 6, unequal. Stamens numerous, inserted upon an elevated receptacle. Ovules scattered over the inner wall of the ovary. Stigma sessile or nearly so. Albumen ruminate. Trees. Leaves undivided. Flowers hermaphrodite.
                              Monodora, **81. Anonaceae.**
     Sepals and petals together 7, 8, 10, or more, rarely (*Flacourtiaceae*) 9, but then ovules attached to 2—10 placentas and either style distinctly developed or stamens 5—15. 259

259. Perianth of 4 sepals and 4 petals, rarely (*Capparidaceae*) of 2 sepals and 6 petals or of 5 sepals and 5 petals ; in the latter case ovary long-stalked. Albumen scanty or wanting. 260
     Perianth of 3—6 sepals and 4 or more petals, but not of 4 sepals and 4 petals. Ovary sessile or nearly so. 262

260. Filaments united throughout their whole length, 8. Placentas 3—5, with 2 ovules each. Calyx 4-lobed. Leaves pinnate. Shrubs or trees. . . . . **118. Meliaceae.**
     Filaments free or united at the base. Placentas 2 or more, in the latter case with numerous ovules. Embryo curved. Leaves simple or digitate. 261

261. Stamens 6, four of them longer than the other two. Ovary sessile or nearly so. Placentas 2. Flowers regular or nearly so. Herbs or undershrubs. Leaves simple, without stipules. . . . **88. Cruciferae.**
     Stamens few or many ; if 6, then not four longer than the rest. Ovary usually stalked. Stigma usually sessile. Flowers mostly irregular.
                              87. Capparidaceae.

262. Filaments united in 3—5 bundles. Sepals 5. Petals 5. Seeds exalbuminous. Leaves opposite, undivided, exstipulate. **149. Guttiferae.**
     Filaments all free or united at the base. Seeds albuminous. . . 263

263. Anthers opening at the apex by pores or very short slits. Sepals 5. Petals 5. Leaves alternate, stipulate, usually lobed. 264
     Anthers opening by longitudinal slits. Leaves entire or toothed. 265

264. Anthers curved. Placentas 2. Petals red. Flowers and flower-stalks clothed with minute scales. . . . . . *Bixa*, **155. Bixaceae.**
Anthers straight. Placentas 3—5. Petals yellow. Flowers and flower-stalks glabrous or clothed with simple hairs.
Cochlospermum, **156. Cochlospermaceae.**

265. Embryo distinctly curved, folded, or rolled up. Ovules usually straight. Disc and corona usually wanting. Anthers opening inwards or laterally. Sepals 3 or 5. Petals 5, with contorted aestivation. Leaves mostly opposite. Herbs, undershrubs, or shrubs. . . . **154. Cistaceae.**
Embryo straight or nearly straight. Ovules inverted. Disc or corona usually present. Anthers usually opening outwards. Leaves alternate. Shrubs or trees. . . . . **159. Flacourtiaceae.**

266. (248.) Leaves opposite, rarely whorled, undivided. Land-plants. . 267
Leaves alternate or all radical, rarely (*Droseraceae*) whorled, but then water-plants with 5 stamens and 5 styles. 268

267. Sepals united below, valvate in bud. Stamens 4—6. Style 2—3-cleft. Seeds with abundant albumen. . . . . **152. Frankeniaceae.**
Sepals free, imbricate in bud. Stamens 9 or more. Seeds without albumen. . . . . *Hypericum*, **149. Guttiferae.**

268. Herbs with glandular hairs or with whorled leaves. Sepals, petals, and stamens equal in number, 4, 5, or 8. Anthers more or less turned outwards. . . . . **92. Droseraceae.**
Herbs or undershrubs without glandular hairs or woody plants; if herbs then anthers turned inwards, at least when young. Leaves alternate or all radical. 269

269. Flowers irregular. Ovary open at the apex. Stigmas sessile. Seeds exalbuminous; embryo curved. . . . . . . **89. Resedaceae.**
Flowers regular. Ovary closed 270

270. Corolla with contorted aestivation, more or less perigynous. Calyx deciduous, callous or glandular within. Sepals, petals, and stamens 5. Anthers turned inwards. Styles 3. . . . . **160. Turneraceae.**
Corolla with imbricate, not contorted, or with valvate aestivation, very rarely with contorted aestivation, but then stamens numerous. . 271

271. Seeds exalbuminous, rarely albuminous, and then placentas finally separating from the wall of the ovary. Anthers usually turned outwards. Leaves exstipulate. . . . . **153. Tamaricaceae.**
Seeds albuminous. Placentas not separating from the wall of the ovary. Anthers turned inwards, rarely outwards, but then, as usually, leaves stipulate. 272

272. Stem erect, rarely climbing, and then stamens numerous or anthers turned outwards. Corona, if present, simple or double. Ovary sessile or nearly so. Shrubs or trees. Leaves simple, undivided. **159. Flacourtiaceae.**
Stem climbing, usually tendril-bearing, rarely erect, but then corona 3- or

more-fold or ovary distinctly stalked. Stamens 4—10. Anthers turned inwards. Sepals 4—6, more or less united, imbricate in bud. Petals as many as sepals. . . . . . .   **161. Passifloraceae.**

273. (190.) Ovules solitary in each ovary-cell. 274
     Ovules 2 or more in each ovary-cell. 319

274. Ovules erect or ascending. 275
     Ovules pendulous, descending, or horizontal. 288

275. Disc outside the stamens, sometimes one-sided or broken up into several glands. Leaves alternate, compound, rarely simple and then stamens 8—10. 276
     Disc or separate glands within or between the stamens or wanting, rarely outside the stamens, but then leaves simple and stamens 4—6. . . 277

276. Flowers hermaphrodite. Petals 5. Stamens 4—5. Ovary 4-celled. Seeds with abundant albumen ; embryo straight.
                              Bersama, **135. Melianthaceae.**
     Flowers unisexual or polygamous. Seeds without albumen ; embryo more or less curved. . . . .   **134. Sapindaceae.**

277. Petals and stamens hypogynous. 278
     Petals and stamens more or less perigynous. Leaves simple, stipulate. Shrubs or trees. 285

278. Sepals 3. Petals 3 or 6. Shrubs or trees. Leaves alternate, undivided, exstipulate. 279
     Sepals 4 or 5, rarely 2. Petals 3—5. 280

279. Sepals valvate in bud. Stamens numerous. Anthers opening outwards. Ovary many-celled. Styles numerous. . . . . **81. Anonaceae.**
     Sepals imbricate or open in bud. Stamens 3. Anthers opening laterally. Ovary 2—9-celled. Style 2—9-cleft. Flowers unisexual or polygamous. . . . .   **125. Empetraceae.**

280. Sepals valvate in bud, 5. Petals with contorted aestivation. Filaments united. Stigmas several. Leaves simple, stipulate. 281
     Sepals imbricate in bud, rarely valvate, but then only 2. Leaves exstipulate. 282

281. Anthers 1-celled. Fertile stamens numerous. Ovary 3- or more celled. Seeds albuminous. . . . .   **142. Malvaceae.**
     Anthers 2-celled. Fertile stamens 5, rarely more, but then ovary 2-celled and seeds exalbuminous. . . . .   **144. Sterculiaceae.**

282. Stamens numerous. Leaves opposite, undivided. Shrubs or trees.
                                            149. Guttiferae.
     Stamens 2—10. Stigmas 1—2. Leaves alternate. 283

283. Leaves pinnate. Shrubs or trees. Stigma 1.   **118. Meliaceae.**
     Leaves simple. Herbs or undershrubs, rarely shrubs. Embryo curved. 284

284. Sepals 4. Petals 4. Stamens 2—6. Glands present between the stamens. . . . . **88. Cruciferae.**
Sepals 5. Petals 3—5. Stamens 5—10, united at the base.

Limeum, 72. **Aizoaceae.**

285. (277.) Flowers irregular. Petals 4—5. Stamens 10—20. Ovary 2-celled. Style basal. Stigma 1. . . *Parinarium*, **103. Rosaceae.**
Flowers regular. Petals 4—8. Stamens 4—8. Style terminal or nearly so. 286

286. Petals, stamens, and carpels 8 each. . *Dirachma*, **107. Geraniaceae.**
Petals 4—5. Stamens 4—5. Carpels 2—5. 287

287. Calyx with valvate aestivation. Stamens opposite the petals. Style 1, with a more or less deeply divided stigma, or several styles.

137. Rhamnaceae.

Calyx with imbricate or open aestivation. Stamens alternate with the petals. Style 1, with an entire or lobed stigma. **129. Celastraceae.**

288. (274.) Flowers unisexual. 289
Flowers hermaphrodite or polygamous. 293

289. Leaves simple. 290
Leaves compound. Shrubs or trees. 293

290. Sepals 2—3, united below, valvate in bud. Petals 5, with contorted aestivation. Stamens numerous. Ovary 2-celled. Style wanting ; stigma lobed. Shrubs or trees. . . *Carpodiptera*, **141. Tiliaceae.**
Sepals, at least in the female flowers, 4—6, sometimes almost wholly united. 291

291. Ovary slightly sunk in the receptacle, 2-celled. Styles 2. Stamens 5. Anthers opening by valves. Sepals and petals valvate in bud. Shrubs.

Trichocladus, **101. Hamamelidaceae.**

Ovary wholly superior, usually 3-celled. Styles usually 3. Anthers opening by longitudinal slits. 292

292. Ovules straight. Stigmas sessile or nearly so. Stamens 10. Calyx-limb nearly entire. Fruit drupaceous. . *Panda*, **106. Pandaceae.**
Ovules inverted. . . . . **122. Euphorbiaceae.**

293. Leaves stipulate. Ovary surrounded by scales. Fruit capsular. Spiny shrubs. . . . . . . *Neoluederitzia*, **113. Zygophyllaceae.**
Leaves exstipulate. Fruit usually drupaceous. . **127. Anacardiaceae.**

294. (288.) Flowers distinctly irregular. 295
Flowers regular or nearly so. 298

295. Leaves compound. Receptacle expanded into a disc or elongated into a stalk. Filaments free. Trees or shrubs. . . **127. Anacardiaceae.**
Leaves simple, undivided. Receptacle small. 296

296. Stamens 10. Shrubs or undershrubs. . . . . **119. Malpighiaceae.**
Stamens 5—8. 297

297. Filaments free. Anthers opening by two longitudinal slits. Petals 5,
perigynous. Style 1 ; stigmas 3. Climbing herbs.

Tropaeolum, **109. Tropaeolaceae.**

Filaments united. Anthers opening by an apical pore. Petals hypogynous. . . . . **120. Polygalaceae.**

298. (294.) Stamens as many as the petals or fewer or more numerous, but less
than twice as many, 2—6. 299

Stamens twice as many as the petals or in greater number, rarely (*Thymelaeaceae*) as many as the petals, but then 8—10. 305

299. Filaments all united below. Fertile and sterile stamens together as many
as the petals, 4—6.· Disc not distinctly developed. Leaves undivided. 300

Filaments free or united in pairs. 301

300. Stamens all fertile. Seeds albuminous. . . . . **110. Linaceae.**

Stamens partly sterile (2 fertile, 3 sterile). Seeds exalbuminous.

Cottsia, **119. Malpighiaceae.**

301. Anthers opening by apical pores. Petals and stamens 5, slightly perigynous. Ovary 3-celled. Style simple ; stigma 3-lobed. Seeds with
abundant albumen. Undershrubs. Leaves rolled inwards when young,
undivided, bearing glandular hairs. . . *Roridula*, **147. Ochnaceae.**

Anthers opening by longitudinal slits. Seeds with scanty albumen or
without any. 302

302. Stamens 6, rarely 2 or 4. Style 1. Sepals 4. Petals 4. Embryo curved.
Herbs or undershrubs, rarely shrubs. Leaves simple. **88. Cruciferae.**

Stamens 5, rarely 4, but then styles 4 and leaves pinnate. Shrubs or
trees. 303

303. Flowers 4-merous. Disc within the stamens. Leaves pinnate.

116. Simarubaceae.

Flowers 5-merous. 304

304. Disc within the stamens. Ovary 3- or 5-celled. Styles or sessile stigmas
3 or 5. Leaves simple. . . . . . . **127. Anacardiaceae.**

Disc outside the stamens. Ovary 2-celled. Style simple. Leaves pinnate.

Filicium, **134. Sapindaceae.**

305. (298.) Filaments free. Shrubs or trees, rarely undershrubs. . . 306

Filaments united into a tube, at least at the base. 312

306. Disc present, more or less ring-, cushion-, or cup-shaped. . . . 307

Disc wanting. Leaves undivided. 310

307. Flowers polygamous, 4—5-merous. Leaves compound, exstipulate.

127. Anacardiaceae.

Flowers hermaphrodite, rarely polygamous, but then 3-merous. . . 308

308. Leaves with glandular dots, compound, exstipulate. Ovary 3—5-celled.
Style simple. . . . . **115. Rutaceae.**

Leaves without dots. 309

309. Leaves stipulate, pinnate with 1—2 pairs of leaflets, more rarely simple and undivided, and then stigma 3-parted. Ovary 3—5-celled. Style simple. . . . . **113. Zygophyllaceae.**
Leaves rarely stipulate, but then undivided and stigma entire or 2-lobed.
116. Simarubaceae.

310. Sepals united into a minute, entire or toothed calyx. Petals 4—6, valvate in bud. Ovary 3—4-celled. Seeds with abundant albumen.
59. Olacaceae.
Sepals free or united at the base only. Seeds without albumen. . . 311

311. Petals 5, imbricate in bud. Ovary 2—3-celled. **119. Malpighiaceae.**
Petals 8—10, rarely 4—5, scale-like, valvate in bud. Sepals free, petaloid. Ovary 4—5-celled. . . . . . *Octolepis*, **171. Thymelaeaceae.**

312. (305.) Stamens numerous. Anthers opening by one slit. Calyx with valvate aestivation. Seeds with curved embryo. Leaves simple, stipulate. . . . . **142. Malvaceae.**
Stamens twice as many as the petals, 6—12, rarely (*Malpighiaceae*) a few more (11—15). Anthers opening by two slits. Calyx with imbricate or open aestivation. 313

313. Style 1, undivided with a single stigma or with two or more stigmas contiguous at the base. 314
Styles 2—5, free or more or less united with separate (not contiguous) stigmas. Stamens 10, rarely 11—15. 316

314. Leaves compound, exstipulate. Seeds without albumen.
118. Meliaceae.
Leaves simple, undivided. Stamens 10. 315

315. Ovary 5-celled. Disc present. Seeds albuminous. Trees. Leaves exstipulate. . . . . *Saccoglottis*, **111. Humiriaceae.**
Ovary 2—3-celled. Disc wanting. Shrubs or undershrubs. . . 316

316. Seeds albuminous. Flowers in axillary fascicles. Leaves alternate, stipulate. . . . . *Nectaropetalum*, **110. Linaceae.**
Seeds exalbuminous. Flowers in racemose inflorescences, rarely solitary. Sepals usually with glands on the outside. **119. Malpighiaceae.**

317. Styles and ovary-cells 5. Herbs or undershrubs, rarely shrubs.
108. Oxalidaceae.
Styles and ovary-cells 2—4. Trees or shrubs, rarely undershrubs. Leaves undivided. 318

318. Flowers solitary or in fascicles. Petals with a scale on the inside. Styles or style-branches 3—4. Fruit a drupe. Seeds usually albuminous. Leaves alternate, stipulate. . . *Erythroxylon*, **112. Erythroxylaceae.**
Flowers in racemose inflorescences. Sepals usually with glands on the outside. Styles or style-branches 2—3. Seeds exalbuminous.
119. Malpighiaceae.

319. (273.) Ovules 2 in each ovary-cell. 320
Ovules 3 or more in each ovary-cell. 389

320. Style 1, undivided, or 2 or more styles united to the base of the stigmas, or 1 sessile stigma. 321

Styles 2 or more, free or united below, but not up to the base of the stigmas, or 2 or more free sessile stigmas. 371

321. Stamens as many as or fewer than the petals. 322

Stamens more than the petals. 339

322. Stamens as many as and opposite to the petals. 323

Stamens as many as and alternate with the petals, or fewer. . . 325

323. Stamens 10. Ovary 10-celled. Herbs. Leaves opposite.

Augea, **113. Zygophyllaceae.**

Stamens 3—7. Leaves alternate. 324

324. Petals with valvate aestivation. Filaments free. Ovary 2-celled. Fruit a berry. . . . . **138. Vitaceae.**

Petals with imbricate-contorted aestivation. Filaments more or less united. Ovary 3- or more-celled. Fruit a capsule. **144. Sterculiaceae.**

325. Stamens 2—4. 326

Stamens 5. 333

326. Sepals 2—4. Petals 3—4. 327

Sepals 5. Petals 2—5. 332

327. Leaves marked with glandular dots, at least at the edges. Stipules wanting. 328

Leaves without glandular dots. 329

328. Leaves simple, undivided. Flowers hermaphrodite. Disc cushion-shaped. Stigmas 3. Fruit separating into 3 drupe-like, 2-celled mericarps. Seeds with curved embryo. *Chamaelea*, **114. Cneoraceae.**

Leaves compound, more rarely simple, but then fruit not drupe-like.

115. Rutaceae.

329. Leaves stipulate. Ovules usually erect. Corolla imbricate in bud. Shrubs or trees. 330

Leaves exstipulate. Ovules usually pendulous. Ovary 2-celled or transversally septate. Flowers hermaphrodite. 331

330. Disc present. . . . . **129. Celastraceae.**

Disc wanting. Flowers unisexual. Ovary 2-celled.

Azima, **131. Salvadoraceae.**

331. Leaves opposite. Petals valvate in bud. Receptacle without glands. Shrubs or trees. . . . . **197. Oleaceae.**

Leaves alternate. Petals imbricate in bud. Receptacle provided with glands. Herbs or undershrubs, rarely shrubs. . . **88. Cruciferae.**

332. (326.) Anthers opening outwards. Stamens 3. Disc present. Ovary 3-celled. Seeds exalbuminous. . . . . . **130. Hippocrateaceae.**

Anthers opening inwards. Disc reduced to separate glands or wholly wanting. Ovary 5-celled. Stigmas 5. Seeds albuminous.

107. Geraniaceae.

333. (325.) Filaments united, at least at the base. 334
  Filaments free. 336

334. Filaments united nearly to the apex. Petals with valvate aestivation.
  Stigma 1. Leaves pinnate, exstipulate.
          Quivisianthe, **118. Meliaceae.**
  Filaments united only at the base. Petals with imbricate or contorted
  aestivation. Leaves stipulate. 335

335. Petals with contorted aestivation. Stigma 1. Seeds with an aril.
  Shrubs. Leaves undivided. . . . *Phyllocosmus*, **110. Linaceae.**
  Petals with imbricate aestivation. Stigmas 5. Seeds without an aril.
            107. Geraniaceae.

336. Leaves gland-dotted, exstipulate, but sometimes with axillary spines.
            115. Rutaceae.

  Leaves not dotted, simple, stipulate. 337

337. Calyx with valvate aestivation. . . . *Triumfetta*, **141. Tiliaceae.**
  Calyx with imbricate or open aestivation. 338

338. Calyx large. Ovules pendulous. Seeds exalbuminous. Leaves alternate.
        Dichapetalum, **121. Dichapetalaceae.**
  Calyx small. Ovules erect, more rarely pendulous, but then leaves
  opposite, at least those of the flowering branches. **129. Celastraceae.**

339. (321.) Stamens fewer than twice as many as the petals, 5—8. . . 340
  Stamens twice as many as the petals, or more. 343

340. Flowers unisexual or polygamous. Disc outside the stamens. Stamens
  8, rarely 5—6 ; in the latter case ovary 3-celled. Ovules ascending,
  at least one of them, or horizontal. Shrubs or trees. . . . 341
  Flowers hermaphrodite. Stamens 5—7. Ovary 2- or 5-celled or transversally septate. Herbs or undershrubs, rarely shrubs. . . . 342

341. Ovary 2-celled. Leaves opposite, lobed. *Acer*, **133. Aceraceae.**
  Ovary 3-celled. Leaves alternate, pinnate. . . . **134. Sapindaceae.**

342. Sepals 4. Petals 4. Stamens 6. Ovary 2-celled or transversally septate.
  Stigmas 1—2. Leaves exstipulate. . . . . . **88. Cruciferae.**
  Sepals 5. Ovary 5-celled. Stigmas 5. Leaves stipulate.
            107. Geraniaceae.

343. (339.) Stamens twice as many as the petals. 344
  Stamens more than twice as many as the petals. 359

344. Filaments free 345
  Filaments evidently united, at least at the base. 354

345. Calyx with valvate aestivation. 346
  Calyx with imbricate aestivation. 349

346. Leaves gland-dotted, without stipules, but sometimes with axillary spines.
            115. Rutaceae.

  Leaves not gland-dotted, usually with stipules. 347

347. Leaves opposite or whorled, undivided, stipulate. Petals valvate in bud. Stamens perigynous. Shrubs or trees. . . **177. Rhizophoraceae.**
Leaves alternate. 348

348. Leaves simple, stipulate. Stamens hypogynous. **141. Tiliaceae.**
Leaves compound, more rarely simple, but then, as usual, exstipulate. Shrubs or trees. . . . . **117. Burseraceae.**

349. Stipules present, but sometimes very small and caducous. . . . 350
Stipules wanting, but axillary spines sometimes present. . . . 352

350. Sepals 3, surrounded by a 6-toothed involucre. Petals 5. Disc cup-shaped. Trees or shrubs. Leaves alternate, undivided.
Leptochlaena, **140. Chlaenaceae.**
Sepals 4—6. Disc ring- or cushion-shaped or reduced to separate scales or wanting. 351

351. Stigma 1, entire or lobed. Filaments usually provided with an appendage. Leaves usually compound. . . . . . . **113. Zygophyllaceae.**
Stigmas 5. Filaments without an appendage. Leaves simple, but sometimes dissected. Fruit beaked, splitting into 5 nutlets.
107. Geraniaceae.

352. Flowers irregular, 4-merous. Disc outside the stamens, one-sided, sometimes indistinct. Ovary 2—3-celled. Leaves pinnate.
134. Sapindaceae.
Flowers regular. 353

353. Bark resinous. Leaves rarely dotted. Ovules pendulous or laterally attached. Fruit drupe-like, but sometimes dehiscing. Seeds exalbuminous. . . . . **117. Burseraceae.**
Bark not resinous. Leaves gland-dotted. Ovules usually ascending.
115. Rutaceae.

354. (344.) Sepals valvate in bud, united below. Leaves stipulate. . . 355
Sepals imbricate in bud. 356

355. Leaves opposite or whorled. Petals toothed or slit, valvate in bud.
177. Rhizophoraceae.
Leaves alternate. Petals nearly always imbricate in bud.
144. Sterculiaceae.

356. Stigmas 5. Ovary lobed. Sepals and petals imbricate in bud. Herbs or undershrubs. Leaves simple, stipulate. . . **107. Geraniaceae.**
Stigmas 1—3. Shrubs or trees. 357

357. Leaves stipulate, undivided. Petals with contorted aestivation. Disc wanting. . . . . **110. Linaceae.**
Leaves exstipulate. Stigma 1, entire or lobed. 358

358. Leaves simple, undivided. Ovary 3-celled. Disc wanting.
Asteropeia, **148. Theaceae.**
Leaves compound, more rarely simple, but then ovary 4—20-celled. Disc usually present. . . . . **118. Meliaceae.**

359. (343.) Petals with valvate aestivation. Trees or shrubs. . . . 360
   Petals with imbricate or contorted aestivation. 362
360. Sepals free. Petals and stamens hypogynous. Anthers opening by an
   apical pore. . . . . *Elaeocarpus*, **139. Elaeocarpaceae.**
   Sepals united below. Petals and stamens more or less perigynous. Anthers opening by two longitudinal slits. 361
361. Calyx entire or nearly so. Leaves alternate. . **145. Scytopetalaceae.**
   Calyx more or less deeply divided. Leaves opposite or whorled.
                                   177. Rhizophoraceae.
362. Calyx with valvate aestivation. 363
   Calyx with imbricate aestivation. 366
363. Leaves exstipulate, undivided, opposite. Ovules ascending or horizontal. Seeds exalbuminous. . . . . . . **149. Guttiferae.**
   Leaves stipulate. Petals 5. 364
364. Filaments free. Anthers opening by two slits. . . . **141. Tiliaceae.**
   Filaments evidently united. 365
365. Anthers opening by a single slit. . . . . . . **142. Malvaceae.**
   Anthers opening by two slits. Stigmas 3 or 5.
                           Dombeya, **144. Sterculiaceae.**
366. Stem herbaceous or woody at the base. 367
   Stem woody throughout. Leaves undivided. 368
367. Sepals and petals with contorted aestivation. Ovary 3-celled. Stigmas
   1—3. Fruit opening loculicidally. Leaves entire. **154. Cistaceae.**
   Sepals and petals with imbricate aestivation. Stamens 15. Ovary 5-
   celled. Stigmas 5. Fruit opening septicidally. Leaves stipulate.
                           107. Geraniaceae.
368. Leaves stipulate. 369
   Leaves exstipulate. 370
369. Sepals 3, surrounded by a 3—5-toothed involucre. Disc cup-shaped.
   Fruit dehiscent. . . . . . *Sarcochlaena*, **140. Chlaenaceae.**
   Sepals 5. Disc wanting. Fruit indehiscent. **150. Dipterocarpaceae.**
370. Leaves alternate. Ovules pendulous. . . . . . **148. Theaceae.**
   Leaves opposite. Ovules ascending or horizontal. **149. Guttiferae.**
371. (320.) Stamens as many to twice as many as petals, 4—12. . . . 372
   Stamens more than twice as many as petals. 382
372. Filaments free. 373
   Filaments obviously united, at least at the base. 377
373. Stipules present, but sometimes very small and caducous. . . . 374
   Stipules wanting, but axillary spines sometimes present. . . . 376
374. Leaves opposite or whorled. Flowers hermaphrodite. Stamens 8—10.
                           98. Cunoniaceae.
   Leaves alternate. 375
375. Style 1, 2—3-cleft, with undivided branches. Stamens 5. Disc present.
   Sepals imbricate in bud. Petals usually 2-cleft. Fruit a drupe or nut.
   Seeds exalbuminous. . . . *Dichapetalum*, **121. Dichapetalaceae.**

C

Styles 2, 3, or 5, free or united at the base, usually 2-cleft. Flowers unisexual. Fruit usually a capsule. . . . **122. Euphorbiaceae.**

376. Leaves with glandular dots. Petals 4—5. Stamens as many or twice as many. . . . . **115. Rutaceae.**
Leaves without glandular dots, lobed, opposite. Petals 5. Stamens 8, inserted at the inner edge of the disc. Ovary-cells and style-branches 2.
Acer, **133. Aceraceae.**

377. Flowers unisexual. Stamens as many as and alternate with the petals. Leaves alternate, undivided, stipulate. ̄ . . **122. Euphorbiaceae.**
Flowers hermaphrodite, rarely polygamous. 378

378. Sepals valvate in bud, united below. Leaves alternate, stipulate.
144. Sterculiaceae.
Sepals imbricate in bud. 379

379. Petals with a callosity or scale on the inside. Ovary-cells and styles or style-branches 3—4. Stamens 10. Flowers solitary or in fascicles. Leaves undivided, stipulate. Shrubs or trees. **112. Erythroxylaceae.**
Petals without an appendage on the inside. Ovary-cells and styles or style-branches 5, more rarely 3—4, but then stamens 4—5 or flowers in racemes or panicles. 380

380. Ovary lobed, 5-celled. Styles 5. Stamens 10. Fruit a capsule. Herbs or undershrubs, rarely shrubs. Leaves alternate, usually compound.
108. Oxalidaceae.
Ovary entire. Stamens 4—5 or 10 ; in the latter case styles 3 or fruit a drupe. Leaves simple, undivided. 381

381. Ovary-cells and styles or style-branches 3. Stamens 10. Flowers in panicles. Leaves alternate, exstipulate. Small trees or climbing shrubs. . . . . *Asteropeia,* **148. Theaceae.**
Ovary-cells and styles or style-branches 5, rarely 3—4, but then stamens 4—5 or flowers in cone-like racemes. . . . . . **110. Linaceae.**

382. (371.) Leaves stipulate, alternate. 383
Leaves exstipulate. 386

383. Calyx imbricate in bud, 4-partite. Stamens 10. Filaments free or united at the base. Anthers turned outwards, 2-celled. Flowers unisexual. Trees. . . . . *Heywoodia,* **122. Euphorbiaceae.**
Calyx valvate in bud. 384

384. Anthers 1-celled (one half only developed). Filaments united. Seeds albuminous ; embryo curved. . . . . **142. Malvaceae.**
Anthers 2-celled (both halves developed, but sometimes finally confluent). 385

385. Filaments united at the base or higher up. Flowers hermaphrodite or polygamous. . . . . **144. Sterculiaceae.**
Filaments free or united at the base ; in the latter case flowers unisexual.
141. Tiliaceae.

386. Leaves opposite, undivided. Ovules ascending or horizontal. Seeds exalbuminous. . . . . **149. Guttiferae.**
Leaves alternate. 387

387. Sepals 2. Petals 4—5, imbricate in bud. Filaments free. Anthers 2-celled. Disc cup-shaped. Ovary 2-celled. Ovules ascending. Style 1, two-cleft. . . . . *Talinella*, **73. Portulacaceae.**
Sepals 5. Disc wanting. Ovary 3—5-celled. Ovules pendulous. Styles 3—5, free or united at the base. 388

388. Flowers unisexual, in glomerules. Petals in the male flowers 3, valvate in bud. Anthers 4-celled. . . . *Junodia*, **122. Euphorbiaceae.**
Flowers hermaphrodite, in panicles. Petals 5, imbricate in bud. Anthers 2-celled. . . . . **148. Theaceae.**

389. (319.) Style 1, undivided, with a single stigma or with two or more stigmas contiguous at the base, or one sessile stigma. 390
Styles 2 or more, free or united below, but not to the base of the stigmas, or two or more free sessile stigmas. 439

390. Stamens fewer than twice as many as the petals. 391
Stamens twice as many as the petals or more. 404

391. Petals and stamens hypogynous. 392
Petals, and usually also the stamens, more or less perigynous. Leaves undivided. 399

392. Stamens 7—9, free. Sepals 3 or 5, petals 5, both with contorted aestivation. Flowers regular. Leaves entire. . . **154. Cistaceae.**
Stamens 2—6. 393

393. Ovary 2-celled. Stamens 6, rarely 2 or 4. Sepals 4, petals 4. Receptacle with glands. Leaves simple, without stipules, but often with auricles at the base. . . . . **88. Cruciferae.**
Ovary 3- or more-celled. Stamens 4—5. 394

394. Sepals valvate in bud, united below. Filaments usually united. Disc wanting. Leaves stipulate. 395
Sepals imbricate or open in bud, free or nearly so, rarely evidently united, but then leaves exstipulate. Filaments free; anthers sometimes united. 396

395. Anthers opening by 1 slit. Leaves palmately compound. Trees.
Ceiba, **143. Bombacaceae.**
Anthers opening by 2 slits or pores. Leaves simple.
144. Sterculiaceae.

396. Anthers united, opening at the apex. Stamens 5. Disc wanting. Petals 3 or 5. Sepals 3 or 5, one of them spurred. Herbs. Leaves undivided, exstipulate. . . *Impatiens*, **136. Balsaminaceae.**
Anthers free, opening lengthwise. 397

397. Flowers irregular. Stamens usually fewer than the petals. Disc present. Ovary 4—5-celled. Albumen abundant. Shrubs or trees. Leaves alternate, pinnate. . . . . . *Melianthus*, **135. Melianthaceae.**

Flowers regular. Stamens as many as the petals. Albumen scanty or
wanting. 398
398. Disc present. Leaves stipulate, usually opposite or compound.

113. Zygophyllaceae.

Disc wanting. Staminodes in bundles alternating with the fertile stamens.
Sepals united below. Leaves exstipulate, alternate, undivided.

Thomassetia, **148. Theaceae.**

399. (391.) Calyx with valvate aestivation. Seeds exalbuminous ; embryo
straight. . . . . **173. Lythraceae.**
Calyx with imbricate or open aestivation. 400
400. Stem herbaceous. Leaves without glandular dots, exstipulate. Sepals
4. Petals 4. Stamens 6. Ovary 2-celled.

Subularia, **88. Cruciferae.**

Stem woody. Stamens 3—5, very rarely 6—8, but then sepals 5 and
petals 5. 401
401. Leaves with glandular dots, alternate, exstipulate. Stamens 5—8.
Ovary 2—3-celled. Seeds exalbuminous.

Heteropyxis, **180. Myrtaceae.**

Leaves without glandular dots. Stamens 3—5. Ovary 3—7-celled. 402
402. Leaves opposite, rarely alternate and then, as usually, stamens 3. Stamens
inserted upon the disc. Filaments dilated. Ovary 3-celled. Seeds
exalbuminous. . . . . **130. Hippocrateaceae.**
Leaves alternate. Stamens 4—5, inserted below the edge of the disc.
Seeds albuminous. 403
403. Leaves stipulate. Ovary 3—5-celled. Fruit a capsule. Seeds with an
aril. . . . . **129. Celastraceae.**
Leaves exstipulate. Ovary 5—7-celled. Fruit a drupe. Seeds without
an aril. . . . . *Brexia,* **96. Saxifragaceae.**
404. (390.) Stamens twice as many as the petals. 405
Stamens more than twice as many as the petals. 416
405. Petals and stamens hypogynous. 406
Petals, and usually also the stamens, perigynous. Leaves undivided. 413
406. Filaments united in a tube, at least at the base. 407
Filaments free, rarely (*Rutaceae*) united in several bundles. . . 408
407. Sepals valvate in bud, very rarely at first imbricate ; in this case many
ovules in each ovary-cell and leaves undivided. Disc wanting. Leaves
stipulate. . . . . **144. Sterculiaceae.**
Sepals imbricate in bud. Ovules few in each ovary-cell, rarely many,
but then leaves pinnate. Disc usually distinctly developed. Leaves
exstipulate. Shrubs or trees. . . . . **118. Meliaceae.**
408. Ovary distinctly stalked, entire. Seeds exalbuminous ; embryo curved.

87. Capparidaceae.

Ovary sessile or nearly so. 409

409. Calyx with valvate aestivation. Disc wanting. Leaves stipulate.
141. Tiliaceae.
Calyx with imbricate, contorted, or open aestivation. 410

410. Calyx with contorted aestivation. Disc wanting. Leaves undivided.
Seeds albuminous ; embryo curved. . . . . . **154. Cistaceae.**
Calyx with imbricate, not contorted, or with open aestivation. Disc
ring-, cushion-, or cup-shaped. 411

411. Disc outside the stamens. Flowers usually irregular. Seeds with a
copious albumen and straight embryo. Shrubs or trees.
135. Melianthaceae.
Disc within the stamens. Flowers regular. 412

412. Leaves with translucent dots, exstipulate. . . . **115. Rutaceae.**
Leaves without dots, stipulate. . . . . . **113. Zygophyllaceae.**

413. (405.) Anthers opening by 1—2 apical pores. Leaves opposite or whorled,
exstipulate.. . . . . **181. Melastomataceae.**
Anthers opening by 2 longitudinal slits. 414

414. Calyx with valvate aestivation. . . . . **173. Lythraceae.**
Calyx with imbricate aestivation. Stamens 10. Ovary 3-celled. Shrubs
or trees. Leaves alternate, exstipulate. 415

415. Flowers polygamous, without bracteoles. Calyx shortly lobed. Filaments
free. Anthers attached by the base. Fruit indehiscent. Leaves with
translucent dots. . . . . . . *Psiloxylon*, **180. Myrtaceae.**
Flowers hermaphrodite. Calyx deeply divided. Anthers attached by
the back. Fruit dehiscing loculicidally. Leaves without dots.
Asteropeia, **148. Theaceae.**

416. (404.) Petals and stamens hypogynous. 417
Petals, and usually also the stamens, perigynous. 433

417. Stipules present, but sometimes minute and caducous. 418
Stipules wanting, but axillary spines sometimes present. 428

418. Calyx with valvate, closed, or open aestivation. 419
Calyx with imbricate or contorted aestivation. 425

419. Corolla with valvate aestivation. 420
Corolla with imbricate or contorted aestivation. 421,

420. Petals toothed or laciniate. Anthers opening by a single pore or slit at the
apex. Trees. Leaves undivided. *Elaeocarpus*, **139. Elaeocarpaceae.**
Petals entire or emarginate. Anthers opening by 2 pores or slits.
141. Tiliaceae.

421. Ovary distinctly stalked. Stigma usually sessile. Petals with imbricate, not contorted aestivation. Seeds exalbuminous.
87. Capparidaceae.
Ovary sessile or nearly so. Petals usually with contorted aestivation. 422

422. Anthers 1-celled, opening by 1 slit or pore. Filaments united. Petals
5. 423
Anthers 2-celled, opening by 2, rarely confluent slits or pores. . . 424

423. Leaves simple. Flowers with an epicalyx. Filaments united to the apex
or nearly so. Pollen-grains spiny. . . . . . . **142. Malvaceae.**
Leaves palmately compound. Flowers without an epicalyx. Filaments
united below. Pollen-grains smooth or nearly so. Trees.
143. Bombacaceae.

424. Filaments more or less united. Staminodes present. **144. Sterculiaceae.**
Filaments free, rarely shortly united at the base, but then staminodes
absent. . . . . **141. Tiliaceae.**

425. (418.) Calyx and corolla with contorted aestivation. Petals 5—6.
Ovary sessile or nearly so. Seeds albuminous. Leaves undivided. 426
Calyx and corolla with imbricate, not contorted aestivation. . . 427

426. Disc present. Ovules inverted. . . . . . . **140. Chlaenaceae.**
Disc absent. Ovules usually straight. . . . . . **154. Cistaceae.**

427. Ovary sessile, 2—3-celled. Style awl-shaped. Ovules ascending. Seeds
with copious albumen. Flowers regular. Leaves undivided.
Sphaerosepalum, **156. Cochlospermaceae.**
Ovary stalked. Seeds without albumen. . . . **87. Capparidaceae.**

428. (417.) Leaves all radical, floating, peltate. Petals numerous. Ovary
6- or more-celled. Stigma sessile. Seeds albuminous ; embryo straight.
Nuphar, **76. Nymphaeaceae.**
Leaves cauline and radical or all cauline, not floating. Petals 4—5. 429

429. Leaves opposite. Calyx with valvate, open, or imbricate, not contorted
aestivation. Filaments usually united in several bundles. Seeds
exalbuminous. . . . . **149. Guttiferae.**
Leaves alternate, more rarely (*Cistaceae*) opposite, but then calyx and
corolla with contorted aestivation, filaments free, and seeds albuminous. 430

430. Leaves compound, with 1—3 leaflets, translucently dotted. Sepals united
below. Ovary sessile, 5- or more-celled. Seeds exalbuminous.
115. Rutaceae.
Leaves simple, undivided, not dotted, rarely digitate or dotted, but then
ovary stalked. 431

431. Ovary stalked. Stigma usually sessile. Disc usually present. Seeds
exalbuminous. . . . . **87. Capparidaceae.**
Ovary sessile. Disc not distinctly developed. Flowers regular. . 432

432. Sepals and petals with contorted aestivation. Ovules usually straight.
Seeds albuminous. . . . . **154. Cistaceae.**
Sepals and petals 5, with imbricate, not contorted aestivation. Ovules
inverted or incurved. Trees or shrubs. . . . . **148. Theaceae.**

433. (416.) Calyx with valvate, closed, or open aestivation. 434
Calyx with imbricate or contorted aestivation. Leaves undivided. 438

434. Corolla with valvate, calyx with open aestivation. Ovary 3—8-celled.
Seeds albuminous. Leaves alternate, undivided. Trees or shrubs.
145. Scytopetalaceae.

Corolla with imbricate or open aestivation ; in the latter case calyx valvate. Seeds exalbuminous, rarely with scanty albumen, but then leaves
digitate. 435

435. Anthers opening by a single slit. Filaments united. Ovary 5—10-
celled, slightly sunk in the receptacle. Petals 5, with contorted aestivation. Seeds albuminous. Leaves digitate, stipulate. Trees.

143. Bombacaceae.

Anthers opening by 2 slits. Seeds exalbuminous. Leaves undivided
rarely digitate, but then ovary stalked and 2-celled. 436

436. Ovary stalked, 2-celled. Embryo curved. Leaves alternate.

87. Capparidaceae.

Ovary sessile. Embryo straight. Leaves undivided, usually opposite. 437

437. Ovary 2—6-celled. . . . . **173. Lythraceae.**

Ovary 10—20-celled. Ovules inserted upon the dissepiments. Petals
linear. Trees or shrubs. Leaves opposite, exstipulate.

Sonneratia, **174. Sonneratiaceae.**

438. Calyx and corolla with contorted aestivation. Petals 5—6. Disc present. Ovary 3-celled. Style present. Trees or shrubs. Leaves alternate, not peltate. . . . . **140. Chlaenaceae.**

Calyx and corolla with imbricate, not contorted aestivation. Petals
numerous. Disc wanting. Ovary 6- or more-celled. Style wanting.
Herbs. Leaves all radical, floating, peltate.

Nymphaea, **76. Nymphaeaceae.**

439. (389.) Stamens as many or twice as many as the petals, 3—10. . . 440

Stamens numerous. 446

440. Petals and stamens perigynous or inserted at the base of an hypogynous
disc. Stamens 8 or 10. Styles free. Seeds albuminous. . . 441

Petals and stamens hypogynous. Disc wanting. 442

441. Stem herbaceous. Leaves usually radical or alternate and exstipulate.
Placentas thick. . . . . *Saxifraga*, **96. Saxifragaceae.**

Stem woody. Leaves opposite or whorled, stipulate. Ovules in two rows.

98. Cunoniaceae.

442. Leaves opposite or whorled, undivided, stipulate. Filaments free.
Styles free. Seeds exalbuminous. Herbs or undershrubs.

151. Elatinaceae.

Leaves alternate or all radical. 443

443. Sepals united below, valvate in bud. Leaves stipulate.

144. Sterculiaceae.

Sepals free or nearly so, imbricate in bud. 444

444. Ovary-cells and styles 5. Petals with contorted aestivation. Seeds
albuminous. . . . . **108. Oxalidaceae.**

Ovary-cells and styles or style-branches 3. Stamens 10. Trees or
shrubs. Leaves undivided. 445

445. Filaments free. Anthers opening at the apex. Style shortly 3-cleft. Ovules in several rows. Albumen abundant. Bracteoles absent.

Clethra, **188. Clethraceae.**

Filaments united at the base. Ovules in two rows. Albumen scanty or wanting. Bracteoles present. . . . *Asteropeia*, **148. Theaceae.**

446. (439.) Petals and stamens perigynous, adnate to the ovary at the base, numerous. Filaments free. Sepals imbricate in bud. Leaves all radical, stipulate. . . . . . . *Nymphaea*, **76. Nymphaeaceae.**

Petals and stamens hypogynous, free from the ovary. Petals 3—9. 447

447. Leaves opposite, undivided, exstipulate. Seeds exalbuminous.

149. Guttiferae.

Leaves alternate. 448

448. Petals 8. Sepals 5, imbricate in bud. Filaments free. Styles free. Seeds with a straight embryo and copious albumen. Herbs. Leaves dissected, exstipulate. . . . . *Nigella*, **78. Ranunculaceae.**

Petals 3—5. Filaments united, at least at the base. 449

449. Sepals 5, free or nearly so, imbricate in bud. Albumen scanty or wanting. Trees or shrubs. Leaves undivided, exstipulate. . **148. Theaceae.**

Sepals 3—5, valvate or open in bud. Leaves stipulate. . . . 450

450. Anthers opening by a single slit or pore. . . . . **142. Malvaceae.**

Anthers opening by two slits or pores. . . . **144. Sterculiaceae.**

451. (189.) Styles united below or throughout their whole length. . . 452

Styles entirely free or loosely cohering above. 457

452. Anthers 1-celled, opening by a single slit. Stamens numerous. Filaments united. Disc not distinctly developed. Calyx with valvate aestivation. Seeds albuminous. Leaves simple, stipulate.

142. Malvaceae.

Anthers 2-celled, opening by 2 slits or pores. Calyx with imbricate, more rarely with open or valvate aestivation, in the latter case leaves exstipulate. 453

453. Ovules solitary in each carpel. Trees or shrubs. 454

Ovules 2 or more in each carpel. Leaves exstipulate. 456

454. Receptacle more or less elongated. Stamens 10 or more. Fruits drupaceous. Seeds exalbuminous. Leaves undivided, stipulate.

147. Ochnaceae.

Receptacle expanded into a disc. Leaves exstipulate. 455

455. Stamens inserted within the disc. Ovules ascending. **134. Sapindaceae.**

Stamens inserted outside the disc. . . . . . **116. Simarubaceae.**

456. Sepals 3. Petals 6. Stamens numerous. Trees or shrubs.

81. Anonaceae.

Sepals 4—5. Petals 4—5. Stamens 4—10. Leaves translucently dotted. . . . . **115. Rutaceae.**

457. (451.) Ovules solitary in each carpel. 458

Ovules 2 or more in each carpel. 470

458. Leaves opposite, exstipulate. 459
  Leaves alternate or the uppermost whorled, or all radical. . . . 462
459. Stamens 3—10. Carpels 3—9. Albumen scanty. Leaves undivided. 460
  Stamens numerous. Carpels 2 or many. Albumen abundant. . . 461
460. Stamens 3—9. Petals white or reddish. Fruit dehiscent.
            Crassula, **95. Crassulaceae.**
  Stamens 10. Petals greenish, fleshy. Fruit indehiscent. Shrubs.
  Flowers in racemes. . . . . . *Coriaria*, **126. Coriariaceae.**
461. Carpels 2. Ovules ascending. Sepals 5. Petals 5. Seeds with an aril.
  Erect shrubs or trees. Leaves undivided.
            Hibbertia, **146. Dilleniaceae.**
  Carpels numerous. Ovules pendulous. Seeds without an aril.
            Clematis, **78. Ranunculaceae.**
462. Leaves stipulate. 463
  Leaves exstipulate. 467
463. Stamens as many as the petals, 3—8, hypogynous or nearly so. Styles
  terminal. Flowers unisexual. 464
  Stamens twice as many as the petals or more, rarely as many as the
  petals or fewer, but then distinctly perigynous and styles basal. Ovules
  inverted. 465
464. Stem erect, tree-like. Leaves lobed. Flowers in heads. Ovules pendulous, straight. Fruit dry. . . . . *Platanus*, **102. Platanaceae.**
  Stem climbing. Leaves undivided. Flowers in racemes or panicles.
  Ovules laterally affixed, half-inverted. Fruit fleshy.
         Tiliacora, **80. Menispermaceae.**
465. Petals and stamens perigynous. . . . . **103. Rosaceae.**
  Petals and stamens hypogynous. Leaves undivided. 466
466. Flowers regular. Sepals 3—4, valvate in bud. Stamens numerous,
  with united filaments. Disc absent. Trees.
         Christiania, **141. Tiliaceae.**
  Flowers irregular. Sepals 5. Disc present. Shrubs.
         Astrocarpus, **89. Resedaceae.**
467. Disc present. Sepals 2—5. Albumen scanty or wanting. Stem woody.
            116. Simarubaceae.
  Disc absent. Albumen abundant, rarely scanty or wanting, but then
  sepals 6 or more. 468
468. Flowers unisexual. Sepals 6 or more. Stamens usually as many as petals
  or fewer. Fruits drupaceous. Stem usually climbing. Flowers usually
  in racemes. . . . . **80. Menispermaceae.**
  Flowers hermaphrodite or polygamous, rarely unisexual, but then sepals
  2—3. Stamens usually more than petals. Albumen abundant. 469
469. Stem woody. Leaves entire or toothed. Sepals 2—3. Albumen
  ruminate. . . . . **81. Anonaceae.**

Stem herbaceous or woody at the base only, rarely throughout, but then leaves lobed or dissected and sepals 4 or more. Albumen uniform.

78. Ranunculaceae.

470. (457.) Leaves stipulate. 471
Leaves exstipulate. 474

471. Petals and stamens perigynous. . . . . . . **103. Rosaceae.**
Petals and stamens hypogynous. 472

472. Disc one-sided, scale-like. Ovary stalked. Stamens 10—15. Flowers irregular, 5-merous. Seeds exalbuminous. Herbs. Leaves undivided.

Caylusea, **89. Resedaceae.**

Disc stalk-like or wanting. Seeds albuminous. Shrubs or trees. 473

473. Calyx with valvate, corolla with contorted aestivation. Stamens 10 or more. Petal-like staminodes within the stamens 5—10. Flowers regular, 5-merous. . . . . **144. Sterculiaceae.**
Calyx and corolla with imbricate aestivation. Stamens numerous. Leaves undivided. . . . . **146. Dilleniaceae.**

474. Stamens as many or twice as many as the petals. 475
Stamens numerous, not exactly twice as many as the petals, hypogynous. Seeds with abundant albumen. 479

475. Sepals 2—3. Petals 3—6. Stamens 6—12, hypogynous. Albumen abundant. Shrubs or trees. Leaves alternate, undivided.

81. Anonaceae.

Sepals 4 or more, rarely 3, but then stamens 3. 476

476. Stem herbaceous or woody at the base, rarely throughout, but then, as usually, ovules numerous. Albumen scanty or wanting.

95. Crassulaceae.

Stem woody throughout. Ovules 2. 477

477. Leaves pinnate, with 3 or more leaflets, alternate, rarely dotted and then stamens 10. Flowers 5-merous. Ovules ascending, straight. Seeds with an aril. . . . . **104. Connaraceae.**
Leaves simple or compound ; in the latter case, as usually, leaves translucently dotted and stamens 3—5. Ovules inverted. Seeds without an aril. 478

478. Style terminal or nearly so. Stamens 3—5. Seeds albuminous, with a thick and hard coat. . . . . *Fagara,* **115. Rutaceae.**
Styles basal or nearly so. Stamens 5—10. Seeds exalbuminous, with a thin coat. Leaves undivided. . . *Suriana,* **116. Simarubaceae.**

479. Sepals 2—3. Petals 3—6. Albumen ruminate. Shrubs or trees. Leaves undivided. . . . . **81. Anonaceae.**
Sepals 4—6, imbricate in bud. 480

480. Seeds with an aril. Sepals persistent. Shrubs or trees. Leaves undivided. . . . . **146. Dilleniaceae.**
Seeds without an aril. Herbs or undershrubs. Leaves more or less deeply divided or compound. . . . . . . **78. Ranunculaceae.**

481. (188.) Ovary 1-celled, sometimes incompletely chambered. . . . 482
Ovary completely or almost completely 2- or more-celled, rarely 2 or more
distinct ovaries. 507
482. Ovules not distinctly differentiated from the placenta. Shrubs parasitic
upon trees or shrubs. Leaves undivided. Calyx-limb little developed.
Petals 2—6, valvate in bud. Stamens as many as and opposite the petals.
Stigma 1. . . . . *Loranthus*, **61. Loranthaceae.**
Ovules distinctly developed. Herbs or non-parasitic shrubs or trees. 483
483. Ovule 1. 484
Ovules 2 or more. 490
484. Ovule erect, straight. Stigmas 2. Stamens numerous. Petals 3—4.
Flowers monoecious, in spikes. Leaves pinnate. Trees.
Juglans, **49. Juglandaceae.**
Ovule pendulous, inverted. Stamens as many as the petals or fewer,
rarely (*Alangiaceae*) more, but then petals 6—10 and flowers hermaphrodite. 485
485. Filaments wholly united. Anthers 5, twisted. Flowers unisexual.
Seeds exalbuminous. Leaves angled or lobed. Climbing, tendril-
bearing plants. . . . . **223. Cucurbitaceae.**
Filaments free or united at the base only. Plants without tendrils. 486
486. Anthers opening by valves. Stigma 1. Seed exalbuminous. Trees or
climbing shrubs. Leaves palminerved. Flowers in panicles.
85. Hernandiaceae.
Anthers opening by longitudinal slits. Flowers hermaphrodite or polygamous. Seed albuminous. 487
487. Flowers 4-merous, in racemes or panicles. Leaves pinnate. Shrubs
or trees. Fruit a drupe. . . . . *Polyscias*, **185. Araliaceae.**
Flowers 5—10-merous. Leaves simple, but sometimes dissected, and then
herbs or undershrubs with the flowers in umbels. 488
488. Flowers in umbels. Leaves more or less deeply divided. Herbs or
undershrubs. Fruit a nut. . . . . . . **186. Umbelliferae.**
Flowers in heads, spikes, or cymes. Leaves undivided. Shrubs or
trees. 489
489. Flowers in cymes. Petals valvate in bud. Fruit a drupe. Embryo large.
Alangium, **178. Alangiaceae.**
Flowers in heads or spikes, 5-merous. Petals imbricate in bud. Fruit a
nut. Embryo small. . . . . **100. Bruniaceae.**
490. (483.) Ovules basal or inserted on a free central placenta. . . . 491
Ovules parietal or inserted at the apex of the ovary-cell. . . . 499
491. Flowers unisexual. Stamens as many as the petals or fewer, 2—5.
Fruit a berry or a nut. Herbs or undershrubs, rarely shrubs. . 492
Flowers hermaphrodite. 493
492. Flowers 4-merous. Styles or sessile stigmas 4, free. Seeds albuminous.
Herbs. Leaves undivided. *Laurembergia*, **183. Halorrhagaceae.**

Flowers 5-merous.   Style 1, entire or cleft.   Seeds exalbuminous.

223.   Cucurbitaceae.

493. Sepals 2.   Fruit opening by a lid.   Herbs.   Leaves alternate, undivided.

Portulaca, **73.   Portulacaceae.**

Sepals 4—8, sometimes united into an entire calyx.   Style simple. Fruit indehiscent.   Trees or shrubs, rarely (*Bruniaceae*) undershrubs. 494

494. Stamens numerous.   Petals 5.   Ovules 2.   Fruit a drupe.   Leaves alternate, stipulate. . . . . **103.   Rosaceae.**

Stamens as many or twice as many as the petals, 4—16.   Leaves undivided. 495

495. Stamens twice as many as the petals, 8—16.   Leaves opposite or whorled. 496

Stamens as many as the petals, 4—6.   Seeds albuminous. . . . 497

496. Leaves stipulate.   Petals 5—8, toothed or lobed, valvate in bud.   Anthers without appendages.   Seeds albuminous.

Carallia, **177.   Rhizophoraceae.**

Leaves exstipulate.   Petals usually 4.   Anthers with appendages.   Seeds exalbuminous. . . . . **181.   Melastomataceae.**

497. Stamens opposite the petals.   Petals valvate in bud.   Ovules pendulous. Fruit a drupe.   Leaves alternate. . . . . . . **59.   Olacaceae.**

Stamens alternating with the petals.   Petals imbricate in bud. . . 498

498. Stigma 1.   Ovules erect.   Fruit a drupe.   Leaves opposite, stipulate.

Pleurostylia, **129.   Celastraceae.**

Stigmas 2.   Ovules pendulous.   Fruit a capsule or a nut.   Leaves alternate, exstipulate. . . . . **100.   Bruniaceae.**

499. (490.) Ovules apical. 500

Ovules parietal. 502

500. Ovules numerous, affixed to 2—3 placentas suspended from the apex of the ovary-cell.   Styles 2—3, free.   Stamens 5.   Flowers hermaphrodite. Fruit capsular.   Seeds with abundant albumen.   Herbs.   Leaves opposite, undivided. . . . . . . *Vahlia*, **96.   Saxifragaceae.**

Ovules 2—6, suspended from the apex of the ovary-cell.   Style 1, entire or cleft.   Seeds without albumen. 501

501. Stamens 2—5.   Flowers unisexual.   Herbs, undershrubs, or shrubs, usually climbing or prostrate. . . . . . **223.   Cucurbitaceae.**

Stamens 8 or more, rarely 4—6, but then flowers hermaphrodite.   Style simple.   Trees, shrubs, or undershrubs.   Leaves undivided.

179.   Combretaceae.

502. Flowers unisexual, rarely polygamous.   Herbs or undershrubs, rarely shrubs. 503

Flowers hermaphrodite.   Shrubs or trees.   Seeds albuminous. . . 504

503. Flowers 5-merous.   Stamens 2—5.   Seeds exalbuminous.   Leaves well-developed. . . . . **223.   Cucurbitaceae.**

Flowers 6-merous.   Stamens 12 or more.   Seeds albuminous.   Leaves scale-like. . . . . *Pilostyles*, **64.   Rafflesiaceae.**

504. Stamens as many as and alternating with the petals, 5. Petals small. Style 2-cleft. Ovary inferior. Ovules many. Fruit a berry. Leaves lobed. . . . . *Ribes*, **96. Saxifragaceae.**
    Stamens as many as and opposite the petals or in greater number. Style simple, more rarely divided, but then ovary half-inferior. Leaves undivided, or wanting. 505

505. Stamens numerous, not collected in bundles. Ovary inferior. Style simple, with several stigmas. Fruit a berry. Succulent, usually leafless plants. . . . . **167. Cactaceae.**
    Stamens as many or twice as many as the petals, or collected in several bundles. Ovary half-inferior. Style simple with an entire or slightly lobed stigma, or more or less deeply divided into 2—6 branches. Leafy plants. 506

506. Petals 5—6, lobed or slit, valvate in bud. Stamens twice their number. Style simple. Ovules 6. Fruit a berry. Leaves opposite or whorled.
                             Ceriops, **177. Rhizophoraceae.**
    Petals 4—8, imbricate in bud. Stamens placed singly or in pairs or bundles opposite the petals ; if in pairs or bundles, then style divided. Fruit a capsule. . . . . **159. Flacourtiaceae.**

507. (481.) Ovules solitary in each ovary-cell. 508
    Ovules two or more in each oyary-cell. 527

508. Ovules erect or ascending. 509
    Ovules pendulous or descending. 513

509. Stamens 10 or more. Sepals 5. Petals 5. Ovary 4—10-celled. Styles or style-branches 2—10. Shrubs or trees. Leaves stipulate.
                             103. Rosaceae.
    Stamens 2—5. 510

510. Flowers 2-merous. Herbs. Leaves opposite, exstipulate.
                      Circaea, **182. Oenotheraceae.**
    Flowers 4—5-merous. 511

511. Stamens, at least apparently (by coalescence), fewer than the petals, 3. Sepals 5. Petals 5. Ovary-cells and stigmas 3. Flowers unisexual. Tendril-bearing herbs. Leaves alternate.
                   Cayaponia, **223. Cucurbitaceae.**
    Stamens as many as the petals, 4—5. Shrubs or trees, rarely under-shrubs. 512

512. Stamens alternating with the petals. Calyx with imbricate or open aestivation. . . . . **129. Celastraceae.**
    Stamens opposite the petals. Calyx with valvate aestivation.
                          137. Rhamnaceae.

513. (508.) Ovary 2-celled. 514
    Ovary 3—15-celled. 522

514. Style 1, with a single stigma. Flowers 4-merous. 515
    Style 1, with 2—3 stigmas, or styles 2. 517

515. Stamens numerous. Flowers hermaphrodite, in cymes. Fruit a berry. Seeds exalbuminous. Trees or shrubs. Leaves opposite.

Pimenta, **180. Myrtaceae.**

Stamens 4. 516

516. Flowers unisexual, in cymes. Fruit a drupe. Seeds albuminous. Trees or shrubs: Leaves opposite. . . . . *Cornus*, **187. Cornaceae.**

Flowers hermaphrodite, solitary. Fruit a nut. Seeds exalbuminous. Herbs. Leaves radical. . . . . . *Trapa*, **182. Oenotheraceae.**

517. Stamens numerous. Petals 5. Stigmas 3. Seeds exalbuminous. Leaves alternate. . . . . *Kissenia*, **164. Loasaceae.**

Stamens as many as the petals. Stigmas 2. Seeds albuminous. 518

518. Fruit a capsule, rarely a nut, and then ovary half-inferior. Trees, shrubs, or undershrubs. Leaves simple, undivided. Flowers in heads or head-like spikes, rarely in racemes or panicles. 519

Fruit a schizocarp (splitting into 2 nutlets), a nut, or a drupe. Ovary inferior, rarely half-inferior, but then leaves compound or divided. Flowers in umbels, more rarely in heads, whorls, spikes, racemes, or panicles. 520

519. Leaves stipulate. Flowers usually 4-merous. Styles 2, free. Fruit a capsule. Albumen scanty. . . . . . **101. Hamamelidaceae.**

Leaves exstipulate, rarely stipulate, but then style 1. Flowers 5-merous. Petals clawed, imbricate in bud. Anthers opening by longitudinal slits. Albumen abundant. . . . . **100. Bruniaceae.**

520. Fruit a schizocarp splitting into two nutlets, rarely a nut, and then, as usually, stem herbaceous or woody at the base only. Flowers 5-merous. Epigynous disc usually 2-parted. Styles free. **186. Umbelliferae.**

Fruit a drupe or a nut. Stem woody throughout. Epigynous disc usually entire. 521

521. Leaves compound or more or less deeply divided. Flowers in umbels, spikes, or racemes. Ovules with ventral raphe. . **185. Araliaceae.**

Leaves simple, undivided, exstipulate. Flowers in racemes or panicles. Ovules with dorsal raphe. Fruit a drupe. . . **187. Cornaceae.**

522. (513.) Stem herbaceous. Fruit dry. 523

Stem woody. Fruit more or less succulent. 524

523. Flowers 4-merous. Stamens 2—8. Fruit indehiscent or splitting into 2—4 nutlets. Seeds albuminous. Leaves exstipulate. Water-plants.

Myriophyllum, **183. Halorrhagaceae.**

Flowers 5-merous. Stamens 10. Fruit capsular. Seeds exalbuminous. Leaves stipulate. Land-plants. . . . . . . **103. Rosaceae.**

524. Leaves compound or more or less deeply divided, rarely the upper ones undivided, and then ovary-cells and styles 5. Flowers in umbels or heads, rarely in spikes or racemes. Stamens as many as petals, 4—16, rarely twice their number, 10. . . . . . . **185. Araliaceae.**

Leaves undivided, exstipulate. Flowers in spikes, racemes, panicles, or fascicles. Ovary 3—4-celled. Styles 1—4. 525

525. Stamens as many as and opposite the petals, 4—5. Style simple. Flowers in racemes or fascicles. . . . . **59. Olacaceae.**

Stamens as many as and alternate with the petals or twice as many. 526

526. Stamens as many as the petals, 4—10. Seeds albuminous.

187. Cornaceae.

Stamens twice as many as the petals, 6—8, but the alternate ones some-times without anthers. Sepals and petals valvate in bud. Styles 3—4. Flowers polygamous. Seeds-exalbuminous. Leaves alternate.

177. Rhizophoraceae.

527. (507.) Ovules 2—4 in each ovary-cell. 528
Ovules more than 4 in each ovary-cell. 537

528. Stamens as many as the petals or fewer. 529
Stamens twice as many as the petals or more. 533

529. Stamens, at least apparently (by coalescence), fewer than the petals, 2—4. Flowers 5-merous, unisexual. Ovary inferior. Usually herba-ceous and tendril-bearing plants. Leaves alternate.

223. Cucurbitaceae.

Stamens as many as the petals, 4—5, free or nearly so. Trees or shrubs, rarely undershrubs. 530

530. Stamens opposite the petals. Petals valvate in bud. Ovary inferior. Style simple ; stigma entire. Leaves opposite, exstipulate.

Olinia, **170. Oliniaceae.**

Stamens alternating with the petals. Ovary usually half-inferior. Leaves opposite, but stipulate, or alternate. 531

531. Leaves exstipulate, alternate. Flowers hermaphrodite, 5-merous. Ovules pendulous. Seeds with a minute embryo and abundant albumen.

100. Bruniaceae.

Leaves stipulate. 532

532. Calyx large. Petals 5, usually two-cleft. Stigmas 2—3. Ovules pendu-lous. Fruit indehiscent. Seeds exalbuminous. Leaves alternate.

Dichapetalum, **121. Dichapetalaceae.**

Calyx small. Petals imbricate in bud. Style simple or wanting. Ovules erect, rarely pendulous, but then leaves, at least those of the flowering branches, opposite. . . . . **129. Celastraceae.**

533. Stamens twice as many as the petals. Petals with valvate aestivation. Style 1. Seeds albuminous. Leaves opposite or whorled, stipulate.

177. Rhizophoraceae.

Stamens more than twice as many as the petals. Petals with imbricate or contorted aestivation. Seeds exalbuminous. 534

534. Style 1, with a single stigma. Ovules in the whole ovary 4 or more. Leaves exstipulate. 535
Style 1, with 2—5 stigmas, or styles 2—5. Sepals 5. Leaves alter-nate. 536

535. Leaves opposite, gland-dotted. Sepals 4—5. Filaments free or united
     into several bundles. . . . . **180. Myrtaceae.**
     Leaves alternate, rarely dotted. Sepals 2—4. Filaments united into a
     cup at the base. Fruit indehiscent. . . . **176. Lecythidaceae.**

536. Stipules absent. Calyx with open aestivation. Filaments collected in
     5 bundles. Ovules in the whole ovary 3, pendulous. Style entire or
     cleft at the top. Fruit a nut. . . . *Kissenia*, **164. Loasaceae.**
     Stipules present. Calyx with imbricate aestivation. Ovules ascending.
     Style more or less deeply divided. Fruit a berry or a drupe.
                                                          103. Rosaceae.

537. (527.) Style 1, undivided, with a single stigma or with 2 or more stigmas
     contiguous at their base. 538
     Styles 2—20, free or united below, the stigmas not contiguous at the
     base. 546

538. Stamens as many or twice as many as the petals or fewer, 2—16. 539
     Stamens more than twice as many as the petals, or stamens and petals
     very numerous. 543

539. Stamens fewer than the petals, at least apparently (by coalescence), rarely
     as many as the petals, but then, as usually, herbs with tendrils. Leaves
     alternate. Flowers unisexual, rarely polygamous, 5-merous. Fruit
     usually succulent and indehiscent. Seeds exalbuminous.
                                                   223.   Cucurbitaceae.
   · Stamens as many or twice as many as the petals. Herbs without tendrils,
     or woody plants. 540

540. Sepals valvate in bud. Stamens twice as many, rarely as many as the
     petals ; in the latter case leaves with small stipules. Anthers opening
     by longitudinal slits. Seeds exalbuminous. **182. Oenotheraceae.**
     Sepals imbricate or open in bud, rarely valvate, but then either stamens
     as many as the petals, leaves without stipules, and seeds albuminous,
     or anthers opening by apical pores. 541

541. Leaves opposite or whorled, undivided, exstipulate, usually with several
     longitudinal nerves. Filaments bent down in bud. Anthers usually
     opening by apical pores. Stigma 1. Seeds exalbuminous.
                                                181.   Melastomataceae.
     Leaves alternate. Stamens as many as the petals. Fruit capsular.
     Seeds albuminous. 542

542. Stem herbaceous or woody at the base. Leaves exstipulate. Flowers
     or inflorescences in the axils of the leaves or terminal. Ovules numerous
     in each ovary-cell. . . . . **224. Campanulaceae.**
     Stem woody throughout. Flowers or inflorescences in the axils or on the
     surface of the leaves. Ovules 6—8 in each ovary-cell. Seeds with an
     aril. . . . . **129. Celastraceae.**

543. Petals numerous. Stigmas 4—20. Seeds albuminous. Herbs or under-
     shrubs. . . . . . . *Mesembryanthemum*, **72. Aizoaceae.**

Petals 4—8. Stigma 1, entire or lobed. Seeds exalbuminous. Shrubs or trees. Leaves undivided, exstipulate. 544

544. Sepals 5—8, red, with valvate aestivation. Petals crumpled in the bud. Ovules at first basal, finally parietal. Leaves not dotted.

Punica, **175. Punicaceae.**

Sepals 2—4, rarely more, but then with imbricate, open, or closed aestivation. Ovules axile. 545

545. Leaves alternate, rarely dotted. Sepals 2—4. Filaments united into a cup at the base. . . . . . . **176. Lecythidaceae.**

Leaves opposite, gland-dotted. . . . . . . **180. Myrtaceae.**

546. (537.) Stamens 2—10. 547

Stamens numerous. 548

547. Stamens fewer than the petals, at least apparently (by coalescence), more rarely as many as the petals, but then, as usually, tendril-bearing herbs. Styles usually 3. Flowers 5-merous, unisexual or polygamous. Fruit more or less berry-like. Seeds exalbuminous.

223. Cucurbitaceae.

Stamens as many as the petals, 4—5, and then styles 2 and stem woody, or twice as many. Fruit capsular. Seeds albuminous, rarely exalbuminous, but then flowers 4-merous. . . . . . **96. Saxifragaceae.**

548. Petals 3—5. Seeds exalbuminous. 549

Petals numerous. Seeds albuminous. Herbs or undershrubs. . . 550

549. Flowers unisexual. Sepals and petals not distinctly differentiated, together 8—9. Ovules many in each ovary-cell.

Begonia, **165. Begoniaceae.**

Flowers hermaphrodite. Sepals and petals distinctly differentiated, together 10. Ovules few in each ovary-cell. Shrubs.

Cydonia. **103. Rosaceae.**

550. Sepals nearly hypogynous, 4. Ovules inserted upon the dissepiments. Fruit bursting irregularly. Embryo straight. Leaves radical, floating, peltate or cordate. Flowers solitary.

Nymphaea, **76. Nymphaeaceae.**

Sepals epigynous, usually 5. Ovules basal or parietal. Fruit opening loculicidally. Embryo curved. Leaves not floating. Flowers in cymes or panicles. . . . . *Mesembryanthemum*, **72. Aizoaceae.**

551. (52.) Ovary superior or nearly so. 552

Ovary inferior to half-inferior. 728

552. Ovary 1, entire or lobed. 553

Ovaries 2 or more, separate or cohering at the base only. . . . 719

553. Ovary 1-celled, sometimes incompletely chambered. 554

Ovary completely or almost completely 2- or more-celled, at least at the time of flowering (sometimes incompletely septate in the bud). 604

554. Ovule 1. 555

Ovules 2 or more. 570

D

118384

555. Ovule erect or ascending. 556
Ovule pendulous or descending. Style simple. 564
556. Style 1, entire or cleft at the top into 2 or more stigmas (or branches stigmatose on the inside). 557
Styles 3—5, free or united at the base. Stamens 5, opposite the petals. 563
557. Stamens free from the corolla or inserted on its base. 558
Stamens inserted on the upper part or near the middle of the corolla. 561
558. Corolla (or corolla-like perianth) with valvate or folded aestivation. Leaves exstipulate. . . . . **69. Nyctaginaceae.**
Corolla with imbricate or open aestivation ; in the latter case leaves stipulate. Stamens as many as the divisions of the corolla. . . 559
559. Flowers 5-merous. Stigmas 3. Herbs. Leaves opposite, stipulate.
Cometes, **75. Caryophyllaceae.**
Flowers 4-merous. Stigma 1. 560
560. Flowers unisexual, solitary or in fascicles. Seeds albuminous. Herbs. Leaves all radical, exstipulate. *Litorella*, **218. Plantaginaceae.**
Flowers hermaphrodite, in racemes or panicles. Seeds exalbuminous. Shrubs or trees. Leaves opposite, stipulate.
Salvadora, **131. Salvadoraceae.**
561. Stamens fewer than the divisions of the corolla, 4. Leaves whorled. Shrubs. . . . . **205. Verbenaceae.**
Stamens as many as the divisions of the corolla. 562
562. Stamens alternating with the divisions of the corolla (or the petaloid staminodes). Seeds albuminous. . . . . . **68. Amarantaceae.**
Stamens opposite the divisions of the corolla (or petaloid perianth), 4. Stigma 1. Seeds exalbuminous. Leaves alternate. Shrubs or trees.
55. Proteaceae.
563. (556.) Sepals 2. Anthers turned outwards. Styles 3. Seeds with curved embryo. . . . . **74. Basellaceae.**
Sepals 5. Anthers turned inwards. Styles 5. Seeds with straight embryo. . . . . **192. Plumbaginaceae.**
564. Petals in the male flowers 2—4, united below, in the female 1—2, free. Sepals in the male flowers 4, in the female 1—2. Stamens 4—10, with united filaments. . . . . **80. Menispermaceae.**
Petals united below in the flowers of both sexes, or flowers hermaphrodite. 565
565. Stamens fewer than the divisions of the calyx or corolla, 4. Anthers opening by a transverse slit. Flowers 5-merous, irregular. Seeds albuminous. 566
Stamens as many as or more than the divisions of the corolla, rarely (*Ericaceae*) fewer, but then only 3. 567
566. Ovary 1-celled from the beginning. Stigma 2-lobed, rarely entire, and then corolla-lobes very unequal. . . . . **215. Globulariaceae.**
Ovary originally 2-celled, one cell becoming rudimentary. Stigma entire. Corolla-lobes almost equal. . . . *Microdon*, **208. Scrophulariaceae.**

567. Stamens as many as and opposite the divisions of the corolla (or corolla-like perianth), 4, inserted on the upper part or near the middle of the corolla. Corolla valvate in bud. Seeds exalbuminous.

                                            55. Proteaceae.

      Stamens as many as and alternate with the divisions of the corolla, or fewer or more numerous, inserted on the base of the corolla or free from it. 568

568. Stamens 10, perigynous. Anthers opening by two longitudinal slits. Flowers regular. . . . . **171. Thymelaeaceae.**

      Stamens 3—8, hypogynous. 569

569. Flowers regular. Sepals 3—4. Corolla-lobes 3—4. Anthers opening by two pores or slits. Seeds albuminous.. . . . . **189. Ericaceae.**

      Flowers irregular. Sepals 5. Corolla-lobes 3 or 5. Stamens 8. Anthers opening by a single pore or slit. Seeds exalbuminous.

                           Securidaca, **120. Polygalaceae.**

570. (554.) Ovules 2. 571

      Ovules 3 or more. 578

571. Stamens 4, fewer than the divisions of the corolla. Flowers irregular. Leaves opposite. 572

      Stamens 3 or more, as many as or more than the divisions of the corolla. 573

572. Anthers opening by pores. Fruit a drupe. Seeds exalbuminous. Climbing shrubs. Flowers in clusters. . *Afromendoncia*, **216. Acanthaceae.**

      Anthers opening by longitudinal slits. Stigmas 2. Fruit a capsule or nut. Seeds albuminous. Prostrate herbs. Flowers solitary.

                           Linariopsis, **210. Pedaliaceae.**

573. Stamens as many as the divisions of the corolla, 4—5. Leaves simple, entire toothed or lobed. Flowers regular. 574

      Stamens more than the divisions of the corolla, rarely the same number, but then, as usually, leaves compound. 576

574. Stamens opposite to the divisions of the corolla. Calyx with valvate, corolla with contorted aestivation. Ovules ascending. Leaves stipulate. . . . . *Waltheria*, **144. Sterculiaceae.**

      Stamens alternating with the divisions of the corolla. Leaves exstipulate. 575

575. Ovules erect. Style 2-parted, rarely simple, and then herbs. Calyx with imbricate, corolla with valvate or folded aestivation.

                           202. Convolvulaceae.

      Ovules pendulous. Style simple or wanting. Shrubs or trees.

                           132. Icacinaceae.

576. Stamens more than the divisions of the corolla, but fewer than twice as many, 4—7, usually 6. Anthers opening by pores. Corolla 4-lobed. Leves whorled, undivided, linear. . . . *Salaxis*, **189. Ericaceae.**

      Stamens as many or twice as many as the divisions of the corolla, or more. Leaves alternate. 577

577. Corolla regular, 5-partite, with imbricate aestivation. Stamens 10, five of them sometimes sterile. Ovules erect, straight. Shrubs or trees. Leaves compound, exstipulate. Flowers in panicles or racemes.

Connarus, **104. Connaraceae.**

Corolla regular, with valvate aestivation, or irregular. Ovules inverted. Leaves usually stipulate. . . . . **105. Leguminosae.**

578. (570.) Ovules basal or inserted upon a free central placenta. . . . 579
Ovules parietal. 587

579. Ovules 3, pendulous. Style simple. Fertile stamens as many as and opposite the corolla-lobes, 5—6, or fewer, 3. Flowers regular. Fruit a drupe. Trees, shrubs, or undershrubs. Leaves alternate.

Olax, **59. Olacaceae.**

Ovules 3, ascending, or more. 580

580. Style 3-cleft. Stamens more than corolla-lobes, 8—30, rarely fewer, 3. Sepals 2. Corolla-lobes 5. Herbs or undershrubs.

73. Portulacaceae.

Style simple or 2-cleft, rarely (*Caryophyllaceae*) 3-cleft, but then sepals corolla-lobes and stamens 5 each. 581

581. Stamens as many as and opposite the divisions of the corolla, 3—7. Style simple. 582
Stamens as many as and alternate with the divisions of the corolla, or fewer or more numerous. 583

582. Fruit a capsule. Herbs or undershrubs. . . . **191. Primulaceae.**
Fruit a nut, berry, or drupe. Shrubs or trees, very rarely herbs or undershrubs. Leaves alternate, gland-dotted. . . . **190. Myrsinaceae.**

583. Stamens 5. Flowers regular. 584
Stamens 2, 4, or 8. 585

584. Leaves opposite, stipulate. Corolla deeply divided, with imbricate aestivation. Styles 1 or 3. Herbs or undershrubs.

75. Caryophyllaceae.

Leaves alternate, exstipulate. Styles 1—2. . **202. Convolvulaceae.**

585. Stamens 4, free from the corolla, or 8. Flowers regular, 4-merous. Stigma 1. Seeds albuminous. Low shrubs. Leaves whorled, narrow.

189. Ericaceae.

Stamens 4, inserted on the corolla-tube, or 2. 586

586. Anthers opening by a transverse slit. Stamens 2. Style wanting. Sepals 2 or 5. Corolla distinctly 2-lipped. Leaves alternate or all radical. Herbs. . . . . **214. Lentibulariaceae.**

Anthers opening by two longitudinal slits. Style present. Ovules 4. Leaves opposite or whorled. . . . . . **205. Verbenaceae.**

87. (578.) Ovules attached to a single placenta. Style simple. Stamens as many as or more than the divisions of the corolla. Leaves alternate, compound or reduced to the dilated petiole. **105. Leguminosae.**

Ovules attached to two or more placentas. 588

588. Style simple or 2-cleft. 589
  Style 3—10-cleft. Flowers unisexual or polygamous. 603
589. Fertile stamens fewer than the divisions of the corolla, 1—4. . . . 590
  Fertile stamens as many as or more than the divisions of the corolla. 595
590. Fertile stamen 1, staminodes 3. Corolla-lobes 4. Stigma 2-cleft. Herbs.
  Leaves opposite, undivided. . . . . . . **199. Gentianaceae.**
  Fertile stamens 2 or 4. 591
591. Fertile stamens 2. Herbs or undershrubs. Leaves undivided. Flowers
  irregular. 592
  Fertile stamens 4. 594
592. Seeds 4, with thin albumen. Fruit a capsule with a drupaceous rind
  Ovules 4—16. Stigma 2-parted. Staminodes 3.
          Martynia, **211. Martyniaceae.**
  Seeds numerous, without albumen. Ovules numerous. 593
593. Disc wanting. Ovary and fruit ovate. Placentas little projecting.
  Staminodes none. Small water-plants. Leaves opposite.
        Dintera, **208. Scrophulariaceae.**
  Disc rarely wanting, and then ovary and fruit linear or oblong and placentas much projecting. . . . . **213. Gesneraceae.**
594. Placentas 2. Fruit a berry or nut. Seeds exalbuminous. Shrubs or
  trees. Leaves compound. . . . . **209. Bignoniaceae.**
  Placentas 4. Fruit a capsule. Seeds albuminous. Herbs without
  green colour. Leaves scale-like. Flowers irregular.
         212. Orobanchaceae.
595. (589.) Stamens as many as the divisions of the corolla, 3—8. . . 596
  Stamens more numerous than the divisions of the corolla, 7 or more.
  Shrubs or trees. 600
596. Style stigmatose beneath the thickened, often 2-lobed apex. Placentas
  2. Corolla with contorted aestivation. Flowers regular or nearly so,
  5-, rarely 4-merous. Juice milky. . . . . **200. Apocynaceae.**
  Style stigmatose at the apex or between the apical lobes. Juice not
  milky. 597
597. Leaves and stem without green colour; stem herbaceous, leaves scale-
  like. Flowers irregular. Stamens 4. Placentas 4.
         212. Orobanchaceae.
  Leaves green, rarely (*Gentianaceae*) without green colour, but then flowers
  regular, stamens 5 and placentas 2. 598
598. Leaves alternate, without stipules. Stem woody. Bark resinous.
  Flowers regular, 5-merous. Stigma 1.
       Pittosporum, **97. Pittosporaceae.**
  Leaves opposite or whorled, rarely alternate or all radical, but then stem
  herbaceous. 599
599. Stem woody. Leaves opposite or whorled, usually stipulate. Flowers
  4-merous. . . . . **198. Loganiaceae.**

Stem herbaceous or woody at the base only, rarely throughout, but then flowers 5-merous. Leaves exstipulate. . . **199. Gentianaceae.**

600. Stamens 7—18, with united filaments. Placentas 3—5. 601
Stamens 23 or more, with free filaments. Leaves undivided. . . 602

601. Sepals 3. Corolla-lobes 4—6. Stamens 7—9 or 14—18. Anthers opening outwards. . . . . *Cinnamosma*, **157. Winteranaceae.**
Sepals 4—5. Corolla-lobes 4—5. Stamens 8—10. Anthers opening inwards or laterally. . . . . **118. Meliaceae.**

602. Corolla-lobes 6. Sepals 3. Filaments and styles very short. Placentas numerous, confluent. Albumen abundant, ruminate. **81. Anonaceae.**
Corolla-lobes 11—14. Sepals 2—4. Filaments and styles long. Placentas 2, two-cleft. Albumen scanty, uniform.
Hoplestigma, **194. Hoplestigmataceae.**

603. (588.) Stamens as many as the corolla-lobes, 3—5. Fruit a capsule. Herbs or undershrubs. . . . . **162. Achariaceae.**
Stamens twice as many as the corolla-lobes, 10. Fruit a berry. Trees
Carica, **163. Caricaceae.**

604. (553.) Ovary 2-celled. 605
Ovary 3- or more-celled. 669

605. Ovules solitary in each ovary-cell. 606
Ovules 2 or more in each ovary-cell. 621

606. Ovules erect or ascending. 607
Ovules pendulous, descending, or horizontal. 611

607. Fertile stamens 2 or 4. 608
Fertile stamens 5 or 6. 609

608. Seeds borne on a hook-like outgrowth of the funicle, exalbuminous. Fruit capsular. . . . . **216. Acanthaceae.**
Seeds not on a hook-like outgrowth of the funicle. **205. Verbenaceae.**

609. Stamens opposite the divisions of the corolla. Anthers opening outwards. Stigma 1. Trees or shrubs. . . . . **193. Sapotaceae.**
Stamens alternate with the divisions of the corolla. Anthers opening inwards. 610

610. Stigma 1. Corolla with imbricate or contorted aestivation. Seeds exalbuminous. Herbs. Leaves alternate, exstipulate.
Rochelia, **204. Borraginaceae.**
Stigmas 2. Corolla with valvate aestivation. Seeds albuminous. Trees or shrubs. Leaves opposite or whorled, stipulate.
Gaertnera, **219. Rubiaceae.**

611. (606.) Fertile stamens 2 or 4. 612
Fertile stamens 5 or more. 618

612. Stamens 4, free from the corolla. Corolla regular or nearly so, 2—4-lobed. Seeds with abundant albumen. . . . . **189. Ericaceae.**
Stamens inserted on the corolla. 613

613. Corolla scarious, regular, 4-lobed. Stamens 4. Stigma 1. Fruit opening by a lid. Seeds albuminous. . . *Plantago*, **218. Plantaginaceae.**
Corolla not scarious, more or less irregular, rarely regular, but then stamens 2 or stigmas 2. 614

614. Corolla regular. Stamens 2, alternating with the ovary-cells. Disc wanting. Seeds with scanty albumen. Shrubs. Leaves compound, but sometimes with a single leaflet. . . *Jasminum*, **197. Oleaceae.**
Corolla more or less irregular, rarely regular, but then stamens 4. Leaves simple. 615

615. Flowers regular. Stamens 4. Anthers opening by two slits. Style 2-cleft. Fruit capsular. Séeds exalbuminous. Low shrubs. Leaves alternate. . . . . *Wellstedia*, **204. Borraginaceae.**
Flowers more or less irregular. Leaves opposite or whorled, rarely alternate, but then anthers opening by a single slit or pore. . . 616

616. Leaves alternate, at least the upper ones. Anthers opening by a single slit or pore. Seeds albuminous. . . . **208. Scrophulariaceae.**
Leaves opposite or whorled. 617

617. Fruit a capsule. Seeds borne on a hook-like process of the funicle, exalbuminous. . . . . **216. Acanthaceae.**
Fruit a drupe or a nut. Seeds not on a hook-like process of the funicle, albuminous. Stamens 4. Anthers opening by two slits. Herbs.
205. Verbenaceae.

618. (611.) Flowers distinctly irregular. Stamens united at the base with one another and with the corolla. Anthers opening by a single pore.
120. Polygalaceae.
Flowers regular or nearly so. Anthers opening by two slits or pores. 619

619. Flowers unisexual. Stamens free from the corolla. **122. Euphorbiaceae.**
Flowers hermaphrodite. Leaves undivided. 620

620. Calyx and corolla of 2—4 divisions each. Stamens 6—8, free from the corolla or nearly so. . . . . **189. Ericaceae.**
Calyx and corolla of 5 divisions each. Stamens 5, attached to the corolla ; filaments free. Stigmas 2. . . . . . . **200. Apocynaceae.**

621. (605.) Ovules 2 in each cell of the ovary. 622
Ovules 3 or more in each cell of the ovary. 640

622. Fertile stamens 2—3. 623
Fertile stamens 4—30. 626

623. Flowers regular. Stamens 2, alternating with the ovary-cells, rarely 3. Disc wanting. . . . . **197. Oleaceae.**
Flowers more or less irregular. Stamens not regularly alternating with the ovary-cells. 624

624. Leaves stipulate, alternate. Style 2-cleft. Petals 2-cleft. Seeds ex-albuminous. Trees or shrubs. . *Tapura*, **121. Dichapetalaceae.**
Leaves exstipulate, opposite or whorled, rarely alternate, but then, as nearly always, style simple. 625

625. Seeds borne on a hook-like outgrowth of the funicle, exalbuminous.
                                                    216. Acanthaceae.
    Seeds not on a hook-like outgrowth of the funicle, albuminous.
                                                    208. Scrophulariaceae.
626. (622.) Fertile stamens 4. 627
    Fertile stamens 5—30. 634
627. Corolla with 4 divisions. 628
    Corolla with 5 divisions. 632
628. Flowers more or less irregular. Seeds exalbuminous. Leaves opposite
    or whorled, without stipules. . . . . . . **216. Acanthaceae.**
    Flowers regular. Seeds albuminous. 629
629. Corolla scarious, regular. Stigma entire. Fruit opening by a lid. Leaves
    sessile. . . . . *Plantago*, **218. Plantaginaceae.**
    Corolla not scarious. 630
630. Leaves alternate. Styles or stigmas 2. Ovules erect
                                                    202. Convolvulaceae.
    Leaves opposite or whorled. Shrubs or trees. 631
631. Leaves provided with stipules or connected at their base by transverse
    lines or ridges. . . . . **198. Loganiaceae.**
    Leaves without either stipules or transverse lines or ridges at their base.
                                                    197. Oleaceae.
632. Leaves alternate, at least the upper ones. Flowers regular or nearly so.
    Corolla white. Stigma entire or 4-lobed. Fruit a drupe. Seeds
    albuminous. . . . . **217. Myoporaceae.**
    Leaves opposite or whorled, rarely the upper ones alternate, but then
    flowers irregular, stigma 2-partite and fruit a capsule or nut. . . 633
633. Seeds with scanty albumen. Plants with glandular hairs.
                                                    210. Pedaliaceae.
    Seeds without albumen. . . . . **216. Acanthaceae.**
634. (626.) Stamens 5. 635
    Stamens 8—30. 639
635. Style (or styles) stigmatose beneath the thickened and sometimes 2-lobed
    apex. Corolla with contorted aestivation. . . **200. Apocynaceae.**
    Style (or styles) stigmatose at the apex or between the apical lobes. 636
636. Leaves opposite or whorled, stipulate or connected by transverse lines
    or ridges. Shrubs or trees. . . . . **198. Loganiaceae.**
    Leaves alternate. 637
637. Ovules erect. Corolla lobed or nearly entire, usually folded in bud.
                                                    202. Convolvulaceae.
    Ovules pendulous. Styles or stigmas 2. Corolla lobed, but imbricate
    in bud, or deeply divided. Shrubs or trees. 638
638. Leaves stipulate. Flowers in axillary cymes or panicles. Fruit a drupe.
                            Dichapetalum, **121. Dichapetalaceae.**
    Leaves exstipulate. Flowers in terminal spikes or heads. Fruit a capsule.
                            Lonchostoma, **100. Bruniaceae.**

639. Stamens 8. Style 1. Flowers hermaphrodite.

Salaxis, **189. Ericaceae.**

Stamens 10—30. Styles 2. Flowers unisexual or polygamous.

Euclea, **195. Ebenaceae.**

640. (621.) Fertile stamens 1—4. 641
Fertile stamens 5—16. 658

641. Flowers more or less irregular. 642
Flowers regular. 652

642. Leaves opposite or whorled. 643
Leaves alternate, at least the upper ones. 648

643. Leaves provided with stipules or connected at their base by transverse
lines or ridges. Shrubs or trees. . . . . . **198. Loganiaceae.**
Leaves rarely with stipules or transverse lines or ridges at their base,
and then herbs or undershrubs. 644

644. Seeds with distinctly developed albumen. 645
Seeds with very scanty albumen or without any. 646

645. Seeds with funicles provided with a wart-like outgrowth. Placentas
remaining attached to the beaked and recurved valves of the capsule.
Disc not distinctly developed. Calyx deeply divided. Corolla-lobes
5, with descending aestivation. Anther-halves not confluent. Stigma
lobed. Flowers in spikes. . . . . **216. Acanthaceae.**
Seeds without an outgrowth from the funicle or without a funicle. Placentas usually separating from the valves of the capsule. Disc more or less
distinctly developed. . . . . . . **208. Scrophulariaceae.**

646. Seeds with scanty albumen. Plants with glandular hairs. Stamens 4.
210. Pedaliaceae.
Seeds without albumen. 647

647. Seeds borne on a large hook-like outgrowth of the funicle, rarely on a small
cushion-shaped one, and then herbs. Fruit a capsule, the valves bearing
the split dissepiment. Ovules usually few. Leaves simple.
216. Acanthaceae.
Seeds not on a hook-like outgrowth of the funicle, more or less distinctly
winged or marginate. Fruit a capsule, the valves usually separating
from the more or less dilated dissepiment, or a nut or berry. Ovules
numerous. Stamens 4. Leaves usually compound. Shrubs or trees.
209. Bignoniaceae.

648 (642.) Corolla with valvate or folded aestivation. Partition of the ovary
usually placed obliquely to the median plane of the flower.
207. Solanaceae.
Corolla with imbricate, not folded aestivation. Partition of the ovary
usually placed transversely to the median plane of the flower. . 649

649. Fruit a drupe. Ovules in each ovary-cell 4—6, in pairs placed one above
the other. Stigma 1. Stamens 4. Anther-halves confluent at the apex.
Shrubs. . . . . *Oftia*, **217. Myoporaceae.**
Fruit a capsule, nut, or berry. Ovules usually numerous. . . . 650

650. Seeds exalbuminous, usually horizontal and winged. Ovules numerous. Stigmas 2. Stamens 4. Shrubs or trees. Leaves usually compound.
209. Bignoniaceae.
Seeds albuminous. Leaves simple, but sometimes dissected. . . 651

651. Albumen very thin, nearly membranous. Stigmas or stigma-lobes 2. Stamens 4. Plants with glandular hairs. Lower leaves opposite.
210. Pedaliaceae.
Albumen distinctly developed. . . . . . **208. Scrophulariaceae.**

652. (641.) Corolla with contorted aestivation. Stamens 4. 653
Corolla with valvate or imbricate, not contorted aestivation. . . 654

653. Style stigmatose below the apex. Mostly shrubs or trees.
200. Apocynaceae.
Style stigmatose at the apex or between the apical lobes. Fruit a septi-cidal capsule. Herbs or undershrubs. . . . **199. Gentianaceae.**

654. Corolla scarious. Stamens 4. Disc wanting. Stigma 1. Fruit dehis-cing by a lid. Flowers in spikes or heads. *Plantago,*
218. Plantaginaceae.
Corolla not scarious. Fruit dehiscing lengthwise or indehiscent. 655

655. Anthers with confluent halves, opening by a transverse slit. Disc more or less distinctly developed. . . . . . **208. Scrophulariaceae.**
Anthers with distinct halves, opening by two longitudinal slits or apical pores. 656

656. Leaves alternate, simple, but sometimes dissected. Corolla usually folded in bud. Partition of the ovary usually placed obliquely to the median plane of the flower. Ovules generally numerous.
207. Solanaceae.
Leaves opposite or whorled, rarely alternate, but then compound. Corolla not folded. Trees, shrubs, or undershrubs. 657

657. Leaves provided with stipules or connected at their base by transverse lines or ridges, simple, opposite or whorled. Ovules usually numerous.
198. Loganiaceae.
Leaves without either stipules or transverse lines or ridges at their base. Ovules 3—4 in each ovary-cell. Disc none. . . . **197. Oleaceae.**

658. (640.) Leaves opposite or whorled. 659
Leaves alternate. 662

659. Leaves provided with stipules or connected at their base by transverse lines or ridges. Shrubs or trees. . . . . . **198. Loganiaceae.**
Leaves without stipules, but sometimes connected by transverse lines ; in this case herbs or undershrubs. Stamens 5. 660

660. Corolla with imbricate, not contorted aestivation. Style stigmatose at the entire apex. Fruit a berry. Shrubs growing upon trees.
Dermatobotrys, **208. Scrophulariaceae.**
Corolla with contorted aestivation. 661

661. Style stigmatose at the apex or between the apical lobes. Fruit a septicidal capsule. Herbs or undershrubs. . . . **199. Gentianaceae.**
Style stigmatose below the apex. Mostly shrubs or trees.

200. Apocynaceae.

662. Corolla with valvate or folded aestivation. 663
Corolla with imbricate or contorted aestivation. 665

663. Stamens free from the corolla. Herbs. *Lightfootia*, **224. Campanulaceae.**
Stamens attached to the corolla. 664

664. Corolla almost entire, somewhat irregular. Trees.

Humbertia, **202. Convolvulaceae.**

Corolla lobed, rarely almost entire, but then herbs or undershrubs.

207. Solanaceae.

665. Corolla with contorted aestivation. Style stigmatose beneath the thickened and sometimes 2-lobed apex. . . . . . **200. Apocynaceae.**
Corolla with imbricate, not contorted aestivation. Style (or styles) stigmatose at the apex or between the apical lobes. 666

666. Styles 2, free or united at the base. Disc wanting. Corolla regular Seeds albuminous ; embryo straight. Herbs or undershrubs.

203. Hydrophyllaceae.

Style 1, undivided. 667

667. Seeds winged, exalbuminous. Fruit a loculicidal capsule. Stigmas 2. Corolla slightly irregular. Shrubs. . . . . **209. Bignoniaceae.**
Seeds not winged, albuminous. 668

668. Seeds with straight embryo. Fruit a capsule opening lengthwise. Stigma 1. Corolla slightly irregular ; tube short. . **208. Scrophulariaceae.**
Seeds with curved embryo. Fruit a capsule opening by a lid, or a berry. Anthers opening by two longitudinal slits. . . . **207. Solanaceae.**

669. (604.) Ovule 1 in each ovary-cell. 670
Ovules 2 or more in each ovary-cell. 685

670. Stamens as many as and alternate with the divisions of the corolla, or fewer. 671
Stamens as many as and opposite the divisions of the corolla, or more. 679

671. Flowers unisexual, regular. Corolla divided almost to the base. Disc wanting. Fruit a drupe. Shrubs or trees. Leaves alternate.

Ilex, **128. Aquifoliaceae.**

Flowers hermaphrodite, rarely polygamous. 672

672. Anthers opening by an apical pore. Stamens 5. Ovary 3-celled. Flowers irregular. . . . . **120. Polygalaceae.**
Anthers opening by two longitudinal slits sometimes confluent at the apex ; in the latter case ovary 4-celled. 673

673. Stamens free from the corolla or scarcely adhering to it, 4. Flowers regular. . . . . **189. Ericaceae.**
Stamens evidently attached to the corolla-tube. 674

674. Corolla scarious, 4-lobed, regular. Stamens 4. Disc wanting. Stigma 1.
Ovules pendulous or laterally affixed. Fruit opening by a lid.

Plantago, **218. Plantaginaceae.**

Corolla not scarious 675

675. Corolla with valvate or folded aestivation, regular. Stamens 5. Leaves
alternate. . . . . **202. Convolvulaceae.**

Corolla with imbricate or contorted aestivation. 676

676. Stamens as many as the divisions of the corolla. Ovules with the micropyle directed upwards. Leaves, all or the upper ones, alternate, undivided. Inflorescences cymose, usually one-sided and coiled when
young. . . . . **204. Borraginaceae.**

Stamens fewer than the divisions of the corolla, rarely the same number,
but then ovules with the micropyle directed downwards and leaves
opposite or whorled. 677

677. Leaves alternate, at least the upper ones, undivided. Corolla regular,
5-lobed. Stamens 4. Anther-halves confluent at the apex. Ovules
pendulous, the micropyle directed upwards. Fruit a drupe. Shrubs.

Myoporum, **217. Myoporaceae.**

Leaves opposite or whorled, rarely alternate, but then corolla 2-lipped.
Ovules with the micropyle directed downwards. 678

678. Ovary deeply divided, more rarely slightly lobed, and then, as usually,
fruit dry. Inflorescence composed of sometimes one-flowered cymes
arranged in false whorls. . . . . **206. Labiatae.**

Ovary entire, rarely slightly lobed, and then fruit succulent, drupaceous.
Inflorescence usually of the racemose type. . . **205. Verbenaceae.**

679. (670.) Anthers 1-celled, opening by a single slit. Stamens numerous.
Calyx with valvate, corolla with contorted aestivation. Leaves simple,
stipulate. . . . . **142. Malvaceae.**

Anthers 2-celled. 680

680. Style 1, undivided. 681

Styles 2 or more, free or partially united. 683

681. Stamens more than the divisions of the corolla, 4—8. Fruit a capsule
or nut. Leaves undivided, exstipulate. . . . . **189. Ericaceae.**

Stamens as many as or more than the divisions of the corolla; in the
latter case, 12 or more. Fruit a berry. 682

682. Corolla with valvate aestivation. Stamens 5. Leaves pinnate.

Leea, **138. Vitaceae.**

Corolla with imbricate aestivation. Leaves undivided. **193. Sapotaceae.**

683. Flowers hermaphrodite. Sepals free. Corolla 5-partite. Stamens 10.
Ovary lobed, 5-celled. Styles 5, free. Herbs or undershrubs, rarely
shrubs. . . . . **108. Oxalidaceae.**

Flowers unisexual or polygamous, rarely hermaphrodite, but then sepals
united below and ovary-cells twice as many as the styles. . . . 684

684. Leaves exstipulate, undivided. Shrubs or trees. Flowers solitary or in cymes, axillary. Corolla with contorted or valvate aestivation.

195. Ebenaceae.

Leaves stipulate, rarely exstipulate, but then herbs or undershrubs, and corolla with imbricate, not contorted aestivation. Flowers in racemes or panicles, unisexual. . . . . **122. Euphorbiaceae.**

685. (669.) Ovules 2 in each ovary-cell. 686

Ovules 3 or more in each ovary-cell. 701

686. Stamens as many as and alternate with the divisions of the corolla, or fewer. 687

Stamens as many as and opposite the divisions of the corolla, or more. 693

687. Stamens 4. 688

Stamens 5—7, rarely (*Dichapetalaceae*) 2—3 only fertile. . . . 691

688. Corolla irregular, 5-lobed. Seeds with scanty albumen. Herbs. Leaves opposite, lobed, stipulate. . . . . *Pretrea*, **210. Pedaliaceae.**

Corolla regular, 4-lobed or 4-parted. Seeds with abundant albumen Leaves opposite and exstipulate, or alternate. 689

689. Flowers unisexual. Corolla deeply divided. Fruit a drupe.

Ilex, **128. Aquifoliaceae.**

Flowers hermaphrodite or polygamous. Fruit a capsule or nut. . 690

690. Stamens free from the corolla or slightly adhering to it at the base.

189. Ericaceae.

Stamens evidently attached to the corolla-tube.

Plantago, **218. Plantaginaceae.**

691. Ovary 4—8-celled. Disc wanting. Corolla deeply divided. Flowers unisexual. . . . . *Ilex*, **128. Aquifoliaceae.**

Ovary 3-celled. Disc present. 692

692. Corolla folded in the bud. Ovules erect. Seeds albuminous.

Ipomoea, **202. Convolvulaceae.**

Corolla not folded in the bud. Ovules pendulous. Stigmas 3. Seeds exalbuminous. Shrubs or trees. Leaves stipulate. **121. Dichapetalaceae.**

693. (686.) Stamens as many to twice as many as the divisions of the corolla. 694

Stamens more than twice as many as the divisions of the corolla. 698

694. Leaves stipulate, alternate. Sepals united below, valvate in bud.

144. Sterculiaceae.

Leaves exstipulate, rarely (*Oxalidaceae*) stipulate, but then sepals free and imbricate in bud. 695

695. Style 1, undivided. 696

Styles 2—8, free or partially united. 697

696. Stamens 8—10 ; filaments united ; anthers opening by longitudinal slits.

118. Meliaceae.

Stamens 4—8 ; filaments free, rarely united, but then anthers opening by apical pores. Leaves undivided. . . . . . . **189. Ericaceae.**

697. Sepals free. Corolla deeply divided. Stamens 10. Filaments united in a cup at the base. Styles 5. Herbs or undershrubs, rarely shrubs. Leaves alternate. Flowers hermaphrodite. . . **108. Oxalidaceae.**
Sepals united below. Filaments free or united in several bundles. Shrubs or trees. . . . . **195. Ebenaceae.**

698. Leaves exstipulate, undivided. Styles 2—8, free or united at the base. Shrubs or trees. . . . . **195. Ebenaceae.**
Leaves stipulate, rarely exstipulate, but then style 1, undivided. 699

699. Corolla with valvate aestivation. Style simple. Shrubs or trees. Leaves undivided. . . . . **145. Scytopetalaceae.**
Corolla with contorted, calyx with valvate aestivation. 700

700. Anthers 1-celled. . . . . **142. Malvaceae.**
Anthers 2-celled. . . . . **144. Sterculiaceae.**

701. (685.) Stamens as many as and alternate with the divisions of the corolla, or fewer. 702
Stamens as many as and opposite the divisions of the corolla, or more. 708

702. Stamens fewer than the divisions of the corolla, 4. Flowers irregular. Albumen scanty. 703
Stamens as many as the divisions of the corolla. 704

703. Anthers opening by a transverse slit. Stigma 1. Ovary 3-celled. Leaves whorled. Shrubs. . . . . *Bowkeria*, **208. Scrophulariaceae.**
Anthers opening by two longitudinal slits. Stigmas 2.
210. Pedaliaceae.

704. Carolla with valvate or folded aestivation. 705
Corolla with imbricate or contorted aestivation. 706

705. Leaves opposite or whorled. Calyx and corolla with valvate aestivation. Ovary 5—7-celled. Embryo straight. Shrubs.
Roussea, **96. Saxifragaceae.**
Leaves alternate. Corolla with folded aestivation. Embryo curved.
207. Solanaceae.

706. Stamens free from the corolla or adhering to it at the base.
189. Ericaceae.
Stamens attached on the middle or the upper part of the corolla-tube. 707

707. Fruit a capsule. Disc wanting. Stamens 4. Leaves without stipules.
Plantago, **218. Plantaginaceae.**
Fruit a berry or a drupe. Leaves opposite or whorled, provided with stipules or connected by transverse lines at the base. Shrubs or trees.
198. Loganiaceae.

708. (701.) Stamens 3—12. 709
Stamens numerous. 714

709. Flowers unisexual. Fruit a berry. Trees or shrubs. 710
Flowers hermaphrodite or polygamous. 711

710. Flowers monoecious. Calyx subentire. Corolla of the male flowers with a long tube, of the female ones with free petals. Staminodes

absent in the female flowers. Ovary sessile. Style short. Stigmas 5. Leaves lobed. . . . . . . *Cylicomorpha*, **163. Caricaceae.**
Flowers dioecious. Calyx of free sepals. Corolla with a short tube. Staminodes present in the female flowers. . Ovary shortly stalked. Style long. Stigma 1, lobed. Leaves undivided.

Cercopetalum, **87. Capparidaceae.**

711. Styles 5, free. Stamens 10, united at the base. Calyx with imbricate, corolla with contorted aestivation. . . . . . **108. Oxalidaceae.**
Style 1, simple or divided ; in the latter case calyx with valvate aestivation. 712

712. Leaves exstipulate, undivided. . . . . **189. Ericaceae.**
Leaves stipulate. Calyx with valvate or closed, corolla with contorted aestivation. 713

713. Anthers 1-celled, opening by a single slit, twisted, 5. Leaves digitate. Trees. . . . . *Ceiba*, **143. Bombacaceae.**
Anthers 2-celled, opening by two slits or pores. **144. Sterculiaceae.**

714. (708.) Corolla of numerous divisions. Styles 5. Leaves without stipules. Herbs. . . . . *Orygia*, **72. Aizoaceae.**
Corolla of 5 divisions. 715

715. Corolla with valvate aestivation. Shrubs or trees.

145. Scytopetalaceae.

Corolla with imbricate or contorted aestivation. 716

716. Calyx with valvate or closed, corolla with contorted aestivation. Leaves stipulate. 717
Calyx with imbricate aestivation. Leaves exstipulate, undivided. Shrubs or trees. 719

717. Anthers 2-celled. . . . . , ... **144. Sterculiaceae.**
Anthers 1-celled. Filaments united. Embryo curved. . . . 718

718. Leaves palmately compound. Trees. . . . . **143. Bombacaceae.**
Leaves simple. . . . . **142. Malvaceae.**

719. Stamens 15. Style simple, with 5 stigmas. Albumen abundant.

Ficalhoa, **189. Ericaceae.**

Stamens more than 15. Albumen scanty or wanting. **148. Theaceae.**

720. (552.) Style 1, or styles 2 or more, united at the base or apex. . . 721
Styles 2 or more, entirely free. 725

721. Stamens numerous. Filaments united. Anthers 1-celled. Ovaries 5 or more. Calyx with valvate, corolla with contorted aestivation. Leaves stipulate. . . . . **142. Malvaceae.**
Stamens 2—5. Ovaries 2—5. 722

722. Fertile stamens 2 or 4. Ovaries 4, one-ovuled. Flowers usually irregular. Leaves usually opposite or whorled. . . . . . **206. Labiatae.**
Fertile stamens 5. Flowers usually regular. 723

723. Ovaries 4, one-ovuled. Style or style-branches stigmatose at the apex or between the apical lobes. Disc present. Leaves, at least the upper

ones, alternate. . . . .   **204. Borraginaceae.**
Ovaries 2, rarely 3 or 5, very rarely 4, but then 2-ovuled. Style or styles
stigmatose beneath the thickened apex. Leaves usually opposite. 724

724. Stylar head with 5 gland-like pollen-carriers alternating with and adhering
to the anthers. Styles 2, united at the top. Pollen-grains cohering.
Disc wanting. . . . .   **201. Asclepiadaceae.**
Stylar head without pollen-carriers, but sometimes adhering to the anthers.
Styles partially or wholly united. Pollen-grains free.
                                        200. Apocynaceae.

725. Styles 2. Ovaries 2 or 4. Ovules together 4. Stamens 5. Corolla
with folded or valvate aestivation. Herbs.   **202. Convolvulaceae.**
Styles 3 or more. Ovaries 3 or more. 726

726. Sepals 2—3. Corolla-lobes 3—6. Stamens 6 or more. Albumen
abundant, ruminate. Shrubs or trees. Leaves undivided, exstipulate.
                                        81. Anonaceae.
Sepals 4 or more, rarely 3, but then stamens 3. Albumen scanty or
wanting. 727

727. Flowers unisexual. Ovules solitary in each ovary. Fruits indehiscent.
Trees. Leaves alternate, lobed, stipulate.
                            Platanus, **102. Platanaceae.**
Flowers hermaphrodite or polygamous. Ovules 2 or more in each ovary,
rarely solitary, but then leaves opposite. Fruits dehiscent. Leaves
exstipulate. 728

728. Ovules 2 in each ovary. Flowers 5-merous. Leaves alternate, pinnate.
Shrubs or trees. . . . .   **104. Connaraceae.**
Ovules numerous, rarely 1—2 in each ovary, but then leaves opposite
and undivided. Herbs or undershrubs, rarely shrubs. **95. Crassulaceae.**

729. (551.) Ovary single, 1-celled. 730
Ovary 2- or more-celled, or 2 separate ovaries. 747

730. Ovules 1—4, not distinctly separated from the tissues of the ovary.
Stamens as many as and opposite the divisions of the corolla. Shrubs
growing upon trees. . . . . . . *Loranthus*, **61. Loranthaceae.**
Ovules distinctly developed. Stamens as many as and alternate with
the divisions of the corolla, or more, or fewer, rarely opposite the divisions,
but then ovules numerous. 731

731. Ovule 1. 732
Ovules 2 or more. 740

732. Ovule erect. 733
Ovule pendulous. 734

733. Stigmas 2. Stamens 3—5 ; anthers coherent. Corolla with valvate or
open aestivation. Calyx little developed. Seed exalbuminous. Flowers
in heads, rarely in spikes or umbels or solitary. Leaves exstipulate.
                                        226. Compositae.
Stigmas 3. Stamens 9—10 ; anthers free. Corolla with contorted,

calyx with imbricate aestivation. Seed albuminous. Flowers in racemes or panicles. Leaves stipulate. Tendril-bearing shrubs.

Ancistrocladus, **166. Ancistrocladaceae.**

734. Leaves alternate. 735

Leaves opposite, whorled, or all radical. 737

735. Flowers unisexual. Seed exalbuminous. Climbing or prostrate plants. Stamens 2—5. . . . . **223. Cucurbitaceae.**

Flowers hermaphrodite. Seed albuminous. Erect shrubs. Leaves undivided. 736

736. Corolla with imbricate aestivation. Stamens 4 or 5. Stigma 1. Fruit dry, indehiscent. Flowers in terminal heads. *Berzelia*, **100. Bruniaceae.**

Corolla with valvate aestivation. Stamens 6 or more. Stigmas 2—6. Fruit succulent, drupaceous. Flowers in axillary cymes.

Alangium, **178. Alangiaceae.**

737. Style 3-parted. Stamens 5. Fruit drupaceous. Shrubs or trees.

Viburnum, **220. Caprifoliaceae.**

Style simple with 1—3 stigmas or 2-parted. Herbs or undershrubs. 738

738. Stamens 5. Corolla with valvate aestivation. . . **219. Rubiaceae.**

Stamens 1—4. Corolla with imbricate aestivation. 739

739. Flowers in heads. Calyx surrounded by an epicalyx. Stamens 2—4. Seed albuminous. . . . . **222. Dipsacaceae.**

Flowers in cymose inflorescences, without an epicalyx. Stamens 1—3. Seed exalbuminous. . . . . **221. Valerianaceae.**

740. (731.) Ovules basal or apical or inserted upon a free central placenta. 741

Ovules inserted upon two or more parietal placentas. 745

741. Calyx of 2, corolla of 4—6 divisions. Stamens as many as and opposite the divisions of the corolla or more. Herbs or undershrubs.

Portulaca, **73. Portulacaceae.**

Calyx and corolla of 4—5 divisions each. Stamens as many or fewer. 742

742. Ovules basal or apical. Stamens as many as and alternate with the divisions of the corolla or fewer. Corolla usually with valvate aestivation. 743

Ovules inserted upon a free central placenta. Stamens as many as and opposite the divisions of the corolla. Corolla with imbricate aestivation. 744

743. Flowers hermaphrodite. Stamens free. Ovules 4, basal. Stigma 2-lobed. Seeds albuminous. Undershrubs.

Merciera, **224. Campanulaceae.**

Flowers unisexual or polygamous. Seeds exalbuminous.

223. Cucurbitaceae.

744. Staminodes alternating with the fertile stamens. Fruit a capsule. Herbs or undershrubs. . . . . *Samolus*, **191. Primulaceae.**

Staminodes wanting. Fruit a berry or nut. Shrubs.

Maesa, **190. Myrsinaceae.**

E

745. Stamens numerous. Flowers hermaphrodite. Fruit a berry. Seeds albuminous. Succulent, usually leafless plants.   **167. Cactaceae.**
Stamens 2—11. Leafy plants. 746

746. Corolla with contorted aestivation. Stamens 5—11. Fruit capsular. Seeds albuminous. Leaves opposite or whorled, undivided, stipulate.
219. Rubiaceae.
Corolla with valvate, rarely with imbricate aestivation. Stamens 2—5. Flowers unisexual or polygamous. Fruit berry- or nut-like. Seeds exalbuminous. Leaves nearly always alternate. **223. Cucurbitaceae.**

747. (729.) Ovaries 2, distinct. Styles more or less united above, stigmatose beneath the thickened apex. Stamens 5. Leaves usually opposite. 748
Ovary 1. 749

748. Stylar head with 5 gland-like pollen-carriers alternating with the anthers, to which the pollen united into masses adheres. Styles free below the thickened apex. Disc wanting. . . . . **201. Asclepiadaceae.**
Stylar head without pollen-carriers, but sometimes adhering to the anthers. Pollen of free grains. . . . . **200. Apocynaceae.**

749. Ovules solitary in each ovary-cell. 750
Ovules 2 or more in each ovary-cell. 758

750. Leaves opposite, whorled, or all radical. 751
Leaves alternate. 753

751. Stamens fewer than the divisions of the corolla, 1—3. Ovary 3-celled. Seeds exalbuminous. Herbs or undershrubs. **221. Valerianaceae.**
Stamens as many as the divisions of the corolla. 752

752. Leaves pinnately dissected. Stamens 5. Anthers opening outwards. Style 3—5-parted. Fruit a drupe.
Sambucus, **220. Caprifoliaceae.**
Leaves undivided. . . . . **219. Rubiaceae.**

753. Flowers unisexual. Stamens as many as or fewer than the divisions of the corolla. Seeds exalbuminous. . . . . **223. Cucurbitaceae.**
Flowers hermaphrodite or polygamous. Stamens as many as or more than the divisions of the corolla. Seeds albuminous. Trees, shrubs, or undershrubs. 754

754. Stamens as many as and opposite the divisions of the corolla. Corolla with valvate aestivation. Ovary 3—4-celled. Leaves undivided.
59. Olacaceae.
Stamens as many as and alternate with the divisions of the corolla or more. 755

755. Flowers irregular. Corolla folded in bud. Ovules erect. Stigma 1, enclosed by a cup. Leaves undivided. *Scaevola,* **225. Goodeniaceae.**
Flowers regular. Ovules pendulous. 756

756. Corolla with imbricate aestivation, divided nearly to the base. Styles or stigmas 2. Leaves undivided. . . . . . **100. Bruniaceae.**
Corolla with valvate aestivation. 757

757. Flowers in cymes. Petals slightly cohering at the base. Leaves undivided.
Alangium, **178. Alangiaceae.**
Flowers in umbels, heads, racemes, or spikes. Petals usually united throughout their whole length. Leaves usually compound.
185. Araliaceae.

758. (749.) Stamens as many as or fewer than the divisions of the corolla. 759
Stamens more numerous than the divisions of the corolla. . . . 769

759. Leaves opposite or whorled. 760
Leaves alternate. 764

760. Leaves stipulate, undivided. Stamens as many as corolla-lobes, inserted on the corolla, with free filaments. . . . . **219. Rubiaceae.**
Leaves exstipulate. 761

761. Flowers unisexual. Seeds exalbuminous. . . **223. Cucurbitaceae.**
Flowers hermaphrodite. Stamens as many as corolla-lobes. Seeds albuminous. 762

762. Stamens free from the corolla or nearly so. Corolla with valvate aestivation. Usually herbs. . . . . **224. Campanulaceae.**
Stamens evidently inserted upon the corolla, 5. Corolla with imbricate or contorted aestivation. Usually shrubs or trees. 763

763. Flowers more or less irregular. Corolla with imbricate aestivation. Style stigmatose at the apex. Fruit a berry. Shrubs.
220. Caprifoliaceae.
Flowers regular. Corolla with contorted aestivation. Style stigmatose below the apex. Ovary 2-celled. . . . . . **200. Apocynaceae.**

764. Leaves stipulate, entire. Stamens 5. Ovary 2—3-celled with 2 ovules in each cell. Seeds exalbuminous. Shrubs or trees.
Dichapetalum, **121. Dichapetalaceae.**
Leaves exstipulate, rarely stipulate, but then more or less deeply divided or stamens fewer than 5 or ovules numerous. 765

765. Flowers unisexual or polygamous, 5-merous, regular, rarely somewhat irregular, in the latter case, as usually, stamens fewer than the divisions of the corolla. Seeds exalbuminous. . . . **223. Cucurbitaceae.**
Flowers hermaphrodite, rarely unisexual or polygamous, but then irregular. Stamens as many as the divisions of the corolla. Seeds albuminous. Leaves entire, toothed, or lobed. 766

766. Corolla with contorted aestivation. Ovary 2-celled. Style simple, stigmatose beneath the thickened apex. . . . . **200. Apocynaceae.**
Corolla with imbricate (not contorted) or valvate aestivation. Style stigmatose at the apex or between the apical lobes. 767

767. Corolla imbricate in bud, regular. Ovary 2-celled, with 2—4 ovules in each cell. Style simple with 2 stigmas or 2-parted. Shrubs or undershrubs. . . . . **100. Bruniaceae.**
Corolla valvate in bud, rarely imbricate, but then irregular or ovules numerous. Style simple. 768

768. Style with hairs or glands in its upper part, rarely without, and then corolla irregular or imbricate in bud. Stigma more or less deeply divided, at least after the period of flowering.   224. **Campanulaceae.**
Style without hairs or glands.   Stigma entire, capitate.   Ovary 3—4-celled with numerous ovules.   Anthers free.   Corolla regular, 5-partite, valvate in bud. · Undershrubs.   .   .   .   *Berenice*, **96. Saxifragaceae.**

769. (758.) Stamens 8—10.   Seeds with a straight embryo and abundant fleshy albumen. .   .   .   . *Vaccinium*, **189. Ericaceae.**
Stamens numerous. 770

770. Corolla of numerous petals united at the base.   Seeds with a curved embryo and mealy albumen.   Herbs or undershrubs.
Mesembryanthemum, **72. Aizoaceae.**

Corolla of 3—6 petals.   Shrubs or trees. 771

771 Petals united at the base, imbricate in bud.   Filaments united at the base.   Ovary inferior.   Seeds exalbuminous.   **176. Lecythidaceae.**
Petals united into a hood throughout their whole length, sometimes finally separating.   Filaments free or nearly so. 772

772. Ovary half-inferior.   Seeds albuminous.
Rhaptopetalum, **145. Scytopetalaceae.**

Ovary inferior.   Seeds exalbuminous.   Leaves gland-dotted.
180. Myrtaceae.

KEY TO THE GENERA

EMBRYOPHYTA SIPHONOGAMA
(PHANEROGAMAE)

SUBDIVISION GYMNOSPERMAE

CLASS I. CYCADALES

FAMILY 1. CYCADACEAE

Stem simple, rarely branched at the top, woody, with mucilagineous juice. Leaves pinnate or pinnatisect, forming a tuft at the top of the stem and intermingled with scales. Flowers solitary, terminal, in the shape of a cone (but sometimes overtopped by the continued growth of the stem), dioecious, without a perianth. Stamens bearing many pollen-sacs on their lower side. Ovules 2—8 to each carpel, straight, with a single coat. Seeds drupe-like, albuminous. Embryo with two more or less united cotyledons. — Genera 3, species 25. Tropical and South Africa. (Plate I.)

1. Stem growing through the female flower, covered with the remains of the old leaves. Leaf-segments one-nerved, coiled in bud. Carpels pinnately toothed or cleft, each with 4—8 ascending ovules.—Species 2, one growing wild in Madagascar and the neighbouring islands, the other cultivated and sometimes naturalized in various parts of Africa. Used as ornamental and medicinal plants ; the fruits are edible and the pith contains starch (sago). [Tribe CYCADEAE.] . . . . **Cycas** L.
   Stem not growing through the female flower. Leaf-segments with several nerves, straight in bud. Carpels each with 2 descending ovules. [Tribe ZAMIEAE.] 2
2. Leaf-segments with pinnate nerves. Stem without remains of old leaves at the base. Cone-scales (stamens and carpels) imbricate.—Species 2. South-east Africa (Natal). Used as ornamental plants.
   Stangeria Th. Moore
   Leaf-segments with parallel nerves. Stem covered with the remains of old leaves. Cone-scales not imbricate.—Species 20. South and Central Africa. The pith (Kaffir-bread) and the seeds of some species are eaten and also used for making a sort of beer. Several species yield gum or serve as ornamental plants. (Plate I.) **Encephalartos** Lehm.

CLASS II. CONIFERAE

FAMILY 2. TAXACEAE

Stem branched, woody, with resinous juice. Leaves alternate, linear or linear-lanceolate. Flowers solitary or the male umbellate, dioecious, without a perianth. Stamens with 2—9 pollen-sacs. Carpels free, one-ovuled, shorter than the seeds, sometimes rudimentary. Seeds 1—2, drupe-like, surrounded by a fleshy aril. Embryo with 2 or more free cotyledons. — Genera 2, species 9. (Under *CONIFERAE*.)

    Stamens with 2 pollen-sacs and a triangular blade. Pollen-grains with air-bladders. Carpels distinctly developed. Ovule inverted, with two coats. Aril enveloping the seed. Leaves with resin-ducts. — Species 8. South and East Africa, Madagascar, Island of St. Thomas. They yield timber and bark for tanning. (Including *Nageia* Gaertn.) [Subfamily **PODOCARPOIDEAE**.] . . . . . . **Podocarpus** L' Hér.

    Stamens with 5—9 pollen-sacs and a peltate blade. Pollen-grains without air-bladders. Carpels rudimentary. Ovule straight, with one coat. Aril cup-shaped. Leaves without resin-ducts. — Species 1. North-west Africa. A poisonous, medicinal and ornamental plant, with hard wood. " Yew." [Subfamily **TAXOIDEAE**]. . . . . . . **Taxus** L.

FAMILY 3. PINACEAE

Stem branched, woody, with resinous juice. Leaves needle- or scale-like. Flowers unisexual, without a perianth. Stamens in catkins, with 2—5 pollen-sacs below the scale-like limb. Carpels arranged in the shape of a cone or bud, leathery woody or fleshy, when ripe. Ovules 2 or more to each carpel, rarely only 1. Seeds hidden by the carpels, without an aril. Embryo with 2 or more free cotyledons. — Genera 6, species 25. (Under *CONIFERAE*.) (Plate 2.)

  1. Leaves alternate (as are also the floral leaves), but sometimes fascicled, needle-like. Stamens with 2 pollen-sacs. Pollen-grains with air-bladders. Carpels divided into an inner and an outer scale, leathery or woody when ripe. Ovules and seeds 2 to each carpel ; ovules turned downwards. [Tribe ABIETINEAE.] 2

    Leaves opposite or whorled. Stamens with 3—5, very rarely 2 pollen-sacs. Pollen-grains without air-bladders. Ovules turned upwards. [Tribe CUPRESSINEAE.] 4

  2. Shoots all alike (all long). Leaves solitary, flat. Pollen-sacs opening obliquely or transversely ; connective without an appendage. Cones ripening the first year ; scales leathery. — Species 2. North-west Africa. The wood and the resin are used, the latter especially for the preparation of turpentine. " Silver fir." . . . . . **Abies** Juss.

    Shoots of two kinds, long and short. Leaves of the short shoots in clusters of two or more, surrounded by scales when young. Pollen-sacs opening longitudinally ; connective with an appendage. Cones ripening the second or third year ; scales woody. 3

J Fleischmann del.

Encephalartos Lemarinelianus De Wild. & Dur.

A Young plant. *B* Male inflorescence. *C* Stamen. *D* Pollen-sacs. *E* Female inflorescence. *F* Carpel. (*A* partly from De Wildeman, Notices sur des plantes utiles ou intéréssantes de la flore du Congo.)

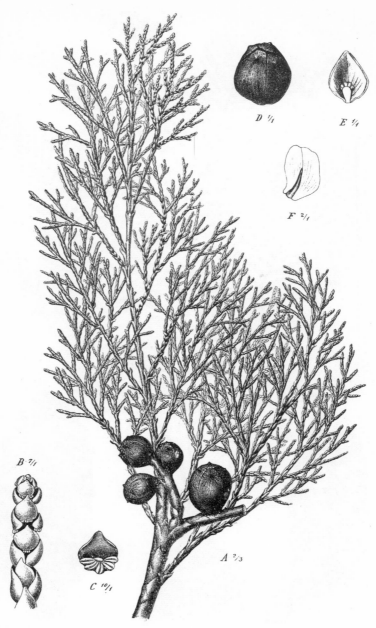

D ⁷/₁   E ⁴/₁

F ²/₁

B ⁷/₁

C ¹⁰/₁

A ²/₃

J. Fleischmann del.

Callitris cupressoides (L.) Schrad.

A Fruiting branch.   *B* Male inflorescence.   *C* Stamen.   *D* Fruit.   *E* Carpel.   *F* Seed.

3. Leaves all needle-like ; those of the short shoots in clusters of many ; those of the long shoots scattered. Flowers inserted upon short shoots, the males solitary. Cone-scales flat, imbricate, without a terminal appendage, deciduous. — Species 2. North-west Africa. They yield timber and medicinal drugs. " Cedar." . . . . **Cedrus** Loud.

Leaves of the short shoots needle-like, in clusters of two or three, very rarely solitary ; leaves of the long shoots scale-like. Male flowers in spikes replacing short shoots ; female flowers towards the end of the branches, replacing long shoots. Cone-scales thick, with a terminal umbonate appendage, persistent. — Species 4. North Africa ; also naturalized in South Africa and St. Helena. Wood, bark, and resin are used for carpenters' and joiners' work, for tanning and for the manufacture of paper, tar, pitch, colophony, turpentine, and other chemical products, as well as in medicine. The seeds of some species (especially those of the stone-pine, *P. Pinea* L.) are edible. " Pine." . . . **Pinus** L.

4. Fruit fleshy, berry- or drupe-like. Seeds not winged, as many as the carpels or fewer. Leaves usually needle-like. — Species 9. North and East Africa. They yield wood, bark for tanning, resin, an essential oil, brandy (gin), and medicines ; some are used as ornamental plants. (Including *Arceuthos* Ant. & Kotschy and *Sabina* Spach). **Juniperus** L.

Fruit woody, cone-like. Seeds winged, as many as the carpels or more. Leaves usually scale-like. 5

5. Carpels 4, valve-like, separating at the apex when ripe, 1—10-seeded.— Species 8, one of them only naturalized. North, South, and southern East Africa, Madagascar and Mauritius. Some of them (especially *C. quadrivalvis* Vent.) yield timber and resin (sandarac) which is used for the preparation of lacquer, varnish, cement, and in medicine. (Including *Tetraclinis* Mast. and *Widdringtonia* Endl.) (Plate 2.)

Callitris Vent.

Carpels 8—10, peltate, separating at the margins when ripe, many-seeded. —Species 1. Cultivated in North Africa as an ornamental plant and sometimes naturalized. It yields timber and is used in medicine. " Cypress." . . . . **Cupressus** L.

CLASS III. GNETALES

FAMILY 4. GNETACEAE

Stem woody. Juice not resinous. Leaves opposite, undivided. Flowers in spikes or panicles or the female solitary, unisexual, but the male sometimes with rudimentary ovules. Perianth of the male flowers tubular or 2—4-parted, of the female bladder-like. Stamens 2—8. Ovule 1, erect, straight. Embryo with 2 cotyledons. — Genera 3 species 8. North and Central Africa.

1. Stem turnip-shaped, very short. Leaves 2, very large, sessile, linear, with parallel nerves. Flowers in panicled spikes ; the male consisting of

a 4-partite perianth, 6 stamens with 3-celled anthers, and a rudimentary ovule. Ovule with a single coat. — Species 1; German South-west Africa and Angola. (*Tumboa* Welw.) [Subfamily **WELWITSCHIOI-DEAE.**] . . . . **Welwitschia** Hook. fil.

Stem shrubby or twining. Leaves numerous, not very large. Male flowers consisting of a 2-partite or a tubular, undivided perianth and 2—8 stamens with 1—2-celled anthers, without rudimentary ovules, but sometimes accompanied by sterile female flowers. 2

2. Leaves large, with a short foot-stalk, lanceolate oblong elliptical or oval, penninerved. Stem climbing. Flowers in spikes or panicles, the male consisting of a tubular, undivided perianth and 2 stamens with 1-celled anthers. Ovule with two coats. — Species 2. West Africa. The young leaves are used as a vegetable. [Subfamily **GNETOIDEAE.**]
Gnetum L.

Leaves scale-like. Male flowers in spikes or panicles, female solitary or in pairs. Male flowers consisting of a 2-partite perianth and 2—8 stamens with 2-celled anthers. Ovule with a single coat exceeding the perianth. — Species 5. North Africa and northern Central Africa. The fruits of some species are eaten or used in medicine. [Subfamily **EPHEDROIDEAE.**] . . . . **Ephedra** L.

SUBDIVISION ANGIOSPERMAE

CLASS IV. MONOCOTYLEDONEAE

ORDER PANDANALES

FAMILY 5. TYPHACEAE

Aquatic or marsh herbs with a creeping root-stock and simple stems. Leaves in two ranks, linear. Inflorescences spadix-like, cylindrical, superposed, interrupted by bracts, the lower female, the upper male. Flowers unisexual, without a perianth, but usually surrounded by hairs. Stamens 2—7; connective thickened; anthers opening lengthwise by two slits. Ovary 1-celled. Ovule 1, pendulous, inverted. Style and stigma simple. Fruit tardily dehiscent. Seed with abundant albumen and a long, axile embryo.

Genus 1, species 4. They are used as ornamental plants and in medicine, and yield potash and also materials for plaiting and stuffing and for the manufacture of paper and felt. The root-stock and the pollen are edible. " Reedmace." . . . . **Typha** Tourn

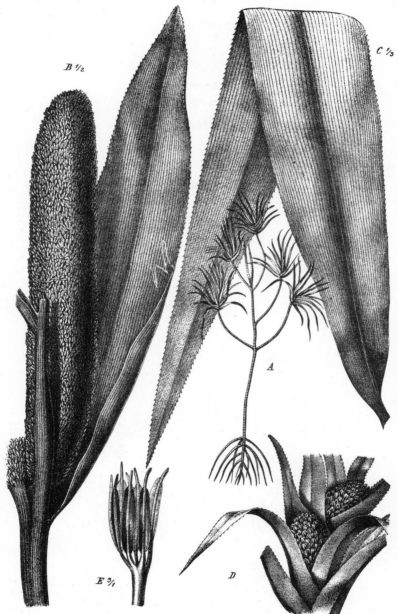

J. Fleischmann del.

Pandanus Candelabrum Beauv.

A Whole plant.   *B* Male inflorescence.   *C* Leaf.   *D* Female inflorescences.   *E* Male flower.   *A* and *D* from Palisot-Beauvois
Flore d'Oware et de Benin.)

J. Fleischmann del

Potamogeton javanicus Hassk.

A Flowering branch. *B* Fruiting branch. *C* Flower. *D* Ovary cut lengthwise. *E* Fruit cut lengthwise

FAMILY 6. PANDANACEAE

Shrubs or trees, usually with aerial roots. Leaves in three ranks, sword-shaped, usually spiny. Flowers dioecious, without bracts, arranged in solitary or panicled, spike- or head-like spadices, which are inserted in the axil of spathe-like bracts. Perianth none. Ovaries connate, 1-celled. Ovule 1, descending, inverted. Stigma 1, sessile. Fruits drupe-like, congested into a globose or ovoid head. Seed with abundant albumen. (Plate 3.)

Genus 1, species 65. Tropics. They yield timber, fibres, flowers used in perfumery, edible fruits, and medicinal drugs. " Screw-pine."

Pandanus L.

FAMILY 7. SPARGANIACEAE

Aquatic or marsh herbs with a creeping root-stock. Leaves in two ranks, linear. Flowers unisexual, in globular heads, the lower of which are female. Perianth of membranous scales. Stamens 3 or more. Ovary superior, 1—2-celled. Ovule 1 in each cell, pendulous, inverted. Style simple , stigmas 1— 2. Fruits drupe-like. Seed with a mealy albumen and a large, axile embryo. (Under *TYPHACEAE*.)

Genus 1, species 2. North-west Africa. " Bur-reed."   **Sparganium** L.

ORDER HELOBIAE

SUBORDER POTAMOGETONINEAE

FAMILY 8. POTAMOGETONACEAE

Aquatic herbs. Leaves with axillary scales. Flowers solitary or spicate, regular, with 1—4-merous whorls. Perianth simple and little developed or wanting. Stamens 1—4. Anthers sessile, opening outwards or laterally. Carpel 1, with a 1-celled ovary, or several distinct or almost distinct carpels. Ovules solitary in each carpel, very rarely 2, pendulous or laterally fixed Fruit indehiscent. Seed exalbuminous. Embryo with a strongly developed radicle. — Genera 8, species 35.   (Including *ZOSTERACEAE*, under *NAIADACEAE*.) (Plate 4.)

1. Flowers in spikes, hermaphrodite or polygamous, without a perianth, but the stamens sometimes provided with a sepal-like connective. 2

  Flowers solitary or in cymes, unisexual. 5

2. Spikes with a flat axis, at the time of flowering enclosed in the sheaths of the uppermost leaves. Stamen 1. Pollen-grains filiform. Carpel 1. Stigmas 2, on a short style. Embryo with a very large radicle and a tail-like cotyledon. Submerged marine plants. — Species 2.   North and South Africa and Madagascar. Used for stuffing and as packing material. " Grass-wrack." [Tribe ZOSTEREAE.] . . . . .   **Zostera** L.

  Spikes with a cylindrical axis, at the time of flowering not enclosed in the sheaths of the uppermost leaves. Stamens 2—4. Stigma 1, undivided or many-parted. 3

3. Spikes compound, submerged. Spikelets shorter than their bracts. Flowers polygamous. Stamens 3, rarely 4. Pollen-grains filiform. Carpel 1. Stigma divided (or provided with narrow appendages). Embryo with a very large radicle and a straight cotyledon resembling the leaves of the plumule. Marine plants. — Species 1. Mediterranean Sea. The leaves are used for packing and thatching, and also in medicine. [Tribe POSIDONIEAE.] . . . . **Posidonia** Koen.

Spikes simple, above the water. Flowers hermaphrodite. Pollen-grains globular or bent. Carpels usually 4. Stigma simple, more or less peltate. Embryo with a curved cotyledon. [Tribe POTAMOGE-TONEAE.] 4

4. Spikes two-flowered. Stamens 2. Anthers with a very short appendage and kidney-shaped cells opening outwards. Pollen-grains bent. Fruit stalked. Embryo with a very thick radicle. Salt-water plants. Leaves subulate. — Species 1. . . . . **Ruppia** L.

Spikes several-flowered. Stamens 4. Anthers with a sepal-like appendage and straight cells opening laterally. Pollen-grains globular. Fruit sessile. Embryo with a slightly thickened radicle. — Species 20. Used for manure ; some have edible root-stocks. " Pondweed." (Plate 4.) **Potamogeton** Tourn.

5. Perianth none. Stamens 2. Pollen-grains filiform. Carpels 2. Stigmas strap-shaped, longer than the style. Embryo with an accumbent cotyledon. Marine plants. [Tribe CYMODOCEEAE.] 6

Perianth present, at least in the female flowers. Stamens 1—2. Pollen-grains globular. Carpels 3—9. Stigma shield- or funnel-shaped, shorter than the style. Embryo with a hooked or rolled cotyledon. Fresh- or brackish-water plants. [Tribe ZANICHELLIEAE.] . 7

6. Stigma 1. Anthers inserted at slightly different heights. Ripe carpels scarcely compressed. — Species 2. Indian Ocean, Red Sea, Angola. (*Halodule* Endl., under *Cymodocea* Koen.)   **Diplanthera** Thouars

Stigmas 2. Anthers inserted at the same height. Ripe carpels compressed and keeled. — Species 5. North Africa, Senegambia, East Africa, Madagascar and neighbouring islands. (Including *Phycagrostis* Ascherson) . . . . **Cymodocea** Koen.

7. Perianth in the male flowers none, in the female cup-shaped and undivided. Anthers stalked, opening by 2 longitudinal slits. Carpels usually 4, slightly curved, with a peltate stigma. — Species 1. North and South Africa, southern West Africa, Madagascar and neighbouring islands. **Zannichellia** Mich.

Perianth in the male flowers 3-toothed, in the female consisting of 1—3 segments. Anthers sessile, opening with one longitudinal slit. Carpels 3, straight, with a funnel-shaped stigma. — Species 1. North-west Africa (Algeria). . . . . **Althenia** Fr. Petit

APONOGETONACEAE.

Pl. 5.

J. Fleischmann del.

Aponogeton leptostachyus E. Mey.

A Plant in flower. *B* Female flower *C* Carpel cut lengthwise.

J. Fleischmann del.   **Limnophyton obtusifolium (L.) Miq.**

A Plant in flower   *B* Male flower from above.   *C* Male flower cut lengthwise.

FAMILY 9. NAIADACEAE

Herbs growing in fresh or brackish water. Leaves linear, toothed or spiny. Flowers axillary, solitary or in glomerules, unisexual. Perianth little developed, in the male flowers simple or double, sack-like, in the female simple and sacklike or wanting. Stamen 1. Anthers 1- or 4-celled. Pollen-grains globular or ovoid. Ovary 1-celled. Ovule 1, erect, inverted. Style 1 ; stigmas 2—3. Seed with a hard coat, exalbuminous. Embryo straight, with a large radicle and a well developed plumule.

Genus 1, species 10. (Including *Caulinia* A. Braun) . . . . **Naias** L.

FAMILY 10. APCNOGETONACEAE

, Aquatic herbs with a tuberous root-stock. Leaves radical, narrow, with several longitudinal and many transverse nerves. Flowers in 1—4 spikes connected at the base, enclosed when young in a sheath, and rising above the water. Perianth of 1—3 more or less brightly coloured segments. Stamens 6 or more, hypogynous, free. Anthers attached by the base, opening with two longitudinal slits. Carpels 3—8, distinct. Ovules in each carpel 2—8, basal or sutural, ascending, inverted. Fruits membranous, dehiscent. Seeds 2 or more, erect, exalbuminous, with a straight embryo. (Under *NAIADA-CEAE.*) (Plate 5.)

Genus 1, species 20. Tropical and South Africa. Some are used as ornamental plants, especially the lattice-leaf (*A. fenestralis* Hook. fil.) with perforated leaves. The tubers are edible and contain starch. (Including *Ouvirandra* Thouars). . . . . **Aponogeton** Thunb.

FAMILY 11. SCHEUCHZERIACEAE

Marsh herbs. Leaves linear, with axillary scales. Flowers in terminal racemes or spikes, regular, hermaphrodite. Perianth of 6 segments, usually green. Stamens 3—6. Anthers turned outwards ; pollen-grains ovoid. Ovary 3—6-celled. Ovule 1 in each cell, ascending, inverted. Stigmas sessile. Seeds exalbuminous, with a straight embryo. (*JUNCAGINEAE,* under *NAIADACEAE.*)

Genus 1, species 4. North, South, and West Africa. The leaves and fruits of some species are edible. (*Juncago* Tourn.) . . . **Triglochin** L.

SUBORDER ALISMATINEAE
FAMILY 12. ALISMATACEAE

Aquatic or marsh herbs, with milky juice. Leaves with axillary scales. Flowers regular. Perianth of 3 sepals and 3 petals, rarely in the female flowers of 3 sepals only. Stamens 6 or more, rarely 3. Anthers opening outwards. Pollen-grains globular. Carpels 6 or more, rarely 3, distinct or united at the base. Ovules solitary in each carpel, rarely two or more, inverted. Seeds without albumen ; embryo curved. — Genera 9, species 15. Tropical and North Africa. (Plate 6.)

1. Carpels on a large and distinctly convex receptacle. Inner perianth-segments petal-like, larger than, or almost as large as the outer. Stamens 6 or more. [Tribe SAGITTARIEAE.] 2

   Carpels on a small and almost flat receptacle. 4

2. Flowers hermaphrodite. Ripe carpels numerous, slightly compressed, with many ribs. — Species 3. Central and North-west Africa. (Under *Alisma* L.) . . . . **Echinodorus** Engelm.

   Flowers unisexual or polygamous. Ripe carpels much compressed later-ally. 3

3. Flowers monoecious or polygamous. Petals a little longer than the sepals. Carpels many. Ripe carpels with two crest-like ribs. — Species 1. Tropics. (*Lophiocarpus* Miq., under *Sagittaria* L.)

   Lophotocarpus Th. Dur.

   Flowers dioecious. Petals shorter than the sepals, white. Carpels 7—9. Ripe carpels with 3 ribs. — Species 1. German South-west Africa.

   Rautanenia Buchenau

4. Petals much smaller than the sepals or wanting. Stamens 3 or 9. [Tribe WIESNEREAE.] 5

   Petals larger than the sepals, coloured. Stamens 6, rarely 9. [Tribe ALISMEAE.] 6

5. Flowers dioecious. Petals in the female flowers wanting. Stamens 9. Carpels about 12. — Species 1. East Africa. . . . **Burnatia** Mich.

   Flowers monoecious. Petals present, but very small and falling off early. Stamens 3. Carpels 3—6. — Species 2. East Africa and Madagascar. (*Wisneria* Mich.) . . . . **Wiesnera** Mich.

6. Carpels 6—8, united at the base and spreading horizontally, containing 2 or more ovules each and opening by a lid when ripe. — Species 2. North Africa. The root-stock is edible. . . . . . **Damasonium** Tourn.

   Carpels 6—20, distinct, with a single ovule in each, indehiscent. . 7

7. Flowers polygamous-monoecious. Carpels 15—20. Pericarp bony within, hollow on either side. Leaves sagittate. — Species 3. Tropics. (Plate 6.) . . . . **Limnophyton** Miq.

   Flowers hermaphrodite. Leaves ovate, cordate, or lanceolate. . . 8

8. Carpels 6—12, irregularly whorled, slightly compressed and 3—5-ribbed when ripe ; pericarp woody within. — Species 2. Tropics and Egypt. (Under *Alisma* L.) . . . . **Caldesia** Parl.

   Carpels 15—20, distinctly whorled, much compressed and 2-ribbed when ripe ; pericarp leathery or parchment-like. — Species 1. North and East Africa. The root-stock contains starch and is used in medicine. "Water-plantain." . . . . **Alisma** L.

SUBORDER BUTOMINEAE

FAMILY 13. BUTOMACEAE

Aquatic or marsh herbs. Leaves linear or lanceolate. Flowers in umbel-like cymes, regular, hermaphrodite. Perianth of 6 segments, all, or the inner ones only, petal-like. Stamens 9, very rarely fewer. Pollen-grains globular. Carpels 6, very rarely fewer, distinct or united at the base only, opening when ripe along the ventral suture. Ovules on irregularly branched parietal placentas, numerous, inverted. Seeds without albumen. — Genera 2, species 2. North and Central Africa. (Under *ALISMACEAE*.)

Perianth-segments nearly equal, all petal-like, pink, persistent. Embryo straight. Leaves linear. Juice not milky. — Species 1. North-west Africa (Algeria). Used as a garden plant. The root-stock is edible. " Flowering-rush." . . . . **Butomus** Tourn.

Perianth-segments unequal, outer sepal-like, inner petal-like, white, falling off very early. Embryo horseshoe-shaped. Leaves elliptical. Juice milky. — Species 1. Northern part of Central Africa. (*Butomopsis* Kunth) . . . . **Tenagocharis** Hochst.

FAMILY 14. HYDROCHARITACEAE

Aquatic herbs. Leaves with axillary scales. Flowers enclosed when young in a one- or several-flowered spathe of one or two bracts, regular, rarely somewhat irregular. Perianth consisting of a calyx and a corolla, rarely simple. Stamens 2—12. Anthers opening outwards or laterally. Ovary inferior, more or less distinctly one-celled, with 2—15 parietal placentas, which sometimes form incomplete dissepiments. Seeds without albumen. — Genera 10, species 40. (Plate 7.)

1. Stigmas 2—5. Placentas as many, slightly raised. 2
   Stigmas 6 or more. Placentas as many, much projecting and generally meeting in the centre of the ovary. 6

2. Petals none. Stamens 3. Pollen-grains filiform. Stigmas several times as long as the sepals. Embryo with a strongly developed radicle. Totally submerged marine plants. Leaves more or less distinctly stalked. — Species 2. Indian Ocean. [Subfamily **HALOPHILOIDEAE**.]
   Halophila Thouars

   Petals present, but sometimes very small and falling off very early. Pollen-grains globular. Stigmas at most twice as long as the sepals. Embryo with a not very strongly developed radicle. Freshwater plants ; flowers raised above the water. Leaves sessile. [Subfamily **VALLISNERIOI-DEAE.**] 3

3. Leaves whorled. Spathes 1-flowered. Flowers unisexual. Stamens 3. — Species 1. Upper Nile, Madagascar, Mauritius. Used in refining sugar. [Tribe HYDRILLEAE.] . . . . **Hydrilla** L. C. Rich.
   Leaves spirally arranged. Spathes of the male flowers several-flowered. 4

4. Spathes of the male flowers 2—10-flowered, not breaking away from the
stem. Stamens 3—9. Ovules inverted. — Species 3. Madagascar and
Angola. [Tribe BLYXEAE.] . . . . . . **Blyxa** Noronha
Spathes of the male flowers many-flowered, breaking away from the stem.
Stamens 2—3. Ovules straight. [Tribe VALLISNERIEAE.]   5

5. Male flowers regular, with 3 fertile and 2—4 sterile stamens. Stigmas
linear, 2-cleft or 2-parted. Leaves one-nerved. Stem elongated —
Species 10. Tropical and South Africa. . . . **Lagarosiphon** Harv.
Male flowers somewhat irregular, with 2—3 fertile stamens and sometimes
a sterile one. Stigmas ovate, notched or two-toothed. Leaves several-
nerved. — Species 2. North and Central Africa. Used in refining sugar.
Vallisneria Mich.

6. Leaves in two rows. Ovules inverted, inserted in the angles formed by the
placentas and the wall of the ovary. Radicle of the embryo strongly
developed. Marine plants. [Subfamily **THALASSIOIDEAE**.]   7
Leaves in rosettes. Ovules inverted, but inserted on the whole surface
of the placentas, or straight. Radicle of the embryo not strongly
developed. Freshwater plants. [Subfamily **STRATIOTOIDEAE**.]   8

7. Scape of the male flowers short, of the female long and at length spirally
twisted. Male spathes several-flowered ; flowers with 3 petals and 3
stamens. — Species 1. Madagascar and Red Sea. Yields fibres and
edible seeds. . . . . **Enalus** L. C. Rich.
Scapes moderately long, not spirally twisted. Male spathes one-flowered ;
flowers without petals, with 6 stamens. — Species 1. East Africa.
Thalassia Soland.

8. Placentas undivided. Ovules straight. Fertile stamens 9. Stem emit-
ting runners. Leaves floating. — Species 1. Algeria and Madagascar.
" Frogbit." [Tribe HYDROCHARITEAE.] . . **Hydrocharis** L.
Placentas two-cleft. Ovules inverted. Seeds very numerous. Fertile
stamens 6—12. Stem very short, without runners. Leaves at least
partially submerged. [Tribe OTTELIEAE.] 9

9. Flowers hermaphrodite. Spathes one-flowered. Stigmas 6. — Species 9.
Tropics and Egypt. Some are used as vegetables. (Plate 7.)
Ottelia Pers.

Flowers dioecious. Spathes of the male flowers several-flowered. Stigmas
9—15. — Species 10. Tropics. Some are used as vegetables.
Boottia Wall.

ORDER TRIURIDALES

FAMILY 15. TRIURIDACEAE

Small, pale, yellowish or reddish herbs. Leaves reduced to scales. Flowers
in racemes, regular, monoecious. Perianth of 6 petaloid, valvate segments
united at the base. Stamens 3 ; filaments short or wanting ; anthers 2-celled,
opening transversely. Carpels inserted on a convex or conical receptacle,

J. Fleischmann del.

Ottelia alismoides (L.) Pers.

A Plant in flower.　*B* Flower.　*C* Stamen,　*D* Pistil cut lengthwise.

J. Fleischmann del.

Chloris Gayana Kunth

A Plant in flower.   B Inflorescence.   C Spikelet.   D Flower.   E Empty glume above the flower.

numerous, distinct ; styles lateral ; ovules solitary, erect, inverted.   Fruits
dehiscing by a longitudinal slit.

Genus 1, species 3.   West Africa and Seychelles.   (Including *Seychellaria*
Hemsl.)   .   .   .   .   **Sciaphila** Blume

ORDER GLUMIFLORAE

FAMILY 16.   GRAMINEAE

Stem usually herbaceous and hollow between the nodes.   Leaves alternate,.
usually linear and furnished at their base with a sheath split open on one side
and ending in a ligule.   Inflorescence consisting of spikelets, rarely of single
flowers, usually enclosed by 2 glumes (outer or empty glumes) and arranged
in spikes, racemes, or panicles.   Flowers in the axil of the flowering glume
(or valve), subtended by the usually 2-keeled palea and sometimes by one or
two, rarely more, minute lodicules.   Perianth none.   Stamens 1—6, usually 3,
Anthers opening by 2 slits or pores.   Ovary 1-celled.   Ovule 1, erect or laterally affixed, slightly curved, with the micropyle turned downwards.   Styles 2,.
rarely 3 or 1.   Fruit indehiscent ; pericarp usually dry and adnate to the seed.
Embryo outside the copious albumen. — Genera 205, species 1600.   "Grasses."
(Plate 8.)

1. Spikelets 1-flowered, rarely 2-flowered, the upper flower fertile, the lower
   male or barren and inserted immediately below the fertile one.   Axis
   of the spikelet not produced beyond the fertile flower, jointed below the
   outer glumes or not jointed ; ripe spikelets falling entire from their
   stalk or from the rachis of the spike, sometimes together with a part of
   it.   [Subfamily **PANICOIDEAE.**]   2
   Spikelets either 1-flowered with the axis produced beyond the flower or
   jointed above the outer glumes, which therefore persist when the spikelet
   falls off, or 2-flowered with both flowers fertile or with a distinct interval
   between the flowers or with a continuation of the axis beyond the flowers,
   or 3- to many-flowered.   65

2. Spikelets distinctly compressed from the side.   Stamens usually 6.   Seed
   with a linear hilum.   [Tribe ORYZEAE.]   3
   Spikelets compressed from front to back or not distinctly compressed.
   Stamens usually 1—3.   Seed usually with a punctiform hilum.   .   .   7

3. Spikelets in terminal clusters of two or three, connate, at length hardened.
   Stamens 3.   Style undivided, papillose. — Species 1.   North Africa..
   One source of the Esparto-grass, which is used for plaiting and paper-
   making.   .   .   .   .   **Lygeum** L.
   Spikelets in panicles.   Stamens nearly always 6.   Style 3-cleft or 3-parted,.
   with feathery stigmas.   4

4. Spikelets unisexual ; 1—2 sessile female and a stalked male on each branch
   of the panicle.   Flowering glume globose.   Stamens 6.   Style 1,

long, 3-cleft. Leaves broad-lanceolate, stalked. — Species 1. Equatorial West Africa. . . . . **Leptaspis** R. Br.
Spikelets bisexual or polygamous. Styles 3, short, free or united at the
very base. Leaves linear or narrow lanceolate. 5

5. Outer glumes rudimentary. Flowering glume awnless. — Species 4.
(*Homalocenchrus* Mieg.) . . . . **Leersia** Swartz
Outer glumes distinctly developed. Stamens 6. 6

6. Flowering glume and palea slightly compressed, awnless. Leaves linear-
lanceolate, more or less distinctly stalked. — Species 4. Madagascar
and Natal. (Under *Potamophila* R. Br.) . . . **Maltebrunia** Kunth
Flowering glume and palea strongly compressed. — Species 3, two wild in
Central Africa, the third (*O. sativa* L., rice) cultivated in various regions.
The seeds are used for food and for the preparation of meal, starch, oil,
and brandy, the straw for plaiting and for the manufacture of paper and
brush-ware. . . . . **Oryza** L.

7. (2.) Flowering glume and palea (if present) stiff or at length hardened,
firmer than the outer glumes and awnless, at least in the hermaphrodite
flowers. Lowest glume usually smaller than the others. Rachis of the
spike or raceme or branches of the panicle rarely jointed. [Tribe
PANICEAE.] 8
Flowering glume and palea (if present) membranous, thinner than the outer
glumes. 26

8. Flowers unisexual, monoecious. Spikelets in panicles, the male in the
lower portion of the panicle or in special panicles. Outer glumes in the
male spikelets none, in the female 2. Lodicules 3. Leaves net-veined.—
Species 2. Tropical and South-East Africa. . . . . . **Olyra** L.
Flowers hermaphrodite or polygamous ; in the latter case spikelets arranged
in spikes. 9

9. Spikelets partly hermaphrodite, partly male or neuter. 10
Spikelets all hermaphrodite. 11

10. Spikelets in short spikes consisting of a lower hermaphrodite and two or
three upper neuter spikelets ; spikes unilateral on the flattened, leaf-
like rachis of a compound spike. Stem erect. Leaves lanceolate,
sagittate. — Species 1. Southern West Africa (Angola).
Phyllorhachis Trimen
Spikelets in a simple spike consisting of 1—2 lower female and 4—6 upper
male spikelets ; rachis of the spike enlarged at the base, but not leaf-like.
Stem creeping. — Species 1. Madagascar. . . . . **Thuarea** Pers.

11. Spikelets in short spikes sunk in pits on a broad rachis. Stem creeping.—
Species 4. Tropical and South Africa. Used for binding the sand
on riverbanks or as fodder ; also in medicine. **Stenotaphrum** Trin.
Spikelets not sunk in pits on a broad rachis. 12

12. Spikelets surrounded or subtended singly or 2—3 together by an involucre formed of one or several bristles or spines or of 2 toothed glumes inserted below the two empty glumes. 13
 Spikelets without an involucre formed of bristles, spines, or toothed glumes. Empty glumes 1—3. Stigmas 2, feathery. 16

13. Involucre formed by two toothed glumes. Stigma 1, papillose. Aquatic herbs. — Species 1. Abyssinia. . . . . **Odontelytrum** Hack.
 Involucre formed by one or several bristles or spines. Stigmas 2, feathery. 14

14. Axis of the spikelet jointed above the persistent involucre. Bristles of the involucre stiff and rough. Styles free from the base. Spikelets in spike-like panicles. — Species 30. Some of them (especially *S. italica* Beauv.) are cultivated as cereals. . . . . . . **Setaria** Beauv.
 Axis of the spikelet jointed below the involucre or not jointed ; involucre falling together with the spikelet ; rarely axis jointed above the persistent involucre, but then styles united at the base. 15

15. Bristles of the involucre numerous, stiff, thickened and often united at the base. Spikelets in spikes or racemes. — Species 10. Tropics and Egypt. Some have edible seeds ; several are fodder-grasses. **Cenchrus** L.
 Bristles of the involucre fine, not thickened at the base. — Species 65. Some (especially the duchn, *P. typhoideum* Rich.) are cultivated as cereals, as fodder, or as ornamental plants. (Including *Gymnothrix* Beauv. and *Penicillaria* Willd.) . . . . **Pennisetum** Pers.

16. Spikelets with 2 outer glumes and 1 flower, or with 1 outer glume and 2 flowers. 17
 Spikelets with 3 outer glumes and 1 flower, or with 2 outer glumes and 2 flowers. 21

17. Spikelets containing an hermaphrodite and a male flower, arranged in panicles. Glumes awnless. Styles free. — Species 1. South-west Africa (Nama-land). . . . . **Anthaenantia** Beauv.
 Spikelets 1-flowered, arranged in one-sided, usually digitate or panicled spikes. 18

18. Rachis of the spike prolonged beyond the spikelets. Style 1, with 2 stigmas. — Species 3. North-west and South Africa. . . . **Spartina** Schreb.
 Rachis of the spike not prolonged beyond the spikelets. Styles 2, free or shortly united. 19

19. Styles united at the base. Flowering glume papery. Upper outer glume awned. Spikelets in digitate racemes. — Species 1. East Africa. (*Stereochlaena* Hack.) . . . . **Chloridion** Stapf
 Styles free. Flowering glume cartilaginous. 20

20. Lower outer glume decurrent into a callous swelling. Flowering glume mucronate. — Species 6. Central Africa. . . . **Eriochloa** Kunth
 Lower outer glume without a callus at the base. — Species 15. Tropical and South Africa. Used as fodder-, medicinal, or ornamental plants.

The seeds of several species (especially those of the fundi *P. exile* Kippist)
are sometimes used as food. . . . . **Paspalum** L.

21. Spikelets containing two hermaphrodite flowers. Axis of the spikelet
jointed above the persistent outer glumes. Outer glumes awnless.
Spikelets arranged in panicles. — Species 6. Tropics. **Isachne** R. Br.
Spikelets containing a single hermaphrodite flower and sometimes also a
male flower. Axis of the spikelet jointed below the outer glumes;
spikelet falling as a whole. 22

22. First (lowest) outer glume awned, as well as the second. Spikelets one-
flowered, directed to one side and disposed in panicles. — Species 4.
Tropical and South Africa. Some are used as fodder. **Oplismenus** Beauv.
First outer glume awnless. 23

23. Second outer glume apparently removed from the first by a conical or
cylindrical, strongly-haired swelling at the base, usually awned or mucronate. Spikelets in panicles. 25
Second outer glume without a basal swelling. 24

24. First outer glume as large as or larger than the second, papery. — Species 1.
South-west Africa to Angola. (Under *Panicum* L.). **Leucophrys** Rendle
First outer glume much smaller than the second. — Species 20. Some are
used as ornamental or fodder-plants. (Including *Monachyron* Parl.
and *Rhynchelytrum* Nees, under *Panicum* L.) **Tricholaena** Schrad.

25. Second outer glume bearing, like the third, a long, twisted awn. — Species 1.
German East Africa. . . . . **Acritochaete** Pilger
Second outer glume unawned. — Species 220. Some (especially *P. milia-
ceum* L., millet, and *P. sanguinale* L.) are cultivated as cereals, others
furnish vegetables, syrup, or fodder, or are used for plaiting-work or as
ornamental plants. (Including *Axonopus* Beauv., *Digitaria* Pers.,
Echinolaena Desv., *Sacciolepis* Nash, and *Syntherisma* Walt.) **Panicum** L.

26. (7.) Outer glumes 3, the lowest smaller than the others, the uppermost
sometimes including a male flower. Rachis and branches of the inflorescence not jointed. [Tribe TRISTEGINEAE.] 27
Outer glumes 1—3; if 3, then the lowest larger than the uppermost. 30

27. Spikelets arranged in spikes. First and second outer glume minute, the
third awned. — Species 3. Abyssinia. . . . . . **Beckera** Fresen.
Spikelets arranged in panicles. Second outer glume not very small.
Flowering glume awnless. 28

28. Lowest outer glume minute, like the second awnless, the third more or less
distinctly awned. Spikelets arranged singly along the branches of
the panicle. — Species 1. Tropical and South-east Africa. Used as a
fodder-grass. . . . . **Melinis** Beauv.
Lowest outer glume not very small; the third awnless, rarely both the
second and third awned. 29

29. Outer glumes, at least the second, awned. Spikelets arranged singly along
the branches of the panicle. (See 24.) . . **Tricholaena** Schrad.

Outer glumes awnless, the first and second about half the length of the third and the flowering glume. Spikelets in clusters along the branches of the panicle. — Species 2. West Africa and Mascarene Islands. Used as ornamental plants. . . . . **Thysanolaena** Nees

30. (26.) Flowers unisexual. Male and female spikelets in different inflorescences, or male spikelets in the upper, female in the lower portion of the inflorescence. [Tribe MAYDEAE.] 31

Flowers hermaphrodite or polygamous, rarely (*Andropogon*) unisexual, but then male and female spikelets in the same inflorescence and arranged in pairs, the male spikelets sometimes rudimentary. 33

31. Male spikelets in a terminal spike, the female at its base, enclosed singly or 2—3 together by a hardened globose bract. Style not very long, 2-cleft. — Species 1 (*C. Lacryma Jobi* L., Job's tears). North-west Africa, Madagascar and neighbouring islands. Used medicinally and for making ornamental articles and rosaries. . . . . **Coix** L.

Male spikelets in spikes arranged in a terminal panicle, female in spikes or spadices with membranous bracts or spathes. Style very long, undivided or shortly 2-cleft. 32

32. Female spikelets in fascicled spikes with a jointed rachis. Style 2-cleft. Fruit enclosed when ripe in a cartilagineous case. — Species 1 (*E. mexicana* Schrad., Teosinte), cultivated as an ornamental or fodder-plant. . . . . **Euchlaena** Schrad.

Female spikelets connate into a spadix with a thick, not jointed rachis. Fruit projecting beyond the membranous glumes, rarely enclosed by leathery glumes. — Species 1 (*Z. Mays* L., maize or Indian corn). Cultivated for the grain or as a fodder- or ornamental plant. The seeds are also used for the preparation of starch, oil, and spirituous drinks. The leaves and spathes yield fibre. . . . . **Zea** L.

33. Spikelets in heads surrounded by 2 or 3 involucral bracts, containing a single hermaphrodite flower. Outer glumes 2, membranous, awnless, the lower one short. Flowering glume larger than the outer glumes, awnless. Stamens 2. — Species 1. North Africa and Senegambia. **Crypsis** Ait.

Spikelets in spikes, racemes, or panicles. 34

34. Spikelets arranged singly or in clusters of 3—6, very rarely in pairs, along the continuous rachis of a spike or raceme. Outer glumes 2. [Tribe ZOYSIEAE.] 35

Spikelets arranged in pairs, one sessile, the other stalked, more rarely singly or in clusters of 3 or more, along the more or less distinctly jointed rachis of a spike or raceme or along the branches of a sometimes very narrow (spike-like) panicle. Outer glumes usually 3. [Tribe ANDROPOGONEAE.] 42

35. Spikelets in clusters of 3—6, falling as a whole 36

Spikelets solitary along the rachis, rarely in pairs. 38

36. Clusters of spikelets enclosed by a hard, urn-shaped involucre formed by the lowest outer glumes.   Rachis of the spike wavy — Species 5. Central and South Africa.   .   .   .   .   **Anthephora** Schreb.
Clusters of spikelets without an involucre.   37

37. Clusters containing 2—4 fertile spikelets and a barren one.   Outer glumes 1—2, the upper one with hooked spines on the nerves.   Rachis of the spike glabrous. — Species 4. (*Nazia* Adans.) .   .   .   .   **Tragus** Hall.
Clusters containing 1—2 fertile and 2—3 barren, often awn-like spikelets. Outer glume 1, with rough nerves, awned. — Species 1. Southern West Africa (Hereroland). .   .   .   .   **Monelytrum** Hack.

38. Styles united at the base; stigmas short, feathery.   Outer glumes 2, glabrous, with a long awn or awnless.   Flowering glume smaller.   Spikelets diverging from the rachis. — Species 4. Tropical and South Africa. Used as fodder-grasses. .   .   .   .   **Perotis** Ait.
Styles free or the stigmas elongated and short-haired all round. .   .   39

39. Outer glume 1, compressed, keeled, awnless.   Styles free.   Spikelets pressed close to the rachis.   Leaves stiff. — Species 1. Mascarene Islands. (*Osterdomia* Neck.) .   .   .   .   **Zoysia** Willd.
Outer glumes 2.   40

40. Outer glumes subulate, with a long awn, short-haired.   Flowering glume somewhat shorter, with a rather long awn.   Palea slightly shorter than the flowering glume, acuminate.   Styles free.   Fruit with a large hilum.   Spikelets in pairs. — Species 1. Northern East Africa.

Tetrachaete Chiovenda
Outer glumes and flowering glume with a short awn or awnless. .   41

41. Outer glumes convex, with hooked spines on the back, awnless.   Flowering glume much shorter, unarmed or mucronate.   Styles free; stigmas feathery.   Spikelets with a flattened stalk. — Species 1. Northern part of Central Africa. .   .   .   .   **Latipes** Kunth
Outer glumes compressed and keeled, not bearing hooked spines.   Flowering glume broad, 3-nerved, mucronate or shortly awned.   Stigmas long, short-haired all round. — Species 5. North Africa. Used as ornamental or fodder-plants. "Foxtail grass." (Including *Colobachne* Beauv.) .   .   .   .   **Alopecurus** L.

42. (34.) Joints of the rachis much thickened, forming, together with the appressed or adnate pedicels of the stalked spikelets, hollows in which the sessile spikelets are sunk.   Flowering glumes awnless.   Lowest outer glume leathery or hardened.   Sessile spikelets hermaphrodite, stalked ones male or neuter, rarely (*Ophiurus*) reduced to the adnate pedicel and therefore apparently absent.   [Subtribe ROTTBOELLIINAE.] 43
Joints of the rachis not much thickened, nor forming hollows for the reception of the spikelets, rarely slightly concave, but then flowering glumes of the sessile spikelets awned or (*Elionurus*) the lowest outer glume membranous or papery and marked with two transparent balsamiferous streaks.   48

43. Lower outer glume awned or tailed, at least in the stalked spikelets. . 44
    Lower outer glume neither awned nor tailed, rarely tailed in the terminal
    spikelet only. 46
44. Lower outer glume with a long tail (or soft awn). Racemes digitate.
    Aquatic herbs. — Species 1. Central Africa. Forming the chief element
    of the grass-barriers (sudd) of the upper Nile. **Vossia** Wall. & Griff.
    Lower outer glume with 1—2 short awns, or in the stalked spikelets with a
    long awn, in the sessile awnless. Racemes solitary or arranged in
    racemes. 45
45. Lower outer glume with 1—2 short awns. Joints of the rachis horizontally
    truncate without an appendage. — Species 7. Central Africa. Used
    for plaiting-work. (*Rhytidachne* Hack., including *Jardinea* Steud.)
    Rhytachne Desv.
    Lower outer glume in the sessile spikelets awnless, in the stalked ones with
    a long awn or tail. Joints of the rachis obliquely truncate with an
    appendage at the tip. — Species 5. Central and South Africa.
    Urelytrum Hack.
46. Lower outer glume globular, pitted. Leaves cordate at the base. —
    Species 1. Tropics. Used in medicine. (Including *Hackelochloa* O.
    Ktze.) . . . . **Manisuris** Swartz
    Lower outer glume more or less ovate, flat or rounded on the back. . 47
47. Stalked spikelets reduced to the adnate pedicel and therefore apparently
    absent. — Species 1. Northern East Africa. (Under *Rottboellia* L. fil.)
    Ophiurus Gaertn.
    Stalked spikelets containing a male flower or reduced to empty glumes.—
    Species 15. (Including *Hemarthria* R. Br.) . . **Rottboellia** L. fil.
48. (42.) Sessile spikelets 2-flowered, the lower flower male, the upper male
    or hermaphrodite. Stalked spikelets 1—2-flowered or reduced to
    empty glumes. 49
    Sessile spikelets 1-flowered, rarely all spikelets stalked and 1- or (*Imperata*)
    2-flowered. 52
49. Sessile spikelets containing 2 male flowers, stalked spikelets a male and a
    female or hermaphrodite flower. Outer glumes of the sessile spikelets
    awned. Flowering glumes awnless. Spikelets in compound racemes.
    Leaves lanceolate. — Species 1. Madagascar. **Cyphochlaena** Hack.
    Sessile spikelets containing a male and an hermaphrodite flower. Flowering
    glumes of the sessile spikelets nearly always awned. [Subtribe
    ISCHAEMINAE.] 50
50. Racemes reduced to the 3 terminal spikelets, surrounded by sheathing
    bracts, fasciculate ; fascicles arranged in panicles. Stamens 2—3. —
    Species 1. Islands of Réunion and Socotra. Used as an ornamental
    plant. . . . . **Apluda** L.
    Racemes consisting of numerous pairs of spikelets, solitary or digitate ;
    one spikelet of each pair sometimes reduced to the pedicel. Stamens
    3. 51

51. Stalked spikelets reduced to the pedicel. Lower outer glume tuberculate. —
Species 1. Abyssinia. . . . .   **Thelepogon** Roth
Stalked spikelets 1—2-flowered or reduced to empty glumes. — Species 7.
Tropical and South Africa. Some are used as fodder- or garden plants.
Ischaemum L.

52. Spikelets all alike, hermaphrodite. [Subtribe SACCHARINAE.] . . . 53
Spikelets of two kinds, the sessile hermaphrodite, rarely female, the stalked
ones male or neuter, sometimes reduced to the pedicel. [Subtribe
ANDROPOGONINAE.] 60

53. Rachis of the raceme jointed. 54
Rachis of the raceme not jointed. 57

54. Racemes more or less palmately arranged on a short main axis, rarely
solitary. 55
Racemes arranged in panicles along a slender main axis, silky. Spikelets
in pairs. 56

55. Spikelets solitary on the branches of the inflorescence, all sessile. Flowering
glumes awned from the back. Leaves cordate-lanceolate. — Species 5.
Tropics. . . . .   **Arthraxon** Beauv.
Spikelets in pairs on the branches of the inflorescence, one sessile, the other
stalked. Flowering glumes awned from the tip, rarely awnless. Leaves
linear or lanceolate with a narrow base. — Species 5. South and East
Africa, Madagascar and the neighbouring islands. (Including *Eulalia*
Kunth) . . . .   **Pollinia** Trin.

56. Flowering glume produced into a bristle or awn. — Species 5. South Africa,
southern Central Africa, and Algeria. Some are used as ornamental
plants or for plaiting mats. . . . . . .   **Erianthus** Michx.
Flowering glume unarmed like the other glumes. — Species 5. One of them
(*S. officinarum* L., sugar-cane) known only in a cultivated state. It
is used for the manufacture of sugar, syrup, rum, and wax, also as a
vegetable and a fodder-plant. . . . .   **Saccharum** L.

57. Spikelets in pairs along the rachis of the raceme, awnless. Outer glumes 3,
membranous, silky. Stamens 1—2. — Species 1 (*I. cylindrica* P.
Beauv.) Sometimes a noxious weed in plantations, but also used for
paper-making, and as a fodder-, medicinal or ornamental plant.
Imperata Cyr.
Spikelets scattered along the rachis of the raceme, awned. . . . 58

58. Outer glumes 3, the two lower stiff. Flowering glume very small, ending
in a long awn. Panicle spreading, hairy. — Species 2. Central Africa.
Cleistachne Benth.
Outer glumes 2. Flowering glume rather large, with a usually short awn
in a terminal notch or on the back. Panicle spike-like. . . . 59

59. Stigmas projecting at the tip of the spikelet, short-haired all round. Outer
glumes awnless, rarely with a short awn. (See 41.)   **Alopecurus** L.

Stigmas projecting near the base of the spikelet, feathery. Outer glumes with usually long awns. — Species 6. North Africa, Abyssinia, and South Africa. Some are used as ornamental plants. " Beardgrass."

Polypogon Desf.

60. (52.) Racemes bearing at their base a false whorl of 4 male or neuter spikelets and subtended by a spathe-like bract, more rarely without a bract. 61

Racemes without a whorl of male or neuter spikelets at their base, rarely surrounded by an imperfect whorl of spikelets, but then racemes in pairs subtended by a common spathe. 62

61. Hermaphrodite spikelets produced at the base into an appendage decurrent along the rachis, easily separating from the whorl of spikelets below them. — Species 2. (*Anthistiria* L. fil.) . . . . . . **Themeda** Forsk.

Hermaphrodite spikelets without a decurrent appendage at the base, falling together with the whorl of spikelets below them. — Species 1. Naturalized in the Island of Mauritius. (Under *Anthistiria* L. fil.)

Iseilema Anders.

62. Spikelets all stalked, in pairs, the longer-stalked hermaphrodite, the shorter-stalked male. Rachis of the raceme indistinctly jointed. Racemes terminal, solitary or 2—3 together. — Species 1. Tropical and South Africa. . . . . **Trachypogon** Nees

Spikelets partly sessile, partly stalked. Rachis of the raceme distinctly jointed, fragile at maturity, rarely indistinctly or not jointed, but then spikelets in clusters of three, arranged in panicles. 63

63. Lowest outer glume marked with two transparent balsamiferous streaks, usually 2-toothed. Glumes awnless. Racemes solitary ; rachis nearly always silky. — Species 10. Tropical and South Africa.

Elionurus Humb. & Bonpl.

Lowest outer glume without balsamiferous streaks. Flowering glumes of the sessile spikelets awned, very rarely awnless and then racemes nearly always panicled. 64

64. Flowering glumes awned from the back. Leaves cordate at the base. (See 55.) . . . . **Arthraxon** Beauv.

Flowering glumes awned from the tip or awnless. Leaves not cordate.— Species 110. The sorghum or Guinea corn (*A. Sorghum* Brot.) is cultivated as a cereal and used for manufacturing sugar, spirituous drinks, dyes, and brushware. Other species are used in perfumery (lemon-grass, vetiver-root) and medicine, for plaiting-work, or as fodder- or garden-plants. (Including *Anatherum* Beauv., *Chrysopogon* Trin., *Cymbopogon* Spreng., *Euclaste* Franch., *Heterochloa* Desv., *Heteropogon* Pers., *Homopogon* Stapf, and *Sorghum* Pers.) . . . . **Andropogon** L.

65. (1.) Leaf-blade jointed with the sheath and finally separating from it, often contracted at the base into a short stalk, usually transversely veined. Stem generally woody. [Subfamily **BAMBUSOIDEAE**.] 66

Leaf-blade passing into the sheath without a joint and without a stalk, rarely transversely veined. Stem herbaceous. [Subfamily **POOI-DEAE.**] 79

66. Stamens 3. Styles 2—3, free. Outer glumes 1—2. Pericarp dry and thin. [Tribe ARUNDINARIEAE.] 67
Stamens 6. 68

67. Spikelets 2-flowered. Upper flowering glume keeled. Herbs. — Species 1 Equatorial West Africa. . . . . . **Microcalamus** Franch.
Spikelets many-flowered. Flowering glumes not keeled. Undershrubs or shrubs. — Species 2. East and South Africa. They yield wood, fibre, vegetables, edible seeds, and medicaments. **Arundinaria** Michx.

68. Fruit a nut or a berry ; pericarp thick, free from the seed. Tall shrubs or trees. 69
Fruit a caryopsis ; pericarp thin, adnate to the seed. [Tribe BAMBU-SEAE.] 72

69. Palea rounded on the back, similar to the flowering glume. Spikelets 1-flowered. [Tribe MELOCANNEAE.] 70
Palea 2-keeled. Fruit a nut. [Tribe DENDROCALAMEAE.] . . 71

70. Spikelets in one-sided spikes, the axis not continued beyond the flower. Outer glumes acuminate. Fruit a large apple-like berry. Trees.— Species 1. Naturalized in the Island of Mauritius. The fruits are edible ; also the wood and the fibres are used. . . . . . **Melocanna** Trin.
Spikelets in panicled clusters, the axis continued beyond the flower in the form of a bristle. Outer glumes rolled inwards. Fruit a small wrinkled nut. Shrubs. — Species 1. Madagascar. Used medicinally.
Schizostachyum Nees

71. Spikelets 1-flowered, in scattered heads. Lodicules 2—3, large. Fruit oblong. — Species 1. Madagascar. . . . **Cephalostachyum** Munro
Spikelets 2- or more-flowered, in panicled glomerules. Lodicules 1—2, very small, or absent. Fruit subglobular, beaked. — Species 1. Naturalized in the Island of Mauritius. Yields wood, fibre, vegetables, edible seeds, and medicaments, and is also used as an ornamental plant.
Dendrocalamus Nees

72. Filaments united into a tube. Palea of the uppermost (hermaphrodite) flower of each spikelet usually 1-keeled. 73
Filaments free. Palea of the uppermost flower 2-keeled, rarely without a keel. 75

73. Spikelets terete. Lodicules none. Tall shrubs. — Species 5. Central Africa. . . . . **Oxytenanthera** Munro
Spikelets compressed. Herbs. 74

74. Outer glumes 2. Fruit spindle-shaped, furrowed ; style much broadened at the base. Spikelets in racemes. — Species 1. Equatorial West Africa. . . . . **Atractocarpa** Franch.
Outer glumes 3—4. Fruit subglobular, not furrowed ; style not broadened. — Species 5. Equatorial West Africa. . . . . **Puelia** Franch.

75. Spikelets 1-flowered. Outer glumes 6—10. Ovary glabrous. Style 2—3-cleft or -parted. Tall shrubs. — Species 3. Madagascar and Mascarenes. . . . . **Nastus** Juss.
    Spikelets 2- or more-flowered. Outer glumes 1—6. 76
76. Lodicules none. Spikelets 2-flowered, in clusters surrounded by two bracts. Ovary glabrous. Style undivided, hairy. — Species 1. German East Africa. . . . . **Oreobambus** K. Schum.
    Lodicules 2-3. Spikelets without bracts. Ovary hairy 77
77. Lodicules 2. Outer glume 1. Palea not winged on the keels. Styles 2, free. Spikelets many-flowered. Herbs with 4 large leaves. — Species 1. West Africa (Cameroons). (Under *Guaduella* Franch.)
    Microbambus K. Schum.
    Lodicules 3. Outer glumes usually 2. 78
78. Palea with winged keels. Spikelets strongly flattened. Herbs. — Species 5. Equatorial West Africa. . . . . **Guaduella** Franch.
    Palea not winged on the keels. Spikelets slightly flattened. Tall shrubs.— Species 2. Cultivated and sometimes naturalized. They yield wood, fibre, vegetables, edible seeds, drinks, and medicaments, and are also used as ornamental plants. " Bamboo." . . . . **Bambusa** Schreb.
79. (65.) Spikelets sessile in the notches on the rachis of a nearly always equal-sided spike, usually 2-ranked. [Tribe HORDEAE.] 80
    Spikelets along a rachis without notches, in usually one-sided spikes or in racemes or panicles. 94
80. Spike one-sided. Spikelets solitary in each notch, 1-flowered. Outer glume 1, minute. Flowering glume awned. Stigma 1. Leaves stiff. — Species 1. Azores. " Matgrass." [Subtribe NARDEAE.]
    Nardus L.
    Spike equal-sided. Stigmas 2. 81
81. Spikelets solitary in each notch of the spike. 82
    Spikelets 2—6 in each notch of the spike. [Subtribe ELYMINAE.] 93
82. Spikelets with the back towards the hollows of the rachis. [Subtribe LOLIINAE.] 83
    Spikelets with the side towards the hollows of the rachis. 88
83. Spikelets 1-flowered, awnless, the terminal one with 2 outer glumes, the others with one. 84
    Spikelets 2- to many-flowered. 86
84. Flowering glumes with a hairy callus at their base. Outer glumes 1—3-nerved. Dwarf herbs. —- Species 2. South and East Africa.
    Oropetium Trin.
    Flowering glumes with a glabrous, sometimes rudimentary callus. . . 85
85. Joints of the rachis of the spike produced into wing-like appendages. — Species 1. Island of Socotra. . . . . . **Ischnurus** Balf. fil.
    Joints of the rachis of the spike without wing-like appendages. — Species 3. Madagascar, South and North-west Africa. . . **Monerma** Beauv.

86. Spikelets 2-flowered. Styles long. Outer glumes 2. Flowering glumes produced into 3 points. — Species 1. North-west Africa (Algeria). (Including *Kralikiella* Coss. et Durieu).　　．　**Kralikia** Coss. et Durieu
Spikelets many-flowered. Styles very short. 87

87. Outer glumes 2, awnless. Flowering glumes with 2 points and a dorsal awn. Lodicules 2-cleft. Fruit hairy at the top. — Species 2. North Africa. (Including *Meringurus* Murbeck)　．　．　．　**Gaudinia** Beauv.
Outer glumes in the terminal spikelets 2, in the lateral single. Fruit glabrous. — Species 6. North, South, and East Africa. Two species (ray-grass) are cultivated on lawns ; - one (the darnel, *L. temulentum* L.) is poisonous. (Including *Arthrochortus* Lowe)　．　．　．　．　**Lolium** L.

88. Spikelets 1-, very rarely 2-flowered, in a slender spike ; joints of the spike separating at maturity together with the lower spikelet. Outer glumes approximate in front. [Subtribe LEPTURINAE.] 89
Spikelets 2- to many-flowered, in usually stout spikes ; joints of the spike separating at maturity together with the upper spikelet or not separating at all. Outer glumes opposite one another. [Subtribe TRITICINAE.] 90

89. Outer glume 1, very small. Flowering glumes awned. Stamen 1. Rachis of the spike with but slightly hollowed joints. — Species 1. North-west Africa (Algeria). . . . . **Psilurus** Trin.
Outer glumes 2, large. Flowering glumes awnless. — Species 4. North Africa, Abyssinia, Socotra. . . . . **Lepturus** R. Br.

90. Flowering glumes decurrent into a callus limited by a furrow, falling with the fruit when ripe. Fruit adhering to the palea. — Species 7　North Africa, Abyssinia, South Africa. The quitch grass (*A. repens* Beauv.) is used for binding the sand, as fodder, for making syrup, and medicinally. (Including *Eremopyrum* Jaub. et Spach)　**Agropyrum** Gaertn.
Flowering glumes without a callus at the base, persisting at maturity. Fruit free. 91

91. Outer glumes ovate, 3- to many-nerved. Fertile spikelets ventricose, 2—5-flowered. Spike usually with a terminal spikelet. — Species 13. Ten species spontaneous in North Africa and Abyssinia, the others (especially the wheat, *T. sativum* Lam. and *polonicum* L.) cultivated in various regions. The latter are used as cereals and for plaiting-work, other species as ornamental plants. (Including *Aegilops* L.)
　　　　　　　　　　　　　　　　　　　　　　　　Triticum L.
Outer glumes oblong lanceolate or subulate, 1—2-nerved. Spikelets not ventricose, 2-, rarely 3-flowered. Spike without a terminal spikelet.　92

92. Outer glumes truncate, two-keeled, with a long awn. Flowering glumes awned from below the tip. Spike very dense. — Species 2. North-west Africa. . . . . **Haynaldia** Schur
Outer glumes acuminate, one-nerved. Flowering glumes awned from the tip. Spike rather loose. — Species 3. North Africa, Abyssinia, and

South Africa. One of them (the rye, *S. cereale* L.) is cultivated as a cereal and also used as fodder, for making brandy and paper, and for plaiting-work. . . . . **Secale** L.

93. Spikelets 1-flowered, sometimes with an empty glume above the flower. Flowering glume awned. — Species 8. North Africa ; some species also cultivated or naturalized in Abyssinia, Madagascar, and South Africa. The barley (*H. sativum* Jessen) is cultivated as a cereal and for making beer ; it is also used as fodder and for medicinal purposes. Other species are used as ornamental plants. . . . . **Hordeum** L.
Spikelets 2—6-flowered. — Species 2. North Africa. Used as ornamental plants. " Lymegrass." . . . . **Elymus** L.

94. (79.) Spikelets in two rows approximated to one another, forming one-sided, sometimes panicled spikes (or spike-like racemes). [Tribe CHLO-RIDEAE.] 95
Spikelets in sometimes spike-like but equal-sided racemes or more frequently in panicles not consisting of one-sided spikes. . . . 123

95. Spikelets containing 1 hermaphrodite flower. 96
Spikelets containing 2 or more hermaphrodite flowers. 108

96. Spikelets bearing no male flowers or empty glumes above the hermaphrodite flower, but sometimes ending in a short bristle. 97
Spikelets bearing above the hermaphrodite flower a male flower or one or several empty, sometimes very small or awn-like glumes. . . . 101

97. Spikelets awned. 98
Spikelets awnless. 99

98. Flowering glume much shorter than the outer glumes, with a very long awn. Spikes 1—4, terminal. — Species 3. Central Africa and Egypt.
Schoenefeldia Kunth
Flowering glume almost as long as the outer glumes, with a short awn. Spikes numerous, arranged along a common axis. — Species 4. Southern West Africa. . . . . **Willkommia** Hack.

99. Spikes solitary, terminal. — Species 3. Central and South Africa. Used in medicine. . . . . **Microchloa** R. Br.
Spikes digitate or in racemes. 100

100. Spikes digitate, 3—5. Flowering glume usually larger than the outer glumes. — Species 5. Some are used as pasture-grasses or in medicine. " Dogstooth." . . . . **Cynodon** Pers.
Spikes arranged along a common axis. Rachis of the spike dilated. Flowering glume much smaller than the outer glumes. — Species 2. East Africa. . . . . **Craspedorhachis** Benth.

101. Outer glumes 4. Second outer glume and flowering glume awned. Spikes solitary, rarely 2—3 together. — Species 5. Tropical and South Africa and Egypt. (Including *Campulosus* Desv.) . . . **Ctenium** Panzer
Outer glumes 2. 102

102. Spike 1, terminal. 103
　　　Spikes 2 or more, sometimes fascile-like. 105
103. Flowering glume many-nerved, awned. Styles united at the base, with
　　　shortly bearded, at length spirally twisted stigmas — Species 1. Central
　　　Africa. . . . . **Streptogyne** Beauv.
　　　Flowering glume 3-nerved. Styles free, with feathery stigmas. 104
104. Spikelets awned, imbricate, in slender spikes. — Species 6. East and
　　　South Africa, Madagascar and Seychelles. . . . **Enteropogon** Nees
　　　Spikelets awnless, crowded, in stout spikes. — Species 1. South Africa.
　　　　　　　　　　　　　　　　　　　　Harpechloa Kunth
105. Spikes in false whorls or closely superposed. — Species 25. Some are used
　　　as ornamental or fodder-plants. (Plate 8.) . . . **Chloris** Swartz
　　　Spikes all distant or the lowest only approximate. 106
106. Spikes very short and very dense. Outer glumes ciliate, with a straight
　　　awn. Flowering glume with 3 awns. Several empty glumes above the
　　　flowering glume. Low grasses. — Species 1. Northern East Africa.
　　　　　　　　　　　　　　　　　　　Melanocenchris Nees
　　　Spikes more or less elongated and loose. Flowering glume with 1 awn
　　　or awnless. Rather tall grasses. 107
107. Flowering glume awned, 2-toothed. Empty glume above the flowering
　　　one awn-like. Spikes very loose, at first erect. — Species 1. Abyssinia.
　　　　　　　　　　　　　　　　　　　Gymnopogon Beauv.
　　　Flowering glume awnless. Spikes rather dense, spreading. — Species 8.
　　　Central Africa. Some have edible seeds. (Including *Cypholepis*
　　　Chiov.) . . . . **Leptochloa** Beauv.
108. (95.) Spikes 1—3, terminal. 109
　　　Spikes more than 3. 114
109. Flowering glumes with 3, sometimes very short awns. Spikelets many-
　　　flowered. Spikes long, rather loose. — Species 4. Central Africa.
　　　　　　　　　　　　　　　　　　　Tripogon Roth
　　　Flowering glumes with one awn or mucro or unarmed. Spikes dense,
　　　usually short. 110
110. Flowering glumes with a rather long awn, long-haired on the back. Spike-
　　　lets 2—3-flowered. — Species 6. Central and North Africa. (Including
　　　Lepidopironia Rich.) . . . . **Tetrapogon** Desf.
　　　Flowering glumes unarmed or mucronate. 111
111. Spikes 2—3 together. Spikelets 3—4-flowered. Fruit almost orbicular.
　　　Leaves rather broad. — Species 1. Egypt and Nubia. (Under *Erag-*
　　　rostis Beauv.) . . . . **Coelachyrum** Nees
　　　Spike solitary. Fruit oblong. Leaves narrow. 112
112. Spikelets 2-flowered. Flowering glumes and paleas delicately mem-
　　　branous. — Species 3. South Africa. (*Prionanthium* Desv.)
　　　　　　　　　　　　　　　　　　　Prionachne Nees
　　　Spikelets 3- to many-flowered. Flowering glumes and paleas firmly
　　　membranous, rather stiff. 113

113. Outer glumes subequal. — Species 1.   North-west Africa (Algeria).
     Wangenheimia Moench
     Outer glumes very unequal or only one present. — Species 50.   Some are used for the manufacture of paper or as ornamental or fodder-plants. " Fescue." (Including *Ctenopsis* De Not., *Nardurus* Reichb., and *Vulpia* (Gmel.)   .   .   .   . **Festuca** L.

114. (108.) Outer glumes 4.   Spikelets falling entire.   115
     Outer glumes 2, usually persisting on the stalk of the spikelet.   .   . 116

115. Outer glumes 1-nerved.   Flowering glumes 5-nerved.   Styles short. — Species 1.   South Africa.   .   .   .   . **Tetrachne** Nees
     Outer glumes 3—8-nerved.   Flowering glumes 7—11-nerved.   Styles long. — Species 2.   South Africa and Angola.   (Under *Tetrachne* Nees).
     Entoplocamia Stapf

116. Outer glumes shortly awned, much longer than the flowering glumes. Spikes short, distant, at length bent downward. — Species 2.   Central Africa and Egypt.   Used as ornamental grasses.   (*Dineba* Jacq.)
     Dinebra Jacq
     Outer glumes unarmed or mucronate,shorter than the flowering glumes. 117

117. Spikelets very densely crowded.   Spikes digitate, at least the upper. 118
     Spikelets not very densely crowded.   Spikes distant.   119

118. Spikes ending in a point.   Outer glumes mucronate. — Species 6.   Used as cereals, fodder-, medicinal, or ornamental plants, and for making beer. (Under *Eleusine* Gaertn.)   .   .   .   .   .   . **Dactyloctenium** Willd.
     Spikes terminated by a spikelet.   Outer glumes usually unarmed.   Pericarp usually loose. — Species 10.   The coracan (*E. coracana* Gaertn.) is cultivated as a cereal and for the preparation of beer ; other species are used as medicinal or ornamental plants.   (Including *Acrachne* Wight & Arn.)   .   .   .   . **Eleusine** Gaertn.

119. Flowering glumes rounded on the back.   Pericarp more or less adhering to the palea.   (See 113.)   .   .   .   . **Festuca** L.
     Flowering glumes keeled.   Pericarp free.   120

120. Glumes thinly membranous, the outer subequal.   121
     Glumes firmly membranous, glabrous, the outer conspicuously unequal. 122

121. Flowering glumes 4-toothed, shortly awned. — Species 3.   East and South Africa.   (Under *Diplachne* Beauv.)   .   . **Leptocarydium** Hochst.
     Flowering glumes entire or obscurely 2—3-toothed.   (See 107.)
     Leptochloa Beauv.

122. Spikelets 2—8-flowered, with a jointed, ciliate axis.   Lodicules very small. Fruit linear-oblong, closely enveloped by the glumes. — Species 2.   South and East Africa.   Used as fodder-grasses.   (Under *Eragrostis* L. or *Leptochloa* Beauv.)   .   .   .   . **Pogonarthria** Stapf
     Spikelets many-flowered, with a tough axis.   Lodicules rather large. Fruit ovate, loosely enveloped by the glumes. — Species 1.   East Africa and Egypt.   (*Stapfiola* O. Ktze., under *Eragrostis* L.) **Desmostachya** Stapf

123. (94.) Spikelets 1-flowered. 124
     Spikelets 2- or more-flowered. 153

124. Outer glumes 4, rarely 3. Palea usually 1-nerved. [Tribe PHALARI-
     DEAE.]   125
     Outer glumes 2, rarely 1 or none. Palea usually 2-nerved. [Tribe
     AGROSTIDEAE.]   129

125. Leaves lanceolate or elliptical, transversely veined. Spikelets in pairs
     on the branches of a panicle. Outer glumes 3. — Species 2. Madagascar.
                                            Poecilostachys Hack.
     Leaves linear. Flowering glume awnless. 126

126. Upper two outer glumes,·or at least the uppermost, larger than the lower.
     Stamens 6, rarely 3. — Species 25.   South and East Africa, Mascarene
     Islands, St. Helena.   .   .   .   . **Ehrharta** Thunb.
     Upper two outer glumes smaller than the lower, more rarely equalling
     them. Stamens 2—3.   127

127. Upper two outer glumes awnless, smaller than the lower. Flowering glume
     and palea hardening. Lodicules present. Stamens 3. — Species 10.
     North, East, and South Africa.   Some species are used as ornamental
     grasses.   The seeds of *Ph. canariensis* L. (Canary-seeds) are used as food
     and in medicine.   .   .   .   . **Phalaris** L.
     Upper two outer glumes awned ; lower two unequal. Flowering glume
     and palea membranous. Lodicules none. Stamens 2. .   .   . 128

128. Upper two outer glumes smaller than the lower. — Species 5.   North-west
     and Central Africa.   The vernal grass (*A. odoratum* L.) imparts a sweet
     scent to new-made hay. .   .   .   . **Anthoxanthum** L.
     Upper two outer glumes about as large as the lower. — Species 5.   South
     Africa and Madagascar.   " Holygrass." (*Ataxia* R. Br., under *Anthox-
     anthum* L.)   .   .   .   . **Hierochloë** Gmel.

129. (124.) Stigmas shortly branched all round, protruding between the tips
     of the slightly gaping glumes. [Subtribe PHLEINAE.]   130
     Stigmas feathery, protruding above the base of the spikelet or enclosed in
     it.   133

130. Flowering glume rather stiff, awned or mucronate.   Axis of the spikelet
     produced beyond the flower into a bristle usually bearing an empty
     glume. — Species 2.   South Africa.   .   .   .   . **Fingerhuthia** Nees
     Flowering glume thinly membranous, unarmed. Axis of the spikelet
     rarely produced beyond the flower into a bristle without empty
     glumes.   131

131. Spikelets in slender simple spikes. Outer glumes obscurely keeled,
     unarmed. Flowering glume somewhat shorter than the outer. Leaves
     awl-shaped. — Species 1. North-west Africa (Algeria). **Mibora** Adans.
     Spikelets in spike-like panicles. Outer glumes distinctly keeled. Leaves
     flat.   132

132. Flowering glume somewhat longer than the outer. Outer glumes unarmed.
— Species 4. North Africa to Senegambia, East Africa, Madagascar.
Heleochloa Host

Flowering glume much shorter than the outer. Outer glumes mucronate
or shortly awned. — Species 5. North Africa to Senegambia. Some
species have edible seeds or are used as ornamental grasses. *Ph. pra-
tense* L. is a valuable fodder-grass. " Timothy-grass." **Phleum** L.

133. Flowering glume harder than the outer glumes at maturity, tightly
enclosing the fruit. Axis of the spikelet not prolonged beyond the
flower. [Subtribe STIPINAE.] 134

Flowering glume thinner than the outer at maturity, loosely enclosing
or not enclosing the fruit, rarely harder or tightly enclosing the fruit,
but then the axis of the spikelet prolonged into a bristle. . . . 137

134. Flowering glume awnless. — Species 1. North-west Africa (Algeria).
Yields edible seeds and is used as an ornamental grass. **Milium** L.

Flowering glume awned. 135

135. Flowering glume narrow, with a 3-branched awn, but the lateral branches
sometimes very short. Lodicules 2. — Species 80. Some of them have
edible seeds or are used as fodder. (Including *Arthratherum* Beauv.)
Aristida L.

Flowering glume with a single awn. 136

136. Flowering glume narrow, with a strong, kneed, usually twisted, persistent
awn. Palea not distinctly keeled. Lodicules usually 3. — Species 15.
North Africa, northern East Africa, Madagascar, and South Africa.
The Esparto-grass (*St. tenacissima* L.) is used for the manufacture of
paper, ropes, and in plaiting-work, other species as ornamental grasses
(feather-grass) ; some have edible seeds. (*Stupa* L., including *Macro-
chloa* Kunth) . . . . **Stipa** L.

Flowering glume broad, with a fine, short, deciduous awn. Palea 2-
keeled. Lodicules usually 2. — Species 3. North Africa, one species
also introduced into South Africa. (*Piptatherum* Beauv.)
Oryzopsis Michx.

137. Fruit not enclosed by the glumes ; pericarp usually loose and dehiscing.
Axis of the spikelet not produced beyond the flower. Glumes unarmed.
Flowering glume usually longer than the outer ones. — Species 60. Some
of them yield edible seeds or are used as fodder and for plaiting-work.
(Including *Triachyrium* Hochst. and *Vilfa* Beauv.) **Sporobolus** R. Br.

Fruit enclosed by the flowering glume and the palea ; pericarp usually
adnate to the seed. 138

138. Spikelets of two kinds, the fertile surrounded by the sterile, which consist
of numerous glumes. Flowering glume 1-nerved, with a dorsal awn. —
Species 1. North Africa and Abyssinia ; also introduced into South
Africa. Used as an ornamental grass. (*Chrysurus* Pers.)
Lamarckia Moench

Spikelets all alike. 139

139. Outer glumes conspicuously shorter than the flowering glume.   Flowering
     glume firmly herbaceous, 3—5-nerved, with a long, straight, terminal
     or subterminal awn.   Panicle loose. — Species 2.   East and South-east
     Africa (Kilimandjaro and Transvaal).   (Under *Brachyelytrum* Beauv.)
                                                        Pseudobromus K. Schum.
     Outer glumes almost equalling the flowering glume or exceeding it.
     Flowering glume membranous, rarely firmer, but then many-nerved
     or with a distinctly dorsal awn or awnless. 140
140. Outer glumes feathery, long.   Flowering glume with two short terminal
     awns or with a long dorsal one.   Panicles spike- or head-like. — Species 1.
     North Africa ; introduced in South Africa.   Used as an ornamental
     grass.   " Harestail-grass." . . . . **Lagurus** L.
     Outer glumes not feathery. 141
141. Outer glumes bladdery at the base, much longer than the flowering glume.
     Panicles spike-like. — Species 2.   North Africa and Abyssinia.   " Nit-
     grass." . . . . **Gastridium** Beauv.
     Outer glumes not bladdery. 142
142. Flowering glume cleft into 9—23 awn-shaped teeth.   Panicles spike-
     like. — Species 13.   Some are used as fodder-grasses.   (Including
     Enneapogon Desv.) . . . . **Pappophorum** Schreb.
     Flowering glume with 1—3 awns or awnless. 143
143. Flowering glume with a delicate dorsal awn and two long and thin lateral
     awns. — Species 2.   Egypt and Abyssinia.   . . . **Trisetaria** Forsk.
     Flowering glume awnless or with a single awn and sometimes 2 short
     bristles. 144
144. Flowering glume with a terminal awn, rounded on the back, sometimes
     keeled towards the tip.   (See 113.)   . . . . . . **Festuca** L.
     Flowering glume with a dorsal awn or with a short mucro or unarmed. 145
145. Flowering glume decurrent into a callus bearing a tuft of long hairs.   146
     Flowering glume with a glabrous or shortly and scantily hairy callus or
     without a callus. 147
146. Flowering glume papery, unarmed or shortly mucronate.   Spikelets
     large, with a glabrous and bristle-like or a club-shaped prolongation
     of the axis. — Species 1 (*A. arundinacea* Host, maram).   North Africa.
     Used for binding sand-dunes and as a fodder-grass ; the root-stock is
     edible. (*Psamma* Beauv.)   . . . . . . **Ammophila** Host
     Flowering glume membranous, awned from the back, very rarely awnless.
     Spikelets rather small, sometimes with a bristle-like and usually hairy
     prolongation of the axis. — Species 6.   Azores, mountains of tropical
     Africa, South Africa.   Some are used as ornamental or medicinal
     plants. (Including *Deyeuxia* Beauv.)   . . . **Calamagrostis** Roth
147. Axis of the spikelet not distinctly continued beyond the flower.   Flowering
     glume shorter than the outer glumes. 148
     Axis of the spikelet produced beyond the flower into a bristle-like appen-
     dage bearing sometimes empty glumes. 149

148. Palea as long as the flowering glume. Panicles few-flowered. — Species
1. South Africa. (Under *Agrostis* L. or *Colpodium* Trin.)

Poagrostis Stapf

Palea shorter than the flowering glume. Panicles many-flowered. — Species
30. North and South Africa and mountains of the tropics. Some are
used as fodder- or ornamental grasses. "Bent-grass." **Agrostis** L.

149. Flowering glume much shorter than the outer glumes, with 2 bristles
at the top and an awn on the back near the base. Continuation of the
axis of the spikelet hairy, without glumes. Panicles spike-like. — Species
1. North-west Africa. (Under *Gastridium* Beauv.) **Triplachne** Link
Flowering glume slightly shorter or longer than the outer glumes. Continuation of the axis of the spikelet glabrous or bearing empty glumes. 150

150. Flowering glume with a very long awn. Outer glumes unequal. Continuation of the axis of the spikelet without glumes. Panicle loose. —
Species 2. North-west Africa (Algeria). Used as ornamental grasses.

Apera Adans.

Flowering glume with a short or moderate awn or awnless. Outer glumes
subequal. Continuation of the axis of the spikelet usually with empty
glumes. 151

151. Lower outer glume 1-nerved. Flowering glume 3—5-nerved, membranous, about as long as the outer glumes. Continuation of the axis
of the spikelet with 1—2 empty glumes or without glumes. — Species
10. North Africa, Abyssinia, South Africa. Some are used as fodder-
grasses. . . . . **Koeleria** Pers.
Lower outer glume 3—9-nerved. Flowering glume 5- to many-nerved,
leathery or longer than the outer glumes. 152

152. Fruit deeply grooved. Flowering glume leathery, rounded on the back,
with a kneed dorsal awn. Outer glumes 7—9-nerved. — Species 20.
Extra-tropical regions and mountains of the tropics. Some (especially
A. sativa L.) are cultivated as cereals (oat) or fodder, and yield also
oil and medicaments; others are used as ornamental grasses. (Including
Avenastrum Juss.) . . . . **Avena** L.
Fruit not deeply grooved. Flowering glume keeled, longer than the
outer ones. Outer glumes 3—7-nerved. Empty glumes above the
flower 2 or more. — Species 10. Extra-tropical regions. Some are
used as ornamental grasses. . . . . **Melica** L.

153. (123.) Flowering glumes, at least one in each spikelet, bearing a twisted
or kneed, generally dorsal awn, usually shorter than the outer glumes,
rarely awnless, and then spikelets 2-flowered with a very short axis not
prolonged beyond the flowers. [Tribe AVENEAE.] . . . 154
Flowering glumes bearing a straight, terminal or subterminal awn, or
unawned, usually longer than the outer glumes. Spikelets 2-flowered,
the axis prolonged between the flowers or above them, or 3—many-
flowered. [Tribe FESTUCEAE.] 177

G

154. Spikelets 2-flowered without a continuation of the axis beyond the upper flower. Flowering glumes usually unawned. 155
Spikelets 2-flowered with a continuation of the axis beyond the upper flower, or 3—many-flowered. Flowering glumes awned. . 161

155. Spikelets solitary, enveloped by a spathe. Flowering glumes connate. Style 1, undivided. Stigma papillose. (See 3.) . . . **Lygeum** L.
Spikelets in panicles, racemes, or spikes. Flowering glumes free. Styles 2, free. Stigmas feathery. 156

156. Outer glumes with a cartilaginous pectinately-toothed keel. Panicle spike-like. (See 112.) . . . . **Prionachne** Nees
Outer glumes membranous. 157

157. Outer glumes hemispherical. Panicle spike-like. — Species 1. North-west Africa (Algeria). . . . . **Airopsis** Desv.
Outer glumes not hemispherical. Panicle spreading. 158

158. Outer glumes shorter than the flowering glumes. Flowering glumes truncate or minutely toothed. — Species 1. North-west Africa. (Under *Aira* L.) . . . . **Molineria** Parl.
Outer glumes somewhat longer than the flowering glumes. . . . 159

159. Flowering glumes blunt, unarmed, hardened at maturity. Axis of the spikelet very short. (See 21.) . . . . **Isachne** R. Br.
Flowering glumes 3-lobed, 2-toothed, or mucronate, usually provided with a dorsal awn, not hardened at maturity. 160

160. Flowering glumes 3-lobed, unarmed. Axis of the spikelet somewhat elongated between the flowers. — Species 1. North-west Africa (Algeria). Used as an ornamental grass. (Under *Aira* L.) . . **Antinoria** Parl.
Flowering glumes 2-toothed or mucronate, nearly always with a dorsal awn. Axis of the spikelet very short. — Species 8. Extra-tropical regions and mountains of the tropics. Some species are used as ornamental grasses. . . . . **Aira** L.

161. (154.) Flowering glumes with a terminal awn inserted between the apical lobes or teeth. 162
Flowering glume with a dorsal awn inserted below the apex. . . . 168

162. Spikelets 2-flowered ; the lower flower male, the upper female or hermaphrodite. 163
Spikelets 2- or more flowered ; all flowers hermaphrodite or the uppermost male. Flowering glumes 5—11-nerved. 165

163. Spikelets in clusters of 3 at the tips of the branches of a raceme or panicle. — Species 13. Tropical and South Africa. . . . **Tristachya** Nees
Spikelets solitary at the tips of the branches of a panicle. 164

164. Palea auricled. Flowering glume of the upper flower not distinctly toothed. Spikelets small. — Species 4. Tropical and South Africa. Some are used for plaiting-work. . . . . . **Arundinella** Raddi
Palea not auricled. Flowering glume of the upper flower distinctly toothed. Spikelets large. — Species 25. Tropical and South Africa. **Trichopteryx** Nees

165. Spikelets with 2 flowers and a minute or bristle-like continuation of the axis. Flowering glumes with 2—4, at least partly bristle-like teeth. 166
Spikelets with 3 or more flowers, the uppermost of which is usually incomplete. Flowering glumes with 2 rarely bristle-like teeth. . 167

166. Fruit globular ; pericarp crusty, almost free from the seed. — Species 5. South Africa. (Under *Danthonia* DC.) . . . **Pentameris** Beauv.
Fruit oblong.'—Species 40. Southern and tropical Africa. The seeds of some species are eaten or used in medicine. (Under *Danthonia* DC.)
Pentaschistis (Nees) Stapf

167. Spikelets falling entire with a part of their stalk. Lowest flowering glume without, the others with side-bristles. — Species 4. South Africa. (Under *Danthonia* DC.) . . . . . . **Chaetobromus** (Nees) Stapf
Spikelets not falling entire ; axis jointed between and below the flowering glumes. — Species 30. Extra-tropical regions and mountains of the tropics. The seeds of several species are eaten or used in medicine.
Danthonia DC.

168. (161.) Spikelets in spikes, many-flowered. (See 87.) **Gaudinia** Beauv.
Spikelets in sometimes spike-like panicles. 169

169. Lower flowers male, upper hermaphrodite. 170
Lower or all flowers hermaphrodite, upper sometimes male or barren. 171

170. Spikelets with 2 flowers and a bristle-like continuation of the axis. Stamens 3. Styles short. — Species 2 North-west Africa They yield fodder and edible seeds. . . . . **Arrhenatherum** Beauv.
Spikelets with 3 flowers, one of which is sometimes reduced to a glume, without a continuation of the axis. Stamens in the male flowers 3, in the hermaphrodite 2. Styles long. (See 128.) **Hierochloe** Gmel.

171. Axis of the spikelets jointed at the base ; spikelets falling entire, 2-flowered, the upper flower usually male, the lower hermaphrodite with the flowering glume unarmed. — Species 6. North-west and South Africa. Some are used as ornamental grasses. . . . . **Holcus** L..
Axis of the spikelets jointed above the persistent outer glumes. 172

172. Fruit grooved in front, usually adherent to the glumes. Spikelets large. 173
Fruit not grooved, free. Spikelets usually small. 174

173. Fruit slightly grooved. Styles inserted laterally below the summit of the ovary. — Species 30. Extra-tropical regions and mountains of the tropics. Some species are poisonous, others are used as fodder-, medicinal, or ornamental plants. . . . . **Bromus** L.
Fruit deeply grooved. Styles inserted at or near the summit of the ovary. (See 152.) . . . . **Avena** L.

174. Flowering glumes 2-cleft or 2-toothed to 2-awned. 175
Flowering glumes irregularly and minutely toothed or 2-lobed with toothed lobes or entire. 176

175. Flowering glume of the lower flower awnless, entire. Outer glumes 3—5-nerved. Spikelets linear-oblong. — Species 1. North-west Africa (Algeria). . . . . **Ventenata** Koeler

Flowering glume of the lower flower awned, 2-toothed. Outer glumes 1—3-nerved. Spikelets lanceolate-elliptical. — Species 20. Extra-tropi-cal regions and mountains of the tropics. Some species are used as fodder- or ornamental grasses. . . . . **Trisetum** Pers.

176. Awns of the flowering glumes jointed, thickened towards the tip. — Species 3. North Africa. (Under *Aira* L.) . . . **Corynephorus** Beauv.
Awns of the flowering glumes not jointed, slender throughout.—Spec. 5. Azores, Canaries, high mountains of Central Africa, subantarctic islands. Used as ornamental grasses. (Under *Aira* L.)
Deschampsia Beauv.

177. (153.) Flowering glumes of the fertile flowers cleft in 3—23 awn-like or awn-bearing lobes. [Subtribe PAPPOPHORINAE.] 178
Flowering glumes entire or 2-lobed, rarely (*Triodia*) 3-lobed, bearing a single awn or unawned. 182

178. Flowering glumes 3-cleft, with 3 awns. Spikelets 5—15-flowered, in panicles. — Species 9. Southern and Central Africa, Sahara, Egypt. Some are used as fodder-grasses. . . . . . **Triraphis** R. Br.
Flowering glumes 4—many-cleft, with 5 or more awns. Spikelets 2—6-flowered. 179

179. Flowering glumes with 5—9 awns springing from the back of the lobes. Style 1, short and broad, 2-cleft. Spikelets 2—3-flowered, in dense panicles. — Species 1. Egypt. . . . . **Boissiera** Hochst.
Flowering glumes with 5—23 awns springing from the tips of the lobes or from the notches between them. Styles 2, free. 180

180. Flowering glumes with 9—23 awn-like lobes. Spikelets 2—3-flowered, in spike-like panicles. (See 142.) . . . . **Pappophorum** Schreb.
Flowering glumes with 5—7 awns or awn-like lobes. 181

181. Flowering glumes with 5—7 subequal, awn-like lobes. Spikelets 2—3-flowered, in heads. — Species 1. North-west Africa. **Echinaria** Desv.
Flowering glumes with 9 lobes, 5 of which are awn-like. Spikelets 4—6-flowered, in rather loose panicles. — Species 3. Central and South Africa and Egypt. Used as fodder and in medicine. (*Antoschmidtia* Steud.) . . . . **Schmidtia** Steud.

182. Axis of the spikelets or flowering glumes covered with long hairs enveloping the glumes. [Subtribe ARUNDINAE.] 183
Axis of the spikelets and flowering glumes glabrous or short-haired.   185

183. Flowering glumes firmly membranous, 5-nerved, hairy like the axis of the spikelets. Ovary hairy at the top. Leaves narrow, more or less rolled up. Low grasses. — Species 1 (*A. tenax* Link). North Africa. Used for making paper, in plaiting-work, as fodder, and as an orna-mental plant. . . . . **Ampelodesma** Beauv.
Flowering glumes delicately membranous, 3-nerved ; if hairy, then axis of the spikelets glabrous. Ovary glabrous. Leaves flat and rather broad. Tall grasses. 184

184. Flowering glumes glabrous, entire, produced into a fine point. Axis of the spikelets hairy. Lowest flower of each spikelet usually male. Panicles lax. — Species 2. Used in house-building, for plaiting-work and divers utensils, and as ornamental grasses; the root-stock is edible and used in medicine. "Reed." (*Trichoon* Roth)   **Phragmites** Trin.

Flowering glumes hairy, 2-toothed, with a mucro in the notch. Axis of the spikelets glabrous. Flowers all hermaphrodite or the uppermost flower or all flowers of the lower spikelets male. Panicles dense. — Species 5. North Africa, Madagascar, South Africa. Used in house-building, for plaiting-work, and as medicinal, fodder-, and ornamental plants. "Reed." (*Donax* Beauv., including *Neyraudia* Hook. fil.) **Arundo** L.

185. Stigmas shortly papillose on all sides, projecting between the tips of the flowering glumes; styles long. [Subtribe SESLERINAE.]   .   . 186

Stigmas feathery, rather short, projecting near the base of the flowering glumes; styles short or almost wanting. 191

186. Styles united at the base. Stigmas spirally twisted   Spikelets in one-sided spikes or spike-like racemes, 2-flowered, very rarely 3—4-flowered. Glumes many-nerved; the outer ones unarmed, the flowering ones awned. Leaves transversely veined. (See 103.)   **Streptogyne** Beauv.

Styles free. Spikelets in sometimes spike-like panicles or in heads.   187

187. Spikelets in spike-like panicles, falling singly and entire, 2-flowered, very rarely 3—4-flowered, the uppermost flower male. Glumes awned or mucronate. (See 130.) . . . . **Fingerhuthia** Nees

Spikelets in heads or head-like panicles or in fascicles arranged in spike-like panicles, not falling entire. 188

188. Spikelets in fascicles arranged in slender spike-like panicles, rarely in heads, and then stamen 1. Glumes 1—3-nerved, mucronate or awned. Spikelets 3—7-flowered. — Species 2. Central Africa.

Elytrophorus Beauv.

Spikelets in head-like panicles. Stamens 3. 189

189. Glumes 4—7-nerved, long-awned. Spikelets 3—7-flowered. Panicles enveloped by the sheath of the uppermost leaf. Leaves awl-shaped. — Species 1. South Africa. . . . . **Urochlaena** Nees

Glumes 1—3-nerved, not awned, but sometimes mucronate. Leaves flat. 190

190. Spikelets 2—3-flowered, in spikes arranged in heads enveloped by the sheath of the uppermost leaf. — Species 1. North-west Africa (Morocco). (Under *Ammochloa* Boiss.) . . . . . **Dictyochloa** (Murb.) Camus

Spikelets 7—15-flowered. Inflorescence not enveloped by a sheath. Species 2. North Africa. . . . . **Ammochloa** Boiss.

191. (185.) Spikelets 2-flowered, the lower flower hermaphrodite, the upper female. Axis of the spikelet elongated between the flowers, but not continued beyond them. Glumes unarmed, with faint nerves. Spike lets in loose panicles. — Species 1. Madagascar. . . **Coelachne** R. Br.

Spikelets 2-flowered, both flowers hermaphrodite or the lower flower hermaphrodite, the upper one male or rudimentary, or 3—many-flowered. 192

192. Flowering glumes 1—3-nerved. [Subtribes TRIODIINAE and ERAGROSTINAE.] 193
   Flowering glumes 5—many-nerved. 207

193. Flowering glumes 2—4-toothed or -cleft, rounded on the back, at least at the base. 194
   Flowering glumes entire or obscurely toothed, rarely (*Diplachne*) distinctly 2-toothed and sometimes awned from the notch, but then keeled. 196

194. Flowering glumes with 3 rather obtuse lobes. — Species 1. North-west Africa. . . . . **Triodia** R. Br.
   Flowering glumes with 2 acute lobes and an awn or mucro between them. 195

195. Flowering glumes with a long awn, the upper ones empty. Outer glumes unequal. Spikes approximate, almost digitate. — Species 1. South Africa. . . . . **Lophacme** Stapf
   Flowering glumes with a short awn or a mucro. Outer glumes subequal. — Species 2. Central and South Africa. (Under *Diplachne* Beauv.) . . . . **Crossotropis** Stapf

196. Spikelets of two kinds, the fertile 2—3-flowered and surrounded by the sterile consisting of numerous two-ranked glumes, arranged in one-sided spike-like panicles. Flowering glumes awned or mucronate. — Species 8. North and South Africa. Some have edible seeds or are used as fodder- or ornamental grasses. "Dogstail." **Cynosurus** L.
   Spikelets all alike. 197

197. Spikelets in spike-like racemes, laterally flattened, falling as a whole, containing 3—4 fertile flowers and two empty glumes above them. — Species 1. Abyssinia. . . . . **Harpachne** Hochst.
   Spikelets in panicles; empty glume above the fertile flowers 1 or none. 198

198. Main branches of the panicles two-ranked, usually branched at their base. 199
   Main branches of the panicles not two-ranked. 203

199. Panicles spreading, with long, thin branches. Spikelets 2—4-flowered, with membranous, unarmed glumes. 200
   Panicles contracted (more or less spike-like) or with very short, rather thick, but somewhat spreading branches. 201

200. Outer glumes slightly unequal. Perennial, creeping grasses, with flat leaves. — Species 1. North Africa. . . . . . **Catabrosa** Beauv.
   Outer glumes very unequal, the lower very small. Stalk of the spikelet somewhat thickened. Delicate, annual grasses with narrow leaves. — Species 2. North Africa. . . . . **Sphenopus** Trin.

201. Panicles with short, rather thick, more or less spreading branches. Glumes hard. Spikelets 3—13-flowered. — Species 5. North Africa.
                                   Cutandia Willk.

Panicles strongly contracted, dense, more or less spike-like. Glumes membranous. Spikelets 2—5-flowered. 202

202. Upper outer glume much broader and somewhat longer than the flowering glumes. Lower outer glume very short, almost bristle-like. Flowering glumes awned below the tip. — Species 1. North-west Africa (Algeria).
Avellinia Parl.

Upper outer glume neither broader nor longer than the flowering glumes. Lower outer glume almost equalling the upper one. (See 151.)
Koeleria Pers.

203. Branches of the panicle spike-like. Flowering glumes 1—3-nerved, usually toothed. 204

Branches of the panicle raceme-like. Flowering glumes 3-nerved, not distinctly toothed, unarmed or mucronate. 205

204. Panicles contracted, spike-like. Flowering glumes entire, acuminate. Lodicules membranous. Fruit terete. — Species 3. South Africa and southern East Africa. (*Triphlebia* Stapf, under *Lasiochloa* Kunth).
Stiburus Stapf

Panicles lax. Lodicules fleshy. — Species 9. Tropical and South Africa and Egypt. Some are used as fodder-grasses. **Diplachne** Beauv.

205. Flowering glumes rounded on the back. Spikelets conical, loosely 2—4-flowered; axis jointed, fragile. Fruit oblong, broadly grooved. — Species 1. North-west Africa (Algeria). Used in plaiting-work and as an ornamental grass. . . . . **Molinia** Schrank

Flowering glumes keeled. Spikelets not conical, densely 5—many-flowered. 206

206. Outer glumes unequal, the lower 3-nerved, the upper 5-nerved. Axis of the spikelet fragile. Fruit broadly grooved. — Species 1. Coast of East Africa. . . . . **Halopyrum** Stapf

Outer glumes 1-nerved, rarely the upper one 3-nerved. Axis of the spikelet usually tough. Fruit usually ovate and not grooved. — Species 130. Some are used as fodder- or ornamental grasses, others as sand-binders or for plaiting-work. The tef (*E. abyssinica* Link) is cultivated in Abyssinia as a cereal. . . . . **Eragrostis** Host

207. (192.) Axis of the spikelet bearing above the fertile flowers two or more empty glumes usually forming a club-shaped body. Flowering glumes keeled. Outer glumes 3—5-nerved. (See 152.) [Subtribe MELICINAE.]
Melica L.

Axis of the spikelet bearing above the fertile flowers a single empty glume or none, rarely several, but then flowering glumes rounded on the back.
208

208. Leaves broadly-lanceolate or ovate, with fine transverse veins between the nerves. [Subtribe CENTOTHECINAE.] 209

Leaves linear or linear-lanceolate, without distinct transverse veins [Subtribes FESTUCINAE and BRACHYPODINAE.] 210

209. Spikelets 2-flowered, in pairs on the spike-like branches of a panicle. Outer glumes 3, the uppermost sometimes bearing a barren spikelet in its axil. (See 125.) . . . . **Poecilostachys** Hack.
Spikelets many-flowered. Outer glumes 2. — Species 4. Tropics.
Centotheca Desv.

210. Spikelets in glomerules arranged in panicles. 211
Spikelets not in glomerules. 212

211. Panicles one-sided. Outer glumes unequal, 1—3-nerved. Flowering glumes larger, firmer, 5-nerved, mucronate or awned, ciliate on the keel. — Species 1. North and South Africa. Used as a fodder- and ornamental grass. "Cocksfoot." . . . . **Dactylis** L.
Panicles equal-sided. Outer glumes subequal, 5—7-nerved, usually hispid. Flowering glumes shorter, thinner, 7—9-nerved, unarmed. — Species 3. South Africa. . . . . **Lasiochloa** Kunth

212. Spikelets tightly imbricate in short spikes arranged in racemes or heads. Flowering glumes broad, 7—9-nerved, somewhat shorter than the palea, mucronate. — Species 4. North and East Africa. **Aeluropus** Trin.
Spikelets tightly imbricate in solitary spikes or not imbricate. . . 213

213. Spikelets very tightly imbricate, arranged in a linear false spike. Flowering glumes sharply keeled from the base, 7-nerved, unarmed. — Species 7. North and South Africa and St. Helena. Used as ornamental plants. (*Brizopyrum* Link). . . . . **Desmazeria** Dumort.
Spikelets not very tightly imbricate; if rather tightly, then flowering glumes not keeled. 214

214. Styles inserted on the front of the ovary, conspicuously below the top. Flowering glumes usually awned. Fruit linear or oblong, adhering to the palea. (See 173.) . . . . **Bromus** L.
Styles inserted on the top of the ovary or close to it. 215

215. Flowering glumes much shorter than the outer ones, 2-lobed or 2-cleft. Outer glumes with white, membranous margins. — Species 4. South and North Africa. . . . . **Schismus** Beauv.
Flowering glumes slightly shorter or longer than the outer ones. . . 216

216. Flowering glumes cordate at the base, very concave, scarious, broader than the outer glumes. Fruit strongly compressed. — Species 5. North Africa, Senegambia, and South Africa. Some are used as ornamental plants. "Quaking-grass." . . . . **Briza** L.
Flowering glumes not cordate. 217

217. Flowering glumes distinctly keeled. 218
Flowering glumes rounded on the back, sometimes slightly keeled towards the tip. 220

218. Flowering glumes shortly awned, scarious. Panicles spike-like. (See 151.) . . . . **Koeleria** Pers.
Flowering glumes unawned, membranous herbaceous or cartilaginous. Panicles usually spreading. 219

219. Flowering glumes cartilaginous at the base, herbaceous towards the tip. Outer glumes unequal. Axis of the spikelet thickened. Panicles one-sided. — Species 1. North-west Africa (Algeria). **Sclerochloa** Beauv. Flowering glumes membranous or herbaceous at the base or throughout. — Species 20. Extra-tropical regions and mountains of the tropics. Some are used as ornamental grasses. . . . . **Poa** L.

220. Spikelets 2-flowered with very approximate flowers and a bristle-like continuation of the axis beyond them. Outer glumes rather stiff, 1—3-nerved. Flowering glumes somewhat shorter, blunt, awnless. — Species 10. South and East Africa. . . . . . **Achneria** Munro Spikelets 2-flowered, with perceptibly distant flowers and usually membranous outer glumes, or 3—many-flowered. 221

221. Outer glumes 7—11-nerved, membranous. Flowering glumes toothed, usually awnless. Paleas narrow, 2-toothed. Spikelets usually 2-flowered. Fruit deeply furrowed. (See 152.) . . . . **Avena** L. Outer glumes 1—5-nerved, rarely 7—9-nerved, and then flowering glumes awned and paleas broad. Spikelets usually 3—many-flowered. 222

222. Flowering glumes 2-cleft, awned, 7—9-nerved. (See 167.) **Danthonia** DC. Flowering glumes entire, rarely toothed or 2-cleft, but then unarmed or 5-nerved. Styles very short. 223

223. Side-nerves of the flowering glumes nearly parallel, not joining the middle-nerve, sometimes obscure. Flowering glumes unarmed. Fruit oblong or ovate. . . . . 224 Side-nerves of the flowering glumes curved, converging towards the middle-nerve. Fruit oblong or linear. 225

224. Lodicules united. Styles distinctly developed. Fruit free, narrowly or not grooved. — Species 1 (*G. fluitans* R. Br., manna-grass). North-west Africa. The seeds are used as food. (Under *Poa* L.)

Glyceria R. Br.

Lodicules free. Styles wanting. Fruit usually adherent to the palea, broadly or not grooved. — Species 4. North-west and South Africa. (Under *Glyceria* R. Br.) . . . . **Atropis** Rupr.

225. Paleas with rigidly ciliate keels. Flowering glumes 7—9-nerved. Outer glumes 3—7-nerved, rather stiff. Spikelets in spike-like racemes. — Species 9. Extra-tropical regions and mountains of the tropics. Some species are used as ornamental grasses. . . **Brachypodium** Beauv. Paleas with finely ciliate or rough keels. Flowering glumes usually 5-nerved. Outer glumes 1—3-nerved. 226

226. Seed with a linear hilum. (See 113.) . . . . . . **Festuca** L. Seed with a punctiform hilum. 227

227. Spikelets upon stout stalks in one-sided panicles. Flowering glumes unarmed. — Species 2. North Africa, also introduced into South Africa. (Under *Festuca* L.) . . . . **Scleropoa** Griseb. Spikelets in spike-like racemes. — Species 3. North-west Africa. (Under *Festuca* L.) . . . . **Catapodium** Link

FAMILY 17. CYPERACEAE

Grass-like herbs, very rarely (*Schoenodendron*) low trees. Stems usually triangular, rarely jointed. Leaves with a closed sheath, sometimes without a blade. Flowers in genuine or spurious spikelets arranged in spikes, heads, or panicles. Perianth much reduced or wanting. Stamens 1—6. Anthers opening by 2 longitudinal slits. Ovary superior or naked, 1-celled. Ovule 1, basal, inverted. Style simple or with 2—3 branches. Fruit a nut or a drupe. Seed free. Embryo lateral, enclosed by the albumen. — Genera 40, species 880. " Sedges." (Plate 9.)

1. Flowers unisexual, but sometimes (*Bisboeckelerieae*) apparently hermaphrodite, single female flowers being surrounded by several male ones ; in this case false spikelets branched at the insertion of one of the lowest bracts. 2

   Flowers hermaphrodite or polygamous. Flowers either in centripetal spikelets without a terminal flower or in centrifugal (false) spikelets branched at the insertion of the uppermost bract below the terminal flower. 13

2. Spikelets unisexual, rarely partly unisexual, partly bisexual ; the female 1-flowered, the male 2- or more-flowered. Stamens 1—2, rarely 3. [Tribe SCLERIEAE.] 3

   Spikelets bisexual, rarely 1-flowered and spicate. 8

3. Perianth consisting of scales or bristles. Partial inflorescences panicled. 4

   Perianth none. 6

4. Perianth of numerous bristles. Spikelets in spikes. — Species 6. Central Africa to Transvaal. . . . . **Eriospora** Hochst.

   Perianth of 2—5 scales. 5

5. Perianth of 2—3 laciniate scales. Spikelets in head-like clusters. Herbs. — Species 1. West Africa. . . . . . . **Microdracoides** Hua

   Perianth of 3—5 ciliate scales. Spikelets in spikes. Small trees. — Species 1. West Africa (Cameroons). . . . . . **Schoenodendron** Engl.

6. Female flowers in the upper portion of the partial inflorescences. Spikelets in panicles. — Species 1. Madagascar. (Under *Eriospora* Hochst.)

   Fintelmannia Kunth

   Female flowers in the lower portion of the partial inflorescences or in special partial inflorescences. 7

7. Style thickened and jointed at the base, deeply 3-cleft. Fruit without a distinct disc. Spikelets in panicles. Leaves broad. — Species 3. Tropics. (Under *Scleria* Berg). . . . . **Acriulus** Ridl.

   Style not thickened at the base. Fruit very hard, surrounded by a disc at the base. — Species 60. Tropical and South Africa. (Including *Diplacrum* R. Br.) . . . . **Scleria** Berg

8. (2.) Spikelets consisting of a terminal female flower surrounded by 3 or more male ones. Stamen 1. Female flowers not enclosed by an utricle-like bracteole. [Tribe BISBOECKELERIEAE, Subtribe CHRYSITRICHINAE.] 9

Spikelets 1-flowered, spicate, rarely 2-flowered or consisting of a basal female flower and several male ones. Stamens usually 3. Female flowers enclosed by an utricle-like bracteole. [Tribe CARICEAE.] 11

9. Male flowers 3. Style-branches 3. Spikelets numerous, in spikes which are sometimes arranged in panicles or heads. — Species 12. Tropics. (Including *Thoracostachyum* Kurz) . . . . **Mapania** Aubl.
Male flowers 6 or more. Spikelets in spikes arranged in heads. . . 10

10. Style-branches 2. Fruit not ribbed. Spikes consisting of numerous spikelets. Leaves reduced to the sheath. — Species 1. Madagascar. Used for plaiting-work. . . . . **Lepironia** Rich.
Style-branches 3. Fruit many-striate. Spikes consisting of 1—4 spikelets. — Species 3. South Africa. . . . . **Chrysithrix** L.

11. Lateral spikelets consisting of one female flower and 1—6 male inserted above the female flower upon the distinctly developed axis of the spikelet ; rarely male flowers reduced to empty glumes or wanting. Utricle usually 2-cleft. — Species 6. South and East Africa. (Including *Hemicarex* Benth.) . . . . **Schoenoxiphium** Nees
Lateral spikelets consisting only of 1 female flower and the usually rudimentary axis. Utricle closed, entire or toothed. 12

12. Axis of the spikelet projecting beyond the utricle and hooked at the tip. — Species 2. Subantarctic islands. . . . . **Uncinia** Pers.
Axis of the spikelet enclosed and straight or more frequently rudimentary and usually early disappearing. — Species 80. Extra-tropical regions and mountains of the tropics. . . . . **Carex** L.

13. (1.) Spikelets (false spikelets) centrifugal, with a terminal flower, branched from the uppermost bract, 1—2-, rarely 3—6-flowered. . . . 14
Spikelets centripetal, without a terminal flower, 3—many-, rarely 1—2-flowered ; flowers hermaphrodite, a male one sometimes added. . 24

14. Spikelets containing 1 terminal male flower and 1—2 lateral hermaphrodite flowers. Style dilated at the base. — Species 30. South Africa. (*Elynanthus* Nees, including *Macrochaetium* Steud.) [Tribe GAHNIEAE.] . . . . **Tetraria** Beauv.
Spikelets containing only hermaphrodite flowers, a male one being sometimes added. [Tribe RHYNCHOSPOREAE.] 15

15. Glumes 2-ranked. Style-branches 3. 16
Glumes not distinctly 2-ranked. 19

16. Perianth-bristles 6, alternately unequal. Fruit crowned by the base of the style. Spikelets in heads. — Species 9. South Africa, Madagascar and Mascarene Islands. (Under *Carpha* R. Br.) . . **Asterochaete** Nees
Perianth-bristles equal or wanting. 17

17. Perianth-bristles stiff, not feathery, or wanting. Fruit not beaked. — Species 6. South Africa, Madagascar and neighbouring islands, Abyssinia, North Africa. (Including *Epischoenus* C.B. Clarke). **Schoenus** L.
Perianth-bristles feathery. 18

18. Perianth-bristles 3. Glumes 4—5. Style with a thickened, persistent
     base. Spikelets in spikes or solitary. — Species 3. South Africa.
     (*Ecklonea* Steud.) . . . .   **Trianoptiles** Fenzl
  Perianth-bristles 6. Glumes numerous. Style slightly thickened. Spike-
     lets in panicles. — Species 2. Madagascar and neighbouring islands.
     (Under *Schoenus* L.) . . . .   **Cyclocampe** Steud.
19. Style-branches 1—2. Perianth of 6 or more bristles or wanting. — Species
     15. (*Rynchospora* Vahl). . . . . .   **Rhynchospora** Vahl
  Style-branches 3. 20
20. Perianth of 3—6 bristles. 21
  Perianth none. 22
21. Perianth of 3 bristles. Upper leaves with red sheaths. — Species 1. South
     Africa. (*Decalepis* Boeck., under *Tetraria* Beauv.) **Boeckeleria** Dur.
  Perianth of 5—6 bristles. Lowest flower male. — Species 6. Madagascar
     and South Africa. . . . .   **Costularia** C. B. Clarke
22. Partial inflorescences arranged in a panicle. — Species 5. **Cladium** R. Br.
  Partial inflorescences arranged in a head. 23
23. Involucre of the inflorescence short. Stem leafless. — Species 1. Mada-
     gascar and neighbouring islands. (*Arthrostylis* Boeck.)
                                           Actinoschoenus Benth.
  Involucre of the inflorescence long. Stem leafy. — Species 1. West Africa
     and Madagascar. Used medicinally. . . . . . . **Remirea** Aubl.
24. (13.) Bracteoles 1—2. [Tribe HYPOLYTREAE.] 25
  Bracteoles none. [Tribe SCIRPEAE.] 28
25. Bracteoles 1—2, parallel with the glume (bract), i.e. placed before or behind
     or before and behind it. Stamens 1—2. [Subtribe LIPOCARPHINAE.] 26
  Bracteoles 2, lateral to the glume, sometimes united. Stamens 2—3.
     [Subtribe HYPOLYTRINAE.] 27
26. Bracteole 1, deciduous. Stamen 1. Spikelets solitary or in clusters of 2—3,
     subtended by a single involucral bract. — Species 2. Central and South
     Africa. (Under *Scirpus* L.) . . . . .   **Hemicarpha** Nees
  Bracteoles 2, persistent. Stamens 1—2. Spikelets in heads surrounded
     by several involucral bracts. — Species 10. Tropical and South Africa.
     (*Hypaelyptum* Vahl). . . . .   **Lipocarpha** R. Br.
27. Bracteoles united in front, longer than the glume. Spikelets solitary
     or in heads. Stem leafy at the base only. — Species 9. Tropical and
     South Africa. . . . .   **Ascolepis** Nees
  Bracteoles free or united behind, as long as or shorter than the glumes.
     Spikelets in heads or panicles. Stem leafy throughout its length. —
     Species 10. Tropics. . . . .   **Hypolytrum** Rich.
28. (22.) Glumes distinctly 2-ranked. Partial inflorescences usually arranged
     in heads or umbels. [Subtribe CYPERINAE.] 29
  Glumes not distinctly 2-ranked. Partial inflorescences usually arranged
     in spikes. or panicles. [Subtribe SCIRPINAE.] 34

29. Perianth consisting of 6 bristles. Spikelets in panicles. — Species 1. Region
of the great lakes. (Under *Carpha* R. Br.) . **Oreograstis** K. Schum.
Perianth none. 30
30. Flowers with a toothed or lobed disc at the base of the ovary. Spikelets
solitary or in heads. — Species 3. South Africa. (Under *Ficinia*
Schrad.) . . . . **Hemichlaena** Schrad.
Flowers without a disc. 31
31. Style-branches 2. Spikelets containing an hermaprodite and sometimes
also a male flower, arranged in heads. — Species 40. Tropical and South
Africa. The root-stock of some species is used in perfumery and medicine ; others yield fodder. (Plate 9.) . . . . **Kyllinga** Rottb.
Style-branches 3, rarely 1—2, but then spikelets many-flowered. . . 32
32. Fertile flowers in each spikelet 1—2. Glumes with a winged keel, the
lower glume enclosing the upper one. Spikelets in umbellately arranged heads. — Species 2. Tropics to Transvaal. **Courtoisia** Nees
Fertile flowers in each spikelet 3 or more, rarely 1—2, but then glumes not
winged or the lower glume not enclosing the upper one. . . . 33
33. Glumes with the margins united into a cylinder at their base, long acuminate
at the top. Spikelets terete .3—4-flowered, in spikes. Stamens 2.—
Species 1. South-east Africa. (Under *Mariscus* Gaertn. or *Cyperus* L.)
Cylindrolepis Boeck.
Glumes with free margins. — Species 300. The root-stocks of some (especially *C. esculentus* L.) are eaten and used for the preparation of oil, per
fume, and medicaments ; the culms (especially of *C. Papyrus* L.) are
used for making paper and for plaiting-work ; some species serve as
fodder- or ornamental plants, others are noxious weeds. (Including
Galilea Parl., *Juncellus* Griseb., *Mariscus* Vahl, *Pycreus* Beauv., and
Torulinium Desv.) . . . . **Cyperus** L.
34. (28.) Style conspicuously thickened at the base. 35
Style not or slightly thickened at the base. 37
35. Perianth none. Style deciduous. — Species 75. Some are used as fodder.
(Including *Abildgaardia* Vahl and *Bulbostylis* Kunth). **Fimbristylis** Vahl
Perianth consisting of 3—8 bristles. Base of the style usually persis-
tent. 36
36. Spikelets in heads. Glumes in 5 rows. — Species 1. Tropics. (Under
Fuirena Rottb. . . . . **Pentasticha** Turcz.
Spikelets solitary. — Species 25. Some are used for plaiting-work or yield
starch. (*Eleocharis* R. Br.) . . . . . . **Heleocharis** R. Br.
37. Flowers with a toothed or lobed, persistent disc at the base of the ovary.
Glumes usually brown or black. — Species 65. South Africa and mountains of East Africa and Madagascar. . . . . . **Ficinia** Schrad.
Flowers without a disc. 38
38. Perianth-bristles 6 or more, much elongated after flowering. Spikelets
solitary or in umbels. — Species 1. South Africa. The cotton-like
perianth-bristles are used for stuffing cushions. " Cotton-grass."
Eriophorum L.

Perianth-bristles not elongated or wanting. 39
39. Glumes hairy, like the whole plant. Perianth of 3—6 toothed scales or
bristles. — Species 20. . . . . **Fuirena** Rottb.
Glumes glabrous. — Species 70. Some are used as ornamental plants or
for plaiting-work, others have edible root-stocks, also used in medicine.
(Including *Isolepis* R. Br. and *Schoenoplectus* Reichb.) **Scirpus** L.

ORDER PRINCIPES

FAMILY 18. PALMAE

Stem woody, usually simple. . Leaves pinnately or palmately split, at least
2-cleft, usually collected in a crown at the top of the stem. Flowers in simple
or branched spadices enveloped by spathes, usually unisexual and provided
with rudimentary stamens or carpels. Perianth-segments 6, similar in texture,
but often unequal in size, leathery or parchment-like, green white or yellow.
Stamens 6 or more, rarely 3, united at the base or adnate below to the perianth.
Carpels 3, superior, distinct or united and then forming a 1—3-celled ovary ;
sometimes 2 carpels empty or reduced to the style. Ovules solitary in each cell,
filling the cell and sometimes adhering to its wall. Fruits berry- or drupe-
like. Seeds with a small embryo and horny albumen. — Genera 36, species
100. (Plates 10 and 11.)
1. Carpels 3, distinct. Fruit consisting of 1—3 smooth berries. Leaf-segments induplicate in bud. [Subfamily **CORYPHOIDEAE**.] . . 2
Carpels 3, united and forming a 1—3-celled ovary, or carpel 1. . . 3
2. Leaves fan-shaped. Spadices with 2 or more incomplete spathes. Flowers
polygamous or dioecious. Perianth of the female flowers as in the male.
Seed ovate, not deeply grooved ; albumen ruminate. Stem short,
usually branched. — Species 1 (*Ch. humilis* L.). North-West Africa.
Used as an ornamental plant ; the leaf-buds are eaten and the fibres
used for making ropes or paper or for stuffing cushions. " Dwarf-
palm." [Tribe SABALEAE.] . . . . . . **Chamaerops** L.
Leaves pinnate. Spadices with one complete spathe. Flowers dioecious.
Perianth of the female flowers differing from the male. Seed oblong,
with a deep longitudinal groove. — Species 5. Some (especially the
date-palm, *Ph. dactylifera* L.) have edible fruits, also used for making
brandy and sugar. They yield also palm wine, wood, and fibres . for
plaiting and stuffing, and are used as ornamental plants. [Tribe PHOE-
NICEAE.] . . . . **Phoenix** L.
3. Leaves fan-shaped. Spadices with many incomplete spathes. Fruit a
drupe with 1—3 distinct stones ; epicarp smooth or minutely dotted.
[Subfamily **BORASSOIDEAE,** tribe BORASSEAE.] 4
Leaves pinnately dissected or 2-cleft. Fruit berry-like or covered with
imbricate scales or containing a single stone ; if fruit drupe-like and
one-seeded, then spadices with 1—4 complete spathes. . . . 8

CYPERACEAE.

Pl. 9.

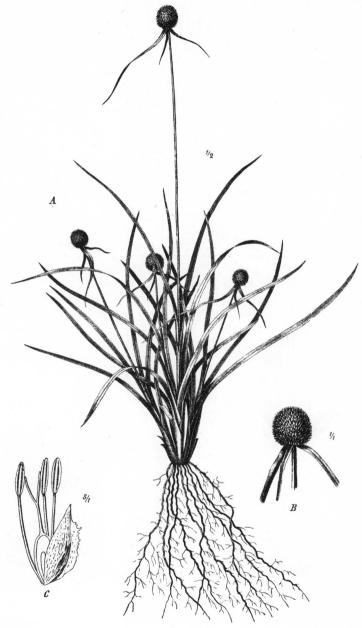

J. Fleischmann del.

Kyllinga alba Nees

A Plant in flower. *B* Inflorescence. *C* Flower (the ovary cut lengthwise)

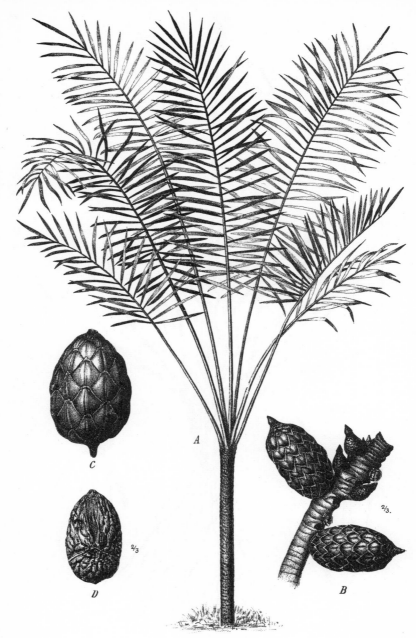

J. Fleischmann del.

Raphia Laurentii De Wild.
A Young plant. *B* Group of fruits. *C* Fruit. *D* Seed. ('*A* from De Wildeman, Expedition Laurent).

4. Male flowers many in each pit of the spadix. 5
  Male flowers solitary in each pit of the spadix. 6
5. Male flowers 20—30 in each pit of the spadix. Stamens about 30. Fruit
  nearly always with a single stone. Seeds deeply 2-lobed. — Species 1.
  Seychelles. The fruit ("double cocoa-nut") is eaten and used in
  medicine. . . . . **Lodoicea** Labill.
  Male flowers 10 in each pit of the spadix. Stamens 6. Fruit with 3 stones.
  Seeds emarginate. Species 1 (*B. flabellifer* L., Palmyra palm). Tropics.
  It yields timber, fibre (piassave), starch (sago), gum, vegetables, edible
  fruits, wine, vinegar, alcohol, sugar, and medicaments. **Borassus** L.
6. Stamens 15—30. Fruit with 3 stones, very rarely with 1—2. Medium-
  sized trees. — Species 3. Madagascar and Mascarene Islands. They
  furnish fibre for plaiting-work and are used as ornamental plants ;
  one species has edible fruits. . . . . **Latania** Comm.
  Stamens 6. Fruit with a single stone. Tall trees. 7
7. Albumen ruminate. Fruit medium-sized (the size of a walnut). Stem
  simple. — Species 3. Upper Nile and Madagascar. They yield timber,
  fibre, edible pith, and alcohol. (Including *Bismarckia* Hildebr. &
  Wendl.) . . . . **Medemia** G. de Wuert. & Braun
  Albumen homogeneous. Fruit large. Stem usually branched. — Species
  13. Tropics to Natal and Egypt. They yield wood, fibre, edible
  fruits, and wine. "Dum palm." . . . . . **Hyphaene** Gaertn.
8. (3.) Ovary and fruit clothed with imbricate scales. Fruit one-seeded.
  Flowers with bracts and bracteoles. Leaf-segments reduplicate in
  bud. [Subfamily **LEPIDOCARYOIDEAE**, tribe METROXYLEAE.] 9
  Ovary and fruit without scales. Flowers usually without bracts. [Sub-
  family **CEROXYLOIDEAE**.] 15
9. Ovary incompletely 3-celled. [Subtribe CALAMINAE.] 10
  Ovary completely 3-celled. [Subtribe RAPHIINAE.] 11
10. Stem erect. Leaves without tendrils. Spadices terminal. Seed depressed-globose. — Species 1 (*M. Rumphii* Mart.) Cultivated in Madagascar and the Mascarenes. It yields wood, fibre for plaiting and
  weaving, vegetables, and starch (sago). (*Sagus* Blume).
  Metroxylon Rottb.
  Stem climbing. Leaves with tendrils. Spadices lateral. — Species 6.
  Tropics. The stems (cane) are used for plaiting-work and for the
  manufacture of walking-sticks and various utensils. "Rattan-palm."
  Calamus L.
11. Stem erect. Flowers monoecious, the male and female on the same branches
  of the much-branched terminal spadices. Seed oblong or ovate. — Species
  10. Tropics. The leaf-stalks (false bamboo) are used for building
  houses and making furniture, the fibres (piassave) for plaiting, weaving,
  and brush-making. The stems, leaf-buds, and fruits of some species
  yield starch, meal, vegetables, wine, and oil. (Plates 10 and 11.)
  Raphia Beauv.
  Stem climbing. Leaves with tendrils. 12

12. Flowers monoecious, in cymes on the primary branches of the lateral
    spadices ; cymes consisting of one female and several male flowers. —
    Species 2. Equatorial West Africa. They furnish cane for plaiting-
    work and for the manufacture of various utensils. (Under *Calamus* L.)

    Oncocalamus Mann & Wendl.

    Flowers hermaphrodite or polygamous, in pairs on the branches of the
    spadices. 13

13. Spadices lateral. Spathes none. — Species 5. West Africa to the upper
    Nile. They furnish cane for plaiting-work and for the manufacture of
    various utensils. (Under *Calamus* L.)

    Eremospatha Mann & Wendl.

    Spadices terminal. Spathes tubular. 14

14. Seed flattened, with a thick raphe. Leaves with a short stalk and narrow
    segments. — Species 1. West Africa to the upper Nile. They furnish
    cane for plaiting-work and for the manufacture of various utensils.
    (Under *Calamus* L.) . . . . . **Ancistrophyllum** Mann & Wendl.

    Seed roundish, deeply grooved, kidney-shaped in transverse section. Leaves
    with a rather long stalk and rather broad segments. — Species 2. West
    Africa. They furnish cane for plaiting-work and for the manufacture of
    various utensils. (Under *Ancistrophyllum* Mann & Wendl. or *Calamus*
    L.) . . . . **Laccosperma** Mann & Wendl.

15. (8.) Fruit a drupe ; endocarp very hard, with 3 pores. [Tribe COCO-
    EAE.] 16

    Fruit a berry ; endocarp membranous, rarely woody. [Tribe ARE-
    CEAE.] 17

16. Flowers sunk singly in deep pits of the spadix-branches. Spadices uni-
    sexual, with 2 deciduous spathes. Stamens united high up. Fruit
    rather small ; pericarp spongy outside ; pores towards the top of the
    stone. — Species 1 (*E. guineensis* L. oil-palm). Central Africa. The
    stem and the leaves furnish wood, fibre, vegetables, and wine ; the fruits
    are edible and used for making oil. [Subtribe ELAEIDINAE.]

    Elaeis Jacq.

    Flowers inserted singly or in groups of three in shallow pits or notches of
    the spadix-branches. Spadices bisexual, with a woody, persistent
    spathe. Stamens free or united at the base. Fruit large ; pericarp
    fibrous ; pores towards the base of the stone. — Species 1 (*C. nucifera* L.,
    coco-nut-palm). Cultivated and sometimes naturalised on the shores
    of the tropics. The stem and the leaves furnish wood, fibre, tanning
    materials, vegetables, wine, and medicaments ; the fruits are edible and
    yield oil, fodder, and a drink. [Subtribe ATTALEINAE.]   **Cocos** L.

17. Leaves with long prickles. Spadices branched ; spathes 2 or more, com-
    plete. Corolla of the female flowers imbricate in bud. Ovary 1-celled,
    with a laterally affixed ovule. Stigmas 3. 18

    Leaves without prickles. 23

18. Leaves with a long sheath. Spadices below the leaves. Seed with homogeneous albumen. 19
    Leaves with a rather short sheath. Spadices between the leaves. Seed with ruminate albumen. 20
19. Seed obtusely triquetrous. Stamens 9. — Species 1. Seychelles.

Deckenia Wendl.

   Seed ellipsoid, slightly compressed laterally. Stamens usually 12. — Species 3. Madagascar and Mascarenes. Used in house-building and as ornamental plants. . . . . **Acanthophoenix** Wendl.
20. Leaves 2-cleft, with pinnately toothed margins. 21
    Leaves irregularly pinnatisect. 22
21. Stamens 6. Seed and endocarp furrowed. Spadices with 3 spathes. Leaf-stalk prickly. — Species 1. Seychelles. Used as an ornamental plant.

Verschaffeltia Wendl.

   Stamens 15—20. Seed and endocarp not furrowed. Spadices with 2 spathes. Leaf-stalk smooth.—Species 1. Seychelles. Used as an ornamental plant. (*Stevensonia* Duncan). **Phoenicophorium** Wendl.
22. Stamens 6. Seed elliptical. Spadices twice branched, with several spathes. — Species 1. Seychelles. Used as an ornamental plant. **Roscheria** Wendl.
   Stamens 40—50. Seed kidney-shaped. Spadices once branched, with 2 spathes.—Species 1. Seychelles. . . . . **Nephrosperma** Balf.
23. (17.) Spadices with many tubular incomplete spathes, twice branched. Stamens 6. Ovary 3-celled. Stem tree-like. — Species 4. Madagascar and Mascarenes. Used as ornamental plants. The fruit is said to be poisonous. . . . . **Hyophorbe** Gaertn.
   Spadices with 1—4 spathes, all or the uppermost complete (i.e. completely enveloping the spadix, when young.) 24
24. Spadices with 4 spathes, simple. Flowers sunk in pits on the spadix. Corolla valvate in bud. Stamens 6. Ovary 3-celled. Stem reed-like. — Species 1. West Africa. The fruit is edible.

Podococcus Mann & Wendl.

   Spadices with 1—3 spathes; if simple, then corolla of the female flowers imbricate in bud or stamens 3 or many. 25
25. Stamens numerous. Stigma 1. Ovary 1-celled. Corolla valvate in bud. Spadices simple. Flowers sunk in pits on the spadix. Stem short. — Species 1. Equatorial West Africa. **Sclerosperma** Mann & Wendl.
   Stamens 3—6. Stigmas usually 3. 26
26. Stamens in the male flowers 3, staminodes in the female 6. Ovary with 1 fertile and 2 empty cells. 27
   Stamens 6. 28
27. Stamens opposite the petals, united at the base. — Species 3. Madagascar.

Trichodypsis Baill.

   Stamens alternating with the petals, free or almost free.— Species 7. Madagascar. Used as ornamental plants. (Including *Adelodypsis* Becc.)

Dypsis Nor.

H

28. Ovary 1-celled. 29
    Ovary 3-celled, but usually one cell only fertile. 34
29. Spadices simple. Leaves deeply forked. Stem short, erect. — Species 5.
    Madagascar. . . . . **Haplophloga** Baill.
    Spadices branched. 30
30. Spadices once branched. Stigma usually 1. Stem tree-like. — Species
    5. Madagascar and neighbouring islands. Used as ornamental plants.
    The fibres of the leaves (piassave) are used in the manufacture of ropes
    and stuffs. . . . . **Dictyosperma** Wendl. & Drude
    Spadices 2—3 times branched. Stigmas usually 3. 31
31. Spadices twice branched. Male flowers with valvate or subimbricate
    sepals. Anthers sagittate, basifixed, opening outwards or laterally.
    Rudimentary pistil 3-cleft. Female flowers larger than the male.
    Stigmas 3, subsessile. Tall trees. — Species 1 (*A. Catechu* L., betel palm).
    Cultivated in East Africa. It yields wood, bark for tanning, fibre,
    vegetables, wine, and medicaments ; the fruits are chewed. **Areca** L.
    Spadices thrice branched. Male flowers with imbricate sepals. Anthers
    ovoid, opening inwards. Rudimentary pistil entire. 32
32. Styles basal. Stem reed-like. — Species 2. Madagascar. (*Chrysalido-
    carpus* Wendl.) . . . . **Neodypsis** Baill.
    Styles or stigmas terminal. 33
33. Leaves irregularly pinnatisect, with lanceolate segments. Stem low,
    reed-like. — Species 1. Madagascar. (Under *Dypsidium* Baill.)
                                            Neophloga Baill.
    Leaves regularly pinnatisect, with linear segments. Stem tall. — Species
    2. Madagascar and Comoro Islands. (Including *Vonitra* Becc.)
                                            Phlogella Baill.
34. Spadices simple. Petals lanceolate. Anther-halves linear. Style conical.
    — Species 3. Madagascar. . . . . **Haplodypsis** Baill.
    Spadices much branched. Petals ovate or orbicular. Anther-halves
    oblong or ovate. Style 3-partite. 35
35. Flowers monoecious. Sepals of the male flowers orbicular. Stamens
    unequal in length. Stigmas awl-shaped. Albumen ruminate. — Species
    5. Madagascar. Leaves used for plaiting-work. . . **Phloga** Nor.
    Flowers dioecious. Sepals of the male flowers elliptical. Stamens subequal.
    Stigmas short and thick. Albumen homogeneous. — Species 2. Mada-
    gascar and Comoro Islands. . . . **Ravenea** Hildebr. & Bouché

ORDER SPATHIFLORAE

FAMILY 19. ARACEAE

Leaves usually net-veined. Flowers in spadices, without bracteoles. Perianth
simple or wanting. Fruit indehiscent or bursting irregularly, usually berry-like.
Seed-coat fleshy. — Genera 33, species 150. (Plate 12.)

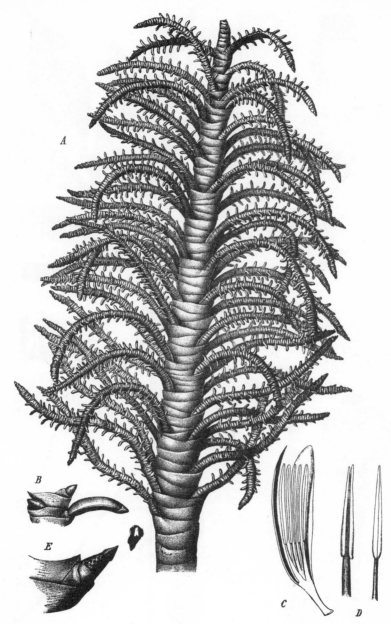

J. Fleischmann del.

Raphia Laurentii De Wild.

A Inflorescence. *B* Male flower-buds. *C* Male flower cut lengthwise. *D* Stamen. *E* Female flower.

J. Fleischmann del.

Hydrosme grata Schott

A Leaf.   *B* Inflorescence and spathe.   *C* Stalk of the inflorescence.   *D* Inflorescence without the spathe.   *E* Stamen.   *F* Stamen from above.   *G* Pistil.   *H* Pistil cut lengthwise.   (*B—H* partly from a drawing in the Vienna Hofmuseum.)

1. Flowers hermaphrodite. 2
   Flowers unisexual. 5
2. Perianth none. Ovary incompletely 2-celled with several ascending
   ovules. Climbing shrubs. Leaves stalked, lanceolate. — Species 2.
   West Africa. Used as ornamental plants. (*Raphidophora* Schott).
   [Tribe MONSTEREAE.] . . . . . **Afroraphidophora** Engl.
   Perianth of 4—6 segments. 3
3. Ovary 1-celled. Ovules 2 or more. Tall herbs. Juice milky. Root-
   stock tuberous. Leaves sagittate ; stalk prickly. — Species 1. West
   Africa. Used for making salt. [Tribe LASIEAE.] **Cyrtosperma** Griff.
   Ovary 2—3-celled. Juice not milky. 4
4. Ovule one in each cell, ascending, inverted. Seeds exalbuminous. Climbing
   shrubs. Leaves stalked, lanceolate to ovate. Spathe oblong or ovate. —
   Species 1. Madagascar and Comoro Islands. [Tribe POTHOEAE.]
   Pothos L.
   Ovules several in each cell, pendulous, straight. Seeds albuminous.
   Herbs with a creeping root-stock. Leaves sessile, linear, sword-shaped.
   Spathe linear, sword-shaped, forming a continuation of the flowering
   stem. — Species 1 (*A. Calamus* L., sweet-flag). Introduced in the
   Mascarene Islands. Yields tanning-materials and is used in the pre-
   paration of perfumes, liquors, snuff, and medicaments. [Tribe ACOR-
   EAE.] . . . . **Acorus** L.
5. Perianth present. 6
   Perianth none. 8
6. Perianth cupular. Ovary 1—4-celled with 2 or more ovules in each cell.
   Juice milky. Leaves sagittate ; stalk not thickened near the middle.
   Spathe-margins connate below. — Species 20. Central and South-East
   Africa. [Tribe STYLOCHITONEAE.] . . **Stylochiton** Leprieur
   Perianth of 4 free segments. Ovary 2-celled with 1 ovule in each cell.
   Juice not milky. Leaves pinnate ; stalk with a thickened joint near
   the middle. Spathe-margins free. [Tribe ZAMIOCULCASEAE.] 7
7. Stamens with free filaments ; anthers opening by slits. Leaves several,
   once pinnate. Spathe upon a short stalk. — Species 1. East Africa
   and Mascarene Islands. Used as an ornamental plant. **Zamioculcas** L.
   Stamens with united filaments ; anthers opening by pores. Leaf 1, thrice
   pinnate in the adult stage. Spathe upon a long stalk. — Species 2.
   East Africa to the upper Congo. . . . . **Gonatopus** Hook. fil.
8. Stamens united throughout their length or almost so. 9
   Stamens free or united in pairs or at the base only. 17
9. Female (inferior) part of the spadix adnate to the spathe, 1-flowered.
   Stamens 2. Floating water-plants. Juice not milky. — Species 1.
   Tropical and South Africa and Egypt. Used medicinally. [Tribe
   PISTIEAE.] . . . . **Pistia** L.
   Female part of the spadix free from the spathe, several-flowered.
   Stamens 3—8, very rarely 2. Land- or marsh-plants. Juice milky. 10

10. Stem creeping. Leaves lanceolate, parallel-veined, with numerous pri-
    mary and secondary lateral veins. Ovary completely or incompletely
    2—3-celled with numerous ovules. — Species 12. West Africa. [Tribe
    ANUBIADEAE.] . . . .   **Anubias** Schott
    Stem erect or tuberous. Leaves ovate ovate-sagittate or dissected, net-
    veined, rarely parallel-veined with 5 primary lateral nerves. . . 11
11. Ovules 1—3. Spadix with barren flowers below and above the male ones.
    Stem short, ascending. Leaves ovate or sagittate, entire, with about
    5 primary lateral nerves and many parallel secondary ones. — Species
    2. Madagascar and neighbouring islands and Zanzibar. They yield
    fibre and edible tubers and seeds and are used in medicine.
    Typhonodorum Schott
    Ovules 4 or more. Leaves sagittate- or cordate-ovate and net-veined,
    or dissected. 12
12. Ovules 4. Female flowers with staminodes. Spadix with a terminal
    appendage. Stem tuberous. Leaves dissected. — Species 1. Seychelles.
    [Tribe PROTAREAE.] . . . .   **Protarum** Engl.
    Ovules more than 4. Leaves sagittate- or cordate-ovate. [Tribe COLO-
    CASIEAE.] 13
13. Ovary completely 1-celled. Ovules straight or almost so. 14
    Ovules incompletely 2—3-celled. Ovules inverted. Spadix without a
    terminal appendage. 16
14. Ovules few, basal. Stem erect. Spadix with a terminal appendage. —
    Species 1. Cultivated and sometimes naturalised in Madagascar and
    the neighbouring islands. Stem and leaves are edible ; also used as an
    ornamental plant. . . . .   **Alocasia** Schott
    Ovules many, parietal. Stem tuberous. 15
15. Spadix with a terminal appendage. Spathe erect. Stamens 3—6. — Species
    1 (*C. antiquorum* Schott, taro or dinde). Cultivated and sometimes
    naturalised in Tropical and North Africa. The tubers and leaves are
    eaten and used in medicine ; also an ornamental plant. (Under *Cala-
    dium* Vent.) . . . .   **Colocasia** Schott
    Spadix without an appendage. Spathes recurved at the top. Stamens
    2—3. — Species 1. Island of Socotra. Used as an ornamental plant.
    Remusatia Schott
16. Style disc-like, adnate to the styles of the neighbouring flowers. Ovules
    with a long funicle. Leaves leathery. — Species 2. Cultivated and some-
    times naturalised in West Africa and the Mascarene Islands. Used as
    ornamental plants or vegetables. . . . . .   **Xanthosoma** Schott
    Style none. Ovules with a short funicle. Leaves herbaceous, usually
    with red spots. — Species 1. Cultivated and sometimes naturalised
    in West Africa. Used as an ornamental plant. .   **Caladium** Vent.
17. (8.) Stem above ground and usually climbing or underground and creeping.
    Spadix without an appendage. Ovary 1—2-celled with 1 ovule in each
    cell. 18
    Stem underground, short and thick, more or less tuberous. Juice milky. 23

18. Juice milky. Leaves cordate or sagittate. Female inflorescence not adnate to the spathe. Ovary 1-celled. [Tribe NEPHTHYTIDEAE.] 19
Juice not milky. Leaves lanceolate oblong or elliptical, acute or obtuse at the base, rarely cordate and then female inflorescence adnate to the spathe or ovary 2-celled. Seed albuminous. 22

19. Stem underground, creeping. — Species 3. West Africa. Used as ornamental plants. (Including *Oligogynium* Engl.) . **Nephthytis** Schott
Stem above ground, climbing, woody. 20

20. Leaves perforated or dissected. Male inflorescence three times as long as the female and contiguous to it. Ovary with a strongly projecting parietal placenta. — Species 2. West Africa.
Rhektophyllum N. E. Brown
Leaves entire or lobed, not perforated. Ovary with a slightly projecting parietal or sub-basal placenta. 21

21. Leaves oblong, shortly cordate at the base. Male inflorescence twice as long as the female and contiguous to it. Stamens 2—3. — Species 1. West Africa (Cameroons). (Under *Cercestis* Schott).
Alocasiophyllum Engl.
Leaves sagittate or hastate. Stamens usually 4. — Species 7. West Africa. . . . . **Cercestis** Schott

22. Stem creeping. Female inflorescence adnate to the spathe, as long as the male. Ovary conical. Style present. — Species 1. Central Africa. Used as an ornamental plant. [Tribe CALLOPSIDEAE.] **Callopsis** Engl.
Stem climbing or erect. Female inflorescence free from the spathe. Ovary subglobose. Style wanting. — Species 17. Central Africa. Some are used as ornamental plants. [Tribe CULCASIEAE.] **Culcasia** Beauv.

23. (17.) Spadix covered with fertile flowers to the top. Ovary with 4 or more ovules. Leaves sagittate or hastate. Spathe funnel-shaped. — Species 10. South Africa and southern Central Africa; one species (*Z. aethiopica* Spreng.) cultivated as an ornamental plant under the name of "Calla" and naturalised in the island of Madeira. (*Aroides* Heist., *Richardia* Kunth). [Tribe ZANTEDESCHIEAE.] **Zantedeschia** Spreng.
Spadix ending in an appendage which is glabrous or covered with rudimentary flowers, rarely without an appendage, but then ovary 1—2-ovuled and leaves dissected. 24

24. Ovules inverted. Ovary usually 2—4-celled. Male and female portions of the spadix contiguous, rarely separated by a glabrous interval without barren flowers. Leaf 1, dissected. [Tribe AMORPHOPHALLEAE.] 25
Ovules straight. Ovary 1-celled. Seeds albuminous. Spadix with a terminal appendage. [Tribe AREAE.] 27

25. Spadix ending in a flowerless appendage. — Species 35. Tropics. Some have edible tubers or are used as ornamental plants. (Under *Amorphophallus* Blume). (Plate 12.) . . . . . **Hydrosme** Schott
Spadix covered with flowers to the top; upper flowers sometimes reduced to barren stamens. 26

26. Ovary 1-celled. Male inflorescence as long as the female. Spathe boat-shaped. — Species 7. Central Africa. Some have edible tubers.

Anchomanes Schott

Ovary 2-celled. Male inflorescence longer than the female. — Species 2. Equatorial West Africa. (Including *Zyganthera* N.E. Brown).

Pseudohydrosme Engl.

27. Spadix unisexual (containing male or female flowers only). Stamens 2—4. Ovules basal. Leaves dissected. — Species 4. East Africa. Some are poisonous. . . . . **Arisaema** Mart.

Spadix bisexual (containing both male and female flowers). . . . 28

28. Male inflorescence contiguous to the female. 29

Male inflorescence separated from the female by a distinct interval usually covered with rudimentary flowers. 30

29. Stamen 1. Anther opening by a slit. Ovules basal. Leaves sagittate or hastate. — Species 2. North Africa. Used as ornamental plants. The tubers are poisonous when raw, but edible when cooked, and furnish starch, medicaments, and a substitute for soap.   **Arisarum** Targ. Tozz.

Stamens 3—4. Anthers opening by pores. Ovules basal or apical. Leaves several, dissected. — Species 2. North-west Africa. Used as ornamental plants. The tubers are poisonous when raw, but edible when cooked, and furnish starch, medicaments, and a substitute for soap.

Dracunculus Schott

30. Interval between the male and the female inflorescence without rudimentary flowers. Spathe divided into two chambers, one of which contains a female flower, the other one several male flowers. Stamens 2. Ovules numerous. Leaves ovate. — Species 1. North-west Africa (Algeria).

Ambrosinia Bassi

Interval between the male and the female inflorescence clothed with rudimentary. flowers. Spathe not 2-chambered. Female flowers several. 31

31. Ovules 6 or more, parietal. Stamens 3—4. Leaves sagittate or hastate. — Species 2. North Africa. Poisonous and sometimes used as ornamental plants. The tubers are edible when cooked and yield starch ; they are also used in medicine and as a substitute for soap. . . . . **Arum** L.

Ovules 1—4, basal. Stamens 1—2. Leaves linear, oblong, ovate, or dissected. 32

32. Ovule 1. Leaves several, entire. — Species 3. North Africa. Used as ornamental plants. The tubers are edible when cooked, and yield starch, medicaments, and a substitute for soap. . . . **Biarum** Schott

Ovules 2—4. Leaf 1, dissected. — Species 2. East Africa and Angola. Used as ornamental plants. The tubers are edible when cooked, and yield starch, medicaments, and a substitute for soap.

Sauromatum Schott

FAMILY 20. LEMNACEAE

Floating herbs without distinct stems or leaves, consisting of leaf- or grain-like fronds. Inflorescence seated in a cavity of the frond and consisting of 1—2 male flowers and a female. Flowers monoecious, without a perianth. Stamen 1. Ovary 1-celled, with 1—6 basal ovules and a funnel-shaped stigma. Seed-coat fleshy. — Genera 3, species 12.

1. Fronds rootless. Inflorescence on the back of the frond, without a spathe and consisting of 1 male and 1 female flower. — Species 6. (Including *Wolffiella* Hegelm., under *Lemna* L.) [Subfamily **WOLFFIOIDEAE.**] **Wolffia** Horkel

   Fronds with roots. Inflorescence at the margin of the frond, consisting of 2 male and a female flower enclosed by a spathe. [Subfamily **LEM-NOIDEAE.**]   2

2. Fronds with one root each, 3—5-nerved. — Species 5. Some are used in medicine. " Duckweed."   .   .   .   . **Lemna** L.

   Fronds with several roots each, many-nerved. — Species 1. (Under *Lemna* L.)   .   .   .   . **Spirodela** Schleid.

ORDER FARINOSAE

SUBORDER FLAGELLARIINEAE

FAMILY 21. FLAGELLARIACEAE

Climbing herbs. Leaves lanceolate, ending in a tendril. Flowers in panicles, regular, hermaphrodite. Perianth-segments 6, free, subpetaloid, yellowish or whitish, the outer somewhat shorter than the inner. Stamens 6. Anthers turned inwards. Ovary superior, 3-celled, with a solitary, inverted ovule in the inner angle of each cell. Style with 3 linear, recurved stigmas. Fruit a 1—2-seeded berry. Seeds with a mealy albumen and a small marginal embryo.

   Genus 1. Species 1. Tropical and South-east Africa. Used in medicine and for plaiting-work.   .   .   .   . **Flagellaria** L.

SUBORDER ENANTIOBLASTAE

FAMILY 22. RESTIONACEAE

Grass-like herbs. Leaves linear or reduced to the sheath. Flowers in spike-lets usually arranged in spikes or panicles, regular, unisexual. Perianth of 3—6 membranous or scarious segments, imbricate in bud, rarely absent in the female flowers. Stamens 2—3. Anthers 1-celled. Ovary superior, 1—3-celled, with 1—3 pendulous, straight ovules. Fruit dry. Seeds with a mealy albumen and a marginal embryo. — Genera 12. Species 230. South Africa to Nyasaland. (Plate 13.)

1. Ovary 1-celled, sometimes 2—3-celled when young. Fruit 1-celled, indehiscent.   2

   Ovary 2—3-celled. Fruit 1—3-celled, dehiscent. Flowers dioecious. **10**

2. Spikelets, all or most of them, bisexual, containing a male and a female flower, arranged in spikes. Styles 2. — Species 1. South Africa.

Phyllocomos Mast.

Spikelets unisexual. 3

3. Female spikelets 1-flowered. Styles or stigmas 2. 4

Female spikelets 2—many-flowered, very rarely 1-flowered, but then stigmas 3 6

4. Glumes distant. Male spikelets in panicles, female in spikes. — Species 10. South Africa (Cape Colony). . (Including *Ceratocaryum* Nees)

Willdenowia Thunb.

Glumes closely imbricate. 5

5. Female flowers on a thick stalk. Style 1, with 2 stigmas. Fruits more or less distinctly stalked. — Species 15. South Africa (Cape Colony).

Hypodiscus Nees

Female flowers on a thin stalk or sessile. Styles 2. Fruits sessile. — Species 20. South Africa to Nyasaland. . . . . **Hypolaena** R. Br.

6. Outer perianth-segments of the female flowers winged on the keel. 7

Outer perianth-segments not winged. Styles 2—3. 8

7. Style 1. Female spikelets in spikes. — Species 15. South Africa (Cape Colony) . . . . **Thamnochortus** Berg

Styles 2—3. Female spikelets solitary or in fascicles. — Species 5. South Africa (Cape Colony). (Under *Thamnochortus* Berg) **Staberoha** Kunth

8. Female spikelets solitary or in clusters of 2—3 on the top of the stem, 2—5-flowered. Outer perianth-segments larger than the inner. Styles 2. — Species 8. South Africa (Cape Colony). **Cannomois** Beauv.

Female spikelets in spikes or panicles. Outer perianth-segments as large as or smaller than the inner, more rarely larger, but then styles 3. . 9

9. Leaf-sheaths persistent. Styles 3. — Species 15. South Africa.

Leptocarpus R. Br.

Leaf-sheaths deciduous, more rarely persistent, but then styles 2.—Species 30. South Africa. (Including *Lamprocaulos* Mast.) . . **Elegia** L.

10. (1.) Leaf-sheaths persistent. — Species 100. South Africa. (Plate 13.) **Restio** L.

Leaf-sheaths, at least the upper ones, deciduous. Spikelets few-flowered. 11

11. Ovary and fruit 2-celled. Female spikelets in short spikes. — Species 1. South Africa (Cape Colony). . . . . . **Askidiosperma** Steud.

Ovary and fruit 3-celled. — Species 15. South Africa. . . **Dovea** Kunth

FAMILY 23. MAYACACEAE

Herbs. Leaves alternate, linear, 2-toothed at the apex. Flowers in axillary, 2—3-flowered umbels, regular, hermaphrodite. Perianth consisting of 3 imbricate sepals and 3 imbricate petals. Stamens 3. Anthers opening by a terminal pore. Ovary superior, 1-celled, with 3 parietal placentas. Ovules numerous, straight. Style and stigma simple. Fruit capsular. Embryo at the apex of the mealy albumen.

Genus 1, species 1. Southern West Africa (Angola). . . . **Mayaca** Aubl.

J Fleischmann del

Restio compressus Rottb.

A Upper part of a plant in flower   *B* Inflorescence.   *C* Male flower.   *D* Male flower cut lengthwise.

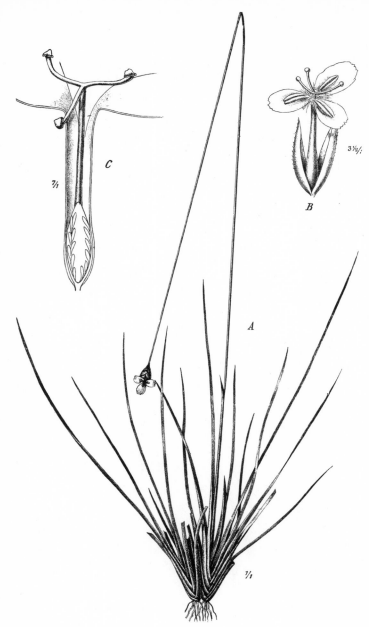

J. Fleischmann del.

Xyris angustifolia De Wi'd. & Dur.

A Plant in flower.   *B* Flower (the third sepal has fallen off).   *C* Lower part of the flower cut lengthwise.

FAMILY 24. XYRIDACEAE

Herbs. Leaves radical, linear. Flowers in spikes or heads with an involucre of imbricate bracts, hermaphrodite. Sepals 3, one much larger than the others and deciduous. Petals 3, united below into a tube. Fertile stamens 3, adnate to the petals ; staminodes 3. Anthers opening by longitudinal slits. Ovary superior, 1-celled or incompletely 3-celled. Ovules numerous, straight. Style 3-cleft. Fruit capsular. Embryo at the apex of the mealy albumen. (Plate 14.)

Genus 1, species 40. Tropical and South Africa. Some are used in medicine.
Xyris L.

FAMILY 25. ERIOCAULACEAE

Herbs. Leaves radical, linear. Flowers in heads surrounded by an involucre, very small, monoecious. Perianth membranous, simple or double, rarely in the female flowers none. Stamens 2—6. Anthers 2-celled. Ovary superior, 2—3-celled, with one pendulous ovule in each cell. Styles or style-branches 2—3. Fruit capsular. Embryo small, at the apex of the albumen. — Genera 4, species 80. Tropical and South Africa. (Plate 15.)

1. Stamens 2—3, opposite the petals. Petals of the male flowers united below, without a gland on the inside. Style-branches 6, three of which bear a stigma, rarely 3. [Subfamily **PAEPALANTHOIDEAE**.]   .   2
   Stamens 4—6, very rarely fewer, but then petals free. Petals usually with a gland on the inside near the apex. Style-branches 2—3, without alternating appendages. [Subfamily **ERIOCAULOIDEAE**.]   .   .   3
2. Petals of the female flowers united at their middle part. — Species 6. Central and South Africa. (Under *Paepalanthus* Mart.) · **Syngonanthus** Ruhl.
   Petals of the female flowers free. — Species 3. West Africa and Mascarene Islands.   .   .   .   . **Paepalanthus** Mart.
3. Petals united into a tube, but free at the base in the female flowers. Inner involucral bracts more or less spreading. Stamens 6. — Species 8. Tropics. Some are used in medicine. (Plate 15.) **Mesanthemum** Koern.
   Petals free or absent. Inner involucral bracts rarely spreading. — Species 60. Tropical and South Africa.   .   .   .   .   .   . **Eriocaulon** L.

SUBORDER BROMELIINEAE

FAMILY 26. RAPATEACEAE

Herbs. Leaves radical, lanceolate. Flowers in heads with 2 large involucral bracts, regular, hermaphrodite. Perianth corolla-like, yellow or whitish, 6-lobed. Stamens 6, inserted in the tube of the perianth. Anthers linear, opening by two terminal pores. Ovary superior, 3-celled, with 1 ascending, inverted ovule in each cell. Style simple. Fruit capsular. Embryo near the apex of the mealy albumen.

Genus 1, species 1. West Africa (Liberia). **Maschalocephalus** Gilg & Schum.

FAMILY 27. BROMELIACEAE

Herbs. Leaves for the most part radical, linear, toothed. Inflorescence terminal, cone-shaped. Flowers regular, hermaphrodite. Perianth consisting of a calyx and a corolla. Petals slightly cohering and bearing two scales at the base. Stamens 6, slightly adhering to the petals. Anthers linear, turned inwards. Ovary inferior or half-inferior, 3-celled, with many axile, inverted ovules. Style 1 ; stigmas 3. Fruits berry-like, united into a cone-shaped head. Embryo near the base of the mealy albumen.

Genus 1, species 1 (*A. sativus* Schult., pine-apple). Cultivated and often naturalised in the tropics. The edible fruit and the fibres of the leaves are used. (*Ananassa* Lindl.) . . . . . . **Ananas** Adans.

SUBORDER COMMELININEAE

FAMILY 28. COMMELINACEAE

Herbs. Leaves alternate. Inflorescence cymose. Flowers hermaphrodite. Perianth-segments 6, more or less distinctly separated into sepals and petals. Fertile stamens 2—6. Ovary superior, 2—3-celled. Ovules straight. Style terminal. Embryo near the apex of the more or less mealy albumen. — Genera 12, species 160. (Plate 16.)

1. Fruit indehiscent, ovate or globular. Ovary 3-celled. Petals free, white, more rarely pale pink or blueish. Inflorescence a panicle without spathe-like bracts. [Tribe POLLIEAE.] 2
   Fruit dehiscing loculicidally. 3
2. Pericarp succulent. Margin of the leaves silky. Perfect stamens 3. — Species 10. West Africa and Upper Nile. Some are used as ornamental plants. . . . . **Palisota** Reichb.
   Pericarp crusty. Margin of the leaves nearly glabrous. Perfect stamens 3 or 6. — Species 5. Tropics. . . . . **Pollia** Thunb.
3. Fertile stamens 2—3, sterile ones 0—4, often bearing empty anthers. [Tribe COMMELINEAE.] 4
   Fertile stamens 5—6. [Tribe TRADESCANTIEAE.] 7
4. Inflorescence in the axil of spathe-like bracts. 5
   Inflorescence without spathe-like bracts. 6
5. Sterile stamens with linear anther-halves cohering at the base. Ovary 2-celled with 1 ovule in each cell. Petals white. Spathes on the elongate branches of a panicle. — Species 1. West Africa.
   Polyspatha Benth.
   Sterile stamens with cross-shaped anthers. Ovary usually 3-celled. Petals usually blue. — Species 80. Some have an edible root-stock or yield vegetables, medicaments, or dyeing-materials ; others are used as ornamental plants. . . . . **Commelina** L.
6. Sepals large, equal, lanceolate, acute. Petals equal. Fruit with 3 equal-sized, many-seeded cells. — Species 1. East Africa. **Anthericopsis** Engl.

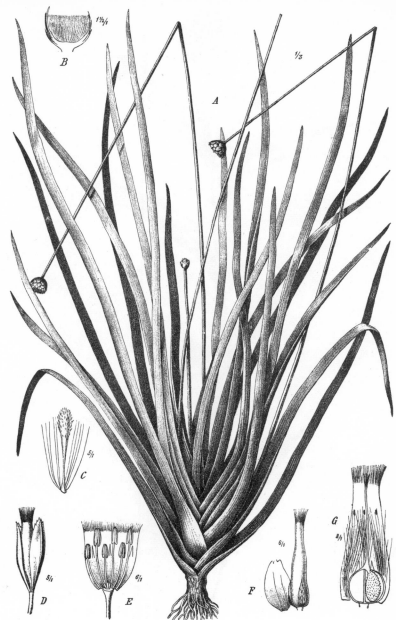

J. Fleischmann del.

Mesanthemum radicans (Benth.) Koern.

A Plant in flower. *B* Inflorescence cut lengthwise. *C* Bract. *D* Male flower. *E* Male flower laid open. *F* Older female flower (from which the sepals have been removed excepting one) *G* Older female flower laid open (the ovary cut lengthwise)

J. Fleischmann **del.**

Aneilema beninense Kunth

A Flowering branch. *B* Flower (the ovary cut lengthwise).

Sepals small, unequal, ovate or oblong-ovate, obtuse. Petals unequal. Fruit with 2 cells, more rarely with 3, one of which is smaller and 1—2-seeded. — Species 30. Tropical and South Africa. Some are used as ornamental plants. (Plate 16.) . . . . . . **Aneilema** R. Br.

7. Petals united below into a tube, but sometimes free at the base, blueish or reddish. Ovary 3-celled with 1—2 ovules in each cell. . . . 8

Petals free or nearly so. 9

8. Stamens inserted towards the top of the corolla-tube. Petals united from the base. — Species 5. Tropical and South Africa. **Coleotrype** C. B. Clarke

Stamens inserted at the base of the corolla. Petals free at the base. — Species 15. Tropical and South Africa. Some are used as ornamental plants. . . . . **Cyanotis** Don

9. Ovary 2-celled with 1 ovule in each cell. Fruit ovate. Filaments glabrous. Petals red or yellow. Inflorescence a panicle. — Species 9. Tropical and South-east Africa. Some are used as ornamental plants.

Floscopa Lour.

Ovary 3-celled. 10

10. Ovules 4—10 in each cell. Fruit oblong. Filaments glabrous. Petals whitish. Inflorescence a panicle. — Species 2. Central Africa.

Buforrestia C. B. Clarke

Ovules 1—2 in each cell. Fruit ovoid or globular. Stamens hairy. Inflorescence spike-, head-, or umbel-like. 11

11. Ovules 2 in each cell ; in the dorsal cell sometimes solitary. Fruit sub-globular. Stamens with a narrow connective. Sepals herbaceous, green. Inflorescence spike- or head-like. Stem long. — Species 3. Equatorial West Africa. . . . . **Forrestia** A. Rich.

Ovule 1 in each cell. Fruit ovoid. Stamens with a broad connective. Sepals subpetaloid. Inflorescence umbel-like and surrounded by an involucre of two bracts. Stem short. — Species 1. West Africa (Congo).

Rhoeo Hance

SUBORDER PONTEDERIINEAE

FAMILY 29. PONTEDERIACEAE

Aquatic herbs. Flowers in spikes racemes or panicles, without bracts, hermaphrodite. Perianth-segments 6, petaloid, white yellow or blue, united below into a tube, rarely nearly free. Stamens 3 or 6, affixed to the perianth. Anthers oblong. Ovary superior, 1- or 3-celled, with numerous inverted ovules. Style simple. Fruit a loculicidal, many-seeded capsule. Seeds with a ribbed testa, a copious mealy albumen, and a long cylindrical embryo. — Genera 3, species 5. Tropics.

1. Stamens 3. Ovary 1-celled or incompletely 3-celled. Perianth funnel-shaped, with a distinct tube. — Species 3. Central Africa.

Heteranthera Ruiz & Pav.

Stamens 6. Ovary 3-celled. Perianth blue or violet. 2

2. Perianth funnel-shaped, with a distinct tube. Filaments thread-like. Anthers attached by the back. Stigma entire or shortly lobed. — Species 1. Tropics. Used as an ornamental plant. . . . . **Eichhornia** Kunth

Perianth bell-shaped, with nearly free segments. Filament of the largest stamen toothed at the base. Anthers attached by the base. Stigma deeply cleft. — Species 1. Central Africa (Upper Nile and Kasai). Used as an ornamental plant, and in medicine. **Monochoria** Presl

FAMILY 30. CYANASTRACEAE

Herbs. Root-stock tuberous. Leaves elliptical or cordate, with curved main-nerves. Flowers in terminal racemes or panicles, provided with bracts. Perianth-segments 6, petaloid, shortly united at the base. Stamens 6, inserted at the base of the perianth, more or less united below. Anthers linear, longer than the filaments, opening by short slits at the apex. Ovary slightly sunk in the receptacle, deeply lobed, 3-celled. Ovules 2 in each cell, ascending, inverted. Style simple, with a 3-lobed stigma. Fruit a 1-seeded nut. Seed with a thin testa, a copious albumen, and a transversely-ovate marginal embryo. (Under *PONTEDERIACEAE* or *HAEMODORACEAE*.)

Genus 1, species 5. Central Africa. Some have edible tubers. (*Schoenlandia* Cornu). . . . . **Cyanastrum** Oliv.

ORDER LILIIFLORAE

SUBORDER JUNCINEAE

FAMILY 31. JUNCACEAE

Leaves linear or reduced to the sheath. Flowers regular, hermaphrodite. Perianth-segments 6, free, stiff, usually green. Stamens 3 or 6. Ovary superior, 1- or 3-celled. Ovules 3 or more, inverted. Style 1 ; stigmas 3, elongated. Fruit capsular. Seeds with a straight axile embryo and abundant albumen. — Genera 3, species 55. (Plate 17.)

1. Stem woody. Leaves at its top, stiff, serrate. Ovary 3-celled, with 2 or few ovules in each cell. Style very short. Seeds with a large embryo and appressed testa. — Species 1. South Africa. It yields fibres and vegetables and is used for plaiting-work. " Palmiet." (Plate 17.)

Prionium E. Mey.

Stem herbaceous. Style thread-like. Seeds with a small embryo. . 2

2. Ovary 1-celled, with 3 basal ovules. Leaves with a closed sheath and ciliate margins.—Species 10. North and South Africa and high mountains of Central Africa. " Wood-rush." . . . . . . **Luzula** DC.

Ovary 1—3-celled, with numerous parietal or axile ovules. — Species 45. Some are used in medicine or for plaiting-work. " Rush." **Juncus** L.

J. Fleischmann del.

Prionium serratum Drege

A Inflorescence. *B* Branch of the inflorescence. *C* Older flower. *D* Younger flower cut lengthwise. *E* Leaf.

½

A

B   1½/1

J. Fleischmann del.

Dracaena Perrotetii Bak.

A Flowering branch.   *B* Flower cut lengthwise.

SUBORDER LILIINEAE

FAMILY 32. LILIACEAE

Perianth more or less corolla-like. Stamens 6, rarely fewer. Ovary superior, usually 2—5-celled, rarely 1-celled with parietal placentas. Seeds with a small embryo and abundant, fleshy or horny albumen. — Genera 79, species 1450. (Including *COLCHICACEAE* and *SMILACEAE*.) (Plate 18.)

1. Underground part of the stem a bulb or a corm. 2
   Underground part of the stem a rootstock or not distinctly developed. 41

2. Leaves all radical, rarely also some much smaller cauline leaves present. 3
   Leaves distributed along the stem or crowded at its top. 31

3. Stem arising out of a corm, very short, underground during the time of flowering, bearing 1—3 flowers at the top. Perianth with a very long, sometimes split tube. Capsule opening septicidally. [Tribe COL-CHICEAE.] 4
   Stem arising out of a bulb. Flowers in racemes or umbels, very rarely solitary. Perianth with a not very long tube or without a tube. Capsule opening loculicidally. 5

4. Perianth-segments free. — Species 2. Algeria and Abyssinia. Used as ornamental plants. . . . . **Merendera** Ram.
   Perianth-segments united below. — Species 5. North Africa. Poisonous and used as medicinal and ornamental plants. . . **Colchicum** L.

5. Flowers in cymose umbels or heads surrounded by 2—3 bracts. Scape distinctly developed. Leaves usually linear. Perianth-segments free or united at the base only. [Tribe ALLIEAE.] 6
   Flowers in racemes, corymbs, or spikes, very rarely solitary, rarely in umbels or heads surrounded by 3 or more bracts, but then scape almost wanting, leaves oblong to ovate, spreading, and perianth-segments united to the middle or higher up. 8

6. Inflorescence surrounded by narrow bracts. Radical leaves 1—3. Perianth usually yellow. — Species 10. North Africa. . . . **Gagea** Salisb.
   Inflorescence surrounded by broad membranous bracts usually united at the base. 7

7. Perianth-segments united into a short tube at the base. Filaments dilated. Ovules in each ovary-cell 6—12. Smell not alliaceous. — Species 2. Cultivated and sometimes naturalised in North Africa, the Mascarene Islands, and St. Helena. Ornamental plants. (*Milla* Cav.)
   Nothoscordum Kunth
   Perianth-segments free or nearly free. Ovules in each ovary-cell 2, rarely 3—6. Smell alliaceous. — Species 30. North Africa, Abyssinia, southern West Africa, and South Africa. Some of them (onion, leek, garlic) are cultivated as vegetables or pot-herbs, and yield also condiments, medicaments, and glue ; others are used as ornamental plants. **Allium** L.

8. Anthers attached by the base.   Stem or inflorescence branched or twining.
   Leaves vanishing before the time of flowering. [Tribe ASPHODE-
   LEAE, Subtribe ERIOSPERMINAE.] 9
   Anthers attached by the back. Stem simple. [Tribe SCILLEAE.] 10

9. Inflorescence twining, bearing flowers on its upper branches only.   Seeds
   oblong, with a small embryo. — Species 1.   South Africa.   Used as an
   ornamental plant. . . . . **Bowiea** Harv.
   Inflorescence bearing flowers on all its branches or not branched.   Seeds
   ovoid or globose, with a large embryo. — Species 7.   South Africa to
   Angola. . . . . **Schizobasis** Bak.

10. Flowers in nearly sessile heads or umbels surrounded by an involucre.
    Perianth-segments united into a tube below. Leaves 2, oblong or
    ovate. 11
    Flowers in racemes or spikes, rarely solitary. 12

11. Perianth-segments very unequal. Filaments free. — Species 3.   South
    Africa.   Used as ornamental plants. . . . . . **Daubenya** Lindl.
    Perianth-segments subequal.   Filaments united at the base. — Species 30.
    South Africa.   Some are used as ornamental plants. **Massonia** Thunb.

12. Perianth-segments free or nearly free. 13
    Perianth-segments united into a tube below. 18

13. Seeds flattened or sharply angled, more or less distinctly winged.   Perianth
    white, yellow, or green. 14
    Seeds globose or obovoid. 15

14. Perianth persistent : inner segments somewhat shorter than the outer,
    connivent at the top, hood-shaped or crested. — Species 70.   South and
    Central Africa.   Some are used as ornamental plants.   **Albuca** L.
    Perianth deciduous ;   segments subequal, spreading or connivent and
    bell-shaped. — Species 55.   Some of them are poisonous or used in medi-
    cine or as ornamental plants. . . . . . . **Urginea** Steinh.

15. Inflorescence racemose, crowned by a tuft of leafy bracts.   Perianth
    greenish. — Species 10.   South Africa to Nyasaland.   Some are used as
    ornamental plants. . . . . **Eucomis** L'Hér.
    Inflorescence without a terminal tuft of bracts. 16

16. Perianth-segments convex, connivent at the top, whitish.   Flowers in
    spikes or spike-like racemes, sessile or short-stalked, the uppermost
    abortive.   Filaments broadened almost to the top. — Species 17.   Central
    and South Africa.   Some are used as ornamental plants.
                                                    Drimiopsis Lindl.
    Perianth-segments spreading or campanulately-connivent at the base.
    Flowers in racemes, long- or short-stalked, in the latter case filaments
    thread-shaped or broadened at the base only. 17

17. Perianth-segments 1-nerved, blue or red, rarely whitish or greenish.   Sta-
    mens affixed to the perianth ; filaments thread-shaped or broadened at
    the base only. — Species 100.   Some have edible bulbs or are used in

medicine or as ornamental plants. " Squill." (Including *Endymion* Dumort.). . . . . **Scilla** L.

Perianth-segments obscurely many-nerved, white or yellow and usually striped, rarely brownish or greenish. Stamens usually free from the perianth and with flattened filaments. — Species 90. Some have edible bulbs. . . . . **Ornithogalum** L.

18. Perianth-tube cylindrical, linear or oblong in section. 19

Perianth-tube bell-, urn-, funnel-, or saucer-shaped. 23

19. Perianth-segments very short and broad, more or less ovate. . . 20

Perianth-segments narrow and more or less elongated. 21

20. Perianth falling off after flowering. Stamens inserted below the throat ; filaments very short. Ovules numerous. Seeds flattened. Leaves awl-shaped. Flowers solitary or in pairs. — Species 1. South Africa. **Litanthus** Harv.

Perianth withering. Stamens inserted in the middle of the tube ; filaments thread-shaped. Ovules 2 in each cell. Seeds thick. Leaves strap-shaped. Flowers in dense racemes. — Species 3. South Africa. Used as ornamental plants. . . . . **Veltheimia** Gled.

21. Seeds flattened. Anthers linear. Perianth-segments unequal, the outer spreading, the inner erect, as long as or shorter than the outer. Leaves linear, usually more than 2. — Species 60. . . . . **Dipcadi** Medik.

Seeds thick. Anthers oblong. Perianth-segments equal or, if unequal, the inner usually longer than the outer. Leaves oblong or lanceolate, more rarely linear, usually 2. 22

22. Perianth-segments equal, lanceolate, shorter than the tube. Stamens inserted at the throat of the perianth. Leaves 2, oblong. — Species 10. South Africa. . . . . **Polyxena** Kunth

Perianth-segments more or less unequal in length, oblong or spatulate. Stamens inserted in the tube of the perianth. — Species 40. South Africa. Some are used as ornamental plants. . **Lachenalia** Jacq.

23. Perianth-segments very short, usually blue. 24

Perianth-segments half as long as the tube or longer. 25

24. Perianth urn-shaped. Ovules 2 in each cell. — Species 7. North Africa. Several species serve as ornamental plants ; the bulbs are used in medicine and as a substitute for soap. . . . . . **Muscari** Mill.

Perianth bell-shaped. Ovules 5—6 in each cell. — Species 1. Madagascar. **Rhodocodon** Bak.

25. Perianth-segments unequal, the inner longer. Leaves 2, rarely 3—5. (See 22.) . . . . **Lachenalia** Jacq.

Perianth-segments nearly equal. 26

26. Perianth with a very short tube and spreading segments. Filaments united at the base. Leaves 2, broad. Flowers in spikes. — Species 1. South Africa (Cape Colony). . . . . . . **Whiteheadia** Harv.

Perianth with a more or less elongated tube, very rarely with a short tube, but with erect segments. Leaves 2, narrow, or more. . . . 27

27. Seeds globular or obovoid, turgid.   Ovules 2—6 in each cell. — Species
    12. North and South Africa, southern East Africa, and Madagascar.
    Some species are used in medicine, perfumery, or gardening. (Including
    Bellevalia Lapeyr.). . . . .   **Hyacinthus** L.
    Seeds flattened or angular. Ovules 6 or more in each cell. Flowers
    whitish.   28

28. Perianth-segments erect or converging. 29
    Perianth-segments spreading or bent back. 30

29. Perianth funnel-shaped ; segments half as long as the curved tube. Stamens
    inserted at the throat.   Ovary oblong.   Style subulate.   Leaves large,
    lanceolate.   Raceme dense, about 100-flowered. — Species 2.   German
    South-west Africa. . . . . **Pseudogaltonia** Kuntze
    Perianth bell-shaped ; segments as long as the tube or longer.   Stamens
    inserted below the throat.   Ovary ovate.   Style short, columnar.
    Leaves short, linear.   Raceme lax, 6—20-flowered. — Species 2.   South
    Africa (Cape Colony).   . . . .   **Rhadamantus** Salisb.

30. Perianth withering ; segments as long as the tube, the outer oblong, the
    inner obovate.   Stamens inserted below the throat.   Seeds angular. —
    Species 3.   South Africa.   Used as ornamental plants. **Galtonia** Decne.
    Perianth falling off after flowering ; segments somewhat longer than the
    tube, linear or oblong.   Stamens inserted at the throat.   Seeds discoid. —
    Species 30.   Southern and tropical Africa.   Some are used as ornamental
    or medicinal plants. . . . .   **Drimia** Jacq.

31. (2.) Anthers turned outwards, opening outwards or laterally.   Styles 3.
    [Tribe ANGUILLARIEAE.]   32
    Anthers turned inwards, opening inwards or laterally.   Style 1, sometimes
    very short, with 1—3 stigmas.   Flowers solitary or in lax, few-flowered
    racemes or umbels. 37

32. Capsule opening loculicidally.   Flowers long-stalked, solitary or in racemes,
    rarely short-stalked and then solitary and axillary.   Perianth dark
    brown.   33
    Capsule opening septicidally.   Flowers sessile or short-stalked, in spikes,
    spike-like racemes, or heads, rarely solitary and terminal.   . . 34

33. Perianth deciduous ; segments without a gland at the base.   Stamens
    with thickened filaments.   Flowers solitary, axillary. — Species 10.
    Tropics and northern South Africa.   . . . . . **Iphigenia** Kunth
    Perianth persistent ; segments with a gland at the base.   Stamens with
    thread-shaped filaments.   Flowers in racemes. — Species 3.   South
    Africa, southern Central Africa, and Madagascar.   Used as ornamental
    plants.   . . . .   **Ornithoglossum** Salisb.

34. Perianth-segments united below, persistent. Stigmas capitate. Flowers
    in spikes, without bracts. — Species 4.   South Africa and mountains
    of Central Africa.   Used as ornamental plants.   . . **Wurmbea** Thunb.

Perianth-segments free, clawed. Flowers in heads or racemes, rarely solitary or in spikes ; in the latter case perianth deciduous and stigmas on the inside of the styles. 35

35. Flowers in spikes, without bracts. Perianth deciduous, whitish. Ovary 3-lobed, obovate. — Species 3. South Africa (Cape Colony). (Including *Neodregea* Wright). . . . . **Dipidax** Salisb.
Flowers in heads or racemes, rarely solitary, provided with bracts. Perianth persistent. 36

36. Flowers in racemes or solitary. Stigmas lateral. Ovary triangular-cylindrical. Perianth yellow or red. Stem distinctly developed. — Species 1. South Africa (Cape Colony). . . . **Baeometra** Salisb.
Flowers in heads. Stigmas minute. Ovary usually ovoid. — Species 20. South, East, and North Africa. (*Erythrostictus* Schlecht.)
Androcymbium Willd.

37. Flowers large, usually solitary. Perianth deciduous, bell- or funnel-shaped, usually white or reddish. Anthers linear or oblong. Stigma usually 3-lobed. [Tribe TULIPEAE.] 38
Flowers rather small, usually umbellate. Perianth persistent, finally more or less wheel-shaped with spreading segments, usually yellow. Anthers ovate or oblong. Stigma usually simple. 40

38 Perianth funnel-shaped, white ; segments recurved at the apex. Anthers attached by the back. Flowers in racemes. — Species 1. North Africa. Used as an ornamental plant. " Lily." . . . . . . **Lilium** L.
Perianth bell-shaped, usually reddish ; segments more or less erect, not recurved. Anthers attached by the base. Flowers usually solitary. 39

39. Flowers drooping. Perianth-segments with a nectar-bearing pit or spot at the base. Style long. — Species 2. North-west Africa (Algeria). Used as ornamental plants. . . . . **Fritillaria** L.
Flowers erect, sometimes slightly drooping before flowering. Perianth-segments without a pit, but often with a nectar-bearing spot at the base. Style very short. — Species 2. North-west Africa (Algeria). Used as ornamental plants. " Tulip." . . . . **Tulipa** L.

40. Perianth funnel-shaped, whitish, with oblong-ovate segments. Style short ; stigma 3-lobed. — Species 1. North Africa (Cyrenaica). **Lloydia** Salisb.
Perianth wheel-shaped, usually yellow and with lanceolate segments. (See 6.)
Gagea Salisb.

41. (1.) Branches leaf-like, but often awl-shaped. Leaves scale-like. Flowers axillary, solitary or in pairs, more rarely in fascicles, umbels, or racemes. Fruit a berry. [Tribe ASPARAGEAE.] 42
Branches not leaf-like ; stem usually simple. Leaves well developed . 44

42. Flowers inserted at the base of the usually linear leaf-like branches. Perianth-segments free or slightly united at the base. Stamens 6, with free filaments. — Species 80 Some of them are used as vegetables, medicinal-, ornamental-, or hedge-plants. (Including *Myrsiphyllum* Willd.)
Asparagus I.

Flowers inserted on the surface or margin of the lanceolate or broader
    leaf-like branches. Stamens with united filaments. 43

43. Flowers hermaphrodite. Perianth-segments united high up. Anthers 6.
    Ovary 3-celled. Style distinctly developed; stigmas 3. — Species 1.
    Canary Islands, Madeira, and Azores. . . . . . .   **Semele** Kunth

Flowers dioecious. Perianth-segments free. Anthers 3. Ovary 1-celled.
    Style very short; stigma lobed. — Species 2. North Africa. Used as
    ornamental and medicinal plants. . . . . **Ruscus** L.

44. Flowers solitary, axillary. Anthers turned outwards. Fruit capsular.
    [Tribe UVULARIEAE.] . . . . 45.

Flowers solitary but terminal or collected into various inflorescences.
    Anthers turned inwards. 47

45. Perianth-segments free, spreading or reflexed. Style bent downwards at
    the base. — Species 5. Tropical and South Africa. Poisonous and used
    as medicinal and ornamental plants; some of them yield starch.

                                   Gloriosa L.

Perianth-segments united below or connivent. Style not bent downwards. 46

46. Perianth-segments free or almost so, with a nectar-bearing cavity at their
    base. — Species 6. Tropical and South Africa. Some are used as orna-
    mental plants. . . . .   **Littonia** Hook. fil.

Perianth-segments united almost to the top into a pitcher-shaped tube,
    with a short spur at the base. — Species 1. South-East Africa. Used as
    an ornamental plant. . . . . . .   **Sandersonia** Hook. fil.

47. Flowers solitary, in 2—3-flowered heads, in axillary cymes, or in umbels,
    the latter sometimes arranged in racemes. 48

Flowers in spikes, racemes, or panicles, which are sometimes contracted
    into many-flowered heads or consist of fascicles or cymes. . . 52

48. Stem herbaceous. Leaves radical, linear, parallel-veined. Inflorescence
    terminal. Fruit a capsule. 49

Stem woody at least at the base, usually climbing. Leaves cauline, oblong
    or broader, net-veined. Inflorescence axillary. Fruit a berry. . 51

49. Flowers solitary or in groups of 2—3, surrounded by an involucre of 5—7
    bracts, sessile. Perianth-segments free. Ovary-cells with a single
    ovule. — Species 1. North Africa. [Tribe APHYLLANTHEAE.]

                               Aphyllanthes L.

Flowers in umbels enclosed by 2 bracts. Perianth-segments united below
    Ovary-cells with many ovules. [Tribe AGAPANTHEAE.] . . 50

50. Perianth with a long tube and a corona at the throat. Style short, colum-
    nar. — Species 20. South Africa and southern Central Africa. Some
    are used as ornamental plants. . . . . **Tulbaghia** L.

Perianth with a short tube, without a corona. Style filiform. Seeds
    winged. — Species 3. South Africa. Used as ornamental plants.

                             Agapanthus L' Hér.

51. Flowers in cymes, hermaphrodite. Perianth-segments united below into
    a long tube. — Species 1. South Africa. [Tribe LUZURIAGEAE.]

                               Behnia Didrichs.

Flowers in umbels, dioecious. Perianth-segments free. — Species 9. Some
of them are used medicinally. [Tribe SMILACEAE.] **Smilax** Tourn.

52. Perianth-segments free or almost so, more or less spreading. Stem herbaceous. Ovary 3-celled. [Tribe ASPHODELEAE.] 53
Perianth-segments evidently united at their base or connivent into a long
tube, rarely almost free and not connivent into a tube, but then stem
woody, very seldom herbaceous plants growing upon trees and having
a 1-celled ovary. 66

53. Anthers attached by the base or between the lobes of the base. . 54
Anthers attached by the back 62

54. Anthers opening by terminal pores, sometimes prolonged into slits. Filaments thickened. Perianth blue, rarely white. Fruit a berry. Leaves
2-ranked, linear. Flowers in lax panicles. — Species 2, one native in
Madagascar and the neighbouring islands, the other one naturalized
in the Island of St. Helena. They are used as ornamental and medicinal plants ; the berries are poisonous. [Subtribe DIANELLINAE.]
Dianella Lam.
Anthers opening by longitudinal slits. Fruit a capsule. Leaves in several
ranks or 1—2 only present. Flowers usually in racemes. . . . 55

55. Anthers without a pit at the base. Perianth more or less campanulate.
Seeds woolly. Root-stock tuberous. Leaves 1—3, usually a single
leaf. — Species 50. South and Central Africa. Some are used as
ornamental or medicinal plants. [Subtribe ERIOSPERMINAE.]
Eriospermum Jacq.
Anthers attached to the filament in a small pit at the base. Perianth more
or less rotate. [Subtribes ANTHERICINAE and ASPHODELINAE.] . 56

56 Perianth spirally twisted after flowering, blue violet or red. Ovules 2
in each ovary-cell. 57
Perianth not twisted, usually white. Ovules 4 or more in each ovary-cell. 58

57. Stamens free or the inner attached to the perianth ; filaments flattened.
Perianth blue. Stem very short, 2—3-flowered. — Species 1. South
Africa (Cape Colony). . . . . **Nanolirion** Benth.
Stamens attached to the perianth ; filaments thread-shaped. Stem long,
many-flowered. — Species 4. South Africa and Madagascar. **Caesia** R. Br.

58. Ovules many in each cell. Filaments short and broad. Perianth funnel-
shaped, with erect segments. — Species 3. West Africa. (*Debesia*
Kuntze). . . . . **Acrospira** Welw.
Ovules 4—8 in each cell. Filaments thread-shaped or slightly broadened
in the middle. 59

59. Stamens as long as or longer than the perianth. Flowers almost sessile. 60
Stamens shorter than the perianth. Flowers distinctly stalked. . . 61

60. Perianth-segments erect. Leaves broadly elliptical. — Species 1. Southern
West Africa. . . . . **Verdickia** De Wild.
Perianth-segments spreading. Leaves linear or lanceolate. — Species 15.
Central Africa. (Under *Chlorophytum* Ker). . . . **Dasystachys** Bak.

76. Leaves herbaceous. Inflorescence few-flowered. Seeds ovate, angled. —
    Species 1. Naturalised in the Mascarene Islands. A garden-plant.
    "Day-lily." . . . . **Hemerocallis** L.
    Leaves leathery. Inflorescence many-flowered. Seeds oblong, winged. —
    Species 1 (*Ph. tenax* Forst., New-Zealand-flax). Cultivated in South
    Africa and the Mascarene Islands. Yields fibre and is used as an
    ornamental and medicinal plant. . . . . . . **Phormium** Forst.
77. Perianth-segments globosely-campanulately converging, slightly cohering
    at the base. Stamens with the filaments thickened at the apex and with
    sagittate basifixed anthers. Ovary 3-celled, each cell with an incomplete
    partition and numerous ovules. Leaves serrate, crowded at the top
    of the woody stem. — Species 2. Cultivated and naturalised in the
    Mascarene Islands and the island of Zanzibar. They yield fibre and
    starch and are used as ornamental plants. [Tribe YUCCEAE.] **Yucca** L.
    Perianth-segments spreading towards the tip. Stamens with thread-
    like filaments or with dorsifixed anthers. Ovary 3-celled with 1—8
    ovules in each cell, or 1-celled. [Tribe DRACAENEAE.] . . 78
78. Ovary 1-celled with numerous ovules. Style short or wanting. Anthers
    attached at or near the base, opening laterally. Flowers polygamous,
    in panicles formed of spikes. Leaves all radical. — Species 1. Mascarene
    Islands. It yields fibre and is used as an ornamental plant.
    Astelia Banks & Soland.
    Ovary 3-celled with 1—8 ovules in each cell. Anthers attached by the
    back. 79
79. Ovules 4—8 in each ovary-cell. Style short and thick. Perianth-segments
    almost free. Flowers in repeatedly branched panicles. Stem woody. —
    Species 2. Mascarene Islands. Used as ornamental plants. (Under
    Cordyline Commers.) . . . . **Cohnia** Kunth
    Ovules solitary in each ovary-cell. Style long and slender. Perianth-
    segments evidently united. 80
80. Leaves all radical, springing from a short root-stock, cartilaginous. Flowers
    in racemes composed of fascicles. Ovary sessile with a large base.
    Fruit an achene with a membranous pericarp. Seed-coat fleshy. —
    Species 25. Tropical and South Africa. Many of them yield fibre and
    are used as ornamental plants. "Bowstring-hemp." (*Sanseverinia*
    Petagna). . . . . **Sansevieria** Thunb.
    Leaves springing from a sometimes very short woody stem, herbaceous
    or leathery. Fruit a berry. — Species 65. Tropical and South Africa
    and Canary Islands. Several species yield a resin (dragon's blood)
    employed medicinally and industrially; some are used for plaiting-work
    or as ornamental plants. . . . . **Dracaena** Vand

FAMILY 33. HAEMODORACEAE

Herbs. Leaves narrow, 2-ranked. Flowers in racemes or panicles, rarely
solitary, hermaphrodite. Perianth yellow; segments 6, petal-like, free or

shortly united at the base. Stamens 3, opposite the inner perianth-segments and attached at their base. Anthers turned inwards. Ovary 3-celled ; two cells sometimes sterile. Style simple, with a simple stigma, rarely 3-parted. Fruit a loculicidal capsule. Seeds flat. Embryo small, enclosed by the base of the albumen. — Genera 4, species 6. South Africa.

1. Ovary superior, 1—3-celled, with 1 ovule in each cell. 2
   Ovary inferior, 3-celled. Flowers regular. 3
2. Ovary with 1 fertile cell. Flowers regular, glabrous, in racemes. — Species
   1. Natal and Kaffraria. . . . . **Barberetta** Harv.
   Ovary with 3 fertile cells. Flowers irregular, hairy, in panicles. — Species 2.
   Cape Colony. Used as ornamental plants. The roots contain a red
   dye-stuff. . . . . **Wachendorfia** L.
3. Ovary with 1 ovule in each cell. Flowers hairy, in panicles. — Species 2.
   Cape Colony. . . . . **Dilatris** Berg
   Ovary with numerous ovules in each cell. Flowers glabrous, solitary. —
   Species 1. Cape Colony. . . . . **Pauridia** Harv.

FAMILY 34. AMARYLLIDACEAE

Flowers hermaphrodite. Perianth corolla-like. Stamens 6, rarely (*Gethyllis*) more. Anthers introrse. Ovary inferior, rarely half-inferior or (*Walleria*) almost superior, 3-celled, with slightly projecting axillary placentas. Ovules inverted. Embryo small, straight, lateral, enclosed by the fleshy albumen. — Genera 33, species 310. (Including *HYPOXIDACEAE*.) (Plate 19.)

1. Underground part of the stem a bulb or a corm, rarely a short root-stock.
   Leaves all radical. Flowers solitary or in umbels ; inflorescence surrounded by a spathe. [Subfamily **AMARYLLIDÓIDEAE.**] . . 2
   Underground part of the stem a root-stock. Flowers in spikes racemes or
   panicles, rarely solitary or in umbels, but without a spathe. . . 27
2. Perianth furnished with a corona, which sometimes is reduced to a narrow
   ring or a crown of hairs. [Tribe NARCISSEAE.] 3
   Perianth without a corona. [Tribe AMARYLLIDEAE.] . . . 8
3. Stamens inserted within the corona. Corona cup- or ring-shaped or consisting of 12 scales. [Subtribe NARCISSINAE.] 4
   Stamens inserted on the edge of the cup- or funnel-shaped corona ; corona
   rarely reduced to a crown of hairs. 6
4. Corona of 12 free scales. Perianth tubular, red. Fruit a berry. — Species
   2. Central Africa (British East Africa and Angola).
                                           Cryptostephanus Welw.
   Corona cup- or ring-shaped, undivided or lobed. Perianth bell-, funnel-,
   or salver-shaped, usually white or yellow. Fruit a capsule. . . 5
5. Perianth funnel-shaped, with a very short tube, yellow. Corona little
   developed, 6- or 12-lobed. — Species 1. North-West Africa. (*Carregnoa*
   Boiss.) . . . . **Tapeinanthus** Herb.

Flowers large, red reddish-yellow or reddish-white.   Stigma 1, simple
    or 3-lobed. 24

24. Flowers almost regular.   Perianth-segments elliptical, about twice as long
    as the tube.   Umbels 6—9-flowered.   Fruit oblong. — Species 1.   South
    Africa (Cape Colony).   Used as an ornamental plant.   **Vallota** Herb.
    Flowers distinctly irregular.   Perianth-segments 3—4 times as long as
    the tube. 25

25. Umbels 2—4-flowered.   Scape hollow.   Perianth hairy within.   Fruit
    globose.   (See 7.) . . . . **Hippeastrum** Herb.
    Umbels many-flowered ; spathe of 2 bracts.   Scape solid. — Species 2.
    South Africa to Damaraland. . . . . . **Ammocharis** Herb.

26. Ovules sunk in the placentas, usually few in each ovary-cell.   Stigma very
    small, capitate.   Anthers linear.   Scape solid. — Species 60.   Tropical
    and South Africa.   Some are used as ornamental or medicinal plants.
    (Including *Stenolirion* Bak.)   (Plate 19.) . . . . . . **Crinum** L.
    Ovules not sunk in the placentas, many in each ovary-cell.   Stigma more
    or less distinctly 3-lobed or 3-parted.   Anthers oblong.   Scape hollow. —
    Species 25. South and East Africa and Angola.   Some are used as
    ornamental plants. . . . . **Cyrtanthus** Ait.

27. (1.) Leaves fleshy, very long (1—2 m.), in a rosette at the base or the
    top of the stem.   Very tall plants.   [Subfamily **AGAVOIDEAE**.] 28
    Leaves not fleshy and not very long.   Smaller plants.   [Subfamily **HY-
    POXIDOIDEAE**.] 30

28. Filaments longer than the perianth.   Flowers in spikes or panicles, usually
    greenish or yellow.   Leaves at the top of a very short stem. — Species
    2.   Cultivated and sometimes naturalised in North and South Africa
    and some tropical islands.   They yield fibre, fodder, drinks, medicaments.
    and a substitute for soap, and are also used as hedge- or garden-plants.
                                       Agave L.
    Filaments shorter than the perianth. 29

29. Filaments strongly thickened at the base.   Flowers in panicles, white.
    Fruit ovoid.   Leaves at the top of a short stem. — Species 1.   Cultivated
    and sometimes naturalised in North and South Africa and some tropical
    islands.   It yields fibre, and is used as a hedge- or garden-plant, also in
    medicine.   (*Furcraea* Vent.) . . . . **Fourcroya** Schult.
    Filaments slightly thickened at the base.   Flowers in capitate spikes,
    red.   Fruit oblong or club-shaped.   Leaves at the base of a long stem. —
    Species 1.   Naturalised in the island of St. Helena.   An ornamental plant.
                                   Doryanthes Correa

30. Ovary inferior with many ovules in each cell.   Perianth yellow, rarely
    white or red.   Leaves all radical, usually hairy like the peduncle.   [Tribe
    HYPOXIDEAE.] 31
    Ovary inferior with 2 ovules in each cell or half-inferior or almost superior.
    Perianth blue, red, or whitish.   Leaves usually radical and cauline.   32

AMARYLLIDACEAE.

Pl. 19.

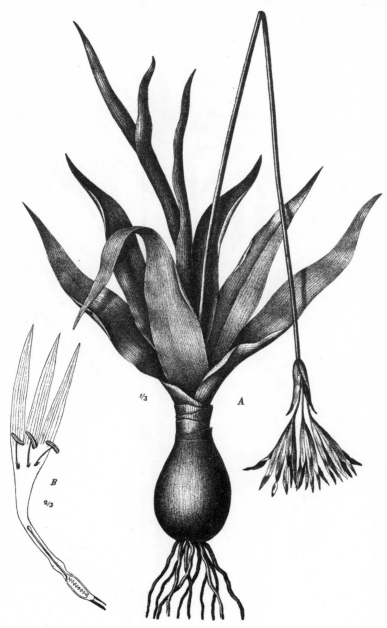

J. Fleischmann del.

Crinum abyssinicum Hochst.

A Plant in flower. *B* Flower cut lengthwise.

J. Fleischmann del.

Barbacenia aequatorialis Rendle

A Inflorescence.   *B* Flower cut lengthwise.

31. Ovary beaked. Fruit a berry. Flowers solitary or in dense spikes or heads. — Species 6. Tropical and South Africa. They yield fibre and are used medicinally and as ornamental plants ; some have an edible root-stock. . . . . **Curculigo** Gaertn.

Ovary not beaked. Fruit a capsule. Flowers solitary or in lax racemes or umbels. — Species 60. Southern and tropical Africa. Some are used as ornamental plants. (Including *Ianthe* Salisb.) . . . **Hypoxis** L.

32. Ovary almost inferior with 2 ovules in each cell. Anthers attached by the back, bursting lengthwise. Perianth with a distinct tube. Fruit 1-seeded. Flowers in panicles. Stem, leaves, and inflorescence woolly. — Species 1. South Africa (Cape Colony). [Tribe CONOSTYLIDEAE.] **Lanaria** Ait.

Ovary half-inferior or almost superior, with several or many ovules in each cell. Anthers attached at the base or near it, bursting at or towards the apex. Perianth divided nearly or quite to the ovary. Stem, leaves, and inflorescence glabrous. [Tribe CONANTHEREAE.] . . . 33

33. Ovary half-inferior. Stamens more or less unequal. Flowers usually without bracteoles, solitary and terminal or arranged in racemes. or panicles. Leaves, all or most of them, crowded at the base of the stem. — Species 7. South Africa to Damaraland. Some have edible root-stocks or are used as ornamental plants. . . . . . . **Cyanella** L.

Ovary almost superior. Stamens equal. Flowers blue, with bracteoles, solitary or in pairs and axillary, or arranged in panicles. Leaves scattered along the stem. — Species 5. Southern tropical Africa. Some have edible root-stocks. . . . . **Walleria** Kirk

FAMILY 35. VELLOZIACEAE

Leaves linear. Flowers solitary, terminal, without bracteoles, regular, hermaphrodite. Perianth-segments free or nearly so, petaloid, usually white. Stamens 6. Anthers attached by the base. Ovary inferior, 3-celled. Placentas projecting and peltately dilated. Ovules numerous. Style simple ; stigma 3-lobed. Fruit a capsule. Seeds black, compressed. Embryo very small, enclosed by the albumen. (Under *AMARYLLIDEAE*.) (Plate 20.)

Genus 1. Species 25. Tropical and South Africa. (*Xerophyta* Juss., under *Vellozia* Vand.) . . . . **Barbacenia** Vand.

FAMILY 36. TACCACEAE

Herbs with a tuberous root-stock. Leaves all radical, large, stalked, twice pinnately divided. Flowers in an umbel-like inflorescence on a leafless scape, regular, hermaphrodite. Perianth greenish-brown, bell- or urn-shaped, with a short tube. Stamens 6. Filaments hooded. Anthers turned inwards. Ovary inferior, 1-celled, with parietal placentas. Ovules numerous, inverted. Style short, umbrella-shaped, 6-lobed. Fruit a berry. Seeds compressed. Embryo small, enclosed by the albumen.

Genus 1, species 2. Tropics. Used as ornamental plants and for plaiting-work ; the tubers yield starch (arrowroot) and are edible when cooked.

Tacca Forst.

FAMILY 37. DIOSCOREACEAE

Root-stock tuberous. Stem twining. Leaves alternate, net-veined, usually cordate. Flowers in racemes, inconspicuous, regular, unisexual. Stamens 6. Ovary inferior, 3-celled. Ovules 2 in each cell, superposed, inverted. Styles or style-branches 3. Embryo enclosed in a horny or cartilaginous albumen.— Genera 2, species 45. (Plate 21.)

> Fruit a berry. Seeds not winged. — Species 3. North Africa. The tubers are eaten and used in medicine ; the berries are poisonous. (*Tamnus* Juss.) . . . . **Tamus** L.
> Fruit a capsule. Seeds winged. — Species 40. Tropical and South Africa. Some are cultivated for their edible tubers (yams) or used in medicine ; others are poisonous. (Including *Testudinaria* Salisb.) (Plate 21.)
> **Dioscorea** L.

SUBORDER IRIDINEAE

FAMILY 38.   IRIDACEAE

Herbs or undershrubs. Inflorescence terminal. Flowers hermaphrodite. Perianth with 6 petaloid segments. Stamens 3, inserted opposite the outer perianth-segments. Anthers turned outwards. Ovary inferior, 3-celled, rarely (*Hermodactylus*) 1-celled. Style-branches usually divided or dilated. Ovules numerous, inverted. Fruit a loculicidal capsule. Embryo enclosed by the horny albumen. — Genera 39, species 600. (Plate 22.)

> 1. Flowers solitary, terminal, sometimes surrounded by several axillary flowers, each flower with a spathe. Perianth regular ; inner and outer segments nearly equal. Leaves not exactly 2-ranked. Stem short or almost wanting. [Subfamily **CROCOIDEAE.**] 2
> Flowers in various inflorescences, rarely spathes solitary, but 2- or more-flowered or (if 1-flowered) the outer perianth-segments very different from the inner ones. Leaves 2-ranked, folded one above the other, rarely (*Geosiris*) reduced to scales. Stem distinctly developed. . . . 5
> 2. Stem underground, very short. Perianth-tube very long. . . . 3
> Stem partly above ground. Perianth-tube short or moderately long.   4
> 3. Style-branches undivided, stigmatose inside. Perianth red or violet, rarely white with red streaks. — Species 6. South Africa (Cape Colony).
> **Syringodea** Hook. fil.
> Style-branches many-lobed or many-parted, stigmatose at the top. — Species 3 ; one of them only cultivated. North-West Africa. Used as ornamental plants ; the tubers are edible. The cultivated species (*C. sativus* L.) yields the saffron, which is used as a condiment and for dyeing. . . . . **Crocus** L.
> 4. Leaves crowded at the top of the very short stem. Perianth with a rather long tube, yellow or violet. Filaments united into a tube. Style-branches dilated above, petal-like. — Species 3. South Africa (Cape Colony). Used as ornamental plants. . . . . **Galaxia** Thunb.

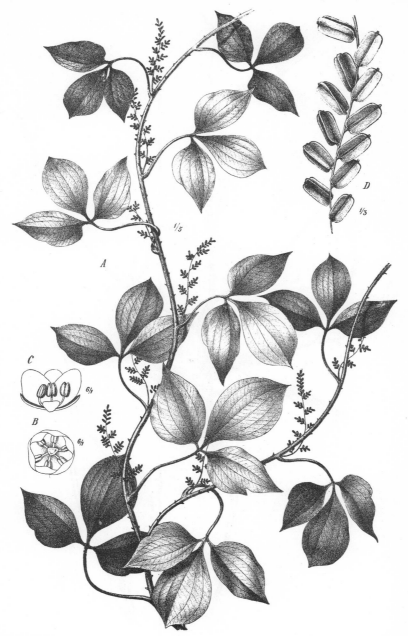

J. Fleischmann del.

Dioscorea dumetorum (Kunth) Pax

A Flowering branch.　*B* Male flower from above.　*C* Male flower cut lengthwise　*D* Group of fruits.

IRIDACEAE.

Pl. 22.

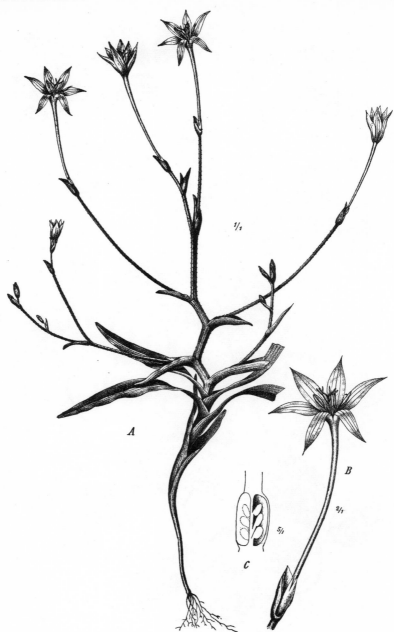

J. Fleischmann del.

Lapeyrousia Fabricii Ker

A Plant in flower. *B* Flower. *C* Ovary cut lengthwise.

Leaves scattered along the stem or crowded at its base. Filaments free, rarely united, but then perianth with a very short tube. Style-branches not petal-like. — Species 50. South and North Africa and mountains of Central Africa. Some are used as ornamental plants. (*Trichonema* Ker). . . . . **Romulea** Maratti

5. (1.) Spathes 1-flowered, in spikes. Style-branches well developed, generally alternate with the anthers, thread-shaped or thickened at the top, more rarely dilated and almost petal-like, but undivided. Flowers usually more or less irregular. Stem leafy. [Subfamily **IXIOIDEAE.**] 6

Spathes 2- or more-flowered, rarely 1-flowered, but then style-branches either reduced to short teeth, or opposite the anthers, petal-like, and 2-lobed. Flowers regular, but the inner perianth-segments often very different from the outer ones. [Subfamily **IRIDOIDEAE.**] . . 23

6. Style-branches 2-parted. [Tribe WATSONIEAE.] 7
Style-branches undivided. 10

7. Flowers small. Perianth with a short tube, red or blue. Ovules 2 in each ovary-cell. — Species 2. South Africa (Cape Colony).
                                                Micranthus Pers.
Flowers large or rather large. Perianth with a long or rather long tube. Ovules many in each ovary-cell. 8

8. Perianth-tube straight or nearly so. Filaments short, inserted at the throat of the perianth. — Species 40. South and Central Africa. Some have edible tubers or serve as ornamental plants. (Plate 22.)
                                                Lapeyrousia Pourr.
Perianth-tube curved. Filaments long, inserted below the throat of the perianth. 9

9. Spathes short, scarious. Perianth yellowish, with unequal segments. — Species 2. South Africa. Used as ornamental plants. **Freesia** Klatt
Spathes rather long, rigid. Perianth red or white, with almost equal segments. — Species 15. South Africa, Madagascar, and Mascarenes. Some are used as ornamental plants. . . . . **Watsonia** Mill.

10. (6.) Flowers distinctly irregular. [Tribe GLADIOLEAE.] . . . 11
Flowers regular or almost so. Filaments and style straight. [Tribe IXIEAE.] 18

11. Perianth curved. 12
Perianth straight. 13

12. Perianth-tube longer than the limb, filiform below, cylindrical above. Stamens inserted in the basal part of the tube. Spathes small. — Species 20. South and Central Africa. Some are used as ornamental plants. (Including *Anisanthus* Sweet). . . . . **Antholyza** L.
Perianth-tube as long as or shorter than the limb, funnel-shaped. — Species 120. Some of them have edible bulbs, others are used in medicine or as ornamental plants. . . . . **Gladiolus** L.

13. Leaves folded, usually hairy. Perianth with a long tube. — Species 30. South Africa and Island of Socotra. Several species have edible bulbs or are used as ornamental plants. . . . . **Babiana** Ker
Leaves flat, glabrous. 14

14. Perianth-segments almost free, thinly acuminate, yellowish-green. Ovules 2—3 in each ovary-cell. Inflorescence paniculate. — Species 1. South Africa (Cape Colony). . . . . **Melasphaerula** Ker
Perianth-segments evidently united below, obtuse or shortly mucronate. Ovules usually numerous. 15

15. Perianth-tube funnel-shaped (distinctly widened above). Style-branches filiform. Spathe-bracts lacerated. 16
Perianth-tube more or less cylindrical (slightly or not widened above). Style-branches usually dilated. Spathe-bracts entire or toothed. 17

16. Perianth 2-lipped, with a long or rather long tube, yellow or violet. Style-branches short. — Species 3. South Africa (Cape Colony). Used as ornamental plants. . . . . **Synnotia** Sweet
Perianth regular, with a short or rather short tube, yellow red or variegated. Style-branches long. — Species 3. South Africa (Cape Colony). Used as ornamental plants. The bulbs are edible. . . . . **Sparaxis** Ker

17. Spathe-bracts long, green, entire. Inflorescence spicate. Perianth nearly always with a long tube. — Species 20. South and Central Africa. Used as ornamental plants. . . . . . . **Acidanthera** Hochst.
Spathe-bracts short, brown, toothed at the top. Inflorescence spicate or paniculate. Perianth with a short or rather short tube. — Species 35. South and Central Africa. Many of them are used as ornamental plants ; some yield edible bulbs or a substitute for saffron. (Including *Crocosmia* Planch., *Montbretia* DC., and *Tritonixia* Klatt).
                                                    Tritonia Ker

18. (10.) Style-branches club-shaped. 19
Style-branches linear or subulate. 20

19. Stigmas notched. Flowers white or yellow. Spathe-bracts lacerated. Leaves short. — Species 2. South Africa (Cape Colony).
                                                Streptanthera Sweet
Stigmas entire. Flowers white or red. Spathe-bracts entire. Leaves long. — Species 2. South and East Africa. Used as ornamental plants.
                                                Dierama C. Koch

20. Style-branches linear, slightly dilated, short. Outer spathe-bract brown. — Species 20. South Africa. Some are used as ornamental plants. (Including *Morphixia* Ker). . . . . **Ixia** L.
Style-branches subulate. Spathe-bracts green or brown at the tip. 21

21. Style long, with short branches. — Species 35. South Africa, southern Central Africa, and Madagascar. Some are used as ornamental or medicinal plants. . . . . **Geissorrhiza** Ker
Style short, with long branches. 22

22. Underground part of the stem a root-stock. Perianth red. Filaments as long as or longer than the anthers. — Species 2. South Africa. Used as ornamental plants. . . . . **Schizostylis** Backh. & Harv.

Underground part of the stem a corm. Filaments short. — Species 35. South Africa and mountains of Central Africa. Some are used as ornamental plants. . . . . **Hesperantha** Ker

23. (5.) Style-branches undivided, very short or thread-shaped or somewhat broadened at the top, but not petal-like, nearly always alternate with the stamens. 24

Style-branches more or less divided or petal-like, opposite the stamens. Perianth with a short tube or without a tube. Fruit not enclosed by the spathe. 32

24. Perianth with a distinct tube. Filaments free. Style-branches very short. Fruit, wholly or for the greater part, enclosed by the spathe. [Tribe ARISTEAE, Subtribe ARISTINAE.] 25

Perianth divided nearly or quite to the ovary. Style-branches usually long. Fruit not enclosed by the spathe. [Tribe SISYRINCHIEAE.] 30

25. Perianth-segments very unequal, the inner much larger than the outer, blueish, the outer black; tube short. Spathes 2—3-flowered, solitary or in corymbs.—Species 1. South Africa (Cape Colony).
Cleanthe Salisb.

Perianth-segments almost equal. 26

26. Stem and leaves without green colour. Leaves short, scale-like. Flowers in umbel-like cymes. Perianth white, with a short tube. — Species 1. Madagascar. . . . . **Geosiris** Baill.

Stem and leaves green. Leaves long, linear or sword-shaped. Perianth blue, rarely yellowish or whitish. 27

27. Spathes 3- or more-flowered, solitary or in spikes racemes or corymbs. Herbs. Perianth with a short tube. — Species 30. Southern and tropical Africa. Some are used as ornamental or medicinal plants. **Aristea** Ait.

Spathes 1—2-flowered. Undershrubs. 28

28. Perianth with a short tube and clawed segments, blue. Filaments long. Spathes in heads. — Species 1. South Africa (Cape Colony).
Klattia Bak.

Perianth with a long tube. Filaments short. 29

29. Perianth blue, glabrous, with a cylindrical tube. Filaments awl-shaped. Anthers small. Spathes solitary or in corymbs. — Species 2. South Africa (Cape Colony). Used as ornamental plants. (Under *Aristea* Ait.)
Nivenia Vent.

Perianth greenish-yellow, hairy outside, with a funnel-shaped tube. Filaments flat. Anthers large. Spathes surrounded by empty bracts and arranged in heads. —Species 1. South Africa (Cape Colony). Used as an ornamental plant; the stem contains sugar. . . **Witsenia** Thunb.

30. Filaments united into a tube. Perianth blue. — Species 1. Naturalised in
    the Mascarene Islands. An ornamental plant. [Subtribe SISYRICHINAE.]
    Sisyrinchium L.
    Filaments free or nearly so. Perianth yellow or red. [Subtribe LIBER-
    TINAE.] 31
31. Stem leafy. Spathes in lax corymbs. Perianth orange-coloured. Style
    filiform, with club-shaped, erect or spreading stigmas. — Species 1.
    Naturalised in the Mascarene Islands. An ornamental and medicinal
    plant. . . . . **Belamcanda** Adans.
    Stem leafless. Spathes solitary or in heads. Perianth pale yellow. Style
    very short, with thread-shaped, recurved stigmas. — Species 6. South
    Africa. . . . . **Bobartia** Ker
32. (23.) Stigmas at the tip of the style-branches. Inner and outer perianth-
    segments almost equal. Filaments united. Underground part of the
    stem a bulb. [Tribe TIGRIDIEAE, subtribe CIPURINAE.] . . 33
    Stigmas on the underside of the dilated style-branches. Inner and outer
    perianth-segments unequal. [Tribe MORAEEAE.] 36
33. Style-branches simple or one of them forked. 34
    Style-branches divided. Perianth-segments usually crisped. . . . 35
34. Perianth white, divided to the ovary. — Species 1. South-east Africa
    (Natal). . . . . **Keitia** Regel
    Perianth yellow or brownish-red, with a short tube. — Species 12. South
    Africa ; one species also naturalised in St. Helena. Used as ornamental
    plants. . . . . **Homeria** Vent.
35. Perianth yellow, divided to the ovary, twisting up in fading. Style-branches
    cylindrical, glabrous. — Species 2. South Africa (Cape Colony).
    Hexaglottis Vent.
    Perianth greenish brownish or red, with a short tube. Style-branches
    dilated, fringed on the margin. — Species 8. South Africa and southern
    West Africa. Some are used as ornamental plants. . . **Ferraria** L.
36. Style-branches broadened, but not petal-like. Perianth blue ; segments
    free, the inner with the edges rolled inwards and the tip recurved. Fila-
    ments free. Scape flattened. — Species 1. Angola and islands of
    equatorial West Africa. Used as an ornamental plant. [Subtribe
    MARICINAE.] . . . . **Marica** Ker
    Style-branches winged, petal-like. [Subtribe IRIDINAE.] . . . 37
37. Perianth-segments free, not bearded. Filaments usually united. — Species
    60. Southern and tropical Africa. Several species have edible root-
    stocks, others are poisonous, many are used as ornamental plants. (In-
    cluding *Dietes* Salisb. and *Vieusseuxia* Delaroche). . . . **Moraea** L.
    Perianth-segments united at the base. Filaments free. 38
38. Ovary 1-celled with parietal placentas. Inner perianth-segments linear,
    acuminate. — Species 1. North-west Africa (Algeria).
    Hermodactylus Adans.

Ovary 3-celled, with axile placentas. — Species 15. North Africa. Many of them are used as ornamental plants, some are poisonous ; the root-stock of several species (orris-root) is edible and yields tanning materials, perfumes, and medicaments. . . . . **Iris** L.

ORDER SCITAMINEAE

FAMILY 39. MUSACEAE

Tall herbaceous plants. Leaves with a large, oblong or ovate, penni-nerved blade. Flowers subtended by large bracts and arranged in usually spicate rows or cymes, irregular. Perianth corolla-like. Fertile stamens 5, rarely 6. Filaments free. Anthers 2-celled. Ovary inferior, 3-celled. Style free from the stamens, 3—6-lobed. Seeds with a straight embryo and mealy albumen. — Genera 4, species 25. (Under *SCITAMINEAE*.) (Plate 23.)

1. Leaves spirally arranged. Partial inflorescences consisting of 1—2 rows of flowers. Flowers monoecious or polygamous. Sepals and two of the petals united below. Fruit berry-like. Seeds without an aril. — Species 15, growing wild in the tropics, besides 4 (especially *M. paràdisiaca*.L.) which are cultivated in various regions. They yield fibre (Manila hemp), tanning and dyeing materials, vegetables, and edible fruits (bananas and plantains), from which also starch, sugar, vinegar, and alcoholic liquor are made. Some species are used as ornamental plants. [Subfamily **MUSOIDEAE.**] . . . . **Musa** L.

   Leaves 2-ranked. Partial inflorescences cymose. Flowers hermaphrodite. Sepals free or the lateral ones united with the petals. Fruit capsular. [Subfamily **STRELITZIOIDEAE.**] 2

2. Odd sepal posterior. Petals united at the base. Ovules solitary in each ovary-cell. Fruit opening septicidally. Seeds without an aril. — Species 1. Naturalised on the Canary Islands. An ornamental plant ; the root-stock is edible. [Tribe HELICONIEAE.]   **Heliconia** L.

   Odd sepal anterior. Petals free, at least one of them. Ovules many in each ovary-cell. Fruit opening loculicidally. Seeds with an aril. [Tribe STRELITZIEAE.] 3

3. Petals very unequal, the two lateral ones elongated, connate on one side, provided with a wing-like appendage on the other, the third petal very short. Stamens 5. Aril yellow. Inflorescence few-flowered. Stem moderately tall. — Species 4. South Africa. Some are used as orna-mental plants. (Plate 23.) . . . . **Strelitzia** L.

   Petals subequal, free, without an appendage. Stamens 6. Aril blue. Inflorescence many-flowered. Stem very tall. Species 1 (*R. madagas-cariensis* Sonn., traveller's tree). Madagascar and Mascarene Islands. The leaves are used in house-building ; their sheaths retain much water ; the sap also furnishes a drink. The seeds are edible and yield a fat.

Ravenala Adans.

K

FAMILY 40. ZINGIBERACEAE

Herbs. Stem simple, springing from a root-stock. Leaves stalked or provided with a sheath, oblong or lanceolate. Flowers in spikes racemes heads or panicles, more or less irregular, hermaphrodite, very rarely dioecious. Perianth consisting of a calyx and a corolla. Sepals united below. Petals subequal, united below. Fertile stamen 1. Anther 2-celled, opening by longitudinal slits. Staminodes 1—3, petal-like, at least one of them (the lip). Ovary inferior, more or less completely 3-celled. Ovules numerous. Style enclosed in a groove of the filament. Stigma funnel-shaped. Fruit a capsule or a berry. Seed with a straight embryo and mealy albumen. — Genera 11, species 120. Tropical and South-east Africa. (Under *SCITAMINEAE*.) (Plate 24.)

1. Leaves spirally arranged ; sheath at first closed, articulated with the petiole. Filaments petal-like. Lateral staminodes wanting. Epigynous glands none. Stem and leaves not aromatic. — Species 35. Central Africa. Some of them are used as ornamental or medicinal plants and in the preparation of rubber. (Including *Cadalvena* Fenzl). [Subfamily **COSTOIDEAE.**] . . . . **Costus** L.

   Leaves two-ranked ; sheath split open, not articulated with the petiole. Epigynous glands present, often style-like. Stem and leaves aromatic. [Subfamily **ZINGIBEROIDEAE.**] 2

2. Lateral staminodes petal-like, but sometimes adnate to the lip, which then appears 3-lobed. [Tribe HEDYCHIEAE.] 3
   Lateral staminodes linear, tooth-like, or wanting ; in the latter case lip not distinctly 3-lobed. [Tribe ZINGIBEREAE.] 5

3. Connective spurred. Lateral staminodes adnate below to the filament of the fertile stamen. — Species 1 (*C. longa* L.). Cultivated and sometimes naturalised in the tropics. The root-stock yields starch, condiments, medicaments, perfumes, and dyeing-materials (turmeric) ; the leaves are used for plaiting-work. . . . . . . **Curcuma** L.

   Connective not spurred. Lateral staminodes free from the filament of the fertile stamen. 4

4. Connective with a crest-like appendage. Filament short. Lateral staminodes broad. — Species 15. Central and South-east Africa. Some are used as ornamental plants. . . . . **Kaempfera** L.

   Connective without an appendage. Filament long. Lateral staminodes narrow. Inflorescence terminating the leafy stem. — Species 3, two of them natives of Madagascar, the third naturalised in the tropics. Ornamental plants ; the tubers yield condiments, perfumes, and medicaments.
   Hedychium Koen.

5. Connective with a distinct appendage. Flowering stem separated from the leafy stem. 6

   Connective without a distinct appendage. 8

J. Fleischmann del.

Strelitzia Reginae Banks ex Ait.

A Plant in flower.   B Flower cut lengthwise.   C Stamens and inner petals.

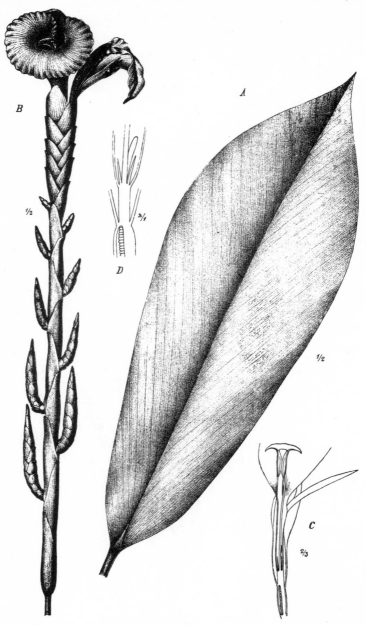

J. Fleischmann del.

Aframomum Laurentii (De Wild. & Dur.) K. Schum.

A Leaf. *B* Inflorescence. *C* Flower cut lengthwise. *D* Lower part of the flower cut lengthwise.

6. Connective with a grooved beak. Lip 3-lobed. — Species 2. Cultivated and sometimes naturalised in the tropics. The root-stock is used as a condiment, especially for the preparation of liquors, and in medicine. "Ginger." . . . . **Zingiber** L.
    Connective with an oblong or 3-lobed, not grooved appendage. Lip not distinctly 3-lobed. 7
7. Connective with an entire, oblong appendage. Filament adnate to the base of the lip. Inflorescence lax. — Species 2. West Africa (Cameroons) and Madagascar. . . . . **Aulotandra** Gagnepain
    Connective with a 3-lobed appendage. Filament free from the lip. Inflorescence dense. — Species 50. Tropics. The fruits (grains of paradise) of several species (especially *A. melegueta* Roscoe) are used as a condiment and for the preparation of perfumes and medicaments ; others serve as ornamental plants. (Under *Amomum* L.) (Plate 24.)
    Aframomum K. Schum.
8. Filament long. Lip not distinctly clawed. Inflorescence terminating the leafy stem. — Species 3. Naturalised in the tropical regions. Ornamental plants. . . . . **Alpinia** L.
    Filament short. Lip clawed. 9
9. Lip entire, rhomboidical, adnate to the filament at the base. Epigynous glands lobed. Flowering stem separated from the leafy stem. Inflorescence very dense, almost head-like, surrounded by a coloured involucre. — Species 1. Madagascar and neighbouring islands. Used as an ornamental plant, the fruit as a condiment. (*Nicolaia* Horan., under *Amomum* L.) . . . . **Phaeomeria** Lindl.
    Lip more or less distinctly 3-lobed, free from the filament. . . . 10
10. Fruit indehiscent. Seeds without an aril. Corolla-tube slightly exceeding the calyx. Stigma small. Inflorescence springing from the base of the leafy stem, lax, paniculate. — Species 1 (*E. Cardamomum* White et Maton). Cultivated in the tropics and naturalised in the Mascarene Islands. The fruits (cardamoms) are used as a condiment and for the preparation of perfumes and medicaments. **Elettaria** Maton
    Fruit dehiscent. Seeds with an aril. Calyx closed in bud. Inflorescence usually terminal. — Species 15. Central Africa. (*Ethanium* Salisb.)
    Renealmia L. f.

FAMILY 41. CANNACEAE

Herbs. Leaves large, penninerved. Inflorescence spicate or formed of cymes. Flowers irregular and asymmetrical, hermaphrodite. Sepals free. Petals united below. Fertile stamen single, 1-celled, the barren half leaf-like. Staminodes leaf-like. Ovary inferior, 3-celled, with numerous inverted ovules. Style and stigma simple. Fruit capsular. Seeds albuminous ; embryo straight. (Under *SCITAMINEAE*.)
    Genus 1, species 5. Cultivated and sometimes naturalised in various regions. They yield starch, vegetables, medicaments, and dyeing materials, and are also used as ornamental plants. "Indian shot." . . **Canna** L.

FAMILY 42. MARANTACEAE

Herbs or undershrubs. Leaves stalked, with a swelling in the upper part of the stalk, penninerved. Inflorescence spicate, capitate, or paniculate. Flowers irregular and asymmetrical, hermaphrodite. Sepals free. Petals united below. Fertile stamen single, 1-celled. Staminodes 2—4, petal-like. Ovary inferior, 1- or 3-celled. Ovules solitary in each cell, inverted. Style simple ; stigma entire or lobed. Seeds with a mealy albumen and a curved embryo. — Genera 12, species 60. Tropics. (Under *SCITAMINEAE*.) (Plate 25.)

1. Ovary 1-celled. [Tribe MARANTEAE.] 2
   Ovary 3-celled, but the ovules of 2 cells sometimes abortive. [Tribe PHRYNIEAE.] 3
2. Corolla-tube very short. Staminodes 3, one of them with two filiform appendages. Fruit indehiscent. Bracts enclosing one pair of flowers each. — Species 7. Central Africa. Used as ornamental plants. **Thalia** L.
   Corolla-tube long. Staminodes 4. Fruit dehiscent. Bracts enclosing 3 pairs of flowers each. — Species 1 (*M. arundinacea* L.) Cultivated and sometimes naturalised in the tropics. The root-stock contains starch (arrow-root). . . . . **Maranta** L.
3. Staminodes 2. Fruit winged. Inflorescence spike-like, springing from the root-stock. Bracts enclosing one pair of flowers each. — Species 1. West Africa. The fruits are edible and contain sugar.
   Thaumatococcus Benth.
   Staminodes 4, rarely 3. 4
4. Bracts approximated in one row, enclosing two pairs of flowers each. Ovary with 1 fertile and 2 sterile cells. — Species 1. Madagascar. (Under *Myrosma* Benth. or *Phrynium* Willd.)   **Ctenophrynium** K. Schum.
   Bracts in two opposite rows. 5
5. Flower-pairs with small, thickened, almost gland-like scales inserted above the bracts and the 2-keeled bracteoles which usually accompany the bracts. 6
   Flower-pairs without gland-like scales above the bracts and bracteoles. 8
6. Ovary and fruit smooth, the latter fleshy. Leaves having the larger half all on the same side. Herbs with a simple stem. Inflorescence panicle-, very rarely spike-like. — Species 13. West Africa. Some have edible fruits. (Under *Phrynium* Willd. or *Phyllodes* Lour.)
   Sarcophrynium K. Schum.
   Ovary and fruit covered with pointed protuberances, the latter dry. Leaves having the larger half some on the right, some on the left side. Under-shrubs or climbing herbs with a branched stem. Inflorescence spike-like. 7
7. Fruit dehiscent, covered with small protuberances. Seeds with an aril. Flower-pairs without a bracteole. — Species 1. West Africa. (Under *Trachyphrynium* Benth.) . . . . . **Hybophrynium** K. Schum.

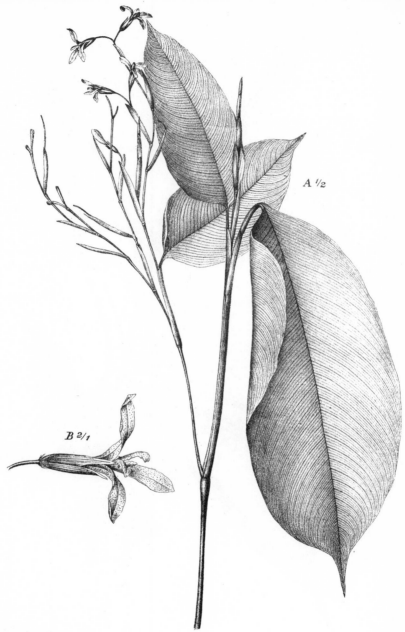

J. Fleischmann del.

Clinogyne arillata K. Schum.

A Flowering branch.   *B* Flower.

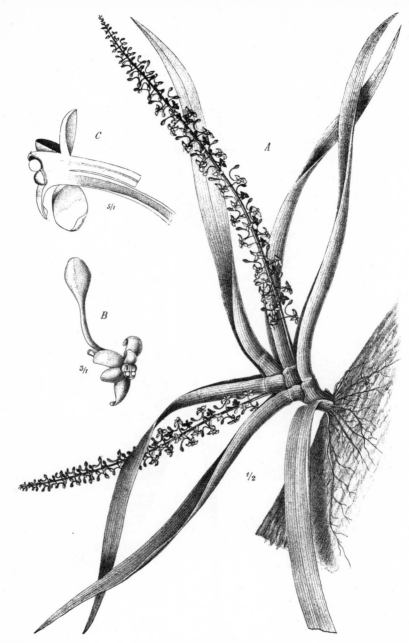

J. Fleischmann del.

Listrostachys vesicata Reichb. fil.

A Plant in flower. *B* Flower. *C* Flower in longitudinal section (the spur cut off near the base).

Fruit indehiscent, covered with large protuberances. Seeds without an aril. Flower-pairs with a bractcole. — Species 6. West Africa.

Trachyphrynium Benth.

8. Inflorescence springing from the root-stock and separated from the 1-leafed stem, spike-like. Inner staminodes, at least one of them, equalling the outer. — Species 1. Equatorial West Africa. (Under *Calathea* Mey.) . . . . **Afrocalathea** K. Schum.
Inflorescence terminating the leafy, sometimes very short stem or its branches. 9

9. Inner staminodes larger than the outer, the hooded one without a strap-shaped appendage. Bracts enclosing 2—4 sessile pairs of flowers each. Inflorescence head-like. Stem branched. — Species 1. Equatorial West Africa (Gaboon). . . . . **Ataenidia** Gagnepain
Inner staminodes smaller than the outer. 10

10. Sepals very unequal. Fruit dry, indehiscent, with adnate seeds. Inflorescence consisting of 2—3 spikes. Bracts enclosing one pair of flowers each, persistent. — Species 1. Equatorial Africa. Used in the preparation of salt. (Under *Clinogyne* Benth. or *Donax* Lour.)

Halopegia K. Schum.

Sepals subequal. Bracts usually enclosing 2—4 pairs of flowers each. 11

11. Inflorescence head-like. Bracts persistent. — Species 2. West Africa. (Under *Calathea* Mey.) . . . . **Phrynium** Willd.
Inflorescence raceme- or panicle-like. Bracts deciduous. — Species 25. West Africa, Upper Nile, and Island of Réunion. Some species yield starch or fibre. (*Donax* Lour., including *Marantochloa* Griseb.) (Plate 25.) . . . . **Clinogyne** Salisb.

ORDER MICROSPERMAE

SUBORDER BURMANNIINEAE

FAMILY 43. BURMANNIACEAE

Herbs. Leaves narrow or scale-like. Flowers solitary or in cymose, usually spike-like inflorescences, regular or nearly so, hermaphrodite or polygamous. Perianth-segments 3 or 6, petaloid, united below. Stamens 3, opposite the inner perianth-segments, or 6. Ovary inferior, 1- or 3-celled. Ovules numerous, inverted. Style 3- or 6-cleft. Fruit dry, dehiscing by slits or irregularly. Seeds albuminous ; testa loose. — Genera 4, species 15. Tropical and South Africa.

1. Anthers erect, opening transversely, 3. Style long, with 3 stigmas. [Tribe BURMANNIEAE.] 2
Anthers recurved, opening lengthwise. Style short. [Tribe THISMIEAE.] 3

2. Ovary 1-celled. — Species 3. Central Africa. . **Gymnosiphon** Blume
Ovary 3-celled. — Species 10. Tropical and South Africa. **Burmannia** L.

3. Corolla regular. Stamens 3 ; connective without an appendage. Stigma 3-parted. — Species 1. West Africa (Cameroons). **Oxygyne** Schlecht.

Corolla irregular. Stamens 6 ; connective with an appendage. Stigma 6-toothed. — Species 2. West Africa (Cameroons). (Under *Thismia* Griff.) . . . . **Afrothismia** (Engl.) Schlecht.

SUBORDER GYNANDRAE

FAMILY 44. ORCHIDACEAE

Leaves with longitudinal nerves. Inflorescence of the racemose type. Flowers irregular. Perianth more or less corolla-like or distinguished into calyx and corolla, one of the petals or segments (the lip) distinctly differing from the others. Receptacle usually continued beyond the ovary and forming the column upon which the stigma and the anther are inserted. Fertile stamen 1, belonging to the outer whorl. Staminodes sometimes present. Ovary inferior, 1-celled, with numerous parietal ovules. Stigmas or stigma-lobes 3, one of them rudimentary or transformed into the rostellum, to which the pollen-masses adhere. Seeds very small, exalbuminous ; embryo imperfectly developed. — Genera 96, species 1600. (Plate 26.)

1. Pollen-masses with basal, stalk-like appendages, which adhere to the sticky, gland-like appendages of the rostellum. Root thickened into tubers. [Tribe OPHRYDEAE.] 2

Pollen-masses with apical appendages or without appendages. . . 37

2. Anther reflected, forming an angle with the column. Lip with 2 spurs or without a spur, but sometimes saccate or bearing appendages on the back. 3

Anther erect, having the same direction as the column, rarely slightly reflected, but then lip with one spur. 14

3. Lip partly adnate to the column, usually bearing on its upper face a large appendage. Petals broad, converging and usually cohering with the middle sepal into a hood. [Subtribe CORYCIINAE.] 4

Lip free from the column, inserted at its base, rarely shortly adnate to it, but then petals not distinctly converging into a hood. [Subtribe SATY-RIINAE.] 7

4. Lateral sepals united nearly to the apex. — Species 10. South Africa. **Corycium** Swartz

Lateral sepals free. 5

5. Lateral sepals spurred or saccate. — Species 30. Southern and tropical Africa. . . . . **Disperis** Swartz

Lateral sepals flat. 6

6. Column short. Lip broad at the base. Connective dilated. — Species 15. South Africa. (Including *Ommatodium* Lindl.) **Pterygodium** Swartz

Column long. Lip clawed. Connective not dilated. — Species 8. South Africa (Cape Colony). . . . . **Ceratandra** Eckl.

7. Lip posticous (uppermost), produced behind into a pair of descending spurs or sacs. — Species 90. Tropical and South Africa. Some are used in medicine. (Including *Aviceps* Lindl. and *Satyridium* Lindl.)

Satyrium Swartz

Lip usually anticous, not spurred, but sometimes with a sac-like cavity.   8
8. Odd sepal spurred or gibbous. 9
   Odd sepal neither spurred nor gibbous. 13
9. Lip more or less saccate at the base. 10
   Lip flat. 11
10. Lip very small, adnate to the column. Stem rather rigid. Leaves in the middle of the stem. — Species 9. South Africa and mountains of the tropics. . . . . **Brownleea** Harv.
    Lip rather large, free from the column. Stem very flexible. Leaves at the base of the stem. — Species 6. South Africa (Cape Colony). (Under *Disa* Berg). . . . . **Schizodium** Lindl.
11. Rostellum with 2 distinct glands, to which the pollen-masses are attached ; side-lobes exceeding the middle-lobe. — Species 110. Southern and tropical Africa. Some are used as ornamental plants. (Including *Penthea* Lindl.) . . . . **Disa** Berg
    Rostellum with one gland ; sides-lobes, if present, not exceeding the middle-lobe. 12
12. Stigma 2-parted. Rostellum with 3 narrow, subequal lobes. — Species 10. South Africa to Nyasaland. (Under *Disa* Berg).

Herschelia Lindl.

Stigma entire. Rostellum more or less hood-shaped, large. — Species 15. South Africa. (Under *Disa* Berg). . . . **Monadenia** Lindl.
13. Petals much narrower than the odd sepal, kneed. Lip kidney-shaped. Stigma not extended in two branches. — Species 1. South Africa (Cape Colony). (Under *Disa* Berg). . . . . . . **Forficaria** Lindl.
    Petals and sepals subequal. Stigma with 2 erect, linear branches. — Species 2. South Africa (Cape Colony). . . . . **Pachites** Lindl.
14. (2.) Stigma extended into two, usually elongated processes. [Subtribe HABENARIINAE.] 15
    Stigma not extended into processes, rather flat. Column very short.   21
15. Stigmatic processes short, adnate to the lip. Rostellum small, not prolonged into anther-channels. Column very short. — Species 10. Tropics. (Under *Habenaria* L. or *Platanthera* Rich.) . . . **Peristylus** Blume
    Stigmatic processes free 16
16. Column long, curved. Rostellum not prolonged into anther-channels. Perianth subglobose. — Species 1. Mascarene Islands. **Acrostylia** Frapp.
    Column short 17
17. Rostellum or stigmatic processes 2-cleft. Base of the anther not enclosed by a channel, but prolonged into solid processes. — Species 7. Central Africa. (Under *Habenaria* Willd.) . . . . . **Roeperocharis** Reichb.

Rostellum and stigmatic processes entire, the former prolonged at the base into two lateral anther-channels. 18

18. Anther reflected. Stigma broad. 19
Anther erect. Stigma more or less slender. 20

19. Middle-lobe of the rostellum exceeding the side-lobes. Lip linear, entire, with a long spur. Petals broad.—Species 1. Southern West Africa. (Under *Habenaria* Willd.) . . . . **Barlaea** Reichb. fil.
Middle-lobe of the rostellum equalling the side-lobes. Lip oblong or broader, usually lobed.—Species 40. Tropical and South-east Africa. (*Cynosorchis* Thouars, including *Amphorchis* Thouars, *Hemiperis* Frapp., and *Camilleugenia* Frapp.) . . . . **Cynorchis** Thouars

20. Stigmatic processes diverging at a right angle. Spur short.—Species 1. North-west Africa. (*Tinea* Biv.) . . . .**Neotinea** Reichb. fil.
Stigmatic processes nearly parallel.—Species 210. (Including *Bonatea* Willd., *Platycoryne* Reichb., and *Podandria* Rolfe). **Habenaria** Willd.

21. (14.) Glands of the rostellum enclosed in 1—2 pouches proceeding from the rostellum and persisting when the glands are removed. [Subtribe SERAPIADINAE.] 22
Glands of the rostellum enclosed by the processes of the anther or naked, rarely covered by a thin pellicle proceeding from the rostellum and carried away with the glands upon removal. [Subtribe GYMNADENIINAE.] 27

22. Glands enclosed in 2 separate pouches. Lip not spurred, usually convex gibbous and hairy. — Species 10. North Africa. The tubers yield medicaments (salep) and mucilage. . . . . **Ophrys** L.
Glands enclosed in a common pouch. 23

23. Glands 2, free. Lip spurred. — Species 20. North Africa. The tubers yield medicaments (salep) and mucilage . . . . . . **Orchis** L.
Glands united into one. 24

24. Connective distinctly elongated. Rostellum laterally compressed. Lip not spurred; middle-lobe entire. — Species 4. North-west Africa. They yield medicaments and mucilage. . . . . . **Serapias** L.
Connective not or scarcely elongated. Rostellum conical at the apex. Lip spurred, rarely without a spur, but then with a 2-cleft middle-lobe. 25

25. Lip with a long spur and two protuberances at the base, equally 3-lobed, flat in the bud. — Species 1. North-west Africa (Algeria). It yields medicaments and mucilage. (Under *Orchis* L.) **Anacamptis** Rich.
Lip with a short spur or without a spur, with unequal lobes, bent inwards or rolled up in the bud. 26

26. Middle-lobe of the lip very long, strap-shaped, spirally coiled in the bud. — Species 1. North-west Africa (Algeria). (Under *Aceras* R. Br. or *Orchis* L.) . . . . **Himantoglossum** Spreng.
Middle-lobe of the lip moderately long, 2-cleft, bent over the anther in the bud. — Species 2. North Africa. (Including **Barlia** Parl.) **Aceras** R. Br.

27. (21.) Glands of the rostellum transversely connate. Rostellum narrow. Stigmatic surface small. Basal appendages of the pollen-masses short. Column short. Lip with a short spur.—Species 40. Tropical and South Africa. (Including *Bucculina* Lindl., *Deroemeria* Reichb. fil., *Monotris* Lindl., *Saccidium* Lindl., *Scopularia* Lindl., and *Tryphia* Lindl.)
Holothrix L. C. Rich.

Glands of the rostellum free. 28

28. Glands large, surrounded by a thin membrane, which proceeds from the rostellum and is removed together with the glands. Lip with a very short spur. Flowers very small. — Species 1. Island of Réunion.
Herminium L.

Glands naked, rarely enclosed by processes of the anther, but then small. 29

29. Petals clawed ; blade deeply concave, fringed. Lip fringed, not spurred. — Species 4. South Africa. (Including *Hallackia* Harv.) **Huttonaea** Harv.

Petals not clawed, flat or slightly concave. 30

30. Rostellum forming a narrow fold between the anther-cells. . . . 31

Rostellum broad, triangular, placed below the anther-cells. . . . 33

31. Column short. Stigmatic surfaces convex. Lip shortly or not spurred. Flowers yellow or white. — Species 5. South Africa and southern East Africa. (*Schizochilus* Sond.) . . . . . . **Gymnadenia** R. Br.

Column long. Stigmatic surfaces concave. 32

32. Petals partly adnate to the column. Lip not spurred. Sepals and petals subequal. — Species 1. South Africa. (Under *Brachycorythis* Lindl.)
Neobolusia Schlecht.

Petals inserted below the column. — Species 25. Tropical and South Africa. (Including *Schwartzkopffia* Kraenzl., under *Platanthera* Rich.)
Brachycorythis Lindl.

33. Lip with a spur. 34

Lip without a spur. 36

34. Lip 3-lobed, the side-lobes inflexed, covering the mouth of the spur.— Species 3. Madagascar. . . . . **Bicornella** Lindl.

Lip 3-lobed, with erect or spreading side-lobes, or undivided. . . 35

35. Lip fringed. Anther-cells approximate and parallel.—Species 2. South Africa. . . . . **Bartholina** R. Br.

Lip entire or crenate. Anther-cells divergent.—Species 20. The tubers yield medicaments (salep) and mucilage. (Including *Gennaria* Parl., under *Habenaria* Willd.) . . . . **Platanthera** L. C. Rich.

36. Lip 3-lobed. Column with 2 basal staminodes. Basal appendages of the pollen-masses very short.— Species 3. South Africa and southern East Africa. . . . . **Stenoglottis** Lindl.

Lip undivided. Column without distinct staminodes. — Species 2. Madagascar and Mascarenes . . . . **Arnottia** A. Rich.

37. (1.) Pollen-masses soft, granular. Anthers usually persistent and withering. Inflorescence terminal. Leaves rolled up in the bud, with overlapping edges. Usually terrestrial herbs. [Tribe NEOTTIEAE] . . . 38

Pollen-masses firm, waxy. Anthers usually deciduous. Inflorescence lateral, more rarely terminal, but then leaves folded lengthwise in the bud. 55

38. Anther erect and greatly exceeding the rostellum, or inclined and incumbent upon the rostellum. Pollen-masses granular or powdery. Rostellum not distinctly notched after the removal of the pollen-masses, or not distinctly cohering with them. 39

Anther about equalling the rostellum, erect, rarely incumbent, but then pollen-masses divided into a number of large angular sections. Rostellum usually distinctly notched after the removal of the pollen-masses. 47

39. Lip distinctly articulated into 2—3 portions placed one behind the other. Anther erect. [Subtribe CEPHALANTHERINAE.] 40

Lip not distinctly articulated, embracing the column. Anther more or less incumbent. 42

40. Lip produced into a spur. Leaves replaced by scales. Plants of a violet colour.—Species 2. North-west Africa (Algeria). **Limodorum** L. C. Rich.

Lip not distinctly spurred. Leaves perfectly developed. 41

41. Lip saccate at the base ; the terminal portion oblong and enclosed by the connivent sepals. — Species 1. North-west Africa (Algeria).

Cephalanthera L. C. Rich.

Lip concave, but not saccate at the base ; the terminal portion broad and projecting between the spreading sepals. —Species 4. North-west Africa and northern East Africa. (*Helleborine* Hill).

Epipactis L. C. Rich.

42. Sepals and petals united below. Leafless herbs. [Subtribe GASTRODIINAE] 43

Sepals and petals free 44

43. Sepals and petals united high up, very unequal. Lip ovate, with 2 gibbosities at the base. Column short. Anther incumbent. Root-stock branched. Flowers large, in few-flowered spikes.—Species 1. West Africa (Cameroons). . . . . **Gastrodia** R. Br.

Sepals and petals united at the base only, subequal. Lip spatulate, not gibbous. Column long. Anther suberect. Rootstock tuberous, spindle-shaped. Flowers very small, in many-flowered racemes.— Species 1. West Africa (Cameroons). . . . **Auxopus** Schlecht.

44. Stem climbing. Seed-coat crusty or winged. [Subtribe VANILLINAE.] 45

Stem erect. Seed-coat membranous, not winged. [Subtribe POGONIINAE.] 46

45. Lip adnate to the column. Fruit fleshy. Seeds not winged. Usually leafy plants. — Species 15. Tropics. Two of the species (especially *V. planifolia* Andr.) are cultivated for their fruits, which are used as condiments and for the preparation of perfumes. Some species are used as ornamental plants. . . . . **Vanilla** Swartz

Lip not adnate to the column. Fruit dry. Seeds winged. Leafless plants. — Species 1. Comoro Islands. . . . . . . **Galeola** Lour.

46. Lip spurred or saccate. Column short. Leaves wanting.—Species 1.
West Africa (Cameroons). (Under *Epipogon* Gmel.)   **Galera** Blume

Lip neither spurred nor saccate. Column long. Leaves stalked, usually
separated from the flowering stem.— Species 10. Tropics to Transvaal.
(Including *Apostellis* Thouars, under *Pogonia* Juss.)   **Nervilia** Gaud.

47. (38.) Pollen-masses divided into a moderate number of rather large, angular
segments. Leaves not folded lengthwise. [Subtribe PHYSURINAE.] 48

Pollen-masses not divided into several large segments. 53

48. Pollen-masses connected with the glands of the rostellum by a strap-shaped
stalk detached from the tissue of the rostellum. 49

Pollen-masses or their appendages adhering directly to the glands of the
rostellum. 50

49. Column with 2 narrow, erect arms. Sepals usually united to the middle.
Lip with two protuberances at the base and with a two-lobed blade.—
Species 4. West Africa, Madagascar, Comoro Islands.

Cheirostylis Blume

Column without erect arms, but sometimes auricled. Sepals free.—
Species 9. Tropical and South-east Africa. (Including *Monochilus*
Blume). . . . . **Zeuxine** Lindl.

50. Lip similar to the other petals, oblong, slightly concave. Stigmas free,
erect, one on each side of the rather long rostellum. —Species 2. Madagascar and Mascarene Islands. . . . . . **Gymnochilus** Blume

Lip distinctly differing from the other petals. 51

51. Column long. Sepals connivent into a tube at the base. Lip with an
oblong blade. — Species 6. Comoro Islands, Seychelles, Natal, West
Africa. . . . . **Platylepis** A. Rich.

Column short. 52

52. Stigma with a papillose protuberance on each side. Lip tubercled at the
base, with a distinctly limited broad blade. — Species 3. Mascarenes,
Seychelles, Comoro Islands, and Cameroons. . . . **Hetaeria** Blume

Stigma simple. Lip not tubercled, but sometimes hairy at the base ; blade
not distinctly separated, undivided, bent back at the tip. — Species 3.
Mascarene Islands and Madeira. Used as ornamental plants.

Goodyera R. Br.

53. (47.) Leaves firm, folded lengthwise. Flowers in panicles. Lip narrow
below, broadened above. Pollen-masses affixed to a slender stalk
arising from the rostellum ; gland peltate. —Species 2. Tropics. (*Corym-
bis* Lindl.) [Subtribe TROPIDIINAE.] . . . **Corymborchis** Thouars

Leaves soft, not folded, sometimes scale-like. Flowers in spikes. . 54

54. Sepals and petals united into a long tube. Lip uppermost, with 2 lateral
appendages. Column elongated, two-winged. —Species 1. West Africa.
[Subtribe CRANICHIDINAE.] . . . . . . **Manniella** Reichb. fil.

Sepals and petals free or almost so, suberect. Lip below. Inflorescence
one-sided. — Species 2. North-west Africa (Algeria). [Subtribe SPIRAN-
THINAE.] . . . . **Spiranthes** L. C. Rich.

55. (37.) Inflorescence terminal.   Leaves folded lengthwise before expansion. 56
    Inflorescence lateral. 65
56. Pollen-masses 8, without an appendage.   Lip saccate at the base.   Leaves
    jointed at the upper end of the sheath.   Inflorescence head-like. —
    Species 1.   Madagascar and Seychelles.   [Tribe GLOMEREAE.]
                                                        Agrostophyllum Blume
    Pollen-masses 2—4. 57
57. Column extended below into a foot forming with the base of the perianth
    a chin or spur. . Pollen-masses attached to a short, sometimes scarcely
    perceptible stalk arising from the rostellum.   Mostly epiphytic plants.
    [Tribe POLYSTACHYEAE.] 58
    Column not extended into a foot.   Pollen-masses without appendages.
    Sepals and petals usually bent backwards.   [Tribe LIPARIDEAE.] 61
58. Lip spurred, 3-lobed.   Pollen-masses 2, grooved.   Leaves not jointed,
    linear.   Joints of the stem swollen. — Species 6.   South Africa. (Under
    Eulophia R. Br.) . . . . **Acrolophia** Pfitz.
    Lip not spurred.   Leaves usually jointed. 59
59. Lip undivided.·   Chin weakly developed.   Column short and thick.   Stem
    slender. — Species 1.   German East Africa. . . **Neobenthamia** Rolfe
    Lip 3-lobed. 60
60. Lateral sepals forming with the column a weakly developed chin.
    Side-lobes of the lip embracing the column.   Column slender.   Stem
    slightly thickened. — Species 6.   Tropical and South-east Africa.   Some
    are used as ornamental plants. . . . . **Ansellia** Lindl.
    Lateral sepals forming with the column a strongly developed chin.   Side-
    lobes of the lip small.   Column short and broad.   Stem usually thickened
    into pseudo bulbs. — Species 120. Tropical and South Africa. Some are used
    as ornamental plants.   (Including *Epiphora* Lindl.) **Polystachya** Lindl.
61. Anther erect.   Leaves not jointed. 62
    Anther inclined to horizontal. 63
62. Anther adnate to the rostellum ; cells widely diverging, opening laterally.
    Column long. — Species 1.   West Africa. . . . . . **Orestia** Ridl.
    Anther deciduous, opening inwards.   Column short.   Lip uppermost.—
    Species 4.   West Africa and Comoro Islands. . **Microstylis** Nutt.
63. Leaves not jointed.   Lip more or less distinctly clawed.   Column slender.—
    Species 30.   Tropical and South Africa. . . . **Liparis** L. C. Rich.
    Leaves jointed between sheath and blade.   Lip not distinctly clawed.   64
64. Stem with pseudobulbs.   Leaf-blade horizontally flattened. — Species 1.
    Mascarene Islands.   (*Cestichis* Thouars, under *Liparis* Rich.)
                                                        Stichorchis Thouars
    Stem without pseudobulbs.   Leaf-blade placed vertically, fleshy.   Lip
    uppermost, concave at the base. — Species 1.   Tropics. **Oberonia** Lindl.
65. (55.) Leaves with convolute praefoliation (i.e. rolled lengthwise in the bud,
    one edge overlapping the other).   Stem not swollen, or several joints
    of the stem equally thickened.   Mostly terrestrial herbs. . . . 66

Leaves with conduplicate praefoliation (i.e. folded together along the midrib in the bud, their edges being applied to each other without overlapping). Mostly epiphytic herbs. 73

66. Pollen-masses 2—4, without appendages, attached to the glands of the
   rostellum by a stalk produced from the latter. Leaves usually jointed.
   [Tribe CYRTOPODIEAE.] 67
   Pollen-masses 8, appendaged, without a stalk produced from the rostellum.
   Leaves usually continuous. [Tribe PHAIEAE.] 71

67. Lip produced into a spur or pouch at the base. 68
   Lip without a spur or pouch. 69

68. Sepals narrower and less coloured than the petals, usually reflexed. Petals
   erect or spreading. — Species 90. Tropical and South Africa. Some
   are used as ornamental plants. . . . . . . **Lissochilus** R. Br.
   Sepals and petals equal or nearly so, spreading. — Species 130. Tropical
   and South Africa. Some species yield medicaments (salep) and mucilage
   or serve as ornamental plants. (Including *Cyrtopera* Lindl. and *Ortho-
   chilus* Hochst.) . . . . **Eulophia** R. Br.

69. Column with 2 basal lobes projecting upon the base of the lip. — Species 4.
   East Africa . . . . **Pteroglossaspis** Reichb. fil.
   Column without appendages. 70

70. Lip and lateral sepals inserted on the foot of the column, the former with
   a narrow, the latter with a broad base. — Species 1. Madagascar.
                                        Eulophiella Rolfe
   Lip inserted on the foot of the column, the lateral sepals on the margin
   of the ovary, both with a narrow base. — Species 1. Madagascar and
   Mascarene Islands. The pseudobulbs yield mucilage.
                                        Cyrtopodium R. Br.

71. Leaves jointed at the upper end of the sheath. Inflorescence 2—3-flowered.
   Lip slightly saccate. Colum rather long, with short, roundish wings.
   Pollen-masses affixed to a single appendage. — Species 2. West Africa.
   Used as ornamental plants. (Under *Pachystoma* Reichb. fil.)
                                        Ancistrochilus Rolfe
   Leaves not jointed. Inflorescence usually many-flowered. Lip clasping
   the column or adnate to it, usually spurred. 72

72. Lip adnate to the column; blade spreading, 3—4-lobed. Column short. —
   Species 9. Tropical and South Africa. Some are used as ornamental
   plants. . . . . **Calanthe** R. Br.
   Lip free, clasping the column or broadly concave at the base. Column
   slender. — Species 7. Madagascar and neighbouring islands, West
   Africa. Some are used as ornamental plants or yield dye-stuffs.
                                        Phaius Lour.

73. (65.) Leafy stems with indeterminate apical growth; side-shoots weakly
   developed or wanting. Inflorescences or solitary flowers axillary.
   Epiphytes without pseudobulbs. Lip continuous with the base of the
   column. [Tribe SARCANTHEAE, subtribe AERIDINAE.] . . 74

Leafy stems with determinate apical growth ; annual shoots arising laterally at their base and forming a sympodium.   Mostly epiphytes with
pseudobulbs.   Lip more or less distinctly articulated with the foot of the
column.   86

74. Lip not spurred.   Sepals and petals long and narrow, spreading.   Pollen-
masses without an appendage.   Leaves broad. — Species 2.   Island of
Réunion.   .   .   .   .   **Bonniera** Cord.
Lip spurred.   75

75. Lateral sepals inserted on the foot of the column, forming a chin.   Lip
entire, smooth, shortly spurred. — Species 10.   Madagascar and neighbouring islands, Cameroons.   Some are used as ornamental plants.
Aeranthus Lindl.
Lateral sepals inserted on the apex of the ovary.   Column not prolonged
into a foot.   76

76. Pollen-masses upon a single, sometimes 2-cleft or almost imperceptible
stalk.   77
Pollen-masses with 2 stalks, which are entirely distinct or united by the
gland only.   81

77. Stalk of the pollen-masses 2-cleft. — Species 10.   Madagascar and the
neighbouring islands, West Africa.   (Including *Ancistrorhynchus* Finet,
Dicranotaenia Finet, and *Monixus* Finet, under *Angrecum* Thouars).
Aerangis Reichb. fil.
Stalk of the pollen-masses simple.   78

78. Stalk of the pollen-masses broadened above or throughout, sometimes
almost imperceptible.   Lip with a long and thin spur. — Species 120
Tropical and South Africa.   Some are used as ornamental or medicinal
plants.   (Including *Lepervenchea* Cord., *Radinocion* Ridl., and *Rhaphi-
dorhynchus* Finet).   .   .   .   .   **Angrecum** Thouars
Stalk of the pollen-masses thread-like.   79

79. Lip hood-shaped, entire, covering the column.   Sepals and petals connivent. — Species 1.   West Africa (Cameroons). (Under *Angrecum* Thou.
or *Saccolabium* Blume).   .   .   .   .   .   .   **Calyptrochilus** Kraenzl.
Lip not covering the column.   80

80. Lip directed upwards.   Flowers fleshy, rather small. — Species 4.   Madagascar and neighbouring islands, Equatorial East Africa.   Used as
ornamental plants.   (Under *Saccolabium* Blume).   **Acampe** Lindl.
Lip directed downwards. — Species 3.   Madagascar and neighbouring
islands, West Africa.   Used as ornamental plants. **Saccolabium** Blume

81. Pollen-masses affixed to the surface of two oblong scales.   Lip entire,
with a long spur. — Species 20.   Madagascar and neighbouring islands,
West Africa.   Some are used as ornamental plants.   (Under *Angrecum*
Thou.)   .   .   .   .   **Macroplectrum** Pfitz.
Pollen-masses affixed to thin, not scale-like, but sometimes very short
stalks.   82

82. Gland of the rostellum covered by scales. Petals 2—4-lobed. Lip with a long spur, a clawed 3—5-lobed middle-lobe, and incurved sickle-shaped side-lobes. — Species 1. Madagascar and Mascarenes.

Cryptopus Lindl.

Gland of the rostellum without scales. 83

83. Lip with a short, conical spur ; side-lobes embracing the column. — Species 9. Madagascar and neighbouring islands. (*Aeonia* Lindl.)

Oeonia Lindl.

Lip with a long, thread- or club-shaped spur. 84

84. Sepals unequal, the lateral much longer than the middle one, united with the petals above. Lip deeply 3-cleft. Stem climbing. — Species 1. German East Africa. . . . . **Angrecopsis** Kraenzl.

Sepals and petals subequal, free. 85

85. Sepals and petals erect. Lip entire. Pollen-masses with very short stalks. — Species 1. Island of Réunion. (*Pectinaria* Cord., under *Angrecum* Thou. *Macroplectrum* Pfitz. or *Mystacidium* Lindl.)

Ctenorchis K. Schum.

Sepals and petals spreading. 86

86. Column bent backwards. Stalks of the pollen-masses attached to a common gland. — Species 70. Tropical and South Africa. Some are used as ornamental plants. (Plate 26.) . . . **Listrostachys** Reichb. fil.

Column straight. Stalks of the pollen-masses usually attached to two separate glands. — Species 40. Tropical and South Africa. Some are used as ornamental plants. (Including *Gussonia* A. Rich.)

Mystacidium Lindl.

87. (73.) Pollen-masses 2, grooved, with a large transverse appendage at the base, attached to the gland of the rostellum by a broad stalk. Lip usually large. Pseudobulbs formed by several internodes, rarely by a single one or wanting. [Tribe CYMBIDIEAE.] 88

Pollen-masses 4, rarely 2, without an appendage and usually without a stalk. Lip usually small. Pseudobulbs formed by a single internode, bearing one or two leaves. 92

88. Lip distinctly spurred. 89

Lip not distinctly spurred. 90

89. Pollen-masses grooved. Stem with a pseudobulb. — Species 5. Madagascar and Mascarenes. (Under *Eulophia* R. Br.) . **Eulophiopsis** Pfitz.

Pollen-masses not grooved. Stem without pseudobulbs.—Species 1. Madagascar. . . . . **Lemurorchis** Kraenzl.

90. Pollen-masses attached to two processes of the stalk. Stem slender, without pseudobulbs, many-leaved. — Species 1. Madagascar. Used as an ornamental plant. . . . . . **Grammatophyllum** Blume

Pollen-masses attached to a common stalk without processes. Stem with more or less distinct pseudobulbs. 91

91. Pseudobulbs enveloped by the sheaths of the leaves inserted below and upon them. — Species 4. Madagascar. Used as ornamental plants.

Cymbidium Swartz

Pseudobulbs bearing leaves at the top only, hence not enveloped by sheaths. Lateral sepals forming with the foot of the column a distinct chin. — Species 2. Madagascar. Used as ornamental plants.

Grammangis Reichb. fil.

92. Pollen-masses attached to a scale-like stalk. Lip spurred, 3-lobed.— Species 2. West Africa. Used as ornamental plants. (Under *Eulophia* R. Br.)¯ [Tribe MAXILLARIEAE.] . . . . **Eulophidium** Pfitz. Pollen-masses without a stalk, rarely with a linear stalk. Lip small, not distinctly spurred, usually entire. [Tribe BOLBOPHYLLEAE.] 93

93. Pollen-masses with a stalk. Lateral sepals somewhat longer than the dorsal one. Flowers in racemes. Stem creeping. — Species 3. West Africa. (Under *Bolbophyllum* Thou. or *Polystachya* Lindl.)

Genyorchis Schlecht.

Pollen-masses without a stalk. 94

94. Lateral sepals much longer than the dorsal one, free at the base, united towards the tip. Inflorescence almost umbel-like. — Species 1. Madagascar, Mascarenes, East Africa. Used as an ornamental plant. (Under *Bolbophyllum* Thou.) . . . . **Cirrhopetalum** Lindl. Lateral sepals shorter or somewhat longer than the dorsal one or equalling it, free or almost so. Flowers in spikes or racemes, rarely solitary. 95

95. Lateral sepals much shorter than the dorsal one. Inflorescence with a dilated, almost leaf-like rachis. — Species 40. Tropical and South-East Africa. Some species are used as ornamental plants. **Megaclinium** Lindl. Lateral sepals about as long as or longer than the dorsal one. Inflorescence with a cylindrical rachis. — Species 90. Tropical and South-East Africa. Some are used as ornamental plants. (*Bulbophyllum* Thou.)

Bolbophyllum Thouars

CLASS V. DICOTYLEDONEAE

SUBCLASS ARCHICHLAMYDEAE

(APETALAE AND CHORIPETALAE)

ORDER VERTICILLATAE

FAMILY 45. CASUARINACEAE

Trees or shrubs. Leaves scale-like, whorled, united into a sheath. Flowers unisexual, the male in spikes, the female in heads. Perianth of the male flowers consisting of two scales, in the female absent. Stamen 1. Anther opening by two longitudinal slits. Ovary 1-celled. Ovules 2, ascending, straight. Style very short, with 2 thread-shaped stigmas. Fruit dry, indehiscent, enclosed by woody bracteoles. Seed 1, without albumen. Embryo straight ; radicle superior.

A ²/₃

B ¹⁰/₁

C ²⁰/₁

Piper guineense Schum.

A Fruiting branch.   *B* Part of the female spike with two flowers and their bracts.   *C* Female flower cut lengthwise.

J. Fleischmann del.

Salix Safsaf Forsk.

A Fruiting branch.   *B* Part of a flowering branch   *C* Male flower.   *D* Female flower cut lengthwise.   *E* Fruit.   *F* Seed cut lengthwise.

Genus 1, species 2.   Spontaneous in Madagascar and the neighbouring islands, cultivated in other tropical countries.   The wood (beaf-wood) and the bark are used, the latter for tanning and dyeing and in medicine.

Casuarina Rumph.

ORDER PIPERALES

FAMILY 46. PIPERACEAE

Flowers in spikes.   Perianth none.   Stamens 2—6.   Ovary 1-celled.   Ovule 1, basal, straight.   Fruit a berry.   Seed with a copious albumen and a small embryo.—Genera 3, species 80.   Tropical and South Africa.   (Plate 27.)
1. Stigma 1, sometimes penicillate.   Flowers hermaphrodite.   Leaves ex-stipulate.   Herbs. — Species 65.   Tropical and South Africa.   Some yield vegetables or condiments or are used in medicine.

Peperomia Ruiz & Pav.

Stigmas 2—5.   Leaves stipulate or sheathing at the base.   Usually shrubs. 2
2. Flowers hermaphrodite.   Spikes axillary, arranged in an umbel.   Stipules united into a sheath.   Shrubs. — Species 1.   Tropics.   Yields edible fruits containing an aromatic oil and is also used in medicine.   (Under *Piper* L.) . . . . **Heckeria** Kunth

Flowers unisexual or polygamous.   Spikes leaf-opposed. — Species 17, two of them only in cultivation.   Tropical and South Africa.   Some species yield spices (pepper) or are used in medicine.   (Including *Cocco-bryon* Klotzsch and *Cubeba* Miq.)   (Plate 27.)   **Piper** L.

ORDER SALICALES

FAMILY 47. SALICACEAE

Trees or shrubs.   Leaves alternate, entire toothed or lobed, stipulate. Flowers in spikes or catkins, dioecious, without a perianth.   Disc cup-shaped or reduced to scales.   Stamens 2 or more.   Anthers opening by two longi-tudinal slits.   Ovary 1-celled, with two or more parietal placentas.   Ovules inverted.   Stigmas 2—4, sessile or nearly so.   Fruit capsular.   Seeds with a basal tuft of hairs, without albumen ; embryo straight.—Genera 2, species 20.   (Plate 28.)

Disc cup- or urn-shaped.   Stamens 4—30.   Bracts jagged.   Leaves, at least those of the uppermost branches, broad (ovate or broader). Buds terminal and lateral, covered by several scales. — Species 6.   North and East Africa.   They yield timber, dyes, and medicaments. " Poplar."

Popᵘlus L.

Disc reduced to one or several scales or teeth sometimes cohering at the base.   Bracts entire.   Leaves narrow or rather broad (linear to ovate). Buds lateral, covered by a single scale. — Species 15, two of them only naturalized. They yield timber, plaiting-, stuffing-, and tanning-materials, and medicaments. " Willow."   (Plate 28.) . . . . . **Salix** L.

ORDER MYRICALES

FAMILY 48. MYRICACEAE

Trees shrubs or undershrubs. Leaves undivided, without stipules. Flowers in simple or compound spikes, unisexual, without a perianth, but usually with 2—6 bracteoles. Stamens 2—12, usually 4. Anthers opening by two longitudinal slits. Ovary 1-celled. Ovule 1, erect, straight. Styles 2, united at the base, thread-shaped, stigmatose on the inside. Fruit a drupe. Seed with a thin coat and a straight embryo, without albumen. (Plate 29.)

Genus 1, species 25. Tropical and South Africa, Canary Islands, Azores. They yield bark for tanning, wax, and edible fruits, and are also used in medicine. . . . . **Myrica** L.

ORDER JUGLANDALES

FAMILY 49. JUGLANDACEAE

Trees. Leaves alternate, unequally pinnate, without stipules. Flowers in spikes or catkins, monoecious, with bracteoles which are adnate to the ovary in the female flowers. Perianth 3—4-parted. Stamens numerous. Anthers opening by two longitudinal slits. Ovary inferior, 1-celled. Ovule 1, basal, straight. Styles 2, united at the base, stigmatose lengthwise. Fruit a drupe with an incompletely septate stone. Seed lobed, with a thin coat, without albumen.

Genus 1, species 2. Cultivated in North Africa. They yield timber, tans and dyes, edible fruits (walnuts), oil, sugar, and medicaments. **Juglans** L.

ORDER FAGALES

FAMILY 50. BETULACEAE

Trees or shrubs. Leaves alternate, undivided, stipulate. Flowers monoecious, in spikes or catkins, with a perianth of bract-like segments or without a perianth. Stamens 4. Ovary 2-celled at the base. Ovules solitary in each cell, descending, inverted. Styles 2. Fruit a nut. Seed 1, exalbuminous, with a membranous coat.—Genera 2, species 2. Extra-tropical regions. (Under *CUPULIFERAE*.)

Male flowers without a perianth, with 2-parted filaments and hairy anthers. Female flowers with a small perianth and a jagged involucre free from the bract but adnate to the fruit. Fruit large. Female spikes bud-shaped, solitary. Leaves folded at the mid-rib in the bud.—Species 1 (*C. Avellana* L., hazel). Cultivated and naturalized in North-west Africa. Fruits edible. [Tribe CORYLEAE.] . . **Corylus** Tourn.

Male flowers with a 4-parted perianth, simple filaments, and glabrous anthers. Female flowers without a perianth, enclosed by a 5-parted involucre formed by the connate bracts and bracteoles. Fruit small. Female spikes cone-shaped, at length woody, arranged in racemes. Leaves

J. Fleischmann del.

Myrica conifera Burm. fil.

A Fruiting branch   *B* Male inflorescence.   *C* Male flower.   *D* Group of fruits.   *E* Female flower.   *F* Ovary cut lengthwise.
G Fruit.   *H* Fruit cut lengthwise.

J. Fleischmann del.

Trema guineensis Schum.

A Flowering branch. *B* Male flower cut lengthwise. *C* Female flower cut lengthwise. *D* Fruit cut lengthwise.

folded along the side-nerves in the bud. — Species 1 (*A. glutinosa* L.,
alder).   North-west Africa, also naturalized in South Africa.   Yields
timber and bark for tanning.   [Tribe BETULEAE.]   **Alnus** Tourn.

FAMILY 51.   FAGACEAE

Trees or shrubs.   Leaves alternate, undivided lobed or pinnately cleft,
stipulate.   Flowers in spikes or catkins, monoecious.   Perianth-segments 4—7,
bract-like, more or less united.   Stamens 4—20.   Ovary inferior, 3—6-celled
at the base.   Ovules 2 in each cell, descending, inverted.   Styles 3—6.   Fruit
a nut surrounded by a cup-shaped involucre.   Seeds without albumen.—
Genera 2, species 9.   Extra-tropical regions.   (Under *CUPULIFERAE*.)

Male flowers in fascicles arranged in erect spikes.   Female flowers in clusters
of 3, surrounded by an involucre.   Filaments long.   Styles 6, thread-
shaped.   Fruit enclosed in a prickly involucre.   Leaves serrate.—Species
1 (*C. vulgaris* Lam., chestnut).   North-west Africa.   Yields timber,
bark for tanning, and edible fruits from which starch and oil are prepared.
Castanea Tourn.

Male flowers in simple, pendulous catkins.   Female flowers each surrounded
by an involucre.   Filaments short.   Styles 3, rarely 4—5, flattened.
Fruit seated in a scaly, cup-shaped involucre. — Species 8.   North-west
Africa ; one species also introduced into South Africa.   They yield
timber, cork, tanning and dyeing materials, chemical and medicinal drugs,
starch, and fodder ; some have edible fruits.   " Oak."   .   **Quercus** L.

ORDER URTICALES
FAMILY 52.   ULMACEAE ·

Trees or shrubs.   Juice not milky.   Leaves simple, stipulate.   Flowers
axillary, solitary or in cymes.   Perianth simple, with 3—8 segments.   Stamens
as many as and opposite the perianth-segments, rarely more, straight in the
bud.   Anthers opening by longitudinal slits.   Ovary superior, 1-celled, very
rarely (*Ulmus*) 2-celled.   Ovule 1, pendulous, inverted.   Styles or stigmas
1—2.   Fruit a nut or a drupe.   Seed with a membranous coat and with scanty
albumen or without albumen. — Genera 5, species 35.   (Under *URTICA-
CEAE*.) (Plate 30.)

1. Stamens twice or thrice as many as the perianth-segments.   Stigma 1.
   Flowers dioecious.   Perianth much enlarged in fruit.   Leaves opposite
   Species 1. Abyssinia.   [Subfamily **BARBEYOIDEAE.**]
   Barbeya Schweint.

Stamens as many as the perianth-segments.   Stigmas 2.   Flowers monoecious polygamous or hermaphrodite.   Leaves alternate.   .   .   2

2. Fruit a compressed, winged nut.   Embryo straight ; cotyledons flat.
   Flower-clusters in the axils of scale-like bracts. — Species 1 (*U. campestris* L., elm).   North-west Africa.   Yields timber, bast, tanning and
   dyeing materials, and medicaments. [Subfamily **ULMOIDEAE.**]
   Ulmus L.

Fruit a more or less globular drupe. Embryo curved ; cotyledons folded
or rolled inwards. Flower-clusters or solitary flowers usually in the
axils of the leaves. [Subfamily **CELTIDOIDEAE.**] 3

3. Stipules united. Leaves entire, penninerved. Spiny shrubs. Flowers
unisexual. Perianth-segments of the male flowers valvate in the bud.
Embryo with narrow cotyledons. — Species 4. Tropical and South
Africa. . . . . **Chaetacme** Planch. & Harv.
Stipules free. Leaves usually 3-nerved. Spineless shrubs or trees.
Flowers usually polygamous. Perianth-segments imbricate in bud,
at least at the apex. 4

4. Embryo with narrow cotyledons. Perianth-segments imbricate at the
apex only. Flowers almost sessile. — Species 10. Tropical and South
Africa. Some species yield timber, fibre, tanning and dyeing materials,
and medicaments. (*Sponia* Commers.) (Plate 30.) **Trema** Lour.
Embryo with broad cotyledons. Perianth-segments imbricate. Stigmas
feathery. Upper flowers upon long stalks. — Species 20. Some of them
yield timber, bast, tanning and dyeing materials, oil, medicaments, and
edible fruits. " Nettle-tree." . . . . **Celtis** L.

FAMILY 53. MORACEAE

Juice usually milky. Leaves stipulate. Flowers unisexual. Perianth
simple or wanting. Stamens as many as and opposite the perianth-segments
or fewer, 1—6. Anthers opening by longitudinal slits. Ovary 1-celled. Ovule
1, pendulous, inverted or curved, rarely erect and straight. Styles 1—2. —
Genera 26, species 260. (Under *URTICACEAE* or *ULMACEAE*.) (Plate 31.)

1. Stamens of the male flowers bent inwards in the bud, subsequently bent
backwards. Ovule pendulous. Leaves folded in bud. Stipules not
leaving a stem-clasping scar. [Subfamily **MOROIDEAE.**] . . 2
Stamens of the male flowers straight from the beginning. 14

2. Flowers in lax cymes consisting of one female flower and several male
ones. Perianth with a distinct tube. Stamens 4. Style 2-cleft. Trees.
Leaves undivided. — Species 1. Madagascar. (Tribe FATOUEAE.]
Bleekrodia Blume
Flowers arranged in spike- raceme- or head-like inflorescences or collected
upon flattened receptacles. 3

3. Flowers on flattened and more or less expanded receptacles, rarely in
spike-like inflorescences ; in the latter case, as usually, male and female
flowers in the same inflorescence. Stamens 1—4, usually 2. [Tribe
DORSTENIEAE.] 4
Flowers in spike- raceme- or head-like, unisexual inflorescences (containing
only male or only female flowers), rarely female flowers solitary. Stamens 4. Trees or shrubs. 7

4. Flowers in false spikes containing male and female flowers or male ones
only. Perianth 4-partite. Stamens 4. Trees. Leaves undivided.—
Species 1. East Africa. . . . . **Sloetiopsis** Engl.
Flowers on flattened receptacles. 5

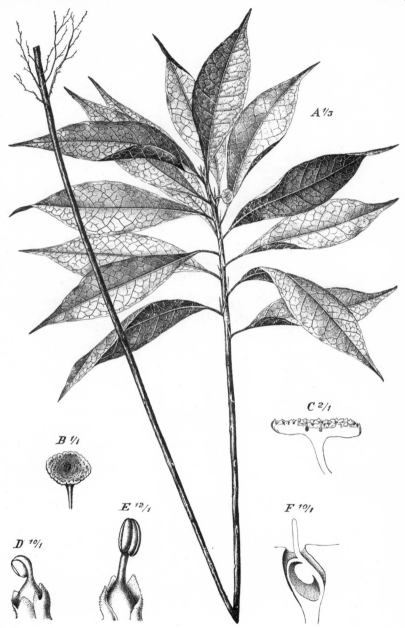

A 1/3

C 2/1

B 1/1

E 12/1

D 10/1

F 10/1

Fleischmann del.

Dorstenia elliptica Bureau

A Plant in flower.   *B* Inflorescence.   *C* Inflorescence cut lengthwise.   *D* Young male flcwer.   *E* Older male flower.   *F* Female flower
cut lengthwise.

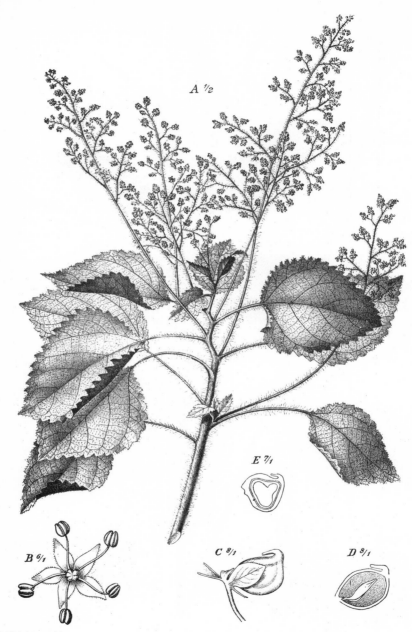

A ½

E ⁷/₁

B ⁶/₁

C ⁸/₁

D ⁸/₁

J. Fleischmann del.

Fleurya aestuans Gaudich.

A Flowering branch,   *B* Male flower,   *C* Older female flower.   *D* Pistil cut lengthwise.   *E* Fruit cut lengthwise.

5. Inflorescences unisexual, the lateral containing many male flowers, the middle one a single female flower. Receptacle covered on the outside by imbricate bracts. Male flowers with a 3—4-partite perianth and 3—4 stamens. Female flowers without a perianth. Trees or shrubs. Leaves undivided. — Species 2. Central Africa.   **Mesogyne** Engl.
Inflorescences bisexual, containing many male flowers and one or several female ones, usually provided with bracts on the margin only. Perianth 2-lobed or wanting. Stamens 2, rarely 1 or 3. 6
6. Receptacles top-shaped, subsequently cupular, bearing many male flowers and a single central female flower. Pericarp membranous. Shrubs. Leaves undivided. — Species 5. Central Africa.

Trymatococcus Poepp. & Endl.
Receptacles expanded, often divided into linear segments, bearing many male flowers and several female ones. Pericarp crusty within, fleshy outside. Herbs or low shrubs. — Species 50. Tropics. Some are poisonous or used medicinally. (Plate 31.) . . . . **Dorstenia** L.
7. Female flowers solitary, axillary ; male flowers in spike-like inflorescences. Perianth 4-toothed. Trees. Leaves undivided. — Species 1. Island of Réunion. Used medicinally. [Tribe STREBLEAE.]

Maillardia Frapp. & Duchartre
Female flowers in spike- or head-like inflorescences. 8
8. Female flowers in head-like, but sometimes elongated (oblong) inflorescences, the male in spike- raceme- or head-like ones. Style simple, with a thread-shaped stigma, rarely with an abortive side-branch. Trees. [Tribe BROUSSONETIEAE.] 9
Female and male flowers in spike-like inflorescences. Perianth of the female flowers divided to the base. Style 2-parted, with thread-shaped, equal or subequal stigmas. [Tribe MOREAE.] 12
9. Male flowers in head-like inflorescences. Perianth of the female flowers 4-lobed. Spinous plants. — Species 1. East Africa and Madagascar. It yields a dye-wood and edible fruits. (Under *Plecospermum* Trecul)

Cardiogyne Bur.
Male flowers in spike- or raceme-like inflorescences. 10
10. Male flowers in lax, raceme-like inflorescences. Spinous plants. Leaves entire. Perianth of the female flowers deeply 4-cleft, persistent and enclosing the fruit. — Species 1. Cultivated in North Africa. The wood is used for joiners' work, the leaves as food for silkworms.

Maclura Nutt.
Male flowers in dense, spike-like inflorescences. Spineless plants. . . 11
11. Perianth of the female flowers deeply 4-cleft or 4-parted. Fruit wholly, or for the greatest part, enclosed by the perianth. Leaves undivided. — Species 2. Central Africa. They yield timber.   **Chlorophora** Gaud.
Perianth of the female flowers shortly toothed. Fruit overtopping the perianth. Leaves usually lobed. — Species 1 (*B. papyrifera* Vent., paper-mulberry). Cultivated in North Africa. Used for making paper ; the fruit is edible.. . . . . **Broussonetia** Vent.

12. Stipules united. Leaves entire, with numerous transverse nerves. Ovary
      subglobose. Seed with leaf-like, folded cotyledons. Shrubs. — Species
      2. Madagascar. . . . . **Pachytrophe** Bur.
    Stipules free. 13
13. Leaves entire, penninerved, leathery. Ovary compressed. Seed without
      albumen ; embryo with thick cotyledons Trees. — Species 2. Madagas-
      car. . . . . **Ampalis** Boj.
    Leaves toothed, 3-nerved at the base. Ovary ovoid or subglobose. Seed
      with copious albumen. — Species 3. Cultivated and naturalized in
      various regions. They yield timber, food for silkworms, edible fruits
      (mulberries), dyes, and medicaments. . . . . . **Morus** L.
14. (1.) Ovule erect, straight. Trees. Leaves folded in the bud. Stipules
      leaving an annular scar. [Subfamily **CONOCEPHALOIDEAE**.] 15
    Ovule pendulous, curved or inverted. Woody plants with the leaves rolled
      inwards in the bud, or herbaceous plants. 16
15. Leaves divided into 11—15 segments. Male flowers in false heads arranged
      in cymes ; perianth with a distinct tube. Stamen 1. Female flowers
      upon a flattened, ovate receptacle. Style long. — Species 1 (*M. Smithii*
      R. Br.). West Africa to the Upper Nile. Yields timber (cork-wood)
      and edible fruits. The aerial roots contain much water. **Musanga** R. Br.
    Leaves undivided, 3-lobed, or 5—7-parted. Male flowers in false spikes
      or heads arranged in cymes ; perianth divided quite or nearly to the
      base. Stamens 2—4. Female flowers in globose or subglobose false
      heads. Style short. — Species 8. Central Africa. Some species yield
      timber or edible fruits. . . . . **Myrianthus** Beauv.
16. Flowers in cymes arranged in spikes or panicles. Fruit dry. Herbs.
      Leaves palmately lobed or dissected. Stipules free. [Subfamily
      CANNABOIDEAE.] 17
    Flowers upon a globe-, club-, disc-, or cup-shaped receptacle. Herbs
      with undivided, lanceolate, penninerved leaves, or more frequently
      shrub or trees. Leaves undivided or lobed, coiled in the bud. Stipules
      usually united and leaving a stem-clasping scar. [Subfamily **ARTO-
      CARPOIDEAE**.] 18
17. Stem twining. Leaves opposite, lobed or the upper ones undivided.
      Female flowers in catkins. Embryo spirally twisted, with narrow coty-
      ledons. — Species 1 (*H. Lupulus* L., hop). Cultivated in the extra-
      tropical regions. It is used for making beer, as a vegetable and a fibre-
      plant, and in medicine. . . . . **Humulus** L.
    Stem erect. Leaves opposite below, alternate above, dissected. Female
      flowers in panicles. Embryo curved, with broad cotyledons. — Species
      1 (*C. sativa* L., hemp). Cultivated in various regions. It yields fibre,
      oil, and an intoxicating drug (hashish). . . . . **Cannabis** Tourn.
18. Flowers enclosed within a pouch-shaped, usually bisexual receptacle pro-
      vided at the top with a small opening surrounded by bracts. Embryo
      curved. Shrubs or trees. — Species 160. Some of them yield timber,

bast-fibres, bark for clothing, india-rubber, shellac, vegetables, medicaments, and edible fruits (especially the figs, from *F. carica* L.) which are
also used for making brandy and a substitute for coffee. Some species
are poisonous or serve as ornamental plants. [Tribe FICEAE.]

Ficus L.

Flowers collected on a globe-, club-, disc-, or cup-shaped receptacle. 19

19. Receptacles more or less cup-shaped, containing many male flowers and a
single central female one. Stamen 1. Embryo straight. [Tribe
BROSIMEAE.] 20
Receptacles of two kinds, some containing only male flowers, the others
only female or many female intermixed with several male. Shrubs or
trees. 22

20. Perianth distinctly developed. Ovary free. Herbs or undershrubs.
— Species 3. Equatorial West Africa. (Including *Cyatanthus* Engl.)

Scyphosyce Baill.

Perianth not distinctly developed. Ovary immersed in and adnate to the
receptacle. Trees. 21

21. Receptacles covered with peltate bracts on their whole surface. Male
flowers with, female without bracts. — Species 2. West Africa (Congo).

Bosqueiopsis De Wild. & Dur.

Receptacles bearing bracts on the margin only. Female flowers with
male without bracts. — Species 6. Tropics. Some yield timber and
dye-stuffs. . . . . **Bosqueia** Thouars

22. Male flowers on a discoid or concave receptacle bearing numerous bracts
on the edge or the whole surface; female flowers on a similar receptacle
or solitary. [Tribe OLMEDIEAE.] 23
Male flowers on a globular or club-shaped receptacle bearing bracts at the
base only and between the flowers, or destitute of bracts; female flowers
on a more or less globular receptacle. [Tribe ARTOCARPEAE.] 24

23. Male inflorescences many-flowered, discoid; female 1-flowered. Male
flowers with, female without a perianth. — Species 3. Central Africa.
Poisonous, used medicinally, and yielding timber and fibre.

Antiaris Leschen.

Male and female inflorescences many-flowered, more or less concave. Male
flowers without, female with a perianth. — Species 2. Cultivated in the
tropics. Yielding india-rubber. . . . . . . **Castilloa** Cerv.

24. Inflorescences without bracts at the base. Flowers monoecious. Stamen
1. — Species 2. Cultivated in the tropics. They yield timber, bark
used for making cloth, bast-fibres, mucilage, starch, edible fruits, and
medicaments. "Breadfruit tree." . . . . **Artocarpus** Forst.
Inflorescences with some bracts at the base. Flowers dioecious. Stamens
1—5. 25

25. Female flowers surrounded each by two rows of very unequal bracts or
perianth-segments, not intermixed with male flowers. — Species 1.
Equatorial West Africa (Cameroons). . . **Acanthotreculia** Engl.

Female flowers surrounded by subequal bracts and intermixed with some male flowers. — Species 9. Tropics. Some species have edible seeds from which also oil and meal are prepared. . . . **Treculia** Decne.

FAMILY 54. URTICACEAE

Juice not milky. Leaves usually stipulate. Flowers unisexual, rarely (*Parietaria*) polygamous Perianth simple, with 1—5 segments, sometimes wanting in the female flowers. Stamens in the male flowers as many as perianth-segments. Filaments broadened at the base, bent inwards in the bud. Anthers attached by the back, opening by longitudinal slits. Ovary 1-celled. Ovule 1, erect or ascending, straight. Style 1 or 0. Fruit indehiscent. Seed with a thin coat and a straight embryo, usually albuminous. — Genera 20, species 150. (Plate 32.)

1. Stamen 1. Perianth of the male flowers entire or divided in 2—3 segments, of the female entire 4-toothed or wanting. Stigma linear. Herbs or undershrubs, rarely shrubs. Hairs not stinging. Stipules free. [Tribe FORSKOHLEAE.] 2
   Stamens 2—5. 4
2. Flower-clusters without an involucre and not surrounded by woolly hairs. Female flowers with a perianth. — Species 4. South and East Africa. (*Didymodoxa* E. Mey.) . . . . **Australina** Gaudich.
   Flower-clusters with an involucre and usually surrounded by woolly hairs. Female flowers without a perianth 3
3. Involucral bracts free or united at the base only. Stem rough. Herbs undershrubs or shrubs. — Species 5. . . . . . **Forskohlea** L.
   Involucral bracts united high up. Stem smooth. Herbs or undershrubs. — Species 5. Tropical and South Africa. ˙ **Droguetia** Gaudich.
4. Stipules absent. Leaves alternate, entire. Plants without stinging hairs. Female flowers in glomerules surrounded by an involucre ; perianth 4-cleft. [Tribe PARIETARIEAE.] 5
   Stipules present, very rarely rudimentary, but then leaves toothed. . . 6
5. Stem herbaceous. Flowers polygamous. Stigma spatulate and recurved. — Species 8. Some are used in medicine. " Pellitory."
                                            Parietaria Tourn.
   Stem woody. Flowers unisexual. Stigma linear. — Species 1. Canary Islands. . . . . ˙ . . **Gesnouinia** Gaudich.
6. Plants with stinging hairs, very rarely (*Fleurya*) almost glabrous, and then stigma linear-oblong and shortly papillose and perianth of the female flowers 3—4-partite. Perianth-segments of the female flowers 4, rarely 1—3. Embryo with orbicular cotyledons. [Tribe UREREAE.] 7
   Plants without stinging hairs. 12
7. Fruit straight. Stigma penicillate. Leaves opposite. Herbs. — Species 10. They yield material for spinning and paper-making and are used as pot-herbs and in medicine. " Nettle." . . **Urtica** Gaudich.
   Fruit oblique. Leaves alternate. 8

8. Stigma more or less capitate. Perianth surrounding the fruit fleshy. Shrubs or trees, rarely undershrubs. — Species 20. Tropical and South-East Africa. . . . . **Urera** Gaudich.
Stigma linear or oblong. 9

9. Perianth of the female flowers reduced to a single, sometimes 2-parted, large segment, more rarely consisting of 2 unequal segments. Herbs with punctiform cystoliths. — Species 3. Tropics. **Girardinia** Gaudich.
Perianth of the female flowers with 4 segments, of which 1—2 are sometimes rudimentary 10

10. Cystoliths linear. Annual herbs. Fruit gibbous, as long as or longer than the perianth. — Species 7. South and Central Africa. They yield fibre and fish-poison. (Plate 32.) . . . . . **Fleurya** Gaudich.
Cystoliths punctiform. Perennial herbs or woody plants. 11

11. Fruit as long as or longer than the perianth, smooth. — Species 3. Central Africa. (*Urticastrum* Heist.) . . . . . **Laportea** Gaudich.
Fruit much shorter than the membranous perianth. Shrubs. — Species 6. Madagascar, Mascarenes, East Africa . . . . **Obetia** Gaudich.

12. (6.) Stigma penicillate. Perianth of the female flowers 3-partite, rarely 4—5-partite or rudimentary, free from the ovary. Embryo with orbicular or ovate cotyledons. Cystoliths linear. Herbs or undershrubs, rarely shrubs; in this case leaves penninerved. Stipules connate. [Tribe PROCRIDEAE]. 13
Stigma filiform, rarely capitate and somewhat hairy, but then shrubs with 3-nerved leaves and perianth shortly toothed and adnate to the ovary. Perianth of the female flowers 2—4-toothed, entire, or wanting. Embryo with elliptical or oblong cotyledons. Cystoliths usually punctiform. Mostly woody plants. [Tribe BOEHMERIEAE.]. 16

13. Leaves opposite, but sometimes the pairs consisting of unequal leaves. Herbs. 14
Leaves alternate or subopposite, i.e., one leaf of each pair very small, stipule-like 15

14. Flowers on a disc- or bell-shaped receptacle. — Species 1. Abyssinia.
Lecanthus Wedd.
Flowers in glomerules arranged in panicles. — Species 35. Tropics. Some are used as vegetables or textile plants. (*Adicea* Rafin.) **Pilea** Lindl.

15. Flowers on an expanded receptacle. Perianth-segments of the female flowers linear or lanceolate. Herbs. Leaves unequal-sided. — Species 15. Tropics. . . . . **Elatostema** Forst.
Flowers in glomerules or heads without an involucre. Perianth-segments ovate. Shrubs or undershrubs. — Species 3. Tropics. **Procris** Juss.

16. Female flowers without a perianth. Stigma filiform. Shrubs. Leaves alternate. Flowers in axillary glomerules. — Species 1. Naturalized on the Island of Mauritius. . . . . **Phenax** Wedd.
Female flowers with a perianth. 17

17. Perianth of the female flowers free or almost free from the ovary, dry or
membranous in fruit. Stipules free or nearly so. Stigma filiform.   18
Perianth of the female flowers adnate to the ovary, more or less succulent
in fruit. Stipules evidently united. Leaves alternate.   Shrubs or
trees.   19
18. Stigma persistent. Perianth surrounding the fruit neither winged nor
ribbed. Leaves toothed. — Species 7. Tropical and South Africa.
Two of them (especially *B. nivea* Hook. & Arn., ramie or Chinese grass-
cloth plant) are cultivated as textile plants .   .   .   **Boehmeria** Jaqu.
Stigma decidous. Perianth surrounding the fruit usually winged or
ribbed. Leaves usually entire. — Species 10. Tropical and South
Africa.   .   .   .   .   **Pouzolzia** Gaudich.
19. Stigma filiform, deciduous. — Species 3. Madagascar and Mascarenes.
Pipturus Wedd.
Stigma capitate, more or less penicillate. — Species 1. Abyssinia.
Debregeasia Gaudich

ORDER PROTEALES

FAMILY 55. PROTEACEAE

Shrubs or trees Leaves alternate, rarely (*Brabeium*) whorled. Stipules
none. Flowers in heads, spikes, or racemes. Perianth with 4 petaloid, valvate
segments, usually surrounded by excrescences of the receptacle. Stamens 4,
opposite the perianth-segments. Anthers opening inwards. Ovary superior,
1-celled. Ovule 1, ascending and inverted, more rarely pendulous and straight,
very rarely ovules 2. Style simple, with a small stigma. Fruit a one-seeded
nut or drupe. Seed exalbuminous. — Genera 13, species 400. Southern and
tropical Africa. (Plate 33.)

1. Stamens inserted at the base of the perianth-segments ; anthers stalked.
Perianth regular, divided to the base. Flowers unisexual or poly
gamous. [Tribe PERSOONIEAE.]   2
Stamens inserted on the middle or the upper part of the perianth-segments ;
anthers usually sessile. Perianth more or less deeply divided, but
rarely to the base. [Tribe PROTEEAE.]   3
2. Receptacle with a short cupular excrescence at the base. Ovule pendulous.
Fruit a drupe. Flowers in fascicles . arranged in racemes. Leaves
whorled, undivided. — Species 1. South Africa. The fruits are
edible and used as a substitute for coffee .   .   .   .   . **Brabeium** L.
Receptacle with 4 scale-like excrescences at the base. Flowers in spikes
arranged in racemes. Leaves alternate, 2-lobed. — Species 1. Madagascar. The wood is used for torches, the seeds yield oil. **Dilobeia** Thouars
3. Flowers unisexual, regular 4
Flowers hermaphrodite 5
4. Male flowers in spikes or racemes, female in heads. Bracts narrow. —
Species 3. South Africa.   .   .   .   . **Aulax** Berg

J. Fleischmann del.

Leucospermum conocarpum R. Br.

A Flowering branch. *B* Flower laid open. *C* Perianth-segment and stamen.

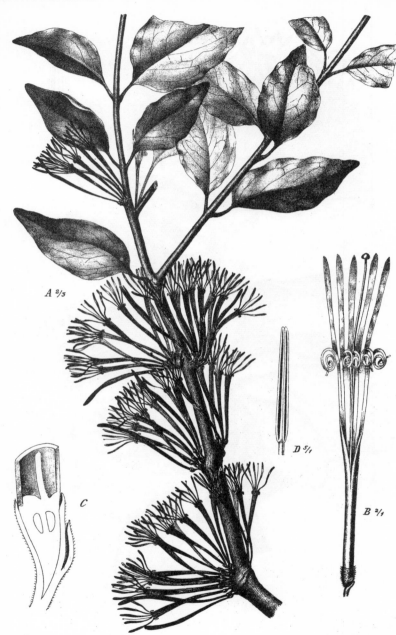

A ²/₃

C

D ⁵/₁

B ²/₁

J. Fleischmann del.

Loranthus capitatus (Spreng.) Engl.

A Flowering branch. *B* Flower. *C* Lower part of the flower cut lengthwise. *D* Anther.

Male and female flowers in heads. Bracts broad. — Species 75. South Africa. Some species yield timber or medicaments ; the silvery-haired leaves of the silver-tree (*L. argenteum* R. Br.) also form an article of commerce. . . . . **Leucadendron** Herm

5. Flowers regular or almost so, disposed in heads which are sometimes reduced to a single flower. Perianth-segments united below, free and recurved above 6

Flowers distinctly irregular. Perianth-segments more or less united, except the hindmost, which is separated from the others . . . 11

6. Leaves, at least the inferior, more or less divided 7

Leaves all undivided 8

7. Heads arranged in sometimes very short spikes, 4-flowered. Ovary glabrous or almost so. Fruit sessile. — Species 15. South Africa. (*Nivenia* R. Br.) . . . . **Paranomus** Salisb. & Knight

Heads solitary or arranged in corymbs or heads, usually many-flowered Ovary hairy, usually woolly or hispid. Fruit short-stalked. — Species 70. South Africa. . . . . **Serruria** Salisb.

8. Heads solitary, 4- or more-flowered. Fruit sessile. — Species 20. South Africa. (Including *Orothamnus* Eckl.) . . . . . **Mimetes** Salisb.

Heads arranged in spikes, racemes, or umbels, 1—6-flowered. Fruit with a short stalk 9

9. Flowers somewhat irregular. Stigma lateral, or very oblique, or seated in the centre of a disc-like expansion of the style-apex. Heads in lax spikes or racemes. — Species 25. South Africa . **Spatalla** Salisb.

Flowers regular. Stigma terminal or nearly so, conical or club-shaped. 10

10. Style more or less lateral, not constricted at the base. Perianth-tube 4-angled. Inflorescence cylindrical. — Species 5. South Africa
Spatallopsis Phillips

Style terminal, constricted at the base. Perianth-tube short, not 4-angled. Inflorescence globose. — Species 12. South Africa. **Sorocephalus** R. Br.

11. (5.) Anterior perianth-segments separating above. Anthers oblong or ovate. Style deciduous. Fruit glabrous. Flowers in sometimes oblong heads, usually yellow. — Species 40. South and East Africa. Some species yield timber and bark for tanning. (Plate 33.)
Leucospermum R. Br.

Anterior perianth-segments united almost to the top into a lip. Anthers linear. Style persistent Fruit covered with dense hairs 12

12. Flowers in spikes or racemes. Anthers obtuse. — Species 15. Tropical and South-east Africa. Some species yield timber. **Faurea** Harv.

Flowers in heads. Anthers usually with a prolonged connective — Species 130. South and Central Africa. Some species yield timber, bark for tanning, or medicaments. (*Leucadendron* L.) . . **Protea** L.

ORDER SANTALALES

SUBORDER SANTALINEAE

FAMILY 56.   SANTALACEAE

Terrestrial plants, sometimes parasitic on roots. Leaves undivided, exstipulate, sometimes scale-like. Flowers regular. Perianth simple. Stamens
3—6, as many as and inserted on the perianth-segments, equalling them or
shorter. Anthers stalked, 2-celled. Ovary inferior, rarely almost superior,
1-celled. Ovule 1, basal, or ovules 2—5, pendulous from the apex of a central
or subparietal placenta. Style simple or wanting. Fruit indehiscent. Seeds
without a testa, with copious fleshy albumen ; radicle of the embryo superior.
— Genera 6, Species 140. (Plate 34.)

1. Ovary superior. Ovule 1. Style absent ; stigma 2-lobed. Stalk of the
   fruit fleshy. Shrubs or trees. — Species 1. Madagascar. Used
   medicinally. [Tribe ANTHOBOLEAE.]   .   .   .   **Exocarpus** Labill.
   Ovary inferior. Ovules 2—5. Style present   2

2. Perianth-tube above the ovary coated by a disc on the inside, or wanting.
   Placenta thick, straight. Ovules recurved. Stigma 3—4-parted or
   4—5-lobed. Fruit a drupe. Shrubs. [Tribe OSYRIDEAE.]   .   3
   Perianth-tube above the ovary not coated by a disc on the inside. Placenta
   thin, usually flexuous. Ovules straight. Stigma entire or obscurely
   2—3-lobed. [Tribe THESIEAE.]   4

3. Leaves, at least most of them, opposite. Flowers in panicles which are
   sometimes composed of false umbels, 4—6-merous, hermaphrodite or
   polygamous. Stigma 4—5-lobed. Embryo with very short cotyledons.
   — Species 2. South Africa. They yield timber and tanning material.
   (*Rhoiocarpus* A. DC.) .   .   .   .   **Colpoon** Berg
   Leaves alternate. Flowers in false umbels, which are often arranged in
   racemes, or the female and hermaphrodite solitary, 3—4-merous,
   dioecious or polygamous. Stigma 3—4-partite. Embryo with long
   cotyledons. — Species 8.   North and East Africa to Natal. Some
   species yield fragrant wood (African sandalwood), tanning and dyeing
   materials, and medicaments. (Plate 34.) .   .   .   .   .   **Osyris** L.

4. Flowers dioecious. Perianth-tube above the ovary very shortly campanulate ; segments usually with a tuft of hairs in the male flowers.
   Anther-halves elliptical. Style short. — Species 6.   South Africa.
   Thesidium Sond.
   Flowers hermaphrodite. Perianth-tube above the ovary campanulate or
   cylindrical ; segments with tufts or rows of hairs. Anther-halves
   usually oblong. Style long or rather short.   5

5. Fruit a drupe. Flowers axillary, solitary or in glomerules. Undershrubs·
   — Species 7. East and South Africa .   .   .   .   **Osyridicarpus** A.DC·
   Fruit a nut. — Species 120 .   .   .   .   **Thesium** L·

J Fleischmann del.

Osyris tenuifolia Engl.

A Flowering branch. *B* Male flower. *C* Male flower from above. *D* Male flower cut lengthwise.

Pl. 36.

A ½

B ⁷/₁

C ¹⁰/₁

J Fleischmann del.

Opilia amentacea Roxb.

A Flowering branch. *B* Flower. *C* Flower cut lengthwise

FAMILY 57. OPILIACEAE

Shrubs or trees. Leaves alternate, entire. Flowers in spikes racemes or umbels, regular, hermaphrodite. Calyx (or calyx-like excrescence of the receptacle) entire or obscurely 4—5-toothed. Petals (or perianth-segments) 4—5, free. Stamens equal in number and opposite to them, free or adnate at the base. Disc present. Ovary superior or nearly so, 1-celled, with a thick central placenta. Ovule 1, pendulous from the apex of the placenta, with no coat. Style simple. Fruit succulent. Seed without a testa ; albumen abundant ; embryo large, with superior radicle. — Genera 2, species 15. (Under *OLACINEAE*) (Plate 35.)

Axis of the inflorescence with cushion-shaped swellings at the base of the pedicels. Flowers in short racemes or umbels. Receptacle broad, cupular. Disc lobed. Petals with inflected tips. Filaments short. Anthers broad. — Species 5. Central Africa.   **Rhopalopilia** Pierre

Axis of the inflorescence without swellings. Flowers in racemes. Receptacle small. — Species 10. Central Africa to Delagoa Bay. (*Groutia* Guill. & Perr., including *Urobotrya* Stapf). (Plate 35.) .   .   . **Opilia** Roxb.

FAMILY 58. GRUBBIACEAE

Shrubs. Leaves opposite, narrow, entire, leathery. Inflorescences axillary, cymose. Flowers regular, hermaphrodite. Perianth 4-partite, with sepaloid, valvate segments. Stamens 8, almost free from the perianth. Anthers 2-celled. Ovary inferior, 1-celled or at first incompletely 2-celled Ovules 2, pendulous from a central or subparietal placenta, straight, with no coat. Style simple ; stigma 2-lobed. Fruit a drupe. Seed 1, with a thin testa and fleshy albumen ; embryo straight, with inferior radicle. (Under *SANTALACEAE* or *HAMAMELIDACEAE*)

Genus 1, species 4. South Africa (Cape Colony). .   .   . **Grubbia** Berg

FAMILY 59. OLACACEAE

Shrubs or trees, rarely undershrubs. Leaves entire. Flowers regular. Calyx usually small. Petals or corolla-lobes 3—6, nearly always valvate in bud. Anthers opening by 2 longitudinal slits. Ovary superior or nearly so, rarely half-inferior or almost inferior, 1-celled, usually septate at the base, rarely 2—5-celled to the top. Ovules 1—5, pendulous from the apex of a usually free placenta, inverted. Style simple Fruit indehiscent. Seed 1 with a small embryo and abundant albumen. — Genera 11, species 70. Tropical and South Africa. (Plate 36.)

1. Ovary superior, 1-celled, sometimes septate at the base. Ovules 2—3, with no coat. 2

Ovary superior, 1-celled with 4—5 ovules, or completely or nearly completely 3—4-celled, or more or less inferior. Ovules with 1—2 coats. 5

2. Filaments united into a long tube. Stamens 4—5, as many as and opposite the divisions of the corolla. Disc 4—5-lobed. Calyx enlarged in fruit. Flowers in racemes or panicles. [Tribe APTANDREAE.] . . . 3
   Filaments free or nearly so. [Tribe OLACEAE.] 4
3. Flowers 4-merous, unisexual. Ovules 2. Calyx cupular, not splitting at the time of maturity. — Species 1. West Africa. **Aptandra** Miers
   Flowers 5-merous. Ovules 3. Calyx splitting into 3 segments at the time of maturity. — Species 2. Equatorial West Africa. They yield timber and oily seeds which are also used in medicine. **Ongokea** Pierre
4. Ovules 2. Stamens 5—10. Calyx not enlarged in fruit. — Species 6. West Africa. . . . . **Ptychopetalum** Benth.
   Ovules 3. Stamens 6—12, of which 3—6 are fertile. Calyx enlarged in fruit. — Species 40. Tropics. Some species yield timber (Plate 36.) . . . . **Olax** L.
5. Stamens as many as and opposite the petals, 4—6, free or nearly so. [Tribe ANACOLOSEAE.] 6
   Stamens 2—4 times as many as the petals. Ovary superior, completely or almost completely 3—4-celled. 9
6. Ovary superior, septate at the base, with 4—5 ovules. Flowers 5-merous, in panicles. — Species 1. Island of Mauritius. . **Stolidia** Baill.
   Ovary inferior or half-inferior. Flowers in axillary spikes racemes or fascicles 7
7. Flowers 6-merous. Calyx entire or toothed. Ovary very incompletely 2-celled. Ovules 2. — Species 1. Madagascar. **Anacolosa** Blume
   Flowers 4—5-merous. Ovary completely or almost completely 3—4-celled. Ovules 3—4 8
8. Flowers 4-merous. Calyx shortly toothed. Ovary 4-celled. Fruit a drupe. — Species 2. Equatorial West Africa. **Strombosiopsis** Engl.
   Flowers 5-merous. Calyx deeply divided. Ovary 3-celled. Fruit a berry. — Species 7. Central Africa. (Including *Lavalleopsis* Van Tiegh.)
   Strombosia Blume
9. Stamens 3—4 times as many as the petals, 12—20. Calyx entire, not enlarged in fruit. Juice resinous. — Species 1. Equatorial West Africa. Yields timber and edible oily seeds. [Tribe COULEAE.]
   Coula Baill.
   Stamens twice as many as the petals, 8—12. Calyx 4—6-toothed. Juice not resinous. 10
10. Anthers globose. Ovary incompletely 3-celled. Style short. Petals 5—6. Calyx much enlarged in fruit. Leaves with milky juice. — Species 3. West Africa. [Tribe HEISTERIEAE.] **Heisteria** Jaqu.
    Anthers linear. Ovary almost completely 3—4-celled. Style as long as the ovary. Petals 4—5. Calyx not enlarged in fruit. Leaves with watery juice. — Species 3. Tropical and South-East Africa. They yield fragrant wood, bark for tanning, edible fruits, and oily seeds, and are also used in medicine. [Tribe XIMENIEAE.] **Ximenia** Plum.

J. Fleischmann del.

Olax Durandii Engl.

A Flowering branch. *B* Branch of another specimen. *C* Flower cut lengthwise.

J. Fleischmann del.

Aristolochia bracteata Retz.

A Plant in flower. *B* Flower. *C* Lower part of the flower (the ovary cut lengthwise).

FAMILY 60. OCTOKNEMATACEAE

Shrubs or trees. Leaves alternate, undivided, without stipules. Flowers in axillary racemes. Petals 5, valvate in bud. Stamens 5, opposite the petals ; filaments short. Disc obscure. Ovary inferior, 1-celled, with a free filiform placenta and 3 pendulous ovules. Style divided into 3—5 two- or three-cleft lobes. Fruit woody, surrounded by the fleshy receptacle. Seeds with a thin coat ; embryo minute, situated at the apex of the 8-furrowed albumen. (Under *OLACACEAE*.)

Genus 1, species 3. Equatorial West Africa.   **Octoknema** Pierre

SUBORDER LORANTHINEAE

FAMILY 61. LORANTHACEAE

Shrubs, parasitic upon trees. Leaves undivided, exstipulate, sometimes scale-like. Perianth simple, with 2—6 valvate segments, often surrounded at the base by a calyx-like outgrowth of the receptacle. Stamens as many as and opposite the perianth-segments and inserted on them. Ovary inferior, with 1—4 indistinctly developed ovules. Style and stigma simple. Fruit succulent. Seeds albuminous. — Genera, 4, species 300. (Plate 37.)

1. Receptacle with a calyx-like outgrowth surrounding the base of the perianth. Flowers usually hermaphrodite. Anthers usually stalked and opening by two longitudinal slits. Style more or less filiform. Leaves well-developed. — Species 250. Tropical and South Africa. Some are used medicinally. (Plate 37). [Subfamily **LORANTHOIDEAE.**]
                                                LORANTHUS L.

    Receptacle without a calyx-like outgrowth. Flowers unisexual. Anthers sessile. [Subfamily **VISCOIDEAE.**] 2

2. Anthers adnate to the perianth ; cells several or many, opening by pores. Placenta basal. Flowers in clusters of 3 or more. — Species 50. Some of them yield bird-lime or are used medicinally. "Mistletoe." [Tribe VISCEAE.] . . . . **Viscum** L

    Anthers seated on the perianth, but not adnate to it ; cells 1—2, opening by longitudinal or transverse slits. Placenta central. Leaves scale-like. 3

3. Anthers 1-celled, opening by a transverse slit. Perianth of the male flowers 2—5-parted, of the female 2-parted. Flowers dioecious, solitary. — Species 1. North-West Africa. [Tribe ARCEUTHOBIEAE.]
                                      Arceuthobium Marsch. Bieb.

    Anthers 2-celled, opening by 2 longitudinal slits. Perianth 3-parted. Flowers monoecious, disposed in rows. — Species 5. Madagascar and neighbouring islands. (*Bifaria* Van Tiegh.) [Tribe PHORADEND-REAE.] . . . . **Korthalsella** Van Tiegh.

SUBORDER BALANOPHORINEAE

FAMILY 62. BALANOPHORACEAE

Succulent herbs without green colour, parasitic on roots, upon which their root-stock is seated. Leaves reduced to scales. Flowers in spadix-like spikes or heads, red, unisexual. Perianth in the male flowers of 3—6 segments, in the female 3-lobed or wanting. Stamens as many as and opposite the perianth-segments, sometimes one of them abortive. Ovary inferior or naked, 1-celled. Ovules 1—3, pendulous from a central placenta or from the apex of the cell or adnate to the wall of the ovary, without coats. Style simple, sometimes very short ; stigma entire or lobed. Fruit a drupe. Seed without a testa ; albumen copious ; embryo small, apical, undivided. — Genera 4, species 6. Tropical and South Africa.

1. Fertile stamens 2. Female flowers with a 3-lobed perianth. Ovules 3. Stigma 3-lobed, borne on a long filiform style. Spadices oblong, solitary. — Species 2. South Africa. [Subfamily **MYSTROPETALOIDEAE.**]

   Mystropetalon Harv.

   Fertile stamens 3 or more. Female flowers without a perianth, but the base of the style sometimes surrounded by a tubular outgrowth of the receptacle. Stigma entire or sessile.   2

2. Stamens free. Anthers globose, many-celled. Ovules 3. Stigma sessile. Spadices panicled. Root-stock not resinous. — Species 1.   South and East Africa. [Subfamily **SARCOPHYTOIDEAE.**]   **Sarcophyte** Sparrm.

   Stamens united. Anthers 2—4-celled. Ovule 1. Style and stigma simple. Spadices solitary. Root-stock resinous. [Subfamily **BALAN-OPHOROIDEAE.**]   3

3. Anthers 3—6, linear, 4-celled. Ovary linear. Ovule adnate to the wall of the ovary. Perianth-segments of the male flowers linear. Spadices hemispherical. — Species 2. Tropics. [Tribe LANGSDORFFIEAE.]

   Thonningia Vahl

   Anthers numerous, 2-celled. Ovule free, pendulous. — Species 1. Comoro Islands. [Tribe BALANOPHOREAE.] .   .   .   **Balanophora** Forst.

ORDER ARISTOLOCHIALES

FAMILY 63. ARISTOLOCHIACEAE

Leaves alternate, entire or lobed. Flowers axillary, solitary or in clusters, irregular, hermaphrodite. Perianth simple, corolla-like, with a distinct tube. Stamens 5—24, adnate to the style. Anthers opening outwards or laterally by longitudinal slits. Ovary inferior, 4—6-celled. Ovules several or many in each cell, pendulous descending or horizontal, inverted. Style or stigma 6-lobed. Fruit capsular. Seeds with a small embryo and copious albumen (Plate 38.)

Genus 1, species 30. Some are used medicinally   .   .   **Aristolochia** L

FAMILY 64. RAFFLESIACEAE

Parasitic herbs, partly immersed in the tissue of the plants upon which they grow. Leaves reduced to scales. Flowers terminal, solitary or in rac mes, regular, unisexual. Perianth-segments 4 or more. Stamens 8 or more ; filaments united into a column. Ovary inferior, 1-celled with 4 or more parietal placentas, or several-celled with axile placentas. Ovules numerous. Style simple ; stigmas situated beneath its thickened apex. Fruit a berry. Seeds minute, with a hard testa, oily albumen, and undivided embryo. — Genera 2, Species 4. (*CYTINACEAE*.)

Ovary 1-celled, with usually 4 slightly projecting parietal placentas. Ovules inverted. Anthers affixed beneath the thickened apex of the staminal column, opening by transverse slits. Perianth-segments free. Flowers solitary. — Species 1. Southern West Africa (Angola). (Under *Apodanthes* Poiteau). [Tribe APODANTHEAE.] **Pilostyles** Guill.

Ovary more or less completely 6- or more-celled ; placentas parietal, but much projecting, sometimes uniting in the middle. Ovules straight. Anthers laterally affixed to the thickened apex of the staminal column, opening by longitudinal slits. Perianth-segments united below. Flowers in spikes, racemes, or panicles. — Species 3.   North and South Africa and Madagascar. They have edible fruits and are used medicinally. [Tribe CYTINEAE.] . . . . **Cytinus** L.

FAMILY 65. HYDNORACEAE

Fleshy, herbaceous, leafless root-parasites with a creeping root-stock Flowers solitary, regular, hermaphrodite. Perianth simple, fleshy, tubular, with 3—4 (very rarely 5) valvate segments. Stamens as many as and alternate with the perianth-segments, inserted in the tube ; filaments united ; anther-cells numerous, linear, opening by longitudinal slits. Ovary inferior, 1-celled, with many placentas hanging down from the top of the cell. Stigma sessile. Fruit succulent. Seeds with a hard testa, copious albumen, and undivided embryo. (Under *CYTINACEAE*).

Genus 1, species 8.   Tropical and South Africa. Some are edible or used for tanning . . . . **Hydnora** Thunb.

ORDER POLYGONALES

FAMILY 66. POLYGONACEAE

Leaves alternate, undivided or pinnately cleft, provided at the base with a stem-clasping sheath. Flowers regular. Perianth-segments 3—6. Stamens 4—50. Ovary superior, 1-celled. Ovule 1. Styles 2—4, free or united at the base. Fruit a nut. Seed with an abundant, mealy albumen and a usually lateral embryo. — Genera 9, species 120. (Plate 39.)

1. Stamens as many as perianth-segments, 6, rarely 4; occasionally fewer than perianth-segments, and then stamens 4—5 and perianth-segments 5—6 in the male, 6 in the female flowers; in this case stem herbaceous and flowers monoecious. [Subfamily **RUMICOIDEAE**, Tribe RUMICEAE.] 2

Stamens more than perianth-segments, rarely equal in number, but then 5. Herbs or undershrubs with hermaphrodite or polygamous flowers, or shrubs. 3

2. Perianth at the time of maturity firm, tubular, tightly clasping the fruit. Flowers unisexual. Annual herbs. — Species 2. North and South Africa, also naturalized in the Mascarene Islands. . **Emex** Neck.

Perianth at the time of maturity more or less membranous, not tubular and not clasping the fruit very tightly. — Species 45. Some are used as vegetables, for tanning and dyeing, or in medicine. " Dock." **Rumex** L.

3. Seed with ruminate albumen. Shrubs with 5, 7—10, or 20—50 stamens. [Subfamily **COCCOLOBOIDEAE**.] 4

Seed with homogeneous albumen. Herbs or undershrubs, more rarely shrubs with 6 or 12—18 stamens. [Subfamily **POLYGONOIDEAE**.] 5

4. Flowers unisexual. Perianth-segments 4 or 6, the outer deciduous. Stamens 20—50. Erect shrubs or trees. — Species 1. West Africa. [Tribe TRIPLARIDEAE.] . . . . **Symmeria** Benth.

Flowers hermaphrodite. Perianth-segments 5, united at the base into a tube becoming two-winged in fruit. Stamens 5—10. Mostly climbing, tendril-bearing plants. — Species 3. West Africa. [Tribe COCCOLO-BEAE.] . . . . **Brunnichia** Banks

5. Stem woody, shrubby. Leaves small. Stamens 6 or 12—18. Filaments united at the base. [Tribe ATRAPHAXIDEAE.] 6

Stem herbaceous or woody at the base only. Stamens 8, more rarely 5—7. Filaments free, but sometimes inserted on a ring-shaped disc. [Tribe POLYGONEAE.] 7

6. Perianth-segments 4, the inner much enlarged in fruit. Stamens 6, the outer with a callosity at the base. Stigmas 2. Fruit glabrous. Embryo lateral. Leaves ovate or orbicular. — Species 1. Egypt. **Atraphaxis** L.

Perianth-segments 5—6, not enlarged in fruit. Stamens 12—18, with a hairy appendage at the base. Stigmas 4. Fruit bristly. Embryo axile. Leaves linear or subulate. — Species 1. North Africa.
Calligonum L.

7. Perianth-segments of the hermaphrodite and female flowers united below into a narrow tube. Flowers polygamous. — Species 17. Central and South Africa. Some are used as vegetables and for making bread. (Including *Raphanopsis* Welw.) (Plate 39.) . . **Oxygonum** Burch.

Perianth-segments not united below into a narrow tube. 8

8. Seed with broad, folded cotyledons. Perianth shorter than the fruit. Leaves cordate. — Species 1 (*F. esculentum* Moench, buckwheat). Cultivated as a cereal or fodder-plant. (Under *Polygonum* L.)
Fagopyrum Gaertn.

A ⁴/₁

B ⁶/₁   *C* ⁴/₁

J. Fleischmann del

Oxygonum sinuatum (Hochst. and Steud.) Benth. and Hook.

A Fruiting plant.   *B* Flower cut lengthwise.   *C* Fruit cut lengthwise.

Traganum nudatum Del.

A Flowering branch. B Part of a fruiting branch. C End of a branch. D Flower with bracts and bracteoles. E Flower cut lengthwise.

Seed with narrow, not folded cotyledons. — Species 50. Some are poisonous, others serve as ornamental, medicinal, or fodder-plants, or yield
tanning and dyeing materials. . . . . . . **Polygonum** L.

ORDER CENTROSPERMAE

SUBORDER CHENOPODIINEAE

FAMILY 67. CHENOPODIACEAE

Stem erect, ascending, or prostrate. Leaves exstipulate, sometimes wanting.
Flowers inconspicuous, greenish. Perianth simple, of 1— 5 imbricate segments,
herbaceous or membranous, persistent, rarely wanting. Stamens as many
as and opposite the perianth-segments or fewer, inserted on the receptacle or the
base of the perianth. Anthers attached by the back, opening inwards or
laterally by longitudinal slits, curved inwards in the bud. Ovary superior,
rarely (*Beta*) half-inferior, 1-celled. Ovule 1, on a basal funicle, curved.
Stigmas 2—5. Fruit dehiscing by a lid or indehiscent. Seed with a curved,
peripheral embryo. — Genera 26, species 120. (*SALSOLACEAE.*) (Plate 40.)
 1. Embryo spiral . Albumen wanting or separated in two parts by the em-
    bryo. 2
    Embryo more or less ring- or horseshoe-shaped or folded together. Albu-
    men wholly or partly enclosed by the embryo, rarely wanting . . . 11
 2. Bracteoles small, scale-like. Perianth herbaceous or fleshy. Stigmas
    thread-shaped, papillose all round. Leaves glabrous, fleshy. — Species
    10. Some are used as vegetables or for making soda. (Including
    Chenopodina Moq., *Lerchia* Hall., *Schanginia* C. A. Mey., *Schoberia* C. A.
    Mey., and *Sevada* Moq.) [Tribe SUAEDEAE.] . **Suaeda** Forsk.
    Bracteoles equalling or exceeding the perianth. Perianth usually mem-
    branous. Stigmas papillose on the inside. Leaves usually hairy.
    [Tribe SALSOLEAE.] 3
 3. Seed horizontal. Disc usually inconspicuous. [Subtribe SODINAE.] . 4
    Seed vertical. Disc usually lobed. [Subtribe ANABASINAE.] . . 6
 4. Perianth 5-lobed, hardening to the top and wingless in the fruit. Filaments
    flattened. Disc inconspicuous. Embryo in a conical spiral. Shrubs
    with continuous branches and alternate leaves. — Species 2. North
    Africa to the Sahara. (Plate 40.) . . . . **Traganum** Del.
    Perianth 4— 5-parted or of 4—5 free segments, not hardening or at the
    base only and furnished with a horizontal wing in the fruit. . . 5
 5. Branches jointed. Leaves scale-like, opposite, connate in pairs. Shrubs.
    Perianth-segments free. Anthers blunt. Disc lobed, enlarged in the
    fruit. Embryo in a flat spiral. — Species 2. North Africa.
                                                    Haloxylon Bunge
    Branches continuous. Disc usually inconspicuous. — Species 20. Some
    of them are used as vegetables or in medicine or furnish soda. "Salt-
    wort." (Including *Caroxylon* Thunb.) . . . . . . **Salsola** L.

6. Perianth of 2 inner and 3 outer segments of which two are in front and one behind. Fruiting perianth winged, not hardened. Seed compressed dorsally. Flowers solitary, more rarely in clusters, and then branches jointed and leaves opposite. 7
Perianth of 3 inner and 2 outer segments of which one is in front and one behind. Fruiting perianth more or less hardened. Seed compressed laterally. Branches continuous. 8

7. Branches jointed. Leaves opposite, sometimes reduced to scales. Filaments awl-shaped. Style short. — Species 5. North Africa and Nubia. Some yield soda or are used medicinally.   **Anabasis** L.
Branches continuous. Leaves alternate. Spinous shrubs. Flowers solitary. Filaments flattened ; connective pointed. Style long. Pericarp membranous. — Species 1. North Africa. . . . . . **Noaea** Moq.

8. Perianth-segments united at the base, wingless in the fruit, but one of them sometimes produced into a prickle. Style long. Shrubs. . . 9
Perianth-segments free, winged in the fruit, at least some of them. Style short. Disc lobed. Leaves alternate. Flowers in clusters. . . 10

9. Leaves opposite. Flowers in pairs, hermaphrodite. Disc indistinct. — Species 1. Sahara. . . . . **Nucularia** Battand.
Leaves alternate. Flowers in clusters, polygamous. Disc lobed. — Species 2. North Africa and Northern Central Africa. **Cornulaca** Del.

10. Inner perianth-segments not winged in the fruit. Stamens with a 2-lobed connective. Shrubs. — Species 1. North Africa. (Under *Halogeton* C. A. Mey.) . . . . **Agathophora** Fenzl
Inner and outer perianth-segments winged in the fruit. Stamens with a blunt connective. Herbs. — Species 1. North-West Africa (Algeria). Used as a vegetable or for making soda. . . **Halogeton** C. A. Mey.

11. (1.) Branches more or less distinctly jointed. Leaves little developed, glabrous. Flowers in clusters, usually of 3, arising in the axils of scale-like bracts or apparently sunk in hollows of the rachis and collected in cone-shaped inflorescences. Stamens 1—2. [Tribe SALICORNIEAE.] 12
Branches continuous. Leaves well developed, usually hairy. Flowers solitary or in clusters, more rarely in spike-like inflorescences. Stamens 3—5, more rarely 1—2. 16

12. Bracts and upper leaves alternate 13
Bracts and upper leaves opposite 14

13. Perianth slightly flattened from the side, 4—5-toothed, surrounded by a wing-like border. Stamens 2. Ovule with a short funicle. Micropyle of the ovule and radicle of the embryo inferior. Low shrubs.— Species 1. North-West Africa (Algeria). . . . . . . **Kalidium** Moq.
Perianth flattened from the back, 3-toothed, without a wing-like border. Ovule with a long funicle. Micropyle and radicle superior or ascending. — Species 2. North Africa to Nubia. Yield soda . **Halopeplis** Bunge

14. Bracts free, peltate, deciduous. Perianth 3-parted. Stamen 1, inserted in front. Ovule on a long, curved, almost ring-shaped funicle. Micropyle and radicle superior. Shrubs. — Species 1. North Africa to Eritrea. Yields soda. . . . . **Halocnemum** Marsch. Bieb.

Bracts united, persistent; flower-clusters apparently sunk in hollows of the branch-joints. Perianth 3—4-toothed or -cleft. Stamen 1, inserted behind, or stamens 2. Ovule on a short funicle. Micropyle and radicle inferior 15

15. Seed smooth or tubercled; embryo curved; albumen abundant, lateral. Stamens 2. Stigmas 2. Shrubs. — Species 3. North and Central Africa. They yield soda and are used in medicine. **Arthrocnemum** Moq.

Seed hairy; embryo folded together; albumen scanty and central or wanting. — Species 4. Sea-coasts. They yield soda and are used in medicine. . . . . **Salicornia** L.

16. Flowers unisexual, sometimes intermixed with a few hermaphrodite, of two kinds, the male and hermaphrodite with a 3—5-parted perianth and without bracteoles, the female without a perianth, but with 2 sometimes united or 2-parted bracteoles. Stamens 3—5. Leaves glabrous, mealy or cottony, usually hastate. [Tribe ATRIPLICEAE.] . .17

Flowers hermaphrodite, sometimes intermixed with similar unisexual ones, all with 4—5 perianth-segments. 19

17. Bracteoles small, narrow, free, unchanged in the fruiting stage, not enclosing the fruit. Flowers monoecious. Stamens 5. Shrubs. — Species 2. South Africa and St. Helena. . . . . **Exomis** Fenzl

Bracteoles large, broad, usually united and hardening, completely enclosing the fruit. 18

18. Bracteoles united nearly to the top, hardened in the fruit and sometimes prolonged into 2—4 prickles. Flowers dioecious. Stigmas 4—5. Stem and leaves glabrous. Herbs. — Species 1 (*S. oleracea* L., spinach). Cultivated in the extra-tropical regions. It serves as a vegetable; the seeds are sometimes used for making bread . . . **Spinacia** L.

Bracteoles free and herbaceous, or more or less united, but not nearly to the top, and at length hardened. Stigmas 2—3. Stem and leaves clothed, when young, with bladdery hairs, afterwards mostly with a close minute whitish pubescence. — Species 20. Some are used as vegetables, for making soda, in medicine, or as ornamental plants. "Orache." (Including *Obione* Gaertn.) . . . . **Atripex** L.

19. Ovary half-inferior. Perianth-segments connivent in the fruit. Fruit dehiscing by a lid. Herbs with a fleshy taproot. Bracteoles usually present. — Species 3. North Africa and Cape Verde Islands; one of them (*B. vulgaris* L., beet) also cultivated in South Africa and Madagascar. The latter species yields sugar, vegetables, fodder, and a substitute for coffee and tobacco. [Tribe BETEAE.] **Beta** L.

Ovary superior. Fruit indehiscent, rarely dehiscing by a lid, but then perianth-segments spreading in the fruit. 20

20. Flowers with bracteoles, solitary. Perianth membranous, unchanged in the fruit ; segments erect. Stigmas 2. Ovule on a long funicle. Pericarp membranous. Herbs or undershrubs. Leaves subulate, rigid, pungent. — Species 1. North-West Africa (Algeria). [Tribe POLYCNEMEAE.] . . . . **Polycnemum** L.
Flowers without bracteoles. 21

21. Perianth 4—5-lobed, membranous. Leaves narrow, clothed with thin hairs. [Tribe CAMPHOROSMEAE.] 22
Perianth 5-parted, rarely 4-parted or 5-lobed, more or less herbaceous. Leaves usually broad and clothed with bladdery hairs. 25

22. Perianth unequally 4-toothed, scarcely changed in the fruit. Stamens 4. Seed erect. Embryo horseshoe-shaped. Flowers in spikes. Undershrubs. — Species 1. North Africa. Used medicinally.
Camphorosma L.
Perianth 5-toothed, 5-lobed, or 5-cleft. Stamens 5. Seed nearly always horizontal. Embryo ring-shaped. Flowers solitary or in clusters, in the axils of the leaves. 23

23. Fruiting perianth unchanged and unappendaged. Undershrubs. — Species 3. North and South Africa. . . . . . . **Chenolea** Thunb.
Fruiting perianth winged, gibbous, or prickly. 24

24. Fruiting perianth gibbous or prickly. — Species 2. North Africa. (*Echinopsilon* Moq., under *Chenolea* Thunb. or *Kochia* Roth) . **Bassia** All.
Fruiting perianth with one or several wings. — Species 3. South Africa to Hereroland and North Africa to Nubia. . . . . . **Kochia** Roth

25. Fruit not enclosed in the perianth, dehiscing with a lid. Perianth-segments spreading, linear-oblong. Stamens 5, much shorter than the perianth. Stigmas 2, short: Leaves elliptical or lanceolate, entire, glabrous. Undershrubs. — Species 1. North-West Africa (Algeria).
Oreobliton Durieu & Moq.
Fruit wholly or partly enclosed in the perianth, indehiscent. Leaves usually broad, toothed, and mealy or glandular-hairy. — Species 25. Some of them yield edible seeds, dyes, and medicaments, or are used as vegetables or ornamental plants ; several are poisonous. " Goosefoot." (Including *Blitum* L. and *Roubieva* Moq.) [Tribe CHENOPODIEAE.]
Chenopodium L.

FAMILY 68. AMARANTACEAE

Leaves without stipules. Perianth more or less dry, simple, of 1—5 imbricate segments. Stamens as many as and opposite the perianth-segments or fewer. Anthers attached by the back, opening inwards by two longitudinal slits. Ovary superior, 1-celled. Ovules erect or suspended from a basal funicle, curved. Fruit dehiscing by a lid or indehiscent. Embryo surrounding the mealy albumen. — Genera 32, species 200. (Plate 41.)

1. Anthers 1-celled. Ovule 1. Herbs or undershrubs. Leaves opposite. Inflorescences head- or shortly spike-shaped. [Subfamily **GOM-PHRENCIDEAE,** tribe GOMPHRENEAE.] 2
Anthers 2-celled. [Subfamily **AMARANTOIDEAE.**] 4

2. Stigma 1, capitate. Fertile stamens alternating with staminodes. — Species 7. Some are used as ornamental plants, others are noxious weeds. (Including *Telanthera* R. Br.) [Subtribe FROEHLICHINAE.]
Alternanthera Forsk.
Stigmas 2—4, subulate. [Subtribe GOMPHRENINAE.] 3

3. Filaments entire. — Species 1. Central Africa. (*Philoxerus* R. Br.)
Iresine L
Filaments fringed, toothed, or 3-parted. — Species 1. Tropical and South East Africa. A weed, sometimes used as an ornamental plant.
Gomphrena L.

4. Ovule 1. [Tribe AMARANTEAE.] 5
Ovules 2 or more, very rarely ovule 1, erect; in this case filaments united below into a membranous tube and flowers hermaphrodite. [Tribe CELOSIEAE.] 32

5. Ovule erect. Radicle of the embryo descending. Filaments free or united in a ring at the base. Flowers unisexual, polygamous, or hermaphrodite but intermixed with sterile ones. Leaves alternate. [Subtribe AMARAN-TINAE.] 6
Ovule pendulous. Radicle of the embryo ascending. [Subtribe ACHY-RANTHINAE.] 9

6. Perianth spreading. Filaments united at the base. Stigmas 3. Fruit a berry. Shrubs. Flowers polygamous, in spikes or racemes. — Species 1. Canary Islands . . . . **Bosia** L.
Perianth erect. Herbs or undershrubs. 7

7. Flowers unisexual or polygamous; no sterile ones. Filaments free. — Species 20. Some of them have edible seeds or are used as vegetables, in medicine or as ornamental plants. (Including *Albersia* Kunth, *Amblogyna* Rafin., and *Euxolus* Rafin.) . . . . . **Amarantus** L.
Flowers hermaphrodite. Partial inflorescences consisting of one fertile and two sterile flowers 8

8. Sterile flowers comb-shaped. Filaments free. Style short; stigma 2-lobed. — Species 1. Tropical and North Africa. Used as a vegetable
Digera Forsk.
Sterile flowers wing-shaped. Filaments united at the base. Style long, stigmas 2. — Species 1. Northern East Africa (Somaliland).
Pleuropterantha Franch.

9. Flowers solitary in the axil of each bract. 10
Flowers in clusters of two or more; usually some of them sterile. . . 20

10. Spurious staminodes (sterile processes) interposed between the fertile stamens 11
Spurious staminodes wanting 18

11. Perianth densely covered with silky or woolly hairs 12
    Perianth glabrous or scantily hairy 15
12. Perianth-segments firmly leathery, silky-hairy, 3-nerved. Shrubs. Leaves
    alternate, fleshy. — Species 1. South Africa to Damaraland. (Under
    Sericocoma Fenzl) . . . . **Calicorema** Hook. fil.
    Perianth-segments more or less membranous 13
13. Branches jointed. Leaves very small, opposite, ovate, acuminate. Under-
    shrubs. — Species 1. Southern West Africa (Hereroland).
    Arthraerua Schinz
    Branches continuous. 14
14. Perianth-segments silky, more or less thickened and hardened at the
    base, 1-nerved. Flowers small. Ovary hairy. Stigma capitate. —
    Species 8. Southern and Central Africa. . . . **Sericocoma** Fenzl
    Perianth-segments woolly, not thickened. Flowers very small, in dense
    spikes. — Species 10. Some are used as vegetables or as ornamental
    plants. (*Ouret* Adans.) . . . . **Aerva** Forsk.
15. Spurious staminodes minute, narrow, acute, unappendaged. Perianth-
    segments brownish-red, stiff-leathery, large, oblong, 3-nerved. In-
    florescence head-like, ovoid. Leaves usually alternate. Undershrubs.
    — Species 1. Southern West Africa (Angola and Congo).
    Mechowia Schinz
    Spurious staminodes more or less quadrate, fringed or appendaged. Leaves
    opposite. 16
16. Spurious staminodes fringed below the top. Perianth-segments erect,
    oblong, blunt, thickened below. Flowers erect, spicate. Leaves small,
    sessile, linear-oblong. Herbs. — Species 1. Southern East Africa.
    (Under *Pandiaka* Hook. fil.) . . . . . . **Argyrostachys** Lopr.
    Spurious staminodes fringed at the top or prolonged into appendages.
    Perianth-segments pointed. Flowers usually bent downwards. . . 17
17. Perianth-segments red or yellow, elliptical, hardened at the base, faintly
    1—5-nerved. Shrubs or undershrubs. — Species 7. Central Africa to
    Transvaal . . . . **Centema** Hook. fil.
    Perianth-segments white green or brown, lanceolate, stiff-leathery,
    usually 3-ribbed. — Species 30. Some of them yield a substitute for
    soap or are used in medicine. (Including *Achyropsis* Moq. and *Pandiaka*
    Moq.) (Plate 41.) . . . . **Achyranthes** L.
18. (10.) Stamens 1—2. Perianth-segments 3—5, membranous, woolly, 1-
    nerved. Herbs. — Species 1. Tropics. . . . **Nothosaerua** Wight
    Stamens 4—5. 19
19. Outer perianth-segments densely clothed with silky hairs, faintly 3-nerved.
    Style slender. Shrubs. — Species 2. Northern East Africa (Somali-
    land). . . . . **Chionothrix** Hook. fil.
    Outer perianth-segments glabrous or scantily hairy, with 3 strong ribs.
    Flowers greenish. — Species 15. Central and South East Africa. (In-
    cluding *Psilostachys* Hochst.) . . . . . . **Psilotrichum** Blume

AMARANTACEAE.

Pl. 41.

J. Fleischmann del.

Achyranthes angustifolia Benth.

A Flowering branch. B Branch of the inflorescence. C Flower cut lengthwise.

Pl. 42.

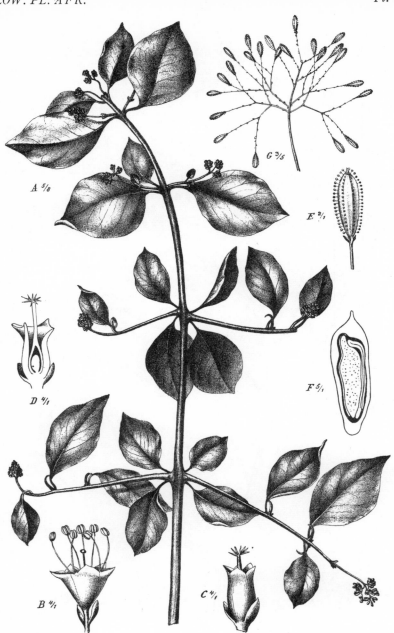

J. Fleischmann del.

Pisonia aculeata L.

A Branch with inflorescences. *B* Male flower. *C* Female flower. *D* Female flower cut lengthwise. *E* Fruit. *F* Fruit cut lengthwise. *G* Group of fruits.

20. (9.) Spurious staminodes interposed between the stamens. 21
Spurious staminodes none. 26
21. Spurious staminodes small, entire. Ovary hairy. Either perianth clothed
with long silky hairs or leaves alternate. 22
Spurious staminodes usually quadrate and fringed, more rarely narrow,
but then perianth not clothed with long silky hairs and leaves (as nearly
always) opposite. 23
22. Ovary with a horn-like appendage. — Species 6. South and Central Africa.
(Under *Sericocoma* Fenzl). . . . . . . **Cyphocarpa** Lopr.
Ovary without a horn. (See 14.) . . . . . **Sericocoma** Fenzl
23. Partial inflorescences consisting of 3 fertile flowers without sterile ones.
Perianth hairy. Erect shrubs. — Species 4. South and Central Africa.
(Under *Sericocoma* Fenzl or *Cyphocarpa* Lopr.) **Sericocomopsis** Schinz
Partial inflorescences consisting of fertile and sterile flowers, or of 2 fertile
ones only. 24
24. Stem woody, climbing. Leaves ovate. Sterile flowers reduced to long
tufts of hairs. Perianth glabrous. Spurious staminodes narrow, entire
or toothed. — Species 2. Equatorial regions (Uganda and Cameroons).
Sericostachys Gilg & Lopr.
Stem herbaceous or woody at the base only, erect or ascending. Sterile
flowers usually reduced to spines. Spurious staminodes usually broad
and fringed. 25
25. Perianth-segments thickened and hardening at the base, yellow or red.
(See 17.) . . . . **Centema** Hook. fil.
Perianth-segments not hardening. — Species 15. Tropical and South
Africa. Some are used in medicine. (*Desmochaeta* DC.) **Cyathula** Lour.
26. (20.) Partial inflorescences consisting of 2 fertile flowers without sterile
ones, and arranged in globose heads. Perianth white, with silky hairs.
Ovary hairy. Shrubs. — Species 1. German South-West Africa.
(Under *Marcellia* Baill., *Sericocomopsis* Schinz, or *Sericocoma* Fenzl)
Leucosphaera Gilg
Partial inflorescences consisting of fertile and sterile flowers, the latter
sometimes reduced to bristles or spines. 27
27. Perianth-segments thickened and hardened at the base, yellow or red.
Ovary glabrous. (See 17.) . . . . . . **Centema** Hook. fil.
Perianth-segments not hardening. 28
28. Sterile flowers consisting of hooked spines. — Species 6. Tropical and
South Africa. . . . . **Pupalia** Juss.
Sterile flowers consisting of not hooked spines, bristles, or hairs. . . 29
29. Partial inflorescences consisting of 2 fertile and 2 sterile flowers, the latter
reduced to bristles or spines. Ovary hairy. Herbs or undershrubs.
— Species 10. Southern West Africa to Namaland. (Under *Sericocoma*
Fenzl). . . . . **Marcellia** Baill.
Partial inflorescences consisting of 1—3 fertile and 4—6 sterile flowers.
Ovary glabrous. 30

30. Partial inflorescences consisting of 1—3 fertile and 4—6 sterile flowers, the
latter reduced to branched spines. Collective inflorescence interrupted
below. Style very short. Herbs. — Species 2. South Africa and
German South-West Africa. (Under *Marcellia* Baill. or *Sericocoma*
Fenzl). . . . . **Sericorema** Lopr.
Partial inflorescences consisting of 3 fertile and 6 sterile flowers, the latter
reduced to long simple spines or bristles. Style thread-shaped. . . 31
31. Sterile flowers elongating in the fruit into yellow spines. Herbs. — Species
1. German East Africa. (Under *Marcellia* Baill.) **Kentrosphaera** Volk.
Sterile flowers elongating in the fruit into yellow or brown, rather soft
bristles. Shrubs. — Species 3. East Africa. (Under *Marcellia* Baill.)
Dasysphaera Volk
32. (4.) Perianth-segments spreading. Style short, with 2—4 stigmas. Fruit
succulent, baccate. Herbs or undershrubs. Leaves ovate. — Species
1. Tropics. . . . . **Deeringia** R. Br.
Perianth-segments erect. Fruit dry. 33
33. Fruit opening lengthwise. Style very short, with 2—3 stigmas. Fila-
ments united at the base only. Leaves narrow. Shrubs. — Species 1.
Madagascar. . . . . **Henonia** Moq.
Fruit opening by a lid. Herbs or undershrubs. 34
34. Spurious staminodes longer than the stamens, 2-lobed. Style short.
Leaves narrow. — Species 10. South Africa and southern Central
Africa . . . . **Hermbstaedtia** Reichb.
Spurious staminodes shorter than the stamens or wanting. — Species 30.
Tropical and South Africa. Some are used as vegetables or as textile,
ornamental, medicinal, or fodder-plants. (Including *Lestiboudesia*
Thou.) . . . . **Celosia** L.

SUBORDER PHYTOLACCINEAE

FAMILY 69. NYCTAGINACEAE

Leaves entire, toothed, or lobed. Flowers regular. Perianth simple,
but often surrounded by a calyx-like involucre, 3—6-lobed, valvate or folded
in the bud persistent. Stamens with the filaments united below ; connective narrow ; anthers opening laterally. Ovary superior, 1-celled. Ovule
1, erect, inverted. Style 1, lateral. Fruit a nut, enclosed by the enlarged and
hardened perianth. Seed albuminous. — Genera 5, species 30. (Plate 42.)
1. Seed with a straight embryo. Shrubs or trees. Leaves opposite. Flowers
in corymbs, inconspicuous. Involucre consisting of 2—3 small bracts.
Perianth tubular or campanulate, 4—5-toothed. Stamens 5—15. —
Species 6. Tropical and South-east Africa. (Plate 42.) [Tribe
PISONIEAE.] . . . . **Pisonia** Plum.
Seed with a curved embryo. Herbs or undershrubs, rarely shrubs or trees,
but then leaves alternate or fascicled and flowers in fascicles. Stamens
1—10. [Tribe MIRABILEAE.] 2

2. Stem woody, spinous. Leaves alternate or fascicled. Flowers in fascicles. Stamens 5—10, unequal. Ovary oblong. [Subtribe BOUGAIN-VILLEINAE.] 3
   Stem herbaceous or woody at the base only, not spinous. Leaves opposite. Flowers hermaphrodite. Ovary ovoid or globose. [Subtribe BOER-HAVIINAE. . . . .
3. Clusters of flowers surrounded by an involucre of 3 large, coloured bracts. Fruit not winged. Leaves scattered. — Species 1. Naturalized in the tropics. Ornamental plant . . . . . **Bougainvillea** Commers
   Clusters of flowers without an involucre. Fruit winged. Leaves fascicled. — Species 2. South Africa, southern West Africa, and Madagascar. (Including *Amphoranthus* S. Moore) . . . . **Phaeoptilon** Radlk.
4. Flowers large, surrounded by a calyx-like, 4—5-cleft involucre. — Species 1 (*M. Jalapa* L., marvel of Peru). Naturalized in various regions. An ornamental and medicinal plant. . . . . **Mirabilis** L.
   Flowers surrounded singly or in clusters by some early deciduous bracts. — Species 20. Some of them are used as vegetables or in medicine.

   Boerhavia L

FAMILY 70. CYNOCRAMBACEAE

Herbs. Leaves undivided, stipulate, the lower opposite, the upper alternate. Flowers monoecious, the male in groups of 2—4 opposite the leaves, the female in axillary clusters of 3. Perianth of the male flowers 2—3-parted, valvate in bud, of the female tubular, 2—4-toothed. Stamens 10—30, free ; anthers linear. Ovary inferior, 1-celled. Ovule 1, basal, curved, with the micropyle turned downwards. Style simple, basal. Fruit a drupe. Seed with a curved embryo and cartilaginous albumen. (*THELIGONACEAE*, under *CHENO-PODIACEAE* or *URTICACEAE*.)

Genus 1, species 1. North Africa. (*Theligonum* L.) **Cynocrambe** Gaertn.

FAMILY 71. PHYTOLACCACEAE

Leaves alternate, entire, without stipules. Flowers in racemes or spikes, bracteolate. Perianth 4—5-parted, herbaceous or membranous, coloured, imbricate in bud, persistent in fruit. Stamens 3—33, hypogynous. Filaments free or united at the base. Anthers affixed at the back, opening by two longitudinal slits. Carpels superior. Ovules solitary in each ovary-cell or in each distinct carpel, basal, curved ; micropyle turned downwards and outwards. Seed with an annular embryo surrounding the albumen. — Genera 5, species 15.

1. Style 1, undivided. Ovary 1-celled. Stamens 4. Anthers linear. Perianth 4-parted. Flowers in racemes. Leaves elliptical. Undershrubs. [Tribe RIVINEAE.] 2
   Styles 2 or more, free or nearly so. Perianth nearly always 5-parted . 3
2. Flowers irregular. Fruit nearly dry. — Species 1. Tropics. Used medicinally. (*Mohlana* Mart.) . . . . **Hilleria** Vell.
   Flowers regular. Fruit succulent. — Species 1. Naturalized in the tropics. Used as an ornamental and a dye-plant. . **Rivina** Plum.

3. Ovary solitary, 1-celled. Stamens 3—5. Anthers ovate or globose. Flowers in spikes. Leaves linear. — Species 4. South Africa and southern West Africa. (Including *Lophiocarpus* Turcz. and *Wallinia* Moq.) . . . . **Microtea** Swartz

Ovary solitary, 2— 16-celled, or several separate ovaries. Stamens 6—33. Leaves lanceolate, elliptical, or ovate. [Tribe PHYTOLACCEAE.] . 4

4. Carpels 2. Stamens numerous. Fruit dry, capsular. Climbing shrubs. — Species 1. Madagascar . . . . **Barbeuia** Thouars

Carpels 5—16. Fruit succulent, baccate. — Species 8, five of them spontaneous in tropical and South Africa, the others cultivated and sometimes naturalized in various regions. They yield vegetables, dyes (chiefly from *Ph. decandra* L.), a substitute for soap, and medicaments ; some are poisonous. " Poke." (Including *Pircunia* Moq.)

Phytolacca L.

FAMILY 72. AIZOACEAE

Herbs or undershrubs, rarely shrubs. Leaves entire, toothed, or lobed Flowers regular. Perianth usually simple. Stamens 3 or more. Ovary usually several-celled. Ovules curved or inverted. Fruit dry. Seeds with a curved embryo and a usually mealy albumen. — Genera 20, species 480. (*FICOIDEAE* or *MESEMBRIACEAE*). (Plate 43.)

1. Perianth divided to the base or nearly so, free from the ovary. [Subfamily **MOLLUGINOIDEAE**.] 2

Perianth with a distinct tube sometimes adnate to the ovary, simple. [Subfamily **FICOIDEAE**.] 11

2. Ovary solitary, 1-celled. Ovule 1, suspended from a basal funicle. Style 1. Stamens 5. Perianth simple. Flowers in panicles. Leaves whorled. — Species 7. South Africa. . . . . **Adenogramma** Reichb.

Ovary solitary but 2- or more-celled, or several separate ovaries. . . . 3

3. Ovary 2-celled. Style 2-cleft. Inflorescence cymose. [Tribe LIMEAE.]

4

Ovary 3—7-celled, or 3—5 separate ovaries.. 5

4. Perianth of 4 thin-membranous, fringed segments, surrounded by bracts. Stamens 4, much exceeding the perianth. Fruit capsular. Flowers in false spikes. Leaves stipulate. — Species 1. South Africa.

Polpoda Presl

Perianth of 5 herbaceous entire segments, to which 3—5 petals are sometimes added. Stamens 5—10, not or scarcely exceeding the perianth. Fruit separating in two nutlets. Leaves exstipulate. — Species 15. South and Central Africa. (Including *Semonvillea* Gay). **Limeum** L.

5. Carpels separate. Ovules solitary. Perianth simple. Flowers in cymes. Leaves opposite. — Species 5. Some of them are used as vegetables or in medicine. . . . . **Giesekia** L.

Carpels united in the ovarial portion. 6

6. Ovary-cells one-ovuled. Stamens 5. Perianth simple. Flowers in panicles. — Species 5. South Africa and southern West Africa.
                                    Psammatropha Eckl. & Zeyh.
Ovary-cells several- or many-ovuled. 7

7. Petals or petaloid staminodes numerous, united at the base. Stamens
numerous. Flowers conspicuous. Leaves exstipulate, fleshy. —
Species 1. . . . . **Orygia** Forsk.
Petals none, but the stamens sometimes intermixed with staminodes.
Leaves stipulate. 8

8. Styles linear or slightly club-shaped. Stipules membranous, entire. . 9
Styles obovate or wedge-shaped. Stipules fringed or sheath-like. . . 10

9. Ovules with a long funicle. Seeds crowned by an appendage of the funicle.
Pericarp firm. — Species 3. Used in medicine. . . . **Glinus** L.
Ovules with a short funicle. Seeds without an appendage of the funicle.
Pericarp thin. Stamens 3—10. Glabrous herbs with narrow leaves.
— Species 10. Tropical and South Africa. Some species are used in
medicine . . . . **Mollugo** L.

10. Disc cup-shaped, lobed or divided. Stamens 3—5. Stipules fringed.—
Species 17. South Africa, Madagascar, St. Helena . **Pharnaceum** L.
Disc none. Stipules sheath-like. Leaves thread-shaped. — Species 4.
South Africa. . . . . **Hyperstelis** E. Mey.

11. (1.) Ovary superior. Petals none. 12
Ovary inferior. [Tribe MESEMBRIANTHEMEAE.] 18

12. Fruit transversely dehiscent, circumscissile. Leaves opposite. [Tribe
SESUVIEAE.] 13
Fruit longitudinally dehiscent, loculicidal or septicidal. [Tribe AIZOEAE.]
                                                          14

13. Ovary 1—2-celled. Ovules solitary or few, basal or subbasal. Pericarp
thick in the upper part. Seed-coat wrinkled. — Species 10. Some of
them are used as vegetables or in medicine. (Plate 43.) **Trianthema** L.
Ovary 3—5- rarely 2-celled. Ovules numerous, axile. Pericarp thin.
Seed-coat smooth. Flowers red. — Species 6. Tropical and South
Africa. Some of them have edible seeds, or serve as vegetables. (Including *Diplochonium* Fenzl and *Halimus* Rumph.) **Sesuvium** L.

14. Stamens 4—5. Ovary-cells and styles 3 15
Stamens 8 or more. 16

15. Ovary-cells 1-ovuled. Filaments long. Fruit roundish. Shrubs with
silky hairs. Leaves all cauline, opposite or alternate, imbricate, tri-
angular-ovate, without stipules. Flowers axillary, yellowish. —
Species 1. South Africa (Cape Colony). . . . . **Plinthus** Fenzl
Ovary-cells several-ovuled. Filaments short. Fruit linear-oblong. Glabrous herbs. Radical leaves lanceolate to ovate, with fringed stipules ;
cauline leaves whorled, filiform. Flowers in cymes, whitish-green.
— Species 2. South Africa . . . . . . **Coelanthum** E. Mey.

16. Stamens numerous. Ovary 4—5-celled. Styles 4—5. Ovules 2 or more in each cell. Flowers yellow. — Species 12. Some of them have edible seeds. . . . . **Aizoon** L.

Stamens 8—10, rarely more, but then ovary 2-celled and styles 2. Ovules 1 or 2 in each cell. 17

17. Stamens 10 or more. Ovary 2-celled. Styles 2. Ovules basal. Stem glabrous. — Species 4. South Africa. . . **Acrosanthes** Eckl. & Zeyh.

Stamens 8, rarely 10, but then ovary 3—5-celled, styles 3—5, and stem hairy or warty Ovules pendulous, 1 in each cell. — Species 20. South Africa to Angola. . . . . **Galenia** L.

18. (11.) Petals (or petaloid staminodes) numerous. Stamens numerous Ovary 4—20-celled, with many basal or parietal ovules. Fruit a capsule. — Species 330. Some of them have edible fruits or seeds or serve as vegetables, as ornamental or medicinal plants, or for making soda . . . . **Mesembrianthemum** L.

Petals (or petaloid staminodes) none. Ovary 2—8-celled with one pendulous ovule in each cell, or ovary 1-celled. Fruit a nut or drupe. Leaves alternate. 19

19. Ovary 1-celled. Styles 4, two of them shorter than the others and without a stigma. — Species 1. South-west Africa (Namaland).

Anisostigma Schinz

Ovary 2—8-, very rarely 1-celled. Styles as many as ovary-cells. — Species 35. Southern and Central Africa. One species (*T. expansa* Murr., New Zealand spinach) is cultivated as a vegetable in various regions.

Tetragonia L.

SUBORDER PORTULACINEAE

FAMILY 73. PORTULACACEAE

Herbs or undershrubs, rarely shrubs. Flowers regular or nearly so, hermaphrodite. Sepals 2, free or united at the base, imbricate in the bud. Petals 4—6, free or united at the base, falling off very early. Stamens as many as and opposite the petals, or fewer, or more numerous. Ovary usually superior and 1-celled. Ovules basal or affixed to a free central placenta, curved, the micropyle lateral or inferior. Style 2—8-cleft or -parted, rarely (*Portulaca*) undivided. Fruit a capsule or a nut. Seeds albuminous ; embryo more or less curved. — Genera 6, species 35. (Plate 44.)

1. Ovary inferior or half-inferior. Ovules numerous. Frui dehiscing by a lid. — Species 12. Some are used as vegetables, fodder-, medicinal, or ornamental plants. " Purslane." [Tribe PORTULACEAE.]

Portulaca L.

Ovary superior. Fruit dehiscing by valves or indehiscent. [Tribe CALANDRINIEAE.] 2

2. Ovary 2-celled with 2 ovules in each cell. Style-branches 2. Stamens numerous. Shrubs. — Species 2. Madagascar. **Talinella** Baill.

Ovary 1-celled with 1, 3, or many ovules. Style-branches 3. . . . 3

J. Fleischmann del.

Trianthema pentandrum L.

A Flowering branch.   *B* Flower.   *C* Flower cut lengthwise.   *D* Mericarp cut lengthwise.

C 2/1   *D* 7/1

A 2/3

B 4/1

J. Fleischmann del.

Talinum cuneifolium Willd.

A Flowering branch. *B* Flower cut lengthwise. *C* Fruit. *D* Seed.

3. Ovule 1. Stamens 4—7. Petals reddish. Fruit indehiscent. Shrubs. —
Species 3. South Africa. Used as ornamental or fodder-plants.

Portulacaria Jacq.

Ovules 3 or more. Stamens 3 or 8—30. Fruit 3-valved. Herbs or undershrubs 4
4. Ovules 3. Stamens 3. Corolla 5-cleft, slightly irregular, white. Calyx
persistent. — Species 1. North Africa and subantarctic islands. Used
as a vegetable . . . . **Montia** L.
Ovules numerous. Stamens 8—30. Corolla of 5 free or almost free
petals, regular. Calyx deciduous. 5
5. Stipules present, but sometimes reduced to a tuft of hairs. Embryo
slightly curved. — Species 15. South Africa. Some are used as
ornamental plants. . . . . **Anacampseros** L.
Stipules absent. Embryo ring-shaped. Funicle of the seed with an
appendage. — Species 4. Central and South Africa. Used as vegetables. (Plate 44.) . . . . **Talinum** Adans.

FAMILY 74. BASELLACEAE

Glabrous, twining herbs. Leaves alternate, broad, entire. Flowers in
spikes racemes or panicles, regular, hermaphrodite. Sepals 2, adnate to the
corolla at the base. Corolla 5-cleft or 5-parted, imbricate in the bud, persistent. Stamens 5, opposite the corolla-lobes and affixed to them at the base.
Filaments straight or bent outwards in the bud. Anthers 2-celled, turned
outwards. Ovary superior, 1-celled. Ovule 1, basal, curved ; micropyle
inferior. Style 3-partite. Fruit indehiscent. Seed albuminous ; embryo
curved or spirally twisted. — Genera 2, species 4, Tropics. (Under *CHEN-
OPODIACEAE* or *PORTULACACEAE*.)

Flowers sessile, in spikes or panicles. Filaments broadened below. Stigmas
entire. Pericarp membranous. Seed subglobose. Embryo spiral. —
Species 3, two spontaneous in East Africa and Madagascar, the third
cultivated in various tropical countries. They are used as vegetables,
in medicine, and as dye-plants. . . . . **Basella** L.
Flowers short-stalked, in racemes. Filaments thread-shaped. Stigmas
forked. Pericarp somewhat fleshy. Seed sublenticular. Embryo semi-
circular. — Species 1. Cultivated in various regions and naturalized in
the Mascarene Islands. Used as a vegetable or an ornamental plant.

Boussaingaultia H. B. & K.

SUBORDER CARYOPHYLLINEAE

FAMILY 75. CARYOPHYLLACEAE

Herbs or undershrubs, rarely shrubs. Leaves undivided. Perianth usually
separated into calyx and corolla. Stamens 1—10. Ovary 1-celled or incompletely 2—5-celled, superior, rarely (*Sclerocephalus*) half-inferior. Ovules on

basal or central placentas, with a distinct funicle, curved or inverted. Seeds albuminous ; embryo usually curved. — Genera 45, species 28o. (Including *PARONYCHIEAE* or *ILLECEBRACEAE, ALSINACEAE,* and *SILE-NACEAE.*) (Plate 45.)

1. Sepals free or united up to the insertion of the stamens. Petals not distinctly clawed, sometimes wanting. Receptacle concave or small and rather flat. [Subfamily **ALSINOIDEAE.**] 2

   Sepals united beyond the insertion of the stamens. Petals present, usually clawed. Receptacle stalk-like or small and flat. Styles free. [Sub-family **SILENOIDEAE.**] 35

2. Fruit indehiscent or irregularly bursting at the base, rarely at the top. Ovule 1, rarely ovules 2, and then sepals 5. Petals usually scale-like or wanting. Leaves stipulate, rarely exstipulate : in the latter case styles 2. 3

   Fruit opening from the top by teeth or valves. Ovules numerous, rarely 2, and then sepals 4, very rarely ovule 1 ; in this case leaves exstipulate and styles 3. Petals usually perfectly developed 16

3. Flowers in clusters of 3, the middle one hermaphrodite, the side flowers male or rudimentary. Stamens nearly hypogynous. Style 1. Ovule one. Embryo almost straight. Leaves opposite, stipulate. [Tribe PTER-ANTHEAE.] 4

   Flowers all alike. Stamens perigynous. 6

4. Stamens 2—3. Staminodes and petals absent. Sepals 5. Stigmas 3. Clusters of flowers on a rather thin stalk, with entire involucral bracts. Shrubs. — Species 1. Canary Islands. . . . **Dicheranthus** Webb

   Stamens 4—5. Clusters of flowers with pinnately divided involucral bracts. Herbs. 5

5. Sepals 4. Petals and staminodes none. Stamens 4. Stigmas 2. Clusters of flowers on a much broadened and hollow stalk. — Species 1. North Africa . . . . **Pteranthus** Forsk.

   Sepals 5. Petals or staminodes 5. Stamens 5. Stigmas 3. Clusters of flowers on a rather thin stalk. — Species 1. Northern East Africa to Egypt. . . . . **Cometes** L

6. Leaves exstipulate. Petals none. Styles 2. Ovule 1. Herbs. Leaves opposite. — Species 3. North Africa, Abyssinia, and South Africa. [Tribe SCLERANTHEAE.] . . . . . . **Scleranthus** L.

   Leaves stipulate. [Tribe PARONYCHIEAE.] 7

7. Ovule 1. 8

   Ovules 2. Undershrubs. 15

8. Style-branches, stigmas, or stigma-lobes 2, very rarely 1, and then style very short. 9

   Style-branches, stigmas, or stigma-lobes 3, very rarely 1, but then style elongated. 13

9. Stem woody, shrubby, nodose. Bracts brown. Sepals mucronate. Petals 5, thread-shaped. Style elongated. Stigmas 2. — Species 1. Island of Socotra. . . . . **Lochia** Balf. fil

   Stem herbaceous, rarely woody at the base; in the latter case sepals obtuse. 10

10. Flowers in globose heads; involucre becoming prickly. Sepals prickly beneath the tip. Petals wanting. Ovary adnate below to the calyx-tube. Fruit bursting at the top. — Species 1. North Africa and Cape Verde Islands. . . . . **Sclerocephalus** Boiss

    Flowers in fascicles; involucre not prickly. Petals thread-shaped or wanting. Ovary free. 11

11. Sepals blunt, green. Style very short; stigmas 2. Embryo curved. Stipules small. — Species 10. North and South Africa, Abyssinia, Cape Verde Islands. Some are used in medicine. . . . **Herniaria** L.

    Sepals more or less hooded, with a dorsal point beneath the tip . . . 12

12. Seed with a straight embryo. Stigma 1, entire or 2-lobed, nearly sessile. Stamens 5. Petals thread-shaped. Sepals white. Leaves in false whorls; stipules very small. — Species 1. North-west Africa. Used in medicine. . . . . **Illecebrum** L.

    Seed with a curved embryo. Stigma 1, two-lobed, or more frequently stigmas 2. Stipules large or rather large. — Species 15. North Africa and northern Central Africa. Some are used in medicine or yield a substitute for tea. . . . . **Paronychia** Juss.

13. Sepals awned. Petals awl-shaped. Style long, with 3 stigmas. Low shrubs with knotty branches. Leaves narrow. — Species 1. North Africa. . . . . **Gymnocarpos** Forsk.

    Sepals blunt. Petals scale-like. Style long with 1 stigma, or short with 3 stigmas. Herbs. 14

14. Style long, with 1 stigma. Leaves whorled, obovate. — Species 1. Island of Socotra. . . . . **Haya** Balf. fil.

    Style short, with 3 stigmas. Leaves opposite or alternate, narrow. — Species 3. North and South Africa and mountains of East Africa and Madagascar. . . . . **Corrigiola** L.

15. (7.) Petals 5. Stamens 5. Embryo curved. Leaves linear, fleshy. — Species 1. Nubia. . . . . **Sphaerocoma** Anders.

    Petals none. Stamens 1—2. Embryo straight or almost so. Leaves lanceolate, flat. — Species 2. South and Central Africa.

    Pollichia Soland.

16. (2.) Styles united below. [Tribe POLYCARPEAE.] 17

    Styles free from the base. 22

17. Sepals 4, concave, minutely toothed. Petals none. Stamens 3. Ovules few. Style short; stigmas 2. Flowers solitary, axillary, with two bracteoles. Leaves very small, densely crowded. — Species 1. Island of Kerguelen. . . . . **Lyallia** Hook.

    Sepals 5. Stamens 3—5. Ovules numerous. Stigmas 3 or 1. . . . 18

N

18. Petals none. Sepals keeled, entire. Stamens 3. Leaves linear. Stipules dark red at the base. — Species 1. North-west Africa (Algeria).

Ortegia Loefl.

Petals 5. 19

19. Petals 2-parted. — Species 1. Tropical and South Africa. **Drymaria** Willd.
Petals entire, notched, or 2-toothed. 20

20. Sepals with a tooth on each side. Leaves awl-shaped. Stipules cut up into bristles. — Species 1. North Africa.   . . .   **Loeflingia** L.
Sepals entire. 21

21. Sepals keeled. Style short, 3-cleft. — Species 6. Some are used medicinally. . . . . **Polycarpon** Loefl.
Sepals rounded on the back. Style long or rather long. — Species 25. Some are used medicinally. (*Polycarpia* Webb, *Polia* Lour., including *Robbairea* Boiss.) (Plate 45.) . . . . . . **Polycarpaea** Lam.

22. (16.) Leaves with scarious stipules. Ovules numerous. [Tribe SPER-GULEAE.]   23
Leaves without stipules. [Tribe ALSINEAE.] 25

23. Ovary incompletely 3-celled. Ovules basal. Styles 3. Stamens 5. Flowers white. Leaves oblong or ovate. — Species 5. North Africa and Madagascar. . . . . **Telephium** L.
Ovary completely 1-celled. Ovules central. Flowers in raceme-like cymes. Leaves linear or subulate. 24

24. Styles and fruit-valves 3. — Species 10. North and South Africa, Abyssinia. Some are used medicinally. (*Lepigonum* Fries, *Tissa* Adans.)

Spergularia Pers.

Styles and fruit-valves 5. — Species 4. North Africa ; also naturalized in Central and South Africa. Used as fodder. " Spurry." **Spergula** L.

25. Ovule 1. Styles 3. Stamens 10. Petals none, but usually 5 thread-like scales opposite the sepals. Fruit 3-valved to the middle. Leaves subulate. Flowers in clusters consisting of fertile and sterile flowers. — Species 1. - North Africa. . . . . **Queria** L.
Ovules 3 or more, rarely (*Buffonia*) 2. 26

26. Petals 2-parted, 2-cleft, or distinctly notched. Flowers solitary or in panicle-like cymes. 27
Petals entire, minutely toothed, obscurely notched, or wanting . . . 28

27. Fruit globose. Styles 2—3, rarely 4—5, alternating with the sepals. — Species 6. Extra-tropical regions and mountains of the tropics. Some are used medicinally. " Stitchwort." . . . **Stellaria** L.
Fruit cylindrical. Styles 5, rarely 3—4, opposite the sepals. — Species 20. Extra-tropical regions and mountains of the tropics. Some are used medicinally. . . . . **Cerastium** L.

28. Petals minutely toothed. Styles 3. Ovules numerous. Fruit cylindrical. Seeds peltate, compressed dorsally. Flowers in umbel-like cymes. — Species 1. North Africa . . . . **Holosteum** L.
Petals entire, slightly notched, or wanting. 29

29. Styles as many as the sepals, 4—5. 30
    Styles fewer than the sepals, 2—4, very rarely 5. 32

30. Styles opposite the sepals. Stamens 8. Fruit opening at the top by 8
    recurved teeth. Leaves lanceolate. — Species 1. North Africa
    (Under *Cerastium* L.). . . . . **Moenchia** Ehrh.
    Styles alternating with the sepals. Stamens 4, 5, or 10. Fruit opening
    to the base in 4—5 valves. 31

31. Stamens as many as and alternating with the sepals. Petals none. —
    Species 2. Subantarctic islands. . . . . . **Colobanthus** Bartl.
    Stamens as many as and opposite the sepals, or twice as many. Leaves
    subulate. — Species 7. North Africa, high mountains of Central Africa
    and subantarctic islands. Some are used as ornamental plants. " Pearl-
    wort." . . . . **Sagina** L.

32. Styles 2. Ovules 2—4. Stamens 2—4. Sepals 4. Fruit opening to the
    base in 2 valves. Seeds 1—2 Leaves subulate. — Species 5. North-
    west Africa. . . . . **Buffonia** L.
    Styles 3—5, rarely 2, but then (as usually) ovules more than 4. Sepals
    nearly always 5. 33

33. Valves of the fruit entire, as many as styles. — Species 8. North Africa
    and northern East Africa. (Including *Minuartia* L., under *Arenaria* L.)
    Alsine Wahlenb.
    Valves of the fruit 2-toothed or 2-parted ; in the latter case apparently
    twice as many as styles. 34

34. Seeds with an appendage at the hilum. Flowers white. — Species 2.
    North-west Africa. (Under *Arenaria* L.) . . . . **Moehringia** L.
    Seeds without an appendage. Stamens 10. — Species 10. North Africa
    and northern Central Africa. " Sandwort." . . . **Arenaria** L.

35. (1.) Calyx with an odd number of ribs. Petals usually with contorted
    aestivation. Styles or stigmas 2. [Tribe DIANTHEAE.] . . . 36
    Calyx with an even number of ribs. Petals usually with quincuncially-
    imbricate aestivation. Styles or stigmas 3—5. [Tribe LYCHNIDEAE.]
    41

36. Calyx with scarious stripes between the lobes and with 5—35 ribs. . . 37
    Calyx without scarious stripes, with 15—55 ribs 38

37. Seeds peltate ; embryo nearly straight. Leaves linear. — Species 2.
    North Africa. (Including *Dianthella* Clauson) . . **Tunica** Scop.
    Seeds reniform ; embryo curved. Leaves lanceolate, oblong, elliptical,
    or ovate. — Species 2 North-east Africa to the Island of Socotra. The
    roots are used in medicine and as a substitute for soap. . **Gypsophila** L.

38 Petals with scales at the base of the blade, which are sometimes reduced to
    hairs. Calyx not surrounded by bracts. 39
    Petals without scales at the base of the blade, but usually with a winged
    claw. 40

39. Flowers small. Calyx tubular, 15-ribbed. Petals notched ; scales small or reduced to hairs. Stamens 5—10. Fruit linear. Seeds with an anterior hilum and a straight embryo. Leaves linear. — Species 1. North Africa. . . . . **Velezia** L.

Flowers rather large. Calyx 15—25-ribbed. Petals with wing-like out-growths on the claw and with scales at the base of the blade. Stamens 10. Seeds with a lateral hilum and a curved embryo. Leaves lanceolate. — Species 4. North Africa. They are used as ornamental or medicinal plants and yield also a substitute for soap. " Soapwort." . **Saponaria** L.

40. Calyx ventricose, acutely angled, with 15—25 ribs, not surrounded by bracts. Petals minutely toothed. Fruit ovoid. Seeds with a lateral hilum and a curved embryo. — Species 1. North Africa. The roots are used as a substitute for soap. (Under *Saponaria* L.)
Vaccaria Medik.

Calyx tubular, with 35—55 ribs, surrounded by two or more bracts at the base. Seeds with an anterior hilum and a straight embryo. — Species 25. North and South Africa and mountains of Central Africa. Many of them are used as ornamental plants or for the preparation of perfumes. " Pink." . . . . **Dianthus** L.

41. (35.) Styles 5, alternating with the sepals. Ovary and fruit completely 1-celled. Petals without scales at the base of the blade. 42

Styles 5, opposite the sepals, or 3—4. Stamens 10. 43

42. Petals with a two-winged claw. Stamens 10. Styles hairy. Ovules numerous. — Species 1. North Africa, also introduced into South Africa. The seeds are poisonous and used in medicine. " Corncockle." (*Githago* Desfont., under *Lychnis* L.) . . . . . **Agrostemma** L.

Petals with a wingless claw. Stamens 5. Styles glabrous. Ovules few. — Species 3. Northern East Africa and Cameroons. **Uebelinia** Hochst.

43. Ovary and fruit completely 1-celled. Calyx more or less inflated, 10—20-ribbed. Petals with scales at the base of the blade. Fruit opening by 6—10 teeth. Seeds tubercled. — Species 6. North-west and South Africa. Some are used as ornamental plants, or as a substitute for soap. (Under *Lychnis* L.) . . . . **Melandryum** Roehl.

Ovary and fruit divided into cells at the base. 44

44. Fruit a berry. Calyx shortly and widely bell-shaped. Petals greenish-white, with a recurved 2-cleft blade provided with two scales at its base. Styles 3. Stem climbing. Leaves ovate or oblong. — Species 1. North-west Africa . . . . **Cucubalus** L.

Fruit a capsule, opening by 6 or more teeth. — Species 75. North and South Africa and mountains of Central Africa. Some are used as a sub-stitute for soap, as vegetables, in medicine or as ornamental plants. (In-cluding *Eudianthe* Rohrb) . . . . **Silene** L

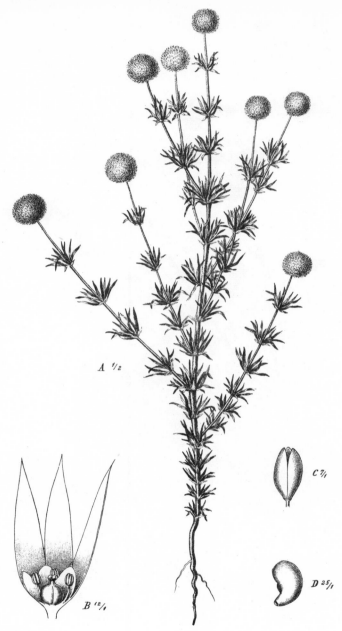

A ¹/₂

B ¹²/₁

C ⁷/₁

D ²⁵/₁

J. Fleischmann del.

Polycarpaea linearifolia DC.

A Plant in flower.   *B* Flower cut lengthwise.   *C* Fruit.   *D* Seed.

J Fleischmann del

Anemone vesicatoria (L. f.) Prantl

A Leaf.   *B* Inflorescence.   *C* Flower cut lengthwise.

ORDER RANALES

SUBORDER NYMPHAEINEAE

FAMILY 76. NYMPHAEACEAE

Aquatic herbs. Leaves floating, undivided, usually peltate. Flowers solitary. Sepals 3 or more. Petals 3 or more. Stamens numerous. Anthers opening inwards by longitudinal slits. Carpels 6 or more, distinct or united below into a many-celled ovary. Stigmas free or partly united. Fruit indehiscent or bursting irregularly. Seeds albuminous. — Genera 3, species 20.

1. Carpels separate, few-ovuled. Sepals 3. Petals 3. Flowers red, axillary. Leaves ovate, without stipules. — Species 1. Southern West Africa (Angola). Used medicinally. (*Hydropeltis* Michx.) [Subfamily **CABOMBOIDEAE.**] . . . . **Brasenia** Schreb.
   Carpels united, at least on the outside, many-ovuled. Sepals 4—5. Petals numerous. [Subfamily **NYMPHAEOIDEAE.**] 2
2. Sepals 4. Ovary more or less free from the calyx, but adnate to the corolla and the stamens. Seeds with an aril. Leaves with a stipule. Leaf- and flower-stalks with 4—7 large air-canals. — Species 20. Used as ornamental and fodder- plants ; the root-stock and the seeds are edible and yield a drink, medicaments, and a dye. " Water-lily." (*Castalia* Salisb.) [Tribe TETRASEPALEAE.] . **Nymphaea** Smith
   Sepals 5. Petals smaller. Flowers yellow. Ovary free. Seeds without an aril. Leaves without stipules. Leaf- and flower-stalks with many small air-canals. — Species 1. North-west Africa (Algeria). Used as ornamental plants, as fodder, and for the preparation of a drink. (*Nymphaea* Salisb.) [Tribe NUPHAREAE.] . . . . **Nuphar** Smith

FAMILY 77. CERATOPHYLLACEAE

Branched submerged aquatic herbs. Leaves whorled, deeply divided into forked, linear segments. Flowers solitary or in pairs in the axils of the leaves, without bracteoles, unisexual. Perianth simple ; segments 9—12, subequal, united at the base, greenish or whitish. Stamens 12—16, inserted upon a convex receptacle ; anthers opening outwards. Ovary superior, 1-celled. Ovule 1, pendulous, straight. Style simple ; stigma entire, grooved. Fruit a nut. Seed with a thin albumen ; embryo with a large, many-leaved plumule.
Genus 1, species 3. . . . . **Ceratophyllum** L.

SUBORDER RANUNCULINEAE

FAMILY 78. RANUNCULACEAE

Herbs, undershrubs, or shrubs. Leaves usually divided. Perianth simple or consisting of a calyx and a corolla of free petals, hypogynous or nearly so. Stamens usually numerous. Anthers opening by longitudinal slits. Carpels superior, solitary or separate, rarely (*Nigella*) united. Ovules inverted. Seeds with a straight embryo and copious albumen. — Genera 11, species 140. (Plate 46.)

1. Carpels containing each a single perfect ovule and sometimes some rudimentary ones, separate, indehiscent. [Tribe ANEMONEAE.] . . 2
   Carpels containing several perfect ovules each, dehiscing at the suture . 7
2. Petals with a pit or scale at the base or the middle. 3
   Petals without a pit or scale, or wanting. Ovule pendulous 4
3. Ovule pendulous. Carpels arranged in a spike. Sepals with a short spur, yellowish. Petals narrow. Stamens few. Pericarp without a hardened layer. Small herbs. Leaves radical, undivided, linear. — Species 2. North-west Africa. Poisonous plants. "Mousetail." **Myosurus** L.
   Ovule ascending. Pericarp with a hardened layer. — Species 50. Many of them are poisonous, some are used as ornamental or medicinal plants. (Including *Ceratocephalus* Pers. and *Ficaria* Dill.) . . **Ranunculus** L.
4. Ovary and fruit with 1—3 longitudinal veins or without veins. Ovule with a single coat. 5
   Ovary and fruit with 4 or more longitudinal or transverse veins. Ovule with 2 coats. Leaves alternate or all radical 6
5. Leaves opposite. Herbs or more frequently climbing shrubs. Perianth-segments 4—8, petal-like, usually valvate in the bud. — Species 40. Many of them are poisonous; some are used as ornamental or medicinal plants . . . . **Clematis** L.
   Leaves radical and alternate, or the uppermost whorled. Herbs, rarely low shrubs. Perianth-segments 4—20, imbricate in the bud. — Species 15. North, South, and East Africa. Several are poisonous ; some are used as ornamental or medicinal plants. (Including *Knowltonia* Salisb.) (Plate 46.) . . . . **Anemone** L.
6. Perianth simple, of 3—5 segments. Carpels inserted upon a flat receptacle, marked with longitudinal veins. Flowers in racemes or cymes. — Species 4. Poisonous plants, used for dyeing and in medicine.

   Thalictrum L.

   Perianth of 5 sepals and 5—16 petals. Carpels inserted upon a cylindrical receptacle, marked with transverse veins. Flowers solitary, terminal. — Species 4. North Africa. Poisonous, also used in medicine and as ornamental plants. . . . . **Adonis** L.
7. (1.) Perianth consisting of 5 or more sepals and 5—8 red, not glandular petals. Stamens united at the base, slightly perigynous. Carpels several, separate, fleshy. Outer coat of the ovules longer than the inner. — Species 1. North-west Africa. Poisonous and used as an ornamental and medicinal plant. [Tribe PAEONIEAE.] **Paeonia** L.
   Perianth consisting of 5 petal-like, usually blue sepals and 1—8 glandular petals (nectaries). Stamens free, hypogynous. Carpels not fleshy. Outer coat of the ovules as long as or shorter than the inner. [Tribe HELLEBOREAE.] 8

8. Perianth regular.   Petals 5—8.   9
  Perianth irregular.   Petals 1—4, usually 2.   10
9. Petals 5, large, with a long spur.   Carpels separate.   Leaves ternately dissected; segments broad.   Tall, perennial herbs. — Species 1.   Northwest Africa.   Used as an ornamental plant and in medicine. " Columbine." . . . .   **Aquilegia** L.
  Petals 8, small, not distinctly spurred.   Carpels more or less united. Leaves pinnately dissected ; segments narrow.   Low annual herbs. — Species 6.   North Africa.   Some (especially *N. sativa* L.) yield condiments and medicaments, others serve as ornamental plants.

  Nigella L.

10. Petals with a long claw, enclosed by the sepals.   Upper sepal erect, helmet-shaped.   Flowers yellow. — Species 1.   North-west Africa (Morocco). Poisonous and used in medicine. . . . . . .   **Aconitum** L.
  Petals sessile, projecting beyond the sepals.   Upper sepal spreading, spur-shaped. — Species 18.   North and East Africa.   Some are poisonous or used in medicine or as ornamental plants. " Larkspur." **Delphinium** L.

FAMILY 79. BERBERIDACEAE

Leaves alternate or all radical.   Flowers in racemes, hermaphrodite.   Sepals 4—9, more or less petal-like and yellow, at least the inner ones.   Petals (nectaries) 4—8.   Stamens 4—6, free.   Anthers turned inwards, opening by valves. Ovary superior, 1-celled.   Ovules 2 or more, basal or inserted along the ventral suture.   Stigma 1.   Fruit a capsule or a berry.   Seeds with a straight embryo and copious albumen. — Genera 3, species 6.   North and East Africa.

  1. Stem woody, shrubby.   Leaves undivided.   Inflorescence terminal.   Flowers 6-merous.   Fruit a berry. — Species 4.   North and East Africa. They yield timber, tanning and dyeing materials, fish-poison, medicaments, and edible fruits which are also used for the preparation of drinks and confectionery. " Barberry." [Tribe BERBERIDEAE.]

  Berberis L.

  Stem herbaceous, low.   Leaves dissected.   Inflorescence lateral.   Fruit a capsule. [Tribe EPIMEDIEAE.]   2
  2. Flowers 4-merous.   Ovules many, inserted along the ventral suture. Fruit opening by two valves.   Seeds with an aril. — Species 1.   North-west Africa. . . . .   **Epimedium** L.
  Flowers 6-merous.   Ovules few, basal.   Fruit bursting irregularly.   Seeds without an aril. — Species 1.   North-west Africa.   The tubers are used in medicine and as a substitute for soap. . . . .   **Leontice** L.

FAMILY 80. MENISPERMACEAE

Stem usually woody and twining.   Leaves alternate, undivided, palmately lobed or digitate, nearly always exstipulate.   Flowers small, unisexual, nearly always dioecious, mostly in racemes or panicles.   Sepals usually 6.   Petals usually 6, smaller than the sepals, sometimes absent. Stamens generally as many as and opposite the petals. Anthers opening by slits. Carpels 3—30, separate, more rarely solitary. Ovule 1, pendulous or laterally affixed, half-inverted with superior micropyle, sometimes accompanied at first by a second which is soon suppressed. Fruits drupaceous. — Genera 27, species 100. (Plate 47.)

1. Sepals 4 in the male flowers, 1—2 in the female. Petals of the male flowers 2—4, united below, of the female 1—3. Stamens united. Carpels solitary. 2
   Sepals 6—24, rarely (*Stephania*) in the female flowers only 3—4. Petals free or wanting. Carpels 3—30, free, rarely (*Stephania*) solitary. . 3
2. Female flowers with 1 sepal and 1 petal, rarely with 2—3 petals, in cymes. Leaves broad. Usually high-climbing plants. — Species 12. Tropical and South Africa. Some are used medicinally. . . **Cissampelos** L.
   Female flowers with 2 sepals and 2 petals, solitary or in pairs. Leaves usually narrow. Low-growing plants. — Species 4. South Africa. (Under *Cissampelos* L.) . . . . **Antizoma** Miers
3. Sepals 6—8, usually 6, rarely in the female flowers 3—4 4
   Sepals 9—24. 22
4. Sepals 6—8 in the male flowers, 3—4 in the female, usually equal in length. Petals 2—4. Carpels solitary. — Species 5. Central and South Africa. (Including *Homocnemia* Miers and *Perichasma* Miers) **Stephania** Lour.
   Sepals 6—8 in both sexes. Petals usually 6. Carpels 3—6. 5
5. Sepals nearly equal in length. 6,
   Sepals very unequal in length, the outer usually much shorter than the inner. 7
6. Petals none. Filaments entirely united. Anthers opening lengthwise. Stigmas thick, entire. — Species 5. Central Africa. (Including *Ropalandria* Stapf) . . . . **Dioscoreophyllum** Engl.
   Petals 6. Anthers opening transversely. Stigmas lobed. Leaves lobed. — Species 2. Tropical and South-east Africa. Used medicinally. "Calumba-root." . . . . **Iatrorrhiza** Miers
7. Petals 3. Stamens 3. Filaments united beyond the middle. Anthers opening by a transverse slit. Flowers in spreading panicles. Leaves sinuated or dissected. — Species 3. Equatorial West Africa.
   Syntriandrium Engl
   Petals 5—8, usually 6, rarely (*Tiliacora*) 3, but then stamens 6—9 and leaves undivided, very rarely (*Penianthus*) petals wanting. . . . 8
8. Stamens 15—30. Filaments united. Anthers opening outwards by a transverse slit. Carpels 4—6. Inner sepals united nearly to the top. Male flowers fascicled, female solitary. — Species 2. Central Africa to Delagoa Bay. . . . . **Epinetrum** Hiern
   Stamers 3—9, usually 6. 9
9. Filaments free or united at the base only. 10
   Filaments, at least the inner ones, united to the middle or beyond . . 17

10. Anthers opening by 1—2 transverse slits. 11
Anthers opening by 2 longitudinal slits 13
11. Anthers opening by two slits. Staminodes in the female flowers 6 or 0.
Stigmas entire. Fruits ovoid, reniform, or globular; scar of the style
nearly basal. Endocarp ribbed. Seeds with a scanty uniform albumen
and thick-fleshy cotyledons. Flowers in fascicles sometimes arranged
in racemes. — Species 5. Tropics to Delagoa Bay, Sahara and Egypt.
They yield dyes, drinks, and medicaments. (*Cebatha* Forsk.) (Plate 47.)

Cocculus L.

Anthers opening by one slit. Fruits oblong or elliptical ; scar of the style
nearly terminal. 12
12. Anthers opening by a slit across the apex. Staminodes in the female
flowers 6 or 0. Stigmas entire. Endocarp smooth. Seeds exalbuminous,
with fleshy cotyledons. Stem erect. Leaves lanceolate to ovate,
penninerved. Flowers in glomerules or false umbels. — Species 2.
West Africa. (Including *Heptacyclum* Engl.) . . **Penianthus** Miers
Anthers opening by a semicircular slit on the inside. Staminodes 3.
Stigmas 3-cleft Endocarp spiny. Seeds with a ruminate albumen and
thin leaf-like cotyledons. Stem climbing. Leaves cordate-ovate, 5-
nerved. Male flowers in spreading panicles, female in racemes. —
Species 4. West Africa. . . . . . . **Kolobopetalum** Engl.
13. Anthers opening laterally, almost outwards. Carpels 3. Leaves cordate-
ovate, palmately 5—7-nerved. 14
Anthers opening inwards. Leaves palmately 3-nerved, peltate, or penninerved. 15
14. Leaves deeply cordate at the base. Styles short. Staminodes in the fe
male flowers 6. — Species 1. Northern Central Africa. **Tinospora** Miers
Leaves slightly cordate. Styles none. Filaments united at the base.
— Species 7. Tropical and South-east Africa. **Desmonema** Miers
15. Leaves palmately 3-nerved, oblong. Carpels 3. Seeds straight. —
Species 1. Madagascar. (Under *Cocculus* DC.) . **Orthogynium** Baill.
Leaves peltate or penninerved. Seeds curved. 16
16. Leaves peltate. Flowers in racemes. Filaments free, flattened. Endocarp
tubercled, hairy. Cotyledons thin, leaf-like. — Species 1. West Africa
(Cameroons). (Under *Tinospora* Miers). . . . **Platytinospora** Diels
Leaves lanceolate to ovate, not peltate. Carpels 6 or more. Staminodes
in the female flowers none. Fruits with a basal style-scar ; endocarp
smooth or wrinkled. Cotyledons thick, fleshy. — Species 12. Central
Africa. (Including *Glossopholis* Pierre under *Limacia* Lour.)

Tiliacora Colebr.

17. (9.) Outer stamens free, inner united to the middle. Carpels 9 ; scar of
the style basal. Seeds spirally twisted, without albumen. Leaves
oblong or lanceolate. Flowers in panicles. — Species 1. Madagascar.

Spirospermum Thouars

Outer and inner stamens more or less united. 18

18. Outer stamens united at the base, inner up to the anthers. Anthers opening lengthwise, the inner laterally, the outer inwards. Carpels 3 ; endocarp spiny. Leaves cordate-ovate. Flowers fascicled in racemes. — Species 1. West Africa. (*Miersiophyton* Engl., under *Chasmanthera* Miers) . . . . **Rhigiocarya** Miers

Outer and inner stamens united to the middle or beyond. 19

19. Anthers opening by a semicircular slit. Carpels 3 ; stigmas 3-cleft. Endocarp spiny. Flowers in panicles. (See 12.) **Kolobopetalum** Engl.

Anthers opening by two longitudinal slits. Endocarp smooth, wrinkled, or tubercled. 20

20. Carpels 6—30. Scar of the style basal. Cotyledons fleshy. Anthers opening inwards. (See 16.) . . . . . . **Tiliacora** Colebr.

Carpels 3. Scar of the style terminal. Flowers fascicled in racemes. . 21

21. Petals unequal. Style none. Leaves undivided. (See 14.)

                                                               Desmonema Miers

Petals subequal. Stamens 6. Styles short. Stigmas cleft. Leaves broadly cordate. — Species 2. Central Africa. One species has edible tubers. ÷ . . . . **Chasmanthera** Hochst.

22. (3.) Inner sepals united nearly to the tip 23

Inner sepals free or nearly so. 24

23. Stamens 6—9. Filaments united at the base. Anthers opening lengthwise. Flowers solitary or in pairs. — Species 1. West Africa.

                                                                Synclisia Benth.

Stamens 15—30. Filaments united throughout their whole length. Anthers opening transversely. Male flowers fascicled, female solitary (See 8.) . . . . **Epinetrum** Hiern

24. Petals none. 25

Petals 3—9, usually 6 27

25. Stamens 3. Filaments united. Anthers opening by two transverse slits. Carpels 3—4. Scar of the style near the base of the fruit. Leaves broad-cordate. Flowers in fascicled glomerules. — Species 2. West Africa. . . . . **Syrrheonema** Miers

Stamens 3, with free filaments, or 5—6. Anthers opening by sometimes confluent longitudinal slits. Scar of the style terminal or lateral. . 26

26. Carpels 3. Styles absent. Stigmas peltate. Anthers opening by confluent slits. Stem erect. Flowers in glomerules. (See 12.)

                                                            Penianthus Miers

Carpels 6 or more. Styles present. Stem climbing. Flowers in lax cymes or in panicles. — Species 12. Tropics. (Including *Pycnostylis* Pierre, *Rameya* Baill., and *Welwitschiina* Engl.) **Triclisia** Benth.

27. Petals 9. Stamens 21. Carpels 12. — Species 1. West Africa.

                                                             Sphenocentrum Pierre

Petals 3—6. 28

28. Stamens 3. 29

Stamens 6—18. 31

J. Fleischmann del.

Cocculus Leaeba DC.

A Flowering branch. *B* Male flower cut lengthwise. *C* Female flower cut lengthwise. *D* Fruit. *E* Seed cut lengthwise.

A ²/₅

c

B ³/₁

D ³/₁

E ³/₂

J. Fleischmann del.

Anona senegalensis Pers.

A Branch. *B* Flower cut lengthwise. *C* Stigma. *D* Anther. *E* Young fruit cut lengthwise.

29. Filaments free.   Sepals hairy.   Stem climbing.   (See 26.) **Triclisia** Benth.
    Filaments united high up.   30
30. Sepals glabrous.   Leaves distinctly 3-nerved.   Stem climbing. — Species 1.
    Madagascar.   . . . .   **Strychnopsis** Baill.
    Sepals hairy.   Leaves not distinctly 3-nerved.   Stem erect. — Species 5.
    Madagascar.   (Including *Gamopoda* Bak. and *Tripodandra* Baill.)
                                                          Rhaptonema Miers
31. Stamens 9—18.   Filaments united throughout their whole length.   Anthers
    opening transversely.   Male flowers with 6 petals, female with 3 petals
    and 3 staminodes.   Carpels 6.   Flowers in false racemes or corymbs.
    Leaves undivided. — Species 7.   Tropics to Delagoa Bay.
                                                          Anisocycla Baill.
    Stamens 9 with the filaments free or united at the base, or 6.   Anthers
    opening lengthwise, but sometimes obliquely. 32
32. Carpels 3—4.   Flowers in racemes.   33
    Carpels 6—30.   Flowers in cymes or panicles, or the female in racemes.
    Leaves undivided.   34
33. Petals ovate.   Fruits ovoid; embryo nearly straight.   Stem erect.   Leaves
    compound, with 3 leaflets. — Species 4.   Madagascar. **Burasaia** Thouars
    Petals oblong, lobed.   Fruits reniform ;   embryo much curved.   Stem
    climbing.   Leaves simple, undivided. — Species 1.   West Africa
    (Congo).   . . . .   **Limaciopsis** Engl.
34. Sepals densely hairy.   Petals minute.   Staminodes in the female flowers
    present.   Carpels hairy.   (See 26.)   . . . . **Triclisia** Benth.
    Sepals glabrous or scantily hairy.   Staminodes in the female flowers
    absent.   (See 16.)   . . . . - . **Tiliacora** Colebr.

SUBORDER   MAGNOLIINEAE.

FAMILY 81.   ANONACEAE.

Shrubs or trees.   Leaves undivided, without stipules.   Flowers usually
hermaphrodite.   Sepals 3, rarely 2, usually valvate in the bud.   Petals 3—6,
fiee or united at the base.   Stamens hypogynous, 6 or more, usually numerous
rarely (*Bocagea*) 3.   Anthers nearly always turned outwards.   Carpels 3 or
more, separate, more rarely united and forming a one- or many-celled ovary.
Ovules inverted.   Fruit usually a berry.   Seeds with a copious, ruminate
albumen and a small embryo. — Genera 27, species 240.   (Plate 48.)

   1. Carpels whorled and united, forming a 1-celled ovary with parietal placen-
      tas.   [Tribe MONODOREAE.]   2
      Carpels spirally arranged, free, more rarely united, and then forming a
      many-celled ovary.   3
   2. Petals unequal, free or the outer united below, frequently with a wavy
      margin. — Species 15.   Tropics to Delagoa Bay.   The seeds of some
      species are used as condiments and in medicine. .   . **Monodora** Dun.

Petals equal, more or less united below, not wavy at the margin. — Species
    15. Tropics. (Under *Monodora* Dun.) . . **Isolona** (Pierre) Engl.

3. Petals 6, the inner greatly exceeding the outer. Carpels 4—6, with united
    stigmas ; ovules 6—10 to each. Trees with long-haired branches.
    Flowers in panicles. — Species 5. West Africa (Cameroons). [Tribe
    MILIUSEAE.] . . . . **Piptostigma** Oliv.

Petals 6, about equal in length, or the inner shorter, or petals 3—4.. . 4

4. Petals thick, more or less distinctly jointed into an inferior hollow portion
    and a superior flat or thickened one, erect or connivent, rarely spreading,
    valvate in the bud, very rarely (*Anona*) the inner imbricate at the apex.
    [Tribe XYLOPIEAE.] 5

Petals thin or rather thin, rarely thick, not jointed and usually spreading,
    but sometimes hollow or with a short claw appressed to the stamens. 10

5. Carpels united in fruit. Ovule 1. Styles oblong. Petals 3, alternate
    with the sepals, or 6. — Species 10, six of them spontaneous in tropical
    and South-east Africa, 4 cultivated in various regions. They yield
    cork-wood, fibre, gum-lac, tans and dyes, poisons, medicaments, a
    substitute for tea, and edible fruits (custard-apple, sour-sop, and others)
    from which also drinks are prepared. (Plate 48.) [Subtribe ANONINAE.]
    Anona L.

Carpels free till maturity. [Subtribe XYLOPIINAE.] 6

6. Ovules solitary. 7
Ovules 2 or more to each carpel. Petals 6. 8

7. Petals 3, opposite the sepals. Stigmas sessile. Trees with a yellow bark
    and yellow hairs. — Species 3. Central Africa. They yield timber,
    dyes, and medicaments. (Under *Xylopia* L.) . . **Enantia** Oliv.

Petals 6, the outer greatly exceeding the inner. Stigmas borne upon
    linear styles. — Species 6. Equatorial West Africa. (Under *Oxymitra*
    Blume) . . . . **Stenanthera** (Oliv.) Engl. & Diels

8. Carpels containing numerous ovules or seeds, coiled spirally when ripe and
    contracted between the seeds. Trees. — Species 1. German East
    Africa. . . . . **Polyceratocarpus** Engl. & Diels

Carpels containing 2—8 ovules or 1—8 seeds, straight or slightly curved
    when ripe. 9

9. Petals spreading, subequal. Ovules 2. Stalks of the inflorescence and the
    flowers usually thickened and hooked. Mostly climbing or scrambling
    shrubs. — Species 18. Tropics to Delagoa Bay. Some have edible
    fruits or are used in medicine. . . . . . . **Artabotrys** R. Br.

Petals suberect or connivent, the inner shorter and triangular above.
    Sepals more or less united. Receptacle usually concave. Ovules
    2—8, inserted along the ventral suture. Styles long. — Species 30.
    Tropics. Some yield timber, spices (guinea-pepper), and medicaments.
    (*Xylopicrum* P. Br.) . . . . **Xylopia** L.

10. (4.) Petals tranversely folded, at least in the bud, united at the base, subequal. Carpels 3—12, hairy ; ovules numerous ; styles 2-cleft. — Species 6. Tropics. [Tribe HEXALOBEAE.] . **Hexalobus** A. DC.
Petals not folded, usually free. [Tribe UVARIEAE.] 11

11. Petals valvate in the bud. Carpels free. [Subtribe UNONINAE.] . . 12
Petals, at least the inner ones, imbricate in the bud. [Subtribe UVAR-IINAE.] 23

12. Petals 3—4. Sepals or calyx-lobes 2. Connective of the stamens not or scarcely prolonged. Carpels and ovules numerous. Flowers unisexual. 13
Petals 6. Sepals 3. Connective usually prolonged beyond the anthercells. 15

13. Petals 3, thick. Flowers in clusters springing from the old wood, the female somewhat larger than the male. Trees. — Species 1. Equatorial West Africa (Congo). . . . . **Thonnera** De Wild.
Petals 4. 14

14. Petals free. Flowers in clusters springing from the old wood, the female much larger than the male. Trees. — Species 2. Equatorial West Africa. . . . . **Tetrastemma** Diels
Petals united below. Flowers solitary, axillary, the female about as large as the male. Shrubs. — Species 1. Equatorial West Africa (Cameroons). . . . . **Uvariopsis** Engl.

15. Petals in 1 row, rather thick. Stamens 12, six of them sometimes sterile. Anther-cells ovate. Carpels numerous, 1-seeded. — Species 2. West Africa (Congo). . . . . **Monanthotaxis** Baill.
Petals in 2 rows. 16

16. Outer petals spreading, inner smaller and converging. — Species 30. Tropical and South-east Africa. (Including *Clathrospermum* Planch.)
Popowia Endl.
Outer and inner petals spreading or erect. 17

17. Stamens 3—6 ; connective ovate, prolonged above, but not dilated. Carpels 3, one-seeded. — Species 1. Madagascar. . . **Bocagea** St. Hil.
Stamens numerous. 18

18. Stamens with an acuminate connective. Ovules several. Style short. Fruit slightly constricted between the seeds. Trees. Flowers in axillary clusters. — Species 1 (*C. odorata* Hook. f. & Thoms., Ylang-Ylang). Cultivated in the tropics for its fragrant flowers, which yield a perfume. . . . . **Cananga** Rumph
Stamens with a truncate or rounded connective. 19

19. Style long. Ovules 2. Peduncles thick and hooked. Climbing shrubs. (See 9.) . . . . **Artabotrys** R. Br.
Style short or wanting. 20

20. Ovules 1—2 to each carpel, rarely 3—8, and then fruits constricted between the seeds, and young branches leaves and flowers glabrous or clothed with simple hairs. Carpels usually numerous. 21

Ovules 10—30 to each carpel, rarely 8, but then fruits not constricted between the seeds, and young branches leaves and flowers clothed with stellate hairs. Carpels usually few. 22

21. Fruit-carpels with a single seed appressed to the pericarp, or with 2—8 seeds, and then constricted between them. Style present. Flowers hermaphrodite. — Species 9. Tropics. . . . . **Unona** L. f
    Fruit-carpels with a single seed not appressed to the pericarp, or with 2 seeds without a distinct constriction between them. Ovules 1—2. — Species 8. Tropics. Several species yield timber. **Polyalthia** Blume

22. Sepals small. Plants covered with stellate hairs. — Species 2. Central Africa. (Under *Unona* L. f.) . . . **Meiocarpidium** Engl. & Diels
    Sepals large. Plants covered with simple hairs or glabrous. — Species 3. Central Africa. . . . . **Uvariastrum** Engl.

23. (11.) Ovules 1—2 in each carpel. 24
    Ovules numerous in each carpel. 26

24. Carpels united as to the ovary and sunk in the receptacle, numerous, one-seeded. Flowers unisexual, with two large bracteoles enclosing the bud. Sepals 3, small. — Species 2. Equatorial West Africa. (Under *Anona* L.) . . . . **Anonidium** Engl. & Diels
    Carpels free. Flowers hermaphrodite. 25

25. Sepals large, leathery, cohering in the bud. Outer petals ovate, scarcely larger than the inner. Receptacle rather flat. Carpels 6—9, one-ovuled ; styles linear. Shrubs. — Species 1. Southern East Africa. (Under *Unona* L. f.) . . . . **Cleistochlamys** Oliv.
    Sepals small, membranous. Outer petals oblong, larger than the inner. Receptacle convex. Carpels usually 2-ovuled ; stigmas usually sessile. — Species 9. West Africa. (Under *Oxymitra* Benth.)
    Cleistopholis Pierre

26. Carpels united, at least in fruit, numerous. Petals much overlapping in the bud. Flowers on dwarf shoots, with a thick stalk and two large bracteoles enclosing the bud. Plants covered with stellate hairs. — Species 2. Equatorial West Africa. **Pachypodanthium** Engl. & Diels
    Carpels free. 27

27. Stigmas lanceolate ; margin not rolled inwards, or at the base only. Carpels about 10. Sepals triangular. Petals lanceolate, united at the base, greatly exceeding the calyx. — Species 1. East Africa. (*Asteran-thopsis* O. Ktze., under *Uvaria* L.) . . **Asteranthe** Engl. & Diels
    Stigmas truncate ; margin rolled inwards all round. Petals usually free. — Species 55. Tropical and South-east Africa. Some species yield edible fruits, dyes, or medicaments. . . . . . **Uvaria** L.

FAMILY 82. MYRISTICACEAE.

Trees or shrubs. Leaves entire, penninerved, without stipules. Flowers dioecious. Perianth simple, 2—5-, usually 3-lobed. Stamens 2—40 ; filaments more or less, usually wholly, united ; anthers 2-celled, turned outwards. Ovary superior, 1-celled ; ovule 1, ascending, inverted ; stigma 1. Fruit fleshy, usually dehiscent. Seed with an aril ; albumen copious ; embryo small. — Genera 9, species 25. Tropics. (Plate 49.)

1. Stamens 30—40 ; filaments united at the base. Style distinctly developed. Aril very small. Inflorescence head-like. — Species 1. Madagascar.
Mauloutchia Warb.

    Stamens 2—24 ; filaments wholly united. Style very short or absent. Aril distinctly developed. 2

2. Flowers with a bracteole at the base of the perianth, rather large, in racemes or panicles, or the female solitary. Anthers 8—24. Fruit ovoid, dehiscent. Aril slit. Albumen ruminate. Embryo with spreading cotyledons. — Species 2. Cultivated in several tropical islands. The seeds (nutmeg) and the arils (mace) are used as spices and medicaments and for the preparation of perfumes ; the pericarp is edible.
Myristica L.

    Flowers, at least the male, without bracteoles. Anthers 2—10. . . . 3

3. Flowers rather large, stalked, in cymosely arranged fascicles. Perianth funnel-shaped. Anthers 4—10, somewhat shorter than the united filaments. Fruit very large, subglobose, indehiscent. Aril entire. Albumen ruminate. Embryo with spreading cotyledons. Lateral nerves of the leaves not forked, joined by distinct arches close to the margin ; transverse veins faint. — Species 3. West Africa. They yield timber and oil. (Including *Ochocoa* Pierre). **Scyphocephalium** Warb.

    Flowers very small, in fascicles or heads, which are sometimes arranged in racemes or panicles. Fruit ovoid or elliptical, dehiscent. Embryo with suberect cotyledons. 4

4. Flowers in simple. fascicle- or head like inflorescences, subsessile. Anthers 3—4. Aril almost entire. Albumen not ruminate. Leaves with forked lateral nerves and distinct transverse veins. — Species 4. West Africa. They yield timber. . . . . **Staudtia** Warb.

    Flowers in heads or fascicles, which are arranged in racemes or panicles. Aril slit. 5

5. Flowers stalked, in fascicles. Anthers 2—7. Albumen ruminate. Lateral nerves of the leaves not distinctly confluent at the margin. . . . 6

    Flowers sessile, in heads. 7

6. Partial inflorescences supported by an involucral disc. Perianth cup-shaped. Anthers 3—5. Albumen with a cavity in the centre. — Species 4. West Africa. They yield timber and oil. **Coelocaryon** Warb.

    Partial inflorescences without an involucral disc. Perianth funnel- or pitcher-shaped. Albumen solid in the centre. — Species 1. Cultivated in the tropics. The seeds yield a fat. . . . . . . **Virola** Aubl.

7. Heads distinctly stalked. Perianth obovoid or club-shaped. Anthers 2—4, shorter than the filaments. Albumen ruminate. Lateral nerves of the leaves joined by arches near the margin. — Species 5. West

Africa and Upper Nile. They yield timber and oil. (Under *Myristica*
L.) (Plate 49.) . . . . **Pycnanthus** Warb.
Heads sessile or nearly so. Perianth cupular. Anthers 3—10. Albumen
uniform. 8
8. Heads large, distant on the branches of a panicle. Anthers 3—4, as long as
   or somewhat shorter than the filaments. Leaves whitish below ; lateral
   nerves joined by arches distant from the margin ; transverse veins faint.
   — Species 1. German East Africa. (Under *Brochoneura* Warb.)
   Cephalosphaera Warb.
   Heads arranged in dense racemes or panicles. Anthers 4—10, usually
   longer than the filaments. Leaves with forked lateral nerves and nearly
   as strong transverse veins. — Species 4. Madagascar. The seeds are
   used as a condiment and yield a fat. (Under *Myristica* L.)
   Brochoneura Warb.

FAMILY 83. MONIMIACEAE

Trees or shrubs. Leaves undivided, without stipules. Flowers unisexual.
Perianth simple, 3—6-lobed. Stamens 10 or more. Carpels solitary or several
and then separate at the time of flowering, often sunk in the receptacle. Ovule
1. Seeds with a small embryo and fleshy albumen. — Genera 6, species 30.
(Plate 50.)

1. Anthers opening by valves. Stamens numerous. Carpels 4 or more
   sunk in the receptacle. Ovules erect. Perianth irregular, strap-
   shaped. Leaves alternate. Flowers solitary or in clusters. — Species
   3. West Africa. (Plate 50.) [Subfamily **ATHEROSPERMOIDEAE,**
   tribe SIPARUNEAE.] . . . . **Glossocalyx** Benth.
   Anthers opening by longitudinal slits. Ovule pendulous. Perianth regular
   or nearly so. [Subfamily **MONIMIOIDEAE.**] 2

2. Receptacle (floral axis) small. Perianth-segments of the female flowers
   falling off singly. Stamens numerous. Carpel 1. [Tribe TRIMEN-
   IEAE.] 3
   Receptacle large, cup- or urn-shaped, at length bursting. Perianth
   falling off entire and lid-like, or little developed and persistent. Carpels
   several or many. 4

3. Perianth of the male flowers protruding beyond the stamens. Flowers
   on long stalks, in lax racemes. Leaves alternate. — Species 2. Equatorial West Africa (Cameroons). . . . . . **Chloropatane** Engl.
   Perianth of the male flowers concealed by the stamens. Flowers on short
   stalks, in dense racemes. Leaves opposite. — Species 3. Tropical and
   South Africa. They yield timber. (Including *Paxiodendron* Engl.)
   Xymalos Baill.

4. Receptacle cup-shaped, subsequently spreading, not enclosing the carpels.
   Perianth falling off as a whole, lid-like. Stamens 10—12. Anther-
   halves confluent above. Leaves opposite. Flowers solitary or in

MYRISTICACEAE.

Pl. 49.

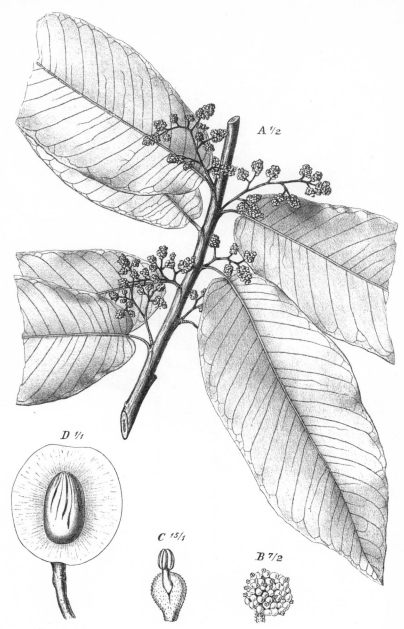

A ½

D ⅟₁

C ¹⁵/₁

B ⁷/₂

J. Fleischmann del.

Pycnanthus Kombo (Baill.) Warb.

A Part of a flowering branch. *B* Male partial inflorescence. *C* Male flower. *D* Fruit, the pericarp cut lengthwise.

J. Fleischmann del.

Glossocalyx longicuspis Benth.

A Flowering branch.   *B* Female flower.   *C* Female flower cut lengthwise.   *D* Carpel (the ovary cut lengthwise).

clusters, monoecious. — Species 1. Madagascar. (Under *Mollinedia* Ruiz & Pav.) [Tribe MOLLINEDIEAE.] . . **Ephippiandra** Decne.

Receptacle narrowly pitcher-shaped, subsequently increasing in size and enclosing the carpels. Perianth little developed. Stamens numerous. Anther-halves separate. [Tribe MONIMIEAE.] 5

5. Stamens with a gland on each side. Carpels few, not sunk in the receptacle. Shrubs. Leaves opposite. Flowers in cymes, dioecious. — Species 4. Madagascar and the neighbouring islands. They yield timber and medi caments . . . . **Monimia** Thouars

Stamens without glands. Carpels numerous, sunk in the receptacle. — Species 20. Madagascar and the neighbouring islands. Some species yield timber, dyes, or medicaments. (*Ambora Juss.*)

Tambourissa Sonn.

FAMILY 84. LAURACEAE

Trees or shrubs. Leaves undivided, without stipules, sometimes scale-like. Flowers regular. Perianth of 4 or 6 segments. Fertile stamens 4—14, perigynous. Anthers opening by 2—4 valves. Ovary superior, very rarely (*Hypodaphnis*) inferior, 1-celled. Ovule 1, pendulous, inverted. Style simple. Seed exalbuminous ; embryo straight. — Genera 15, species 75. (Plate 51.)

1. Anthers 2-celled. [Subfamily **LAUROIDEAE.**] 2
Anthers 4-celled. [Subfamily **PERSEOIDEAE.**] 11

2. Anthers all turned inwards, 8—14, usually 12. Perianth 4-cleft. Flowers in umbels, dioecious or polygamous. Leafy shrubs or trees. — Species 2. North Africa. They yield timber, oil, perfumes, spices, and medicaments, and are also used as ornamental plants. " Laurel." [Tribe LAUREAE.] . . . . **Laurus** L.

Anthers partly (the outer) turned inwards, partly outwards, 4—12, usually 9. Flowers hermaphrodite or polygamous, usually panicled. . . 3

3. Stem thread-shaped, twining, parasitic. Leaves reduced to minute scales. Perianth 6-cleft, the outer segments much smaller than the inner. Fertile stamens 9. — Species 4. Southern and tropical Africa. Some are used medicinally. [Tribe CASSYTHEAE.] . . **Cassytha** L.

Stem shrub- or tree-like. Leaves perfectly developed. Perianth with 6, rarely 4, subequal segments. 4

4. Receptacle accrescent, cupuliform, enclosing the fruit. Perianth-segments 6. Fertile stamens 9, rarely 12. [Tribe CRYPTOCARYEAE.] . 5

Receptacle scarcely or not accrescent, not enclosing the fruit. [Tribe APOLLONIADEAE.] 6

5. Fruit incompletely 6-celled. Pericarp adnate to the receptacle, but free from the seed. Cotyledons 6-lobed. Leaves penninerved. — Species 8. Madagascar. They yield timber, oil, condiments, and medicaments. (*Agathophyllum* Juss.) . . . . **Ravensara** Sonn.

O

Fruit completely 1-celled. Pericarp easily separable from the receptacle,
but adnate to the seed. — Species 10. Madagascar, South and East
Africa. . . . . **Cryptocarya** R. Br.

6. Perianth 4-parted. Fertile stamens 4. Shrubs. Leaves linear-lanceolate.
— Species 2. Madagascar. . . . .   **Potameia** Thouars
Perianth 6-parted or 6-cleft. Fertile stamens 6—9. 7

7. Fertile stamens 6, each with 2 glands. Flowers in racemes. — Species 1.
Madagascar. . . . . **Berniera** Baill.
Fertile stamens 9, rarely 6, all or the outer ones without glands. Flowers
in panicles. 8

8. Staminodes within the fertile stamens none. Filaments oblong or obovate,
the inner ones each with 2 oblong, wholly adnate glands. — Species 3
Equatorial West Africa (Cameroons). They yield timber.

Tylostemon Engl.

Staminodes within the fertile stamens present. Inner fertile stamens
with 2 roundish glands at their base. 9

9. Perianth persistent. Leaves herbaceous. — Species 1. Canary Islands
and Madeira. Yields timber. . . . . **Apollonias** Nees
Perianth deciduous. Leaves leathery. — Species 20. Tropics. Some
species yield timber or edible seeds. (*Afrodaphne* Stapf, *Hufelandia*
Nees, *Nesodaphne* Hook., under *Tylostemon* Engl.) **Beilschmiedia** Nees

10. (1.) Anthers 9—14 (usually 12), all turned inwards. Flowers dioecious, in
umbels. — Species 2. Naturalized in the Mascarenes and Seychelles.
They yield timber, a fat, and medicaments. (*Tetranthera* Jaqu.) [Tribe
LITSEEAE.] . . . . **Litsea** Lam.
Anthers 9, the outer turned inwards, the inner outwards. Flowers her-
maphrodite or polygamous, usually in panicles. [Tribe CINNA-
MOMEAE.] 11

11. Staminodes very small and awl-shaped or wanting. Receptacle accrescent.
Flowers usually polygamous. 12
Staminodes well developed, thickened at the apex. Receptacle scarcely
or not accrescent. Flowers usually hermaphrodite. 13

12. Anther-valves side by side. Ovary inferior. — Species 1. West Africa
(Cameroons). (Under *Ocotea* Aubl.) . . . . **Hypodaphnis** Stapf
Anther-valves in superposed pairs. Ovary superior. — Species 15. Tropical
and South Africa, Canary Islands, Azores. They yield timber, fat,
condiments, and medicaments. (Including *Mespilodaphne* and *Oreo-
daphne* Nees). (Plate 51.) . . . . **Ocotea** Aubl.

13. Leaves trinerved. Perianth-segments falling singly after the time of
flowering. — Species 2 (*C. zeylanicum* Breyn, cinnamon, and *C. cam-
phora* Nees & Eberm., camphor). Cultivated in the tropics. They
yield timber, spices, and drugs for industrial and medicinal uses.

Cinnamomum Blume

Leaves penninerved: Perianth persisting or falling off as a whole. . . 14

F ⁴/₁　A ¹/₂　E ⁵/₁　D ⁶/₁　G ³/₂　B ⁴/₁　C ⁶/₁

J. Fleischmann del.

Ocotea bullata (Burch.) Benth.

A Flowering branch.　*B* Male flower cut lengthwise.　*C* Stamens.　*D* Staminode.　*E* Female flower cut lengthwise.　*F* Group of fruits.　*G* Young fruit cut lengthwise.

PAPAVERACEAE.

Pl. 52

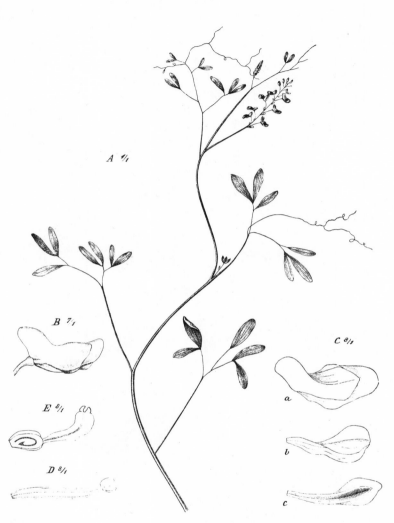

J. Fleischmann del.

Trigonocapnos curvipes Schlecht.

A Flowering branch. *B* Flower. *C* Petals (*a* the upper *b* one of the lateral, *c* the lower). *D* Bundle of stamens (the third anther not visible). *E* Pistil (the ovary cut lengthwise).

14. Perianth yellow, with oblong segments, deciduous.   Fruit large, greenish.
— Species 1 (*P. gratissima* Gaertn., avocado-pear).   Cultivated in the
tropics.   It yields edible fruit, from which also a fat and a dye are
prepared, and is used in medicine.   .   .   .   .   .   **Persea** Gaertn.
Perianth white, with ovate segments, persistent.   Fruit small, blackish.
— Species 1.   Canary Islands and Azores.   Yields timber.   (Under
Persea Gaertn.)   .   .   .   .   **Phoebe** Nees

FAMILY 85. HERNANDIACEAE

Trees or shrubs.   Leaves alternate, palminerved, without stipules.   Flowers
in panicles, regular, hermaphrodite polygamous or monoecious.   Perianth
4—10-parted.   Fertile stamens 3—5, alternating with the inner perianth-
segments.   Anthers 2-celled, turned inwards, opening by valves.   Ovary
inferior, 1-celled.   Ovule 1, pendulous, inverted.   Style and stigma simple.
Seed exalbuminous.   Embryo with folded or coiled cotyledons. — Genera 3,
species 7.   Tropics.   (Under *LAURACEAE* or *COMBRETACEAE*.)
1. Flowers without bracteoles, polygamous.   Perianth very small. Stigma
capitate.   Fruit with 2 terminal wings.   Cotyledons spirally twisted.
Trees.   Leaves undivided or lobed. — Species 1.   East Africa, Angola,
Madagascar.   Yields timber.   [Subfamily **GYROCARPOIDEAE.**]
Gyrocarpus Jaqu.
Flowers with bracteoles, which sometimes form an involucre, hermaphrodite
or monoecious.   Perianth rather small.   Stigma discoid and more or
less lobed.   Cotyledons more or less folded or crumpled.   [Subfamily
HERNANDIOIDEAE.]   2
2. Flowers hermaphrodite.   Perianth 10-parted.   Fertile stamens 5, with 2
scales at the base.   Fruit with 2—4 lateral wings.   Climbing shrubs.
Leaves digitate. — Species 1.   Southern West Africa (Angola).
Illigera Blume
Flowers monoecious, the female surrounded by a cupular, truncate or
lobed, ultimately inflated involucel.   Perianth of the male flowers
6—8-parted, of the female 8—10-parted.   Fertile stamens 3—4.   Trees.
Leaves undivided.   Partial inflorescences surrounded by an involucre
of several bracts, and consisting of a female flower and two or more
male. — Species 5.   Tropics.   They yield timber and are used in
medicine.   .   .   .   .   **Hernandia** L.

ORDER RHOEADALES

SUBORDER RHOEADINEAE

FAMILY 86. PAPAVERACEAE

Herbs.   Leaves more or less lobed or divided.   Flowers hermaphrodite.
Sepals 2, very rarely 3.   Petals 4, very rarely 6, free, hypogynous.   Anthers
opening by slits.   Ovary superior, 1-celled or incompletely 2- or more-celled.

Ovules parietal, curved or inverted. Fruit a capsule or a nut. Seeds with a small embryo and a copious, oily albumen. — Genera 11, species 50. (Including *FUMARIACEAE*.) (Plate 52.)

1. Petals, at least one of them, prolonged into a spur. Stamens 2, tripartite (or 6 in two bundles) ; the middle segment of each stamen bearing a two-celled anther, the lateral ones a one-celled. Juice not milky. [Subfamily **FUMARIOIDEAE**.] 2

    Petals not spurred. Stamens 4 or many, all with 2-celled anthers. . . 5

2. Ovary with 3 or more ovules. Fruits, at least some of them, dehiscent, 3- or more-seeded. — Species 9. South and North Africa and high mountains of Central Africa. Some are used as ornamental plants. (Including *Cysticapnos* Adans.) . . . . **Corydalis** DC.

    Ovary with 1—2 ovules. Fruit indehiscent, 1—2-seeded. Seeds not appendaged. 3

3. Ovary with 2 ovules. Fruit 2-seeded, compressed, with 3 nerves on each side. Leaves fleshy. — Species 1. North-west Africa (Algeria). **Sarcocapnos** DC.

    Ovary with 1 ovule. Fruit 1 seeded, compressed but 1-nerved on each side, or triquetrous, or globular. 4

4. Fruit triquetrous, pendulous. Superior petal helmet-shaped, inferior spoon-shaped, lateral ones clawed. Stem climbing. — Species 1. South Africa (Cape Colony). (Plate 52.) . **Trigonocapnos** Schlecht.

    Fruit globular or compressed, erect. — Species 15. North, South, and East Africa ; also naturalized in West Africa and the Mascarene Islands. " Fumitory." (Including *Discocapnos* Cham. & Schlechtend. and *Platycapnos* Bernh.) . . . . **Fumaria** L.

5. Stamens 4. Petals 3-cleft. Placentas and styles 2. Juice not milky. — Species 7. North Africa. Some are used as ornamental plants. [Subfamily **HYPECOIDEAE**.] . . . . **Hypecoum** L.

    Stamens numerous. [Subfamily **PAPAVEROIDEAE**.] 6

6. Juice not milky. Flowers solitary. Petals yellow. Placentas 2. Stigma subsessile, with 4 spreading lobes. Fruit linear, 10-ribbed, 1-celled, 2-valved to the base. Seeds unappendaged. — Species 1. Naturalized in the Canary Islands. Fodder-plant. [Tribe ESCHSCHOLTZIEAE.] **Hunnemannia** Sweet

    Juice milky. Placentas 4 or more, more rarely 2, but then stigmas or stigma-lobes only 2, or at least partly erect. 7

7. Stigmas (or style-branches) 2, alternating with the 2 placentas and borne upon a short, but distinct style. Ovary and fruit linear. Seeds appendaged. Flowers in umbels, yellow. Juice reddish-yellow. — Species 1. North-west Africa. Poisonous and used medicinally. " Celandine." [Tribe CHELIDONIEAE.] . . **Chelidonium** L.

    Stigmas (or style-branches) 3 or more, rarely 2, as many as and opposite to the placentas or more numerous, sessile or nearly so. [Tribe PAPA-VEREAE.] 8

8. Fruit linear, dehiscing to the base. Placentas, stigmas, and fruit-valves
   2—4. Juice yellow. 9
   Fruit oblong, ovoid, or globular, dehiscing near the top only or indehiscent.
   Placentas, stigmas, and fruit-valves 4—16.. 10
9. Petals yellow or reddish-yellow, twisted in the bud. Style ending in 2
   erect and 2 spreading lobes. Fruit with a false partition. — Species 2.
   North Africa and Cape Verde Islands. Used as ornamental or medicinal
   plants ; the seeds yield oil. . . . . **Glaucium** Juss.
   Petals violet or red, crumpled in the bud. Style ending in 2—4 connivent
   lobes. Fruit 1-celled. — Species 4. North Africa. Used as ornamental
   plants . . . . **Roemeria** Medik.
10. Stigmas in the sinuses between the connivent style-lobes. Petals yellow
    or whitish. Fruit oblong, usually bristly. Juice yellow. — Species 1.
    Naturalized in Tropical and South Africa. Used as an ornamental and
    medicinal plant ; the seeds yield oil. . . . . **Argemone** L.
    Stigmas radiating upon a disc-like expansion of the style-apex. Ovary in-
    completely septate. Juice white. Buds nodding. — Species 12.
    North and South Africa, Abyssinia, and Cape Verde Islands ; also
    cultivated in various regions. Some species are poisonous or are used
    as ornamental, medicinal, or dye-plants. *P. somniferum* L. yields
    opium, oil, and edible seeds. " Poppy " . . . . . **Papaver** L.

SUBORDER CAPPARIDINEAE.

FAMILY 87. CAPPARIDACEAE

Leaves alternate, simple or digitate. Flowers solitary or in racemes or
umbels, usually irregular. Petals wanting or free, usually 4, rarely (*Cercopetalum*) united at the base. Disc ring- or scale-like, rarely tubular. Ovary
superior, usually stalked. Ovules 4 or more, rarely (*Dipterygium*) 1—2, curved,
usually parietal. Seeds reniform, exalbuminous. Embryo curved, with folded
or coiled cotyledons. — Genera 20, species 260. (Plate 53.)

1. Fruit succulent, baccate, indehiscent, rarely at length dehiscing in two
   valves to which the placentas remain attached. Embryo coiled. Shrubs
   or trees. [Subfamily **CAPPARIDOIDEAE.**] 2
   Fruit dry, capsular and usually siliquiform, rarely nut-like. Embryo
   curved. Herbs or undershrubs, rarely shrubs or trees. . . . 14
2. Calyx-tube distinctly developed. Stamens very numerous. Ovary with
   a long stalk. [Tribe MAERUEAE.] 3
   Calyx-tube indistinct or wanting, rarely distinctly developed, but then
   stamens 10 and ovary with a very short stalk. [Tribe CAPPARIDEAE] 4
3. Calyx bursting transversely. Petals none. Stamens inserted upon
   a convex receptacle. Placentas 6—10. — Species 10. East Africa,
   Madagascar and Mauritius. . . . . **Thylachium** Lour.
   Calyx bursting lengthwise. Stamens usually inserted upon an elongated,
   stalk-like receptacle. Placentas 2—4. — Species 50. Some of them

yield timber, vegetables, or medicaments. (Including *Niebuhria* DC.
and *Streblocarpus* Arn.) . . . .   **Maerua** Forsk.

4. Calyx-tube distinctly developed. Petals none. Stamens about 10. Disc
and androphore wanting. Ovary with a very short stalk. Placentas 2.
Leaves digitate. — Species 2. South Africa. . .   **Bachmannia** Pax
    Calyx-tube indistinct or wanting. Petals present, more rarely wanting,
    but then leaves undivided. 5

5. Receptacle produced behind into a tube- or strap-shaped appendage. Sta-
mens 4—8, inserted upon a stalk-like androphore. Leaves undivided.
— Species 20. Tropical and South Africa. Some are used in medicine.
(Including *Schepperia* Neck.) . . . .   **Cadaba** Forsk.
    Receptacle produced into scale-like appendages or unappendaged. Sta-
    mens rarely upon a distinct stalk-like androphore, and then fertile and
    sterile stamens together 10 or more. 6

6. Petals none. Stamens without a distinct androphore. Leaves undivided. 7
    Petals 4 or more. Ovules numerous. 9

7. Ovary 2-, rarely 3-celled, with 2 ovules in each cell, supported upon a long
stalk. Stamens numerous. Disc cup-shaped, crenate. Sepals 3,
rarely 2 or 4, united at the base. — Species 6. Central Africa.
                                     Courbonia Brongn.
    Ovary 1-celled, sometimes incompletely 2-celled. Ovules 6 or more.
    Sepals 4, rarely 5. 8

8. Disc cup-shaped, crenate, accrescent. Stamens numerous. Ovules
numerous. Stigma 4-lobed. — Species 3. West Africa. **Buchholzia** Engl.
    Disc ring-shaped. Stamens 6—20. Ovules 6—12. Stigma entire. —
    Species 30. Central Africa, northern South Africa, and Sahara. The
    fruits and roots of some are eaten or used medicinally. **Boscia** Lam.

9. Flowers dioecious. Sepals 5. Petals 5, united at the base. Stamens
10—13, borne upon a short androphore. Ovary 5-celled, with axile
ovules. Leaves undivided. — Species 1. West Africa.
                                     Cercopetalum Gilg
    Flowers hermaphrodite or polygamous, very rarely dioecious, but then
    stamens numerous. Flowers nearly always 4-merous 10

10. Stamens inserted on an elongated stalk-like androphore, united in two
bundles, one of which contains 5—9 fertile, the other as many sterile
stamens. Petals 4. Placentas 2. Leaves ternately compound. —
Species 3. East Africa. . . . .   **Cladostemon** A. Br. & Vatke
    Stamens inserted on a very short androphore or without an androphore 11

11. Petals very unequal, two much larger than the others, wing-like. Stamens
5—7. Placentas 2. Leaves ternately compound. — Species 1. West
Africa. Used as an ornamental plant. (*Pteropetalum* Pax)
                                     Euadenia Oliv.
    Petals not very unequal. Stamens 8 or more. 12

12. Petals open in aestivation, with a long claw ; sepals imbricate or open.
Stamens upon a short androphore bearing scales within. Ovary upon a

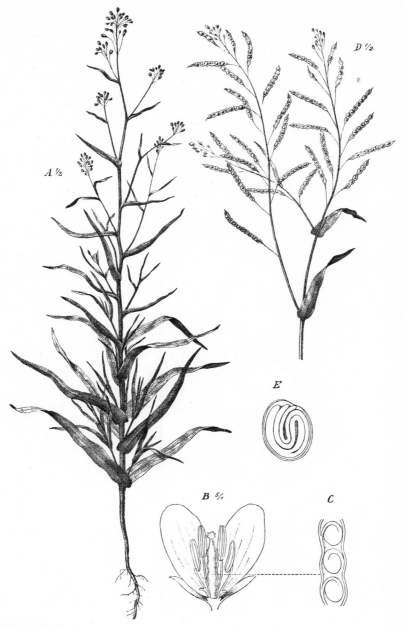

J. Fleischmann del.

Heliophila amplexicaulis L. fil.

A Plant with inflorescences.   *B* Flower cut lengthwise.   *C* Ovary cut lengthwise.   *D* Fruiting branch   *E* Seed cut lengthwise.

J. Fleischmann del.

Polanisia hirta (Klotzsch) Sond.

A Branch with flowers and fruits. *B* Flower cut lengthwise. *C* Anther. *D* Ovary cut lengthwise. *E* Seed.

long gynophore, 1- or incompletely 2-celled, with 2 placentas. Leaves ternately compound. — Species 6. Tropics. Some species yield timber, edible fruit, or medicaments. . . . . **Crataeva** L.
Petals imbricate in aestivation ; sepals usually valvate. Disc and androphore little developed or wanting. 13

13. Leaves ternately compound, rarely simple and undivided, and then petals numerous. Petals clawed. Ovary with a long stalk, 1-celled. — Species 25. Central Africa. . . . . . . **Ritchiea** R. Br.
Leaves simple, undivided. Petals 4, very rarely 5. — Species 50. Some of them yield timber, salad, condiments (capers from *C. spinosa* L.), edible fruits, and medicaments ; some are poisonous. **Capparis** L.

14. (1.) Fruit indehiscent, winged, 1-seeded. Petals 4. Stamens 6. Ovary with a very short stalk, 1-celled. Ovules 1—2. Style short. Undershrubs. Leaves undivided. — Species 1. Egypt and Nubia. [Subfamily **DIPTERYGIOIDEAE.**] . . . . . **Dipterygium** Decne.
Fruit dehiscing by 2 or more valves. Ovules 4 or more 15

15. Fruit 1-seeded, dehiscing by many valves. Sepals 2. Petals 5. Stamens 40—60. Ovary sessile, 1-celled. Ovules 4—6. Style long. Shrubs. Flowers fascicled. — Species 2. East Africa. [Subfamily **CALYP-TROTHECOIDEAE.**] . . . . **Calyptrotheca** Gilg
Fruit several- or many-seeded, dehiscing by 2 valves which separate from the persistent placentas. Sepals 4. Petals 4. Ovules numerous. [Subfamily **CLEOMOIDEAE.**] 16

16. Calyx-tube distinctly developed. Petals violet. Stamens 10—12, borne upon a short androphore. Ovary with a long stalk. Herbs. Leaves ternately compound. — Species 2. East Africa. (Under *Cleome* L.)
Chilocalyx Klotzsch
Calyx-tube none. 17

17. Stamens inserted upon a stalk-like androphore, 6 all fertile. Ovary stalked. Herbs. Leaves digitate. — Species 1. Tropical and South Africa and Egypt. Yields vegetables, condiments, and medicaments, and is also used as an ornamental plant. (*Pedicellaria* Schrank) **Gynandropsis** DC.
Stamens inserted upon the receptacle, which is not prolonged into a distinct androphore. 18

18. Stamens numerous or intermixed with staminodes. Herbs. Leaves digitate. — Species 20. Some of them are used as vegetables. (Including *Dianthera* Klotzsch and *Tetratelia* Sond., under *Cleome* L.) (Plate 53.) . . . . **Polanisia** Raf.
Stamens 4—6, all fertile. 19

19. Disc reduced to 4 small glands. Ovary sessile. Style long. Trees. Leaves undivided. — Species 1. Northern East Africa (Somaliland).
Cleomodendron Pax
Disc ring- or saucer-shaped, sometimes produced into scales. Herbs or undershrubs. — Species 30. Some of them are used as ornamental or medicinal plants. . . . . **Cleome** L.

FAMILY 88. CRUCIFERAE

Herbs or undershrubs, rarely shrubs.   Leaves alternate, rarely the lower
opposite, simple, but often divided, without stipules, but frequently with
auricles at the base.   Flowers without bracteoles, usually in racemes, regular
or nearly so, hermaphrodite.   Sepals 4.   Petals 4, rarely 0.   Stamens 6, of
which 4 are longer, rarely 2—4, hypogynous, rarely subperigynous.   Glands at
the base of the stamens more or less developed.   Ovary superior, 1—2-celled or
transversely septate, very rarely 3-celled.   Ovules parietal, curved.   Style
simple, with 1—2 stigmas.   Fruit dry, usually 2-valved.   Albumen scanty or
wanting.   Embryo curved. — Genera 88, species 420.   (Plate 54.)

1. Hairs, all or some of them, branched, at least at the base.   Stigma more
     developed above the placentas than between them.   [Tribe HESPERI-
     DEAE.]   2
   Hairs simple or wanting.   37
2. Fruit at least 4 times as long as broad.   3
   Fruit less than 4 times as long as broad, or broader than long   .   .   .   19
3. Fruit-valves with a horn-like appendage.   Radicle of the embryo accum-
     bent   4
   Fruit-valves without an appendage, but the style sometimes appendaged.   7
4. Fruit-valves with a basal appendage.   Seeds margined.   Style appendaged
     at the base.   Petals violet.   Lateral sepals gibbous at the base.
     Herbs covered with glandular tubercles. — Species 1.   North Africa.
                                                    Lonchophora Dur.
   Fruit-valves with an apical appendage.   Seeds not margined.   Petals
     white, yellow, or red.   Plants without glandular tubercles.   .   .   .   5
5. Fruit-valves with a forked appendage.   Petals pink.   Leaves linear,
     entire.   Undershrubs. — Species 1.   Canary Islands. **Parolinia** Webb
   Fruit-valves with an entire appendage.   6
6. Fruit-valves with a blunt appendage below the apex.   Petals red.   Leaves
     oblong or ovate, sinuate or toothed.   Undershrubs with star-shaped
     hairs. — Species 5.   East Africa.   .   .   .   .   .   **Diceratella** Boiss.
   Fruit-valves with a pointed appendage at the apex.   Petals white or
     yellow.   Leaves linear.   Herbs with 2-cleft hairs. — Species 1.   North
     Africa.   .   .   .   .   **Notoceras** R. Br.
7. Lateral glands alone present, one on each side of the lateral stamens.
     Stigmatic lobes usually long and erect, but sometimes united.   .   .   8
   Lateral and median (anterior and posterior) glands present, sometimes
     blended into a ring.   Stigmatic lobes usually short and spreading or
     indistinctly developed.   14
8. Plants covered with glandular tubercles.   Style with a dorsal gibbosity ;
     stigma not sharply limited.   Seeds flat ; radicle accumbent. — Species
     15.   North, East, and South Africa.   Some are used as ornamental
     plants or in medicine.   "Stock."   .   .   .   .   .   **Matthiola** R. Br.
   Plants without glandular tubercles.   Stigma more or less sharply limited
     at the base .   .   .   .

9. Longer filaments united to the top. Sepals connivent. Petals linear, white or pink. Seeds minute, in two rows. Bracts leaf-like. Leaves divided into narrow segments. — Species 1. North-east Africa (Egypt).
Leptaleum DC.
Longer filaments free or slightly cohering. 10

10. Seeds thick ; radicle incumbent. Fruit-valves more or less convex. Petals white or pink. — Species 10. North Africa. Some are used as ornamental plants. (Including *Maresia* Pomel). . . **Malcolmia** R. Br.
Seeds flat ; radicle accumbent. 11

11. Fruit-valves convex, with a faint middle-nerve, constricted between the seeds. Sepals saccate at the base. Petals pink. Hairs stellate. — Species 3. North Africa. (Under *Farsetia* Desv. or *Malcolmia* R. Br.).
Eremobium Boiss.
Fruit-valves flat, sometimes keeled. 12

12. Fruit-valves projecting inwards between the seeds, thick, obtusely angled. Stigma acutely 2-lobed. Sepals erect. Petals pink. — Species 3. North and East Africa . . . . **Morettia** DC.
Fruit-valves not projecting between the seeds. 13

13. Petals purple, narrow. Sepals erect, not saccate. Stigma acutely 2-lobed. Seeds winged. Leaves narrow. Hairs 2-cleft. — Species 13. East and North Africa. Some are used medicinally. . . **Farsetia** Desv.
Petals white, rarely yellowish, reddish, or bluish. Fruit-valves with a faint middle-nerve. Seeds in one row. — Species 15. North, East, and South Africa. Some are used as ornamental plants. " Rock-cress."
Arabis L.

14. (7.) Median glands 4. Style 2-lobed ; stigma dilated, not sharply limited. Fruit-valves convex or keeled. 15
Median glands 2, usually confluent with the lateral ones into a ring. Style short, truncate or somewhat depressed at the apex ; stigma usually sharply limited. 16

15. Seeds flat ; radicle accumbent. — Species 4. North Africa. Used as ornamental plants or in medicine. " Wallflower." (Including *Di-chroanthus* Webb). . . . . **Cheiranthus** L.
Seeds thick ; radicle incumbent. — Species 5. North Africa to Abyssinia. Some are used as ornamental plants or in medicine. **Erysimum** L.

16. Partition of the fruit with two bundles of fibres ; valves with a strong midrib. Radicle incumbent. Petals yellow. Leaves pinnatipartite. — Species 4. North Africa to Abyssinia. (Under *Sisymbrium* L.).
Descurainia Webb & Berth.
Partition of the fruit without bundles of fibres. Petals white, rarely yellowish, reddish, or bluish. 17

17. Fruit-valves flat, with a faint middle-nerve. Seeds in one row ; radicle accumbent. (See 13.). . . . . **Arabis** L.
Fruit-valves more or less convex, with a strong middle-nerve. . . . 18

18. Seeds with an accumbent radicle, in 2 rows. — Species 1. South Africa.
   (Under *Arabis* L.). . . . . **Turritis** L.
   Seeds with an incumbent radicle, usually in 1 row. — Species 2. East,
   South, and North Africa, and Cape Verde Islands. (Under *Arabis* L. or
   Sisymbrium L.). . . . . **Stenophragma** Celak.

19. (2.) Fruit 1-seeded. 20
   Fruit 2- or more-seeded. 22

20. Sepals petal-like. Petals reddish. Glands none. Ovary 3-celled. Style
   very short. Fruit elliptical, much compressed. Shrubs. — Species
   1. South Africa (Cape Colony). . . . . . **Schlechteria** Bolus
   Sepals not petal-like. Petals yellow or whitish. Glands present. Ovary
   2-celled. Fruit orbicular. Herbs. 21

21. Filaments with a tooth-like appendage. Style none. Fruit flat, without a
   partition. Radicle accumbent. Fruit-stalk bent back. Leaves linear.
   Hairs star-shaped. — Species 2. North Africa. . . **Clypeola** L.
   Filaments not appendaged. Style thread-shaped. Fruit thick, with a
   rudimentary partition. Radicle incumbent. Fruit-stalk erect or
   spreading. Cauline leaves sagittate. Hairs 2—3-cleft. — Species 1.
   North Africa. Used medicinally. (*Vogelia* Medik.) . **Neslia** Desv.

22. Fruit 2—4-seeded. 23
   Fruit many-seeded. 30

23. Petals yellow. 24
   Petals white or reddish. 26

24. Sepals, at least the lateral, saccate at the base. Filaments without an
   appendage. Stigma 2-lobed. Fruit with laterally compressed, boat-
   shaped valves and a linear partition. Seeds 2—3 ; radicle incumbent.
   Shrubs. Leaves entire. Flowers solitary, axillary. — Species 1.
   Island of Socotra. . . . . **Lachnocapsa** Balf.
   Sepals not saccate. Herbs or undershrubs. Flowers in spikes or racemes. 25

25. Median and lateral glands present. Filaments without an appendage.
   Stigma 2-lobed. Fruit winged, 4-celled, indehiscent. Seeds 4 ; funicle
   very short. Embryo spirally twisted ; radicle incumbent. Plants
   covered with glandular tubercles. Leaves toothed. — Species 1.
   North Africa. Used medicinally. . . . . **Bunias** L.
   Median glands absent. Filaments usually appendaged. Stigma obscurely
   lobed. Fruit dehiscing in two valves. Embryo not spiral ; radicle
   accumbent. Plants without glandular tubercles. — Species 13. North
   and South Africa. Some are used in medicine or as ornamental plants.
   (Including *Meniocus* Desv.) . . . . **Alyssum** L.

26. Fruit-valves with a large, wing-like appendage near the top, projecting
   inwards between the seeds. Style long. Seeds 4. Leaves toothed. —
   Species 1. North Africa. " Rose of Jericho." . . **Anastatica** L.
   Fruit-valves without an appendage. 27

27. Fruit-valves boat-shaped, laterally compressed ; partition narrow. Stigma sessile. Seeds 4. — Species 2. North Africa. (Including *Hinter-hubera* Reichb. and *Hornungia* Reichb.) . . . . **Hutchinsia** R. Br.
Fruit-valves flat or convex, dorsally or not compressed ; partition broad. 28

28. Fruit-valves strongly convex ; partition thick, woody. Fruit elliptical, tapering into the style. Seeds 2. Median glands wanting. Flowers short-stalked. — Species 1. North-west Africa (Algeria).
Euclidium R. Br.
Fruit-valves flat or slightly convex ; partition thin, membranous. . . 29

29. Median glands wanting. Partition of the fruit without fibres. Fruit orbicular. Spinous undershrubs. — Species 1. North-west Africa. (Under *Alyssum* L.). . . . . **Ptilotrichum** C. A. Mey.
Median and lateral glands present. Partition of the fruit with scattered fibres. — Species 6. North and South Africa, Cape Verde Islands, and St. Helena. Some are used as ornamental or medicinal plants. (*Koniga* Adans., under *Alyssum* L.) . . . . **Lobularia** Desv.

30. Petals yellow. 31
Petals white or red. 34

31. Sepals, at least the lateral, saccate at the base. Shorter filaments with a tooth-like appendage. Fruit elliptical, flat. Seeds numerous, winged. — Species 1. North-east Africa (Egypt). (Under *Farsetia* Desv.)
Fibigia Medik.
Sepals not saccate. 32

32. Filaments, at least some of them, with an appendage, more rarely without, but then, as usually, seeds 2—8. Fruit-valves marked with a mid-rib at the base. (See 25.) . . . . **Alyssum** L.
Filaments without an appendage. Seeds 10 or more. Fruit-valves with the mid-rib extending to the top. 33

33. Fruit ovate or elliptical, with rather flat valves and a faint middle-nerve. Radicle accumbent. — Species 5. North-west Africa. Some are used as ornamental or medicinal plants. (Including *Erophila* DC.)
Draba L.
Fruit obovate or pear-shaped, with very convex valves and a strong middle-nerve. Radicle incumbent. Leaves sagittate. — Species 3. North Africa. They yield oil and medicaments. . . . **Camelina** Crantz

34. Petals red. Stigma 2-cleft. Seeds winged. Hairs 2-cleft. (See 13.).
Farsetia Turr.
Petals white. Stigma entire or notched. Seeds not winged. . . . 35

35. Valves of the fruit flat or slightly convex, with a faint middle-nerve ; partition broad. Radicle accumbent. Leaves undivided. (See 33.)
Draba L.
Valves of the fruit boat-shaped ; partition narrow. Radicle incumbent. 36

36. Fruit broadened or notched at the apex. — Species 1. North Africa and
northern East Africa, also naturalized in South Africa and the islands
of St. Helena and St. Thomas. Used medicinally. " Shepherds purse."
                                                            Capsella DC.
Fruit rounded or pointed at the apex. (See 27.).   .   **Hutchinsia** R. Br.

37. (1.) Stigma equally developed all round. Style-apex entire, rarely notched
at right angles to the placentas. Cotyledons usually folded or twisted.
[Tribe THELYPODIEAE.] 38
Stigma more developed above the placentas than between them. Style-
apex entire or 2-lobed. [Tribe SINAPEAE.]. 45

38. Fruit at least 4 times as long as broad. 39
Fruit less than 4 times as long as broad. Cotyledons transversely folded
or spirally twisted.   42

39. Fruit without a partition, oblong, with convex, angled valves. Seed-
coat spongy. Cotyledons neither folded nor twisted ; radicle accumbent.
Leaves roundish. — Species 1. Island of Kerguelen. Used as a vegetable and in medicine. . . . .   **Pringlea** Hook. fil.
Fruit with a partition. Cotyledons folded or twisted ; radicle incumbent. 40

40. Sepals connivent, the lateral saccate at the base. Petals white. Fruit
oblong. Seeds flat. Cotyledons twice inflected lengthwise. Leaves
reniform-cordate. — Species 1. South Africa (Cape Colony).
                                                            Chamira Thunb.
Sepals erect, not saccate. Cotyledons rolled inwards or folded transversely. 41

41. Seeds turgid, separated by transverse partitions. Fruit linear. Petals
blue or red. Leaves linear. — Species 1. South Africa (Cape Colony).
                                                            Carponema Sond.
Seeds flat, not separated by transverse partitions, but the fruit often constricted between the seeds. — Species 60. South Africa. Some are
used as ornamental plants. (Plate 54.) . . . .   **Heliophila** L.

42. Fruit 1-seeded. Seed winged. Leaves thread-shaped. — Species 1.
South Africa (Cape Colony). . . . . . .   **Palmstruckia** Sond.
Fruit 2- or more-seeded. 43

43. Fruit dehiscent, rather flat, with usually more than 2 seeds. (See 41.)
                                                            Heliophila L.
Fruit indehiscent, 2-seeded. Leaves linear or lanceolate. 44

44. Fruit compressed dorsally ; valves with elevated ridges radiating from
the centre. Style long. Seeds flat ; cotyledons folded. Petals red.
— Species 2. South Africa (Cape Colony). .   **Cycloptychis** E. Mey.
Fruit compressed laterally ; valves ventricose ; dissepiment very narrow.
Style short. Seeds subglobose ; cotyledons involute. Petals yellow
or red. — Species 2. South Africa (Cape Colony). **Brachycarpaea** DC.

45. (37.) Fruit at least 4 times as long as broad. 46
Fruit less than 4 times as long as broad, or broader than long. . . . 77

46. Fruit traansversely divided into two or more fertile cells. Cotyledons folded ; radicle incumbent. [Subtribe BRASSICINAE.] 47
Fruit not transversely septate, but sometimes produced into a seedless beak. 59

47. Fruit with 2 transverse cells (joints). 48
Fruit with 3 or more transverse cells. 56

48. Upper joint of the fruit 3—4-seeded, flat. Seeds oblong. Petals yellow. Undershrubs. — Species 1. North-west Africa (Morocco).
Hemicrambe Webb
Upper joint of the fruit 1-seeded. 49

49. Fruit-valves flat, usually 1-nerved. 50
Fruit-valves convex. 51

50. Sepals connivent, the lateral saccate. Petals violet. Stigmatic lobes long, erect, connate. — Species 7. North Africa. . **Moricandia** DC.
Sepals spreading, not saccate. Stigmatic lobes short. Leaves pinnatipartite. — Species 10. North Africa, northern Central Africa, and Island of St. Thomas ; one species also naturalized in South Africa. The seeds of some species are used as a condiment. . **Diplotaxis** DC.

51. Beak of the fruit flat, sharp-edged. Valves usually 3-nerved. . . . 52
Beak of the fruit cylindrical or conical, terete or but slightly flattened. . 53

52. Petals red. Lateral sepals saccate. Seeds ovoid. Fruits erect. Leaves dissected. — Species 2. North Africa. (Under *Erucaria* Gaertn.)
Reboudia Coss. & Durieu
Petals yellow or whitish with violet veins. Seeds globose. Leaves lyrate. — Species 5. North Africa, one species also cultivated in the Mascarene Islands. The white mustard (*S. alba* L.) yields salad, oil, condiments, and medicaments. (Under *Brassica* L.) . **Sinapis** L.

53. Lower joint of the fruit indehiscent, narrower than the upper one, 3—4-seeded. Petals yellow. Lateral sepals saccate. — Species 1 North-west Africa. (Under *Rapistrum* Desv.) . . . **Cordylocarpus** Desf.
Lower joint of the fruit dehiscing in two valves, as broad as the upper one, rarely narrower, but then petals violet. 54

54. Seeds globular, sometimes slightly flattened. Cotyledons 2-lobed. Petals yellow or white, sometimes with violet veins. — Species 25, five of them only cultivated or naturalized. Some species yield vegetables, salad, oil, condiments, or medicaments, especially *B. oleracea* L., cabbage, *B. campestris* L., rapeseed, *B. Napus* L., turnip, and *B. nigra* Koch, black mustard. (Including *Melanosinapis* Schimp. & Spenn.)
Brassica L.
Seeds ovoid or oblong. Leaves pinnatipartite. 55

55. Fruit-valves net-veined with a strong midrib. Cotyledons truncate. Sepals spreading. Petals white or yellow. — Species 6. North and East Africa. (Including *Hirschfeldia* Moench, under *Brassica* L.)
Erucastrum Presl

Fruit-valves with several longitudinal nerves. Sepals connivent. Petals violet. — Species 4. North Africa. (Including *Hussonia* Coss.)

Erucaria Gaertn.

56. Seeds pendulous. 57
    Seeds partly (the upper ones) erect.. 58

57. Fruit flat or 4-angled. Stem very short. Leaves radical. Flowers solitary, axillary. — Species 3. North-west Africa. (*Raffenaldia* Godr.) . . . . **Cossonia** Durieu

Fruit turgid. Stem branched. Leaves radical and cauline. Flowers racemose. — Species 2, one spontaneous in North Africa and naturalized in South Africa, the second (*R. sativus* L.) cultivated and naturalized in various regions. The latter yields salad, oil, and medicaments. "Radish." (*Raphanus* L.) . . . . **Rhaphanus** L.

58. Lower joint of the fruit 1-celled, indehiscent, 1—4-seeded. Hispid herbs. Leaves lyrate, the upper toothed. Flowers, at least the lower, subtended by bracts. — Species 4. North Africa to Nubia. **Enarthrocarpus** Labill.

Lower joint of the fruit 2-celled lengthwise, usually dehiscing in two valves, 4—12-seeded. Almost glabrous herbs. Leaves dissected. Flowers without bracts. (See 55). . . . . **Erucaria** Gaertn.

59. (46.) Fruit 1-seeded, flat, winged, 6-nerved, indehiscent. Stigma sessile. Radicle incumbent. Petals yellow. Leaves undivided. — Species 5. North Africa. Woad (*I. tinctoria* L.) yields a dye, other species are used medicinally. . . . . **Isatis** L.

Fruit 2- or more-seeded.. 60

60. Fruit-valves flat, but sometimes with a prominent midrib. 61
    Fruit-valves convex or keeled. 67

61. Stigmatic lobes long, erect, sometimes connate. Median glands none. Radicle incumbent ; cotyledons folded. Lateral sepals saccate. Petals violet or purple. Glabrous plants. 62

Stigmatic lobes short or not developed. Median, sometimes confluent, glands besides the lateral ones present, rarely only the latter, but then radicle accumbent. Radicle accumbent or incumbent ; in the latter case cotyledons flat, rarely folded, but then sepals not saccate. . 63

62. Seeds broadly winged, in a single row. Fruit broadly linear. Petals with a broad claw. Shrubs. Leaves linear-oblong, sessile, entire. — Species 1. North-west Africa (Algeria). (Including *Oudneya* R. Br.)

Henophyton Coss. & Durieu

Seeds narrowly or not winged. Fruit narrowly linear. Herbs or under-shrubs. Leaves undivided, the upper stem-clasping, or pinnately divided. (See 50.). . . . . **Moricandia** DC.

63. Radicle of the embryo incumbent. Seeds usually in 2 rows. Leaves, at least the lower, pinnately divided. 64

Radicle of the embryo accumbent. Seeds usually in a single row . . 65

64. Seeds oblong. Cotyledons not folded. Sepals converging or erect, the lateral saccate at the base. Petals purple or violet. — Species 2. North Africa. . . . . **Ammosperma** Hook. fil.
 Seeds ovoid or globose. Cotyledons folded. Fruit-valves 1-nerved. Sepals erect or spreading, not saccate. (See 50.). **Diplotaxis** DC.

65. Fruit-valves without distinct veins, opening elastically. Fruit linear or linear-lanceolate. Seeds in a single row, oblong or elliptical, not winged. Sepals not saccate. Leaves usually pinnately divided. — Species 8. Some of them are used as salad or in medicine. " Bittercress." **Cardamine** L.
 Fruit-valves with distinct veins, not elastic. Fruit linear. Leaves usually undivided. 66

66. Fruit-valves with a faint midnerve. Seeds in a single row. (See 13.) **Arabis** L.
 Fruit-valves with a prominent midnerve. Seeds in two rows, ovoid. Sepals spreading. Petals white. Leaves undivided. (See 18.) **Turritis** L.

67. (60.) Median glands absent. Fruit-valves with a prominent midnerve. Cotyledons convex or folded ; radicle incumbent. Sepals erect or converging. Petals yellow or violet. Glabrous plants. 68
 Median and lateral glands present, sometimes blended into a ring, rarely (*Nasturtium*) median glands absent, but then fruit-valves with a faint or scarcely visible midnerve. Sepals erect or spreading. Petals white or yellow, sometimes with red or violet veins. 69

68. Petals violet. Stigmatic lobes long, erect, sometimes cohering. Cotyledons folded. (See 50.) . . . . **Moricandia** DC.
 Petals yellowish. Stigmatic lobes short or imperceptible. Seeds in a single row, oblong. Cotyledons convex. Leaves undivided. — Species 1. North Africa to Nubia. Used as a vegetable. . **Conringia** Heist.

69. Radicle of the embryo accumbent. Sepals not saccate 70
 Radicle of the embryo incumbent ; cotyledons usually folded. . . . 71

70. Fruit-valves with a strong midnerve. Seeds in a single row. Petals yellow. — Species 3. North, East, and South Africa, also naturalized in the Mascarene Islands. Used as vegetables, salad, or fodder. " Wintercress." . . . . **Barbarea** R. Br.
 Fruit-valves with a faint midnerve not reaching to the top. Seeds usually in two rows. — Species 15. Some of them (especially *N. officinale* R. Br., watercress) yield salad, condiments, and medicaments. (Including *Roripa* Scop.) . . . . **Nasturtium** R. Br.

71. Cotyledons not folded. Fruit not beaked ; valves with 1—3 strong ribs. Glands confluent into a ring. 72
 Cotyledons folded. Fruit usually beaked. 73

72. Style-apex truncate beneath the stigma. Seeds striate. Petals white. Leaves broad-cordate, toothed. — Species 1. North-west Africa. Used medicinally. (Under *Sisymbrium* L.) . . **Alliaria** Adans.

Style-apex notched beneath the stigma. Petals usually yellow. — Species
  25. Some are used as vegetables or in medicine. (Including *Kibera*
  DC. and *Nasturtiopsis* Boiss.) . . . . **Sisymbrium** L.
73. Fruit with a flat, sharp-edged beak, dehiscing in two valves. Seeds
  globular. Herbs with lyrate leaves. 74
  Fruit with a cylindrical or conical, terete or slightly flattened beak, or
  without a beak. 75
74. Fruit-valves with a single strong longitudinal nerve. Seeds in 2 rows.
  Sepals converging. Fruits erect, pressed against the stem. — Species 4.
  North Africa and northern East Africa. The seeds are used as a condiment or in medicine. (Including *Rytidocarpus* Coss.) . **Eruca** Lam.
  Fruit-valves with 3 longitudinal nerves. Seeds in 1 row. Sepals spreading.
  (See 52.). . . . . **Sinapis** L.
75. Seeds oblong. Fruit-valves with a strong midrib. Lateral sepals saccate.
  Petals yellow. Undershrubs. Leaves undivided. — Species 6. Madeira
  and Cape Verde Islands. (Under *Brassica* L.) **Sinapidendron** Lowe
  Seeds globular, sometimes slightly flattened. Herbs 76
76. Fruit indehiscent, spongy. Leaves lyrate. (See 57.) . **Rhaphanus** L.
  Fruit dehiscing in two valves. (See 54.) . . . . . **Brassica** L.
77. (45.) Fruit indehiscent, transversely divided into 2—7 cells (joints), the
  lowest cell sometimes seedless. 78
  Fruit not transversely septate, but sometimes prolonged into a seedless
  beak. 82
78. Fruit 3—7-jointed, oblong, flat. Style rather long. Seeds solitary in
  each cell, pendulous. Sepals erect or connivent, the lateral saccate.
  Stem very short. Leaves radical, lyrate. Flowers solitary, axillary.
  (See 57.) . . . . **Cossonia** Durieu
  Fruit 2-jointed. Flowers racemose. 79
79. Fruit compressed, the lower joint with a pendulous, the upper with
  an erect seed. Stigma sessile. Radicle accumbent. Lateral sepals
  saccate. Petals pale-violet or rose-coloured. — Species 1. North
  Africa. Used medicinally. . . . . **Cakile** Gaertn.
  Fruit not essentially compressed. Radicle incumbent. Cotyledons folded.
  Petals white or yellow. 80
80. Upper joint of the fruit with a partition and an erect seed; lower joint
  1—2-seeded or seedless. Sepals spreading. Leaves pinnatipartite. —
  Species 7. North Africa; one species also naturalized in South Africa.
  (Including *Ceratocnemon* Coss. et Balansa, *Didesmus* Desv., *Otocarpus*
  Durieu, and *Rapistrella* Pomel). . . . . . . **Rapistrum** Desv.
  Upper joint of the fruit without a partition, one-seeded; lower joint
  seedless. Sepals not saccate. Petals white. 81
81. Upper joint of the fruit tubercled, beaked. Seed erect or pendulous from
  the top of the cell. Cotyledons not lobed. Sepals suberect. Filaments
  not toothed. Leaves lobed. — Species 2. North-west Africa. (Including *Kremeria* Coss.). . . . . **Muricaria** Desv.

Upper joint of the fruit ribbed or smooth, not beaked. Seed pendulous from the long, ascending funicle. Cotyledons 2-lobed. Sepals spreading. — Species 7. North and East Africa. Some are used as vegetables (sea-kale). . . . . **Crambe** L.

82. (77.) Fruit prolonged into a broad beak. Radicle incumbent. Petals yellow, often marked with violet veins. 83
Fruit not distinctly beaked. 87

83. Fruit indehiscent, 1- or 3-celled, with a single perfect seed and usually a rudimentary one below it. Seed oblong. Herbs. Leaves toothed, lobed, or cleft. 84
Fruit dehiscing in 2 valves, completely or incompletely 2-celled, with 2 or more seeds, but the seed of one cell sometimes rudimentary (in this case shrubs). Seeds globose or nearly so. Cotyledons folded. . . . 85

84. Fruit 1-celled, with an oblique, sword-shaped beak. — Species 1. North-east Africa (Egypt). . . . . . . **Schimpera** Hochst. & Steud.
Fruit 3-celled, with a broad, hollow, chambered beak. — Species 1. North-west Africa (Algeria). . . . . **Myagrum** L.

85. Fruit with 2 seeds. Longer filaments united in pairs. Small shrubs. Leaves entire. — Species 1. North-west Africa. . . . . **Vella** L.
Fruit with 6 or more seeds. Filaments free. Herbs. Leaves divided, at least some of them. 86

86. Fruit with 6—8 seeds and a leaf-like beak. Leaves twice pinnately dissected. — Species 1. North Africa. . . . . **Carrichtera** Adans.
Fruit with many seeds and a sword-shaped beak. Leaves lyrate or undivided. (See 74.) . . . . **Eruca** Lam.

87. (82.) Fruit 1-seeded. 88
Fruit 2- or more-seeded. 91

88. Fruit slightly or not compressed, ovoid, with a crusty rind. Seed globular. Cotyledons folded; radicle incumbent. Petals white. Filaments without an appendage. Glands confluent. Radical leaves pinnately divided. Fruit-stalks spreading-erect. — Species 1. North-west Africa (Algeria). . . . . **Calepina** Adans.
Fruit much compressed. Leaves undivided. 89

89. Sepals petal-like. Petals rose-coloured. Filaments without an appendage. Glands wanting. Ovary 3-celled. Fruit elliptical. Radicle accumbent. Shrubs. Leaves entire. (See 20.) . . **Schlechteria** Bolus
Sepals not petal-like. Glands present. Ovary 2-celled. Herbs or undershrubs. 90

90. Petals rose-coloured. Longer filaments with a tooth-like appendage. Median glands wanting. Apex of the style truncate beneath the stigma. Fruit discoid, winged. — Species 2. North-west Africa (Algeria). Used as ornamental plants. . . . . **Aethionema** R. Br.
Petals yellow. Filaments without an appendage. Median and lateral glands confluent into a ring. Apex of the style more or less 2-lobed

P

beneath the stigma. Fruit with 6 longitudinal nerves. Fruit-stalks
bent downwards. (See 59.) . . . . **Isatis** L.

91. (87.) Fruit 2-seeded. 92
Fruit 4- or more-seeded. 99

92. Fruit much compressed from the back, oblong, with a soon vanishing
partition and flat, net-veined valves. Seeds horizontal, winged ;
radicle accumbent. Lateral sepals saccate. Petals pale-violet. Leaves
pinnatisect. — Species 1. North-east Africa (Egypt). . . **Ricotia** L.
Fruit compressed from the side, and then with a narrow partition, or not
compressed ; partition well developed. 93

93. Fruit distinctly compressed laterally. 94
Fruit not distinctly compressed. 97

94. Fruit moderately compressed, with a lanceolate or elliptical partition,
opening by 2 valves. Seeds pendulous ; radicle incumbent, rarely
obliquely accumbent ; cotyledons inserted behind the bend of the
embryo. Petals white, more rarely yellowish or wanting. — Species 20.
Some of them (especially *L. sativum* L., garden-cress) yield salad, oil, and
medicaments. . . . . **Lepidium** L.
Fruit strongly compressed, with a linear partition. 95

95. Seeds horizontal, inserted in the middle of the cell. Radicle short, accumbent ; cotyledons inserted behind the bend of the embryo. Petals
yellow. Median and lateral glands present. — Species 6. North
Africa. Some are used medicinally. . . . . . . **Biscutella** L.
Seeds pendulous from the top of the cell. Petals, when present, white
red or violet. 96

96. Radicle incumbent ; cotyledons inserted behind the bend of the embryo.
Style very short. Fruit reniform, wrinkled, indehiscent. — Species 7.
Some of them are used medicinally. (*Senebiera* Poir.) **Coronopus** Gaertn.
Radicle accumbent ; cotyledons inserted at the bend of the embryo.
Style distinctly developed. Fruit ovate. Outer petals larger than
the inner. Median glands wanting. — Species 4. North-west Africa.
Some are used as ornamental plants or in medicine. " Candytuft."
                                                              Iberis L.

97. Fruit dehiscing by two valves, globular, prickly, with a pierced partition.
Style subulate, with short, blunt lobes. Seeds globose, with a thread-
shaped funicle. Radicle incumbent ; cotyledons folded, inserted
at the bend of the embryo. Sepals erect. Petals yellow. Herbs.
Leaves pinnatisect. — Species 1. North-west Africa. **Succowia** Medik.
Fruit indehiscent, with a thick partition. Style conical. Seeds with a
very short funicle. 98

98. Fruit angular-subglobose, tubercled. Style very short, with short lobes.
Seeds oblong. Radicle obliquely accumbent ; cotyledons inserted
behind the bend of the embryo. Sepals spreading. Petals yellow.
Herbs. Leaves pinnately divided. — Species 1. North-east Africa
(Egypt). . . . . **Ochthodium** DC.

Fruit ovoid. Style rather long, with long lobes. Radicle incumbent ; cotyledons folded, inserted at the bend of the embryo. Sepals erect. Petals rose-coloured. Spinous shrubs. Leaves undivided. — Species 2. North Africa to Nubia. . . . . **Zilla** Forsk.

99. (91.) Fruit compressed from the back or not compressed ; hence partition as broad as the fruit. 100
Fruit laterally compressed ; partition narrower than the fruit. . . . 104

100. Seeds 4, in a single row, flat, with a long free funicle ; radicle accumbent. Fruit with a soon vanishing partition ; valves flat, without a distinct median nerve ; style very short. Lateral sepals saccate. Petals violet. Only two lateral glands present. Leaves pinnately dissected. Fruit-stalks bent downwards. (See 92.). . . . . . **Ricotia** L.
Seeds more than 4, nearly always in two rows. Fruit with a persistent partition. Sepals not saccate. 101

101. Seeds flat, winged. Funicle adnate to the partition at the base. Radicle incumbent ; cotyledons folded. Fruit with a stalk-like appendage at the base ; valves slightly convex. Petals rose or violet. Leaves undivided or lobed. — Species 2. North Africa. Used medicinally.
Savignya DC.
Seeds turgid or flat but not winged. Funicle free. Radicle accumbent. Petals white or yellow. 102

102. Fruit-valves with a very faint median nerve not reaching the top, or without a distinct median nerve, convex. Seeds turgid. Style-apex lobed. Median and lateral glands developed. (See 70.) **Nasturtium** R. Br.
Fruit-valves with a distinct median nerve reaching the top. Median glands wanting. 103

103. Fruit-valves distinctly convex. Seeds turgid. Style-apex truncate beneath the stigma. Petals white. Filaments curved. — Species 1. Naturalized in the Island of St. Helena. (Under *Cochlearia* L.)
Kernera Medik.
Fruit-valves rather flat. Style-apex lobed or depressed beneath the stigma. Glands 4. Leaves undivided. (See 33.). . . **Draba** L.

104. (99.) Median and lateral glands present. Sepals erect. Fruit winged. Style long. Seeds numerous. Radicle incumbent ; cotyledons folded. Leaves undivided. 105
Median glands absent. Style short, rarely long, but then radicle accumbent. Cotyledons not folded. 106

105. Petals white, with dark veins. Fruit obcordate. Style-apex shortly and obtusely lobed. Hispid herbs. — Species 1. North-west Africa.
Psychine Desf.
Petals violet or red. Fruit ovoid. Style-apex distinctly and acutely lobed. Glabrous herbs. — Species 1. North Africa and Abyssinia.
Schouwia DC.

106. Stamens more or less perigynous.   Petals white.   Seeds 4—6.   Cotyledons
     inserted behind the bend of the embryo. 107
     Stamens hypogynous.   Cotyledons inserted at the bend of the embryo. 108
107. Filaments with an appendage at their base.   Fruit winged above.   Style
     short.   Seeds 4.   Radicle accumbent.   Leaves lanceolate, ovate, or
     pinnatipartite. — Species 2.   North-west Africa.   Used as vegetables.
                                                          Teesdalia R. Br.
     Filaments without an appendage.   Fruit not winged.   Style absent.
     Seeds 6.   Radicle incumbent.   Leaves linear. — Species 1.   High
     mountains of East Africa. . . . . **Subularia** L.
108. Filaments, at least the longer ones, with a tooth-like appendage.   Lateral
     sepals saccate at the base.   Petals rose-coloured.   Style short.   Radicle
     incumbent.   Flowers in racemes.   (See 90.). . . **Aethionema** R. Br.
     Filaments without an appendage.   Sepals not saccate. 109
109. Flowers solitary in the axils of the radical, undivided leaves.   Petals
     rose-coloured.   Fruit-valves wingless, separating from the laterally
     dilated placentas.   Seeds 6.   Radicle incumbent. — Species 2.   North-
     west Africa.   Used as ornamental plants.   . . **Ionopsidium** Reichb.
     Flowers in racemes.   Fruit-valves separating from the narrow or thickened
     but not dilated placentas, or fruit indehiscent. 110
110. Fruit-valves not winged.   Fruit oblong or ovate.   Petals white.   Leaves
     pinnately divided.   (See 27.) . . . . **Hutchinsia** R. Br.
     Fruit-valves winged 111
111. Radicle accumbent.   Petals white or rose.   Leaves undivided. — Species
     6.   North Africa and Abyssinia.   Used medicinally.   " Penny-cress."
                                                          Thlaspi L.
     Radicle incumbent.   112
112. Fruit oblong or elliptical.   Stigma sessile.   Petals white or yellow.
     Leaves undivided. — Species 2.   North-west Africa (Algeria).   (In-
     cluding *Pastorea* Tod.) . . . . **Bivonaea** DC.
     Fruit obcordate.   Stigma borne upon a short style.   Funicle free.   Petals
     white.   (See 36.). . . . . **Capsella** DC.

SUBORDER RESEDINEAE

FAMILY 89.   RESEDACEAE

Leaves alternate, stipulate.   Flowers in terminal spikes or racemes, irregular.
Sepals 4—8.   Petals 2—8, free, rarely 0.   Disc hypogynous, one-sided, rarely
wanting.   Stamens 3—40, free or united at the base.   Carpels 2—6, superior
and usually stalked, open at the top, distinct or united and then forming a 1-
celled ovary.   Ovules inverted.   Stigmas sessile.   Seeds reniform, exalbuminous, with a curved embryo. — Genera 6, species 45.   (Plate 55.)
     1. Carpels 5—6, distinct or cohering at the base only.   Petals 5.   Leaves
        lanceolate, entire. 2

Pl. 55.

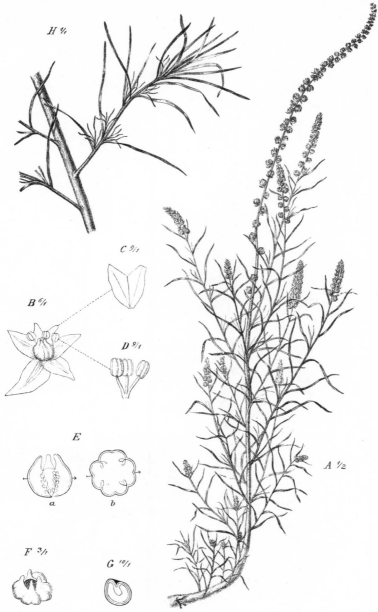

J. Fleischmann del.

Oligomeris glaucescens Cambess.

A Flowering branch. *B* Flower. *C* Petal. *D* Stamens. *E* Ovary cut lengthwise and across. *F* Fruit. *G* Seed cut lengthwise.
H Part of a branch with clusters of leaves.

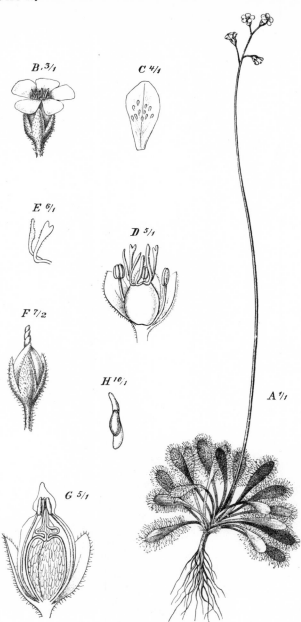

J. Fleischmann del.

Drosera Burkeana Planch.

A Plant in flower. *B* Flower, *C* Petal. *D* Flower without the corolla (the calyx cut lengthwise). *E* Style. *F* Older flower.
G Older flower cut lengthwise. *H* Seed

Carpels 2—4, united at least to the middle, forming a 1-celled ovary open at the top with parietal placentation ; if carpels united to the middle only, then petals 4. 3

2. Carpels with a single descending ovule attached in the middle of the cell, stellately spreading when ripe. Shrubs. — Species 1. North-west Africa (Algeria). . . . . **Astrocarpus** Neck.

Carpels with 2—3 basal ovules. Herbs. — Species 3. North and Central Africa. . . . . **Caylusea** St. Hil.

3. Petals none. Sepals 6. Stamens 10—30, hypogynous. Stigmas 3. Fruit berry-like, closed at the top. Shrubs. Leaves linear. — Species 5. North Africa and northern East Africa. . . **Ochradenus** Del.

Petals 2—8. Fruit capsular, open at the top. 4

4. Petals 2. Disc wanting. Stamens 3—10, hypogynous. Ovary sessile. Stigmas 4. Herbs or undershrubs. — Species 6. South Africa and North Africa to Nubia. (Plate 55.) . . . . . **Oligomeris** Cambess.

Petals 4—8. Disc present. 5

5. Petals perigynous, 6—8. Stamens perigynous, numerous. Disc double. Stigmas 2—3. Shrubs. — Species 2. North Africa and northern East Africa. . . . . **Randonia** Coss.

Petals hypogynous, 4—7. Stamens hypogynous. Ovary stalked. Herbs or undershrubs. — Species 30. North Africa and northern East Africa ; one species also introduced in South Africa. Some species (especially *R. luteola* L.) yield a dye, oil, and medicaments, others (especially *R. odorata* L.) are used as ornamental plants and in perfumery. " Mignonette." (Including *Luteola* Tourn.). . . . . . **Reseda** L.

SUBORDER MORINGINEAE
FAMILY 90. MORINGACEAE

Trees. Leaves alternate, pinnate. Stipules gland-like or wanting. Flowers in panicles, irregular, hermaphrodite. Petals 5, perigynous, imbricate in bud. Fertile stamens 5, perigynous, alternating with 5 staminodes. Anthers 1-celled, turned inwards. Ovary short-stalked, 1-celled, with 3 parietal placentas. Ovules numerous, pendulous, inverted. Style simple. Fruit capsular. Seeds exalbuminous ; embryo straight. (Under *CAPPARIDACEAE*.)

Genus 1, species 6. Five species spontaneous in northern East Africa, Madagascar, and Egypt ; the sixth (*M. oleifera* Lam., horse-radish-tree) cultivated and sometimes naturalized on the coasts of the tropics. This species yields gum, fibre, tanners' bark, fodder, vegetables, oil, condiments, and medicaments. . . . . **Moringa** Juss.

ORDER SARRACENIALES
FAMILY 91. NEPENTHACEAE

Shrubs or undershrubs. Leaves alternate, undivided, terminating in a pitcher. Flowers regular, dioecious. Perianth-segments 4. Stamens 4 or more, with united filaments ; anthers 2-celled, opening outwards. Ovary superior, 4-celled. Ovules numerous, axile, inverted. Stigmas 4, sessile, 2-lobed. Fruit a loculicidal capsule. Seeds with a straight, axile embryo and fleshy albumen.

Genus 1, species 2. Madagascar and Seychelles. Used as ornamental plants. " Pitcher plant." . . . . **Nepenthes** L.

FAMILY 92. DROSERACEAE

Herbs or undershrubs. Leaves usually covered with glandular hairs and rolled up in the bud. Flowers regular, hermaphrodite. Calyx 4—8-lobed or -parted, imbricate in bud. Petals 4—8, usually 5, free, clawed, imbricate or contorted in aestivation. Stamens 4—20, as many as or more than the petals, hypogynous or nearly so, free. Anthers usually turned outwards, opening by longitudinal slits. Ovary superior, 1-celled. Ovules numerous (10 or more), inverted. Styles or style-branches 2—5. Fruit a loculicidal capsule. Seeds albuminous, with a small embryo. — Genera 3, species 15. (Plate 56.)

1. Stamens 10—20. Styles 5, free, with capitate stigmas. Ovules basal or nearly so. Undershrubs. Leaves linear, glandular-hairy, rolled up in the bud. Flowers in corymbs. — Species 1. North-west Africa (Morocco). . . . . **Drosophyllum** Link

Stamens 4—8. Styles or style-branches 2—5, with not much thickened stigmas. Ovules parietal. Herbs. 2

2. Blade of the leaves jointed to the stalk, folded lengthwise, surrounded by bristles, without glands at the edges. Leaves whorled. Flowers solitary, axillary. Stamens 5. Styles 5, free, with branched stigmas. Ovules few, affixed at the middle of the placentas. Floating water-plants. — Species 1. Upper Nile. . . . . . **Aldrovanda** L.

Blade of the leaves not jointed, flat, rolled up in the bud, bearing long-stalked glands at the edges. Ovules numerous. — Species 13. Southern and tropical Africa. Some species are used in the preparation of liquors and in medicine. " Sundew." (Plate 56.) . . . . . **Drosera** L.

ORDER ROSALES

SUBORDER PODOSTEMONINEAE

FAMILY 93. PODOSTEMONACEAE

Aquatic herbs resembling mosses or algae. Flowers solitary or in cymes, usually enclosed when young in a spathe, hermaphrodite. Perianth of 2—3 minute scales, rarely larger and 3-parted. Stamens 1—4, hypogynous. Anthers opening by longitudinal slits. Ovary superior, 1—3-celled, with a central placenta. Ovules numerous, sub-sessile, inverted. Fruit capsular. Seeds exalbuminous. — Genera 9, species 25. Tropical and South Africa. (Plate 57.)

A ⁴/₃

B ⁶/₁

C.⁶/₁

J. Fleischmann del.

Tristicha alternifolia Tul.

A Plant in flower.   *B* Flower.   *C* Flower cut lengthwise.

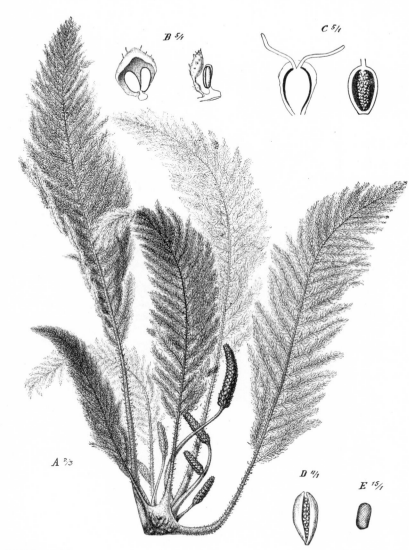

J. Fleischmann del.

Hydrostachys multifida A. Juss.

A Plant in flower.   *B* Male flower with its bract.   *C* Female flower, and ovary cut lengthwise.   *D* Fruit.   *E* Seed.

1. Flowers without a spathe, regular. Perianth 3-parted. Stamen 1.
   Ovary 3-celled. Styles 3. Leaves undivided. — Species 5. Tropical
   and South Africa. (Plate 57.) [Tribe TRISTICHEAE.]

   Tristicha Thouars

   Flowers at first enclosed in a spathe, irregular. Perianth of 2, rarely of
   3 small scales. Stamens 2—4. Ovary 1—2-celled. Styles 1—2.
   Leaves usually dissected. 2
2. Style 1, very short ; stigma entire. Ovary 1-celled. Stamens 3—4 ;
   filaments free or nearly so. Stem elongate. Spathe close to the flower.
   — Species 1. Southern West Africa (Angola). [Tribe MARATHRE-
   AE.] . . . . **Angolaea** Wedd.
   Styles 2, free or united at the base. Stamens 2, rarely (*Winklerella*) 3,
   but then filaments united about halfway up. [Tribe PODOSTE-
   MONEAE.] 3
3. Filaments free or nearly so. Ovary stalked. 4
   Filaments obviously united. 5
4. Fruit with unequal valves, the persistent valve 5-nerved, the deciduous
   one 3-nerved. Stem little branched. Leaves linear or the lower with
   two teeth at the base. — Species 1. West Africa (Cameroons).

   Ledermanniella Engl.

   Fruit with two equal, persistent, linear, 5-nerved valves. Stem much
   branched. Leaves divided in 2—5 narrow segments. — Species 2.
   West Africa. Used as salad. . . . . . **Dicraeanthus** Engl.
5. Ovary and fruit 1-celled, the latter with somewhat unequal valves. Flowers
   drooping. — Species 4. Central and South Africa. Used as salad.
   (Including *Isothylax* Baill.) . . . . **Sphaerothylax** Bisch.
   Ovary and fruit 2-celled. 6
6. Fruit with unequal valves, one of which falls off, and with prominent ribs.
   Pollen-grains united in pairs. — Species 1. Madagascar.

   Podostemon Mich.

   Fruit with equal valves. 7
7. Fruit smooth, without distinct ribs. Pollen-grains separate. Flowers
   drooping. — Species 3. Southern Central Africa. (*Leiocarpodicraea*
   Engl., under *Dicraea* Thouars). . . . . . . **Leiothylax** Warm.
   Fruit with prominent ribs. 8
8. Fruit 2-toothed at the top, with boat-shaped valves , one of them or both
   falling off. Pollen-grains separate. — Species 1. West Africa (Cameroons). . . . . **Winklerella** Engl.
   Fruit with persistent valves. Pollen-grains united in pairs. — Species 9.
   Tropics. (Under *Podostemon* Mich.) . . . . . **Dicraea** Thouars

FAMILY 94. HYDROSTACHYACEAE

Aquatic herbs. Stem tuberous. Leaves with a sheath and a ligule. Flowers
in spikes, bracteate, without a perianth, dioecious. Stamen 1, with separated

anther-halves (or 2 with united filaments), hypogynous. Anthers turned
outwards.   Pollen-grains united in groups of 4.   Ovary 1-celled, with 2 parietal
placentas. Ovules numerous, inverted. Styles 2. Fruit capsular. Seeds
exalbuminous.   (Under *PODOSTEMONACEAE*.)   (Plate 58.)

Genus 1, species 15.   Tropical and South-east Africa.

Hydrostachys Thouars

SUBORDER SAXIFRAGINEAE

FAMILY 95.   CRASSULACEAE

Herbs or undershrubs, rarely shrubs.   Stem and leaves usually succulent.
Leaves without stipules. Flowers regular, hermaphrodite. Petals 3—20,
free or united below, hypogynous or nearly so.   Stamens as many or twice as
many as the petals. Filaments free. Anthers turned inwards. Carpels as
many as the petals, free or united at the base, usually with a scale-like appendage. Ovules numerous, rarely (*Crassula*) 1—2 in each carpel. Fruit-carpels
follicular.   Seeds with a very scanty albumen or without albumen. — Genera
10, species 400.   (Plate 59.)

1. Petals free or nearly so.   2
   Petals united below into a distinct, usually long tube.   5

2. Stamens as many as the sepals or petals, 3—9, usually 5.   Sepals free or
   nearly so.   Petals white or reddish.   Leaves opposite. — Species 180.
   Some of them are used as ornamental or medicinal plants.   (Including
   Bulliarda DC., *Dinacria* Harv., *Helophytum* Eckl. & Zeyh., and *Tillaea*
   L.) . . . .   **Crassula** L.
   Stamens twice as many as the sepals, rarely (*Sedum*) equalling the sepals in
   number, but then leaves alternate.   3

3. Flowers 4—5-merous, very rarely 6—7-merous. Sepals free or nearly
   so. Leaves usually scattered. — Species 25.   North Africa and high
   mountains of East Africa.   Some species are used as vegetables or as
   medicinal or ornamental plants. . . . .   **Sedum** L.
   Flowers 6—20-merous, very rarely 5-merous. Sepals more or less united.
   Leaves usually rosulate.   4

4. Scale-like appendages of the carpels broad, petaloid. Petals linear-
   lanceolate, inconspicuous, reddish or yellowish. — Species 10. North-
   west Africa. (*Petrophyes* Webb) . . . . .   **Monanthes** Haw.
   Scale-like appendages of the carpels small or wanting. Petals lanceolate,
   brightly coloured. — Species 70. North Africa and northern Central
   Africa. Some are used as ornamental or medicinal plants. " Houseleek.'' (Including *Aeonium* Webb, *Aichryson* Webb, and *Greenovia*
   Webb & Berth.) . . . .   **Sempervivum** L.

5. Flowers 4-merous.   Leaves opposite.   6
   Flowers 5—6-merous.   8

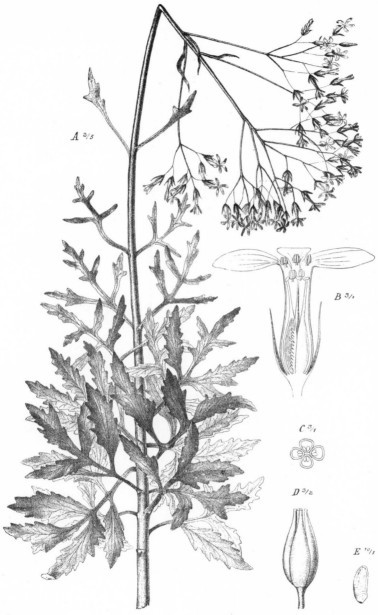

J. Fleischmann del.

Kalanchoë laciniata DC.

A Flowering branch.   *B* Flower cut lengthwise.   *C* Cross-section of carpels.   *D* Fruit   *E* Seed.

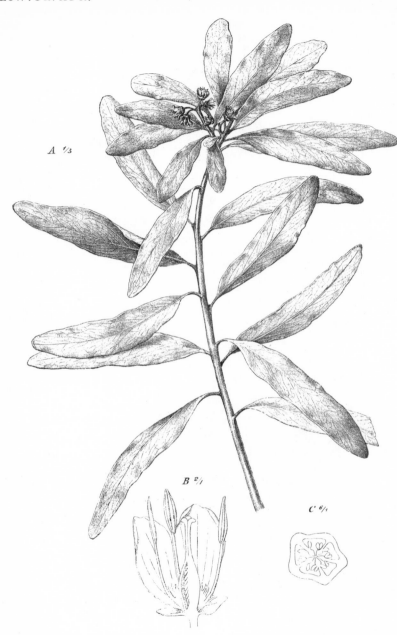

A ⅓

B ²/₁

C ⁶/₁

J. Fléischmann del.

Brexia madagascariensis Thouars

A Flowering branch.   *B* Flower cut lengthwise.   C Cross-section of ovary.

6. Calyx cleft nearly to the middle, large, inflated. Corolla urn- or almost bell-shaped. Stamens 8. Carpels not diverging. Stigmas capitate. Undershrubs. — Species 5. Tropical and South Africa. Some are used as ornamental or medicinal plants. (*Crassuvia* Comm.)

Bryophyllum Salisb.

Calyx divided to the middle or beyond, usually small. 7

7. Calyx divided to the middle, small, bell-shaped. Corolla tube- or bell-shaped ; segments short and broad, triangular to orbicular. Stamens 8. Carpels diverging. Stigmas capitate. — Species 15. Madagascar. (Under *Kalanchoe* Adans.) . . . .   **Kitchingia** Bak.

Calyx divided nearly to the base, rarely only to the middle, but then corolla with oblong, elliptical, or ovate segments. Corolla usually salver-shaped, with spreading segments. Stigmas obliquely truncate. — Species 45. Tropical and South Africa. Some yield an aromatic resin or are used in medicine. (Plate 59.) . . . **Kalanchoë** Adans.

8. Stamens twice as many as the sepals or petals, 10, rarely 12. — Species 40. Some of them are used as ornamental or medicinal plants. (Including *Echeveria* DC., *Mucizonia* DC., *Pistorinia* DC., and *Umbilicus* DC.)

Cotyledon L.

Stamens as many as the sepals or petals, 5, rarely 6. Leaves opposite .   9

9. Calyx as long as the corolla-tube, bell-shaped, divided to about the middle. Corolla bell-shaped, yellow. Small, stiff, glaucous herbs. — Species 1. South Africa. . . . . **Grammanthes** DC.

Calyx shorter than the corolla-tube, divided nearly or quite to the base. Corolla funnel-shaped. Thick, succulent herbs or undershrubs. — Species 4. South Africa. Used as ornamental plants. **Rochea** DC.

FAMILY 96. SAXIFRAGACEAE

Petals 4—5, free or united below. Stamens as many or twice as many as the petals, perigynous or epigynous. Anthers opening by two longitudinal slits. Ovary 1—7-celled. Ovules numerous, inverted. Seeds with copious albumen, rarely (*Montinia*) without albumen. — Genera 11, species 25. (Including *GROSSULARIACEAE*.) (Plate 60.)

1. Stem herbaceous. Styles 2—5, free. [Subfamily **SAXIFRAGOIDEAE.**]   2
Stem woody, rarely (*Berenice*) herbaceous above, but then style simple. Leaves without stipules. Placentas parietal or septal.   3

2. Calyx with valvate aestivation. Stamens 5. Ovary inferior, 1-celled, with 2—3 placentas suspended from the apex of the cell. Leaves opposite, entire. — Species 4. Tropical and South Africa and Egypt.

Vahlia Thunb.

Calyx with imbricate aestivation. Stamens 8—10. Ovary 2—5-celled, with the placentas attached to the dissepiments. — Species 9. North Africa and Abyssinia. Some species are used as ornamental or medicinal plants. . . . . **Saxifraga** L.

3. Stamens 8—10. Ovary inferior or half-inferior, completely or incompletely 2—5-celled. Styles 2—5, free or united at the base. Corolla with valvate aestivation. Outer flowers of the inflorescence often barren with enlarged sepals. Leaves opposite. — Species 1 (*H. Hortensia* DC.) Naturalized in several islands (Madeira, St. Helena, Réunion). An ornamental plant. [Subfamily **HYDRANGEOIDEAE.**] **Hydrangea** L.

Stamens 4—5. Styles 1—2. 4

4. Ovary 1-celled, inferior. Style simple with 2 stigmas, or styles 2. Fruit a berry. Leaves alternate. Flowers hermaphrodite. — Species 2. North-west Africa (Algeria). One of them (*R. Grossularia* L., gooseberry) yields edible fruit, from which also a drink is prepared. (Including *Grossularia* A. Rich.) [Subfamily **RIBESOIDEAE.**] **Ribes** L.

Ovary 2—7-celled, rarely 1-celled, but then leaves opposite and flowers unisexual. [Subfamily **ESCALLONIOIDEAE.**] 5

5. Ovary 1-celled, inferior. Ovules 8—10. Style simple ; stigma 2-lobed. Flowers unisexual. Leaves opposite. — Species 1. Madagascar.
Grevea Baill.

Ovary 2—7-celled. Style simple with an entire or 5—7-lobed stigma, or 2-parted. 6

6. Ovary superior, 5—7-celled. Style simple with a 5—7-lobed stigma. Fruit a berry or drupe. 7

Ovary inferior or half-inferior, 2—4-celled. Style simple with an entire stigma or 2-parted. Fruit a capsule. Leaves alternate. . . . 8

7. Sepals persistent. Petals united at the base, campanulately connivent, rolled back at the tip. Stamens inserted between the lobes of the disc. Anthers opening outwards. Ovary pyramidal. Fruit a berry Embryo shorter than the seed. Climbing shrubs. Leaves opposite. Flowers solitary or in few-flowered clusters. — Species 1. Mascarene Islands.
Roussea Smith

Sepals deciduous. Petals free, blunt. Stamens inserted on the margin of the disc. Anthers opening inwards or laterally. Ovary ovoid. Fruit a drupe with a woody, 1-celled stone. Embryo as long as the seed. Low trees. Leaves alternate. Flowers in umbel-shaped cymes. — Species 2. East Africa, Madagascar and Seychelles. The fruits are edible. (*Venana* Lam.) (Plate 60.) . . . . **Brexia** Thouars

8. Ovary 3—4-celled. Style 1, simple. Petals 5, united at the base. Seeds linear-oblong. Undershrubs. Leaves serrate. Flowers in panicles. — Species 1. Island of Réunion. . . . . . **Berenice** Tul.

Ovary 2-celled. Styles 2, free or united at the base (sometimes also at the top, when young). Shrubs or trees. 9

9. Ovary inferior. Flowers 4-merous, unisexual. Petals imbricate in bud. Seeds winged, exalbuminous. Leaves entire. Male flowers panicled, female solitary. — Species 1. South Africa. . . . **Montinia** L.f.

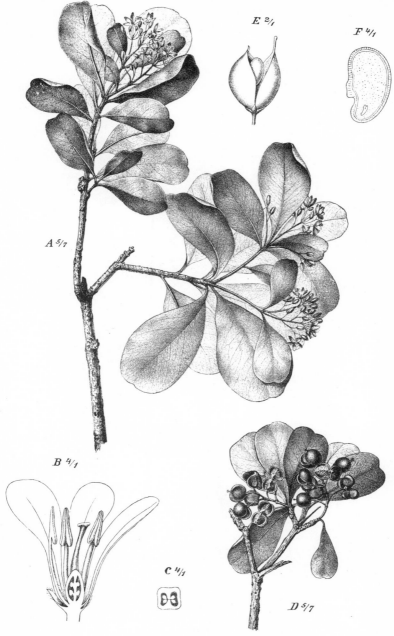

E ^{2}/$_1$

F ^{4}/$_1$

A ^{5}/$_7$

B ^{4}/$_1$

C ^{4}/$_1$

D ^{5}/$_7$

J. Fleischmann del.

Pittosporum viridiflorum Sims

A Flowering branch.   *B* Flower cut lengthwise.   *C* Cross-section of ovary.   *D* Fruiting branch.   *E* Fruit.   *F* Seed cut lengthwise.

A ⁴/₇

B ⁷/₁

C ⁷/₁

D ⁴/₁

E ⁴/₁

J. Fleischmann del.

Weinmannia Hildebrandtii Baill.

A Flowering branch.   *B* Flower cut lengthwise   *C* Cross-section of ovary.   *D* Fruit.   *E* Seed.

Ovary half-inferior. Flowers 5-merous. Petals valvate in bud. Seeds albuminous. Leaves glandular-serrate. Flowers in panicles or in umbel-shaped cymes. 10

10. Sepals subulate. Petals ovate. Filaments thin. Seeds oblong. Shrubs with thin branches. Flowers small, polygamous. — Species 2. South Africa and southern East Africa . . . . . . **Choristylis** Harv.

Sepals lanceolate to ovate. Petals linear or oblong. Filaments thick. Trees with thick branches. Flowers rather large. — Species 1. Island of Réunion. . . . . **Forgesia** Comm.

FAMILY 97. PITTOSPORACEAE

Shrubs or trees. Leaves alternate, undivided, exstipulate. Flowers regular, hermaphrodite. Sepals 5, free or nearly so. Petals 5, free or united below. Stamens 5, hypogynous. Disc none. Ovary superior, sessile or short-stalked, 1-celled or incompletely 2—5-celled. Style simple ; stigma entire or lobed. Ovules numerous, ascending or horizontal, inverted, with a single coat. Fruit a loculicidal capsule. Seeds with a hard albumen and a small embryo situated near the hilum. (Under *SAXIFRAGACEAE*.) (Plate 61.)

Genus 1, species 35. Tropical and South Africa and Canary Islands. Some are used as ornamental plants. . . . . . **Pittosporum** Banks

FAMILY 98. CUNONIACEAE

Shrubs or trees. Leaves opposite or whorled, stipulate. Flowers in spike-, raceme-, or panicle-like inflorescences, hermaphrodite. Sepals 4—5, free or united at the base. Petals 4—5. Stamens 8—10, inserted beneath the disc. Ovary superior, 2—3-celled , ovules 2 or more to each cell. Styles 2—3, free. Fruit capsular. Seeds albuminous. — Genera 3, species 17. South Africa, Madagascar and neighbouring islands. (Under *SAXIFRAGACEAE*.) (Plate 62.)

1. Calyx valvate in bud. Petals 3-cleft or 3-toothed, shorter than the calyx. Disc perigynous, deeply 4—5-lobed. Connective acuminate. Ovary 2-celled, with 2 pendulous ovules in each cell. Trees. Leaves of 3 leaflets. Stipules free. Flowers in panicles. — Species 1. South Africa (Cape Colony). . . . . **Platylophus** Don

Calyx imbricate in bud. Disc 8—10-lobed. Stipules united in pairs. Flowers in clusters arranged in spikes or racemes. 2

2. Disc perigynous, adnate to the base of the ovary. Stamens 10. Ovary 2-celled, with numerous ovules. Seeds compressed, with a narrow wing. Leaves compound, with 3 or more leaflets. — Species 1. South Africa. Yields timber. . . . . **Cunonia** L.

Disc hypogynous, free from the ovary. Seeds hairy. — Species 15. Madagascar and the neighbouring islands. Some species yield timber, tans, dyes, and medicaments. (Plate 62.) . . . . . **Weinmannia** L.

FAMILY 99. MYROTHAMNACEAE

Balsamiferous shrubs. Leaves opposite, folded fan-like, undivided, stipulate. Flowers in spikes, dioecious, without a perianth. Stamens 3—8 ; connective produced into a point ; anthers attached at the base, opening by lateral slits ; pollen-grains cohering in groups of four. Ovary lobed, 3—4-celled. Ovules numerous, inverted. Styles 3—4, free, short and thick, with broadened stigmas. Fruit capsular or separating into 2—4 nutlets. Seeds with copious albumen. (Under *HAMAMELIDEAE* or *SAXIFRAGACEAE*.)

Genus 1, species 2. Tropical and South Africa. The resin is used as a fumigant and in medicine. (Including *Myosurandra* Baill.)

Myrothamnus Welw.

FAMILY 100. BRUNIACEAE

Undershrubs or shrubs. Leaves alternate, small, undivided, without stipules, rarely (*Staavia*) with gland-like stipules. Flowers in heads, more rarely in spikes or racemes or solitary, hermaphrodite, 5-merous, very rarely 4-merous. Calyx with imbricate or open aestivation. Petals free or united below, imbricate in bud. Stamens as many as and alternate with the petals. Anthers opening inwards by longitudinal slits. Ovary inferior or half-inferior, rarely (*Lonchostoma*) almost superior, 1—3-celled. Ovules 1—4 in each cell, pendulous, inverted. Style 1—3. Fruit a capsule or nut. Seeds with a copious albumen and a minute embryo next the hilum. — Genera 12, species 55. South Africa. (Plate 63.)

1. Anthers linear or oblong, with parallel, wholly adnate cells. Petals clawed, the claw without distinct glands. Ovary and receptacle (calyx-tube) glabrous. Style 1, with 2—3 punctiform stigmas. [Tribe AUDOUINI-EAE.] 2

   Anthers sagittate or cordate, with partly free and divergent cells. [Tribe BRUNIEAE.] 4

2. Ovary 3-celled. Ovules 6. Stigmas 3. Connective prolonged beyond the anther-cells, strap-shaped. Receptacle obconical. Petals red. Flowers in head-like spikes. Bracteoles 7—10. — Species 1. Cape Colony. . . . . **Audouinia** Brongn.

   Ovary 2-called or later on 1-celled. Ovules 4 or 8. Stigmas 2. Connective not prolonged. Fruit a 1-seeded nut. Flowers solitary or in racemes. 3

3. Ovary inferior. Receptacle obconical or cupular. Sepals hairy, deciduous. Petals lanceolate. Flowers solitary. — Species 5. South Africa.

   Thamnea Soland.

   Ovary half-inferior. Ovules 4. Receptacle globular-urceolate. Sepals glabrous, persisting in fruit. Petals obovate, white. Flowers in racemes. Bracteoles 6. — Species 1. Cape Colony. **Tittmannia** Brongn.

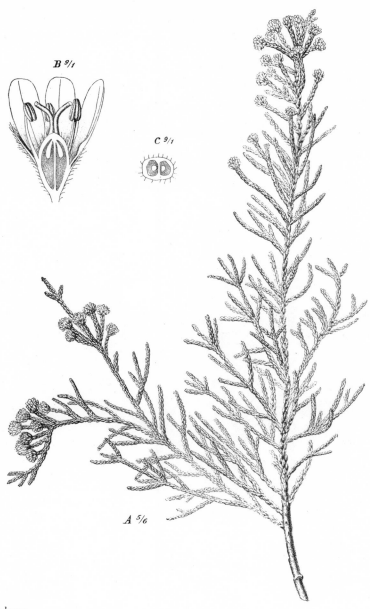

B 9/1

C 9/1

A 5/6

J. Fleischmann

Raspalia microphylla (Thunb.) Brongn.

A Flowering branch. *B* Flower cut lengthwise. *C* Cross-section of ovary.

J. Fleischmann del.

Trichocladus ellipticus Eckl. and Zeyh.

A Flowering branch. *B* Flower cut lengthwise (the petals cut off excepting one). *C* Cross-section of ovary.

4. Anthers sagittate. Petals sessile or with a glandless claw. Ovary 2-celled with 2 ovules in each cell. Fruit consisting of 2 dehiscing parts. Flowers in spikes. 5

   Anthers cordate. Petals clawed, the claw with 2 glands. 6

5. Petals with the claws united into a tube. Sepals, anthers, and ovary hairy. Ovary almost superior. Bracteoles 2. — Species 3. Cape Colony. . . . . **Lonchostoma** Wickstr.

   Petals sessile, free. Flowers glabrous. Sepals very short. Ovary almost inferior. Styles free. Bracteoles 4—8. — Species 3. Cape Colony.

   Linconia L.

6. Ovary 1-celled. Ovule 1. Style and stigma simple. Glands at the base of the petals crest-like. Flowers hairy. Fruit indehiscent. . . . 7

   Ovary 2-celled. Styles 2, or a single style with 2 stigmas. Glands at the base of the petals tubercle- or pouch-like. 8

7. Sepals short and broad, triangular. Stamens curved inwards, shorter than the petals : anthers shortly cleft. Flowers solitary, axillary, spicately arranged. Bracteoles thread-shaped. — Species 1. Cape Colony. (Under *Berzelia* Brongn.) . . . . **Mniothamnea** Oliv.

   Sepals awl-shaped. Stamens curved outwards, longer than the petals ; anthers deeply cleft. Flowers in heads. Bracteoles club- or spoon-shaped. — Species 9. South Africa. . . . . **Berzelia** Brongn.

8. Fruit one-seeded, usually indehiscent. 9

   Fruit consisting of two dehiscent, usually one-seeded parts. Flowers in heads. 10

9. Receptacle obconical. Sepals united beyond the ovary. Petals short, with a very short, 2-tubercled claw. Stamens shorter than the petals, equal. Anthers adnate, shortly cleft. Style short and thick, kneed. — Species 8. South Africa. (Under *Brunia* L.) **Pseudobaeckea** Nied.

   Receptacle cylindrical. Sepals free above the ovary. Petals long, with a long claw bearing a 2-lobed pouch. Stamens longer than the petals, unequal, the anterior longer. Anthers versatile, deeply cleft. Style long or rather long, almost straight. Ovules 2 in each cell. Flowers in heads. — Species 4. South Africa. . . . . . . **Brunia** L.

10. Style 1, short and thick ; stigmas 2, obliquely terminal, slightly thickened. Anthers pointed at the apex. Receptacle rather long. Sepals united beyond the ovary. Petals oblong, shortly clawed, 2-tubercled at the base. Bracteoles thread-shaped. — Species 9. South Africa.

    Staavia Thunb.

    Styles 2, free or more or less cohering, but then long and thread-shaped : stigmas simple, terminal. Anthers rounded at the apex. . . . 11

11 Sepals united beyond the ovary, triangular. Petals oblong, with a short claw bearing two tubercles at the base. Styles free, kneed above. Bracts broad, shorter than the flowers. Bracteoles linear. — Species 8. South Africa. (Under *Berardia* Sond.) (Plate 63.) **Raspalia** Brongn.

Sepals free above the ovary, linear. Petals strap-shaped, with a long claw
    bearing two tubercles in the upper part. Styles more or less cohering,
    long, almost straight. Bracts narrow, longer than the flowers. Bract-
    eoles spatulate or sickle-shaped. — Species 5. South Africa. (*Berardia*
    Brongn.) . . . .   **Diberara** Baill.

FAMILY 101. HAMAMELIDACEAE

Trees or shrubs. Leaves undivided, stipulate. Flowers in heads or head-
like spikes, 4—5-merous. Petals narrow, sometimes wanting in the female
flowers. Fertile stamens as many as and alternating with the petals, sometimes accompanied by staminodes. Filaments free. Anthers opening by
lateral slits or by valves. Ovary 2-celled. Ovules 1 in each cell, pendulous,
inverted. Styles 2, free. Fruit capsular. Seeds with a straight embryo and
thin albumen. — Genera 3, species 20. Tropical and South Africa. (Plate
64.)

1. Flowers unisexual, rarely polygamous, 5-merous. Staminodes none.
    Anthers ovoid. opening by valves. Shrubs. Stipules short and narrow.
    Flowers in many-flowered heads. — Species 3. South and East Africa.
    (Plate 64.) . . . .   **Trichocladus** Pers.
    Flowers hermaphrodite, usually 4-merous. Sepals short. Ovary inferior
    or almost so. 2

2. Staminodes none. Anthers opening by longitudinal slits. Trees. Flowers
    in many -flowered heads, 4-merous. — Species 1. Madagascar.
                                                Franchetia Baill.
    Staminodes as many as and alternate with the stamens. Anthers oblong.
    Shrubs. Stipules long and broad. Flowers in 3—8-flowered head-like
    spikes. — Species 15. Madagascar and Comoro Islands. Some species
    yield timber and medicaments. . . . . .   **Dicoryphe** Thouars

SUBORDER ROSINEAE

FAMILY 102. PLATANACEAE

Trees. Leaves alternate, palmately lobed ; stipules connate. Flowers on a
thickened receptacle in spicately arranged globose heads, monoecious. Sepals
3—8, free, hairy. Petals the same number, nearly hypogynous. Stamens as many
as and alternating with the petals ; connective peltate ; anthers opening inwards or laterally by longitudinal slits. Carpels the same number, free.
Ovules solitary, pendulous, straight. Fruit consisting of achenes densely
crowded in a head. Seed with scanty albumen ; cotyledons linear.
    Genus 1, species 2. Cultivated in North Africa as avenue-trees. They also
    yield timber. " Plane." . . . .   **Platanus** L.

FAMILY 103. ROSACEAE

Leaves alternate, stipulate. Receptacle (floral axis) more or less concave, saucer-, cup-, urn-, or tube-shaped, in the male flowers sometimes very small. Stamens curved inwards in the bud, usually numerous. Anthers opening inwards by longitudinal slits. Carpels superior, solitary or free, or inferior and then more or less united. Ovules inverted. — Genera 32, species 230. (Including *AMYGDALACEAE* and *POMACEAE*.) (Plate 65.)

1. Ovaries 1—10, inferior (adnate to the concave receptacle) and usually connate. Petals 5   Flowers hermaphrodite or polygamous.   .   . 2
   Ovaries (or ovary) superior, free from the receptacle, but sometimes tightly enclosed by it.   10
2. Stem herbaceous. Leaves lobed or dissected. Petals yellow. Stamens 10. Carpels 1—10, one-ovuled. Fruiting receptacle dry. [Subfamily **NEURADOIDEAE.**]   3
   Stem woody. Petals white or red. Carpels 1—5. Fruiting receptacle succulent. [Subfamily **POMOIDEAE.**]   4
3. Flowers small, with a persisting epicalyx. Carpels 10. Leaves lobed. — — Species 2. North Africa to Nubia, German South West Africa.
   Neurada L.
   Flowers large. Epicalyx none. — Species 6. South Africa.
   Grielum L.
4. Carpels 2—5, distinct from each other on their inside, 2-ovuled. Fruit small. Endocarp bony. Leaves undivided. — Species 3. Northwest Africa (Algeria). Used medicinally. .   .   . **Cotoneaster** Medik.
   Carpels 2—5, united as to the ovaries, or carpel 1.   5
5. Carpels 3—5, incompletely divided in two cells each ; hence cells twice as many as the style-branches and containing a single ovule each. Fruit small. Endocarp membranous. Petals narrow. Leaves undivided. Flowers in racemes. — Species 1. North-west Africa (Algeria). Used as an ornamental plant.   .   .   .   .   . **Amelanchier** Medik.
   Carpels not divided, containing 2 or more ovules each.   6
6. Ovules and seeds more than 2 to each carpel (or ovary-cell). Carpels 5. Fruit large. Endocarp cartilagineous. Seed-coat mucilagineous. Leaves undivided. — Species 1 (*C. vulgaris* Pers., quince). Cultivated in North and South Africa and in some tropical islands. The fruit is edible and used for the preparation of confectionery and in medicine. (Under *Pyrus* L.)   .   .   .   . **Cydonia** Tourn.
   Ovules and seeds 1—2 to each carpel (or ovary-cell).   7
7. Fruit with a bony endocarp and a mealy mesocarp. Ovules 2, one of them sterile and covering the fertile one.   8
   Fruit with a membranous, parchment-like, or cartilagineous endocarp. Carpels 2—5.   9
8. Style furrowed. Carpel 1. Embryo with coiled cotyledons. Stamens 10—15. Flowers in racemes. Leaves undivided, persistent. — Species 1. Madeira.   .   .   .   . **Chamaemeles** Lindl.

Style not furrowed. Embryo with flat cotyledons. Leaves usually
lobed or divided and deciduous. — Species 5. North-west Africa.
They yield timber, tanners' bark, edible fruits (medlars) and medicaments and are also used as ornamental plants (hawthorn). (Including
Crataegus L.) . . . .   **Mespilus** L.

9. Carpels projecting above the receptacle ; hence cells of the fruit reaching
to the cavity at its top. Styles 5, free. Fruit with a membranous
endocarp. Seeds very large, with thick cotyledons. Leaves undivided, persistent. — Species 1 (*E. japonica* Lindl., loquat). Cultivated in North Africa and some tropical islands for its edible fruits.
(Under *Photinia* Lindl.) . . . .   **Eriobotrya** Lindl.

Carpels completely enclosed in the receptacle ; hence cells of the fruit
not reaching to its top. Leaves usually deciduous. — Species 8, of
which 6 are growing wild in North Africa, the other two (*P. communis*
L., pear, and *P. Malus* L., apple) cultivated in North and South Africa
and Madagascar. They yield timber, tanners' bark, and edible fruits,
from which also drinks and medicaments are prepared. Several species
are used as ornamental plants. (*Pyrus* L., including *Malus* Tourn. and
Sorbus L.). . . . .   **Pirus** Tourn.

10. (1.) Carpels 2 or more, with 1—2 ovules each, rarely carpel 1, with a
single ovule. Flowers regular. [Subfamily **ROSOIDEAE.**] . . . 11
Carpel 1, with 2 ovules, sometimes more or less completely 2-celled or
one ovule abortive; in this cases flowers distinctly irregular. Fruit
a drupe. Shrubs or trees. Leaves undivided. 25

11. Receptacle of the female flowers deeply concave, tube- or urn-shaped,
tightly enclosing the carpels, especially in fruit. 12
Receptacle flat, convex, or moderately concave (cup- or saucer-shaped),
not tightly enclosing the carpels. Carpels 5 or more. Stamens numerous 21

12. Carpels numerous. Ovules pendulous. Stamens numerous. Petals 4—6,
large, red white or yellow, imbricate in bud. Sepals imbricate. Flowers
hermaphrodite. Receptacle becoming succulent in fruit. Shrubs.
Leaves pinnate. — Species 10. North Africa and Abyssinia ; also
naturalized in several tropical islands. Used as ornamental plants, and
in the preparation of perfumes and medicaments ; some have edible
fruits. [Tribe ROSEAE.] . . . . **Rosa** Tourn.
Carpels 1—4. Petals small, yellow or white, or wanting. [Tribe SAN-
GUISORBEAE.] 13

13. Perianth consisting of an epicalyx, a calyx, and a corolla. Carpels 2—4. 14
Perianth consisting of calyx and corolla, or of epicalyx and calyx, or of the
calyx only. 15

14. Flowers hermaphrodite. Epicalyx of 5—6 small segments. Petals broad.
Stamens 10—12. Shrubs. Leaves pinnatipartite. Flowers in racemes.
— Species 1. South Africa. . . . .   **Leucosidea** Eckl. & Zeyh.

Flowers polygamous-dioecious. Epicalyx of 4—5 large segments. Petals narrow. Stamens 20. Trees. Leaves pinnate. Flowers in panicles. — Species 1. East Africa. Used medicinally. (*Brayera* Kunth)

Hagenia Gmel.

15. Perianth consisting of a corolla and a calyx surrounded by several rows of hooked bristles. Stamens 10 or more. Styles 2, subterminal. Herbs. Leaves pinnate. Flowers in spikes. — Species 1. North and South Africa. Yields tanning and dyeing materials, and is also used in medicine. . . . . **Agrimonia** L.
Perianth consisting of a calyx with an epicalyx, or only of a calyx. . 16

16. Epicalyx of 4—5 segments alternating with the sepals. Stamens 1—5. Ovules ascending. Styles basal. Stigmas capitate. Leaves lobed or digitate. — Species 25. Some of them yield tanning and dyeing materials and medicaments. "Lady's mantle." (Including *Aphanes* L.) . . . . **Alchimilla** L.
Epicalyx none. Stigmas more or less penicillate 17

17. Flowers hermaphrodite or monoecious ; in the latter case receptacle of the male flowers resembling that of the female. Leaves pinnate. Flowers in spikes or heads 18
Flower dioecious. Stamens numerous. Receptacle of the male flowers very small. Shrubs or trees 20

18. Receptacle armed with hooked bristles, at least in fruit. Flowers hermaphrodite. Stamens 2—5. Herbs or undershrubs. — Species 3. South Africa. Used medicinally . . . . **Acaena** Vahl
Receptacle without bristles 19

19. Flowers hermaphrodite or polygamous. Fruiting receptacle dry, not coloured, wrinkled and pitted or winged. Herbs. — Species 10. North Africa, one species also introduced in South Africa. Some species yield tans, dyes, and medicaments, or are used as potherbs. (Under *Poterium* L.) . . . . **Sanguisorba** L.
Flowers monoecious. Fruiting receptacle somewhat fleshy, coloured, smooth. Stamens numerous. Spinous shrubs. — Species 1. North Africa. Used medicinally. (*Sarcopoterium* Spach) . . . **Poterium** L.

20. Leaves pinnate, with several pairs of leaflets. Flowers in spikes. Fruiting receptacle somewhat fleshy. — Species 2. Canary Islands and Madeira . . . . **Bencomia** Webb
Leaves 1—3-foliolate. Flowers solitary, axillary. Fruiting receptacle cartilaginous, rarely somewhat fleshy. — Species 40. South Africa and southern Central Africa . . . . **Cliffortia** L.

21. (11.) Filaments narrowed towards the base. Petals 5, white. Ovules 2. Styles terminal. Ripe carpels dry and indehiscent. Herbs. Leaves pinnatisect. Flowers in panicles. — Species 1. North-west Africa (Algeria). Used as an ornamental plant. (*Ulmaria* Tourn., under *Spiraea* L.) [Tribe FILIPENDULEAE]. . . . . **Filipendula** L.

Q

Filaments broadened at the base. Sepals valvate in bud. Carpels usually
   inserted on an elevated receptacle. [Tribe POTENTILLEAE]. . 22
22. Carpels with 2 ovules each, drupe-like when ripe. Style subterminal.
   Epicalyx none. — Species 30. Many of them yield edible fruits, from
   which also drinks are prepared ; some are used as ornamental plants,
   for tanning, and in medicine. " Bramble." [Subtribe RUBINAE.]
                                                          Rubus L.
   Carpels with 1 ovule each, nut-like when ripe. Epicalyx nearly always
   present 23
23. Ovule ascending. Style persistent, terminal. Herbs. Radical leaves
   pinnatisect. — Species 4. North and South Africa ; one species also
   naturalized in St. Helena. They yield tanning and dyeing materials and
   medicaments. " Avens." [Subtribe DRYADINAE.] . . . **Geum** L.
   Ovule pendulous. Style deciduous. [Subtribe POTENTILLINAE.] . 24
24. Ripe carpels on a greatly enlarged, coloured, and succulent receptacle.
   Petals white. Herbs. Leaves usually trifoliolate. — Species 5. Cultivated in various regions ; one species also growing wild in the Azores,
   Madeira, and the Canary Islands. They yield edible fruits (strawberries),
   dyeing and tanning materials, and medicaments . . . **Fragaria** L.
   Ripe carpels on a slightly or not enlarged, not coloured, dry (sometimes
   spongy, but not succulent) receptacle. Flowers hermaphrodite. —
   Species 10. Some of them yield tanning and dyeing materials, or serve
   for the preparation of ink and medicaments, or as ornamental plants.
                                                       Potentilla L.
25. (10.) Style terminal or nearly so. Ovules pendulous. Flowers regular.
   [Subfamily **PRUNOIDEAE**.] 26
   Style basal. Ovules erect. [Subfamily **CHRYSOBALANOIDEAE**.] . 27
26. Petals sepaloid. Flowers in racemes. — Species 1. Central and South-east
   Africa . . . . **Pygeum** Gaertn.
   Petals petaloid. — Species 9 ; six of them spontaneous in North Africa,
   the others, as well as the former, cultivated in various regions. They
   yield timber, tanners' bark, gum, oil, medicaments, and edible fruits
   (plums, cherries, apricots, peaches, almonds), from which also drinks and
   confectionery are prepared. Several species are used as ornamental
   plants. (Including *Amygdalus* L., *Armeniaca* Juss., *Cerasus* Juss., and
   Persica Tourn.) . . . . **Prunus** L.
27. Flowers almost regular. Stamens 10 or more. Carpel inserted at or
   near the base of the bell- or funnel-shaped receptacle. [Subtribe
   CHRYSOBALANINAE.] 28
   Flowers distinctly irregular. Fertile stamens 3—20, all on one side of the
   flower. Carpel inserted at or near the upper margin of the more or less
   tubular receptacle. [Subtribe HIRTELLINAE.] 29
28. Receptacle swelling on one side ; carpel slightly excentrical. Stamens
   10—15. Fruit with a 3-angled stone. Flowers in racemes. — Species 2.
   Madagascar and Mascarenes. Used medicinally . . **Grangeria** Comm.

A ⅔

D ³/₂   *C* ²/₁   *B* ⁴/₁

J. Fleischmann del.

Parinarium congoense Engl.

A Flowering branch. *B* Flower cut lengthwise. *C* Flower from above. *D* Unripe fruit.

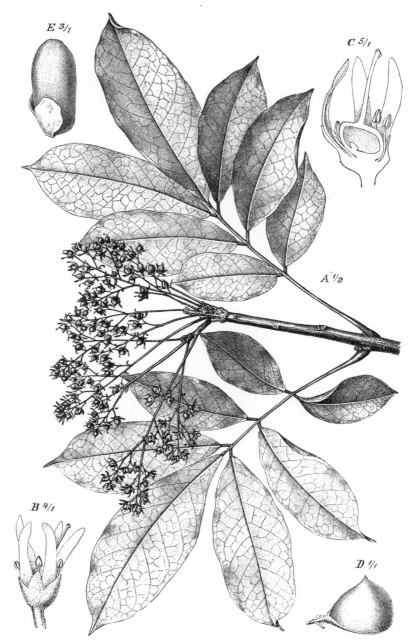

E 3/1

C 5/1

A 1/2

B 4/1

D 1/1

J. Fleischmann del.

Connarus Smeathmannii DC.

A End of branch with young fruits. *B* Flower. *C* Flower cut lengthwise. *D* Fruit. *E* Seed with aril.

Receptacle not swelling on one side ; carpel central. Stamens numerous. Fruit with an irregularly 5-angled stone. Flowers in panicles. — Species 3. Central Africa. They yield tanning and dyeing materials, oil, medicaments, and edible fruits (cocoa-plums) . . . **Chrysobalanus** L.

29. Filaments united in a long strap. Anthers 10—20. Ovary completely 1-celled. — Species 17. Central Africa. Some species yield timber. (*Griffonia* Hook. fil.) . . . . **Acioa** Aubl.

Filaments free or united at the base only 30

30. Receptacle prolonged above into a scale-like appendage. Stamens 6—7. Ovary completely 1-celled. Stipules large. — Species 3. West Africa.
Magnistipula Engl.

Receptacle without a scale-like appendage. Stipules small. . . . 31

31. Ovary completely 1-celled. Fertile stamens 3—10. Fruit 1-seeded. — Species 3. East Africa and Madagascar . . . . . **Hirtella** L.

Ovary completely or incompletely 2-celled. Fertile stamens 10—20. Fruit usually 2-seeded. — Species 25. Tropical and South Africa. Some of them yield timber, tanners' bark, medicaments, and edible fruits, from which also oil, glue, and an inebriating drink are prepared. (*Parinari* Aubl.) (Plate 65). . . . . **Parinarium** Juss.

FAMILY 104. CONNARACEAE.

Shrubs or trees. Leaves alternate, pinnate, but sometimes with 3 leaflets only, exstipulate. Flowers in fascicles racemes or panicles, regular, hermaphrodite or polygamous. Calyx 5-cleft or 5-parted. Petals 5, free, rarely slightly united, imbricate in the bud. Stamens 5—10, free or united at the base. Carpels 1—5, free, superior. Ovules 2 to each carpel, erect or ascending, straight. Ripe carpels dry, dehiscing by a longitudinal slit, rarely indehiscent, usually solitary. Seeds with an aril often adnate to the testa. — Genera 12, species 140. Tropical and South Africa. (Plate 66.)

1. Sepals imbricate in the bud. Seeds exalbuminous. [Tribe CON-NAREAE.]. 2

Sepals valvate in the bud. Seeds albuminous. Stamens 10. Carpels 5. [Tribe CNESTIDEAE.] 8

2. Ripe carpel indehiscent, nearly always 2-seeded. Seeds with a large, adnate aril. Calyx hardened in fruit. Petals greatly exceeding the sepals. Stamens 10, very unequal, surrounded by a disc. Carpel 1. Flowers in clusters, springing from the old wood. — Species 3. Equatorial West Africa (Gaboon). (*Anthagathis* Harms). **Jollydora** Pierre

Ripe carpel (or carpels) dehiscing lengthwise, usually 1-seeded. . . 3

3. Fruit-carpels narrowed at the base into a distinct stalk. Seeds attached to the ventral suture, with a free aril. Calyx not enlarged in fruit. — Species 18. Central Africa. Some are used medicinally. (Plate 66.)
Connarus L

Fruit-carpels not stalked. Seeds attached at their base. Carpels (at the time of flowering) 3—5 4

4. Calyx scarcely or not enlarged in fruit, small, usually flaccid . . . 5
  Calyx conspicuously enlarged and hardened in fruit, leathery to woody
      Stamens 10. Carpels 5 6
5. Leaves trifoliolate. — Species 25. Tropics. Some are used medicinally.
                                                Agelaea Sol.
  Leaves pinnate, with several pairs of leaflets. Stamens 10. Carpels 5.
      Styles 2-cleft at the apex. Calyx persistent. — Species 7. Tropics.
      Some are poisonous. (Under *Rourea* Aubl.)
                                        Byrsocarpus Schum. & Thonn.
6. Calyx tightly clasping the fruit, herbaceous at the time of flowering. Styles
      short ; stigmas capitate. Seeds with very convex cotyledons. —
      Species 40. Tropics. Some are poisonous or used in medicine.
                                                Rourea Aubl.
  Calyx not clasping the fruit. Stamens very unequal. Styles long   7
7. Stem twining. Inflorescence paniculate. Calyx leathery at the time
      of flowering. Seeds with flat cotyledons. — Species 2. Equatorial
      West Africa . . . . **Paxia** Gilg
  Stem erect. Inflorescence racemose-fasciculate. Anther-halves distant
      from one another, the pollen-sacs placed crosswise. — Species 1. Equa-
      torial West Africa. (*Jaundea* Gilg). . . . . . **Yaundea** Gilg
8. (1.) Ripe carpel indehiscent, not stalked, with a crusty pericarp. Seeds
      enveloped by a thin aril. Carpel 1. Stamens 5—7, alternating with as
      many glands. Calyx deeply divided, persistent, but not enlarged in
      fruit. Low trees. Leaves unifoliolate. Flowers in clusters. — Species 2.
      West Africa. . . . . **Hemandradenia** Stapf
  Ripe carpel (or carpels) dehiscing lengthwise 9
9. Receptacle prolonged into a stalk-like androphore. Sepals red, free. Petals
      yellow, clawed, with 2 glands above the claw. Styles long. Erect
      shrubs. — Species 1. Northern West Africa (Liberia). **Dinklagea** Gilg
  Receptacle not prolonged. Petals without glands. Mostly climbing
      shrubs 10
10. Sepals united to the middle, ovate-triangular. Petals linear, four times
      as long as the calyx, rolled inwards at the tip. Stamens very unequal.
      Styles long ; stigmas lobed. — Species 6. West Africa. **Spiropetalum** Gilg
  Sepals free or nearly so. Petals not more than twice as long as the calyx.
      Styles short ; stigmas capitate 11
11. Fruit-carpels glabrous on the inside, short-haired on the outside, pro-
      longed into a stalk at the base. Seeds without a distinct aril, but with
      a fleshy testa. Embryo long and narrow. Petals longer than the
      calyx. — Species 10. West Africa. . . . . . **Manotes** Sol.
  Fruit-carpels covered with long stiff hairs on the inside and usually also
      on the outside. Seeds with a very small adnate aril at the base. Petals
      as long as or shorter or somewhat longer than the calyx. Stamens
      subequal. — Species 30. . Tropical and South Africa. Some are used
      medicinally . . . . **Cnestis** Juss.

FAMILY 105. LEGUMINOSAE

Leaves usually compound and stipulate. Anthers 2-celled. Ovary superior, 1-celled. Ovules inserted at the ventral suture. Style simple, but sometimes with a tooth near the apex. Stigma entire. Fruit 1-, 2-, or transversely several-celled, opening in two valves or along the ventral suture, or separating transversely in two or more joints, or indehiscent. — Genera 261, species 3300 (*FABACEAE*, including *PAPILIONACEAE*, *CAESALPINIACEAE* and *MIMOSACEAE*.) (Plate 67.)

1. Petals valvate in bud. Flowers regular. Leaves twice pinnate, rarely (*Acacia*) reduced to the broadened stalk. [Subfamily **MIMOSOIDEAE.**] 2
   Petals imbricate in bud or wanting. Flowers more or less irregular (some-times nearly regular.) 28
2. Calyx with imbricate aestivation. Unarmed trees. [Tribe PARKIEAE]. 3
   Calyx with valvate aestivation 4
3. Flowers in long spikes, yellowish. Fertile stamens 5, sterile ones 10—15. — Species 3. West Africa. They yield timber, oil, and edible seeds (ovala-seeds) . . . . **Pentaclethra** Benth.
   Flowers in globular or club-shaped heads. Fertile stamens 10. — Species 7. Tropics. They yield timber, tanners' bark, vegetables, medica-ments, edible fruits, from which a drink is prepared, and oily seeds, which are also used as a condiment, a substitute for coffee, a fish-poison, and for improving bad water . . . . . . **Parkia** R. Br.
4. Stamens as many or twice as many as the petals 5
   Stamens more than twice as many as the petals. Trees or shrubs . . 25
5. Anthers without glands. [Tribe MIMOSEAE.] 6
   Anthers crowned, at least in the bud, by a sometimes caducous gland. Stamens 10. 9
6. Fruit dehiscing by two valves which separate from the persistent sutures. Petals united below 7
   Fruit dehiscing by two valves which do not separate from the sutures, or indehiscent 8
7. Fruit and seeds slightly 4-angled, the former prickly. Petals red. Stamens 8—10. Herbs or undershrubs. Flowers in heads. — Species 1. West Africa . . . . **Schranckia** Willd.
   Fruit and seeds flat. — Species 20. Tropics to Egypt, one species naturalized. Some yield timber or medicaments or serve as ornamental plants . . . . **Mimosa** L.
8. Fruit broadly linear. Seeds placed transversely. Petals free, white. Stamens 10. Ovary stalked. Unarmed shrubs or trees. Flowers in heads. — Species 1 (*L. glauca* Benth.). Naturalized in the Tropics. It yields timber, fodder, edible fruits, ornamental seeds, and medicaments.
   Leucaena Benth.
   Fruit narrowly linear. Seeds placed obliquely or longitudinally. — Species 7. One of them naturalized in the Tropics, the others natives of Mada-gascar. Seeds used as ornament. (*Acuan* Medik.) **Desmanthus** Willd.

9. Seeds albuminous.   [Tribe ADENANTHEREAE.]   10
Seeds exalbuminous.   [Tribe PIPTADENIEAE.]   19

10. Flowers in heads   11
Flowers in spikes or racemes   12

11. Flowers partly (the upper) hermaphrodite, partly (the lower) male or
neuter. Ovary stalked. Ovules numerous. Fruit obliquely-oblong,
opening by two valves. Herbs or undershrubs. Stipules membranous,
cordate. — Species 1. Tropics. Used as a vegetable. **Neptunia** Lour.
Flowers all hermaphrodite. Ovary sessile. Ovules 1—2. Fruit sickle-
shaped, indehiscent. Shrubs. Stipules spinous, recurved. — Species
1. South Africa .   .   .   .   **Xerocladia** Harv.

12. Flowers partly (the upper) hermaphrodite and yellow, partly (the
lower) neuter and white or red. Fruit not winged. Shrubs or trees. —
Species 12. Tropical and South Africa. Some species yield ebony-like
wood and medicaments. (*Cailliea* Guill. & Perr.) **Dichrostachys** DC.
Flowers partly hermaphrodite, partly male or female, or all hermaphrodite ;
no neuter flowers. Trees   13

13. Fruit winged or distinctly 4-angled, transversely septate, indehiscent. 14
Fruit neither winged nor distinctly 4-angled   16

14. Fruit 2-winged. Ovary stalked. Flowers sessile. — Species 1. Madagascar and Mauritius   .   .   .   .   **Gagnebina** DC.
Fruit 4-winged or 4-angled. Ovary sessile or nearly so. Flowers stalked.
15

15. Fruit 4-winged. — Species 3. Central Africa. They yield timber, a
substitute for soap, poison, and medicaments .   .   **Tetrapleura** Benth.
Fruit 4-angled. Leaves with 4—5 pairs of pinnae.—Species 1. Central
Africa .   .   .   .   **Amblygonocarpus** Harms

16. Fruit distinctly dehiscing in two valves   17
Fruit indehiscent   18

17. Seeds few, very flat, winged, with a long funicle. — Species 3. Equatorial West Africa   .   .   .   .   **Newtonia** Baill.
Seeds numerous, thick, red. Leaflets numerous. — Species 1 (*A. pavo-
nina* L.). Naturalized in the tropics. It yields timber, gum, dyes,
medicaments, and edible oily seeds, which are also used as ornaments.
Adenanthera L.

18. Calyx large, tube- or urn-shaped, with ovate, acute teeth. Stamens
inserted at the base of the petals. Leaves with one pair of pinnae
and several pairs of very large oblong leaflets. Spikes arranged in
panicles. — Species 1. Equatorial West Africa (Cameroons). Yields
timber and medicaments. .   .   .   .   **Calpocalyx** Harms
Calyx small, bell-shaped, with short segments. Stamens free. Leaves
with 2—5 pairs of pinnae and small or rather small leaflets. — Species 3.
North and Central Africa. They yield timber and edible fruits. (Including *Anonychium* Benth.) .   .   .   .   **Prosopis** L.

19. (9.) Flowers in heads. Ovary sessile, with many ovules. Fruit trans-
    versely septate. Trees. — Species 5. Tropics. They yield timber
    and a substitute for soap. (Under *Parkia* R.Br.) **Xylia** Benth.

    Flowers in spikes or racemes. Shrubs or trees. 20

20. Flowers sessile 21

    Flowers short-stalked 23

21. Calyx saucer-shaped, cleft to the middle. Petals free. Disc cupular,
    thick. Fruit large, elliptical, 1-celled. Seeds winged, with a long
    funicle. Trees. Leaves with 1—2 pairs of pinnae. Spikes panicled. —
    Species 1. Equatorial West Africa. Yields timber. **Fillaeopsis** Harms

    Calyx bell-shaped, shortly toothed. Disc inconspicuous or wanting . 22

22. Petals obviously united below. Fruit 1-celled, opening in two valves. —
    Species 13. Tropics to Delagoa Bay. Some species yield ebony-like
    wood . .. . **Piptadenia** Benth.

    Petals free or nearly so. Fruit with thick, persistent sutures, the valves
    splitting transversely into one-seeded joints. Endocarp separating
    from the exocarp and persisting round the seeds. Shrubs. — Species 10.
    Tropical and South Africa. Some species (especially *E. scandens* L.
    with fruits attaining a yard in length) yield soap-bark, fibre, vegetables,
    fish-poison, and edible oily seeds which are also used in medicine and as
    ornaments. (*Gigalobium* P.Br., *Pusaetha* L.) . . **Entada** Adans.

23. Disc cupular, thin. Ovary stalked. Seeds winged. Trees. Leaves
    with one pair of pinnae. Flowers with a very short stalk. — Species 1.
    Equatorial West Africa. Yields timber. (Including *Cyrtoxiphus* Harms)
    Cylicodiscus Harms

    Disc inconspicuous or wanting. Ovary sessile or nearly so. Shrubs.
    Leaves with 3—12 pairs of pinnae 24

24. Calyx-teeth more or less unequal. Buds oblique. Fruit woody, trans-
    versely septate, opening in two valves. Leaves with 3—6 pairs of pinnae.
    — Species 1. German East Africa.. . . **Pseudoprosopis** Harms

    Calyx-teeth equal. Fruit leathery, with persistent sutures, the endocarp
    separating from the exocarp. Leaves with 6—12 pairs of pinnae. —
    Species 5. South Africa and southern Central Africa. They yield
    fish-poison and are used in medicine . . **Elephantorrhiza** Benth.

25. (4.) Filaments free or the inner united into a ring. Petals white or yellow
    — Species 80. They yield timber, fibre, soap-bark, gum (especially
    from *A. Senegal* Willd., Verek), tanning and dyeing materials, perfumes,
    oil, and medicaments ; some are used as ornamental plants. (Including
    Vachellia Arn.) [Tribe ACACIEAE.] . . . . **Acacia** Willd.

    Filaments united into a tube, at least at the base. Petals white or red.
    Flowers in heads. Unarmed plants. [Tribe INGEAE.] . . . 26

26. Fruit strongly curved or coiled, thick, leathery, separating into one-seeded
    joints or indehiscent. Petals united beyond the middle. Trees. —

Species 3. Tropics ; one species naturalized. They yield timber, gum, tanning and dyeing materials, edible fruits, and medicaments.
Pithecolobium Mart.

Fruit straight or nearly so. 27

27. Fruit dehiscing elastically. Petals united to the middle. Shrubs. — Species 5. Tropics. They yield timber, gum, and medicaments, and are used also as ornamental plants. . . . . **Calliandra** Benth.

Fruit dehiscing in two straight and thin, not elastic valves, or indehiscent. Petals united to the middle or beyond. — Species 45. Tropical and South-east Africa ; several species also cultivated in Egypt. Some species (especially *A. Lebbek* Benth.) yield timber, tanners' bark, gum, condiments, and medicaments, or serve as ornamental plants. (Including *Zygia* Benth.) . . . . **Albizzia** Durazz.

28. (1.) Petals 1—6, the posterior one (the one next the placenta) inside of all in the bud, not forming a papilionaceous corolla, or wanting altogether. Embryo usually with a straight radicle. [Subfamily **CAESALPINIOI-DEAE.**] 29

Petals 5, the posterior outside in bud, usually constituting a papilionaceous corolla. Sepals united below. Stamens 10, more rarely 5—9. Embryo usually with an inflexed radicle. Leaves simple, unifoliolate, digitate, or once pinnate. [Subfamily **PAPILIONATAE.**] 104

29. Calyx undivided or shortly lobed in the bud, usually more deeply divided at the time of flowering 30

Calyx, already in the bud, divided down to the receptacle or nearly so . 39

30. Stamens 1—10. Corolla of 5 petals, nearly regular. Trees or shrubs. 31

Stamens 16 or more. Corolla of 6 petals, or of a single petal, or wanting. Calyx undivided in bud. Leaves imparipinnate or unifoliolate. Trees. [Tribe SWARTZIEAE.] 37

31. Leaves undivided, 2-lobed, 2-parted, or of 2 leaflets. [Tribe BAUHI-NIEAE.] 32

Leaves pinnate, with many leaflets. Stamens 10. 34

32. Ovary and fruit with a very long stalk, the fruit turgid. Ovules few. Style short. Stamens 10. Petals red. Calyx 5-lobed, imbricate in bud. Climbing shrubs. Leaves undivided, penninerved or faintly trinerved. — Species 3. West Africa. (*Bandeiraea* Welw.)
Griffonia Baill.

Ovary and fruit with a short or rather short stalk, the fruit not turgid . 33

33. Receptacle (calyx-tube) very long. Petals yellowish. Stamens 10, partly sterile. Leaves undivided, ovate or elliptical. Racemes many-flowered. — Species 1. Madagascar. (Under *Bauhinia* L.). . **Gigasiphon** Drake

Receptacle (calyx-tube) not very long. — Species 40. Tropical and South Africa, and Egypt. Some species yield timber, fibre, tanning and dyeing materials, edible roots, oily seeds, and medicaments, or serve as ornamental plants. (Plate 67.) . . . . **Bauhinia** L.

34. Leaves once pinnate, with a terminal leaflet. Calyx campanulate, subequally 5-lobed. Petals subequal, white or red. Ovules numerous Fruit opening by two valves. Shrubs. Flowers solitary or in racemes. — Species 8. Madagascar and East Africa. . . . . **Cadia** Forsk.
Leaves twice pinnate. [Tribe DIMORPHANDREAE.] 35

35. Ovary sessile or nearly so. Ovules 2. Style very short. Fruit with a thin, leathery rind, indehiscent. Seeds suborbicular. Flowers in spikes. — Species 2. Central Africa to Transvaal. They yield gum . . . . **Burkea** Hook.
Ovary stalked. Ovules more than 2. Fruit with a thick, leathery rind. Flowers in racemes. Trees. 36

36. Calyx-lobes unequal. Petals with a long claw. Stamens with a glandular connective. Style long. Fruit long, wavy, indehiscent. Leaflets small. — Species 1. Madagascar and Seychelles. **Brandzeia** Baill.
Calyx-lobes subequal. Stamens with a glandless connective. Style short. Fruit oblong, dehiscing by two valves. Seeds oblong. Leaflets large. — Species 5. Tropics. They yield timber, tanning and dyeing materials, medicaments, and poisons especially used in ordeals. "Sassy tree." (*Fillaea* Guill. & Perr.). . . . . **Erythrophloeum** Afz.

37. (30.) Corolla of 6 petals, almost regular. Stamens 16—18. Ovary sessile. Ovules 2. Leaves unifoliolate. — Species 2. West Africa to the Great Lakes. They yield timber. . . . . . **Baphiopsis** Benth.
Corolla reduced to a single petal or wanting. Ovary stalked. Ovules more than 2. Leaves pinnate. 38

38. Receptacle (calyx-tube) very short, almost wanting. Petal 1. Fruit linear. — Species 2. Tropics. Yielding timber. (*Tounatea* Aubl.).
                                                                Swartzia Schreb.
Receptacle bell-shaped. Petals none. Fruit ovate. — Species 1 (*C. africana* Lour.). Central Africa. Yields timber, gum, edible fruits, and medicaments. . . . . **Cordyla** Lour.

39. (29.) Leaves, at least some of them, twice pinnate. [Tribe CAESALPINIEAE.] 40
Leaves all once pinnate, rarely simple 52

40. Common petiole very short, ending in a spine ; rachis of the pinnae very long, flattened, leaf-like ; leaflets very small. Stipules spinous. Trees or shrubs. Calyx imbricate in bud. Petals 5, subequal, yellow. Stamens 10. Ovules numerous. Fruit linear, tardily dehiscing or indehiscent. Seeds oblong, placed lengthwise, albuminous. — Species 2 one of them a native of South Africa, the other naturalized in the tropics They yield timber, bast for paper-making, a substitute for coffee, and medicaments, and serve also as garden- or hedge-plants.
                                                                Parkinsonia L.
Common petiole distinctly developed ; rachis of the pinnae not leaf-like. 41

41. Stem herbaceous or woody at the base only. Petals 5, subequal, yellow. Stamens 10. Ovules numerous. Fruit dehiscing by two valves,

membranous or thin-leathery. Seeds transverse, ovoid, exalbuminous.
— Species 3. South Africa and southern Central Africa (*Melano-
sticta* DC.) . . . . **Hoffmannseggia** Cav.
Stem woody throughout, shrub- or tree-like 42

42. Flowers sessile, in elongate panicled spikes. Calyx 5-cleft, with semiorbi-
cular lobes. Petals 5, equal, oblong, much exceeding the calyx. Stamens
10, unequal. Anthers basifixed. Ovules 2—3. Trees. — Species 1.
West Africa (Cameroons). . . . . . **Stachyothyrsus** Harms
Flowers more or less stalked, in racemes or panicles 43

43. Flowers polygamous. Calyx slightly imbricate in bud. Petals 3—5,
subequal, white or greenish. Stamens 6—10. Seeds transverse, albuminous. Trees. Leaves without stipules. — Species 2, one a native of
Central Africa, the other naturalized in North Africa. Used as hedge-
plants and yielding timber. . . . . **Gleditschia** L
Flowers hermaphrodite. Stamens 10. 44

44. Petal 1, greenish-yellow. Calyx valvate in bud. Ovules very numerous.
Styles long. Trees. — Species 1. Madagascar. . . **Aprevalia** Baill.
Petals 5. 45

45. Sepals united high up, excepting one, valvate in bud. Petals unequal,
red. Ovules numerous. Fruit straight, turgid, dehiscing by two
valves. Seeds transverse. Trees. Bracts coloured. — Species 1.
Madagascar. Used as an ornamental plant. . . . **Colvillea** Boj.
Sepals free above the receptacle 46

46. Sepals valvate in bud. Petals yellow or red. Ovules numerous. Style
thread-shaped. Fruit dehiscing by two valves. Seeds transverse,
oblong, albuminous. Trees. Stipules indistinct. Flowers large. —
Species 3. Tropics: also cultivated in various regions. Ornamental
plants. "Flame-tree." . . . . **Poinciana** L.
Sepals imbricate in bud. Seeds exalbuminous. 47

47. Ovule 1, very rarely ovules 2. Seed 1, placed lengthwise. Fruit winged
at the top, indehiscent. Petals subequal, white or yellow. Spinous
climbing shrubs. Flowers small. — Species 1. Abyssinia. (*Cantuffa*
Gmel.). . . . . **Pterolobium** R.Br.
Ovules 2 or more. Seeds placed transversely. 48

48. Fruit woody, not winged, 2-seeded, opening by two valves. Ovary short-
stalked, 2-ovuled. Stigma peltate. Stamens hairy at the base. Petals
unequal. Receptacle oblique. — Species 2. German East Africa.
(Under *Peltophorum* Vog.). . . . . **Bussea** Harms
Fruit membranous or leathery 49

49. Fruit winged at both sutures, indehiscent. Stigma broad-peltate. Filaments hairy at the base. Petals subequal, yellow. Trees. — Species 1.
Central Africa and northern South Africa. . . . . **Peltophorum** Vog.
Fruit winged at one suture only or not winged. Stigma small, sometimes
concave 50

50. Fruit winged, indehiscent. Receptacle (calyx-tube) very oblique. Petals subequal, yellow. Stamens bent downwards. — Species 5. West Africa and Madagascar . . . . **Mezoneurum** Desf.

Fruit not winged. Receptacle not very oblique 51

51. Fruit membranous, lanceolate, dehiscing in the middle of the valves. Seeds oblong. Sepals subequal. Petals oblong, subequal, yellow. Stamens erect, hairy at the base. Ovary short-stalked. Ovules 2—3. Trees. — Species 1 (*H. campecheanum* L.). Cultivated in the tropics. Yields timber (log-wood), dyes, gum, and medicaments, and serves also as a garden- and hedge-plant . . . . . **Haematoxylon** L.

Fruit leathery, dehiscing at the sutures or indehiscent. Seeds ovoid or globose. Petals yellow or red. Stamens bent downwards. Ovules few. — Species 10, of which 7 are natives of tropical and South Africa, 3 naturalized there as well as in Egypt and Madeira. They yield timber, tanning and dyeing materials, oily seeds, and medicaments, and are also used as garden- and hedge-plants. (Including *Guilandina* L.).

Caesalpinia L.

52. (39.) Anthers attached by the base or nearly so, rarely by the back, and then opening by apical pores. Seeds usually albuminous. [Tribe CASSIEAE.] 53

Anthers distinctly attached by the back, opening by longitudinal slits. Seeds usually exalbuminous. Trees or shrubs. 58

53. Petals 1—2 or 0. Ovules 2—3. Fruit indehiscent, 1-2-seeded. Trees. Leaves unequally pinnate 54

Petals 3—5 55

54. Stamens 2—3. — Species 10. Tropics. They yield timber and edible fruits from which an intoxicating drink is prepared. . **Dialium** L.

Stamens 8—10. Petals none. — Species 1. East Africa. Yields timber.

Andradia Sim

55. Petals 3, narrow, yellow. Fertile stamens 2 ; anthers opening by a terminal pore. Staminodes 3, petaloid. Ovules 4—5. Trees. Leaves unequally pinnate. — Species 1. Equatorial West Africa. Yields timber. . . . . **Distemonanthus** Benth.

Petals 5. Stamens 4—10 56

56. Sepals 4. Petals unequal, red. Stamens 4—5, some of them with cohering anthers. Ovules 2. Fruit 4-winged. Leaves unequally pinnate. — Species 1. Equatorial West Africa. (*Oligostemon* Benth.)

Duparquetia Baill.

Sepals 5. Leaves equally pinnate or simple 57

57. Leaves simple, undivided. Stamens 10. Filaments thickened above. Anthers opening below the top. Ovules few. Fruit fleshy, with transverse partitions. Trees. — Species 2. Madagascar.

Baudouinia Baill.

Leaves pinnate. — Species 40. They yield timber, gum, tanning and dyeing materials, fish-poison, medicaments (especially senna-leaves), fodder, vegetables, edible fruits, and a substitute for coffee ; several species are used as ornamental plants.   .   .   .   .   .   **Cassia** L.

58. (52.) Ovules 2, rarely 3 or 1, occasionally in some flowers 4. Ovary or its stalk usually free at the base of the receptacle, more rarely adnate to it. [Tribe CYNOMETREAE.].   59
Ovules 4 or more, occasionally in some flowers only 3. Ovary or its stalk usually adnate to the receptacle by the back. Leaves pinnate. [Tribe AMHERSTIEAE.]   80

59. Petals none.   60
Petals 1—5   64

60. Sepals 6, very small and unequal. Stamens 6. Ovary sessile. Shrubs. Leaves pinnate. Bracteoles large. —Species 1. Southern West Africa (Congo).   .   .   .   .   **Dewindtia** De Wild.
Sepals 4—5. Stamens 8—10 or 4. Trees. Leaves abruptly pinnate. Bracteoles small or wanting.   61

61. Sepals 5, distinctly imbricate in bud. Stamens 10. Ovary sessile. Stigma acute. Bracteoles present. — Species 2. West Africa (Cameroons). They yield timber.   (Under *Copaiba* Mill. or *Hardwickia* Roxb.)
Oxystigma Harms
Sepals 4.   62

62. Stamens 4, inserted on the outside of a spathe-like disc cleft on one side. Sepals imbricate in bud. Ovary nearly sessile. Bracteoles present. — Species 1. West Africa (Cameroons).   .   .   .   **Stemonocoleus** Harms
Stamens 8—10.   63

63. Ovary sessile. Fruit sessile, drupe-like, indehiscent. Bracteoles present. — Species 3. Central Africa. They yield timber, fragrant resin, arrow-poison, and medicaments. The fruits of one species are edible, of another poisonous. " Dattock."   .   .   .   .   **Detarium** Juss.
Ovary stalked. Fruit stalked, oblique, with a leathery rind, dehiscing by two valves. Bracteoles none. — Species 9. Central Africa. They yield timber, a resin (copal) used for making ornaments lacs and varnishes, dye stuffs, medicaments, and edible seeds. (*Copaiba* Mill.)
Copaifera L.

64. Petals 1—2. Bracteoles large. Trees. Leaves pinnate 65
Petals 5.   67

65. Stamens 3. Sepals 4, small, scale-like. Petals 1, orbicular. — Species 10. Central Africa.   .   .   .   .   **Cryptosepalum** Benth.
Stamens 10.   66

66. Sepals reduced to minute teeth or wanting. Leaves with a single pair of leaflets. — Species 1. Equatorial West Africa.   .   **Aphanocalyx** Oliv.
Sepals 5, three of them very small, the other two larger and connate. Petal 1, spatulate. Filaments united at the base, excepting one. Leaves with many pairs of leaflets. — Species 2. West Africa.
Monopetalanthus Harms

67. Fertile stamens 3. Ovules 3. Bracteoles large. Trees. — Species 20. Central Africa. Some species yield timber. (*Vouapa* Aubl.)

Macrolobium Schreb.

Fertile stamens 10, rarely (*Cynometra*) more. 68

68. Petals very unequal.ꞏ Leaves pinnate 69

Petals equal or nearly equal. 71

69. Corolla of 1 large and 4 very small petals. Receptacle shortly cup-shaped. Bracteoles minute. Leaves with 1—2 pairs of leaflets. — Species 1. Equatorial West Africa. . . . . . . **Eurypetalum** Harms

Corolla of 3 large and 2 small petals 70

70. Bracteoles petal-like. Receptacle cup- or top-shaped. — Species 4. West Africa. (Under *Cynometra* L.) . . . **Hymenostegia** Harms

Bracteoles sepal-like, hairy outside, equalling the bracts. Receptacle funnel-shaped. Sepals 4. Shrubs. Leaves with 3—4 pairs of leaflets. — Species 1. ꞏWest Africa . . . . . . **Loesenera** Harms

71. Sepals 5, very unequal, the lowest very large. Receptacle very short Trees. Leaves pinnate. — Species 1. Madagascar.

Cymbosepalum Bak.

Sepals 4—5, equal or nearly equal 72

72. Receptacle (calyx-tube) long and narrow. Sepals 4. Stalk of the ovary obliquely adnate to the receptacle 73

Receptacle short and usually broad 75

73. Bracteoles large, petaloid, enclosing the bud. Receptacle with a thick disc on one side. Shrubs. Leaves pinnate, with 2—4 leaflets. — Species 1. West Africa (Cameroons.) . . . **Plagiosiphon** Harms

Bracteoles small, not enclosing the bud, or wanting. Leaves simple or pinnate with many leaflets 74

74. Leaves simple. Shrubs. — Species 2. West Africa (Cameroons).

Zenkerella Taub.

Leaves abruptly pinnate. Trees. — Species 1. West Africa (Cameroons). The bark is used as a condiment. . . . **Scorodophloeus** Harms

75. Ovule 1. Stalk of the ovary obliquely adnate to the receptacle. Sepals 4. Trees. Leaves simple. — Species 1. East Africa. **Podogynium** Taub.

Ovules 2, rarely 3. Leaves abruptly pinnate 76

76. Filaments united into a ring at the base, unequal, hairy. Sepals 5. Ovary glandular. Trees. Leaves with 3—6 pairs of leaflets. Flowers in terminal, many-flowered racemes. — Species 1. East Africa.

Stuhlmannia Taub.

Filaments free. Bracteoles none 77

77. Flowers in panicles. Sepals short. Petals white. Filaments hairy at the base. Fruit flat, lanceolate, opening by two valves. Trees. — Species 1. South Africa (Cape Colony). Yields timber.

Umtiza Sim

Flowers in racemes or corymbs. Sepals usually long 78

78. Flowers in terminal, few-flowered corymbs. Filaments hairy at the base. Fruit flat, ovate, beaked, opening by two valves. Low, glandular shrubs. — Species 1. East Africa (Somaliland). The seeds are edible.
Cordeauxia Hemsl.

Flowers in racemes springing from the axils of the leaves or from the old wood. 79

79. Fruit lanceolate, flat, bursting in the middle of the valves, but remaining closed at the sutures. Sepals 5. Corolla yellow. Filaments erect, hairy at the base. Stalk of the ovary free. Trees. (See 51.)
Haematoxylon L.

Fruit more or less ovate and turgid, opening in two valves. Filaments usually glabrous. — Species 20. West Africa and Madagascar. Some species yield timber and resin (copal). . . . . **Cynometra** L.

80. (58.) Petals reduced to minute scales or wanting. Trees. . . . 81
Petals well developed 87

81. Bracteoles large, enclosing the bud, persisting during the time of flowering. Calyx consisting of 1—5 scale-like sepals, or replaced by a 10-lobed disc, or wanting altogether 82
Bracteoles small, not enclosing the bud, falling off early. Calyx of 4—5 well-developed sepals. 83

82. Disc fleshy. Petals 5, awl-shaped. Stamens 5—6. Stipules small, connate. — Species 4. West Africa. . . . . . **Didelotia** Baill.
Disc none. Stamens 10—20, more or less united at the base. Ovules few. Fruit oblong or linear, opening in two valves. Seeds exalbuminous. — Species 20. Central Africa. The seeds of some species are eaten and the bark is used as a substitute for cloth. (Under *Didelotia* Baill.)
Brachystegia Benth.

83. Sepals 5. Petals 0. Stamens 5. Disc expanded. Ovary in its centre, subsessile. Ovules numerous. Style very short; stigma peltate. Fruit linear, indehiscent. Seeds albuminous. Leaves equally pinnate. Flowers polygamous-dioecious. Bracteoles very small, deciduous. — Species 1 (*C. Siliqua* L., carob-tree). North Africa. The fruits are edible, and used as fodder and for preparing brandy and medicaments; the seeds serve as a substitute for coffee . . . . **Ceratonia** L.
Sepals 4. Stamens 8—10. Disc not expanded. 84

84. Petals 5, scale-like. Stamens 10. Leaves equally pinnate. Flowers in panicles. — Species 12. Central and South Africa. They yield timber, gum, and edible seeds from which meal is prepared. (*Theodora* Medik.)
Schotia Jaqu.

Petals none. 85

85. Stamens 8, alternatingly unequal. Ovary sessile. Ovules numerous. Leaves unequally pinnate. Flowers in compound racemes. Bracteoles linear. — Species 1. Equatorial West Africa (Gaboon).
Hylodendron Taub.

Stamens 10, rarely 8, but then equal in length. Ovary short-stalked.
Ovules few. 86

86. Stamens unequal, 10. Fruit oblong, winged, indehiscent. Seeds pendulous. Leaves equally pinnate. Flowers in simple racemes. —
Species 1. Madagascar . . . . **Apaloxylon** Drake
Stamens equal in length. Fruit broad-oblong to orbicular, dehiscing in
two valves. Leaves unequally pinnate. — Species 5. Central Africa
to Delagoa Bay. (*Apalatoa* Aubl.) . . . . **Crudia** Schreb.

87. (80.) Well developed petal 1 ; sometimes 2—4 rudimentary petals in
addition. Trees. 88
Well developed petals 3—6. Leaves abruptly pinnate. 93

88. Petal sessile. Sepals 4. Leaves abruptly pinnate. 89
Petal with a long claw. 90

89. Receptacle minute. Sepals scale-like. Petal orbicular. Stamens 3,
short. Ovary with a short stalk. Ovules 4. Stigma truncate. Brac-
teoles large, enclosing the bud, persistent at flowering. (See 65.)
Cryptosepalum Benth.
Receptacle rather large, narrowly top-shaped. Sepals large, coloured.
Petal oblong. Stamens 10, long. Ovary with a long stalk. Ovules
numerous. Stigma capitate. Bracteoles falling off early. — Species 3.
West Africa. They yield timber and an aromatic resin.
Daniella Benn.

90. Fertile stamens 3. 91
Fertile stamens 5—10. 92

91. Bracteoles enclosing the bud, persisting at flowering. Petal folded
together in the bud. Flowers small or middle-sized. (See 67.)
Macrolobium Schreb
Bracteoles shorter than the bud, falling off during the time of flowering.
Receptacle elongated. Sepals 4. Fruit oblong. Flowers rather large.
— Species 1. Madagascar and neighbouring islands. It yields timber,
edible seeds, and medicaments. (Under *Afzelia* Smith).
Intsia Thouars

92. Fertile stamens 6—8. Sepals 4. Bracteoles shorter than the bud. Seed
with an aril. — Species 4. Central Africa to Delagoa Bay. They yield
timber ; the aril is edible, the seeds are poisonous and used medicinally.
(Under *Intsia* Thouars) . . . . **Afzelia** Smith
Fertile stamens 5 or 10. Sepals usually 5. Petal folded in bud, whitish.
Bracteoles enclosing the bud. — Species 15. Central Africa. The
wood and the bark are used, the latter for making cloth.
Berlinia Soland.

93. (87.) Sepals 6—7. Petals 6, subequal. Fertile stamens 6—8, barren ones
4—7. Trees. — Species 1. East Africa. . **Englerodendron** Harms
Sepals 4—5. 94

94. Sepals 5. Trees. 95
Sepals 4. 96

95. Petals more or less unequal, white or yellowish.   Stamens 5 or 10.   Fruit
    dehiscent.   Bracteoles enclosing the bud.   (See 92.)   **Berlinia** Soland.
    Petals subequal, red.   Stamens 10.   Fruit winged, indehiscent.   Seeds
    pendulous. — Species 1.   Madagascar   .   .   .   .   **Bathiaea** Drake
96. Fertile stamens 3.   Petals unequal, 3 of them larger than the other two.
    Trees.   97
    Fertile stamens 10 or more.   98
97. Filaments united nearly half their length.   Petals yellowish or red-striped.
    Fruit indehiscent.   Leaves with many pairs of leaflets.   Bracteoles
    narrow, falling off early. — Species 3.   Tropics.   They yield timber,
    tanning and dyeing materials, edible fruits from which drinks and
    medicaments are prepared, and oily seeds   .   .   .   **Tamarindus** L.
    Filaments free.   Fruit dehiscent.   Bracteoles large, enclosing the bud.
    (See 67.)   .   .   .   .   **Macrolobium** Schreb.
98. Stamens numerous, united at the base.   Anthers linear.   Petals subequal.
    Bracteoles enclosing the bud.   Trees. — Species 1.   West Africa.
                                    Polystemonanthus Harms
    Stamens 10.   99
99. Bracteoles large, enclosing the bud.   100
    Bracteoles small, not enclosing the bud, falling off early.   101
100. Petals very unequal, 3 large, 2 very small.   Filaments united at the base.
    Ovules numerous.   Leaves with several pairs of leaflets.   Flowers in
    panicles. — Species 3.   West Africa.   They yield timber and resin.
    (Under *Daniella* Benn.)   .   .   .   .   .   .   **Cyanothyrsus** Harms
    Petals subequal.   Ovules few.   Shrubs.   Leaves with 1—2 pairs of
    leaflets.   Flowers in racemes.   Bracteoles petaloid.   (See 73.)
                                    Plagiosiphon Harms
101. Filaments, excepting one, united high up.   Petals pink, narrow ; blade
    passing gradually into the claw.   Sepals unequal, subvalvate in bud.
    Receptacle very short.   Flowers in racemes or panicles.   Leaflets 7—9,
    alternate. — Species 1.   Equatorial West Africa.   **Tessmannia** Harms
    Filaments free or united at the base.   102
102. Petals sessile or nearly so, subequal, red.   Leaves with 2—16 pairs of
    leaflets.   Flower in panicles.   (See 84.)   .   .   .   .   **Schotia** Jacq.
    Petals with a long or rather long claw.   Trees.   103
103. Sepals slightly imbricate.   Petals subequal.   Filaments, excepting one,
    united at the base.   Leaves with 1—4 pairs of leaflets.   Flowers large, in
    racemes. — Species 7.   West Africa to the Great Lakes.   **Baikiaea** Benth.
    Sepals much imbricate.   Petals white.   Filaments free.   Ovules few.
    Leaves with one pair of leaflets.   Flowers in panicles. — Species 2.
    Tropics.   They yield timber and resin (copal) which is used for turnery
    and carving and for making lacs and varnishes.   (Under *Hymenaea* L.)
                                    Trachylobium Hayne
104. (28.) Filaments free or nearly so.   Shrubs or trees.   105
    Filaments, all or all excepting one, united into a tube or sheath .   .   126

105. Stamens 4-5. Filaments very short. Anthers attached by the base, opening at the top; 2-3 of them united. Ovary 4-winged. Ovules 2. Stigma terminal. Calyx-lobes 4, unequal. Petals 5, shorter than the calyx, unequal, red. Leaves pinnate. (See 56.) **Duparquetia** Baill.
Stamens 8—10. [Tribes SOPHOREAE and PODALYRIEAE] . . 106
106. Leaves simple and undivided or unifoliolate. Corolla papilionaceous. 107
Leaves pinnate or palmately trifoliolate 112
107. Calyx shortly toothed, not slit. Corolla whitish ; petals of the keel slightly cohering. Ovules few. Shrubs with arched or climbing branches. Stipules ovate or lanceolate. Flowers in racemes or panicles. Bracteoles large, enclosing the flower, persistent. — Species 1. West Africa. . . . . **Dalhousiea** Grah.
Calyx shortly toothed but slitting as the flower expands, on one or both sides, or deeply cleft. Bracteoles not enclosing the flower, rather large but deciduous, or small 108
108. Calyx shortly toothed, but deeply slit in one or two places. Corolla white or yellow ; petals of the keel free or nearly so. Ovules few. . . 109
Calyx subequally 4—5-cleft. Stipules awl-shaped or wanting . . 110
109. Anthers longer than the filaments. Ovary long-stalked. Calyx slit on one side. Corolla white : petals of the keel free. Fruit long-stalked, falcate-ovate, turgid. Seeds oblong, with a thick aril. Flowers in panicles. Bracteoles small. — Species 1. West Africa.
Leucomphalus Benth.
Anthers shorter than the filaments. Ovary nearly sessile. Fruit compressed. Seeds ovate or orbicular. — Species 50. Tropical and South-east Africa. Some of them yield timber (camwood), dye-stuffs, or edible fruits. (Including *Bracteolaria* Hochst.) . . . **Baphia** Afz.
110. Petals of the keel free. Flowers in 5—10-flowered racemes. — Species 1. West Africa . . . . ' . **Ormosia** Jacks.
Petals of the keel united. Flowers solitary or in 2—4-flowered fascicles. 111
111. Corolla yellow ; keel shortly beaked. Fruit compressed. Leaves sessile, without stipules. Flowers solitary. — Species 10. South Africa. The leaves are used as a substitute for tea or as a medicament.
Cyclopia Vent.
Corolla red or reddish-white ; keel blunt. Ovary sessile. Fruit turgid. Leaves short-stalked, with deciduous stipules. Hairy plants. — Species 20. South Africa . . . . **Podalyria** Lam.
112. (106.) Leaves palmately trifoliolate. Corolla papilionaceous . . 113
Leaves pinnate 115
113. Petals subequal, yellow, those of the keel united Ovary sessile or nearly so. Fruit oblong, not septate. Erect shrubs. Leaves sessile, leathery, exstipulate. Flowers solitary, axillary, with bracteoles. (See 111.)
Cyclopia Vent.
Petals of the keel free. Ovary stalked. Fruit linear. Leaves stalked, stipulate. Flowers in racemes. 114

R

114. Standard shorter than the wings. Petals yellow. Fruit septate between
the seeds. Erect shrubs. Leaves herbaceous ; stipules connate.
Flowers without bracteoles. — Species 2. North Africa. Poisonous
and medicinal . . . .   **Anagyris** L.
Standard as long as or longer than the wings. Petals clawed, yellowish-
white. Climbing shrubs. Leaves leathery. Flowers with small, deciduous bracteoles. — Species 3. West Africa. (*Giganthemum* Welw.)
Camoënsia Welw.

115. Corolla nearly regular ; petals subequal 116
Corolla papilionaceous ; petals conspicuously unequal, at least one of
them (the standard) very different from the others 118

116. Petals entire. Anthers linear. Ovules more than 2. (See 34.)
Cadia Forsk.

Petals 2-lobed or 2-cleft. Anthers ovate. Ovules 1—2 117

117. Petals shortly lobed. Ovary short-stalked. Leaflets 9—11. Flowers
in racemes. — Species 1. Northern East Africa (Somaliland).
Dicraeopetalum Harms

Petals deeply left. Ovary long-stalked. Leaflets 13—19. Flowers in
panicles. — Species 2. Equatorial West Africa (Gaboon).
Amphimas Pierre

118. Petals of the keel united 119
Petals of the keel free 121

119. Petals long-clawed, red. Ovary sessile. Ovules few. Fruit compressed, not winged, leathery, dehiscing in two valves. Trees. Flowers
in racemes. Bracteoles none. — Species 1. South Africa and St.
Helena. Yields timber and is used as an ornamental plant.
Virgilia Lam.

Petals short- or not clawed, white yellow or violet. Ovary more or less
distinctly stalked. Fruit tardily or not dehiscing. 120

120. Fruit compressed, winged at the upper suture, membranous. Calyx-lobes
unequal. Petals yellow ; those of the keel curved. Flowers in racemes.
Bracteoles none. — Species 9. South and Central Africa.
Calpurnia E. Mey.

Fruit terete or nearly so, constricted between the seeds, 4-winged or
wingless, leathery woody or fleshy. — Species 6. Tropical and South-
east Africa. They yield timber, dye-stuffs, and medicaments, and are
also used as ornamental plants. . . . . . .   **Sophora** L.

121. Standard broad-oblong or narrow-ovate, clawed and auricled. Calyx
very shortly toothed. Filaments slightly united at the base, excepting
one. Ovary long-stalked, hairy. Style very short, almost straight.
Ovules numerous. Trees. Flowers in panicles. — Species 1. Madagascar. (Under *Cadia* Forsk.) . . . .   **Pseudocadia** Harms
Standard broad-ovate or orbicular. Ovary short-stalked or almost
sessile. 122

122. Calyx shortly toothed or entire. Stigma terminal. Fruit almost terete, constricted between the seeds.   123
    Calyx deeply cleft. Fruit flat.   124

123. Stalk of the ovary obliquely adnate to the curved receptacle (calyx-tube). Standard suborbicular, slightly exceeding the other petals. Filaments free. Flowers in racemes arising from the old wood. — Species 5. Central Africa.   .   .   .   . **Angylocalyx** Taub.
    Stalk of the ovary not adnate to the receptacle. Style curved at the apex. Flowers in terminal racemes or panicles. (See 120.) **Sophora** L.

124. Ovule 1. Stigma terminal. Flowers in racemes. Leaflets 5—7. — Species 1. East Africa.   .   .   .   .   .   . **Platycelephium** Harms
    Ovules 2 or more. Leaflets 7—13.   125

125. Stigma terminal. Corolla blue. Flowers in racemes. Leaflets curved and pointed. — Species 1. South Africa.   .   . **Bolusanthus** Harms
    Stigma lateral. · Corolla red or green. Flowers in panicles. — Species 2. West Africa. They yield timber.   .   .   .   . **Afrormosia** Harms

126. (104.) Filaments all, or the alternate ones, broadened at the apex. [Especially tribe LOTEAE.]   127
    Filaments not broadened at the apex.   147

127. Filaments monadelphous, i.e., all united into a tube or sheath, at least when young.   128
    Filaments diadelphous, i.e., united into a sheath, excepting one, which is free from the others, at least at the base, but sometimes connate with them in the middle or slightly cohering with them at the very base . 131

128. Leaves equally pinnate or reduced to the broadened stalk, usually ending in a tendril or bristle. Stipules large, leaf-like. Flowers solitary or in racemes, without bracteoles. Petals short-clawed. Anthers all alike. Ovary more or less distinctly stalked. Style-apex bearded on the inner face. Fruit opening by two valves. Herbs. — Species 35. North Africa and the mountains of the tropics. Several species yield edible tubers or seeds, vegetables, fodder, medicaments, or perfumes ; some are poisonous or used as ornamental plants. (Including *Orobus* L.)
                                                                    Lathyrus L.
    Leaves unequally pinnate, digitate, or unifoliolate. Style glabrous . 129

129. Leaflets minutely toothed, 1 or 3, very rarely more. Stipules adnate to the leaf-stalk. Flowers solitary or in racemes. Calyx-lobes long, subequal. Petals short-clawed. Anthers usually of two kinds. Ovary more or less distinctly stalked. Fruit dehiscing by two valves. — Species 60. North Africa and Abyssinia. Some are used as vegetables or in medicine.   .   .   .   . **Ononis** L.
    Leaflets entire. Stipules small or wanting. Flowers in heads or umbels, sometimes almost solitary. Petals long-clawed. Anthers all alike. Fruit not or tardily dehiscing.   130

130. Ovary sessile. Ovules 2. Fruit protruding beyond the calyx, linear, shortly or not beaked, slightly 4-angled, spirally coiled. Silky herbs.

Flowers in umbels, very small, reddish-yellow, without bracteoles. —
Species 1. Abyssinia. . . . . . **Helminthocarpum** A. Rich.
Ovary more or less distinctly stalked. Fruit enclosed by the calyx or
slightly protruding ; in the latter case beaked. Flowers in heads or
nearly solitary. — Species 12. North Africa and Abyssinia. Some
species (especially *A. Vulneraria* L.) are used as fodder-, dyeing-, medi-
cinal-, or ornamental plants. (Including *Cornicina* Boiss., *Dorycnopsis*
Boiss., and *Physanthyllis* Boiss.) . . . . . . **Anthyllis** L.

131. (127.) Keel beaked. 132
Keel blunt or somewhat pointed 138

132. Ovary short-stalked. Ovules 2. Calyx deeply and equally divided.
Corolla yellow. Fruit spirally coiled, flat, margined, indehiscent.
Herbs. Lowermost leaves simple, with adnate stipules, upper pinnate,
without stipules. Flowers in few-flowered heads. -- Species 1. North
Africa. (*Circinus* Medik.) . . . . . . **Hymenocarpos** Savi
Ovary sessile. Ovules more than two. Calyx more or less unequally
divided. Flowers solitary or in umbels 133

133. Leaves simple, undivided. Stipules adnate to the leafstalk. Upper
calyx-teeth united high up. Petals long-clawed, yellow. Fruit spirally
coiled, almost terete, ribbed. Herbs. — Species 5. North Africa and
Abyssinia. . . . . **Scorpiurus** L.
Leaves pinnate, sometimes apparently digitate 134

134. Fruit jointed. 135
Fruit not jointed. Herbs or undershrubs. 136

135. Joints of the fruit and seeds curved. Fruit more or less flattened, with
the upper edge notched at each seed. Corolla yellow. Leaves with 5
or more leaflets. — Species 9. North Africa. . . . **Hippocrepis** L.
Joints of the fruit and seeds straight, oblong. Fruit not or slightly
flattened. Leaves with 3 or more leaflets, stipulate. — Species 12.
North Africa. Some species are poisonous or used as ornamental or
medicinal plants. . . . . **Coronilla** L.

136. Leaves with many leaflets. Stipules small, membranous. Corolla
yellow. Fruit flat, slightly curved. Seeds quadrate. Glabrous herbs.
— Species 1. North Africa. (*Bonaveria* Scop., *Securidaca* Gaertn.).
Securigera DC.
Leaves with 4—5 leaflets, of which the 1—2 lowest have usually the
appearance of stipules. Stipules very small or wanting. Keel gibbous
on each side. Seeds globular or lenticular. 137

137. Fruit longitudinally 4-winged or 4-angled. — Species 5. North Africa.
Used as fodder or as vegetables. (Under *Lotus* L.)
Tetragonolobus Scop.
Fruit neither 4-winged nor 4-angled. — Species 50. Some of them are
used as vegetables, fodder, or ornamental plants. (Including *Heine-
kenia* Webb, *Lotea* Medik., and *Pedrosia* Lowe). . . . . **Lotus** L.

138. (131.) Petals, at least the lower, adnate below to the staminal tube
Standard oblong or ovate. Erect or prostrate herbs. Leaves pinnate
or palmate; leaflets 3—5, usually toothed. Stipules adnate to the
leafstalk. Flowers solitary or in umbels, heads, or spikes. — Species 70.
North and South Africa and mountains of Central Africa. Many of
them are used as fodder or in medicine. " Clover " .   **Trifolium** L.
Petals free from the staminal tube. Leaflets entire, rarely toothed, but
then more than 5. Stipules usually free or wanting. 139

139. Leaves unifoliolate, stipellate; stalk winged. Flowers in spikes. Calyx-
lobes unequal. Uppermost stamen free at the base, but united with
the others in the middle. Ovary sessile. Ovules 3—4. — Species 4.
Central Africa. (Under *Desmodium* Desv.) **Droogmansia** De Wild.
Leaves pinnate, digitate, or reduced to the usually broadened stalk . 140

140. Leaves equally pinnate or reduced to the stalk. Leaflets entire. Stipules
leaf-like. Flowers solitary or in racemes. Ovary more or less distinctly stalked. Style-apex broadened and bearded. Fruit 2-valved.
Seeds with an outgrowth near the hilum. Herbs or undershrubs. . 141
Leaves unequally pinnate or digitate. Ovary sessile or nearly so . 142

141. Style-apex laterally compressed with reflexed edges, hence grooved
above. Corolla white or red; wings adhering to the keel. Herbs with
tendrils. Leaflets 2—6. — Species 3. North Africa, also cultivated
in the tropics. They yield fodder and edible seeds (peas), from which
also starch is prepared. . . . .   **Pisum** L.
Style-apex compressed dorsally, with the edges bent downwards or
straight. (See 128.)   . . . .   **Lathyrus** L.

142. Stem woody throughout. Leaves unequally pinnate. Flowers in
racemes or fascicles. Upper calyx-teeth united for the greatest part.
Corolla red or violet; wings slightly adhering to the keel; standard
with a callus at the base. Fruit linear, flat. — Species 15. Tropical
and South-east Africa. The seeds of some species are used as a fish-
poison. . . . .   **Mundulea** DC.
Stem herbaceous or woody at the base only. 143

143. Flowers in racemes. Calyx-teeth unequal. Corolla blue; standard
suborbicular, with a callus and two auricles; keel somewhat longer
than the wings and the standard. Uppermost stamen cohering with
the others at the base. Style-apex bearded. Ovules 2. Twining undershrubs. — Species 1. Equatorial East Africa (Kilimandjaro).
                                        Spathionema Taub.
Flowers solitary or in umbels or heads 144

144. Leaflets toothed. Stipules leaf-like. Flowers solitary. Corolla white
or blue. Fruit ovate to oblong, turgid, 2-valved. — Species 2. North
Africa and Abyssinia; one species also cultivated in Angola. They
yield edible seeds (chick-peas) and are used medicinally. **Cicer** L.
Leaflets entire. Flowers in umbels or heads, rarely solitary, but then
corolla yellow. 145

145. Leaflets numerous. Leaf-stalk long. Flowers very small, in heads or umbels. Keel nearly straight. Fruit jointed. — Species 6. North Africa and high mountains of Central Africa. Some are used as fodder. "Birds-foot." (Including *Arthrolobium* Desv.) . . . **Ornithopus** L.

Leaflets 3—5, the lower usually stipule-like. Leaf-stalk short or wanting. 146

146. Corolla yellow; standard suborbicular, with a long claw. Fruit jointed. Undershrubs with long silky hairs. Stipules small. Flowers solitary or 2—3 together in the axils of the leaves. — Species 1. North-west Africa (Algeria). (*Ludovicia* Coss.) . . . . . **Hammatolobium** Fenzl

Corolla white or red; standard oblong or ovate, short-clawed; wings coherent towards the apex, longitudinally folded or transversely gibbous; keel gibbous on each side. Fruit continuous, terete, 2-valved. Stipules very small or wanting. — Species 6. North Africa. (Including *Bonjeania* Reichb.) . . . . **Dorycnium** Vill.

147. (126.) Anthers of two kinds, five shorter and attached by the back, the others longer and attached by the base, or the alternate ones rudimentary 148
Anthers all alike 205

148. Leaves digitate, unifoliolate, simple, or wanting. [Tribe GENISTEAE.] 149
Leaves pinnate, but sometimes with three leaflets 195

149. Uppermost stamen free or nearly so. 150
Uppermost stamen united with the others into a tube or sheath . . 158

150. Stem herbaceous or woody at the base only. Leaves stipulate. . . 151
Stem woody throughout. Leaves usually exstipulate 154

151. Keel with a straight beak. Anthers bearded. Stigma lateral. Fruit linear. Leaves simple, sessile. Flowers in axillary racemes. — Species 2. Southern West Africa. (Under *Indigofera* L.) **Rhynchotropis** Harms
Keel with a spirally twisted beak or without a beak. Anthers not bearded. Stigma terminal. Leaves unifoliolate or digitate 152

152. Keel spirally beaked. Fruit oblong. Flowers opposite the leaves, solitary or 2—3 together. Bracteoles 2. — Species 2. South Africa to Amboland . . . . **Bolusia** Benth.
Keel curved inwards, not beaked. Flowers in axillary or terminal inflorescences. Bracteoles none 153

153. Keel somewhat pointed. Ovules several. Fruit linear. Leaves digitate. Corolla reddish. — Species 1. East Africa. **Parochetus** Hamilt.
Keel blunt. Ovule 1. Fruit ovate. Gland-dotted plants. — Species 60. Some are used as ornamental or medicinal plants. . . **Psoralea** L.

154. Keel with a lateral gibbosity or spur. Anthers distinctly unequal. Leaves simple 155
Keel without a lateral appendage. Anthers nearly equal . . . 156

155. Keel beaked. Corolla yellowish-green, shorter than the calyx. Ovule
1. Flowers in small terminal heads. — Species 1. South Africa (Cape
Colony) . . . . **Lathriogyne** Eckl. & Zeyh.
Keel blunt. Corolla red or white, longer than the calyx. — Species 10.
South Africa. . . . . **Amphithalea** Eckl. & Zeyh.

156. Corolla blue, red, or white. Ovule 1. Leaves unifoliolate or digitate,
stipulate. (See 153.) . . . . **Psoralea** L.
Corolla yellow. Ovules 2 or more. Leaves simple, exstipulate . . 157

157. Calyx-lobes very unequal, the lowest very large and petaloid. Standard
ovate or oblong; wings oblong. Inflorescence surrounded by large
bracts. — Species 4. South Africa. . . . . . . **Liparia** L.
Calyx-lobes about equal. Standard suborbicular; wings obovate. Bracts
not very large. — Species 15. South Africa. . . **Priestleya** DC.

158. (149.) Filaments united into a sheath which is slit above 159
Filaments united into a tube which is closed all round 180

159. Style bearded or ciliate on the inside towards the apex. 160
Style glabrous inside 161

160. Fruit flat, oblong or ovate, stalked, downy, 2-seeded. Shrubs. Leaves
trifoliolate. — Species 1. Island of Socotra. **Priotropis** Wight & Arn.
Fruit turgid. — Species 220. Tropical and South Africa and Egypt.
Some yield fibres, dyes, vegetables, and medicaments, or serve as ornamental plants. . . . . **Crotalaria** L.

161. Ovule 1. 162
Ovules 2 or more. 163

162. Leaves stipulate. Flowers ebracteolate, blue pink or white. Keel
incurved. Fruit indehiscent. Seeds without an outgrowth at the
hilum, adhering to the pericarp. Gland-dotted plants. (See 153.)
Psoralea L.
Leaves exstipulate. Flowers bracteolate, red yellow or white. Keel
almost straight, gibbous at each side. Fruit dehiscing by two valves.
Seeds with an outgrowth at the hilum. Silky-hairy shrubs. Leaves
simple, sessile. Flowers usually in pairs in the axils of the leaves. —
Species 8. South Africa. . . . . . . **Coelidium** Vog.

163. Leaves simple and undivided or unifoliolate, usually exstipulate. . 164
Leaves digitate, with 3, rarely 5—7 leaflets, usually stipulate. . . 171

164. Calyx-lobes distinctly unequal, the 1—3 lowest usually narrower than
the rest 165
Calyx-lobes about equal 169

165. Petals adnate at the base to the staminal tube, yellow; wings auricled
at the base; keel with a blunt spur at each side. Ovules 2. Shrubs
clothed with long hairs. Leaves stalked, linear. Flowers axillary.
Bracteoles leaf-like. — Species 1. South Africa (Cape Colony).
Walpersia Harv.
Petals free from the staminal tube 166

166. Petals red, long-clawed, glabrous. Fruit ovate, turgid. Prostrate undershrubs clothed with long reddish-brown hairs. Leaves imbricate sessile, lanceolate. Flowers in short racemes. — Species 1. South Africa (Cape Colony) . . . . . . **Euchlora** Eckl. & Zeyh.
Petals yellow, rarely white or red, but then short-clawed and leaves fascicled 167

167. Leaves in tufts of 3 or more, usually thread-shaped. — Species 150. South Africa . . . . **Aspalathus** L.
Leaves scattered, flat. Petals yellow. Fruit linear or lanceolate, more or less flattened 168

168. Plant hairy. Leaves stalked. — Species 90. . . . **Lotononis** DC·
Plant glabrous. — Species 30. South Africa. Some are used medicinally . . . . **Rafnia** Thunb.

169. Leaves more or less distinctly stalked, narrow, usually thread-shaped. Flowers in racemes, yellow. Fruit linear. Funicle very short. — Species 25. South Africa. . . . . **Lebeckia** Thunb.
Leaves sessile 170

170. Leaves many-nerved, flat, stiff. Calyx 5-cleft, with pungent segments· Corolla yellow; standard villous. Fruit linear or lanceolate, slightly flattened. — Species 15. South Africa. . . . . . **Borbonia** L.
Leaves one- or few-nerved, usually thread-shaped and in tufts. Fruit obliquely-ovate or -lanceolate. Funicle filiform. (See 167.)
Aspalathus L.

171. (163.) Calyx 2-lipped, the upper lip 2-toothed or 2-parted, the lower 3-toothed or 3-parted. Corolla yellow. Fruit linear 172
Calyx not 2-lipped; all segments subequal or the 4 upper ones united in pairs 174

172. Keel longer than the standard and the wings. Calyx deeply two-lipped· Fruit flat, somewhat constricted and with thin partitions between the seeds, not glandular. Undershrubs. Leaves exstipulate. Flowers solitary. Bracteoles small. — Species 4. South Africa.
Dichilus DC.
Keel shorter than the standard. Leaves stipulate. 173

173. Fruit glandular-hairy or viscid, flat, usually constricted between the seeds. Calyx tubular, usually shortly two-lipped. Shrubs or undershrubs. Flowers in spikes or racemes. Bracteoles mostly leaf-like. — Species 12. South Africa. . . . **Melolobium** Eckl. & Zeyh.
Fruit hairy, but not glandular. Calyx deeply two-lipped. Standard suborbicular. Bracteoles usually small. — Species 60. (*Tephrothamnus* Sweet, including *Macrolotus* Harms)
Argyrolobium Eckl. & Zeyh.

174. Calyx-lobes distinctly unequal, the upper 4 united in pairs, the lowest separate and narrow. 175
Calyx-lobes about equal. 177

175. Keel and style straight. Standard spatulate. Bracteoles bristle-like. — Species 3. South Africa. (*Pleiospora* Harv.)

Phaenohoffmannia O. Ktze.

Keel and style curved inwards. Bracteoles none. 176

176. Fruit flattened, repeatedly folded and twisted from side to side. Corolla yellow; keel exceeding the standard. Stigma oblique. Herbs. Flowers in racemes. -- Species 1. South Africa (Cape Colony).

Listia E. Mey.

Fruit slightly flattened or turgid, straight or curved. (See 168.)

Lotononis L.

177. Fruit winged, flat, ovate or oblong, stalked, indehiscent. Petals long-clawed, yellow; keel exceeding the standard. Ovary stalked. Ovules few. Shrubs. Flowers in racemes. — Species 7. South Africa. (*Viborgia* Thunb.) . . . . **Wiborgia** Thunb.

Fruit not winged. Ovules usually numerous. 178

178 Fruit ovate, 1—3-seeded. Corolla white, yellowish, or red; standard with a long claw, clothed with long hairs. Shrubs. Flowers in spikes or heads, without bracteoles. — Species 10. South Africa.

Buchenroedera Eckl. & Zeyh.

Fruit linear, lanceolate, or oblong. 179

179. Seeds with a very short funicle. Fruit linear. Corolla yellow. Shrubs or undershrubs. Leaves exstipulate. Flowers in terminal racemes. (See 169.) . . . . **Lebeckia** Thunb.

Seeds with a long funicle. Fruit flattened or slightly inflated. Leaves usually stipulate. (See 168.) . . . . . . **Lotononis** L.

180. (158.) Ovule 1. Fruit ovate, indehiscent; pericarp adhering to the seed. Gland-dotted plants. Stipules stem-clasping. Corolla blue, rose, or white. Bracteoles none. (See 153.) . . . . . **Psoralea** L.

Ovules 2 or more. 181

181. Calyx 2-lipped. 182

Calyx subequally 5-toothed or 5-cleft. Leaves 1- or 3-foliolate. . 191

182. Calyx deeply 2-lipped. 183

Calyx slightly 2-lipped. Leaves 1—3-foliolate or wanting. 188

183. Leaves reduceed to scales or spines. Spinous shrubs. Calyx and corolla yellow. Fruit oblong or ovate, 1—4-seeded. — Species 6. North Africa; one species (*U. europaeus* L.) also naturalized in South Africa, the Mascarenes, and St. Helena. This species is used as a garden- or hedge-plant and furnishes a dye-stuff, fodder, and a substitute for tea. "Furze." . . . . **Ulex** L.

Leaves digitate, with 2—9 leaflets. 184

184. Leaflets 5—9. Stipules adnate to the leafstalk. Keel beaked; wings cohering at the apex. — Species 10. North and Central Africa. They yield manure, fodder, vegetables, medicaments, and edible seeds which

serve also as a substitute for coffee ; several species are used as orna
mental plants. .   .   .   .   **Lupinus** L.
Leaflets 2—4.   Stipules usually free.   Wings free. 185

185. Leaflets 2 or 4, very rarely 3.   Lateral calyx-lobes much shorter than the
others.   Fruit jointed, bristly or spiny, indehiscent.   Herbs or undershrubs. — Species 3.   Tropical and South Africa.   Used as fodder.
Zornia Gmel.
Leaflets 3.   Fruit not jointed, dehiscing by two valves. 186

186. Fruit covered with glandular tubercles or hairs.   Seeds without an
outgrowth at the hilum.   Corolla yellow ;   keel curved inwards.
Shrubs. — Species 7.   North and Central Africa.   .   **Adenocarpus** DC.
Fruit not glandular, but usually hairy. 187

187. Seeds with an outgrowth at the hilum   Shrubs. — Species 15.   North
Africa.   Some are poisonous or are used as ornamental or medicinal
plants.   (Including *Sarothamnus* Wimm., *Spartocytisus* Webb, and
Teline Medik.) .   .   .   .   **Cytisus** L.
Seeds without an outgrowth at the hilum.   Herbs or undershrubs, rarely
shrubs.   Corolla yellow.   (See 173.)   **Argyrolobium** Eckl. & Zeyh.

188. (182.) Calyx sheath-like, split on one side after flowering.   Corolla
yellow ;   keel and wings adnate below to the staminal tube ;
keel acuminate, curved inwards ;   wings obovate.   Stigma oblique.
Fruit linear.   Seeds without an outgrowth at the hilum.   Shrubs or
trees.   Leaves unifoliolate, without stipules. — Species 1 (*S. junceum*
L., Spanish broom).   North Africa.   Yields fibres and medicaments
and is used as an ornamental plant. .   .   .   .   .   **Spartium** L.
Calyx not sheath-like.   Keel obtuse or free from the staminal tube.   . 189

189. Seeds with an outgrowth at the hilum.   Fruit linear or oblong, flat.
Petals free from the staminal tube.   Shrubs.   (See 187.)   **Cytisus** L.
Seeds without an outgrowth at the hilum. 190

190. Keel distinctly curved inwards ;   wings and keel free from the staminal
tube ;   standard suborbicular.   Fruit linear or oblong, flat, covered
with glandular tubercles or hairs.   Shrubs.   Leaves trifoliolate, with
small stipules.   Flowers in racemes, yellow.   (See 186.)
Adenocarpus DC.
Keel straight or nearly so, blunt, gibbous at each side ;   wings and keel
usually adnate to the staminal tube ;   the former oblong ;   standard
ovate.   Fruit usually inflated.   Shrubs or undershrubs. — Species 40.
North Africa.   Some species yield fibres, dyes, and medicaments, or
serve as ornamental plants.   (Including *Retama* Boiss.)   **Genista** L.

191. (181.) Calyx deeply divided.   Ovary more or less distinctly stalked.
Leaflets minutely toothed.   Stipules adnate to the leaf-stalk.   (See
129.) .   .   .   .   **Ononis** L.
Calyx shortly toothed.   Filaments not broadened above.   Ovary sessile
or nearly so.   Leaflets entire. 192

192. Calyx obscurely toothed, coloured.   Corolla yellow, free from the staminal
tube.   Fruit thickened or winged at the upper suture.   Seeds without
an outgrowth at the hilum.   Spinous shrubs.   Leaves digitate, without
stipules.   Flowers solitary or in fascicles. — Species 3.   North Africa.
Used medicinally. . . . .   **Calycotome** Link
Calyx distinctly toothed.   Corolla red, blue, or white. 193

193. Petals with a long claw, blue or violet ; wings and keel adnate at the
base to the staminal tube.   Fruit oblong, glandular-hairy.   Seeds
without an outgrowth at the hilum.   Spinous shrubs.   Leaves trifoliolate on the young branches, unifoliolate on the older.   Flowers
solitary or in fascicles.   Bracteoles small, leaf-like. — Species 1.
North Africa (Algeria).   Used medicinally. . . . **Erinacea** Boiss.
Petals with a short claw or sessile, free from the staminal tube.   Seeds
with an outgrowth at the hilum.   Unarmed plants.   Leaves trifoliolate.   Flowers in racemes or panicles. 194

194. Keel shorter than the standard.   Corolla red or violet.   Fruit linear,
many-seeded.   Shrubs.   Bracteoles bristle-like. — Species 1.   South
Africa (Cape Colony). . . . . **Hypocalyptus** Thunb.
Keel longer than the standard.   Corolla red or white.   Fruit ovate-
lanceolate, few-seeded.   Undershrubs. — Species 1.   South Africa
(Cape Colony). . . . . **Loddigesia** Sims

195. (148.) Leaves equally pinnate. 196
Leaves unequally pinnate. 197

196. Leaflets 4.   Flowers solitary or in spikes.   Calyx with a long, narrow
tube and unequal lobes.   Corolla yellow or whitish ; keel beaked.
Filaments all united.   Ovules 2—3.   Fruit oblong, inflated, continuous within, indehiscent, ripening beneath the soil.   Stem herbaceous. — Species 1 (*A. hypogaea* L., ground-nut).   Cultivated.
The seeds are edible and yield oil ; the leaves are used as a vegetable
or as fodder. . . . . **Arachis** L.
Leaflets numerous.   Flowers in racemes.   Calyx with a wide tube,
truncate or with subequal lobes.   Keel blunt or somewhat pointed.
Filaments united, excepting one.   Ovules numerous.   Fruit linear,
with transverse partitions. — Species 15.   Tropics to Natal and Egypt.
Some species yield timber, fibre, fodder, or medicaments, or serve as
garden- or hedge-plants. . . . . **Sesbania** Pers.

197. Leaflets 3. 198
Leaflets numerous. 203

198. Leaflets with stipels. 199
Leaflets without stipels. 201

199. Filaments all united.   Corolla red ; standard unappendaged ; keel almost
straight, blunt, shorter than the wings.   Style short and thick.   Flowers
very small.   Twining herbs. — Species 3.   Tropical and South-east
Africa.   Used medicinally. . . . . **Teramnus** Swartz

Filaments united, excepting the uppermost, which is free at least at the base. Standard auricled at the base ; keel curved. Flowers large or rather large. 200

200. Uppermost stamens free at the base, but united with the others at the middle. Corolla red ; keel somewhat shorter than the wings. Twining shrubs. — Species 1. Tropics. . . . . . **Dioclea** H. B. & K.

Uppermost stamens free throughout. Corolla red or yellowish-green ; keel as long as or longer than the wings. — Species 20. Tropics. Some of them yield poisons, medicaments, vegetables, fodder, and dyes, or serve as ornamental plants. (*Stizolobium* P. Br.).

Mucuna Adans.

201. Stipules free, stem-clasping, Corolla red, blue, or white ; keel blunt. Ovule 1. Fruit ovate, indehiscent. Gland-dotted plants. (See 153.)

Psoralea L.

Stipules adnate to the leaf-stalk. Corolla red or yellow ; keel usually beaked. Ovules 2 or more. 202

202. Leaflets toothed. Calyx with a short tube and subequal segments. Fruit dehiscing by two valves, usually terete. (See 129.) . **Ononis** L.

Leaflets entire. Calyx with a thread-shaped tube and unequal segments, four of which are connate. Corolla yellow. Ovules 2—3. Base of the style persistent. Fruit flat, separating in two joints or indehiscent. Herbs. Flowers usually intermixed with feathery bristles. — Species 5. Tropical and South Africa. . . . . . **Stylosanthes** Swartz

203. (197.) Stem woody. Corolla white or red ; wings free. Stamens diadelphous at the base, at first monadelphous at the middle. Ovary stalked. Style hairy at the apex. Fruit flat. — Species 1 (*R. Pseudacacia* L.). Naturalized in North Africa. Yields timber and medicaments and is used as an ornamental plant. The bark and the leaves are poisonous.

Robinia L.

Stem herbaceous. Corolla blue, yellow, or whitish. Ovary sessile. . 204

204. Filaments united, excepting one, or all united into a sheath split above. Wings free. Fruit oblong or ovate, flat or constricted between the seeds. — Species 2. North Africa. They yield medicaments (liquorice), dyes, and material for papermaking. . . **Glycyrrhiza** L.

Filaments all united into a closed tube. Wings slightly adhering to the keel. Style glabrous. Fruit linear, subterete. — Species 1. North Africa (Algeria). Used as an ornamental, medicinal, or fodder-plant. "Goats rue." . . . . **Galega** L.

205. (147.) Leaves abruptly pinnate. [Especially tribe VICIEAE.] . . 206

Leaves imparipinnate, digitate, unifoliolate, simple, or wanting. . . 220

206. Calyx distinctly two-lipped, the upper lip entire or shortly 2-toothed, the lower one entire, 3-toothed, or 3-parted. Corolla yellow ; standard suborbicular. Fruit jointed. Flowers in racemes. 207

Calyx equally or subequally toothed or divided, or entire. 210

207. Bracts very large, imbricate, hiding the flowers and fruits. Bracteoles none. Flowers very small. Filaments all united. Ovules 2. Herbs. Stipules produced at the base into a spur-like appendage. — Species 9. Central Africa. . . . . **Geissaspis** Wight & Arn.
Bracts not hiding the flowers, usually small and deciduous. Bracteoles present. . . . . 208.

208. Fruit enclosed by the enlarged calyx. Filaments all united. Ovules more than two. — Species 30. Tropical and South-east Africa. (*Damapana* Adans., including *Kotschya* Endl.) . . . . . . **Smithia** Ait.
Fruit much exceeding the calyx. 209

209. Ovary sessile. Uppermost stamen free. Keel obtuse. Fruit ring-shaped or spirally twisted, flat, glabrous except at the shortly spinous sutures, 2-valved. Herbs. Leaves with 2—4 pairs of leaflets. Stipules spurred at the base. Bracts not spurred. — Species 1. West Africa. . . . . **Cyclocarpa** Afz.
Ovary stalked. Fruit straight, curved, or spirally twisted; in the latter case covered with glandular hairs. — Species 60. Tropical and South Africa. Some species (especially the ambatch, *A. Elaphroxylon* Taub.) yield cork-wood, fibre, and medicaments. (Including *Herminiera* Guill. & Perr.) . . . . **Aeschynomene** L.

210. Style hairy, usually bearded lengthwise. Fruit more or less flattened, 1-celled, 2-valved. Seeds with an outgrowth near the hilum. Herbs. Bracteoles rudimentary or wanting. 211
Style glabrous. 214

211. Staminal tube obliquely truncate at its mouth. 212
Staminal tube evenly truncate. 213

212. Style bearded on the inner face. Flowers small. Corolla bluish-white; keel somewhat pointed. Uppermost stamen free. Ovary almost sessile. Ovules 2. Seeds flat. — Species 3. North Africa; also cultivated in northern Central Africa. The seeds of *L. esculenta* Moench (lentils) are used as food, for the preparation of starch, and in medicine. (Under *Ervum* L.) . . . . **Lens** Gren. & Godr.
Style hairy all round or on the back only; in the latter case flowers large or middle-sized. Seeds globose or slightly flattened. — Species 40. North and East Africa; some species also naturalized in South Africa and the Mascarene Islands. They yield fodder, edible fruits and seeds (especially beans from *V. Faba* L.), and medicaments; some are used as ornamental plants. "Vetch." (Including *Ervum* L. and *Faba* Tourn.) . . . . **Vicia** L.

213. Style-apex compressed laterally, with the margins bent upwards, hence grooved above. Ovary subsessile. Ovules more than 2. Corolla white or red; keel blunt. Uppermost stamens free at the base. Leaves with 1—3 pairs of leaflets. (See 141.). . . . **Pisum** L.
Style-apex compressed dorsally, with the margins straight or bent downwards. (See 128.) . . . . **Lathyrus** L.

214. Stamens 9. Calyx-teeth very short. Corolla white or pink; standard adhering to the staminal tube at its base; wings oblong, shorter than the keel. Shrubs or undershrubs. Leaves ending in a bristle. Bracteoles present. — Species 6. Tropical and South Africa. Several species (especially *A. praecatorius* L.) yield fibres, poisonous ornamental seeds (crab-eyes), and medicaments. . . . . **Abrus** L.
Stamens 10. 215

215. Connective of the stamens ending in a small point, a gland, or a tuft of hairs. Keel gibbous or spurred on each side. Fruit transversely chambered, opening by two valves. Herbs undershrubs or shrubs, clothed with appressed hairs fixed at the middle. Bracteoles none. — Species 320. Tropical, South, and North-east Africa. Several species yield a dye (indigo), or are used in medicine or as ornamental plants.
Indigofera L.
Connective without an appendage. 216

216. Fruit indehiscent, not jointed. Calyx-teeth obscure or wanting. Standard auricled at the base; petals of the keel free. Alternate filaments with a scale at the base. Trees. Leaflets alternate. — Species 1. Madagascar. . . . . **Xanthocercis** Baill.
Fruit dehiscent or jointed. Herbs, undershrubs, or shrubs. . . . 217

217. Fruit jointed, dehiscing on one side or indehiscent. Corolla yellow; standard orbicular. Stamens usually all united. (See 209.)
Aeschynomene L.
Fruit not jointed, dehiscing by two valves. 218

218. Fruit transversely septate. Bracteoles bristle-like, deciduous. Uppermost stamen free. (See 196.). . . . . . . **Sesbania** Pers.
Fruit longitudinally septate or 1-celled. Wings adhering to the keel . 219

219. Fruit 1-celled, compressed. Petals with a short claw. Herbs. Leaves ending in a bristle or a tendril. Bracteoles none. (See 212.). **Vicia** L.
Fruit 2-celled, rarely 1-celled but then turgid. — Species 70. North and East Africa to Transvaal and the Cape Verde Islands. Several species yield fodder, tragacanth-gum, manna-like exudations, or edible seeds which are also used as a substitute for coffee. (Including *Acanthyllis* Pomel, *Erophaca* Boiss., and *Phaca* L.) . . . **Astragalus** L.

220. (205.) Leaves unifoliolate, simple, or wanting. 221
Leaves digitate or pinnate, with 3 or more leaflets 251

221. Leaves exstipulate or wanting 222
Leaves stipulate. 224

222. Branches leaf-like. Leaves usually wanting. Trees. Corolla red. Fruit turgid, indehiscent. — Species 5. Madagascar. They yield timber. (Including *Neobaronia* Bak.) . . . . . . **Phylloxylon** Baill.
Branches not leaf-like. Leaves present. Shrubs. Corolla yellow. Fruit flat, dehiscing by two valves. Seeds with an outgrowth near the hilum. 223

223. Flowers in heads surrounded by large imbricate bracts. Lowest calyx-lobe very large, petaloid. Standard ovate or oblong ; wings oblong. (See 157.) . . . . **Liparia** L.
     Flowers solitary or in racemes, umbels, or heads with small or medium-sized bracts. Lowest calyx-lobe equalling or slightly exceeding the others. Standard suborbicular ; wings obovate. Bracteoles bristle-like. (See 157.). . . . . **Priestleya** DC.

224. Stem herbaceous or woody at the base only. 225
     Stem woody throughout. 241

225. Uppermost stamen united with the others at least in its lower half. . 226
     Uppermost stamen free from the others throughout or at the base. . 229

226. Ovule 1. Ovary sessile. Style slender. Calyx-teeth long and pointed. Petals shortly clawed. Fruit enclosed by the calyx, ovate, indehiscent. Flowers 1—3 in the axils of the leaves. — Species 6. South Africa (Cape Colony). . . . . **Hallia** Thunb.
     Ovules 2 or more. Fruit dehiscing by two valves. 227

227. Style bearded. Ovary more or less distinctly stalked. Seeds with an aril. Leaves reduced to the broadened or tendril-bearing petiole. (See 128.) . . . . **Lathyrus** L.
     Style glabrous. Leaves unifoliolate. 228

228. Style short and broad. Ovary sessile. Petals red, long-clawed. Fruit compressed. Leaflets entire. Stipules awl-shaped. Flowers very small, in axillary racemes. — Species 5. Central Africa to Transvaal.
                                                    Microcharis Benth.
     Style awl-shaped. Ovary more or less distinctly stalked. Calyx deeply divided. Petals short-clawed. Leaflets toothed. Stipules adnate to the leaf-stalk. Flowers 1—3 in the axils of the leaves. (See 129.)
                                                              Ononis L.

229. Uppermost stamen united with the others in the middle, at least when young, free at the base, later sometimes free throughout. . . . 230
     Uppermost stamen free from the base or nearly from the base. . . 234

230. Fruit jointed. 231
     Fruit not jointed. 232

231. Upper calyx-lobes separate. Wings small ; standard subsessile. Ovary stalked. Ovules 1—3. Leaflets without stipels. Flowers in axillary, few-flowered racemes, with small bracteoles. — Species 5. Nileland and Island of Socotra. . . . . **Taverniera** DC.
     Upper calyx-lobes more or less united. Wings oblong, adhering to the keel. Ovules 2 or more. Leaflets usually with stipels. — Species 40. Tropical and South Africa. Some are used as ornamental, medicinal, or textile plants. (*Meibomia* Moehr.). . . . **Desmodium** Desv.

232. Flowers very small, in pairs in the axils of the leaves, with minute bracteoles. Fruit oblong, with a membranous pericarp, indehiscent. Leaflets without stipels. — Species 2. South Africa to Angola.
                                                        Sylitra E. Mey.

Flowers not very small, in usually terminal or leaf-opposed racemes. Fruit with a more or less herbaceous pericarp, dehiscing by two valves.

233

233. Flowers with rather large bracteoles, violet. Ovary shortly stalked. Stigma penicillate. Fruit 4-winged, septate. Stem twining. Leaflets with stipels. Stipules spurred. — Species 4. Tropics. The roots and the fruits are used as vegetables. (*Botor* Adans.) **Psophocarpus** Neck.
Flowers without bracteoles. Ovary sessile. Fruit flat. Leaflets without stipels, usually with numerous parallel side-nerves. — Species 130. Some of them yield dyes, poisons, and medicaments. (*Cracca* L., including *Pogonostigma* Boiss. and *Requienia* DC.) **Tephrosia** Pers.

234. Connective of the stamens ending in a small point, a gland, or a tuft of hairs. Keel straight or slightly curved. Fruit with transverse partitions. Plants clothed with appressed hairs fixed by the middle. . 235
Connective without an appendage. Hairs rarely affixed by the middle.

236

235. Keel beaked. Anthers bearded at base and apex. Style boat-shaped below. Ovules 4—6. Fruit short-stalked, turgid. (See 151.)
Rhynchotropis Harms
Keel blunt or somewhat pointed, gibbous or spurred on each side. Style thread-shaped. Fruit sessile or nearly so. (See 215.) **Indigofera** L.

236. Ovule 1. 237
Ovules 2 or more. 238

237. Leaflets with stipels. Flowers in racemes, with broad bracteoles. Calyx-lobes narrow, subequal. Fruit dehiscing by two valves. — Species 2. Madagascar. .   .   .   . **Leptodesmia** Benth.
Leaflets without stipels. Leaves gland-dotted. Fruit indehiscent ; pericarp adnate to the seed. (See 153.) .   .   .   . **Psoralea** L.

238. Ovules 2. Corolla usually yellow. 239
Ovules 3 or more. Corolla usually red. 240

239. Seeds oblong, without an outgrowth at the hilum ; hilum linear, the funicle affixed at its apex. Upper calyx-lobes separate or shortly united. Standard oblong or obovate. Erect or decumbent, rarely twining plants. — Species 55. Tropical and South Africa. The roots of one species are used in making beer. .   .   .   .   . **Eriosema** DC.
Seeds orbicular or reniform, with a more or less distinct outgrowth at the hilum ; hilum orbicular or oblong, the funicle affixed at or nearly in the middle. Upper calyx-lobes more or less united. Standard orbicular or obovate. Twining or decumbent, more rarely erect plants. — Species 100. Tropical and South Africa and Egypt. (*Dolicholus* Medik.)
Rhynchosia Lour.

240. Calyx-lobes long, stiff, very unequal, the two upper ones united high up. Style thread-shaped, glabrous. Fruit jointed, indehiscent. Leaves unifoliolate, usually stipellate. Stipules membranous. Flowers small,

in racemes, with bracteoles. — Species 9. Tropical and South Africa. (*Fabricia* Scop.). . . . . **Alysicarpus** Neck.

Calyx-lobes subequal. Style flattened, bearded towards the apex. Fruit not jointed, dehiscing by two valves. Seeds with a small aril. Leaves reduced to the broadened or tendril-bearing petiole. Stipules leaf-like. Flowers without bracteoles. (See 128.) . **Lathyrus** L..

241. (224.) Filaments all united into a tube split on one or on both sides, Bracteoles present. 242

Filaments united into a tube, excepting one which is free, at least at the base. 240

242. Ovary sessile. Ovules numerous. Standard suborbicular. Fruit jointed. Seeds oblong. Shrubs, usually erect. Flowers in few-flowered racemes. — Species 10. Tropics. (*Diphaca* Lour., including *Arthro·carpum* Balf. f.) . . . . **Ormocarpum** Beauv.

Ovary stalked. Ovules 2—3. Anthers basifixed. Fruit not jointed, indehiscent. Seeds reniform. Trees or climbing shrubs. Flowers in cymes arranged in many-flowered raceme- or panicle-like inflorescences. — Species 65. Tropical and South-east Africa. Some species yield timber (Senegal-ebony) and gum-resin. (*Amerimnon* P.Br., including *Ecastaphyllum* Rich.) . . . . **Dalbergia** L. f.

243. Uppermost stamen united with the others in the middle, at least when young. 244

Uppermost stamen free throughout. 245

244 Fruit jointed, indented at one or at both sutures. Leaflets usually with stipels. (See 231.). . . . . **Desmodium** Desv.

Fruit not jointed, very thinly or not septate, opening by two valves. Standard clawed, suborbicular. Ovary sessile. Stigma usually hairy. Leaflets usually with numerous parallel side-nerves and without stipels. Bracteoles none. (See 233.) . . . . **Tephrosia** Pers.

245. Connective of the stamens ending in a gland, a point, or a tuft of hairs. Keel straight or slightly curved. Fruit transversely septate. Shrubs with appressed hairs fixed by the middle. Bracteoles none. . . 246

Connective without an appendage. Hairs rarely fixed by the middle. . 247

246. Fruit separating into joints. Petals red, clawed. Ovules numerous. Leafstalk not jointed at the apex. — Species 1. Mascarene Islands.

Bremontiera DC.

Fruit not jointed, dehiscing by two valves. Standard sessile or short-clawed; keel gibbous or spurred on each side. (See 215.) **Indigofera** L.

247. Bracteoles present. Trees. Petals yellow, more rarely white marked with violet ; those of the keel free or slightly cohering. Ovules 2—4. Fruit compressed, more or less winged, indehiscent. — Species 15. Tropical and South Africa. Several species yield timber (rose-wood) and a resin (kino) used for tanning and dyeing and for medicinal purposes, also edible fruits and seeds. . . . . **Pterocarpus** L.

Bracteoles wanting. Shrubs. 248

S

248. Ovule 1. Petals blue, red, or white ; standard short-clawed ; keel
curved. Fruit ovate, indehiscent ; pericarp adhering to the seed.
Gland-dotted plants. Stipules stem-clasping. (See 153.) **Psoralea** L.
Ovules 2 or more. 249
249. Ovules 3 or more. Petals red. Fruit subterete, constricted between
the seeds, indehiscent. Spinous shrubs. Racemes with the rachis
ending in a spine. — Species 1. Egypt and Nubia. The resinous
exudations (Persian manna) are used for food and in medicine.

Alhagi Desv.

Ovules 2. Petals red or yellow ; standard auricled at base. Fruit
dehiscing by two valves. 250
250. Fruit compressed. Seeds with a linear hilum. (See 239.) **Eriosema** DC.
Fruit turgid. Seeds with a short hilum. — Species 5. Tropical and
South-east Africa. Used for dyeing and in medicine. (*Moghania*
St. Hil.) . . . . **Flemingia** Roxb.
251. (220.) Leaflets 3. 252
Leaflets 4 or more 330
252. Leaves digitate. 253
Leaves pinnate. 264
253. Uppermost stamen united with the others into a tube or sheath. Ovules
numerous. Bracteoles bristle-like. 254
Uppermost stamen free from the others, at least at the base. . . . 257
254. Filaments united into a closed tube. Seeds with an outgrowth at the
hilum. Herbs or hairy shrubs. 255
Filaments united into a sheath split above. Seeds without an outgrowth
at the hilum. Glabrous undershrubs, shrubs, or trees. 256
255. Calyx-lobes unequal, the upper approaching in pairs. Standard spatulate ;
wings obliquely ovate. Anthers slightly unequal. Fruit ovate-
lanceolate, dehiscing by two valves. Tall shrubs with brownish
hairs. Flowers in head-like spikes. (See 175.)

Phaenohoffmannia O. Ktze.

Calyx-lobes subequal. Standard ovate or oblong ; wings narrow ; petals
of the keel scarcely cohering. Fruit linear or lanceolate, dehiscing
at the upper suture. Decumbent herbs. Flowers very small, solitary
or in short racemes. — Species 1. Central Africa. . . **Rothia** Pers.
256. Keel longer than the standard. Fruit ovate-lanceolate, few-seeded.
Undershrubs. (See 194.) . . . . **Loddigesia** Sims
Keel shorter than the standard. Fruit linear, many-seeded. Shrubs
or trees. (See 194.) . . . . **Hypocalyptus** Thunb.
257. Uppermost stamen united with the others in the middle, at least when
young. 258
Uppermost stamen free. Bracteoles absent. 260
258. Petals, at least the four lower ones, adnate below to the staminal tube.
Fruit not jointed, scarcely dehiscent. Herbs. Leaflets usually

toothed. Stipules adnate to the leafstalk. Flowers solitary or in spikes, heads, or umbels. Bracteoles absent. (See 138.) **Trifolium** L.
Petals free from the staminal tube. Ovary sessile. Fruit flat. Leaflets entire. 259

259. Flowers very small, solitary or in pairs in the axils of the leaves, with small bracteoles. Petals yellowish. Fruit oblong ; pericarp membranous. Undershrubs. (See 232.) . . . . . **Sylitra** E. Mey.
Flowers not very small, in racemes, without bracteoles. Petals usually red. Fruit dehiscing by two valves ; pericarp more or less herbaceous. (See 233.) . . . . **Tephrosia** Pers.

260. Connective of the stamens ending in a gland, a tuft of hairs, or a small point. Keel gibbous or spurred on each side. Fruit transversely septate, dehiscing by two valves. Plants with appressed hairs fixed by the middle. (See 215.) . . . . **Indigofera** L.
Connective without an appendage. 261

261. Ovule 1. Keel curved. Fruit ovate, indehiscent ; pericarp adhering to the seed. Gland-dotted plants. (See 153.) . . . **Psoralea** L.
Ovules 2 or more. 262

262. Ovules 2. Petals free from the staminal tube ; standard auricled at base. Fruit turgid, 1-celled, 2-valved. Shrubs. (See 250.)
Flemingia Roxb.
Ovules 3 or more, rarely 2, but then lower petals adnate to the staminal tube. Wings exceeding the keel. Herbs. Stipules adnate to the leafstalk. 263

263. Petals, at least the four lower ones, adnate to the staminal tube. Keel blunt. Ovules 2—8. Fruit scarcely dehiscent. (See 138.)
Trifolium L.
Petals free from the staminal tube, red. Keel somewhat pointed, curved. Ovary sessile. Ovules numerous. Fruit dehiscing by two valves. Flowers solitary. (See 153.) . . . . . . **Parochetus** Hamilt.

264. (252.) Leaflets with stipels. [Especially tribe PHASEOLEAE.] . . 265
Leaflets without stipels. 310

265. Stem herbaceous or woody at the base only. 266
Stem woody throughout. 303

266. Uppermost stamen united with the others from the base. Flowers small, red, in racemes, with the rachis not thickened. — Species 20. Tropical and South-east Africa ; one species (*G. hispida* Maxim., soybean) only cultivated. The latter yields edible oily seeds. . **Glycine** L.
Uppermost stamen free or almost so, or united with the others in the middle only. 267

267. Uppermost stamen, at least when young, free at the base, but united with the others in the middle. 268
Uppermost stamen free from the base or nearly so. 272

268. Flowers in racemes, the rachis of which is thickened at the insertion of the pedicels. Bracteoles present. Wings usually free from the keel. Fruit not jointed, opening in two valves. 269

Flowers in racemes with the rachis not thickened, or in fascicles, or solitary. Wings adhering to the keel. Fruit compressed. . . . 271

269. Fruit 4-angled or 4-winged. Seeds oblong. Stigma villous. Corolla violet. Bracteoles rather large, falling off tardily. Stipules spurred. (See 233.) . . . . **Psophocarpus** Neck.

Fruit 2—3-angled or 2-winged.. Stigma small. Bracteoles small, falling off early. Stipules small. 270

270. Calyx-lobes very unequal, the upper much larger than the lower. Seeds ovate or orbicular. — Species 5. Tropical and South Africa. The seeds of several species are eaten and used for dyeing and in medicine.

Canavalia Adans.

Calyx-lobes not very unequal, the upper united higher up, but not considerably larger than the lower. Seeds oblong. — Species 1. East Africa. . . . . **Pueraria** DC.

271. Fruit more or less distinctly jointed. Bracteoles usually present. (See 231.) . . . . **Desmodium** Desv.

Fruit not jointed, opening by two valves. Stigma usually penicillate. Flowers in terminal or leaf-opposed racemes. Bracteoles wanting. (See 233.) . . . . **Tephrosia** Pers.

272. Style hairy above. 273

Style glabrous or hairy at the base only, sometimes with a hairy stigma. 287

273. Flowers solitary or in fascicles or racemes with the rachis not thickened at the insertion of the pedicels. Keel curved. Ovules numerous. Fruit linear. 274

Flowers in racemes, the rachis of which is thickened at the insertion of the pedicels. 277

274. Calyx tubular ; upper lobes united high up. Corolla white, blue, or violet ; wings oblong, adhering to the much shorter and pointed keel. Ovary stalked. Style broadened above, bearded lengthwise. — Species 5. Tropics. Used as medicinal, dyeing, and ornamental plants.

Clitoria L.

Calyx campanulate. Wings obovate. Ovary almost sessile. . . . 275

275. Upper calyx-teeth united to the middle. Corolla red or violet ; standard equalling the wings, spurred or gibbous on the back ; keel not beaked. Style-apex broadened, hairy round the stigma. Fruit flat. Seeds without an outgrowth at the hilum. Climbing herbs. — Species 1. Naturalized in West Africa. Used as a medicinal and ornamental plant. (*Bradburya* Rafin., under *Clitoria* L.) . . **Centrosema** DC.

Upper calyx-teeth united wholly or for the greatest part. Standard not spurred at the back, but auricled at the base. Style-apex slightly or not thickened. Fruit more or less inflated. Seeds with an outgrowth near the hilum. 276

276. Style with a crown of hairs beneath the large ovoid stigma. Wings longer than the keel, but shorter than the standard. Stipules long-spurred. — Species 1. Southern West Africa (Congo).

Vignopsis De Wild.

Style bearded on the inner face towards the top, or penicillate round the small terminal stigma. Wings adhering to the keel. — Species 60. Tropical and South Africa. Some species yield fodder and edible fruits or seeds, or serve as ornamental plants. . . . **Dolichos** L.

277. Keel spirally twisted. Ovary surrounded by a cupular disc. Stigma lateral or oblique. 278

Keel more or less curved inwards, but not spiral. 279

278. Keel with a long spur ; wings free. Ovary stalked. Ovules 2—3. Style with a pointed dorsal appendage at the apex. Flowers violet or whitish, without bracteoles. — Species 3. Central Africa. One species (*Ph. venenosum* Balf., Calabar bean) has poisonous seeds used in ordeals and medicinally. . . . . . . **Physostigma** Balf.

Keel without a spur, but sometimes with two gibbosities ; wings adhering to the keel. Ovary almost sessile. Ovules numerous. Style without a dorsal appendage at the apex. — Species 20. Tropical and South-east Africa ; one species (*Ph. vulgaris* L.) cultivated also in extra-tropical regions. The fruits and seeds of some species (beans) are eaten and used for preparing starch and medicaments, those of others are poisonous. Several species are used as ornamental or fodder-plants.

Phaseolus L.

279. Stigma lateral, situated beneath the apex of the style. 280

Stigma terminal, but sometimes oblique. 283

280. Style-apex bent down towards the stigma. Stigma globose, blunt or notched. Wings oblong, equalling the blunt keel. Fruit flat. Leaf-lets usually toothed. — Species 2. Cultivated in the tropics. They yield fibre used for rope-making, and edible roots and seeds, from which also starch and medicaments are prepared. (*Cacara* Thouars).

Pachyrrhizus Rich.

Style-apex bent back. Fruit turgid. 281

281. Fruit subglobular, 1—2-seeded, ripening under ground. Ovules 2—3. Stigma 2-lobed. Corolla yellow ; keel blunt. Creeping herbs. Race-mes 1—3-flowered. — Species 1 (*V. subterranea* Thouars). Culti-vated in Tropical and South Africa. Yields edible fruits and oily seeds. . . . . **Voandzeia** Thouars

Fruit linear, several- or many-seeded, ripening above ground. Ovules several or many. 282

282. Calyx deeply 4-cleft, with acuminate segments. Keel pointed ; wings auricled. Undershrubs with erect or ascending branches. — Species 1. South Africa. (Under *Vigna* Savi). . . . . . **Otoptera** DC.

Calyx 4—5-toothed or 5-cleft. Keel blunt or beaked. — Species 65. Tropical and South Africa and Egypt. Some species yield fibre used for rope-making, and edible fruits or seeds. (Including *Liebrechtsia* De Wild.) . . . . **Vigna** Savi

283. Stigma very oblique. Style-apex wedge-shaped, hairy. Calyx-teeth very short and broad. Keel blunt. Fruit linear. — Species 5. Central and South-east Africa. (Under *Vigna* Savi) . **Sphenostylis** E. Mey. Stigma slightly oblique or straight. 284

284. Upper lip of the calyx entire. Style bearded lengthwise. Fruit oblong, 2—4-seeded. . . . . 285 Upper lip of the calyx notched. 286

285. Keel almost straight, blunt. Standard oblong, straight, folded over the other petals. Corolla yellow-green. Style flat at base, hairy above. — Species 1. South Africa. (Under *Dolichos* L.) **Chloryllis** E. Mey. Keel sharply bent upwards, pointed. Standard orbicular, bent back, expanded. Corolla white or red. Style flat and bearded above. — Species 1 (*L. vulgaris* Savi). Tropical and South-east Africa ; also cultivated in Egypt. It yields edible fruits and seeds, fodder, and medicaments, and serves also as an ornamental plant. (Under *Dolichos* L.) . . . . **Lablab** Savi

286. Ovules 2. Style flattened and hairy above. Keel pointed. Upper calyx-teeth united to about the middle. Glandular plants. — Species 10. Central Africa. (Under *Dolichos* L.) . **Adenodolichos** Harms Ovules 3 or more. Style thread-shaped. Keel shortly beaked. Gland-less plants. (See 276.) . . . . **Dolichos** L.

287. (272.) Ovules 1—2. . . . . 288 Ovules 3 or more. 295

288. Connective of the stamens produced into a gland, a tuft of hairs, or a short point. Calyx-teeth subequal. Corolla usually red ; keel gibbous or spurred on each side. Fruit more or less turgid, with transverse partitions. Plants clothed with appressed hairs fixed by the middle. Bracteoles none. (See 215.) . . . **Indigofera** L. Connective without an appendage. Fruit more or less compressed . 289

289. Ovule 1. Calyx-teeth about equal, bristle-like. Keel obtuse. Fruit enclosed by the calyx. Bracts broad. (See 237.) **Leptodesmia** Benth. Ovules 2, rarely ovule 1, but then calyx-teeth unequal (the upper ones more or less united). 290

290. Bracteoles present. . . . . 291 Bracteoles absent. Corolla usually yellow ; standard auricled at the base. 293

291. Style hairy at the base, bent almost at a right angle above the middle. Ovary surrounded at the base by a cupular disc. Calyx-teeth and bracteoles ending in a club-shaped gland. Corolla spotted with violet. Fruit 1-celled. Leaflets toothed. — Species 5. Central Africa. (Under *Rhynchosia* Lour.) . . . . . **Eminia** Taub. Style glabrous, slightly curved. Fruit transversely chambered. . . 292

292. Corolla yellowish ; keel as long as the wings ; standard not auricled.
Flowers two or several together in the axils of the leaves, subsessile.
Fruit ripening under ground. — Species 1. West Africa. Cultivated
for its edible seeds. . . . .   **Kerstingiella** Harms
    Corolla red ; keel shorter than the wings ; standard slightly auricled.
Flowers in axillary racemes or false-racemes. Fruit ripening above
ground. (See 266.) . . . .   **Glycine** L.

293. Calyx-lobes very unequal. Standard oblong or ovate ; wings shorter
than the keel, auricled at the base. Style downy below. — Species 4.
Tropics. . . . .   **Cylista** Ait.
    Calyx-lobes about equal, but the two upper ones sometimes more or less
united. 294

294. Seeds oblong, without an outgrowth at the hilum ; hilum linear, the
funicle affixed at its apex. Upper calyx-teeth free or shortly united.
Standard oblong or obovate. Erect or decumbent, rarely twining
plants. (See 239.) . . . .   **Eriosema** DC.
    Seeds orbicular or reniform, with a more or less distinct outgrowth at the
hilum ; hilum orbicular or oblong, the funicle affixed in the middle.
Upper calyx-teeth more or less united. Standard orbicular or obovate.
Twining or decumbent, more rarely erect plants. (See 239.)
                                         Rhynchosia Lour.

295. (287.) Calyx entire or obscurely toothed, gibbous at the base. Corolla
yellow or red. Ovary surrounded at the base by a tubular disc.
Style broadened in the middle. Fruit flattened, 2-valved. Twining
herbs. Bracteoles present. — Species 1. South and East Africa and
Madagascar. . . . .   **Dumasia** DC.
    Calyx distinctly toothed. 296

296. Upper sepals wholly united ; hence calyx 4-toothed or 4-cleft. Twining
herbs. 297
    Upper sepals more or less separate ; calyx 5-toothed or 5-cleft. . . 298

297. Calyx-lobes short. Corolla red ; keel shorter than the wings. Rachis
of the inflorescence not thickened at the insertion of the pedicels.
Bracts striate. — Species 1. Mountains of Central Africa.
                              Shuteria Wight & Arn.
    Calyx-lobes long. Corolla yellow ; keel as long as or longer than the
wings. Rachis of the inflorescence thickened at the insertion of the
pedicels. Bracts bristle-like. — Species 2. East Africa to Natal
and Mascarene Islands. . . . .   **Galactia** P. Browne

298. Wings free from the keel. Flowers small, red. Leaflets large. . . 299
    Wings adhering to the keel. 300

299. Fruit septate between the seeds, oblong. Seeds globose. Ovules 3—5.
Style thickened below. Standard auricled at the base. — Species 1.
German South-west Africa. . . . . .   **Neorautanenia** Schinz
    Fruit not septate between the seeds, flat, with transversely veined valves.
Seeds reniform. Style awl-shaped. Upper calyx-lobes united high up.

Hairy plants. — Species 5. Central and South-east Africa (*Anarth-rosyne* E. Mey.) . . . . **Pseudarthria** Wight & Arn.

300. Bracteoles wanting. Keel gibbous or spurred on each side. Connective ending in a gland, a point, or a tuft of hairs. Plants with appressed hairs fixed by the middle. (See 215.) . . . . . **Indigofera** L.
Bracteoles present. 301

301. Standard spurred or gibbous at the apex of the claw. Style broadened above. Fruit flat. Seeds oblong. Stem twining. Flowers large. Bracteoles larger than the bracts. (See 275.) **Centrosema** DC.
Standard neither spurred nor gibbous. Flowers small or medium-sized. 302

302. Fruit jointed, flat, usually indehiscent. (See 231.) **Desmodium** Desv.
Fruit not jointed, but septate between the seeds, dehiscing by two valves. Corolla red ; standard auricled at the base ; wings exceeding the keel. Bracts bristle-like. (See 266.) . . . . **Glycine** L.

303. (265.) Uppermost stamen united with the others in the middle. Calyx-lobes blunt and very short. Fruit not jointed, indehiscent. — Species 30. Tropics. Some species yield timber, dyes, fish-poison, and medicaments. . . . . **Lonchocarpus** H. B. & K.
Uppermost stamen free from the base or nearly so, rarely (*Desmodium*) united with the others in the middle, but then calyx-lobes pointed. Fruit jointed or dehiscent. 304

304. Connective of the stamens produced in a gland, a point, or a tuft of hairs. Calyx-teeth subequal. Keel gibbous or spurred on each side. Ovary sessile or nearly so. Fruit transversely septate. Shrubs with appressed hairs fixed by the middle. Bracteoles none. (See 215.)
Indigofera L.
Connective without an appendage. 305

305. Standard with two auricles at the base. 306
Standard without an appendage at the base. 308

306. Calyx-teeth blunt, nearly equal. Corolla usually red ; keel beaked. Bracteoles deciduous. — Species 6. Madagascar and Mascarenes.
Strongylodon Vog.
Calyx-teeth pointed, unequal, the upper united high up. Corolla yellow ; keel blunt. Bracteoles none. 307

307. Standard oblong or ovate ; keel longer than the wings. Ovary and base of the style hairy. Style thread-shaped. Ovules 2. — Species 1. Madagascar. . . . . **Baukea** Vatke
Standard orbicular ; keel somewhat shorter than the wings. Ovary and base of style glabrous or downy. Style thickened in the middle and at the apex. Ovules numerous. — Species 1 (*C. indicus* Spreng., pigeon-pea). Tropics, also cultivated. Yields edible, pea-like fruits and seeds, medicaments, fodder, food for silkworms, and manure.
Cajanus DC.

308. Style bearded above.   Upper calyx-teeth almost entirely united.   Wings
    adhering to the shorter and pointed keel.   Fruit not jointed.   Bracteo-
    les persistent.   (See 274.) . . . .   **Clitoria** L.
    Style glabrous. 309
309. Fruit separating into joints, when ripe.   Flowers usually small.   Wings
    adhering to the keel.   (See 231.) . . . . . .   **Desmodium** Desv.
    Fruit not jointed.   Flowers large.   Wings much shorter than the standard,
    sometimes wanting.   Ovary stalked. — Species 20.   Tropical and
    South Africa.   Several species yield wood, vegetables, and medicaments,
    or serve as ornamental plants. . . . .   **Erythrina** L.
310. (264.) Uppermost stamen united with the others from the base. . . 311
    Uppermost stamen free from the others, at least at the base. . . . 314
311. Ovule 1.   Fruit ovate, not jointed, indehiscent.   Gland-dotted plants.
    Bracteoles absent.   (See 153.) . . . .   **Psoralea** L.
    Ovules 2 or more.   Fruit linear or oblong, dehiscent or separating into
    joints.   312
312. Staminal tube split.   Ovary sessile.   Fruit breaking up into several
    joints.   Shrubs.   Bracteoles persistent.   (See 242.)
                                          Ormocarpum Beauv.
    Staminal tube closed.   Fruit not jointed, opening by two valves.   Herbs
    or undershrubs.   Bracteoles absent. 313
313. Connective of the stamens ending in a small point.   Ovary sessile.   Cor-
    olla red ; keel blunt.   Fruit slightly 4-angled, transversely septate.
    Stipules bristle-like.   Flowers small, in racemes, without bracteoles.
    — Species 2.   Central Africa. . . . .   **Cyamopsis** DC.
    Connective without an appendage.   Ovary stalked.   Calyx deeply
    divided.   Standard suborbicular.   Leaflets minutely toothed.   Stip-
    ules adnate to the leaf-stalk.   (See 129.) . . . . .   **Ononis** L.
314. Bracteoles present.   Calyx-teeth subequal.   Wings short.   Ovary
    stalked.   Ovules few. 315
    Bracteoles absent.   316
315. Keel beaked.   Standard clawed, auricled.   Uppermost stamen free.
    Fruit opening by two valves.   Seeds subglobular.   Twining shrubs.
    Rachis of the raceme thickened at the insertion of the pedicels.   (See
    306.) . . . .   **Strongylodon** Vog.
    Keel not beaked.   Standard scarcely clawed.   Uppermost stamen at
    first united with the others in the middle.   Fruit breaking up into
    several joints.   Seeds reniform.   Erect undershrubs.   (See 231.)
                                          Taverniera DC.
316. Petals, at least the lower ones, adnate to the staminal tube.   Herbs.
    Leaflets usually toothed.   Flowers solitary or in spikes, heads, or
    umbels.   (See 138.) . . . .   **Trifolium** L.
    Petals free from the staminal tube. 317
317. Connective of the stamens produced into a gland, a point, or a tuft of
    hairs.   Keel straight or slightly curved inwards, gibbous or spurred on

each side. Fruit transversely septate. Plants with appressed hairs
fixed by the middle. (See 215.) . . . . **Indigofera** L.
Connective without an appendage. 318

318. Ovule 1. Corolla red, blue, or white ; standard clawed. Fruit ovate,
indehiscent ; pericarp adhering to the seed. Gland-dotted plants.
Stipules stem-clasping, not adnate. Bracts membranous. (See 153.)
Psoralea L.

Ovules 2 or more, rarely ovule 1, but then fruit more or less curved or
coiled, corolla usually yellow, standard almost sessile, and stipules
adnate to the leafstalk. 319

319. Uppermost stamen, at least when young, united with the others in the
middle. Corolla red or white ; standard suborbicular, clawed ; wings
adhering to the keel. Stigma usually hairy. Fruit dehiscing by two
valves. Leaflets entire, usually with numerous parallel side-nerves.
Flowers in terminal or leaf-opposed racemes, more rarely in axillary
racemes or clusters. Bracts distinctly developed. (See 233.)
Tephrosia Pers.

Uppermost stamen free from the base, rarely united with the others
in the middle, but then standard oblong or ovate, sessile or nearly so,
corolla usually yellow, fruit not or tardily dehiscent, leaflets usually
toothed, stipules adnate to the leafstalk, inflorescence axillary, and
bracts minute or wanting. 320

320. Ovules 1—2. 321
Ovules more than 2. 325

321. Calyx-lobes very unequal, the upper two almost wholly united, the
side ones small, the lowest the longest, enlarged after flowering, scarious. Corolla reddish-yellow ; standard auricled at base. Fruit
falcate-ovate, enclosed by the calyx, 1-seeded, 2-valved. Twining
undershrubs. (See 293.) . . . .   **Cylista** Ait.
Calyx-lobes about equal, but the upper ones sometimes more or less united,
not or scarcely enlarged after flowering. 322

322. Fruit dehiscing by two valves, more or less flattened, straight or nearly
so. Upper calyx-teeth usually more or less united. Standard auricled
at base. Leaflets usually entire. 323
Fruit not or very tardily dehiscing, turgid or curved to spiral, exceeding
the calyx. Upper calyx-teeth scarcely or not united. Leaflets usually
toothed. Stipules adnate to the leafstalk.. 324

323. Seeds orbicular or reniform, with a more or less distinct outgrowth at
the hilum ; hilum orbicular or oblong, the funicle attached in the
middle or nearly so. Standard orbicular or obovate. Twining or
decumbent, rarely erect plants. (See 239.) . **Rhynchosia** Lour.
Seeds oblong, without an outgrowth at the hilum ; hilum linear, the
funicle attached at its apex. Upper calyx-teeth not or shortly united.
Standard oblong or obovate. Erect or decumbent, rarely twining
plants. (See 239.) . . . .   **Eriosema** DC.

324. Fruit straight, globular or ovoid, thick, wrinkled. Flowers in slender, more or less spike-like racemes, yellow, rarely white. Herbs. — Species 10. North Africa and Abyssinia ; several species also naturalized in South Africa. Used as fodder or in medicine. **Melilotus** Juss.

Fruit more or less curved (sickle- or kidney-shaped) or spirally coiled, usually flattened. Flowers in short racemes or in heads. — Species 35. North Africa to Abyssinia and South Africa ; several species also naturalized in the Mascarene Islands. Some of them (especially *M. sativa* L.; lucern) are used as fodder, or medicinal plants, and for making paper and brush-wares, others are noxious as burs.

Medicago L.

325. Upper calyx-lobes more or less, sometimes entirely united. Corolla yellow. Standard suborbicular, auricled at base. Fruit linear or oblong, constricted between the seeds, dehiscing by two valves. Leaflets entire, gland-dotted. 326

Upper calyx-lobes not or scarcely united. Standard oblong or obovate. Fruit dehiscing at the upper suture or indehiscent, rarely tardily dehiscing by two valves. Leaflets usually toothed. Stipules adnate to the leafstalk. 328

326. Upper calyx-lobes shortly united. Keel exceeding the wings. Fruit oblong, curved, turgid, 1-celled. Seeds with an outgrowth at the hilum. Viscid, twining herbs or undershrubs. — Species 1. South Africa and Madagascar. . . . . **Fagelia** Neck.

Upper calyx-lobes united for the greater part or entirely. Fruit compressed and transversely septate. 327

327. Fruit oblong, blunt or shortly pointed. Seeds with an outgrowth at the hilum. Herbs or undershrubs. Stipules persistent. Flowers in fascicles or short racemes. — Species 2. Madagascar and Mascarenes. (Under *Atylosia* Wight & Arn.) . **Cantharospermum** Wight & Arn.

Fruit linear, ending in a long point. Seeds without an outgrowth at the hilum. Style broadened in the middle and towards the apex. Erect shrubs or undershrubs. Stipules deciduous, awl-shaped. Flowers in racemes. (See 307.) . . . . **Cajanus** DC.

328. Flowers in long, more or less spike-like racemes. Ovules few. Fruit oblong to globose, thick, straight, indehiscent, 1—3-seeded. Herbs. (See 324.) . . . . **Melilotus** Juss.

Flowers solitary or in short racemes, heads, or umbels. 329

329. Fruit linear or oblong, straight or slightly curved. Herbs. — Species 25. North Africa, Nile-land, and South Africa. *T. foenumgraecum* L. is cultivated for its seeds, which are used as food, fodder, vermin-poison, in medicine, and in the manufacture of cloth ; it is also used as a vegetable. . . . . **Trigonella** L.

Fruit spirally twisted, more rarely sickle- or kidney-shaped. (See 324.)

Medicago L.

330. (251.) Stem herbaceous or woody at the base only. 331
     Stem woody throughout. 347
331. Uppermost stamen united with the others from the base, at least when
     young. 332
     Uppermost stamen free from the others, at least at the base. . . . 336
332. Filaments united into a closed tube, at least when young. Corolla red,
     blue, or white. Fruit dehiscing by two valves. 333
     Filaments united into a sheath split on one or both sides. Corolla yellow,
     sometimes veined with red. Fruit breaking up into joints, more
     rarely indehiscent. 335
333. Stem twining. Leaflets 5—7, stipellate. Bracteoles present. Upper-
     most stamen finally separating from the others. (See 266.)
                                              Glycine L.
     Stem erect or decumbent. Leaflets not stipellate. Bracteoles absent.
     Uppermost stamen remaining united with the others. 334
334. Leaflets 5—7. Stipules bristle-like. Corolla red ; standard sessile ;
     wings free. Connective ending in a short point. Fruit septate.
     (See 313.) . . . . **Cyamopsis** DC.
     ·Leaflets numerous. Stipules semi-sagittate. Corolla blue or white ;
     standard short-clawed ; wings adhering to the keel. Connective
     without an appendage. Fruit 1-celled. (See 204.) . . **Galega** L.
335. Fruit enclosed by the enlarged calyx, folded, with 2 or more flat joints.
     Calyx 2-lipped. (See 208.) . . . . **Smithia** Ait.
     Fruit much exceeding the calyx. Ovary stalked. (See 209.)
                                          Aeschynomene L.
336. Uppermost stamen united with the others in the middle, at least when
     young. 337
     Uppermost stamen free throughout. 339
337. Standard clawed. Wings adhering to the keel. Ovules several or
     many, very rarely only 2. Stigma usually penicillate. Fruit linear,
     rarely oblong or ovate, dehiscing by two valves. Leaflets usually
     with many parallel side-nerves. Flowers white or red, in terminal or
     leaf-opposed racemes, rarely in axillary fascicles or racemes ; in this
     case ovules numerous. Bracteoles absent. (See 233.)
                                          Tephrosia Pers.
     Standard nearly sessile. Wings short. Ovules 1—3. Fruit oblong to
     orbicular, indehiscent, very rarely dehiscing by two valves. Flowers
     in axillary spikes or racemes. 338
338. Calyx-lobes much longer than the tube, feathery. Corolla red ; keel
     adhering to the staminal tube. Fruit enclosed by the calyx, oblong
     or ovate. Unarmed, hairy plants. Stipules connate. — Species 2.
     North Africa. . . . . **Ebenus** L.
     Calyx-lobes as long as or shorter than the tube. Fruit projecting beyond
     the calyx, hemispherical or spirally twisted. — Species 10. North

Africa and Abyssinia. Sainfoin (*O. sativa* Lam.) is cultivated in
various regions for fodder, sometimes also as a medicinal or ornamental
plant. . . . . **Onobrychis** Gaertn.

339. Style bearded lengthwise towards the top. Fruit 2-valved. . . . 340
Style glabrous above or penicillate round the stigma. 343

340. Style thread-shaped, bearded on the outside or all round. Calyx-teeth
subequal. Petals red or white, clawed ; standard exceeding the
wings and the keel. Seeds kidney-shaped, with a filiform funicle.
Flowers in racemes. — Species 40. South Africa to Angola. Some are
used medicinally. (*Coluteastrum* Heist.) . . . . . **Lessertia** DC.
Style flattened, bearded on the inner side. 341

341. Calyx-teeth unequal, the two upper ones united high up. Corolla blue
or white. Seeds without an outgrowth at the hilum. Leaflets usually
stipellate. Bracteoles persistent. (See 274.) . . . **Clitoria** L.
Calyx-teeth about equal. Seeds with a small aril covering the hilum.
Leaflets not stipellate. Bracteoles rudimentary or wanting . . 342

342. Staminal tube obliquely truncate. Keel somewhat pointed. Ovary
almost sessile. Ovules 2. Aril ovate or oblong. Flowers small,
bluish-white. (See 212.) . . . . **Lens** Gren. & Godr.
Staminal tube evenly truncate. Keel shorter than the wings, usually
blunt. Ovules 3 or more. Aril usually linear. (See 128.)

Lathyrus L.

343. Connective of the stamens bearing a gland, a point, or a tuft of hairs.
Fruit transversely septate, 2-valved. Plants with appressed hairs
fixed by the middle. (See 215.) . . . . . **Indigofera** L.
Connective without an appendage. Hairs rarely fixed by the middle . 344

344. Leaflets stipellate, 5—7. Flowers in terminal racemes, without bracteoles.
Fruit jointed, enclosed by the calyx ; joints ovate, slightly flattened.
— Species 1. Central Africa. Used as an ornamental and medicinal
plant. . . . . **Uraria** Desv.
Leaflets not stipellate. Fruit jointed, with orbicular or quadrate flattened
joints, or not jointed. 345

345. Fruit breaking up into joints, flat. Wings clawed, auricled, shorter than
the scarcely clawed standard. Flowers in axillary racemes, with
bristle-like bracteoles. — Species 12. North Africa. Some are used as
fodder- or ornamental plants. . . . . **Hedysarum** L.
Fruit not jointed, usually septate lengthwise. 316

346. Fruit sessile, linear, flat, longitudinally 2-celled, indehiscent, the valves
boat-shaped with a wavy and toothed keel. Hairy herbs. Leaflets
emarginate. Stipules adnate to the leafstalk. Flowers in axillary
spikes or fascicles, bluish or whitish. — Species 1. North Africa and
Abyssinia. . . . . **Biserrula** L.
Fruit not flat and with wavy and toothed valves, tardily dehiscent.
(See 219.) . . . . **Astragalus** L.

347. (330.) Uppermost stamen united with the others from the base into a
      tube usually split in one or two places, rarely (*Dalbergia*) wanting. . 348
      Uppermost stamen free from the others, at least at the base.   .   .   . 354

348. Fruit breaking up into two or more joints, very rarely reduced to a single
      ovate, not winged joint. Calyx usually two-lipped. Corolla yellow or
      white, sometimes with red stripes or veins. Standard suborbicular.
      Erect shrubs. 349
      Fruit not jointed, indehiscent, more or less distinctly winged, rarely
      not winged but curved. Ovules few. Trees or climbing, very rarely
      erect shrubs. 351

349. Fruit enclosed by the enlarged calyx, folded, jointed. Seeds 2 or more,
      reniform or orbicular, flat. Calyx two-lipped. Racemes short.
      Bracteoles persistent. (See 208.) .   .   .   .   . **Smithia** Ait.
      Fruit much exceeding the calyx. 350

350. Joints of the fruit 2 or more, oblong, usually striate. Ovary sessile,
      with several or many ovules. Racemes few-flowered. Bracteoles
      persistent. (See 242.)   .   .   .   .   .   **Ormocarpum** Beauv.
      Joints of the fruit quadrate to semiorbicular, not striate. Ovary usually
      stalked. (See 209.) .   .   .   . **Aeschynomene** L.

351. Staminal tube closed all round. Calyx subtruncate, very shortly or
      obscurely toothed. Wings adhering to the keel. Leaflets opposite
      — Species 15. Tropics. Some are poisonous. (*Deguelia* Aubl.,
      including *Leptoderris* Dunn) .   .   .   . **Derris** Lour.
      Staminal tube split in one or two places. Leaflets usually alternate. . 352

352. Anthers attached by the base, with erect cells opening by a short apical
      slit, or with divergent cells opening lengthwise. Calyx-lobes unequal.
      Ovary stalked. Seeds kidney-shaped. Flowers in copious panicles
      composed of cymes. (See 242.) .   .   .   .   **Dalbergia** L. f.
      Anthers attached by the back, opening by parallel longitudinal slits.
      Fruit more or less oblique or curved. 353

353. Bracteoles persistent. Calyx bell-shaped, obtuse at base. Corolla
      violet ; standard silky outside. Ovary stalked. Ovules 1—2. Fruit
      thick-leathery, crescent-shaped, not winged. Seed 1, kidney-shaped.
      Small spiny trees. — Species 1. West Africa. **Drepanocarpus** G. F. Mey.
      Bracteoles deciduous. Calyx more or less top-shaped at the base. Corolla
      yellow, more rarely white marked with violet ; standard glabrous.
      Ovules 2—6. Fruit membranous or leathery, hardened in the middle,
      more or less distinctly winged. (See 247.) .   .   **Pterocarpus** L.

354. (347.) Uppermost stamen united with the others in the middle, at least
      when young. 355
      Uppermost stamen free throughout. 361

355. Wings free from the keel. Ovules more than two. Fruit 2-valved.
      Leaflets usually with stipels. 356
      Wings adhering to the keel. Leaflets usually without stipels. .   . 357

356. Flowers in axillary racemes, without bracteoles. Corolla white. Ovary
     stalked, not surrounded by a disc. Style hairy at the apex. Stipules
     spine-like. (See 203.) . . . .   **Robinia** L.
     Flowers in terminal racemes or panicles, with bracteoles. Corolla red,
     bluish, or white. Ovary usually surrounded at the base by a disc.
     Style glabrous. — Species 60. Tropical and South-east Africa. Some
     species yield timber, dyes, and poison. . . **Millettia** Wight & Arn.
357. Calyx-teeth distinctly developed. Fruit dehiscing by two valves. Shrubs.
     Bracteoles absent. 358
     Calyx-teeth very short or wanting. Fruit indehiscent. Trees or climbing
     shrubs. Bracteoles present. 359
358. Petals acuminate, red; standard lanceolate; keel beaked. Style
     glabrous. — Species 10. Madagascar. . . . . . **Chadsia** Boj.
     Petals obtuse or subacute, white or red; standard suborbicular; keel
     not beaked. (See 233.) . . . . **Tephrosia** Pers.
359. Fruit winged. Seeds flat. Ovary sessile or short-stalked. (See 351.)
                                                   Derris Lour.
     Fruit not winged. 360
360. Fruit with a thick-leathery, almost woody pericarp, oblique-oblong, not
     thickened at the sutures. Seed 1, kidney-shaped, rather thick. Ovary
     subsessile, with 2 ovules. Climbing shrubs. Flowers in racemes,
     reddish. — Species 1. Seychelles. The wood and the oily seeds are
     used. (*Galedupa* Lam.) . . . . **Pongamia** Vent.
     Fruit with a membranous or leathery pericarp. Seeds flat. (See 303.)
                                               Lonchocarpus H. B. & K.
361. (354.) Stem shrubby, erect or climbing. 362
     Stem tree-like. 371
362. Style bearded lengthwise towards the apex. Ovules numerous. Fruit
     indehiscent or dehiscing at the top only. Flowers in axillary racemes.
                                                   363
     Style glabrous, or hairy at the base only, or bearing a penicillate stigma.
                                                   365
363. Style bearded on the back or all round. Stigma terminal. Corolla red
     or white; keel blunt, shorter than the standard. Fruit finally de-
     hiscing at the top. (See 340.) . . . . **Lessertia** DC.
     Style bearded on the inner side only. Ovary stalked. Fruit inflated,
     indehiscent. 364
364. Stigma terminal. Corolla red; keel pointed, exceeding the standard.
     Bracteoles present. — Species 1. South Africa. Used as an orna-
     mental plant. . . . . **Sutherlandia** R. Br.
     Stigma placed beneath the hooked apex of the style. Corolla yellow;
     keel blunt; standard with two callosities on the inner side. — Species
     2. North Africa and Abyssinia. They (especially *C. arborescens* L.
     bladder senna) are used as ornamental plants and yield a dye and
     medicaments. . . . . **Colutea** L.

365. Connective of the stamens bearing a gland, a short point, or a tuft of hairs. Wings adhering to the keel. Fruit 2-valved. Hairs fixed by the middle. Bracteoles absent. (See 215.) . . . . **Indigofera** L.
Connective without an appendage. Bracteoles usually present. . . 366

366. Ovule 1. Fruit ovate, indehiscent; pericarp adhering to the seed. Gland-dotted plants. (See 153.) . . . . **Psoralea** L.
Ovules 2 or more. 367

367. Calyx 2-lipped, the upper lip hooded, notched, equalling the standard, the lower lip divided into 3 narrow teeth. Corolla yellowish. Ovary sessile. Ovules 5—7. Flowers in panicles, with large persistent bracteoles. — Species 8. West Africa. . . **Platysepalum** Welw.
Calyx obscurely 2-lipped, with a not very large upper lip, or equally 4—5-toothed, or almost entire. 368

368. Wings adhering to the keel. 369
Wings free from the keel. 370

369. Calyx-teeth very short or wanting. Fruit flat, narrowly winged, transversely chambered or 1-celled, indehiscent. Usually climbing plants. (See 351.) . . . . **Derris** Lour.
Calyx-teeth distinctly developed. Fruit longitudinally 2-celled, more rarely 1-celled, but turgid, finally dehiscing by two valves. (See 219.) . . . . **Astragalus** L.

370. Inflorescence axillary. Corolla yellowish. Ovary sessile. Ovules free. Fruit leathery, suborbicular, not winged, indehiscent. Seed 1, oblong or ovate. Climbing plants. Leaflets without stipels. — Species 3. West Africa. . . . . **Ostryocarpus** Hook. fil.
Inflorescence terminal. Ovary usually surrounded by a disc. Fruit linear or oblong, tardily dehiscing by two valves. Seeds orbicular or reniform. (See 356.) . . . . . . **Millettia** Wight & Arn.

371. (361.) Calyx 2-lipped, with large entire lips. Corolla yellow; wings free; petals of the keel free. Ovary subsessile, surrounded by a lobed disc. Ovules 3—4. Bracteoles small, deciduous. — Species 1. West Africa (Congo). . . . . **Dewevrea** Mich.
Calyx 2-lipped with divided lips, or more or less equally 4—5-toothed. 372

372. Calyx 2-lipped, the upper lip hooded, notched, equalling the standard, the lower lip divided into 3 narrow teeth. Corolla yellow. Ovary sessile. Ovules 5—7. Flowers in panicles. Bracteoles large, persistent. (See 367.) . . . . **Platysepalum** Welw.
Calyx obscurely 2-lipped, with a not very large upper lip, or equally 4—5-toothed, or almost entire. 373

373. Fruit dehiscing by two valves. 374
Fruit indehiscent. Ovules 2—6. 375

374. Leaflets alternate, gland-dotted on the lower face. Petals gland-dotted. Ovary long-stalked. Ovules 3—4. Fruit woody, turgid. — Species 2. Central Africa. . . . . **Schefflerodendron** Harms

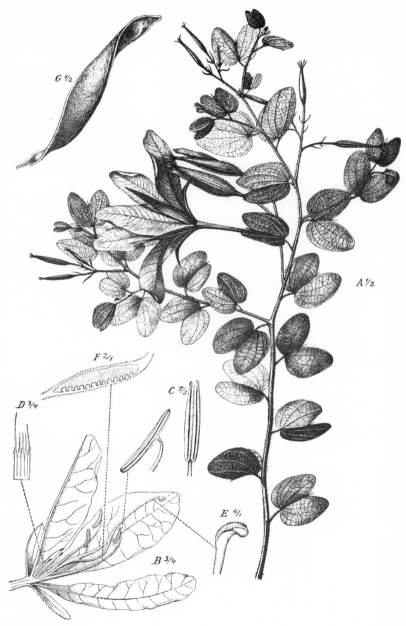

J. Fleischmann del.

Bauhinia macrantha Oliv.

A Flowering branch.   *B* Flower cut lengthwise.   *C* Anther from the side and the front.   *D* Staminodes.   *E* Stigma.   *F* Ovary cut lengthwise.   *G* Fruit.

J. Fleischmann del.

Monsonia biflora DC.

A Whole plant.   *B* Flower cut lengthwise.   *C* Sepal.   *D* Cross-section of ovary.   *E* Unripe fruit.   *F* Ripe fruit.   *G* Mericarp

Leaflets opposite. Petals not gland-dotted. Fruit more or less leathery and flattened. Inflorescence terminal. (See 356.)

Millettia Wight & Arn.

375. Calyx-teeth very short or wanting. Corolla red or white; standard distinctly clawed; petals of the keel free. Ovary stalked. Fruit drupe-like with a woody endocarp and a more or less fleshy exocarp. Seed 1. Inflorescence terminal. — Species 2. West Africa. They yield timber and are used in medicine. (*Vouacapoua* Aubl.)

Andira Lam.

Calyx-teeth distinctly developed. Corolla yellow or white, sometimes marked with red or violet. Fruit more or less distinctly winged, with a membranous or leathery pericarp. Leaflets alternate or sub-opposite. (See 247.) . . . . **Pterocarpus** L.

ORDER PANDALES

FAMILY 106. PANDACEAE

Trees. Leaves alternate. Flowers in fascicled racemes, or in false racemes formed of fascicles, or in panicles, unisexual. Calyx small, slightly toothed. Petals 5, large, oblong, red. Stamens 10. Ovary superior, slightly lobed, 3—4-celled. Ovule 1 in each cell, pendulous, straight. Stigmas 3—4, sessile or nearly so, oblong. Fruit a drupe; stone with many pits and cavities, 3—4-seeded. Seeds with a large axile embryo and an oily albumen.

Genus 1, species 1. Equatorial West Africa. The seeds yield oil. (*Porphyranthus* Engl.) . . . . **Panda** Pierre

ORDER GERANIALES

SUBORDER GERANIINEAE

FAMILY 107. GERANIACEAE

Herbs, undershrubs, or shrubs. Leaves stipulate. Flowers hermaphrodite. Sepals 5, imbricate, rarely 4, valvate in bud. Petals 2—8, more or less distinctly perigynous, imbricate in bud. Stamens twice or thrice as many as the petals, some frequently sterile, the outer opposite the petals. Anthers opening inwards. Ovary lobed, 5-celled, with 2 ovules in each cell, rarely 8-celled with 1-ovuled cells. Fruit beaked, the carpels separating at maturity. Seeds albuminous. — Genera 6, species 350. (Plate 68.)

1. Sepals 4, valvate in bud. Petals 8, white. Stamens 8, opposite the petals, free. Ovary 8-celled, with 1 ascending ovule in each cell. Tails (awns) of the carpels not recurved at maturity. Shrubs. Flowers solitary, with 4 bracteoles. — Species 1. Island of Socotra. [Tribe DIRACHMEAE.] . . . . **Dirachma** Schweinf.

Sepals 5, imbricate in bud. Petals 2—5. Stamens 10 or 15, some frequently sterile. Ovary 5-celled, with 2 ovules in each cell. Tails (awns) of

T

the carpels curved or twisted backwards at maturity. [Tribe GER-
ANIEAE.]   2
2. Flowers irregular, with a spur-like appendage along the pedicel and without
   glands at the base of the stamens. Fertile stamens 5—7, rarely 2—4.
   — Species 250. Southern and tropical Africa ; two species also naturalized in North Africa. Many of them are used as ornamental plants,
   some have edible roots or yield perfumes or medicaments.
                                              Pelargonium L'Hér.
   Flowers regular or almost so, without a spur-like appendage, with glands
   at the base of the stamens. Fertile stamens 5, 10, or 15.   3
3. Stamens 10, all or 5 of them fertile.   4
   Stamens 15, all fertile.   5
4. Tails of the carpels spirally twisted, hairy. Fertile stamens 5. Petals
   entire. Flowers usually in umbels. — Species 40. North Africa to
   Abyssinia and South Africa. Some are used medicinally ; hygro-
   metres are made from the carpel-tails. " Storks-bill."
                                              Erodium L'Hér.
   Tails of the carpels arched, generally glabrous. Fertile stamens usually 10.
   Petals mostly notched. Flowers usually solitary or in pairs. — Species
   30. North and South Africa and mountains of the tropics. Some
   species are used as ornamental plants or yield tanning and dyeing
   materials or medicaments. " Cranes-bill." . . . . **Geranium** L.
5. Filaments united in 5 bundles. Stem herbaceous. — Species 25. Some
   are used medicinally. (Plate 68.) . . . . . .   **Monsonia** L.
   Filaments free almost to the base. Stem fleshy, armed with spines formed
   from the persistent leafstalks. — Species 7. South Africa, southern
   Central Africa, and Madagascar. Some species yield an aromatic
   resin. (Under *Monsonia* L.) . . . .   **Sarcocaulon** DC.

FAMILY 108. OXALIDACEAE

Leaves alternate. Flowers regular, hermaphrodite. Sepals 5. Petals 5,
free or united at the base, with contorted aestivation. Stamens 10, rarely
5 of them sterile. Filaments united at the base. Anthers opening inwards.
Glands at the base of the stamens present. Ovary superior, 5-celled. Ovules
axile. Styles 5, free. Fruit a capsule or a berry. Seeds with a fleshy albumen
and a straight embryo. — Genera 3, species 160. (Under *GERANIACEAE*.)
(Plate 69.)
1. Fruit a berry. Trees. Leaves unequally pinnate, sensitive. Flowers in
   cymes. — Species 2. Cultivated in the Mascarene Islands. They
   yield timber, medicaments, and edible fruits, which are also used for
   preparing a scouring water. . . . . **Averrhoa** L.
   Fruit a capsule. All stamens fertile. Herbs or undershrubs, rarely
   shrubs.   2

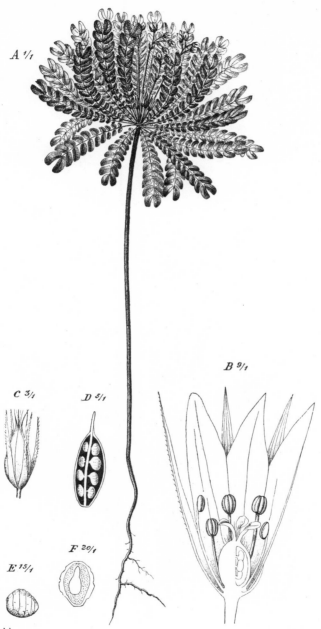

J. Fleischmann del.

Biophytum sensitivum (L.) DC.

A Plant in flower. *B* Flower cut lengthwise. *C* Fruit. *D* Fruit-valve. *E* Seed. *F* Seed cut lengthwise.

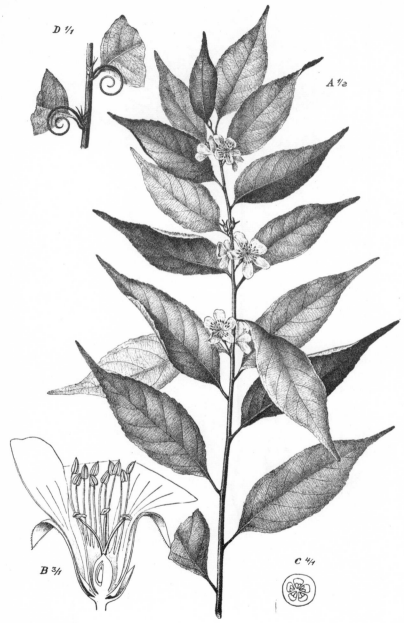

J. Fleischmann del.

Hugonia acuminata Engl.

A Flowering branch, *B* Flower cut lengthwise. *C* Cross-section of ovary. *D* Tendrils.

2. Valves of the fruit finally spreading. Leaves pinnate, sensitive. — Species
  15. Tropics. Some are used medicinally. (Under *Oxalis* L.) (Plate
  69.) . . . . **Biophytum** DC.
  Valves of the fruit persisting around the central column. Leaves usually
  digitate. — Species 140. Some are used as salad or fodder or for preparing chemical drugs and medicaments. (Including *Bolboxalis* Small).

  Oxalis L.

FAMILY 109. TROPAEOLACEAE

Twining, succulent herbs. Leaves alternate, undivided, peltate. Flowers
solitary, axillary, irregular, hermaphrodite. Sepals 5, the hindmost spurred.
Petals 5, yellow or red, imbricate in bud. Stamens 8, free ; anthers opening
inwards or laterally. Ovary superior, 3-celled. Ovule 1 in each cell, pendulous,
inverted. Style 1, with 3 stigmas. Fruit separating in 2—3 nutlets. Seeds
without albumen. (Under *GERANIACEAE*.)

  Genus 1, species 1 (*T. majus* L., Indian cress). Naturalized in the Island
    of St. Helena. Ornamental plant, also yielding salad, condiments,
    and medicaments. . . . . **Tropaeolum** L.

FAMILY 110. LINACEAE

Leaves undivided. Flowers regular, hermaphrodite. Calyx imbricate in
bud. Petals free, with imbricate or contorted aestivation. Stamens as many
or twice as many as the petals. Filaments united at the base. Ovary 2—10-
celled. Ovules 1—2 in the inner angle of each cell, pendulous, inverted.
Fruit a capsule or a drupe. Seeds with fleshy albumen. — Genera 7, species
60. (Plate 70.)

  1. Fertile stamens as many as the petals, 4—5, furnished with glands at their
    base. Styles or style-branches 2—5. Petals deciduous. Fruit cap-
    sular. Herbs or undershrubs, very rarely shrubs. [Tribe LINEAE.] 2
  Fertile stamens twice as many as the petals, 10, rarely the same number,
    5, but then without glands at their base and style simple. Shrubs or
    trees. [Tribe HUGONIEAE.] 4
  2. Sepals 3-toothed at the tip. Petals very small, white. Flowers 4-merous.
    Stem repeatedly forked. Leaves opposite. — Species 1. North Africa
    and high mountains of Central Africa. "Alseed." **Radiola** Gmel.
  Sepals entire. Flowers nearly always 5-merous. 3
  3. Stipules bristle-like. Corolla yellow. Stamens partly (2—4 of them)
    with, partly without glands. Styles 3. Stigmas kidney-shaped.
    Shrubs or undershrubs. — Species 1. Naturalized in the Mascarene
    Islands. Ornamental plant. (Under *Linum* L.) **Reinwardtia** Dumort.
  Stipules gland-like or wanting. Stamens all furnished with glands.—
    Species 25. North, East, and South Africa and Madagascar. *L.
    usitatissimum* L. is cultivated for fibre and oil and yields also fodder and
    medicaments ; other species are used as ornamental plants. "Flax."

    Linum L.

4. Styles 5, free or united at the base. Stamens 10. Petals deciduous.
Fruit a drupe. — Species 25. Tropics. Some are used medicinally.
(Plate 70.) . . . . **Hugonia** L.
Style 1, undivided or 2—3-cleft at the top. 5
5. Style shortly 2-cleft. Ovary 2-celled, with 1 ovule in each cell. Stamens
10. Anthers linear or oblong. Petals elongated, with a glandular pit
at the claw. — Species 2. East Africa. . **Nectaropetalum** Engl.
Style 3-cleft or undivided. Ovary 3—5-celled. 6
6. Style shortly 3-cleft. Ovary 3-celled with 2 ovules in each cell. Stamens
10. Anthers ovoid or globose. Petals short. Inflorescence racemose,
cone-shaped when young, with roundish vaulted bracts. — Species 1.
West Africa (Cameroons). . . . . **Lepidobotrys** Engl.
Style undivided. Stamens usually 5. Corolla persistent. Fruit capsular. Inflorescence racemose with small bracts, or paniculate. —
Species 5. Central Africa. (Under *Ochthocosmus* Benth.)
Phyllocosmus Klotzsch

FAMILY 111. HUMIRIACEAE

Trees. Leaves alternate, undivided. Flowers in cymes or panicles, regular,
hermaphrodite. Sepals 5, imbricate in bud. Petals 5, yellow or greenish,
imbricate in bud, deciduous. Stamens 10, at first united below, with a prolonged connective and 1-celled anther-halves. Ovary surrounded by a cupular
disc, superior, 5-celled. Ovules solitary in each cell, pendulous, inverted.
Style simple. Fruit a nut or drupe. Seeds with fleshy albumen.
Genus 1, species 1. West Africa. Yields timber and edible fruits from
which a spirituous drink is prepared. (*Aubrya* Baill., under *Humiria*
Aubl.) . . . . **Saccoglottis** Mart.

FAMILY 112. ERYTHROXYLACEAE

Shrubs or trees, rarely undershrubs. Leaves entire, stipulate. Flowers
solitary or in clusters, regular, hermaphrodite, rarely polygamous. Sepals 5,
imbricate in bud. Petals 5, free, with a callosity or an appendage on the
inner face, imbricate or contorted in aestivation. Stamens 10. Filaments
united at the base. Anthers opening by two longitudinal slits. Ovary 3-,
rarely 4-celled, usually a single cell fertile. Ovules 1—2, pendulous, inverted.
Styles or style-branches 3, rarely 4. Fruit a drupe. Seeds with fleshy albumen,
rarely without albumen ; embryo straight. — Genera 2, species 40. Tropical
and South Africa. (Under *LINACEAE*.) (Plate 71.)
Petals scarcely clawed, provided with a longitudinal callosity. Filaments
united into a ring. Ovary with 3—4 two-ovuled cells. Fruit 3—4-
celled. Leaves opposite. Stipules 2. — Species 1. Equatorial West
Africa. . . . . **Aneulophus** Benth.
Petals distinctly clawed, with a usually 2-cleft scale. Filaments united
into a cup. Ovary with 1 fertile one-ovuled cell and 2 empty ones.

J. Fleischmann del.

Erythroxylon pictum E. Mey.

A Flowering branch. *B* Flower cut lengthwise. *C* Petal from within. *D* Stamen from front and back. *E* Cross-section of
ovary. *F* Fruit. *G* Fruit cut lengthwise.

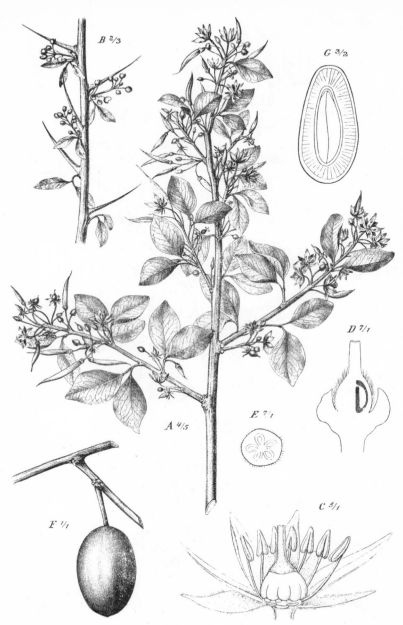

J. Fleischmann del.

Balanites aegyptiaca Del.

A Branch with flowers and young fruits.   *B* Part of branch with spines.   *C* Flower cut lengthwise.   *D* Ovary and disc cut lengthwise.   *E* Cross-section of ovary.   *F* Fruit.   *G* Fruit cut lengthwise.

Fruit 1-celled. Leaves alternate. Stipule 1. — Species 40. Tropical and South Africa. Some species yield timber or medicaments. (Plate 71.) . . . . **Erythroxylon** P. Browne

FAMILY 113. ZYGOPHYLLACEAE

Leaves stipulate. Flowers regular, hermaphrodite, rarely (*Neoluederitzia*) dioecious. Petals 4—5, free, rarely wanting. Stamens 1—3 times as many as the petals. Filaments usually with an appendage at the base. Anthers attached by the back. Ovary superior, 3—10-celled, lobed angled or winged. Style simple, rarely (*Seetzenia*) styles 5. — Genera 12, species 90. (Plate 72.)

1. Fruit drupaceous, one-seeded. Seeds without albumen. Ovary 3—5-celled with 1 pendulous ovule in each cell. Filaments without an appendage. Corolla yellowish-green. Leaves alternate, simple and undivided or of 2 leaflets. Shrubs or trees. [Subfamilies **BALANITOIDEAE** and **NITRARIOIDEAE.**] 2

  Fruit capsular or separating into several nutlets, several- or many-seeded. Leaves opposite, at least the lower ones, more rarely all alternate, but then dissected or pinnate with many leaflets. 3

2. Fruit with a very thick endocarp. Ovary 5-celled, surrounded by a cupular disc; ovules attached at the top of the cells. Style rather long; stigma 1. Stamens 10. Petals oblong. Sepals hairy. Leaves with two leaflets. Spiny plants. — Species 3. Central Africa, Sahara, Egypt. They yield timber, fish-poison, vegetables, medicaments, oily seeds, and edible fruits which are also used as a substitute for soap and for preparing a spirituous drink. " Zachun-oil-tree." (*Agialid* Adans.) (Plate 72.) . . . . **Balanites** Del.

  Fruit with a thin endocarp, opening finally by 6 teeth at the top. Ovary 3-celled; ovules attached near the middle of the cells. Style very short; stigmas 3, converging. Stamens usually 15. Petals concave, induplicate-valvate in bud. Sepals fleshy, imbricate in bud. Leaves simple, undivided, fleshy. — Species 2. North Africa and northern Central Africa. They yield soda and edible fruits which are said to be inebriating. " Nitre bush." . . . . **Nitraria** L.

3. Leaves pinnately dissected or irregularly many-cleft, alternate. Filaments without an appendage. Ovary 3—4-celled with several or many ovules in each cell. Seeds albuminous. Herbs. [Subfamilies **TETRADICLIDOIDEAE** and **PEGANOIDEAE.**] 4

  Leaves undivided, unifoliolate, digitate, or pinnate, usually opposite. Ovary 4—10-, usually 5-celled. [Subfamily **ZYGOPHYLLOIDEAE.**] 5

4. Leaves pinnately dissected. Flowers small. Calyx 3—4-toothed. Petals 3—4, obovate. Stamens 3—4. Ovary deeply lobed, the lobes incompletely 3-celled, 6-ovuled. — Species 1. North-east Africa.

Tetradiclis Stev.

Leaves irregularly many-cleft. Flowers rather large. Sepals 4—5, linear. Petals 4—5, oblong. Stamens 8—15. Ovary slightly lobed, with undivided, many-ovuled cells. — Species 1. North Africa. The seeds are used medicinally, as a condiment, and for dyeing. **Peganum** L.

5. Leaves unequally pinnate or digitate, rarely unifoliolate ; in the latter case disc indistinct and ovules ascending. Filaments without an appendage. Ovary 5-celled with 1—2 ovules in each cell. . . . 6

Leaves equally pinnate or undivided, rarely reduced to the stalk. Disc distinctly developed. Ovules pendulous. 8

6. Leaves alternate, with 4—6 pairs of leaflets. Flowers dioecious. Ovary surrounded by strap-shaped scales. Spiny shrubs. — Species 1. South-west Africa (Namaland). . . . . . . **Neoluederitzia** Schinz

Leaves opposite, with 1 or 3 leaflets. Flowers hermaphrodite. Herbs or undershrubs. 7

7. Calyx valvate in bud. Petals none. Disc 5-lobed. Stamens 5. Ovule 1 in each ovary-cell, pendulous. Styles 5, with capitate stigmas. Prostrate undershrubs. Leaflets 3. — Species 2. South and North-east Africa. . . . . **Seetzenia** R. Br.

Calyx imbricate in bud. Petals 5, rose violet or yellowish. Disc obscure. Stamens 10. Ovules 2 in each ovary-cell, suspended from ascending funicles. Style 1 ; stigma simple. — Species 15. North Africa, northern Central Africa, and South-west Africa. Some are used medicinally. **Fagonia** Tourn.

8. Leaves alternate, abruptly pinnate, with 6—8 pairs of leaflets. Flowers large. Sepals saccate at base. Corolla yellow. Disc lobed, with 5 glands projecting into the sacks of the sepals. Stamens 10, unappendaged. Ovary 5-lobed, with 2 ovules in each cell. Shrubs. — Species 1. East Africa (Somaliland). . . . **Kelleronia** Schinz

Leaves opposite, at least the lower ones. 9

9. Ovary 10-celled, with 2 ovules in each cell. Calyx valvate in bud. Petals narrow, 3-cleft. Disc cupular, 10-toothed. Stamens 10, with awl-shaped appendages at the base. Fruit winged. Seeds exalbuminous. Erect, succulent herbs. Leaves undivided, club-shaped. — Species 1. South Africa. . . . . **Augea** Thunb.

Ovary 4—5-celled. Calyx imbricate in bud. 10

10. Ovary-cells with one ovule in each. Style long ; stigma club-shaped. Disc 5-lobed, with five 3-cleft scales opposite the sepals. Stamens 10, appendaged. Fruit capsular. Seeds exalbuminous. Shrubs. — Species 1. South Africa. . . . . **Sisyndite** E. Mey.

Ovary-cells with 2 or more ovules in each 11

11. Ovary-cells later on transversely chambered, 3—5-ovuled. Style very short, with a large stigma. Disc thin, lobed. Fruit separating into nutlets, bristly or warty, usually with outgrowths. Seeds exalbuminous. Herbs. Flowers cymose, 5-merous. — Species 12. Some of them have edible seeds or serve as ornamental or medicinal plants . **Tribulus** Tourn.

Ovary-cells undivided. Style awl-shaped, with a small stigma. Disc fleshy. Filaments usually appendaged. Fruit capsular. Seeds albuminous. Flowers solitary or in pairs, whitish or yellowish. — Species 55. Some of them yield soda, edible seeds, medicaments, or poison.

Zygophyllum L.

FAMILY 114. CNEORACEAE

Shrubs. Leaves alternate, simple, entire, gland-dotted, without stipules. Flowers in cymes, 3—4-merous, hermaphrodite, with an elongated receptacle. Petals free, imbricate in bud. Stamens 3—4, alternating with the petals; filaments without an appendage. Ovary 3—4-lobed, 3—4-celled. Ovules 2 in each cell, one above the other, pendulous, curved. Style simple; stigmas 3. Fruit separating in two 2-celled drupes. Seeds with a curved embryo and fleshy albumen. (Under *SIMARUBACEAE*.)

Genus 1, species 1. Canary Islands. Used medicinally. (Under *Cneorum* L.) . . . . **Chamaelea** Tourn.

FAMILY 115. RUTACEAE

Leaves gland-dotted, at least at the margin, rarely (*Empleuridium*) without dots. Petals free, rarely (*Empleurum*) wanting. Disc usually present. Anthers versatile, opening inwards or laterally by longitudinal slits. Embryo rather large, the radicle turned upwards. — Genera 33, species 320. (Including *AURANTIACEAE* and *XANTHOXYLEAE*.) (Plate 73.)

1. Fruit dehiscent and more or less dry. Carpels, at least when ripe, more or less separate, rarely only one present. [Subfamily **RUTOIDEAE**.]   2
   Fruit indehiscent and more or less fleshy. Carpels usually united, even when ripe, rarely only one present. Shrubs or trees. Leaves compound, but sometimes with a single leaflet. 19
2. Stem herbaceous or woody at the base only. Flowers hermaphrodite. Corolla yellow. Stamens 8—10. Ovules 2, or more frequently more than 2 in each carpel. Seeds albuminous; embryo curved. [Tribe RUTEAE.] 3
   Stem woody. Corolla green, white, red, or violet, rarely (*Empleurum*) wanting. Fertile stamens 3—5, rarely (*Pelea*) 8—10. Ovules 2 in each carpel. 4
3. Carpels 2, with 5—6 ovules in each. Flowers 4-merous. Petals entire. Seeds spiny. Undershrubs. Leaves undivided or 3-parted. — Species 2. German South-west Africa (Hereroland) and Island of Socotra.

Thamnosma Torr.

   Carpels 4—5. Seeds tubercled. — Species 8. North Africa and northern Central Africa. Some species yield condiments and medicaments. "Rue." (Including *Desmophyllum* Webb and *Haplophyllum* Juss.)

Ruta L.

4. Seeds albuminous. Corolla greenish or whitish. Leaves usually compound. [Tribe XANTHOXYLEAE.] 5

Seeds exalbuminous, Corolla white, red, violet, or wanting. Leaves
simple, undivided. [Tribe DIOSMEAE.] 7

5. Stamens 8—10. Carpels 4—5. Trees. Leaves alternate, undivided.
Flowers polygamous. — Species 1. Madagascar. (Under *Melicope*
Forst.) . . . . **Pelea** A. Gray
Stamens 3—5. 6

6. Leaves opposite. Flowers unisexual. Carpels 4—5. Styles united.
Seeds oblong. Unarmed plants. — Species 15. Madagascar and
neighbouring islands. Some are used medicinally. . **Evodia** Forst.
Leaves alternate. Carpels 1—5. Styles free or united above. — Species
30. Tropical and South Africa. Some species yield timber, vegetables,
condiments, and medicaments. (Including *Pterota* P. Br., under
Zanthoxylum L.) . . . . **Fagara** L.

7. Carpels 1—2. Fertile stamens 4. Flowers unisexual or polygamous.
Shrubs. [Subtribe EMPLEURINAE.] 8
Carpels 4—5. Fertile stamens 5. Flowers hermaphrodite or polygamous. 9

8. Flowers dioecious. Sepals united at the base. Petals 4. Disc 4-lobed.
Anthers roundish, without terminal glands. Leaves needle-like, three-
edged, without glandular dots. — Species 1. South Africa (Cape
Colony). . . . . **Empleuridium** Sond.
Flowers polygamous-monoecious. Sepals united beyond the middle.
Petals wanting. Disc none. Anthers oblong, with a gland at the top.
Ovary beaked. Stigma entire. Leaves linear-lanceolate, flat, gland-
ular-serrate. — Species 1. South Africa (Cape Colony). Used medicin-
ally. . . . . **Empleurum** Soland.

9. Endocarp cartilaginous, adnate at the back and separating from the
tubercled exocarp at the margins only. Seeds with thick cotyledons.
Ovules one above the other. Ovary with a long and thin stalk. Stam-
inodes linear, glandulose. Trees. — Species 2. East and South Africa.
[Subtribe CALODENDRINAE.] . . . . . . **Calodendron** Thunb.
Endocarp separating from the exocarp. Seeds with flat cotyledons.
Ovules usually side by side. Shrubs. [Subtribe DIOSMINAE.] . . 10

10. Staminodes 5. 11
Staminodes none 15

11. Style long. Stigma small 12
Style short or rather short. Stigma capitate or discoid. Inflorescences
terminal 13

12. Petals clawed. Stamens with glabrous filaments and gland-tipped anthers.
Staminodes petaloid, with hairy claws. Disc crenate or lobed. Carpels
2—4. Flowers in terminal umbels or heads, rarely solitary and axillary.
— Species 100. South Africa (Cape Colony). Some are used as orna-
mental or medicinal plants. (Plate 73.) . . **Agathosma** Willd.
Petals subsessile, glabrous. Carpels 5. Flowers solitary or in cymes in
the axils of the leaves. — Species 20. South Africa (Cape Colony).
Some are used medicinally. . . . . **Barosma** Willd.

13. Petals with a very short, glabrous claw. Anthers ending in a stalked gland. Staminodes exceeding the fertile stamens. Disc lobed. Ovary covered with stalked glands. Flowers rather large. — Species 25. South Africa (Cape Colony). Several species are used as ornamental or medicinal plants, or as a substitute for tea . . **Adenandra** Willd.
Petals with a long or rather long, usually channelled or bearded claw. Anthers with a sessile gland or without a gland. 14

14. Petals channelled inside, glabrous. Anthers bearing a sessile gland. Staminodes adnate below to the petals or enclosed by their channelled claw. Ovary glabrous. Leaves alternate. — Species 6. South Africa (Cape Colony). Some are used as ornamental or medicinal plants.
Coleonema Bartl. & Wendl.
Petals not channelled, usually with a hairy claw. Stamens short. Staminodes very small. — Species 15. South Africa (Cape Colony).
Acmadenia Bartl. & Wendl.

15. Style long. Stigma small. Petals with a hairy claw. 16
Style short or rather short. Stigma capitate. Filaments glabrous. . 17

16. Disc 5-parted. Filaments and style hairy. Carpels 5. Flowers solitary or in clusters, white. — Species 1. South Africa (Cape Colony).
Phyllosma Bolus
Disc entire, urn-shaped. Filaments glabrous. Carpels 3—5. — Species 10. South Africa (Cape Colony). . . **Macrostylis** Bartl. & Wendl.

17. Petals sessile, obovate, glabrous. — Species 15. South Africa (Cape Colony). Some are used medicinally . . . . . **Diosma** L.
Petals clawed, hairy within. . . . . 18.

18. Petals oblong or lanceolate, slightly exceeding the calyx. Anthers with a terminal gland. Flowers very small. — Species 6. South Africa (Cape Colony). . . . . **Euchaetis** Bartl. & Wendl.
Petals obovate. (See 14.) . . . . . **Acmadenia** Bartl. & Wendl.

19. (1.) Fruit a drupe. Flowers usually unisexual. Stigma sessile or nearly so. [Subfamily **TODDALIOIDEAE**, tribe TODDALIEAE.] . . 20
Fruit a berry. Flowers usually hermaphrodite. [Subfamily **AURAN-TIOIDEAE**, tribe AURANTIEAE.] 27

20. Fruit 1-celled. Seed 1, exalbuminous. Ovary 1-celled. Petals imbricate in bud. Leaflets 1—3. [Subtribe AMYRIDINAE.] . . . 21
Fruit 2—7-celled or consisting of 2—4 carpels cohering at the base only, 1—3 of them sometimes abortive. Ovary 2—7-celled. 22

21. Flowers hermaphrodite. Fertile stamens 10. Disc cup-shaped. Style long, with a minute stigma. Ovule 1. — Species 1. Equatorial West Africa (Cameroons) . . . . **Eriander** H. Winkl.
Flowers dioecious. Fertile stamens 4—5. Disc ring-shaped. Style short, with a broad stigma. Ovules 2. — Species 18. Tropical and South Africa. (Under *Toddalia* Juss.) . . . . . **Teclea** Del.

22. Carpels almost free when ripe, some of them rudimentary. Seeds ex-
    albuminous. Ovary distinctly 2—4-lobed. Stamens 4. Petals valvate
    in bud. Leaves digitate. [Subtribe ORICIINAE.] 23
    Carpels united up to maturity, forming a 2—7-celled fruit. Ovary not
    or obscurely lobed. Petals imbricate in bud. [Subtribe TODDALIINAE.] 24
23. Carpels 2, one of them rudimentary at maturity. Seeds with equal cotyle-
    dons. Ovary almost glabrous. Petals oblong. Flowers in racemes.
    — Species 1. Equatorial West Africa (Gaboon). . . **Diphasia** Pierre
    Carpels 4, of which 1—3 are rudimentary at maturity. Seeds with unequal
    cotyledons. Ovary very hairy. Petals oval. Flowers in panicles, uni-
    sexual. — Species 4. West Africa. . . . . . . **Oricia** Pierre
24. Fruit with 2-seeded cells. Seeds albuminous. Flowers 4-merous. Trees.
    Leaves digitate, with 5 leaflets. — Species 1. Equatorial West Africa
    (Gaboon). . . . . **Araliopsis** Engl.
    Fruit with 1-seeded cells. Flowers unisexual. Leaves digitate with
    3 leaflets, rarely pinnate with 7—9 leaflets. 25
25. Fertile stamens as many as the petals. Flowers 5-merous. Seeds albumin-
    ous; embryo curved. Climbing shrubs. Leaves digitate. — Species 1.
    Tropics. Yields condiments and is used in medicine. (*Cranzia* Schreb.)
    Toddalia Juss.
    Fertile stamens twice as many as the petals. Flowers 2—4-merous.
    Embryo straight or almost so 26
26. Filaments awl-shaped. Flowers 4-merous. Seeds exalbuminous. Shrubs.
    Leaves digitate. — Species 1. East Africa. . **Toddaliopsis** Engl.
    Filaments flattened. Seeds albuminous. — Species 30. Tropical and
    South Africa. Some species yield timber and medicaments. (Under
    Toddalia Juss.) . . . . **Vepris** Comm.
27. (19.) Ovary 2—5-celled, with 1—2 ovules in each cell. Stamens twice
    as many as the petals. [Subtribe LIMONIINAE.] 28
    Ovary 5- or more-celled, with 4 or more ovules in each cell. Leaves with
    1—3 leaflets. [Subtribe CITRINAE.] 32
28. Ovules solitary in each ovary-cell. 29
    Ovules two or more in each ovary-cell. Unarmed plants 30
29. Flowers solitary or in groups of three in the axils of the leaves, 3-, rarely
    4-merous. Calyx toothed. Seeds usually with unequal and lobed
    cotyledons. Spiny shrubs. Leaflets 3, unequal. — Species 1. Cul-
    tivated in the tropics. Yields timber, fragrant flowers, and edible
    fruits. . . . . **Triphasia** Lour.
    Flowers in racemes or panicles, 4—5-merous. Calyx lobed or more deeply
    divided. Leafstalk winged. — Species 10. Tropics. They yield
    timber, edible fruits, oily seeds, and medicaments. . **Limonia** L.
30. Style very short, not jointed with the ovary. Leaves unifoliolate. —
    Species 1. West Africa. . . . . **Glycosmis** Correa
    Style long or rather short, jointed with the ovary. Leaves unequally
    pinnate. 31

J. Fleischmann del.

Agathosma ciliata Link

A Flowering branch. B Flower. C Petal. D Stamen. E Staminode. F Flower cut lengthwise. G Cross-section of ovary.
H Fruit.

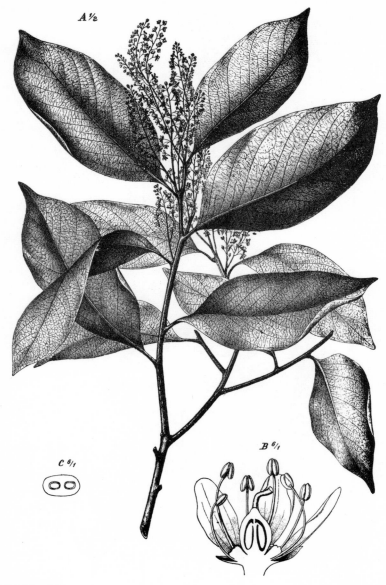

A ½

C ⁶/₁

B ⁶/₁

J. Fleischmann del.

Irvingia Barteri Hook. fil.

A Flowering branch. *B* Flower cut lengthwise. *C* Cross-section of ovary.

31. Filaments awl-shaped. Petals 5, linear lanceolate or oblong. Flowers
    rather large. — Species 1. Cultivated and naturalized in the tropics.
    Yields timber, fragrant flowers, and medicaments . . . **Murraya** L.
    Filaments broadened below. Petals 4—5, elliptical or roundish. Flowers
    rather small. — Species 6. Central and South Africa. Some are used
    medicinally. (Including *Myaris* Presl). . . . . **Clausena** Burm.
32. Ovary with 4—8 ovules in each cell. Anthers oblong. Pericarp leathery.
    Seed-coat white, leathery. Leaves leathery. — Species 4. Cultivated ;
    also naturalized in the tropics. They serve as ornamental plants and
    afford wood, fragrant flowers, and edible fruits (especially oranges and
    citrons) from which drinks, medicaments, and perfumes are prepared.
    Citrus L.
    Ovary with numerous ovules in each cell. Anthers linear. Pericarp
    hard. Leaves with 3 leaflets. 33
33. Stamens 10. Seed-coat smooth. Leaves leathery. — Species 1. Region
    of the great lakes. . . . . **Balsamocitrus** Stapf
    Stamens numerous. Seed-coat woolly and sticky. Leaves herbaceous.
    — Species 1. West Africa. Yields timber and is used in medicine.
    Aegle Correa

FAMILY 116. SIMARUBACEAE

Shrubs or trees. Leaves simple or pinnate, not gland-dotted. Flowers in
spikes racemes or panicles, regular. Sepals 2—5. Petals 3—9, free. Disc
usually present. Anthers versatile, opening inwards by longitudinal slits.
Carpels free or united and then forming a several-celled ovary. Ovules 1—2,
pendulous or laterally attached. Seeds with a very thin albumen or without
albumen. — Genera 16, species 40. Tropical and South Africa. (Under
RUTACEAE.) (Plate 74.)

1. Carpels 5, free, 2-ovuled. Disc indistinct. Stamens 5—10, without an
   appendage. Corolla yellow. Fruit drupe-like. Embryo curved, with
   a large radicle. Shrubs. Leaves undivided. — Species 1. Tropics.
   [Subfamily **SURIANOIDEAE.**] . . . . **Suriana** L.
   Carpels united at least by the base or the apex of the style, 1-ovuled.
   Disc distinctly developed. Embryo with a very short radicle. [Sub-
   family **SIMARUBOIDEAE.**] 2
2. Filaments with a scale-like appendage at the base. [Tribe SIMARUBEAE] 3
   Filaments without a scale at the base. 9
3. Stamens 6—14, twice as many as the petals. Anthers oblong or oval . 4
   Stamens 15—18, thrice as many as the petals or more. Anthers linear.
   Ovaries 5. Style 1. Corolla red. Trees. Leaves pinnate. [Sub-
   tribe MANNIINAE.] 8
4. Ovaries and style-tips united. Fruit a drupe with 4—5 stones. Embryo
   curved. Shrubs. Leaves compound. — Species 2. Central Africa.
   [Subtribe HARRISONIINAE.] . . . . . **Harrisonia** (R.Br.) Juss.

Ovaries free. Styles united. Fruit consisting of 1—5 nuts or drupes.
[Subtribe SIMARUBINAE.] 5
5. Leaves undivided. Flowers in umbels. Calyx 3—5-lobed, imbricate in
bud. Petals with contorted aestivation. Filaments with a minute
scale at the base. Style long ; stigma small, entire. Fruits woody.
Trees. — Species 2. Madagascar. Used medicinally.
Samadera Gaertn.
Leaves pinnate. Flowers in racemes or panicles. 6
6. Calyx 5-parted, imbricate in bud. Petals 5, with contorted aestivation.
Filaments with a short scale. Style long ; stigma slightly 5-lobed.
Leaflets lanceolate, acuminate. — Species 1. West Africa. Yields
arrow-poison and is used in medicine. . . . . . . **Quassia** L.
Calyx 2—4-lobed or -cleft. Petals with imbricate aestivation. Filaments
with a long scale. Style short. Flowers in panicles. 7
7. Calyx 4-, rarely 5-lobed. Petals 4, rarely 5. Fruits woody. Leaflets
oblong or obovate. — Species 3. Equatorial regions. The seeds
yield a fat. (Under *Quassia* L.) . . **Odyendea** (Pierre) Engl.
Calyx at first closed, later on unequally 2—4-cleft. Petals 5, rarely 6—9.
Stigma 5-parted. Fruits drupe-like. — Species 4. Central Africa.
They yield timber, oily seeds, and medicaments. . **Hannoa** Planch.
8. Calyx shortly lobed. Anthers shorter than the filaments. Ovaries
united below. Leaflets with a spoon-shaped appendage at the tip. —
Species 1. West Africa (Cameroons) . . **Pierreodendron** Engl.
Calyx deeply divided. Anthers longer than the filaments. Ovaries free.
Leaflets with an awl-shaped appendage at the tip. — Species 1. West
Africa. . . . . **Mannia** Hook. fil.
9. (2.) Stamens 4—6. Carpels free, either as to the ovaries or as to the
styles. Flowers usually polygamous. 10
Stamens 8—10. Fruit drupe-like. Trees. 12
10. Sepals 3. Petals 3. Stamens 6. Carpels 2, united at the base. Stigma
subsessile, discoid. Fruit 2-celled, winged. Leaves undivided. —
Species 1. Seychelles. [Tribe SOULAMEEAE.] **Soulamea** Lam.
Sepals, petals, stamens, and carpels 4. Stigma small. Leaves pinnate. 11
11. Ovaries and styles free or united at the base only. Petals short. Fruit
consisting of 4 drupes. Rusty-hairy plants. — Species 5. Central
Africa. Used medicinally. [Tribe PICRASMEAE.] **Brucea** J. S. Muell
Ovaries united ; styles free. Petals long. Fruit separating into 4 leathery
mericarps suspended from a central column. — Species 5. Central
Africa. [Tribe KIRKIEAE.] . . . . **Kirkia** Oliv.
12. Carpels free for the greater part. Leaves pinnate. — Species 1. Madagascar. Poisonous. . . . . **Perriera** Courchet
Carpels wholly united. Leaves undivided. Flowers hermaphrodite . 13
13. Stigma 2-parted. Ovary 2-celled. Disc ring-shaped, lobed. Anthers
oblong. Flowers solitary or in clusters in the axils of the leaves. —
Species 1. South Africa. (Under *Nectaropetalum* Engl.) **Peglera** Bolus

Stigma entire. Disc cushion-shaped. Anthers ovate. Flowers in panicles. [Tribe IRVINGIEAE.] 14

14. Ovary 4—5-celled. Fruit broader than long, angled, 4—5-celled, with a thin fleshy layer. — Species 3. Equatorial West Africa.
Klainedoxa Pierre

Ovary 2-celled. Fruit oblong, 1—2-celled. 15

15. Fruit much compressed, broadly winged all round, 2-celled, 2-seeded, with a thin fleshy layer. — Species 2. Equatorial West Africa. (Under *Irvingia* Hook. fil.) . . . . **Desbordesia** Pierre

Fruit slightly compressed, not winged, 1-celled, 1-seeded, with a thick fleshy layer. — Species 5. Central Africa. They yield timber, edible fruits, and oily seeds (dika). (Including *Irvingella* van Tiegh.) (Plate 74.) . . . . **Irvingia** Hook. fil.

FAMILY 117. BURSERACEAE

Trees, rarely shrubs. Bark resinous. Leaves usually pinnate. Flowers panicled, regular, mostly polygamous. Perianth consisting of a calyx and a corolla of 3—5 free petals. Stamens twice as many as the petals, inserted on the margin or the outside of the disc, rarely within. Anthers versatile, opening inwards by longitudinal slits. Ovary 2—5-celled. Ovules 2 in each cell, pendulous or attached laterally. Style simple or wanting; stigma lobed. Fruit drupe-like, but sometimes dehiscent. Seeds exalbuminous. Embryo with a superior radicle and usually folded or twisted cotyledons. — Genera 7, species 160. Tropical and South Africa. (Under *TEREBINTHACEAE*). (Plate 75.)

1. Receptacle concave; tube-, cup-, or urn-shaped; sepals, petals, and stamens inserted at its upper rim. Sepals 4 and petals 4, valvate in bud. Ovary 2—3-celled. Fruit drupaceous, but dehiscent, with a 2—3-celled stone; one cell only fertile. — Species 110. Tropical and South Africa. Several species yield timber and odorous resins (especially myrrh) which are used for preparing varnish, incense, and medicines. Some are also used as hedge plants. (*Balsamea* Gled., *Balsamodendron* Kunth, including *Hemprichia* Ehrenb. and *Hitzeria* Klotzsch). **Commiphora** Jacq.

Receptacle flat or convex, usually bearing a free disc, outside of which the sepals and petals are inserted. Leaves pinnate. Trees. . . . 2

2. Flowers 3-merous. Petals valvate in bud. Fruit with a 2—3-celled stone, indehiscent, sometimes only one cell fertile. 3

Flowers 4—5-merous. Fruit with 2—5 stones. 5

3. Fruit depressed, obliquely hemispherical, broader than long, with a lateral style and 1—2 fertile cells; endocarp thin, mesocarp rather thick. Embryo with a short radicle and thick, pinnately divided cotyledons. Stamens inserted outside the thick disc. Ovary 3-celled; one cell sterile. — Species 6. Equatorial West Africa. They yield timber,

edible fruits, and medicaments. (Under *Pachylobus* Don or *Santiria* Blume) . . . . **Santiriopsis** Engl.
Fruit oblong, ovate, or subglobose. 4

4. Fruit with 2 cells, one of which is sterile, and with a terminal style or style-scar ; endocarp thin crusty, mesocarp thick fleshy. Embryo with a long radicle and thick, much divided cotyledons. Ovary 2-celled. Sepals united at the base. — Species 13. West Africa. They yield timber, resin, and edible oily fruits (safu). (Under *Canarium* L.) (Plate 75.) . . . . **Pachylobus** Don
Fruit with 3 cells, two of them sometimes sterile ; endocarp usually thick, woody or bony ; mesocarp usually thin. Embryo with a short radicle and slightly divided cotyledons. Ovary 3-celled. Sepals united high up. — Species 13. Tropics. Some species yield timber, resin (elemi) used in medicine and manufacture, and edible oily fruits and seeds.
Canarium L.

5. Disc situated outside the stamens. Petals 5, imbricate in bud. Ovary 5-celled. Fruit top-shaped, with 5 stones, dehiscent. — Species 1. Equatorial West Africa. Yields timber and an aromatic resin.
Aucoumea Pierre
Disc situated inside the stamens. 6

6. Petals 4—5, valvate in bud. Ovary 4—5-celled. Fruit globular or ovoid. Species 4. Madagascar and Mascarenes. They yield timber and resin. (*Marignia* Comm.) . . . . **Protium** Burm.
Petals 5, imbricate in bud. Ovary 2—3-celled. Fruit with 2—3 stones, dehiscent. Flowers hermaphrodite. — Species 15. Central Africa. The resin of several species (frankincense) is used as an incense and in medicine. . . . . **Boswellia** Roxb.

FAMILY 118. MELIACEAE

Trees or shrubs. Leaves without stipules, usually pinnate. Flowers regular, mostly panicled. Petals 3—6, usually free. Stamens as many or more frequently twice as many as the petals. Filaments usually united. Anthers 2-celled, opening inwards or laterally by longitudinal slits. Ovary superior, usually 2- or more-celled. Ovules inverted. Style simple or wanting ; stigma entire or lobed. — Genera 23, species 150. (Including *AITONIEAE*, *CEDRELEAE*, and *PTAEROXYLEAE*.) (Plate 76.)

1. Filaments free. Ovule 1 in each ovary-cell. Seeds winged. Leaves pinnate. [Subfamily **CEDRELOIDEAE.**] 2
Filaments more or less united into a tube. 3

2. Ovary and fruit 2-celled. Petals 4. Stamens 4. — Species 2. South and East Africa. They yield timber (sneezewood).
Ptaeroxylon Eckl. & Zeyh.
Ovary and fruit 5-celled. — Species 1. Madagascar. . **Cedrelopsis** Baill.

J. Fleischmann del.

Pachylobus edulis G. Don

A Flowering branch. B Male flower cut lengthwise. C Stamen. D Female flower cut lengthwise. E Staminode. F Cross-section
of ovary.

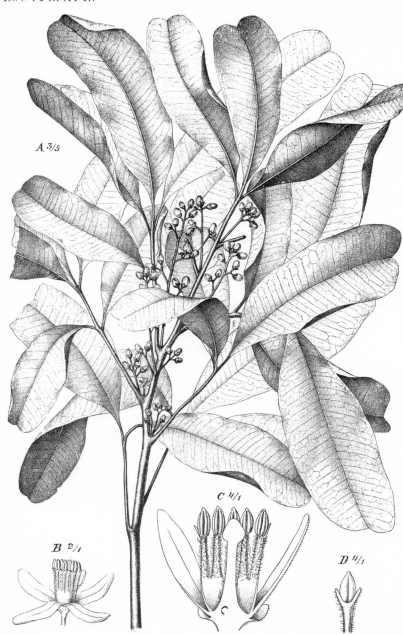

A 3/5

B 2/1

C 4/1

D 4/1

J Fleischmann del.

Trichilia retusa Oliv.

A Flowering branch. *B* Flower. *C* Flower cut lengthwise. *D* Anther.

3. Seeds winged. Ovules 4 or more, rarely 2 in each ovary-cell. Stamens
   8—10. [Subfamily **SWIETENIOIDEAE.**] 4
   Seeds not winged. Ovules 1—2, rarely 3—8 in each ovary-cell or on
   each placenta. [Subfamily **MELIOIDEAE.**] 9
4. Ovules 2 in each ovary-cell. Ovary 5-celled. Stigma small. Disc
   wanting. Anthers 10, seated between the teeth of the staminal tube.
   Leaves whorled, undivided. Flowers in panicles. — Species 2. West
   Africa. . . . . **Pynaertia** De Wild.
   Ovules 4 or more in each ovary-cell. Leaves pinnate. 5
5. Ovules 4 in each ovary-cell. Disc shortly stalk-shaped. Staminal tube
   campanulate, the mouth crenate and with short teeth bearing the
   anthers. Petals imbricate in bud. — Species 7. Central Africa.
                                                        Lovoa Harms
   Ovules 6 or more in each ovary-cell. 6
6. Ovules 6 in each ovary-cell. Ovary sessile. Disc none. Staminal tube
   entire at the mouth, or with short teeth bearing the anthers. Petals
   with imbricate aestivation. Flowers 5-merous. — Species 2. Southern
   West Africa. . . . . **Wulfhorstia** C. DC.
   Ovules 12 or more in each ovary-cell. Petals with contorted aestivation. 7
7. Disc shortly stalk-shaped, connected with the staminal tube by longitudinal
   ridges. Seeds winged below. Leaflets entire. — Species 15. Central
   Africa. They yield timber, gum, and a dye-stuff. (Including *Leioptyx*
   Pierre, under *Swietenia* L.) . . . . . **Entandophragma** C. DC.
   Disc cup- or cushion-shaped, not connected with the staminal tube by
   longitudinal ridges. 8
8. Disc cup-shaped. Fruit oblong. Seeds about 5 in each cell of the fruit,
   winged below. — Species 1. Central Africa. Yields timber and
   gum. (Under *Cedrela* L.) . . . . **Pseudocedrela** Harms
   Disc cushion-shaped. Flowers 4-merous. Fruit globose. Seeds numerous
   in each cell, winged all round. — Species 7. Tropics. They yield
   timber (African mahogany), tanning bark, gum, and medicaments.
                                                        Khaya Juss.
9. (3.) Ovules more than 2 in each ovary-cell. Ovary 4—5-celled. Anthers
   8—10, inserted between the lobes of the staminal tube. Seeds large,
   pyramidal ; seed-coat woody or corky. 10
   Ovules 1—2 in each ovary-cell or on each placenta. Seeds small or medium-
   sized ; testa crustaceous, leathery, parchment-like, or membranous. 11
10. Flowers 4-merous. Staminal tube with 2-toothed lobes. Seed-coat
   corky or spongy. Radicle of the embryo lateral. Leaves pinnate,
   with 1—3 pairs of leaflets, or simple. Panicles rather small, lax, few-
   flowered. — Species 3. Tropics. They yield timber, tanning bark,
   and oily seeds. (Under *Carapa* Aubl.) . . . **Xylocarpus** Koen.
   Flowers 5-merous. Staminal tube with entire lobes. Ovules 6—8 to
   each ovary-cell. Seed-coat woody. Radicle superior. Leaves pinnate,

with many pairs of leaflets. Panicles very large, many-flowered. — Species 4. Tropics. They yield timber, oily seeds, and medicaments.

Carapa Aubl.

11. Ovary 2—3-celled, rarely 1-celled with 2—3 placentas. Stamens 6—12. 12
Ovary 4—20-celled, rarely later on 1-celled with 4—5 placentas. . . 19

12. Anthers inserted below the mouth of the staminal tube, entirely or almost included. Disc stalk-like or wanting. Seeds exalbuminous. Leaflets 6—25. 13
Anthers inserted at the upper edge of the staminal tube, or at the top of its lobes, or in the notches between them. 14

13. Leaflets serrate. Flowers 5-merous. Anthers inserted at the base of the lobes of the staminal tube. Disc none. Ovary septate. Stigma 2—3-parted. Fruit a 1-seeded drupe. Radicle of the embryo exserted. — Species 1. East Africa. Yields timber, oily seeds, and medicaments. (Under *Melia* L.) . . . . .   **Azadirachta** Juss.
Leaflets entire. Stigma discoid. Fruit a 2- or more-seeded capsule or berry. Radicle included. — Species 7. West Africa. Yield timber. (Including *Bingeria* A. Chev. and *Heckeldora* Pierre) . .   **Guarea** L.

14. Filaments united at the base only, 2-toothed at the top ; anthers inserted between the teeth. Petals 5, valvate in bud. Fruit a berry or drupe Seeds albuminous. Leaves 3-foliolate. — Species 2. Madagascar and Comoro Islands. . . . .   **Cipadessa** Blume
Filaments united high up, rarely (*Trichilia*) at the base only, but then fruit a capsule and seeds exalbuminous. 15

15. Ovary 1-celled, adnate to the staminal tube. Stigma sessile. Anthers inserted at the rim of the almost entire staminal tube. Disc stalk-like. Flowers 4-merous. Leaflets usually 5. — Species 1. Madagascar.

Symphytosiphon Harms

Ovary 2—3-celled. 16

16. Flowers solitary, axillary, rarely in spikes. Anthers 10, inserted at the tips of the teeth of the staminal tube. Disc ring-shaped. Style long. Fruit capsular, subglobose. Seeds with 3 narrow wings and with fleshy albumen. Small shrubs. Leaves with a narrowly winged stalk and 3 woolly leaflets. — Species 1. Southern West Africa (Angola). Used medicinally. (*Nelanaregam* Adans.)   **Naregamia** Wight & Arn.
Flowers in panicles, rarely in racemes. Leaves with 5 or more leaflets, rarely with 3, but then seeds exalbuminous. 17

17. Leaflets 5—7, toothed, clothed with stellate hairs ; leafstalk winged. Anthers 10, inserted between the lobes of the staminal tube, which are divided in filiform segments. Disc ring-shaped. Style short. — Species 1. West Africa (Cameroons). The bark is eaten and used medicinally.

Pterorhachis Harms

Leaflets entire, very rarely toothed, but then anthers 8, inserted at the entire mouth of the staminal tube. Seeds exalbuminous. . . . 18

18. Fruit a berry or a drupe. Seed-coat crustaceous. Staminal tube entire or shortly toothed. — Species 15. Tropical and South Africa. Some of them yield timber, tanners' bark, and medicaments. (Including *Charia* C. DC.) . . . . **Ekebergia** Sparm.

Fruit a capsule with a leathery rind. Seed-coat thin-leathery. Staminal tube usually more or less deeply divided. — Species 35. Tropical and South Africa. Some of them yield timber, dyes, oily seeds, and medicaments. (Plate 76.) . . . . **Trichilia** L.

19. (11.) Leaves simple, undivided. Flowers solitary or in cymes or racemes. Fruit capsular. Seeds albuminous. 20

Leaves pinnate. Flowers in panicles, racemes, or cymes. Stamens united high up. 21

20. Stamens united at the base only, 8. Disc cup-shaped. Stigma small. Flowers solitary. — Species 1. South Africa. (*Aitonia* Thunb., *Carruthia* O. Ktze.) . . . . **Nymania** Lindb.

Stamens united high up, 8—10. Disc ring-shaped or absent. Stigma usually thick. — Species 50. Tropical and South Africa. Some are used medicinally. (Including *Calodryum* Desv., *Grevellina* Baill., and *Quivisia* Comm.) . . . . **Tourraea** L.

21. Leaves twice pinnate, with usually serrate leaflets. Anthers 10—12, inserted between the teeth of the staminal tube. Fruit a drupe. Seeds with scanty albumen. — Species 4, two natives of Central Africa, the others (especially *M. Azederach* L., beadtree or Persian lilac) cultivated as ornamental plants and sometimes naturalized. They yield timber, gum, oil, and medicaments, and are also used for the preparation of liquors. The fruits are poisonous. . . . . **Melia** L.

Leaves once pinnate, with entire leaflets. Seeds exalbuminous . . 22

22. Leaves equally pinnate. Anthers 5 or 8. 23

Leaves unequally pinnate. Anthers 8 or 10. 24

23. Leaflets 2—6. Flowers 4-merous. Petals with contorted aestivation. Anthers 8, inserted below the notches between the lobes of the staminal tube. (See 10.) . . . . **Xylocarpus** Koen.

Leaflets 10—16. Flowers 5-merous. Petals with valvate aestivation. Anthers 5, inserted at the rim of the nearly entire staminal tube. — Species 1. Madagascar. . . . . **Quivisianthe** Baill.

24. Anthers inserted at the upper margin of the staminal tube or at the top of its teeth. Disc ring- or cup-shaped. Style short, with a lobed stigma. Leaflets opposite. (See 18.) . . . **Ekebergia** Sparm.

Anthers inserted below the mouth of the staminal tube, included. Leaflets usually alternate. 25

25. Petals united high up and adnate to the staminal tube, valvate in bud. Ovary at first 4—5-celled, with 2 ovules in each cell, later 1-celled. — Species 4. West Africa. . . . . . . **Turraeanthus** Baill.

U

Petals free, or united at the base only. 2
26. Ovary 4-celled, with 1 ovule in each cell. (See 13.)   .   **Guarea** L.
  Ovary 4—5-celled, with 2 ovules in each cell. (See 10.) **Carapa** Aubl.

SUBORDER MALPIGHIINEAE

FAMILY 119. MALPIGHIACEAE

Shrubs or undershrubs, with branched hairs, usually climbing. Leaves undivided, usually stipulate. Flowers in racemose inflorescences, bracteolate. Sepals 3—5, free or united at the base, mostly furnished with glands on the outside. Petals 5, free, imbricate in bud, usually clawed and toothed. Stamens usually 10, hypogynous. Filaments free or united at the base. Anthers opening inwards by two longitudinal slits. Ovary 2—3-celled, with 1 pendulous and inverted ovule in each cell. Styles 1—3. Fruit usually separating into 3 mericarps. Seeds exalbuminous. — Genera 16, species 80. Tropical and South Africa. (Plate 77.)

 1. Fruiting receptacle flat. Mericarps not winged. Calyx without glands. Petals clawed, almost entire. Stamens 10. Leaves stipulate. Flowers in terminal racemes. 2
    Fruiting receptacle pyramidal. Mericarps winged. 3
 2. Fruit covered with short hairs, dehiscent. Petals equal. Anthers glabrous. Ovary covered with short hairs. Styles free, long and thin, with small stigmas. Leaves opposite. — Species 1. Madagascar. [Tribe GAL-PHIMIEAE.] . . . . **Galphimia** Cav.
    Fruit covered with long, soft, hairy, spine-shaped processes. Petals unequal. Anthers hairy. Ovary clothed with long hairs. Styles converging, rather short and thick, with oval reflexed stigmas. Leaves alternate or subopposite. — Species 1. Madagascar. [Tribe TRI-COMARIEAE.] . . . . **Echinopteris** Juss.
 3. Mericarps with a large dorsal wing, without a lateral wing. Petals more or less distinctly clawed. [Tribe BANISTERIEAE.] 4
    Mericarps with a large, sometimes divided, lateral wing and a small dorsal wing, or without a dorsal wing. Stamens 10. [Tribe HIRAEEAE.] 10
 4. Style 1. Ovary 3-celled, 3-lobed. Stamens 5, two only fertile. Sepals with two large glands each. Flowers solitary, terminal. Leaves mucronate. — Species 1. Madagascar. . . **Cottsia** Dubard & Dop
    Styles 2—3. Stamens 10—15. 5
 5. Styles 2, long. Ovary with 2 perfect and 1 rudimentary cell. Stamens 10. Petals with a long claw. Leaves usually alternate. 6
    Styles 3. Ovary with 3 perfect cells. Corolla regular. Leaves usually opposite. 7
 6. Corolla distinctly irregular. Mericarps with an almost semi-circular, cockscomb-shaped, palmately nerved dorsal wing. Bracteoles awl-shaped. — Species 1. West Africa. . . . . . **Rhinopteryx** Nied.

MALPIGHIACEAE.

Pl. 77

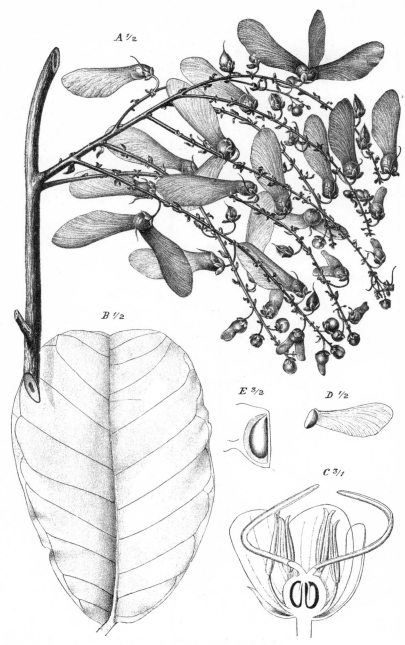

J. Fleischmann del.

Acridocarpus macrocalyx Engl.

A Part of branch with fruits. *B* Leaf. *C* Flower cut lengthwise. *D* Mericarp. *E* Mericarp cut lengthwise.

J. Fleischmann del.

Securidaca longepedunculata Fresen.

A Branch with flower-buds.   B Flower (from which one of the lateral sepals has been removed).   C Flower without the perianth, cut lengthwise.   D Group of fruits.   E Fruit cut lengthwise.

Corolla regular. Mericarps with a more or less parallel-nerved dorsal wing. — Species 20. Tropical and South-east Africa. Some species are used as ornamental plants or in medicine. (Plate 77.)

Acridocarpus Guill. & Perr.

7. Styles very long, divaricate; stigmas small, capitate. Stamens 10. Petals with a very short claw. Sepals with very scantily developed glands. — Species 4. Central and South-east Africa.

Sphedamnocarpus Planch.

Styles short or rather short, erect or slightly divergent; stigmas obliquely truncate, hooked, or broadened. 8

8. Stigmas broadened, semi-orbicular. Ovary with 3 tufts of hairs. Stamens 11—15. Petals with a very short claw. Sepals without glands. — Species 1. Madagascar. . . . . . **Tricomariopsis** Dubard & Dop

Stigmas not broadened. Stamens 10. 9

9. Styles hooked at the apex, bearing the stigma at the bent. Petals with a distinct claw. Sepals with glands. – – Species 1. West Africa.

Heteropteris Juss.

Styles not hooked above, bearing the stigma at the obliquely truncate tip. Petals with a very short claw. Sepals without glands. — Species 1. Madagascar. (Under *Sphedamnocarpus* Planch.)

Banisterioides Dubard & Dop

10. (3.) Styles shorter than the ovary. Stigma terminal. Petals with a short claw. Calyx without glands. Mericarps with an undivided side-wing. 11

Styles longer than the ovary 12

11. Ovary 2-celled. Petals slightly toothed. Leaves alternate. — Species 1. East Africa. . . . . **Diaspis** Nied.

Ovary 3-celled. Mericarps with an air-cavity extending all round. Leaves usually opposite and crowded upon dwarf-shoots. — Species 4. East Africa. . . . . **Caucanthus** Forsk.

12. Petals sessile, entire. Calyx without glands. Styles 3, very long, with the stigma on the inside of the thickened apex. Mericarps with an undivided side-wing. — Species 1. West Africa to the upper Nile.

Flabellaria Cav.

Petals clawed. 13

13. Petals with a very short claw, entire. Calyx without glands. Styles 3, rather short, with a 2-lobed stigma. Flowers polygamous-dioecious, in umbels. Mericarps with a 3-parted side-wing. — Species 5. Madagascar. . . . . **Microsteira** Bak.

Petals with a long or rather long claw. Style long. Flowers usually hermaphrodite. 14

14. Stigma at the inside of the thickened style-apex. Styles 3, all perfectly developed. Calyx without glands. Petals more or less toothed or fringed. Mericarps with a shield-shaped, usually notched side-wing. — Species 25. Tropical and South Africa. . . . . **Triaspis** Burch.

Stigma small, at the slightly or not thickened style-apex. Usually a
single style perfectly developed. 15
15. Flowers distinctly irregular. Calyx with a large gland. Petals fringed.
Mericarps with a 3-parted side-wing.—Species 2, one a native of West
Africa, the other one naturalized in the Mascarene Islands. Ornamental
plants. (*Gaertnera* Roxb.) . . . . **Hiptage** Gaertn.
Flowers more or less regular. Calyx with several small glands or without
glands. Petals entire. Mericarp with a stellate, many-parted side-
wing. — Species 17. Madagascar, East and South-east Africa.
Tristellateia Thouars

SUBORDER POLYGALINEAE
FAMILY 120. POLYGALACEAE

Leaves simple, entire. Inflorescence racemose, bracteolate. Flowers irregular. Sepals 5, the two inner usually petal-like. Petals 3—5, more or less
adnate to the staminal tube, the lowest more or less concave and boat-shaped.
Stamens 5—8. Filaments more or less united. Anthers attached by the base,
at length one-celled, opening towards the apex. Ovary superior, 1—3-celled.
Ovule 1 in each cell, pendulous, inverted. Style simple or 2-cleft, usually
curved and flattened. — Genera 6, species 240. (Plate 78.)
1. Petals 5, all well-developed, unappendaged. Stamens 5. Ovary 2—3-
celled. 2
Petals 3, 4, or 5, two of which are rudimentary. Stamens 6—8. Ovary
1—2-celled. 3
2. Petals unequal, clawed, the lowest boat-shaped. Stigma capitate. Fruit
a drupe. Seeds ellipsoid. — Species 3. West Africa. They yield
timber, edible fruits, and medicaments. . . . . **Carpolobia** Don
Petals subequal, sessile, the lowest not boat-shaped. Stigma punctiform. Fruit a nut. Seeds globose. — Species 4. West Africa. (Under
Carpolobia Don) . . . . **Atroxima** Stapf
3. Ovary 1-celled ; a second rudimentary cell sometimes present. Stigma
entire or lobed. Sepals unequal. Concave petal with an appendage.
Stamens 8. Fruit a winged nut. Seeds without an aril, exalbuminous.
Shrubs or trees. — Species 3. Central and South Africa. They yield
bast-fibres, soap-bark, oily seeds, and medicinal drugs ; the roots are
said to be poisonous. (*Lophostylis* Hochst.) (Plate 78.)
Securidaca L.
Ovary 2-celled. Fruit a capsule or a drupe. 4
4. Sepals subequal. Concave petal with an appendage. Stamens 7, rarely
8. Style almost straight. Fruit a capsule. Seeds with an aril, albuminous. — Species 60. South Africa to Nyasaland. **Muraltia** Neck.
Sepals unequal, the two inner usually wing-like. 5
5. Fruit a drupe. Seeds albuminous. Style almost straight. Stamens 7,
rarely 8. Filaments united quite or nearly to the top. Concave

A ²/₃

C ⁵/₁

B ⁷/₂

D ⁵/₁

J. Fleischmann del.

Dichapetalum leucosepalum Ruhl.

A Flowering branch. B Flower C Flower cut lengthwise. D Cross-section of ovary.

EUPHORBIACEAE.

Pl. 80.

J. Fleischmann del.

Phyllanthus floribundus Müll. Arg.

A Flowering branch.   *B* Male flower.   *C* Stamens and disc.   *D* Fruit.   *E* Female flower cut lengthwise.   *F* Cross-section of ovary.

petal with an appendage. Shrubs. — Species 1. South Africa (Cape Colony). The fruits are edible. (*Mundtia* Kunth). **Mundia** Kunth
Fruit a capsule. Stamens 8, rarely 6 or 7. — Species 170. Some of them yield fibres or fat from the seeds, others serve as ornamental or medicinal plants. " Milkwort." . . . . **Polygala** L.

SUBORDER DICHAPETALINEAE

FAMILY 121. DICHAPETALACEAE

Shrubs or trees. Leaves alternate, undivided, stipulate. Inflorescence cymose. Sepals 4—5, imbricate in bud. Petals 4—5, usually 2-cleft. Disc present, but sometimes reduced to separate glands. Stamens 5, sometimes only 2—3 fertile. Anthers opening inwards. Ovary 2—3-celled, usually superior. Ovules 2 in each cell, pendulous, inverted ; raphe ventral. Style 2—3-cleft or undivided with 2—3 stigmas. Fruit a nut or drupe. Seeds 1—2, exalbuminous. — Genera 2, species 75. Tropical and South Africa. (*CHAILLETIACEAE.*) (Plate 79.)

   Petals unequal, united below into a long tube, 2-cleft, imbricate in bud. Sepals united below, unequal. Fertile stamens 2—3. Disc semi-annular. — Species 2. Central Africa. . . . . . **Tapura** Aubl.
   Petals equal, free or united at the base, rarely higher. Fertile stamens 5. — Species 75. Tropical and South Africa. Some are poisonous. (*Chailletia* DC.) (Plate 79.) . . . . . **Dichapetalum** Thouars

SUBORDER TRICOCCAE

FAMILY 122. EUPHORBIACEAE

Flowers unisexual. Stamens hypogynous, rarely (*Bridelia*) perigynous. Anthers 2-celled. Ovary superior or naked, usually 3-celled. Ovules solitary in each cell, or 2 side by side, pendulous, inverted ; raphe ventral ; micropyle usually covered by an outgrowth of the placenta. Fruit generally separating into 3 dehiscing mericarps. Seeds usually albuminous ; embryo axile, radicle superior. — Genera 122, species 1200. (Including *DAPHNIPHYLLA-CEAE.*) (Plate 80.)

   1. Ovule 1 in each ovary-cell. [Subfamily **CROTONOIDEAE.**] . . . 2
      Ovules 2 in each ovary-cell. Juice not milky. [Subfamily **PHYLLANTHOI-DEAE.**] 76
   2. Inflorescence consisting of partial inflorescences having the appearance of a single flower and containing one female flower and several or many male ones surrounded by a lobed involucre with glandular appendages. Petals none. Stamen 1. Ovary 3—4-celled. Juice milky. [Tribe EUPHORBIEAE.] 3
      Inflorescence not consisting of partial inflorescences looking like a single flower. 11

3. Male flowers with a cupular, entire or 3—6-lobed perianth. Female
   flowers with a 3—4-toothed or -cleft perianth. Trees or shrubs. . . 4
   Male flowers without a perianth. 5

4. Involucre of the partial inflorescences split at one side and consisting of 4
   or more bracts. Ovary 3-celled. Style 3- or 6-cleft. Trees. — Species
   3. Tropics. Poisonous and used medicinally. . . **Anthostema** Juss.
   Involucre closed all round and consisting of 4 bracts. Ovary 4-celled.
   Style 4-parted. — Species 3. Equatorial West Africa.
                                                  Dichostemma Pierre

5. Involucre of the partial inflorescences with unequal lobes and with an
   appendage, in the axil of which the glands are inserted. Shrubs. —
   Species 2. Madagascar. . . . . **Pedilanthus** Neck.
   Involucre with equal lobes, but sometimes surrounded by a one-sided
   gland. 6

6. Involucre irregular, with a single gland sometimes embracing the partial
   inflorescence and split at one side only. 7
   Involucre regular, with several glands sometimes united into a ring or
   cup. 9

7. Involucre with a narrow gland not enveloping the partial inflorescence.
   Female flowers with a perianth. Bracts subtending the involucres united
   high up. Spiny shrubs. — Species 1. East Africa. **Stenadenium** Pax
   Involucre with a broad gland enveloping the partial inflorescence. Herbs. 8

8. Female flowers with a perianth. Bracts subtending the involucres united
   at the base. — Species 2. East Africa. (Under *Monadenium* Pax).
                                                     Lortia Rendle

   Female flowers without a perianth. Bracts subtending the involucres
   united high up. — Species 10. Central Africa. . . **Monadenium** Pax

9. Glands of the involucre united into a ring or cup. — Species 10. Tropical
   and South-east Africa. Some are poisonous. . . **Synadenium** Boiss.
   Glands of the involucre separate. 10

10. Fruit a drupe. — Species 1. West Africa. (Under *Euphorbia* L.)
                                                Elaeophorbia Stapf
    Fruit a capsule. — Species 320. Many of them are poisonous, some yield
    timber, gum, rubber, oil, and medicaments, or serve as garden- or
    hedge-plants. "Spurge." . . . . **Euphorbia** L.

11. (2.) Filaments bent inwards in the bud. Calyx 4—6-partite, imbricate
    or subvalvate in bud. Corolla present, at least in the male flowers.
    Inflorescence spike- or raceme-like. Leaves and young shoots clothed
    with scales or stellate hairs. — Species 100. Tropical and South Africa.
    Several species are poisonous, some yield gum-lac, incense-wood, oil,
    and medicaments, or serve as ornamental plants. [Tribe CROTON-
    EAE.] . . . . **Croton** L.
    Filaments straight in the bud 12

12. Calyx of the male flowers with valvate or closed aestivation. [Especially tribe ACALYPHEAE.] 13

Calyx of the male flowers with imbricate or open aestivation. . . . 59

13. Corolla present in the male flowers. 14

Corolla absent in the male flowers. 24

14. Petals of the male flowers more or less united. Rudimentary pistil cup-shaped or wanting. Style-branches 2. Flowers dioecious. Hairy undershrubs, shrubs, or trees. 15

Petals of the male flowers free from each other, but sometimes (*Caperonia*) adnate to the staminal tube ; in this case rudimentary pistil club-shaped and style with many branches 17

15. Petals united high up. Calyx bursting irregularly. Disc of 5 glands alternating with the petals. Stamens 12—20. Rudimentary pistil absent. Climbing shrubs with reddish-brown hairs. Leaves 3—7-nerved. Flowers in panicles. — Species 5. West Africa. Fibre-yielding plants. . . . . **Manniophyton** Muell. Arg.

Petals united at the base only. Calyx 4—5-parted. Stamens 4—5. Undershrubs or trees. 16

16. Flowers 4-merous. Anthers turned inwards. Disc within the stamens. Trees. Leaves 3-nerved. Young shoots with rusty-brown hairs. Flowers in panicles. — Species 1. West Africa (Cameroons).

Schubea Pax

Flowers 5-merous. Anthers turned outwards. Glands alternating with the stamens ; a cupular disc also present within them. Undershrubs. Young shoots with white hairs. Flowers in axillary clusters. — Species 1. East Africa (Somaliland). . . . . **Gilgia** Pax

17. Style many-cleft. Rudimentary pistil of the male flowers club-shaped. Stamens 5—10, united below. Petals adnate to the staminal tube. Disc indistinct. Flowers in racemes. Herbs or undershrubs, usually hispid. — Species 9. Tropics. Several species yield fibre.

Caperonia St. Hil.

Style 2—4-cleft. Rudimentary pistil of the male flowers 2—3-cleft or wanting. 18

18. Stem herbaceous or woody at the base only, hairy or cottony. Flowers in racemes, monoecious. Male flowers without a disc. — Species 7. Northern and tropical Africa. Some are poisonous or yield dyes and medicaments. "Turnsole." (*Tournesolia* Scop.) . . **Chrozophora** Neck.

Stem woody. Male flowers usually with a disc reduced to separate glands. 19

19. Young branches and leaves clothed with scales. Inflorescence spicate or racemose. Flowers dioecious. Stamens 15—20. — Species 12. West Africa. . . . . **Crotonogyne** Muell.Arg.

Young branches and leaves glabrous, downy, or clothed with star-like hairs. Inflorescence spicate, racemose, or paniculate ; in the two former cases stamens 6—14. 20

20. Young branches and leaves clothed with 2-cleft or star-like hairs. Trees. Leaves palmately nerved. Flowers in panicles, monoecious. Stamens 8—20. Fruit a drupe. — Species 2. Cultivated and naturalized in the tropics. They yield timber, gum-lac, tanning bark, dye-stuffs, and edible oily seeds (" candle-nuts ") . . . . .   **Aleurites** Forst.
    Young branches and leaves clothed with simple hairs, or glabrous. Shrubs. Inflorescence spicate or racemose, more rarely paniculate, but then leaves pinnately nerved. Fruit a capsule. 21
21. Flowers in panicles, dioecious. Calyx 2—3-partite in the male flowers, 4-partite in the female. Corolla in the female flowers falling off very early, or wanting. Stamens numerous, free. Male flowers without a rudimentary pistil. Branches downy, at least when young. — Species 2. West Africa (Cameroons) . . . .   **Grossera** Pax
    Flowers in spicate or racemose inflorescences. Stamens 6—13. . . . 22
22. Flowers monoecious. Calyx 5-partite. Stamens 10, united at the base. Anthers attached by the back. Male flowers without a rudimentary pistil. Branches glabrous. — Species 1. Madagascar and Comoro Islands. . . . .   **Tannodia** Baill.
    Flowers dioecious. 23
23. Branches glabrous. Anther-halves suspended from the connective. — Species 2. West Africa and Comoro Islands. .   **Agrostistachys** Dalz.
    Branches hairy. Styles 2-cleft. Leaves stalked. — Species 2. East Africa. . . . .   **Holstia** Pax
24. (13.) Styles united to about the middle or beyond. 25
    Styles free or united at the base only. 32
25. Styles united nearly to the top into a usually hollow column. . . . 26
    Styles united about to the middle, undivided. Ovary 3-celled. . . 31
26. Calyx of the female flowers entire or shortly toothed. Anthers 3—4-celled. Ovary 1—2-, rarely 3-celled. Trees or shrubs. — Species 50. Tropical and South Africa. (Including *Mappa* Juss.) . .   **Macaranga** Thouars
    Calyx of the female flowers 4—12-partite. Anthers 2-celled. Ovary 3—4-, rarely 5-celled. 27
27. Flowers dioecious. Calyx of the female flowers 4-partite. Ovary 4-celled, winged. Style rather long, columnar, with a 4-lobed stigma. Seeds with an outgrowth at the hilum. Trees. — Species 1. West Africa (Cameroons). . . . .   **Tetracarpidium** Pax
    Flowers monoecious. Calyx of the female flowers 5—12-, rarely 4-partite. Seeds usually without an outgrowth. 28
28. Calyx of the male flowers 3-partite, of the female 5—6-partite. Stamens 3, with united filaments. Ovary 3-celled. Style united into a globose body. Climbing shrubs. Flowers in spikes. — Species 1. Madagascar. . . . .   **Sphaerostylis** Baill.
    Calyx of the male flowers 4—6-partite. Stamens 4—30 29
29. Stamens 4—6. Rudimentary pistil of the male flowers columnar. Ovary 3-celled. Trees or shrubs, with stellate hairs. Leaves undivided,

palmately nerved. Flowers in spikes. — Species 1. Madagascar and Comoro Islands. (Including *Niedenzua* Pax) . **Adenochlaena** Baill. Stamens 8—30, inserted upon an elevated receptacle. Rudimentary pistil none. Shrubs or undershrubs, usually climbing. 30

30. Flowers in cymes surrounded by two large, brightly coloured bracts. Anther-halves parallel. Style columnar. — Species 15. Tropical and South Africa. Some are used for dyeing, in medicine, or as ornamental plants. . . . . **Dalechampia** L. Flowers in racemes, without conspicuous bracts. Anther-halves spreading. Climbing plants. Leaves undivided. — Species 5. Central and South Africa. . . . . **Plukenetia** L.

31. Stem herbaceous or woody at the base only, usually climbing, often with stinging hairs. Stamens 3, rarely more. — Species 45. Tropical and South Africa. Some are used medicinally. (Including *Ctenomeria* Harv.) . . . . **Tragia** L. Stem woody throughout. Stamens numerous, free. — Species 20. Tropics. The fruits of some species are used for tanning. . . **Pycnocoma** Benth.

32. (24.) Filaments repeatedly branched. Anther-halves numerous, separate, globose. Tall herbs or shrubs. Leaves palmately lobed. Flowers monoecious. — Species 1 (*R. communis* L., castor-oil-plant). Spontaneous in the tropics, naturalized in other parts of Africa. An ornamental plant yielding fibre, fodder, and poisonous oily seeds used in medicine. . . . . **Ricinus** L. Filaments not branched. 33

33. Anther-halves plainly separate, oblong or linear, often twisted. Filaments 6—20, free. Styles free, usually divided. Trees or shrubs. . . . 34 Anther-halves contiguous or nearly so, oblong to globular. 35

34. Bracts of the female flowers leaf-like. Sepals of the female flowers 3—5, small. Stamens usually 8. Disc none. Male flowers spicate, female spicate, paniculate, or solitary. — Species 80. Tropical and South Africa. Some are used as ornamental or medicinal plants. . . **Acalypha** L. Bracts of the female flowers small. Sepals of the female flowers 4—6, broad. Disc absent in the male flowers, flat and lobed in the female. Flowers spicate. — Species 4. West Africa. . . . . . **Mareya** Baill.

35. Anthers 2-celled, at least after opening. . . . . 36 Anthers 3—4-celled, even after opening. Trees or shrubs. 57

36. Anther-halves oblong, attached lengthwise or above the middle. . . 37 Anther-halves ovoid or globose, attached by the base or the tip, rarely in the middle. 50

37. Stamens 3—10. Trees or shrubs. . . . . 38 Stamens numerous. 43

38. Calyx valvate in bud. Stamens 5—10; filaments united throughout. Rudimentary pistil exceeding the staminal tube. Styles very short, 2-lobed. Trees. Leaves 3-foliolate. Flowers in panicles, monoecious.

— Species 2.   Cultivated in the tropics.   They yield rubber (para-rubber):
(*Siphonia* Schreb.)   .   .   .   .   **Hevea** Aubl.
Calyx closed in bud.   Stamens 3—10 ;   filaments free or united at the
base only.   Styles distinctly developed.   Leaves simple, undivided.   39

39. Male flowers with a rudimentary pistil.   Stamens 6—10.   Filaments free,
bent twice.   Styles divided into many branches.   Flowers monoecious.
Shrubs with stellate hairs.   40
Male flowers without a rudimentary pistil.   Filaments united at the base.
Styles undivided or with 2 branches.   Flowers usually dioecious.   .   41

40. Sepals of the female flowers 6, entire, united halfway up.   Styles free. —
Species 1.   Island of Socotra.   (Under C*ephalocroton* Hochst.)
                                    Cephalocrotonopsis Pax
Sepals of the female flowers pinnately dissected.   Styles united at the
base. — Species 8.   East Africa to Transvaal, Madagascar, and German
South-west Africa.   .   .   .   .   **Cephalocroton** Hochst.

41. Styles at first united, finally free.   Seeds with an outgrowth at the hilum.
Glabrous shrubs.   Leaves 3—5-nerved at the base.   Male inflorescences
catkin-like, springing from the old wood. — Species 5.   Tropics.   Some
yield dye-stuffs.   .   .   .   .   **Lepidoturus** Baill.
Styles free or nearly so.   Seeds without an outgrowth.   Male inflorescences
spike- or panicle-like, axillary.   42

42. Styles united at the base, two-cleft.   Trees.   Leaves penninerved. —
Species 2.   Madagascar.   (Including *Orfilea* Baill., under *Alchornea*
Swartz) .   .   .   .   **Lautembergia** Baill.
Styles free, undivided. — Species 10.   Tropics to Delagoa Bay.   Some
of them yield dye-stuffs.   .   .   .   .   **Alchornea** Swartz

43. (37.) Styles laciniate.   Ovary nearly glabrous.   Disc in the male flowers
consisting of glands situated outside the stamens, in the female indistinct.   Sepals 5.   Trees.   Leaves penninerved, without stipules.
Flowers dioecious, the male in clusters arising from the old wood, the
female in axillary racemes. — Species 1.   East Africa.
                                    Crotonogynopsis Pax
Styles two-cleft or undivided, but usually ciliate within.   Ovary usually
hairy.   Disc indistinct in the male flowers.   Sepals 2—4, very rarely 5.
Flowers in spikes or panicles.   44

44. Styles two-cleft.   45
Styles undivided.   47

45. Flowers dioecious, in panicles.   Calyx of the male flowers 2-partite.   Disc
indistinct.   Plants clothed with stellate hairs.   Leaves palminerved. —
Species 5.   Central Africa.   .   .   .   .   .   **Neoboutonia** Muell. Arg.
Flowers monoecious, all or the female in spikes.   Calyx of the male flowers
4—5-partite.   Disc distinctly developed in the female flowers.   Trees.
Leaves penninerved.   46

46. Disc of the female flowers expanded.   Styles thick.   Leafstalk rather
short.   Stipules lanceolate, persistent. — Species 1.   West Africa.
                                    Necepsia Prain

Disc of the female flowers cupular. Styles awl-shaped. Leafstalk very
short. Stipules awl-shaped, deciduous. Spikes unisexual. — Species 1.
Madagascar. (Under *Alchornea* Swartz) . . . . . **Palissya** Baill.

47. Calyx of the male flowers 2-partite. Stamens numerous. Styles thickish,
united at the base. Shrubs. Leaves narrow, penninerved. Flowers in
axillary spikes, monoecious. — Species 1. Equatorial West Africa.

Neopycnocoma Pax

Calyx of the male flowers 3—5-partite 48

48. Flowers in leaf-opposed spikes, monoecious. Calyx 4-partite. Styles 4.
Stem herbaceous. Leaves broad. — Species 2. Southern West Africa
(Amboland). . . . . **Pseudotragia** Pax

Flowers in axillary or terminal spikes or panicles. Stem woody. . . 49

49. Leaves narrow, penninerved. Flowers monoecious, in spikes. Calyx
of the male flowers 3-partite. Styles thin. — Species 1. Central
Africa. . . . . **Argomuellera** Pax

Leaves broad, palminerved. Flowers usually dioecious. — Species 10.
Tropical and South Africa. (Including *Echinus* Lour.) **Mallotus** Lour.

50. (36.) Anther-halves attached at the middle. Stamens 6—12. Calyx
5-partite. Ovary 3-celled. Styles 3, united at the base, 2-cleft. Herbs.
Flowers in cymes. — Species 8. South Africa. (Including *Para-
denocline* Muell. Arg.) . . . . **Adenocline** Turcz.

Anther-halves attached at the base or the top. Styles undivided or many-
cleft. 51

51. Anther-halves attached at the top, pendulous, spreading downwards.
Styles 2, rarely 3, undivided. Herbs or undershrubs. 52

Anther-halves attached at the base, erect, spreading upwards . . . 54

52. Stamens 8—20. Disc of the female flowers reduced to two scales. Calyx
3-partite. Leaves opposite. — Species 3. North Africa ; also introduced in South Africa. Used as dye-plants, pot-herbs, and in medicine.
" Mercury." . . . . **Mercurialis** L.

Stamens 2—7. Disc none. Flowers monoecious. Leaves alternate. . 53

53. Calyx of the female flowers 3-partite. Stamens 2—3. Leaves narrow,
entire. Flowers in clusters. — Species 1. South Africa.

Seidelia Baill.

Calyx of the female flowers reduced to a single scale or absent. Stamens
4—7. Leaves broad, more or less toothed. Flowers in racemes. —
Species 2. South Africa. . . . . **Leidesia** Muell. Arg.

54. Stem herbaceous. Flowers monoecious. Calyx of the female flowers
imbricate in bud. Stamens 3—10. Disc of the female flowers reduced
to 3—4 linear scales. Ovary 3—4-celled. Styles undivided. — Species
1. Central Africa. . . . . **Micrococca** Benth.

Stem woody. Flowers dioecious, rarely monoecious, but then calyx of
the female flowers valvate in bud. Ovary 2—3-celled. 55

55. Styles undivided. Disc of the female flowers entire or lobed. Stamens 5
or more, usually numerous. — Species 25. Tropical and South Africa.

Several species yield timber or are used in medicine. **Claoxylon** Juss. Styles many-cleft. Stamens 3—12. Flowers dioecious. Shrubs. Stipules spiny. 55

56. Disc of the female flowers consisting of numerous, more or less ciliate scales ; also 3 staminodes present. Sepals of the female flowers broad. Ovary 3-celled. Fruit a 3-celled capsule. Female flowers in pendulous spikes. — Species 1. Southern West Africa. . . **Poggeophyton** Pax

Disc of the female flowers consisting of 2 narrow scales ; no staminodes. Fruit a drupe. Female flowers in clusters. — Species 8. Central Africa. . . . . **Erythrococca** Benth.

57. (35.) Disc of the female flowers formed of 3 petal-like scales. Styles recurved, appressed to the ovary, united at the base, 2-cleft. Ovary 3-celled. Stamens 3. Anthers 4-celled. Flowers dioecious, the male ones in spikes, the female solitary or 2—3 together. Leaves pinnately nerved. — Species 3. West Africa. Yielding timber.

Hasskarlia Baill.

Disc absent. Styles erect or spreading. Flowers in spikes, racemes, or panicles. 58

58. Calyx of the female flowers 3—5-partite. Stamens numerous. Anthers 4-celled. Ovary 2—3-celled. Styles long and thin, 2-parted. Seedcoat leathery. Trees or shrubs. Inflorescence spicate or racemose. — Species 3. Central Africa. . . . . **Cleidion** Blume

Calyx of the female flowers entire or shortly toothed. Connective not prolonged. Ovary 1—2-, rarely 3-celled. Styles undivided, usually short and thick. Seed-coat crustaceous. Leaves usually palmately nerved. (See 26.). . . . . **Macaranga** Thouars

59. (12.) Corolla present in the male flowers 60

Corolla absent in the male flowers 66

60. Flowers in corymb- or panicle-like inflorescences composed of cymes, nearly always monoecious. Stamens 5 or more, all or the outer opposite the petals, all or the inner united below. [Tribe JATROPHEAE.] . 61

Flowers solitary or in clusters or panicles, dioecious. Stamens free, but often inserted on a stalk-like process of the receptacle. Shrubs or trees. [Tribe CLUYTIEAE.] 62

61. Flowers dioecious. Petals free. Stamens 16—17, the five outer nearly free, the inner irregularly united. Seeds without an outgrowth. Leaves undivided. — Species 2. East Africa. . . . . **Neojatropha** Pax

Flowers monoecious. Stamens in 2—6 whorls, usually 8—10. Seeds with an outgrowth at the hilum. — Species 50. Central and South Africa ; two species cultivated and naturalized in the tropics. Several species yield gum, oil, and medicaments ; some are poisonous or used as garden- or hedge-plants. . . . . **Jatropha** L.

62. Stamens 5. Male flowers with a rudimentary pistil. Petals free. Flowers solitary or in clusters in the axils of the leaves. Leaves undivided. . 63

Stamens 12 or more. Male flowers without a rudimentary pistil. Flowers in panicles. 64

63. Stamens opposite the sepals, inserted upon a flat receptacle, free. Fruit a drupe. — Species 1. West Africa . . . . **Microdesmis** Planch.

. Stamens opposite the petals, inserted upon a stalk-like receptacle. Fruit a capsule. — Species 40. South and Central Africa. Some are used as ornamental plants. . . . . **Cluytia** L.

64. Petals free. Stamens free. Fruit a capsule. Leaves undivided, pinnately nerved. Shrubs. — Species 1. Equatorial West Africa (Congo).

Mildbraedia Pax

Petals united below. Fruit a drupe. Leaves lobed or dissected, palmately nerved at the base. Trees. 65

65. Leaves lobed. — Species 1. Madagascar. . . . . **Givotia** Griff.

Leaves dissected. — Species 3. West Africa. Yield timber and fat from the seeds. . . . . **Ricinodendron** Muell. Arg.

66. (59.) Stamens 1—4, rarely more, and then ovary many-celled. Disc little developed or wanting. Male flowers without a rudimentary pistil. Style-branches undivided. [Tribe HIPPOMANEAE.] 67

Stamens 5 or more. Ovary 2—4-celled. Style-branches two-cleft or lobed. Sepals 4—8. Shrubs or trees. 74

67. Stamens 8 or more. Calyx cup-shaped, almost entire. Ovary many-celled. Style columnar, many-branched at the top. Fruit a capsule. Trees. Inflorescence spicate; bracts adnate to the rachis throughout their whole length, at first enclosing the flower-buds. Flowers monoecious. — Species 1 (*H. crepitans* L., sandbox-tree). Naturalized in the tropics. Ornamental tree, yielding oil and medicaments; the fruits are used as sand-boxes; the juice is poisonous. . . . . **Hura** L.

Stamens 1—4. Ovary 2—4-celled. Bracts adnate to the rachis of the inflorescence by their base only. 68

68. Stamens 1—3, the filaments entirely or almost entirely united. Shrubs or trees. Flowers monoecious. 69

Stamens 2—4, the filaments free or united at the base only. Styles free or united at the base. Ovary 2—3-celled. 71

69. Calyx 3-lobed. Stamens 1—3; filaments free at the top, connective not broadened. Ovary 3—4-celled. Styles united high up. Fruit a capsule. Seeds with a large outgrowth at the hilum. Flowers in panicles. — Species 3. Central Africa. . . . . . . **Maprounea** Aubl.

Calyx 4—5-parted. Stamens 2—3; filaments united into a short column. Anthers turned outwards. Ovary 2—3-celled. Fruit a capsule or a drupe. Seeds without an outgrowth. 70

70. Calyx-segments broad. Connective broadened, peltate. Styles united high up. Flowers in panicles. — Species 2. Tropics. **Omphalea** L.

Calyx-segments narrow. Connective not broadened. Styles free or united at the base. Flowers in spikes. — Species 2. Central Africa.

Excoecariopsis Pax

71. Calyx of the male flowers 2—3-toothed or -lobed.   Inflorescence terminal.
    Bracts with two glands.   Flowers monoecious. 72
    Calyx of the male flowers 2—5-parted.   Fruit a capsule with a persistent
    central column. 73
72. Ripe carpels separating from a 3-parted central column.   Seeds without an
    outgrowth. — Species 10.   Tropical and South Africa.   They yield
    timber ; one species (*S. sebiferum* Roxb.) is cultivated for its oily seeds.
    (Including *Conosapium* Muell. Arg.) . . . . **Sapium** P. Browne
    Ripe carpels separating from the base of the pericarp, leaving no central
    column.   Seeds with an outgrowth at the hilum. — Species 5.   Tropical
    and South Africa.   Some are poisonous. . . . **Stillingia** L.
73. Seeds with an outgrowth at the hilum.   Flowers monoecious.   Inflor-
    escences terminal or terminal and lateral.   Leaves alternate. — Species
    3.   Central Africa.   (*Cnemidostachys* Mart.) . . **Sebastiania** Spreng.
    Seeds without an outgrowth at the hilum.   Flowers usually dioecious.
    Inflorescences usually lateral. — Species 20.   Tropical and South Africa.
    Some are poisonous or are used as ornamental plants.   (Including
    Taenosapium Muell. Arg.) . . . . **Excoecaria** L.
74. (66.) Flowers in racemes, monoecious, with a disc.   Sepals of the male
    flowers evidently united below.   Stamens 10, free.   Leaves palmately
    divided, sometimes alternating with undivided ones. — Species 3.
    Cultivated in the tropics.   *M. Glaziovii* Muell. Arg. yields rubber,
    M. utilissima Pohl and *M. dulcis* Pax (cassava or mandioc-plants)
    furnish vegetables, medicaments, and edible roots, from which meal,
    starch (tapioca), and a spirituous drink are prepared.   **Manihot** Adans.
    Flowers in glomerules, dioecious, rarely monoecious, but then without a
    disc.   Sepals of the male flowers free or nearly so.   Leaves undivided.
    [Tribe GELONIEAE.] 75
75. Sepals 5.   Filaments free.   Male flowers without a disc and without a
    rudimentary pistil. — Species 6.   Tropical and South Africa.   (*Cerato-
    phorus* Sond., including *Suregada* Roxb.) . . . . **Gelonium** Roxb.
    Sepals of the female flowers 7—8, the inner petaloid.   Filaments united. —
    Species 1.   West Africa. . . . . . . **Chaetocarpus** Thwait.
76. (1.) Calyx of the male flowers with valvate aestivation.   Stamens 5—7
    Male flowers with a rudimentary pistil.   Shrubs or trees. 77
    Calyx of the male flowers with imbricate or open aestivation. . . . 81
77. Petals absent.   Disc none.   Styles 2, undivided.   Ovary-cells 2, each
    with an incomplete partition. — Species 1.   West Africa.
                                                    Martretia Beille
    Petals small.   Disc outside the stamens.   Styles 2-parted.   Ovary-cells
    undivided.   [Tribe BRIDELIEAE.] 78
78. Ovary 2-celled.   Styles 2.   Stamens borne upon a short androphore.
    Leaf-veins of the third order almost parallel. 79
    Ovary 3-celled.   Styles 3.   Disc of the female flowers cup-shaped.   Fruit a
    capsule.   Leaf-veins of the third order netted. 80

79. Disc of the female flowers bottle-shaped, enclosing the ovary to the top.
    Inflorescence paniculate. — Species 1. East Africa. (Under *Bridelia*
    Willd.) . . . . **Neogoetzea** Pax
    Disc of the female flowers double, the outer cup-shaped, adhering to the
    calyx, the inner consisting of 5 scales. Fruit usually a drupe. — Species
    25. Tropical and South-east Africa. Some species yield dye-stuffs.
    (Including *Gentilia* Beille) . . . . **Bridelia** Willd.

80. Receptacle of the male flowers elevated, forming a short androphore. —
    Species 10. Tropics. . . . . **Cleistanthus** Hook.
    Receptacle not prolonged into an androphore. Flowers clustered, dioecious.
    — Species 1. Madagascar and Comoro Islands. . **Stenonia** Baill.

81. (76.) Anthers 4-celled, even after opening, numerous. Filaments united.
    Male flowers with 5 sepals and 3 valvate petals. Ovary 3—4-celled.
    Styles 3, undivided. Carpels enlarging and separating after the time of
    flowering. Downy shrubs. Leaves without stipules. Flowers in
    axillary glomerules. — Species 1. South-east Africa. [Tribe JUN-
    ODIEAE.] . . . . **Junodia** Pax
    Anthers 2-celled, at least after opening. 82

82. Seeds with a very small embryo. Fruit an oblong drupe. Ovary 2-celled.
    Styles 2, undivided. Male flowers with 9—18 free, central stamens,
    without a disc and without a rudimentary pistil. Corolla none. Flowers
    dioecious, in racemes. Trees. — Species 1. West Africa. [Tribe
    DAPHNIPHYLLEAE] . . . . **Daphniphyllum** Blume
    Seeds with a large embryo. Ovary-cells and styles usually 3 ; if 2, then
    stamens 2—6 or surrounding a central disc. [Tribe PHYLLANTH-
    EAE.] 83

83. Corolla present, at least in the flowers of one sex. 84
    Corolla absent. 95

84. Stamens 8—10. Anthers opening outwards. Sepals, petals, and carpels
    4—5. Flowers dioecious, in glomerules. Trees. — Species 1. South
    Africa. Yields timber. . . . . **Heywoodia** Sim
    Stamens 4—5. [Subtribe ANDRACHNINAE.] 85

85. Flowers 3-merous, dioecious. Petals exceeding the sepals in the male
    flowers, absent in the female. Male flowers without a rudimentary
    pistil. Stamens 6, each surrounded at the base by a gland ; anthers
    opening transversely. Ovary 4—5-celled. Shrubs. Flowers in glo-
    merules. — Species 1. East Africa (Somaliland). . **Bricchettia** Pax
    Flowers 4—6-merous. Male flowers with a rudimentary pistil . . . 86

86. Ovary 5-celled. Styles 5, two-cleft. Disc cup-shaped, lobed in the male
    flowers, entire in the female. Stamens inserted upon a short androphore.
    Petals exceeding the sepals. Flowers fascicled, monoecious. Shrubs. —
    Species 1. Seychelles. (Under *Savia* Willd.) . . **Wielandia** Baill.
    Ovary 3-celled. Styles or sessile stigmas 3. 87

87. Styles very short, undivided. 88
    Styles well developed, two-cleft. 90

88. Flowers monoecious, in spikes or fascicles. Petals short. Rudimentary
    pistil 3-lobed. Stigmas thick. Seeds solitary in each cell, exalbuminous,
    with thick-fleshy cotyledons. Trees or shrubs. — Species 6. Tropics.

    Amanoa Aubl.

    Flowers dioecious, in panicles. Fruit a loculicidal capsule. Trees. . 89

89. Panicles terminal. Petals small. Disc of the male flowers of separate
    glands. Rudimentary pistil obconical, flattened at the top. Seeds with
    a spongy coat, scanty albumen, and flat cotyledons. — Species 2.
    Equatorial regions. . . . .   **Megabaria** Pierre

    Panicles axillary. Petals large. Disc of the male flowers cupular. Rudi-
    mentary pistil narrowed above. Seeds with copious albumen. —
    Species 1. Equatorial West Africa. . . . . **Centroplacus** Pierre

90. Stamens inserted upon a prolonged, stalk-like receptacle. Petals shorter
    than the sepals. Disc and ovary densely woolly. Seeds with scanty
    albumen and folded cotyledons. Shrubs. Flowers dioecious, the
    male ones fascicled, the female solitary. — Species 1. South Africa.

    Lachnostylis Turcz.

    Stamens inserted upon a receptacle which is not stalk-like. 91

91. Stamens inserted upon the disc. Seeds exalbuminous, with folded cotyle-
    dons. Trees or shrubs. Flowers in fascicles. — Species 1. Equatorial
    West Africa. (*Pentabrachium* Muell. Arg.) . . . **Actephila** Blume

    Stamens inserted inside the disc round the rudimentary pistil. Seeds
    with copious albumen. 92

92. Male flowers without a corolla, with 4 sepals and 6 stamens. Female
    flowers with 2 sepals and 5 petals. Flowers dioecious, the male in
    glomerules, the female solitary. Shrubs or trees. — Species 1. West
    Africa (Congo). . . . . **Neochevaliera** Beille

    Male flowers with a corolla, rarely without, but then with 5 sepals and 5
    stamens. Flowers dioecious, the male in spikes racemes or panicles,
    or monoecious. 93

93. Lobes of the disc alternating with the petals. Flowers monoecious, in glo-
    merules or the female solitary. Shrubs. — Species 8. Madagascar and
    neighbouring islands. (Under *Savia* Willd.) . . **Petalodiscus** Baill.

    Lobes of the disc opposite the petals. Male flowers in spikes, racemes, or
    fascicles. 94

94. Flowers monoecious. Anther-halves adnate lengthwise. Rudimentary
    pistil of the male flowers columnar or 3-partite. Styles short. Herbs,
    undershrubs, or shrubs. — Species 6. . . . . . **Andrachne** L.

    Flowers dioecious. Anther-halves at first suspended from the thick con-
    nective. Rudimentary pistil thick, usually obovate. Styles long.
    Shrubs or trees. — Species 9. West Africa and Madagascar.

    Thecacoris Juss.

95. (83.) Leaves digitate. Male flowers in glomerules, with a 5—8-partite
    calyx. Trees. [Subtribe BISCHOFIINAE.] 96

    Leaves simple, undivided. 98

96. Leaflets 1—3. Flowers monoecious. Stamens 14—15. — Species 1. Southern West Africa (Angola). . . . . . . **Aristogeitonia** Prain
Leaflets 5—7. Flowers dioecious. Stamens 4—10. 97

97. Leaves opposite. Leaflets stalked. Fruit a capsule. — Species 1. West Africa. Yields timber (African teak) . . . . . **Oldfieldia** Hook.
Leaves alternate. Leaflets sessile. Male flowers with a 6—8-cleft calyx and 6—8 stamens. Female flowers solitary, with 3 bracteoles, a disc consisting of 6—7 scales, a 2-celled ovary, and 2 short, thick, undivided styles. Fruit a drupe. — Species 1. Southern West Africa (Angola).

Paivaeusa Welw.

98. Leaves opposite or whorled. Flowers dioecious, the male in fascicles or panicles, the female solitary. Stamens numerous. Disc none. Fruit a capsule. Trees. [Subtribe TOXICODENDRINAE.] 99
Leaves alternate. 100

99. Sepals 2—5. Stamens inserted upon a stalk-like receptacle. Styles united high up. — Species 1. Southern East Africa (Mosambic). Yields timber. . . . . **Androstachys** Prain
Sepals 5—12. Stamens inserted upon a flat receptacle. Styles united at the base only. — Species 1. South Africa (Cape Colony). Fruit poisonous. (*Hyaenanche* Lamb.) . . . . **Toxicodendron** Thunb.

100. Male flowers in catkins, spikes, racemes, or panicles, more rarely in heads or umbels with a calyx-like involucre. Flowers dioecious. [Subtribe ANTIDESMINAE.] 101
Male flowers in axillary glomerules, fascicles, or short cymes, rarely in umbels without an involucre. 112

101. Male flowers in umbels or heads with a calyx-like involucre, female solitary. Male flowers without a disc, but with a rudimentary pistil. Stamens 4—5. Ovary 2—4 celled. Styles branched. Fruit fleshy, indehiscent. Trees. — Species 30. Tropics. Some yield timber or edible fruits.

Uapaca Baill.

Male flowers in spikes racemes or panicles without an involucre. . . 102

102. Ovary 1-celled. Fruit a drupe. Trees or shrubs. 103
Ovary 2—5-celled. 105

103. Styles 3, 2-lobed. Male flowers with a disc. Stamens 2—5. — Species 25. Tropical and South-east Africa. Some yield timber and dye-stuffs. . . . . **Antidesma** L.
Style 1, undivided. Male flowers without a disc. 104

104. Sepals in the male flowers 3—5. Stamens 3—5. Disc of the female flowers ring-shaped. — Species 2. Madagascar. . **Cometia** Thouars
Sepals in the male flowers 6—8. Stamens numerous. Disc none. — Species 1. Equatorial West Africa. The seeds yield oil.

Plagiostyles Pierre

105. Ovary 2-celled. Male flowers with a rudimentary pistil. Trees or shrubs. 106
Ovary 3-, rarely 4—5-celled. 108

X

106. Ovary and fruit winged. Styles long, undivided. Disc none. Stamens
4—6. — Species 12. Central and South Africa. . **Hymenocardia** Wall.
Ovary and fruit not winged. Styles short. 107
107. Disc in the male flowers consisting of 5 scales, in the female cup-shaped,
entire. Stamens 5. Fruit one-seeded. — Species 4. West Africa and
Upper Nile. . . . . **Maesobotrya** Benth.
Disc, especially in the female flowers, little developed or absent. Styles
shortly lobed. Fruit several-seeded. — Species 10. West Africa.
Baccaurea Lour.
108. Disc indistinct or wanting. Styles short, very shortly lobed. (See 107.)
Baccaurea Lour.
Disc distinctly developed. Stamens 4—5. 109
109. Disc entire or nearly so. Styles undivided, united high up. Rudimentary
pistil salver-shaped. Shrubs. — Species 1. Equatorial regions.
Baccaureopsis Pax
Disc lobed or divided. Styles more or less deeply two-cleft. . . . 110
110. Stem herbaceous or woody at the base only. Stipules hair-like. Flowers
very small. Rudimentary pistil salver-shaped. Styles free, thick, 2-
cleft. — Species 5. Central Africa. . . **Cyathogyne** Muell. Arg.
Stem woody. Rudimentary pistil not salver-shaped. 111
111. Stipules large, kidney-shaped. Inflorescence springing from the old
wood. Seeds with an aril. — Species 5. West Africa. (Under *Maesobotrya* Benth.) . . . . **Staphysora** Pierre
Stipules not kidney-shaped. Flowers 5-merous. Anther-halves at first
suspended from the thickened connective. Styles long. (See 94.)
Thecacoris Juss.
112. (100.) Styles or sessile stigmas much broadened, sometimes wholly united.
Flowers dioecious. Disc present. Fruit indehiscent. Trees or shrubs.
[Subtribe DRYPETINAE.] 113
Styles or style-branches rather thin or broadened at the apex only. [Sub-
tribe PHYLLANTHINAE.] 115
113. Stamens 3. Ovary 1-celled. Stigmas peltate, nearly sessile. Disc cup-
shaped in the male flowers, ring-shaped in the female. Sepals unequal.
— Species 1. West Africa. . . . . **Sibangea** Oliv.
Stamens 4 or more. 114
114. Fruit 1-seeded. Ovary 1—2-celled. Stamens usually 4. — Species 4.
Central Africa. . . . . **Drypetes** Vahl
Fruit 2—4-seeded. Ovary 2—4-celled. Stamens usually numerous. —
Species 20. Tropical and South Africa. . . . **Cyclostemon** Blume
115. Male flowers with a rudimentary pistil and a disc usually divided into
glands. 116
Male flowers without a rudimentary pistil. 120
116. Receptacle of the male flowers prolonged into an androphore. Stamens
5—6. Shrubs, undershrubs, or herbs. 117

Receptacle not prolonged into an androphore. Disc of the male flowers divided into glands alternating with the sepals, rarely entire. Seeds without an outgrowth at the hilum. Shrubs and trees. 118

117. Disc of the male flowers nearly entire, of the female divided into 5 glands alternating with the sepals. Fruit a drupe. Seeds with an outgrowth at the hilum. Shrubs. Male inflorescence many-flowered. — Species 3. Central Africa. . . . . **Pseudolachnostylis** Pax

Disc of the male flowers 5-lobed or divided into 5 glands opposite the sepals. Fruit a capsule. Seeds without an outgrowth at the hilum. Flowers monoecious, fascicled. — Species 4. Central Africa.
Cluytiandra Muell. Arg.

118. Disc of the male flowers slightly lobed. Styles undivided. Flowers monoecious, large. Stipules large. — Species 1. German East Africa.
Zimmermannia Pax

Disc of the male flowers deeply lobed or divided. Styles two-cleft. Flowers usually dioecious. 119

119. Anthers opening outwards. Disc of the female flowers lobed. Seeds grooved on the ventral face ; testa thick ; embryo curved. — Species 8. Tropical and South Africa. Some yield timber. (Under *Securinega* Juss.) . . . . **Flueggea** Willd.

Anthers opening inwards or laterally. Disc of the female flowers undivided. Seeds not grooved ; testa thin ; embryo straight. — Species 6. Some of them yield timber. . . . . . . **Securinega** Juss.

120. Disc present. 121
Disc absent. Shrubs or trees. 124

121. Disc of the male flowers consisting of 5—6 scales adnate below to the sepals which consequently appear much thickened. Stamens 3. Filaments very short, united. Anthers opening outwards. Style-branches 2-cleft. Flowers monoecious. Herbs or undershrubs. — Species 1. Madagascar and neighbouring islands. . . . . **Agyneia** Vent.

Disc of the male flowers not adnate to the sepals ; hence sepals not much thickened. 122

122. Stamens 2—10. Styles usually two-cleft. — Species 80. Tropical and South Africa ; one species naturalized in Egypt. Some of them serve as garden- or hedge-plants or yield timber, tanning and dyeing materials, edible fruits, and medicaments. (Including *Cicca* L. and *Pleiostemon* Sond.) (Plate 80.) . . . . **Phyllanthus** L.

Stamens 12—18. Disc many-lobed or many-parted. Styles 3. Shrubs or trees. 123

123. Flowers monoecious. Sepals 5. Disc lobed. Styles entire or notched, flattened. — Species 1. Madagascar and Comoro Islands.
Humblotia Baill.

Flowers monoecious with 6 sepals, or dioecious with 5. Disc deeply divided. Styles two-cleft. Stipules gland-like. — Species 2. Equatorial West Africa. . . . . **Lingelsheimia** Pax

124. Flowers monoecious. Calyx 6-lobed. Stamens 3 ; filaments united ;
    anthers opening outwards. Male flowers in glomerules. — Species 1.
    Naturalized in the Mascarene Islands. (*Melanthesopsis* Muell. Arg.)

    Breynia Forst.

    Flowers dioecious. Calyx 5-parted. Stamens 5 ; filaments free ; anthers
    opening inwards. Male flowers in umbels. — Species 1. Madagascar.

    Leptonemea Juss.

FAMILY 123. CALLITRICHACEAE

Herbs. Leaves opposite, simple, entire. Flowers solitary or in clusters
in the leaf-axils, minute, without a perianth, but sometimes with two bracteoles,
monoecious. Stamens 1. Anther 2-celled. Ovary 4-celled. Ovules solitary
in each cell, pendulous, inverted, with a single coat and a ventral raphe. Styles
2, free, awl-shaped. Fruit separating into 4 drupe-like mericarps. Seeds
albuminous ; embryo axile. (Under *HALORRHAGIDACEAE*.)

Genus 1, species 6. North and South Africa and high mountains of Central
    Africa ; one species also naturalized in Madagascar and the Mascarene
    Islands. . . . . **Callitriche** L.

ORDER SAPINDALES

SUBORDER BUXINEAE

FAMILY 124. BUXACEAE

Shrubs or trees. Juice not milky. Leaves opposite, simple, entire. Flowers
in lateral fascicles heads or spikes, regular, monoecious. Perianth simple, of 4
segments in the male flowers, of 4—6 in the female. Disc absent. Stamens 4,
opposite the sepals, or 6. Filaments free. Anthers 2-celled. Ovary superior,
3-celled. Ovules 2 in each cell, pendulous or nearly so, inverted, with dorsal
raphe. Styles 3, free, short and thick, undivided, persisting in fruit. Fruit a
loculicidal capsule. Seeds albuminous ; embryo axile, straight. — Genera 3 ;
species 8. (Under *EUPHORBIACEAE*.)

1. Stamens 4 ; filaments long. Male flowers with a rudimentary pistil.
    Perianth of the female flowers of 4—6 segments. — Species 6. The box
    (*B. sempervirens* L.) is used as a garden-plant and yields wood and
    medicaments ; another species affords arrow-poison. [Tribe BUXEAE.]

    Buxus L.

    Stamens 6 ; filaments very short or absent. Male flowers without a
    rudimentary pistil. Perianth of the female flowers of 4 segments.
    [Tribe STYLOCEREAE.] 2

2. Flowers in fascicles, the male on long pedicels, very small. Leaves nar-
    rowed into a long point. — Species 1. Central Africa.

    Macropodandra Gilg

    Flowers in groups of 3, nearly sessile, not very small. Leaves blunt or
    slightly pointed. — Species 1. South-east Africa.   **Notobuxus** Oliv.

SUBORDER EMPETRINEAE
FAMILY 125. EMPETRACEAE

Low shrubs. Leaves alternate, sometimes almost whorled, undivided, grooved on the under surface, without stipules. Flowers solitary or in heads, bracteolate, unisexual or polygamous. Sepals 3. Petals 3 or none. Stamens 3, hypogynous, opposite to the sepals, free. Disc absent. Ovary superior, 2—9-celled. Ovules solitary in each cell, erect, inverted, with ventral raphe. Style branched. Fruit a drupe. Seeds without an outgrowth at the hilum, albuminous. Embryo axile ; radicle turned downwards. — Genera 2, species 2. North and South Africa.

Flowers, at least the male, crowded in terminal heads. Ovary cells, style-branches, and fruit-stones 2—5. Style with linear branches. — Species 1. Canary Islands and Azores. The fruits are used as a condiment and in medicine., ... **Corema** Don

Flowers solitary, on lateral dwarf-shoots. Ovary-cells, style-branches, and fruit-stones 6—9. Style with broadened branches. — Species 1. Island of Tristan da Cunha. The fruits (crawberries) are eaten and used for preparing drinks and medicaments. . . . . . **Empetrum** L.

SUBORDER CORIARIINEAE
FAMILY 126. CORIARIACEAE

Shrubs. Leaves opposite, simple, entire, 3-nerved, without stipules. Flowers in racemes, hermaphrodite or polygamous. Sepals 5, imbricate in bud. Petals shorter, fleshy, enlarged after flowering. Stamens 10. Anthers opening inwards. Carpels 5, distinct. Ovule 1 in each carpel, pendulous, inverted, with dorsal raphe. Fruit with a crustaceous rind, indehiscent. Seeds with scanty albumen.

Genus 1, species 1. North-west Africa. Poisonous and used for tanning and dyeing . . . . **Coriaria** L.

SUBORDER ANACARDIINEAE
FAMILY 127. ANACARDIACEAE

Trees or shrubs. Juice resinous. Leaves usually alternate, without stipules. Flowers in panicles, usually polygamous. Corolla present, rarely (*Pistacia*) absent. Ovary superior, 1—5-celled. Ovules solitary in each cell, inverted, with dorsal raphe. Fruit usually a drupe. Albumen of the seeds scanty or wanting. — Genera 29, species 250. (*TEREBINTHACEAE*.) (Plate 81.)

1. Carpel 1. Style simple, lateral ; stigma entire. Funicle basal. Fertile stamen 1, rarely 5. Leaves simple, entire. Trees. [Tribe MAN-GIFEREAE.] 2

Carpels 2—5, sometimes 1—4 of them rudimentary. Style simple with a lobed stigma, or more or less deeply divided, or several free styles. Fertile stamens 3 or more. Leaves usually compound. 5

2. Stamen 1. Filament broad. Calyx 4-lobed. Petals 4. Disc one-sided. Leaves lanceolate. — Species 2. West Africa. The fruits are edible. (Under *Mangifera* L.) . . . .   **Fegimanra** Pierre
Stamens 5—10, but usually 1 only fertile. Petals 5.   3
3. Fertile stamens 5. Calyx bursting-irregularly. — Species 1. Madagascar. The juice is used for preparing varnishes and medicaments. **Gluta** L.
Fertile stamen 1, usually accompanied by 4 or 9 sterile ones, which bear small anthers. Calyx 5-partite.   4
4. Stamens and staminodes together 5. Disc cushion-shaped. Fruit egg-shaped, with a fleshy pericarp and a slightly thickened stalk. Leaves lanceolate. — Species 1 (*M. indica* L., mango-tree). Cultivated in the tropics. Yields timber, gum, tanning and dyeing materials, edible fruits from which a spirituous drink is prepared, starch from the seeds, and medicaments. . . . . **Mangifera** Burm.
Stamens and staminodes together 10. Disc indistinct. Fruit kidney-shaped, with a resinous pericarp and a much thickened, fleshy stalk. Leaves obovate. — Species 1 (*A. occidentale* L., cashew-tree). Cultivated in the tropics. Yields timber, gum, tanning and dyeing materials, oil, vermin-poison, edible seeds and fruit-stalks from which vinegar and brandy are prepared, and medicaments. . . . . **Anacardium** L.
5. (1.) Ovary with 1 fertile cell and sometimes 1—2 empty and usually rudimentary ones, rarely (*Protorhus*) with 3 fertile cells ; in this case stamens 5 and leaves simple. [Tribe RHOIDEAE.]   6
Ovary with 3—5 fertile cells. Stamens 6—15 and leaves compound, rarely stamens 5 and leaves simple, but then ovary-cells and styles 5. [Tribe SPONDIEAE.]   20
6. Perianth simple, consisting of 1—2 segments in the male, of 2—5 in the female flowers. Stamens 3—5. Style 3-cleft. Leaves compound. — Species 5, one of them only cultivated. North Africa and northern East Africa. They yield timber, tanning and dyeing materials, resins (mastic and turpentine) which are used industrially, in medicine, as fumigatories, masticatories, or condiments, and for preparing spirituous drinks, also edible oily fruits and seeds (pistachio-nuts) and various medicaments.
Pistacia L.

Perianth consisting of a calyx and a corolla.   7
7. Style 1, undivided, rarely (*Micronychia*) shortly cleft at the top, or a slightly lobed sessile stigma.   8
Styles 3, free or united at the base, sometimes recurved and adnate to the ovary, or 3 free sessile stigmas.   13
8. Leaves simple, undivided.   9
Leaves compound, pinnate.   11
9. Stamens 6—10, twice as many as the petals. Ovary with 1 fertile and 1 sterile cell. Style absent. Trees with small flowers. — Species 2. Madagascar and Seychelles. . . . . .   **Campnosperma** Thwait.
Stamens 4—5, as many as the petals. Ovary 1-celled. Style present .   10

10. Corolla of the male flowers equalling the calyx. Disc broad, fleshy. Filaments thread-shaped. Ovary and fruit much compressed. Style short, undivided, with a 3-lobed stigma. Shrubs. Leaves serrate. Flowers small. Female inflorescence finally with broadened branches and hardened bracts. — Species 1. South Africa (Cape Colony). (*Botryceras* Willd.) . . . . **Laurophyllus** Thunb.

    Corolla much exceeding the calyx. Disc cup-shaped. Filaments broad. Ovary and fruit slightly compressed. Style long, shortly 3-cleft at the top. Trees. Leaves entire. Flowers rather large. — Species 1. Madagascar. . . . . **Micronychia** Oliv.

11. Receptacle deeply cupular ; hence petals and stamens distinctly perigynous. Calyx valvate, corolla imbricate in the bud. Stamens 5—10. Ovary sessile. Style thin. Fruit dry, indehiscent. — Species 1. West Africa. . . . . **Thyrsodium** Benth.

    Receptacle flattish or convex ; hence petals and stamens hypogynous or nearly so. Style thick or wanting. 12

12. Petals imbricate in the bud ; sepals imbricate. Stamens 4—5, as many as the petals. Ovary and fruit with a compressed stalk. Stigma sessile. Fruit sickle-shaped, dry, indehiscent. — Species 1. Madagascar.

                                  Faguetia March.

    Petals valvate in the bud. Stamens 5—20, usually more than petals. Ovary and fruit sessile, the latter drupaceous. — Species 20. Tropics. Some species yield timber, gum, and edible fruits. **Sorindeia** Thouars

13. (7.) Ovule basal or suspended from a basal funicle. 14

    Ovule suspended from the top or the flank of the cavity. 16

14. Ovule subbasal, ascending. Styles lateral, thread-shaped. Ovary compressed. Stamens 5, alternating with 2-cleft scales. Petals of the male flowers longer, of the female shorter than the sepals. Sepals lanceolate, enlarged in the fruit. Flowers dioecious. Leaves pinnate ; stalk winged. — Species 1. South Africa. . . . . . **Loxostylis** Spreng. fil.

    Ovule suspended from the basal funicle. Styles terminal. Flowers polygamous. 15

15. Endocarp crusty or bony, finally separating from the mesocarp. Seed-coat thin. Leaves alternate, usually compound. — Species 100. Some of them yield timber, tanning and dyeing materials (sumac), condiments, medicaments, and edible fruits ; others are used as ornamental plants.

                                          Rhus L.

    Endocarp leathery, not separating from the mescarp. Seed-coat thick. Leaves undivided, narrow, with numerous parallel side-nerves. — Species 18. Tropical and South Africa. Some yield timber. (*Anaphrenium* E. Mey.) . . . . **Heeria** Meissn.

16. Leaves simple, undivided. Stamens 5. 17

    Leaves compound, trifoliolate or pinnate. 18

17. Filaments broadened. Ovary 1-celled. Ovule attached laterally. Styles sickle-shaped, united at the base, with capitate stigmas. Fruit trans-

versely oblong ; endocarp very thin. Embryo with thick cotyledons. —
Species 1. Madagascar. Used medicinally. . . .   **Baronia** Bak.
Filaments awl-shaped. Ovary usually 3-celled. Ovule attached at
the top of the cell. Stigmas sessile. Fruit oblong ; endocarp woody.
Leaves opposite or nearly so, with numerous parallel side-nerves. —
Species 10. Madagascar and South-east Africa. Some species are
poisonous or used medicinally. . . . .   **Protorhus** Engl.

18. Leaflets 3, toothed. Stamens 5. Ovary compressed. Styles lateral,
thread-shaped. Fruit winged ; endocarp very thin, mesocarp resinous.
Shrubs. — Species 1. South Africa.   . .   **Smodingium** E. Mey.
Leaflets 5 or more. Styles more or less terminal. 19

19. Stamens 4—5. Fruit with a crusty endocarp, a fibrous mesocarp, and a
fleshy exocarp. Embryo with a short radicle. — Species 30. Central
Africa. Some have edible fruits. (*Emiliomarcelia* Hel. et Th. Dur.)
Trichoscypha Hook. fil.
Stamens 10. Fruit with a hard endocarp, an oily mesocarp, and a parch-
ment-like exocarp. Embryo with a long radicle. Shrubs. — Species 2.
Cultivated in North Africa, the Cape Verde Islands, and the Mascarenes.
They yield timber, resin used industrially and medicinally, tanning
and dyeing materials, vinegar, syrup, and medicaments.
Schinus L.

20. (5.) Stamens 5, as many as the petals. Disc consisting of 5 scales. Styles
5. Leaves simple, undivided. — Species 2. West Africa.
Spondianthus Engl.
Stamens 6—15, twice as many as the petals or more. Leaves compound. 21

21. Petals valvate in bud. 22
Petals imbricate in bud. 23

22. Flowers dioecious, 4-merous. Petals lanceolate, with inflexed tips. Male
flowers with a sterile ovary and a simple style. Leaflets 3, serrate. —
Species 1. Equatorial East Africa. . . . .   **Spondiopsis** Engl.
Flowers polygamous, usually 5-merous. Petals oblong ovate or elliptical,
finally recurved. Styles in the female and hermaphrodite flowers 4—5,
free. Leaflets 5 or more, usually with a marginal nerve. — Species 4,
two of them growing wild in equatorial West Africa, the others cultivated in the tropics. They yield timber, gum, tanning material, medicaments, and edible fruits from which a spirituous drink is prepared.
(Including *Antrocaryon* Pierre). . . . .   **Spondias** L.

23. Sepals free. Stone of the fruit with 3—4 lids at the top. 24
Sepals more or less united. 25

24. Flowers dioecious, 3—4-merous. Anthers subglobose, versatile. Seeds
oblong, terete. — Species 2. Central Africa. The fruits are edible.
(Under *Spondias* L.). . . . .   **Pseudospondias** Engl.
Flowers polygamous, 4—5-merous. Anthers oblong, continuous with the
filament. Ovary-cells and styles usually 3. Seeds club-shaped, some-

A ⅓

E ²/₁

C ⁶/₁

D ⁴/₁

B ⁷/₂

J. Fleischmann del.

Lannea Schimperi (Hochst.) Engl.

A Flowering branch.   *B* Male flower.   *C* Male flower cut lengthwise.   *D* Older female flower cut lengthwise.   *E* Fruit.

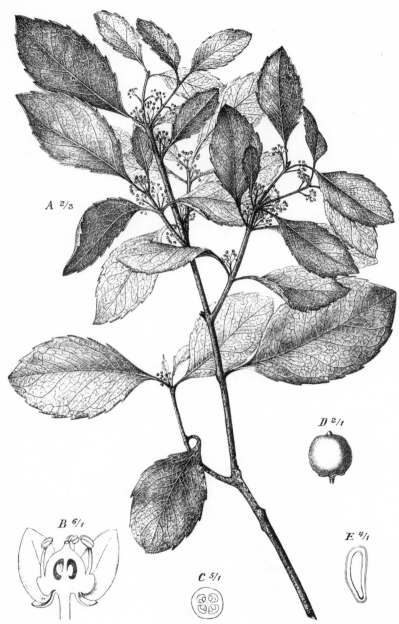

A ²/₃

D ²/₁

B ⁶/₁

C ⁵/₁

E ⁴/₁

J. Fleischmann del.

Elaeodendron croceum (Thunb.) DC.

A Flowering branch.   *B* Flower cut lengthwise.   *C* Cross-section of ovary.   *D* Fruit.   *E* Seed cut lengthwise.

what compressed. — Species 5. Tropical and South Africa. They
yield timber, gum, dyes, oil, medicaments, and edible fruits and seeds
from which a spirituous drink is prepared. . . **Sclerocarya** Hochst.
25. Flowers 3-merous, dioecious. Fruit 1—2-seeded. Leaflets numerous. —
Species 2. West Africa. They yield timber and edible fruits (blood-
plums). . . . . **Haematostaphis** Hook. fil.
Flowers 4—5-merous. 26
26. Flowers 4-merous. Fruit usually 1-seeded. 27
Flowers 5-merous. Fruit 2—5-seeded. Leaflets 5 or more. Sepals
united at the base only. 28
27. Sepals united high up. Petals oblong. Disc 4-partite. Style simple,
club-shaped. Flowers in panicled fascicles. Leaflets numerous, alternate. — Species 1. West Africa (Cameroons). **Nothospondias** Engl.
Sepals united at the base only. Petals obovate. Disc 8-crenate. Styles
3—4. Stone of the fruit with 1—2 fertile cells bearing a lid at the top
and with 2—3 sterile cells. Seeds 1 or 2 ; in the latter case leaflets 3. —
Species 30. Tropical and South Africa. Several species yield timber,
bark used for making cloth, gum, edible fruits, and medicaments.
(*Calesiam* Adans., *Odina* Roxb., including *Lanneoma* Del.) (Plate 81.)
Lannea Rich.
28. Male flowers with a narrow disc and 3 styles. Stone of the fruit with 2
fertile and 2 sterile cells. — Species 1. South Africa.
Harpephyllum Bernh.
Male flowers with a broad disc and 5 styles. Ovary 5-celled. Stone of the
fruit with 3—5 fertile cells. Panicles spike-like. — Species 5. Madagascar and Mascarenes. They yield timber, resin, and edible fruits·
(Under *Spondias* L.) . . . . **Poupartia** Comm.

SUBORDER CELASTRINEAE
FAMILY 128. AQUIFOLIACEAE

Shrubs or trees. Leaves alternate, entire toothed or lobed. Flowers
regular, dioecious. Calyx 4—7-cleft. Petals 4—7, united at the base, imbricate in bud. Stamens as many as the petals, hypogynous. Anthers 2-
celled, opening inwards by longitudinal slits. Disc none. Ovary superior,
4—8-celled. Style short or absent ; stigma lobed. Ovules solitary in each
cell or two side by side, pendulous, inverted, covered by a cupular expansion
of the funicle. Fruit a drupe with 4—8 one-seeded stones. Embryo minute,
at the apex of the albumen (*ILICINEAE*.)
Genus 1, species 5. They yield timber, bird-lime, tea, and medicaments.
The holly (*I. Aquifolium* L.), with poisonous fruits, is also planted as a
garden- or hedge-plant. . . . . **Ilex** L.

FAMILY 129. CELASTRACEAE

Shrubs or trees. Leaves simple, stipulate. Flowers regular. Sepals 4—5,
imbricate or open in bud. Petals 4—5, free, imbricate in bud. Disc present.

Stamens as many as and alternating with the petals. Filaments free. Anthers opening by two longitudinal slits sometimes confluent at the top. Ovary superior, but sometimes sunk in the disc and adnate to it, 2—5-celled, rarely (*Pleurostylia*) 1-celled. Ovules 1—8 in each cell, inverted. Style 1 or 0. Seeds usually albuminous. Embryo axile, with leaf-like cotyledons. — Genera 15, species 160. (Plate 82.)

1. Fruit a loculicidal capsule. Seeds with an aril. [Subfamily **CELAS-TROIDEAE.**] 2

   Fruit a drupe or a nut. Seeds without an aril. 7

2. Leaves opposite, at least those of the flowering and fruiting branches. Un-armed shrubs. Ovules 2 in each ovary-cell. 3

   Leaves alternate. 4

3. Petals spreading. Disc thick. Anthers opening by 1 slit. Ovary-cells and stigmas 4—5. Seeds enveloped by a red aril. Leaves elliptical. — Species 1. North-west Africa (Algeria). Yields timber and medicaments and serves as an ornamental plant ; the fruits are poisonous. " Spindle-tree." . . . . **Evonymus** L.

   Petals erect. Disc thin. Anthers opening by 2 slits. Ovary-cells and stigmas 3. Seeds with a white, wing-like aril. Leaves lanceolate. — Species 1 (*C. edulis* Forsk.). Central and South Africa. The wood and the leaves are used, the latter for chewing and for preparing a tea and medicaments. (*Methyscophyllum* Eckl. & Zeyh.) . **Catha** Forsk.

4. Flowers in axillary racemes or umbels, or more frequently solitary or in clusters and inserted upon the leaves, 5-merous. Ovary-cells and stigmas 5, very rarely 3—4. Seeds with a laciniate aril. Unarmed shrubs or trees. — Species 7. Madagascar. (Under *Celastrus* L.).

   Polycardia Juss.

   Flowers in axillary fascicles or cymes. Ovary 2—3-celled, very rarely 4—5-celled. 5

5. Ovules 3—6 in each cell of the ovary. Disc thick, almost hemispherical, ribbed, red. Seeds enveloped by the aril. Spiny shrubs. — Species 2. South Africa. (Under *Celastrus* L.) . . . . **Putterlickia** Endl.

   Ovules 2 in each cell of the ovary. Ovary 2—3-celled. Disc not hemis-pherical. 6

6. Fruit with usually wing-like appendages. Seeds with a gaping aril. Ovary usually ribbed. Stigmas 2—3. Disc 5-lobed or 5-parted. Flowers 5-merous. Unarmed shrubs or trees. Leaves entire. — Species 9. South Africa. . . . . **Pterocelastrus** Meissn.

   Fruit without appendages. Ovary not ribbed. Disc faintly lobed, not ribbed. — Species 80. Some of them yield timber, rubber, or medica-ments. (Including *Scytophyllum* Eckl. & Zeyh., under *Celastrus* L.)

   Gymnosporia Wight & Arn.

7. (1.) Fruit broadly winged, with a leathery rind. Flowers 4-merous. Stamens inserted within the disc. Anthers opening outwards. Ovary

2-celled, with 1 erect ovule in each cell. Stigma 1, small. Shrubs. Leaves opposite, entire. Inflorescences terminal and axillary. — Species 1. Madagascar. [Subfamily **TRIPTERYGJOIDEAE.**]

Ptelidium Thouars

Fruit not winged. Stamens inserted on the edge or outer face of the disc. Anthers usually opening inwards. [Subfamily **CASSINIOIDEAE.**] . 8

8. Ovary 1-celled. Ovules 2—8, erect. Style lateral. Stigma peltate. Flowers 5-merous. Fruit with a thin endocarp and a thin-fleshy mesocarp. Seeds with copious albumen. Leaves opposite. — Species 5. East and South Africa and Malagasy Islands. (Including *Cathastrum* Turcz.) . . . . **Pleurostylia** Wight & Arn.

Ovary 2—4-celled, with 1—2 ovules in each cell. Style terminal, rarely lateral in the fruit. 9

9. Ovules pendulous. Flowers 5-merous. Fruit a drupe. Glabrous shrubs. Upper leaves opposite, broad. — Species 1. South Africa (Cape Colony). Yields timber. (Under *Cassine* L.) . . . . . **Maurocenia** L.

Ovules erect. 10

10. Stigma entire. Anthers turned inwards. Petal-like staminodes usually present. Flowers hermaphrodite. Leaves opposite, unequal, the lower lanceolate, the upper oval. Trees. — Species 1. Isle of Réunion.

Herya Cordem.

Stigma 2—4-lobed, very rarely entire, but then anthers turned outwards. Petal-like staminodes none. 11

11. Flowers in short racemes, unisexual, 4-merous. Stamens inserted at the margin of the thin disc ; filaments strap-shaped. Fruit almost dry. Glabrous shrubs. Leaves opposite. — Species 1. South Africa (Cape Colony). (Under *Elaeodendron* Jacq.) . **Lauridia** Eckl. & Zeyh.

Flowers solitary or in fascicles or cymes ; usually hermaphrodite . . 12

12. Leaves alternate. Flowers 5-merous. Fruit almost dry. — Species 20. Tropical and South Africa. (Under *Cassine* L. or *Elaeodendron* Jacq.)

Mystroxylon Eckl. & Zeyh.

Leaves opposite or the upper alternate. 13

13. Pericarp neither fleshy nor hardened. Seeds exalbuminous. Anthers opening outwards. Glabrous shrubs. Leaves more or less distinctly toothed. — Species 3. South Africa and Madagascar. (Under *Schrebera* Thunb.) . . . . **Hartogia** Thunb.

Pericarp more or less fleshy or hardened. Seeds albuminous. Anthers usually opening inwards. 14

14. Pericarp fleshy. Leaves opposite. — Species 10. South Africa.

Cassine L.

Pericarp dry. — Species 17. Tropical and South Africa. Some species yield timber, dyes, edible fruits, and medicaments. (Under *Cassine* L.) (Plate 82.) . . . . **Elaeodendron** Jacq.

FAMILY 130. HIPPOCRATEACEAE

. Shrubs or trees. Leaves simple. Flowers regular. Calyx 5-partite, imbricate in bud. Petals 5, free, inserted below the disc. Stamens 3—5, inserted upon or within the disc. Filaments free, strap-shaped. Ovary 3-celled, with 2—10 inverted ovules in each cell. Style 1 or 0. Fruit drupaceous or capsular or separating into several mericarps. Seeds exalbuminous. — Genera 3, species 110. Tropical and South Africa. (Under *CELASTRINEAE*.) (Plate 83.)

1. Stamens 5. Anthers opening inwards by a transverse slit. Disc indistinct. Ovules 6—8 to each ovary-cell. Leaves opposite, serrate. — Species 4. West Africa. . . . . . **Campylostemon** Welw.
   Stamens 3. Anthers opening outwards . Disc distinct. 2
2. Fruit drupaceous. Petals imbricate in bud. Flowers usually in fascicles or in fascicled cymes. — Species 60. Tropical and South Africa. Several species yield rubber or edible fruits. (Plate 83.) . **Salacia** L.
   Fruit capsular or separating into several mericarps. Anthers roundish. Leaves opposite. Flowers usually in simple cymes. — Species 50. Tropics to Delagoa Bay. Some are used medicinally. (Including *Helictonema* Pierre) . . . . **Hippocratea** L.

FAMILY 131. SALVADORACEAE.

Shrubs or trees. Leaves opposite, simple, entire, with minute stipules. Flowers solitary or in spikes racemes or panicles, regular. Calyx 2—4-cleft. Petals 4, very rarely 5, free or united at the base, with imbricate or contorted aestivation. Stamens as many as and alternate with the petals ; sometimes 4—5 staminodes also present. Ovary superior, 1—2-celled. Ovules 1—2 in each cell, erect, inverted. Style simple, short. Fruit a berry or a drupe. Seeds exalbuminous ; embryo with the radicle turned downwards. — Genera 3, species 6.

1. Flowers dioecious. Petals 4, free, narrow. Filaments free from one another and from the corolla. Glands between the stamens absent. Ovary 2-celled. Shrubs with 2—6 spines in the axils of the leaves. — Species 2. Tropical and South Africa. Used medicinally. (*Monetia* L'Hér.) . . . . **Azima** Lam.
   Flowers hermaphrodite or polygamous. Filaments united together or to the corolla. Glands between the stamens nearly always present. Ovary 1-celled. Unarmed shrubs or trees. 2
2. Petals free, narrow. Filaments united at the base. Anthers oblong. — Species 3. East Africa. Yielding timber. (Including *Platymitium* Warb.) . . . . **Dobera** Juss.
   Petals united at the base, broad, 4. Filaments free. Anthers ovoid or globose. — Species 1 (*S. persica* Garcin). North-east and Central Africa to Delagoa Bay. Yields edible fruits and medicaments ; the twigs are used as tooth-brushes. . . . . . . **Salvadora** Garcin

J. Fleischmann del.

Salacia Dusenii Loesen.

A Flowering branch. *B* Flower from above. *C* Flower cut lengthwise. *D* Cross-section of ovary.

A ²/₃

B ⁸/₁

D ²/₁

C ³/₂

J. Fleischmann del.

Apodytes dimidiata E. Mey.

A Flowering branch.   *B* Flower cut lengthwise.   *C* Fruit.   *D* Fruit cut lengthwise.

SUBORDER ICACININEAE

FAMILY 132. ICACINACEAE

Trees or shrubs. Leaves entire toothed or lobed, without stipules. Flowers regular, 3—5-merous. Stamens as many as the petals or perianth-segments and alternate with them. Anthers opening by 2 longitudinal slits. Ovary superior, 1-celled. Ovules 2, pendulous, inverted, with dorsal raphe. Style 1 or 0. Fruit a drupe. Seed 1, with a thin testa, without an aril. — Genera 19, species 90. Tropical and South Africa. (Under *OLACINEAE*.) (Plate 84.)

1. Pericarp warty or spiny on the inner face. Embryo equalling the albumen. Climbing or twining shrubs. Leafstalk terete. [Tribe PHYTO-CRENEAE.] 2
  Pericarp smooth or wrinkled on the inside. Leaves entire. 7
2. Perianth simple, 3—5-parted. Stigma sessile. Leaves palminerved. . 3
  Perianth, at least in the female flowers, consisting of a sometimes very small calyx and a corolla of united petals. Leaves penninerved. . 5
3. Flowers solitary or in pairs in the axils of the leaves, hermaphrodite. Stem tuberous, with slightly twining branches. Leaves undivided, wavy at the margin. — Species 1. East Africa (Somaliland).
  Trematosperma Urban
  Flowers in heads or spikes, dioecious. 4
4. Flowers in heads arranged in spikes or panicles. Perianth of the male flowers 3-lobed. — Species 3. West Africa. . **Polycephalium** Engl.
  Flowers in spikes. Perianth usually 4-parted. — Species 15. Tropical and South Africa . . . . **Pyrenacantha** Hook.
5. Calyx minute. Corolla not enlarged in the fruit. Flowers in spikes arising from the lower part of the stem. Leaves oval. — Species 1. Madagascar. . . . . **Endacanthus** Baill.
  Calyx distinctly developed, at least in the female flowers. Corolla enlarged in the fruit. 6
6. Calyx of the male flowers 5-toothed. Petals 5. Filaments rather long. Anthers linear. Flowers in spikes at the nodes of the older branches. Leaves lanceolate. — Species 1. West Africa (Cameroons).
  Stachyanthus Engl.
  Calyx of the male flowers indistinct or wanting Petals 4. Filaments short. Anthers ovate. Flowers in spikes or heads. — Species 7. West Africa. . . . . **Chlamydocarya** Baill.
7. (1.) Flowers dioecious, with a corolla of united petals, with or without a calyx. Stamens with flat filaments ; anthers opening inwards. Embryo nearly equalling the albumen. Climbing shrubs, usually with tendrils. Leaves opposite. Flowers in panicles. — Species 6. Tropics. [Tribe IODEAE.] . . . . **Iodes** Blume
  Flowers hermaphrodite or polygamous, rarely unisexual, but then with a calyx and a corolla of free petals, or without a corolla, and the anthers opening outwards. Embryo usually much shorter than the albumen.

Trees or erect, rarely climbing shrubs ; in the latter case leaves alternate
or flowers in spikes. [Tribe ICACINEAE.] 8

8. Flowers unisexual, dioecious. Calyx 5-partite. Petals minute and free,
or wanting. Anthers turned outwards. Ovary with a ring-shaped
appendage at the top. Trees. Leaves alternate. Flowers in panicles.
— Species 2. Madagascar and neighbouring islands. **Grisollea** Baill.
Flowers hermaphrodite or polygamous. Perianth consisting of a calyx
and a corolla. 9

9. Petals free. Sepals usually united high up. 10
Petals more or less united. Sepals usually united at the base only. . . 14

10. Embryo nearly as long as the albumen. 11
Embryo much shorter than the albumen. 12

11. Petals bearded within. Disc present. Style long ; stigma small or shield-
shaped. Fruit with a crusty endocarp. Embryo with flat cotyledons.
Shrubs with ascending or somewhat twining branches. — Species 7.
Tropics. Some have edible fruits or seeds. . . . . **Icacina** Juss.
Petals not bearded within. Disc absent. Fruit with a woody endocarp
and a fleshy mesocarp. Embryo with folded cotyledons. Climbing
shrubs. — Species 2. Equatorial West Africa. The fruits and seeds are
eaten and used medicinally. . . . . **Lavigeria** Pierre

12. Stem climbing. Flowers in spikes. Petals hairy outside. Disc present.
Ovary without swellings. Style terminal ; stigma slightly lobed. —
Species 6. Tropics. . . . . . **Desmostachys** Planch. & Miers
Stem erect, tree-like. Flowers in fascicles or panicles. Ovary with 2
swellings. Style lateral. 13

13. Flowers in axillary fascicles. Filaments broadened below. Ovary usually
with two narrow swellings at the top. — Species 12. Central Africa.
(Under *Apodytes* Mey.) . . . . **Rhaphiostyles** Planch.
Flowers in terminal panicles. Filaments awl-shaped. Ovary with two
broad swellings on the ventral face. — Species 10. Tropical and South
Africa. Several species yield timber or edible fruits. (Plate 84.)
                                 Apodytes E. Mey.

14. Petals united at the base or nearly to the middle. 15
Petals united beyond the middle. 16

15. Petals imbricate in the bud. Style short. Leaves opposite. Flowers in
repeatedly forked cymes. — Species 4. South Africa and Madagascar.
                                 Cassinopsis Sond.
Petals valvate in the bud. Style long. Leaves alternate. Flowers in
few-flowered fascicles or panicles. — Species 9. Central Africa. (Including *Alsodeiidium* Engl.) . . . . . . **Alsodeiopsis** Oliv.

16. Petals imbricate in the bud. Sepals and stamens unequal. Disc indistinct. Stigma sessile. Leaves opposite, elliptical. Flowers in
panicles. — Species 1. Madagascar. . . . . . **Tridianisia** Baill.
Petals valvate in the bud. 17

17. Petals bent backwards at the tip. Disc thick. Style short. Leaves opposite, lanceolate. Flowers in few-flowered axillary cymes. — Species 1. West Africa (Congo). . . . . **Acrocoelium** Baill.
Petals bent inwards at the tip. Disc absent. Leaves alternate. . . 18

18. Sepals united at the base only. Filaments adnate to the corolla-tube throughout their whole length, without appendages. Style long, filiform. Ovary and fruit without a swelling. — Species 5. Tropics.

Leptaulus Benth.

Sepals united high up. Filaments free from the corolla, with two tufts of hairs at the apex. Style short, conical. Ovary and fruit with a lateral swelling. Flowers in head-like cymes. — Species 1. West Africa. . . . . **Lasianthera** Beauv.

SUBORDER SAPINDINEAE

FAMILY 133.   ACERACEAE

Trees or shrubs. Leaves opposite, palmately lobed, without stipules. Flowers in terminal corymbs, regular, polygamous. Sepals 5, free. Petals 5, free. Stamens 8, very rarely 4 or 12, perigynous, inserted on the inner edge of the thick disc. Filaments free. Ovary superior, 2-lobed and 2-celled, with 2 ovules in each cell. Styles 2 or a single style with 2 branches or stigmas. Fruit winged, splitting into 2 mericarps. Seeds exalbuminous. (Under *SAPINDACEAE*.)

Genus 1, species 4. North-west Africa. They yield timber, tanning bark, and sugar, and serve as ornamental plants. " Maple." . . **Acer** L.

FAMILY 134.   SAPINDACEAE

Trees or shrubs, rarely (*Cardiospermum*) herbs or undershrubs. Leaves alternate, usually compound. Flowers in racemes or panicles, rarely solitary or in clusters, polygamous, rarely unisexual. Petals 4—5, mostly with a scale on the inner face, or absent. Stamens 4—24, usually 8, inserted within the disc, rarely upon it ; sometimes disc indistinct. Anthers opening inwards by 2 longitudinal slits. Ovary superior, 2—8-, usually 3-celled, sometimes not quite completely septate or with a single fertile cell, frequently lobed. Ovules 1—2, rarely (*Cossignia*) 3 in each ovary-cell, curved. Style 1, undivided, rarely cleft. Seeds exalbuminous ; embryo usually curved. — Genera 51, species 200. (Including *DIDIEREACEAE*.)   (Plate 85.)

1. Ovary with 1 fertile cell and sometimes 2 sterile ones. Ovule 1. Style 3—4-cleft. Stamens 8—10, inserted on the edge of the ring-shaped disc. Petals 4. Sepals 2. Flowers dioecious. Leaves undivided deciduous. Spiny trees. — Species 6. Madagascar. Some species yield timber. (Including *Alluaudia* Drake). [Tribe DIDIEREAE.]

Didierea Baill.

Ovary with 2—8 fertile cells. Stamens inserted within the disc, rarely upon it (*Pistaciopsis*) or no distinct disc present (*Dodonaea*) ; in both these cases petals wanting. 2

2. Ovule 1 in each cell of the ovary. 3
Ovules 2, very rarely 3, in each cell of the ovary. 45

3. Ovule pendulous. Ovary 2-celled. Style undivided, with 2 decurrent stigmatic lines at the apex. Stamens 5. Disc regular. Petals 5, small. Sepals 5, slightly imbricate in bud. Fruit succulent, indehiscent. Seeds without an aril. Embryo with pinnately cut cotyledons. Branches and leaves with a resinous coating. Leaves equally pinnate, with a winged rachis. — Species 2. Equatorial East Africa and Madagascar.
Filicium Thwait.
Ovule erect or ascending. Stamens usually 8. 4

4. Flowers irregular, with a one-sided disc. Petals 4. 5
Flowers regular or nearly so, with a complete disc. Petals 5 or 0. Leaves exstipulate, equally pinnate, rarely unequally pinnate (*Pistaciopsis*) or simple (*Pappea*). 14

5. Leaves stipulate, unequally pinnate with 5 leaflets or twice ternate. Herbs or undershrubs or climbing tendril-bearing shrubs. Petals with a crested, and hooded scale. Stamens 8. Ovary 3-celled. . . . 6
Leaves exstipulate, simple trifoliolate or equally pinnate. Trees or shrubs without tendrils. Seeds without an aril. 8

6. Stem herbaceous or woody at the base only. Fruit capsular, inflated, with a membranous rind. Seeds without an aril. — Species 5. Tropical and South Africa, one species (*C. Helicacabum* L.) also naturalized in North Africa. They yield fodder, vegetables, oil, and medicaments, and serve also as decorative plants. " Heartseed." . **Cardiospermum** L.
Stem woody, climbing, bearing tendrils. Fruit capsular, not inflated, with a leathery or woody rind, or separating into mericarps. Seeds with a more or less distinct aril 7

7. Leaves twice ternate. Fruit 3-winged below, separating into 3 nutlets. — Species 1. Madagascar. . . . . **Serjania** Schum.
Leaves pinnate. Fruit wingless, capsular. — Species 1. Tropics. Poisonous and yielding fibres and medicaments. . . . . . **Paullinia** L.

8. Leaves simple or trifoliolate. Sepals 4, broadly imbricate in bud. Petals with a crestless, notched or 2-parted scale. Stamens 8. Ovary deeply lobed. Fruit of 1—3 drupes. — Species 50. Tropical and South Africa. Some species yield timber, edible fruits, and medicaments. (Under *Schmidelia* L.) . . . . **Allophyllus** L.
Leaves abruptly pinnate. Sepals 5. 9

9. Sepals free, broadly imbricate in bud. Petals with a notched scale. Stamens 8. Fruit separating into 3 mericarps. Seed-coat hard. — Species 3. Naturalized in the Mascarenes and Seychelles. The wood and the fruits (soap-berries) are used ; the latter afford a substitute for soap,

mucilage, oil, poison, and medicaments ; the seeds serve as ornaments and for making buttons and rosaries. (Including *Dittelasma* Hook.)

Sapindus L.

Sepals more or less united, narrowly imbricate or valvate in bud. Fruit furrowed or lobed, indehiscent. 10

10. Calyx shortly bell- or top-shaped ; sepals united at the base only. Petals with a 2-crested scale. Stamens 6—8. Pericarp crustaceous or leathery.
11

Calyx deeply. urn-shaped or almost globular ; sepals united high up. Pericarp more or less fleshy. 12

11. Disc obliquely cupular. Ovary 2-celled. Sepals imbricate in bud. Petals with a very broad scale. Shrubs. Leaflets 10. — Species 1. Madagascar. . . . . **Plagioscyphus** Radlk.
Disc not cupular. Ovary 3-celled. Leaflets 4—8. — Species 7. West Africa. (Under *Erioglossum* Blume) . . . . . **Pancovia** Willd.

12. Stamens 12—15. Petals sessile ; scale adnate below by the margin, bearing a short crest. Ovary 6—8-celled. Trees. Leaflets 10—12. — Species 1. West Africa (Cameroons). . . . **Glossolepis** Gilg
Stamens 6—8. Petals clawed. 13

13. Scales of the petals adnate below by the margins, bearing an incurved crest ; claws elongate. Calyx subglobose, shortly toothed. Ovary 7-celled. Trees. Leaflets numerous. — Species 1. West Africa (Cameroons). . . . . **Radlkofera** Gilg
Scales of the petals adnate by a ridge, more rarely free. Ovary 3—4-celled, rarely 7—8-celled, but then petals with a free and crestless scale. Species 10. West Africa. Some have edible fruits. **Chytranthus** Hook. fil.

14. (4.) Petals absent. 15
Petals present. 23

15. Sepals 4—6, united at the base only, valvate or almost valvate in bud . 16
Sepals 5, united high up. 19

16. Stamens 4. Ovary 2-celled. Sepals 4. Leaves with 4—6 leaflets. — Species 1. Madagascar. . . . . **Crossonephelis** Baill.
Stamens 5—8. Ovary 3-celled. 17

17. Flowers in racemes or panicles. Sepals 4—5, hairy outside. Stamens 7—8. Seeds without an aril. Leaves with 4—6 leaflets. — Species 2. Central Africa. . . . . **Melanodiscus** Radlk.
Flowers in clusters. Stamens 5, rarely 6—7, but then seeds with an aril. 18

18. Stamens inserted inside the disc ; filaments short, not exceeding the calyx ; anthers linear. Sepals 5—6, hairy above. Seed 1, with an aril. Leaves abruptly pinnate, with 4—10 leaflets. — Species 2. East Africa. . . . . **Haplocoelum** Radlk.
Stamens inserted at the edge of the disc, 5 ; filaments long, much exceeding the calyx ; anthers oblong or oval. Sepals 5. Leaves with a narrowly winged rachis. — Species 4. Central Africa. . **Pistaciopsis** Engl.

19. Sepals imbricate in bud, finally slashed.   Stamens 8—10, bent twice in the
    bud.   Ovary 3-celled.   Seeds with an aril ; embryo almost straight.
    Trees.   Flowers in axillary racemes or panicles. — Species 2.   Central
    Africa.   Flowers fragrant, used for preparing an aromatic water.

                                              Lecaniodiscus Planch
    Sepals valvate in bud.   Stamens 8. 20
20. Ovary 2-celled.   Fruit indehiscent.   Seeds with an aril. 21
    Ovary 3-celled. 22
21. Fruit covered with wart-like protuberances.   Aril free from the seed-
    coat. — Species 1 (*L. chinensis* Sonn.)   Cultivated in the tropics
    and naturalized in the Mascarene Islands.   It yields timber, edible
    fruits, and medicaments.   (Under *Nephelium* L. or *Euphoria* Commers.)

                                                      Litchi Sonn.
    Fruit covered with soft spine-like processes or glabrous.   Aril adnate to
    the seed-coat. — Species 1 (*N. lappaceum* L., Rambutan).   Cultivated
    in the tropics.   It yields edible fruits and fat-containing seeds.   (Under
    Euphoria Comm.) . . . . **Nephelium** L.
22. Fruit dehiscent.   Seeds with an aril.   Calyx cup-shaped.   Flowers in
    axillary panicles. — Species 1.   Mascarene Islands.   Yields timber
    (iron-wood), edible fruits, and oily seeds.   (Under *Nephelium* L.)

                                                  Stadmannia Lam.
    Fruit indehiscent.   Seeds without an aril.   Calyx top-shaped.   Flowers
    in racemes or panicles springing from the older parts of the stem. —
    Species 3.   Central Africa. . . . . **Placodiscus** Radlk.
23. (14.) Calyx 5-lobed ; lobes open or slightly imbricate in bud.   Stamens
    6—10. 24
    Calyx 5-parted. 27
24. Calyx urn-shaped.   Petals with a scale adnate by a ridge.   Fruit indehiscent,
    3-lobed, with a leathery pericarp.   Seeds without an aril.   Inflorescences
    arising from the older branches.   Leaves pinnate.   (See 13.)

                                              Chytranthus Hook. fil.
    Calyx cup- or saucer-shaped, small.   Petals with a scale adnate by the
    margins, or with a free scale, or without a scale.   Fruit dehiscent.
    Seeds with an aril. 25
25. Petals hairy, without a scale or with the inflexed margins prolonged into
    small scales.   Ovary lobed.   Pericarp leathery.   Leaves simple, un-
    divided, oblong. — Species 4.   East and South Africa.   They yield
    timber, edible fruits, and oily seeds.   (Under *Sapindus* L.)

                                              Pappea Eckl. & Zeyh.
    Petals with a free scale or with a scale adnate by the margins.   Leaves
    pinnate.· 26
26. Petals with a scale adnate by the margins, hence funnel-shaped.   Disc
    clothing the base of the calyx.   Filaments hairy.   Fruit 3-angled, almost
    glabrous.   Inflorescences axillary. — Species 5.   Central Africa.
    Some yield timber.   (Under *Blighia* Koen.) . . **Phialodiscus** Radlk.

Petals with an almost free, notched scale. Disc free. Filaments glabrous. Fruit almost globose ; pericarp crustaceous or woody, hispid on the outside, woolly within. — Species 3. West Africa. Yielding timber.

Eriocoelum Hook. fil.

27. (23.) Sepals narrowly imbricate in bud. 28
Sepals broadly imbricate in bud. 33

28. Stamens 5. Petals hooded, without scales. Disc 5-lobed. Ovary 2-celled. Fruit indehiscent, with a crustaceous pericarp. Seeds with an aril. Leaves with numerous leaflets. Inflorescences arising from the older parts of the stem. — Species 1. Madagascar. **Pseudopteris** Baill.
Stamens 6—10. 29

29. Stamens 6—7. Petals hairy, with 1—2 scales adnate by their edges. Ovary 2-celled. Fruit compressed, dehiscent, with a cartilagineous endocarp. Seeds with an adnate aril. Leaves with 4—11 pairs of leaflets. Flowers in terminal panicles. — Species 3. Central Africa.

Aporrhiza Radlk.
Stamens 8—10. 30

30. Ovary 2-celled. Fruit indehiscent. Stamens 8. 31
Ovary 3-celled. Fruit tardily dehiscent. Stamens 8—10. Petals furnished at the base with a scale adnate at each side. 32

31. Leaflets in 3—4 pairs, toothed, pellucidly dotted, beset with scaly glands when young. Fruit 2-lobed, with a fleshy pericarp. Seeds without an aril. — Species 1. South Africa (Cape Colony). (Under *Sapindus* L.)

Smelophyllum Radlk.
Leaflets in 5 pairs, entire, beset with stellate hairs. Fruit with a crust-aceous pericarp. Seeds with a free aril. — Species 1 (*E. Longana* Lam.). Cultivated in the tropics and in Egypt and naturalized in the Mascarene Islands. Yields timber and edible fruits. (Under *Nephelium* L.) . . . . **Euphoria** Commers.

32. Petals saccate at the base. Stamens 8, rarely 10. Fruit large, bluntly 3-angled. Seeds enveloped at the base by an adnate aril. — Species 3. West Africa. The aril is poisonous when unripe or over-ripe, but edible when ripe, and used for preparing oil and medicaments ; from the fragrant flowers an aromatic liquid is prepared. " Akee-tree." (Under *Cupania* L.) . . . . **Blighia** Koen.
Petals funnel-shaped. Stamens 10. Seeds enclosed in the fleshy testa. Leaflets in 4—6 pairs, toothed. — Species 3. West Africa.

Lychnodiscus Radlk.

33. (27.) Stamens 5. Ovary 2-celled. Fruit compressed, dehiscent, with a spongey pericarp. Seeds with a free aril. — Species 1. Madagascar.

Tinopsis Radlk.
Stamens 8—24. 34

34. Stamens 8. 35
Stamens 10—24. Seeds without an aril. 42

35. Leaves twice pinnate. Petals small. Fruit 1-celled, indehiscent, with a crustaceous pericarp. Seeds with a membranous aril and a crustaceous testa. — Species 10. Madagascar and East Africa. **Macphersonia** Blume
    Leaves once pinnate. 36
36. Petals with 1 scale. Seeds without an aril; testa membranous, leathery, or crustaceous. 37
    Petals with 2 scales, usually formed by the inflexion of their edges, rarely (*Molinaea*) without scales. Seeds with an aril, rarely (*Sapindus*) without, but then with a bony testa. 39
37. Leaflets prickly toothed, in several pairs. Stem shrubby. Inflorescences springing from the older parts of the stem. Petals with a hooded scale. Disc cup-shaped, crenate. — Species 1. Madagascar.
    Cotylodiscus Radlk.
    Leaflets entire. Stem tree-like. Fruit lobed. 38
38. Leaflets in 2 pairs. Fruit drupaceous, not separating into mericarps. Seeds with a thin testa; embryo nearly straight. — Species 1 (*A. senegalensis* Radlk.). Central Africa. It yields timber and edible fruits which are also used as a substitute for soap; the seeds are poisonous. (Under *Sapindus* L.) . . . . **Aphania** Blume
    Leaflets in 3 or more pairs. Fruit separating into 2—3 berry-like mericarps. Seeds with a leathery testa. — Species 20. Tropical and South Africa. Some have edible fruits. (Plate 85.)
    Deinbollia Schum. & Thonn.
39. Petals with large scales. Ovary 2-celled. Fruit capsular. — Species 10. Madagascar. (Under *Cupania* L., *Jagera* Blume, or *Ratonia* DC.).
    Tina Roem. & Schult.
    Petals with small scales or without scales. Ovary 3-celled. 40
40. Petals very small, with 2 linear scales at the base. Filaments bent twice in the bud. Shrubs. Leaflets in 6—10 pairs. — Species 1. Madagascar. . . . . **Eriandrostachys** Baill.
    Petals small or rather large, with the margins bent inwards at the base or without any appendage. Usually trees. 41
41. Seeds with an aril and a crustaceous testa. Fruit winged, capsular. — Species 8. Madagascar and Mascarenes. Some species yield timber and medicaments. (Under *Cupania* L.). . . . . **Molinaea** Comm.
    Seeds without an aril; testa bony. Fruit not winged, drupaceous or separating into mericarps. (See 9.) . . . . . **Sapindus** L.
42. (34.) Petals without a scale. Stamens 10. Ovary 3-celled. Fruit capsular, bristly. Climbing shrubs clothed with rust-coloured hairs. Leaflets in 3—4 pairs, toothed. — Species 1. West Africa. (Under *Cupania* L.) . . . . **Laccodiscus** Radlk.
    Petals with a scale. Trees or erect shrubs. 43
43. Ovary entire. Stamens 10—12. Leaves without glands. — Species 1. East Africa. (Under *Deinbollia* Schum. & Thonn.)
    Camptolepis Radlk.

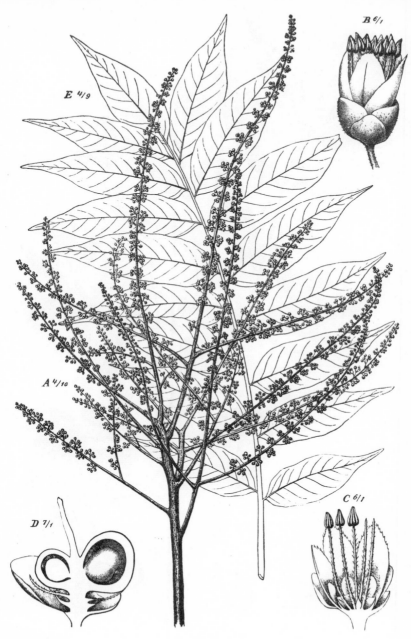

J Fleischmann del,

Deinbollia pycnophylla Gilg

A Inflorescence.   *B* Male flower.   *C* Male flower cut lengthwise (two anthers have fallen off).   *D* Older female flower cut lengthwise.
E Leaf.

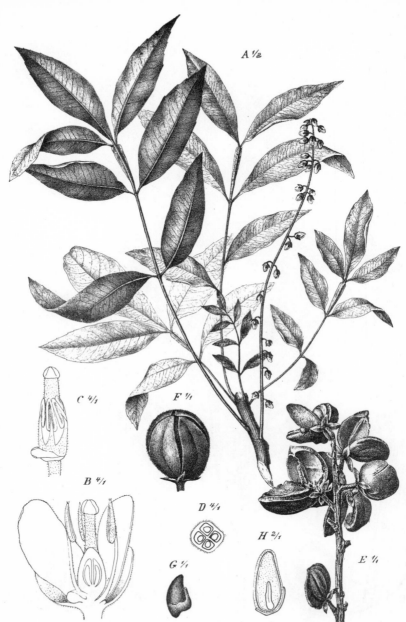

J. Fleischmann del.

Bersama abyssinica Fresen.

A Flowering branch. *B* Flower cut lengthwise. *C* Flower without the perianth. *D* Cross-section of ovary. *E* Group of fruits.
F Fruit. *G* Seed with aril. *H* Seed cut lengthwise.

Ovary lobed or divided. Stamens 12—24. Leaves with sunken glands. Fruit separating into mericarps. 44

44. Fruit winged; pericarp leathery. Ovary 2-celled. Stamens 20—24. Sepals densely clothed with silky hairs. Leaflets 4, with conspicuous veins. — Species 1. Island of Mauritius. The seeds contain oil.

Hornea Bak.

Fruit not winged ; pericarp fleshy. (See 38.) **Deinbollia** Schum. & Thonn.

45. (2.) Flowers irregular. Petals 4. Disc one-sided. Ovary 3-celled. Fruit capsular. 46

Flowers regular or nearly so. Petals 5 or 0. Disc complete or indistinct. 48

46. Petals with a long claw and a crisped scale, red. Disc cup-shaped. Stamens 8. Ovary stalked. Fruit inflated, bursting irregularly. Seeds with a red, bony testa and a spiral embryo. Shrubs. Leaves unequally pinnate with a winged rachis and 11—13 leaflets. — Species 2. South Africa and Madagascar. . . . . . **Erythrophysa** E. Mey.

Petals with a short claw and without a scale. Disc flat. Ovary sessile. Fruit opening regularly. Seeds with a leathery or crusty testa. Leaves with 3—10 leaflets clothed with stellate hairs. 47

47. Stamens 5—6. Fruit with septifragal dehiscence. Embryo spirally twisted. Leaves unequally pinnate, with 3—7 leaflets. — Species 2. Madagascar and Mascarenes. Yielding timber. . **Cossignia** Comm.

Stamens 8. Fruit with loculicidal dehiscence. Embryo curved. Leaves equally pinnate, with 6—10 leaflets. — Species 3. Tropics. (*Majidea* Kirk) . . . . **Harpullia** Roxb.

48. Petals present. Stamens 8. Ovary 3-celled. Leaves equally pinnate. 49

Petals absent. 51

49. Disc somewhat one-sided. Petals green or yellowish. Fruit capsular. Leaves with 8—10 leaflets. (See 47.) . . . **Harpullia** Roxb.

Disc equal-sided. Petals red or reddish. 50

50. Leaves with 4—6 leaflets. Petals with the margins bent back at the base. Fruit capsular, 3-celled. — Species 1. Madagascar.

Conchopetalum Radlk.

Leaves with 8—14 usually serrate leaflets along a winged rachis. Petals minutely toothed. Fruit indehiscent, leathery, usually 1-celled. — Species 1. South Africa. . . . . **Hippobromus** Eckl. & Zeyh.

51. Disc indistinct. Stamens 5—15, usually 8. Ovary 2—6-, usually 3-celled. Stigma lobed. Fruit capsular, 2—6-celled. Embryo spirally twisted. Leaves usually simple. — Species 4. Tropical and South Africa. They yield timber, medicaments, and edible fruits ; the beaten branches are used as torches. . . . . . **Dodonaea** L.

Disc distinctly developed. Stamens 4—5. Ovary 2-celled. Fruit indehiscent, usually drupaceous and 1-celled. Embryo not spiral. Leaves pinnate. 52

52. Flowers 4-merous. Leaves unequally pinnate. Tall trees. — Species 1.
Southern West Africa (Angola). . . . . . .   **Zanha** Hiern
Flowers 5-merous. Leaves equally pinnate. 53
53. Calyx slightly lobed. Seeds with a thin testa and short radicle. Leaflets
elliptical, entire. Flowers in panicles. — Species 1. West Africa.
Talisiopsis Radlk.

Calyx deeply divided. 54
54. Stamens alternating with the sepals. Stigma 2-lobed. Seeds with a thin
testa and short radicle. Leaflets oval, crenate. Flowers in few-
flowered cymes. — Species 1. East Africa. The seeds are edible.
Dialiopsis Radlk.

Stamens opposite to the sepals. Stigma entire. Seeds with a leathery
testa and long radicle. Leaflets lanceolate oblong or elliptical, entire.
Flowers in panicles. — Species 1. Mascarene Islands. It yields timber,
edible fruits, and medicaments. (Under *Hippobromus* Eckl. & Zeyh.
or *Melicocca* L.) . . . .   **Doratoxylon** Thouars

SUBORDER MELIANTHINEAE
FAMILY 135. MELIANTHACEAE

Trees or shrubs. Leaves alternate, unequally pinnate or simple and undivided. Flowers in racemes, more or less irregular, hermaphrodite. Sepals
4—5, free or united at the base, imbricate in bud. Petals 4—5, imbricate in
bud, sometimes cohering in the middle. Stamens 4—10, inserted within the
disc. Anthers opening lengthwise by lateral slits. Ovary superior, 4—5-celled.
Style simple ; stigma entire or lobed. Fruit a capsule. Seeds with a straight
embryo and copious albumen. — Genera 3, species 30. (Under *SAPINDACEAE*)
(Plate 86.).

1. Leaves simple, undivided, exstipulate. Flowers almost regular. Disc
equal-sided, with 10 processes. Petals sessile. Stamens 10. Ovary 5-
celled, with numerous ovules in each cell. Capsule septicidal. —
Species 3. South Africa. [Tribe GREYIEAE.] **Greyia** Hook. & Harv.
Leaves pinnate, stipulate. Flowers more or less irregular. Disc one-
sided. Petals clawed. Stamens 4—5. Ovary usually 4-celled. Ovules
1—12 in each cell. Capsule loculicidal. [Tribe MELIANTHEAE.]   2
2. Sepals very unequal. Petals 4, rarely 5, cohering in the middle, shorter
than the sepals. Disc pouch-shaped. Stamens 4. Ovules 4—12 in
each ovary-cell. Seeds without an aril. — Species 5. South Africa ;
one species also naturalized in the Canary Islands. The latter serves
as an ornamental plant and is said to render honey poisonous.
Melianthus L.

Sepals nearly equal. Petals 5, free, longer than the sepals. Disc semi-
orbicular. Ovules solitary in each ovary-cell. Seeds with an aril.
— Species 20. Central and South-east Africa. (Including *Natalia*
Hochst.) (Plate 86.) . . . .   **Bersama** Fres.

BALSAMINACEAE.

Pl. 87.

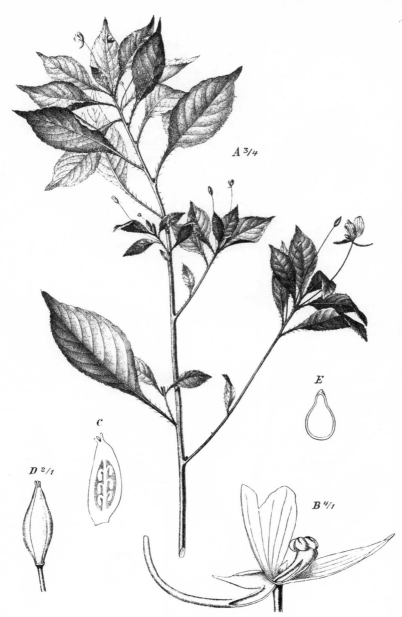

J. Fleischmann del.

Impatiens capensis Thunb.

A Flowering branch.   B Flower cut lengthwise.   C Ovary cut lengthwise.   D Fruit.   E Seed cut lengthwise.

J. Fleischmann del.

Ventilago leiocarpa Benth.

A Flowering branch.　*B* Flower cut lengthwise.　*C* Sepal.　*D* Petal expanded.　*E* Younger and older stamen　*F* Fruit.　*G* Lower part of the fruit cut open.

SUBORDER BALSAMININEAE
FAMILY 136. BALSAMINACEAE

Succulent herbs. Leaves herbaceous, undivided, penninerved, without stipules. Flowers solitary or in clusters or racemes, without bracteoles, irregular, hermaphrodite. Sepals 3, rarely 5, imbricate in bud, the hindmost more or less distinctly spurred. Petals 3 or 5. Stamens 5; filaments short and broad; anthers united, turned inwards, opening towards the apex. Disc none. Ovary superior, 5-celled. Ovules 3 or more, in the inner angle of each cell, pendulous, inverted, with dorsal raphe. Style 1; stigmas 1 or 5. Fruit succulent, dehiscing elastically. Seeds exalbuminous. (Under *GERANIA-CEAE*.) (Plate 87.)

Genus 1, species 100. Tropical and South Africa. Some are used as ornamental plants (balsams), others yield dyes, medicaments, or edible oily seeds. (Including *Trimorphopetalum* Bak.) . . . . **Impatiens** L.

ORDER RHAMNALES
FAMILY 137. RHAMNACEAE

Shrubs or trees, rarely (*Helinus*) undershrubs. Leaves undivided, stipulate, more rarely (*Phylica*) exstipulate. Flowers regular, hermaphrodite or polygamous. Receptacle more or less cup-shaped. Sepals 4—5, valvate in bud. Petals 4—5 or 0. Stamens as many as and alternate with the sepals. Anthers opening by 1—2 slits. Disc within the stamens, sometimes indistinct. Ovary 2—4-celled, sometimes not quite completely septate, rarely (*Maesopsis*) 1-celled. Ovules solitary in each cell, basal, inverted. Style undivided or cleft. Seeds with a large, straight embryo. — Genera 18, species 140. (Plate 88.)

1. Ovary superior or almost so. 2
   Ovary inferior or half-inferior. 9
2. Ovary 1-celled. Stigma 5-lobed. Fruit one-seeded, indehiscent. Leaves opposite or nearly so, penninerved. — Species 2. Equatorial regions. The fruits are edible. (Including *Karlea* Pierre) . **Maesopsis** Engl.
   Ovary completely or almost completely 2—4-celled. Stigma 2—4-lobed, or 2—4 stigmas. 3
3. Anthers opening outwards. Sepals with a far projecting ledge on the inside. Disc ring-shaped. Style undivided, with a 2-lobed stigma. Leaves opposite or nearly so, crenate, with 2—4 lateral nerves on each side. Flowers in axillary spikes or in terminal panicles. — Species 1. Abyssinia. . . . . **Lamellisepalum** Engl.
   Anthers dehiscing inwards or laterally. Flowers solitary or in cymes, rarely in racemes or panicles, but then style 2—4-cleft or with 3 stigmas. 4
4. Leaves 3-, more rarely 5-nerved from the base. Style 2—4-cleft. Fruit wingless, fleshy, indehiscent, with a 1—4-celled stone. — Species 10. Some of them yield timber, tanning and dyeing materials, gum-lac, food for silk-worms, medicaments, and edible fruits (jujubes) from which

a sort of bread and a beverage are prepared ; others have poisonous fruits ; some are used as hedge plants. . . . . **Zizyphus** Juss.
Leaves penninerved. 5

5. Flowers in terminal panicles, 5-merous. Stigmas 3. Fruit with 3 stones. Shrubs with spiny branches. Leaves opposite. — Species 1. Northern East Africa. The fruits are edible. . . . **Sageretia** Brongn.
Flowers in axillary inflorescences. 6

6. Receptacle united with the fruit for the greatest part. Fruit with 2—4 indehiscent stones. Seeds not grooved. Disc thick. Spines in the axils of the leaves. — Species 3. Tropical and South Africa. (*Adolia* Lam.) . . . . **Scutia** Brongn.
Receptacle free from the fruit for the greatest part. Disc thin, rarely thick, but then spines, as usually, wanting. 7

7 Fruit with 1 two-celled stone. Disc thick. Style 2-cleft. Flowers 5-merous. Leaves alternate. — Species 1. East Africa. The fruits are edible. . . . . **Berchemia** Neck.
Fruit with 2—4 stones. Disc thin. 8

8. Fruit with a red skin and a woody stone separating into 3 elastically dehiscing portions. Seed-coat crustaceous, shining. Flowers 5-merous. Leaves alternate. — Species 1. Madagascar. . **Macrorhamnus** Baill.
Fruit with 2—4 leathery or thin-woody, scarcely or not dehiscing stones. Seed-coat thin. — Species 17. North, East, and South Africa. They yield timber, dyes, a substitute for hop, fish-poison, and medicaments. " Buckthorn." . . . . **Rhamnus** L.

9. (1.) Ovary half-inferior. 10
Ovary inferior. 15

10. Style simple ; stigma 3-lobed. Leaves penninerved, serrate or crenate. 11
Style 2—4-cleft. 12

11. Ovary incompletely 2—3-celled, 1—2-ovuled. Fruit drupaceous, 1 celled, 1—2-seeded. Trees. Leaves opposite or nearly so. Flowers in axillary, raceme-like cymes. (See 2.) . . . . **Maesopsis** Engl.
Ovary completely 3-celled, 3-ovuled. Fruit separating into 3 dehiscing mericarps, 3-seeded. Shrubs. Leaves alternate. Flowers in axillary and terminal cymes or panicles. — Species 1. South Africa and St. Helena. . . . . **Noltia** Reichb.

12. Leaves 3—5-nerved from the base, alternate. Fruit a drupe. Stem erect or decumbent. 13
Leaves penninerved. Fruit a nut, a schizocarp, or a capsule. . . . 14

13. Fruit with a horizontal wing ; epicarp leathery, endocarp woody. Leaves 3-nerved, serrate ; stipules transformed into spines. Flowers in axillary and terminal, raceme-like cymes. — Species 1. Cultivated and naturalized in Algeria. Used medicinally and as a hedge-plant.
Paliurus Juss.
Fruit not winged ; epicarp fleshy, endocarp horny woody or leathery. (See 4.) . . . . **Zizyphus** Juss.

14. Ovary 2-celled. Style 2-cleft. Fruit with a long wing-like appendage, dry, 1-seeded, indehiscent. Climbing shrubs. Leaves alternate. — Species 3. Madagascar and neighbouring islands, West Africa. They yield fibres, tanning and dyeing materials, and medicaments. (Plate 88.)
Ventilago Gaertn.

Ovary 3-celled. Style 3-cleft or 3-parted. Fruit not winged, 3-seeded. Erect or almost erect, hairy shrubs or trees. Leaves opposite. Flowers in lateral inflorescences. — Species 6. Tropics. **Lasiodiscus** Hook. fil.

15. (9.) Style simple, sometimes very short, with 1—3 stigmas. Fruit separating into 3 dehiscing mericarps. Seed-coat hard. Hairy plants. Leaves alternate, entire, nearly always exstipulate. Flowers solitary or in spikes, racemes, or heads. — Species 80. South Africa, southern Central Africa, Madagascar and the neighbouring islands. Some are used as ornamental plants. . . . . **Phylica** L.

Style 2—4-cleft. Leaves stipulate. Flowers in cymes sometimes arranged in false spikes or racemes, very rarely flowers solitary. 16

16. Receptacle top-shaped, not prolonged beyond the ovary. Fruit separating into 3 elastically dehiscent mericarps. Erect shrubs or low trees. Leaves alternate, 3-nerved at the base, serrate. Flowers in axillary cymes. — Species 1. East and South-east Africa, including the islands.
Colubrina Brongn.

Receptacle prolonged beyond the ovary. 17

17. Stem tree-like. Leaves opposite, entire, penninerved, hairy beneath. Flowers in axillary cymes. Anthers dehiscing by longitudinal slits which are confluent at the apex. Fruit separating into dehiscent mericarps; epicarp somewhat fleshy. — Species 1. Island of St. Helena. . . . . **Nesiota** Hook. fil.

Stem shrubby, half-shrubby, or climbing. Leaves alternate. Flowers in axillary and terminal inflorescences. 18

18. Stem not climbing, without tendrils. Leaves few, lanceolate, entire. Flowers solitary or in few-flowered cymes. — Species 1. South Africa (Betchuanaland). . . . . **Marlothia** Engl.

Stem climbing, bearing tendrils. Leaves oval. Flowers in usually many-flowered cymes, false spikes, or panicles. Mericarps 3, separating from a central column. 19

19. Flowers in cymes. Disc entire. Fruit wingless; mericarps dehiscing elastically. Leaves entire, penninerved. — Species 3. Tropical and South Africa. . . . . **Helinus** E. Mey.

Flowers in false spikes or racemes. Disc usually lobed. Fruit 3-winged; mericarps dehiscing by a narrow slit or indehiscent. — Species 12. Tropics. Some are used medicinally. . . . . **Gouania** L.

FAMILY 138. VITACEAE.

Shrubs or trees, usually climbing, rarely (*Cissus*) herbs or undershrubs. Leaves alternate, stipulate. Flowers regular, in cymose inflorescences. Calyx small, entire or lobed.   Petals 3—7, sometimes cohering at the base or at the apex, valvate in bud.   Stamens as many as and opposite to the petals, inserted outside the hypogynous, sometimes indistinct disc.   Anthers opening inwards by two longitudinal slits.   Ovary 2—8-celled, seated upon the disc or more or less sunk in it.   Ovules solitary in each cell or two side by side, ascending, inverted, with ventral raphe.   Style simple, sometimes indistinct.   Stigma entire or 2—4-lobed.   Fruit a berry, usually septate.   Seeds with a bony or crustaceous testa and a fleshy or cartilaginous, more or less ruminate albumen enclosing a small straight embryo. — Genera 5, species 200. (*AMPELIDEAE.*)   (Plate 89.)

1. Filaments united with one another and with the petals.   Ovary 3—8-celled, with 1 ovule in each cell.   Erect shrubs or trees, without tendrils. Leaves 1—3 times pinnate. — Species 3.   Tropics.   They yield vegetables, edible fruits, dyes, and medicaments, and serve as ornamental plants.   [Subfamily **LEEOIDEAE.**]   . . . .   **Leea** L.
   Filaments free from each other and from the petals.   Ovary 2-celled, with 2 ovules in each cell.   [Subfamily **VITOIDEAE.**]   2

2. Flowers polygamous-dioecious.   Petals 5, cohering at the top and falling off together.   Disc 5-lobed.   Style very short, conical.   Seeds pear-shaped, with two pits on the ventral face.   Climbing shrubs.   Leaves more or less distinctly 3—5-lobed.   Inflorescences paniculate, often with tendrils. — Species 1 (*V. vinifera* L., grape-vine).   North Africa, also cultivated in other regions.   It yields edible fruits, also used for preparing wine vinegar and brandy, oily seeds, and medicaments.
   Vitis Tourn.
   Flowers hermaphrodite or polygamous-monoecious.   Petals usually spreading at the time of flowering, very rarely cohering at the top, but then only 4.   Seeds more or less egg-shaped.   3

3. Style short-conical or wanting.   Petals usually 5.   Disc ring-shaped. Seeds egg- or boat-shaped.   Climbing shrubs.   Inflorescences with tendrils. — Species 30.   Tropics.   Some have edible fruits.   (Under *Cissus* L. or *Vitis* Tourn.) . . . . . .   **Ampelocissus** Planch.
   Style filiform or columnar, usually rather long.   Inflorescences mostly without tendrils.   4

4. Petals 5 or 6, very rarely 4 or 7, thickened, fleshy, persistent.   Disc adnate to the ovary.   Style usually short.   Climbing shrubs.   Inflorescences compact. — Species 15.   Central and South Africa.   (Under *Cissus* L. or *Vitis* Tourn.) . . . .   **Rhoicissus** Planch.

5. Petals 4, not thickened.   Disc usually saucer-shaped, 4-lobed and adnate to the ovary at the base only.   Style usually long. — Species 150. Tropical and South Africa and Egypt.   Some of them yield edible fruits or tubers, mucilage, or medicaments.   (Under *Vitis* Tourn.)   (Plate 89.)
   Cissus L.

VITACEAE.

Pl. 89.

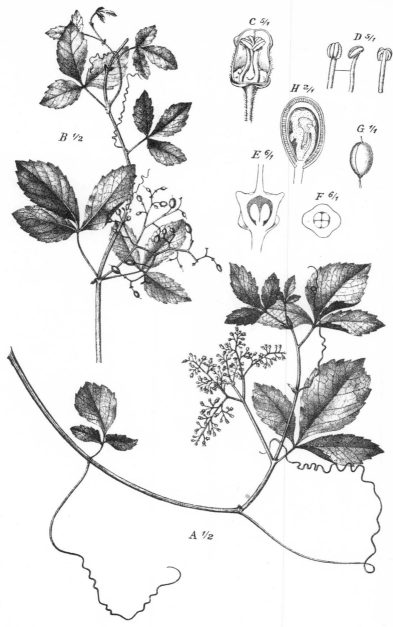

C 5/1

D 5/1

B 1/2

H 2/1

G 1/1

E 6/1

F 6/1

A 1/2

J. Fleischmann del.

Cissus cirrhosa (Thunb.) Planch.

A Flowering branch.   *B* Fruiting branch.   *C* Male Flower, the corolla cut lengthwise.   *D* Stamens.   *E* Ovary cut lengthwise.
F Ovary cut across.   *G* Fruit.   *H* Fruit cut lengthwise.

J. Fleischmann del.

Leptochlaena multiflora Thouars

A Flowering branch.   *B* Flower cut lengthwise.   *C* Cross-section of ovary.

ORDER MALVALES

SUBORDER ELAEOCARPINEAE

FAMILY 139. ELAEOCARPACEAE

Trees. Leaves undivided, stipulate. Flowers in axillary racemes, regular, hermaphrodite or polygamous. Sepals 4—6, valvate in bud. Petals 4—6, hypogynous, free, flat at the base, toothed or fringed at the apex, valvate in bud. Stamens numerous, inserted upon a cushion-shaped receptacle. Filaments free. Anthers linear, 2-celled, opening by a terminal pore. Ovary superior, 2—5-celled. Ovules 2 or more in the inner angle of each cell, inverted, pendulous, with ventral raphe, or one of them ascending. Style simple. Fruit a drupe with a septate stone. Seeds albuminous; embryo straight. (Under *TILIACEAE*.)

Genus 1, species 15. Madagascar, Mauritius, and Socotra. **Elaeocarpus** L.

SUBORDER CHLAENINEAE

FAMILY 140. CHLAENACEAE

Trees or shrubs, rarely climbing. Leaves alternate, simple, entire, stipulate. Flowers solitary or in panicles, regular, hermaphrodite, each flower or pair of flowers usually surrounded by an involucre. Sepals 3—5, imbricate in bud. Petals 5—6, free, hypogynous, with contorted aestivation. Disc ring- or cup-shaped, rarely 5-parted or indistinct. Stamens 10 or more, inserted within the disc or at its edge. Filaments free or united below with the disc, very rarely in 5 bundles. Anthers roundish, opening by 2 sometimes confluent longitudinal slits. Ovary superior, 3-celled, with 2 or more ovules in each cell. Style simple; stigmas 1 or 3. Fruit a capsule or a nut. Seeds with a leathery testa and copious albumen. — Genera 7, species 25. Madagascar. (Under *TERNSTROEMIACEAE*.) (Plate 90.)

1. Involucre large, calyx-like, 3—10-lobed or many-parted. Sepals 3. Disc cupular. Ovules 2—4 in each ovary-cell, pendulous. 2

   Involucre not calyx-like, either 2-parted or shortly cup-shaped or indistinct or wanting; in the two former cases ovules numerous in each ovary-cell. Stamens 12 or more. 4

2. Involucre consisting of numerous densely crowded bracts, fleshy. Stamens numerous. Ovules 2 in each ovary-cell. Fruit a capsule. — Species 5. Madagascar. Used medicinally. (*Sarcolaena* Thouars)

   Sarcochlaena Thouars

   Involucre cup-shaped, lobed, dry. 3

3. Stamens 10. Ovules 2 in each ovary-cell. Involucre 6-toothed. Fruit a one-seeded nut. — Species 7. Madagascar. (*Leptolaena* Thouars). (Plate 90.) . . . . **Leptochlaena** Thouars

   Stamens numerous. Fruit a capsule. — Species 4. Madagascar.

   Xerochlamys Bak.

4. Involucre cup-shaped, enlarged in fruit.   Sepals 5, the two outer somewhat smaller than the others. Disc consisting of 5 scales. Filaments
   united in 5 bundles. Ovules many in each ovary-cell, descending.
   Fruit a nut. — Species 1. Madagascar. (*Sclerolaena* Bak., *Xyloolaena*
   Baill.) . . . . **Xylochlaena** Baill.
   Involucre of two bracts or rudimentary or wanting. Sepals 5, the two
   outer much smaller than the others, or 3. Disc ring- or cup-shaped.
   Filaments not united in bundles. 5
5 Ovules many in each ovary-cell, descending. Involucre enclosing two
   flowers, usually consisting of two laciniate bracts enlarged in fruit.
   Sepals 3. Disc cup-shaped. Fruit a capsule splitting to the base. —
   Species 5. Madagascar. (*Schizolaena* Thouars). **Schizochlaena** Thouars
   Ovules few in each ovary-cell.   Involucre rudimentary or wanting.   . 6
.6. Ovules axile, descending. Outer stamens inserted on the inside of the
   disc. Fruit a capsule dehiscing at the top only. — Species 4. Madagascar. (*Rhodolaena* Thouars). . . . . . **Rhodochlaena** Thouars
   Ovules basal, ascending. Sepals 5. Outer stamens inserted at the edge
   of the ring-shaped disc. Stigma 3-lobed. — Species 1. Madagascar.
   (*Eremolaena* Baill.) . . . . **Eremochlaena** Baill.

SUBORDER MALVINEAE

FAMILY 141. TILIACEAE

Leaves toothed or lobed, more rarely entire or deeply divided. Stipules
present. Flowers regular. Calyx valvate in bud. Petals entire or notched
at the apex, rarely (*Grewia*) wanting. Stamens hypogynous, 10 or more,
rarely 5—9, free or united in 4—10 bundles. Anthers 2-celled, the cells sometimes confluent at the top. Ovary superior, completely or almost completely
2- or more-celled, rarely (*Christiania*) deeply divided. — Genera 18, species 260.
(Plate 91.)
   1. Sepals combined into an entire, crenate, or 2—6-lobed calyx. Petals
      with contorted aestivation. Stamens numerous. Anthers roundish,
      opening by usually confluent, longitudinal slits. Style 4—5-parted or
      wanting. Ovules 1—2 in each ovary-cell. Trees or shrubs. Leaves
      cordate. Flowers panicled. [Tribe BROWNLOWIEAE.] . . . 2
      Sepals free or nearly so. Anthers opening by separate slits or by pores.
      Style simple. 4
   2. Ovary 2-celled, with 1 ovule in each cell. Stigma sessile, petal-like, lobed.
      Calyx 2—3-lobed. Flowers dioecious. Fruit 4-winged. — Species
      2. East Africa and Madagascar. . . . . . **Carpodiptera** Gris.
      Ovary 4—6-celled. Styles 4—6, free or united at the base. 3
   3. Flowers dioecious or polygamous. Calyx 3—4-lobed. Filaments united
      at the base. Ovary 5—6-parted. Stigmas horizontal, laciniate.
      Fruit with one-seeded cells. — Species 2. Tropics. **Christiania** DC.

Flowers hermaphrodite. Calyx 5—6-cleft. Ovules 2 in each ovary-cell. Stigmas twisted, almost entire. — Species 1. Madagascar.

Speirostyla Bak.

4. Petals with a gland at the base, rarely (*Grewia*) petals wanting. Receptacle nearly always prolonged into a more or less stalk-like androphore. Anthers roundish. [Tribe GREWIEAE.] 5
Petals without a gland at the base. Receptacle not stalk-like, rarely (*Corchorus*) somewhat prolonged. Anthers linear or oblong, rarely (*Sparmannia*) oval. 11

5. Flowers dioecious or polygamous. Stamens 10. Ovary 3—5-celled, with numerous ovules in each cell. Leaves elliptical. Inflorescence raceme-like. — Species 1. West Africa (Congo). **Pentadiplandra** Baill.
Flowers hermaphrodite. Stamens numerous, rarely (*Triumfetta*) 5—10, but then ovary-cells with 2 ovules in each. 6

6. Fruit a spiny. nut or schizocarp. Herbs or undershrubs, rarely shrubs. Flowers in cymes, yellow. Stigma lobed. Ovules 2 in each ovary-cell. — Species 50. Tropical and South Africa. Some species yield fibres, vegetables, or medicaments. . . . . . . **Triumfetta** L.
Fruit an unarmed nut or drupe. Shrubs or trees. 7

7. Fruit few-seeded, usually fleshy. Ovary 2—5-celled, with usually 2 ovules in each cell. Filaments free. — Species 140. Tropical and South Africa and the Sahara. They yield timber, fibre, edible fruits from which drinks are prepared, and medicaments. (Plate 91.) **Grewia** L.
Fruit many-seeded, fibrous. Ovary 4—10-celled, with numerous ovules in each cell. Petals 4—5, small. Trees. 8

8. Flowers 2—3 together surrounded by an involucre of 3—4 bracts. Filaments free. Ovary 6—8-celled. 9
Flowers without a distinct involucre. Filaments united at the base. Stipules cleft. 10

9. Involucral bracts 3, enclosing 3 flowers. Ovary 8-celled. Fruit with 8 furrows. Stipules awl-shaped. — Species 1. West Africa. The seeds are used as a substitute for coffee. . . . . **Duboscia** Bocq.
Involucral bracts 4, enclosing 2 flowers. Petals 4. Ovary 6—7-celled. Fruit with 6—7 ribs. Stipules large, oblique. — Species 1. West Africa (Cameroons). . . . . **Diplanthemum** K. Schum.

10. Ovary and fruit 4—5-celled. Fruit oblong. Seeds winged. — Species 1. West Africa. . . . . **Desplatzia** Bocq.
Ovary and fruit 8—10-celled. Fruit ovoid or globose. — Species 3. Equatorial West Africa. Used medicinally. (*Grewiopsis* De Wild. & Dur.)

Grewiella O. Ktze.

11. (4.) Anthers linear, surmounted by a two-tipped or scale-like appendage. Stamens numerous. Ovary 6—10-celled. with 3 or more ovules in each cell. Shrubs or trees. [Tribe APEIBEAE.] 12
Anthers without an appendage at the top, rarely surmounted by a short point. Ovary 2—5-celled, rarely 6-celled. [Tribe TILIEAE.] . . 13

12. Petals 4, white, shorter than the calyx. Filaments united in 4 bundles. Anthers with a two-tipped appendage. Ovary 6-celled. Fruit globular, spiny. — Species 2. West Africa. (Including *Acrosepalum* Pierre).

                                                  Ancistrocarpus Oliv.

    Petals 4—5, yellow, equalling the calyx. Filaments almost free. Anthers with a scale-like appendage. Ovary 8—10-celled. Fruit spindle-shaped, many-celled. — Species 5. Tropics. Some are used for dyeing and in medicine. . . . . **Glyphaea** Hook. fil.

13. Staminodes 5 or more. Shrubs or trees. 14

    Staminodes none.   17

14. Staminodes 5, within the stamens. Anthers ending in a short point. Petals 5, white. Ovary 5-celled with 2 ovules in each cell. Stigma 5-parted. Leaves undivided, oblong or oval. — Species 3. Central Africa. . . . . **Cistanthera** K. Schum.

    Staminodes numerous, outside the stamens. Ovary 4—6-celled, with 3 or more ovules in each cell. 15

15. Fertile stamens 7—10. Anthers linear. Petals 4—5, violet. Fruit oblong, prickly, not winged. — Species 3. West Africa to the Great Lakes. They yield fibre. . . . . **Honckenya** Willd.

    Fertile stamens numerous. Petals 4, white or yellow. 16

16. Petals white. Ovary 4-celled. Fruit globose, prickly. — Species 6. South and East Africa and Madagascar. *S. africana* L. is used as an ornamental, medicinal, and textile plant. . . . **Sparmannia** L. f.

    Petals yellow. Ovary 5—6-celled. Fruit oblong, with bristly ciliate wings. — Species 1. Equatorial West Africa. Yields fibre.

                                                Cephalonema K. Schum.

17. Stem woody, shrubby. Leaves 6—7-parted. Sepals united at the base, bearing a small horn at the top. Petals 5, notched at the top or minutely toothed, shorter than the sepals. Stamens very numerous. Ovary 5—6-celled with 2 ovules in each cell. — Species 1. East Africa.

                                              Ceratosepalum Oliv.

    Stem herbaceous or woody at the base only. Leaves undivided. Sepals free. Petals yellow. Ovary 2—5-celled, with more than 2 ovules in each cell. Fruit more or less elongate, not prickly. — Species 30. Tropical and South Africa and Egypt ; one species also cultivated in other parts of North Africa. Some of them yield fibre (jute), vegetables, and medicaments. . . . . **Corchorus** L.

FAMILY 142. MALVACEAE

Leaves simple, stipulate. Calyx valvate in bud. Petals 5, adhering to the staminal tube, with contorted aestivation. Stamens numerous ; filaments united into a tube ; anthers 1-celled ; pollen-grains large, prickly. Ovary superior, sessile, 3- or more-celled, or many distinct ovaries. Ovules inverted. Seeds albuminous ; embryo curved. — Genera 21, species 300. (Plate 92.)

J. Fleischmann del.

Grewia occidentalis L.

A Flowering branch. *B* Flower cut lengthwise. *C* Ovary cut lengthwise. *D* Fruiting branch. *E* Fruit. *F* Cross-section of fruit.

J. Fleischmann del.

Pavonia praemorsa Willd.

A Flowering branch. *B* Flower cut lengthwise. *C* Anther. *D* Fruit. *E* Mericarp cut lengthwise.

1. Carpels in several rows placed one above the other, one-seeded, indehiscent, falling singly. Staminal tube beset with anthers to the top. Flowers with an epicalyx of 3 bracteoles. Herbs. — Species 3. North Africa. Used as ornamental and medicinal plants. [Tribe MALOPEAE.]

Malope L.

Carpels placed side by side in one plane. 2

2. Style-branches 10, twice as many as the ovary-cells. Ovules solitary in each cell. Staminal tube truncate or minutely toothed at the top. Fruit splitting into mericarps. [Tribe URENEAE.] 3

Style-branches as many as the ovary-cells, or a simple style. . . . 5

3. Flowers without an epicalyx, but inflorescence with an involucre. Carpels opposite to the petals. Hispid herbs. — Species 2. Tropics. Yielding fibre. . . . . **Malachra** L.

Flowers with an epicalyx of 5 or more bracteoles. 4

4. Mericarps covered with hooked bristles, indehiscent. Carpels alternating with the petals. Epicalyx of 5 bracteoles. Leaves glandular beneath. — Species 2. Tropical and South Africa ; one species only cultivated. Used as medicinal and textile plants. . . . . . . **Urena** L.

Mericarps winged, tubercled, or with 1—3 awns, rarely smooth. Leaves without glands on the under surface. — Species 25. Tropical and South Africa. Some of them are used as ornamental, medicinal, or textile plants. (*Malache* Vogel). (Plate 92.) . . . **Pavonia** L.

5. Fruit splitting into mericarps. Carpels 5 or more. Style cleft. Staminal tube loaded with anthers to the top. [Tribe MALVEAE.] . . . 6

Fruit capsular, loculicidal. Staminal tube beset with anthers on the outer face, truncate or minutely toothed at the top. [Tribe HIBISC-EAE.] 14

6. Carpels with 1 ovule. 7

Carpels with 2 or more ovules, sometimes transversely septate. [Subtribe ABUTILINAE.] 11

7. Ovule pendulous. Stigmas terminal. Epicalyx absent. — Species 20. Some of them yield fibre, fodder, tea, and medicaments. [Subtribe SIDINAE.] . . . . **Sida** L.

Ovule ascending. Epicalyx usually present. [Subtribe MALVINAE.] 8

8. Style-branches bearing the stigma at the thickened, capitate apex. Shrubs or undershrubs. — Species 20. Tropical and South Africa. Some of them are used as ornamental or medicinal plants. . **Malvastrum** A. Gray

Style-branches pointed, bearing the stigma on the inner face. . . . 9

9. Epicalyx consisting of 3 free bracteoles or wanting. Central column of the fruit overtopping the mericarps. — Species 15. Some of them are used as ornamental or medicinal plants. " Mallow." . . **Malva** L.

Epicalyx consisting of 3—9 bracteoles united below. 10

10. Central column of the fruit overtopping the mericarps. Epicalyx 3—6-cleft. — Species 12. North Africa ; one species also introduced into

South Africa. Some are used as ornamental or medicinal plants. (Including *Navaea* Webb & Berth. and *Saviniona* Webb & Berth.)

Lavatera L.

Central column of the fruit not overtopping the mericarps. Epicalyx 6—9-cleft. Herbs. — Species 7. North and South Africa, Mascarene Islands, and St. Helena. Several species yield fibres, dyes, mucilage, and medicaments, or serve as ornamental plants. (Including *Alcea* L.)

Althaea L.

11. Carpels completely or nearly completely divided into two compartments by a transverse partition. Style-branches capitate at the top. Ovules 2—3 in each carpel. 12
    Carpels without a partition. Style-branches filiform throughout or club-shaped. 13

12. Flowers with an epicalyx of 3 bracteoles. Petals red. Carpels numerous. Mericarps with 2 prickles at the back. Prostrate herbs. Leaves lobed. — Species 1. South Africa ; naturalized in the Island of Madeira.

Modiola Moench

Flowers without an epicalyx. Petals yellow. Carpels 5. Mericarps beaked. Shrubs or undershrubs. Leaves undivided. — Species 3. Tropics. They yield fibres. . . . . **Wissadula** Med.

13. Flowers with an epicalyx of 3 bracteoles. Carpels numerous ; ovules 2—3 in each. — Species 5. South Africa. Used as ornamental plants. (Including *Sphaeroma* Harv.) . . . . . . **Sphaeralcea** St. Hil.
    Flowers without an epicalyx. Ovules 3—9 in each carpel. — Species 30. Some of them yield fibres, medicaments, and a substitute for coffee, or serve as ornamental plants. . . . . **Abutilon** Gaertn.

14. (5.) Style split into long or rather long branches. Ovary 5-celled. Seeds kidney-shaped. 15
    Style split into very short, erect branches, or simple. 17

15. Ovules solitary in each carpel. Stigma capitate. Epicalyx of 7—10 bracteoles. — Species 9. Tropical and South Africa.

Kosteletzkya Presl

    Ovules 2 or more in each carpel. 16

16. Ovules 2 in each carpel. Epicalyx consisting of 3 large, cordate bracteoles. Shrubs. — Species 1. East Africa. . . . . . . **Senra** Cav.
    Ovules 3 or more in each carpel. Epicalyx consisting of 3 or more narrower bracteoles or wanting. — Species 130. Some of them yield timber, fibres, dyes, perfumes, oil, vegetables, condiments, and medicaments, or serve as ornamental plants. (Including *Abelmoschus* Medik., *Lagunaea* Cav., and *Paritium* St. Hil.) . . . . **Hibiscus** L.

17. Epicalyx of partly united bracteoles. Calyx deeply divided. Ovary 5-celled. Leaves small, undivided. 18
    Epicalyx of free bracteoles. Calyx not deeply divided. 19

18. Epicalyx 5-parted, large. Calyx 5-parted. Trees. Leaves ovate. — Species 1. Madagascar. . . . . . **Macrocalyx** Cost. & Poisson

Epicalyx 11-toothed. Calyx 2-parted. Corolla yellow. Shrubs. Leaves reniform or orbicular. — Species 1. East Africa.

Symphyochlamys Guerke

19. Epicalyx of 3 large, cordate bracteoles. Ovary 5-celled. Seeds woolly. Species 5, three of them growing wild in Central and South Africa, the others (cotton-plants) cultivated in various regions. They yield cotton, oil, dyes, vegetables, and medicaments.   .   .   .   .   . **Gossypium** L.

Epicalyx of small or narrow bracteoles.   20

20. Calyx sprinkled with black dots. Ovary 3—4-celled. Fruit readily dehiscing. Cotyledons not dotted. Shrubs or undershrubs. — Species 7. Central and South Africa. (*Fugosia* Juss.)   **Cienfuegosia** Cav.

Calyx not dotted. Ovary 5-celled. Fruit not or hardly dehiscing. Seeds woolly. Cotyledons usually marked with black dots. Trees or shrubs. Leaves undivided. — Species 5. Tropics to Delagoa Bay. They yield timber, fibres, dyes, and medicaments.   .   .   .   . **Thespesia** Corr.

FAMILY 143. BOMBACACEAE

Trees. Leaves digitate, stipulate. Flowers solitary or fascicled, hermaphrodite, without an epicalyx. Calyx with valvate, closed, or open aestivation. Petals 5, adhering at the base to the staminal tube, with contorted aestivation. Stamens 5 or more, united below. Anthers 1-celled. Pollen-grains smooth or almost so. Ovary superior or nearly so, 5—10-celled, the cells opposite to the petals. Ovules numerous in each cell, ascending or horizontal, inverted. Style simple. Fruit a capsule or a nut. Seeds with a scanty albumen and a curved embryo with folded or coiled cotyledons. — Genera 3, species 13. Tropics. (Under *MALVACEAE* or *STERCULIACEAE*.)   (Plate 93.)

1. Stamens 5. Anthers twisted. Calyx lobed. Stigma capitate. Fruit leathery, woolly within, dehiscent. — Species 1 (*C. pentandra* Gaertn., silk-cotton-tree). Central Africa ; naturalized in Madagascar and the Mascarenes. Yields timber, bast, tanning materials, wool for stuffing, oil, condiments, vegetables, and medicaments. (*Eriodendron* DC.)

Ceiba Gaertn.

Stamens numerous.   2

2. Calyx truncate or irregularly 3—5-cleft, with open or closed aestivation. Stigma 5-partite or capitate. Fruit hairy within, dehiscent. — Species 6. Central Africa. They yield timber, wool for stuffing, and medicaments (Including *Pachira* Aubl.) (Plate 93.)   .   .   .   .   . **Bombax** L.

Calyx 5-cleft, with valvate aestivation. Stigma 5—10-partite. Fruit woody, filled with pulp, indehiscent. Flowers solitary, pendulous. —- Species 6. Tropics. They yield wood, fibres, tanning materials, vegetables, oil, condiments, and medicaments. The pulp of the fruits and the seeds are edible ; from the former a drink is prepared. "Baobab."

Adansonia L.

z

FAMILY 144. STERCULIACEAE

·Leaves alternate, stipulate, rarely *(Hua)* exstipulate. Sepals more or less united, valvate in bud, rarely *(Cotylonychia)* at first imbricate. Petals 5, with contorted, rarely *(Hua)* valvate aestivation, sometimes adnate to the staminal tube, or rudimentary, or wanting. Stamens as many as the sepals or more. Filaments usually more or less united. Anthers 2-celled, rarely *(Triplochiton)* 1-celled. Ovary superior, 3- or more-celled, or several free ovaries, rarely ovary 1—2-celled. Ovules inverted, usually 2 or more to each carpel. — Genera 28, species 470. (Including *BUETTNERIACEAE* and *TRIPLOCHITONACEAE*.) (Plate 94.)

1. Flowers unisexual or polygamous, without a corolla. Filaments united. Male flowers without staminodes. Styles free at the base or throughout. Trees. [Tribe STERCULIEAE.] 2

   Flowers hermaphrodite, rarely polygamous, but then, as nearly always, provided with a corolla. 7

2. Carpels numerous, in several rows. Calyx-lobes 6—8, yellow or brown. Anthers numerous, arranged in a ring. — Species 2. West Africa.
                                                   Octolobus Welw.

   Carpels 3—12, in a single row. Calyx-lobes 4—5. 3

3. Anthers arranged irregularly, crowded in a head, numerous. Seeds albuminous. 4
   Anthers arranged in a ring. 5

4. Calyx tubular, red. Ovules 2 in each carpel. Fruit with a membranous rind, one-seeded, dehiscing before the time of maturity. Leaves undivided. — Species 1. West Africa. Yields fibre. (Under *Sterculia* L.)
                                                   Firmiana Marsigli

   Calyx campanulate. Ovules more than 2 in each carpel. Fruit with a woody or leathery rind, dehiscing at maturity. — Species 25. Tropical and South Africa. Some species yield timber, fibre, gum (African tragacanth), vegetables, edible fruits, oily seeds, and medicaments. (Including *Eribroma* Pierre). . . . . **Sterculia** L.

5. Anthers 4—5, inserted below the apex of the staminal column. Ovules 2 in each carpel. Calyx shortly lobed. Ripe carpels woody, winged, indehiscent. Seeds exalbuminous. — Species 3. Tropics. They yield timber, bark for tanning, and medicaments. . . . . **Heritiera** Ait.

   Anthers 8 or more, rarely 5, but then inserted at the apex of the staminal column. Ovules 3 or more in each carpel. Ripe carpels dehiscent. 6

6. Seeds winged, albuminous. Leaves undivided. — Species 4. Central Africa. (Under *Sterculia* L.) . . . . **Pterygota** Endl.

   Seeds wingless, exalbuminous. — Species 45. Central and South-east Africa. Some species yield timber, vegetables, and edible seeds (colanuts) which are also used medicinally. *(Edwardia* Rafin.) **Cola** Schott

B ³/₂ C ³/₂ A ¹/₃

J. Fleischmann del.

Bombax lukayensis De Wild. and Dur.

A Flowering branch. *B* Flower-bud cut lengthwise (the anthers cut off excepting one). *C* Anther.

A ³⁄₈

C ⁴⁄₁

B ⁴⁄₁

J. Fleischmann del.

Dombeya Bruceana A. Rich.

A Flowering branch. B Flower cut lengthwise. C Cross-section of ovary.

7. (1.) Petals minute or wanting. Stamens 5, free or almost free. Ovary 3—5-celled, with 3 or more ovules in each cell. Shrubs. — Species 1. Madagascar. [Tribe LASIOPETALEAE.] . . **Keraudrenia** Gay
   Petals distinctly developed. 8
8. Carpels distinct, surrounded by 5—10 petal-like staminodes twisted in the bud. Stamens 10—30, inserted upon a raised receptacle, free. Fruit winged. Trees. Flowers panicled. [Tribe MANSONIEAE.] 9
   Carpels not surrounded by petal-like staminodes. Anthers 2-celled. . 10
9. Calyx spathe-like. Petals oblong, with a gland at the base. Stamens 10, inserted upon a long androphore. Staminodes 10, oblong-linear, glabrous. Leaves toothed. Panicles terminal, many-flowered. — Species 1. West Africa. Yields timber. . . . **Achantia** A. Chev.
   Calyx 5-parted. Petals obovate, without glands. Stamens 30, upon a short androphore. Staminodes 5, ovate, downy. Leaves lobed. Panicles lateral, few-flowered. — Species 1. West Africa. Yields timber. . . . . **Triplochiton** K. Schum.
10. Petals or their lower part hooded. 11
    Petals or their lower part flat or slightly boat-shaped, sometimes one of them hooded, the others flat. 18
11. Ovary 1-celled, with a single ovule. Stamens united in pairs. Staminodes none. Petals clawed, with a spur-like appendage. Trees. — Species 1. Equatorial West Africa. The bark and the seeds are used as condiments.
    Hua Pierre
    Ovary 2- or more-celled, with two or more ovules in each cell. [Tribe BUETTNERIEAE.] 12
12. Staminodes absent. Fertile stamens 10, united at the base. Sepals at first imbricate. Petals with a saucer-shaped claw and a lanceolate blade. Ovary 5-celled, with numerous ovules. Shrubs. Leaves undivided. Flowers in racemes. — Species 1. West Africa (Congo).
    Cotylonychia Stapf
    Staminodes present. 13
13. Stamens united in pairs or bundles. Shrubs or trees. [Subtribe THEOBROMINAE.] 14
    Stamens united below in a ring or tube; anthers solitary between the barren lobes. Petals with a blade. Ovules 2—3 in each ovary-cell. [Subtribe BUETTNERINAE.] 17
14. Petals with a blade above the hood. Ovules numerous in each ovary-cell. 15
    Petals without a blade. 16
15. Petals with a 2-parted blade. Staminodes short. Fruit with a woody, prickly rind, dehiscent. Cotyledons coiled. Trees. Leaves serrate. Flowers in panicles. — Species 1. Cultivated in the tropics, naturalized in the Mascarene Islands. Yields timber, fibre, a mucilage used for clarifying sugar, fodder, edible fruits, and medicaments.
    Guazuma Plum.

Petals with an entire blade. Staminodes long. Fruit with a leathery rind, indehiscent. Cotyledons wrinkled. Leaves entire or sinuate. Flowers in cymes. — Species 3 (chiefly *Th. Cacao* L.). Cultivated in the tropics. The seeds are used for the preparation of cocoa, chocolate, and cocoa-butter, the pericarp for making a beverage. They yield also fibres and are used in medicine. . . . . **Theobroma** L.

16. Staminal tube bell-shaped. Anthers in short-stalked clusters of 3. Staminodes solitary, leaf-like, bent outwards. Shrubs. — Species 10. West Africa. . . . . **Scaphopetalum** Mast.
    Staminal tube ring-shaped. Anthers singly upon long filaments. Staminodes in bundles, thread-like. — Species 10. Central Africa.
    Leptonychia Turcz.

17. Petals clawed, adhering to the cupular staminal tube. Anthers sessile or nearly so. Seeds exalbuminous. — Species 13. Tropics.
    Buettnera L.
    Petals sessile, free from the annular staminal tube. Anthers stalked. Seeds albuminous. — Species 2. Madagascar. . **Ruelingia** R. Br.

18. (10.) Stamens and carpels inserted on a long gynophore. Petals unequal, one of them hooded, red, deciduous. Stamens in bundles of 3 alternating with staminodes. Ovary 5-celled with 3—5 ovules in each cell. Trees. — Species 1. Comoro Island. Yields timber. [Tribe HELICTEREAE.] . . . . **Kleinhofia** L.
    Stamens and carpels inserted on a very short gynophore or without a gynophore. Petals equal or subequal, flat or slightly convex, not hooded. 19

19. Fertile stamens 5 ; staminodes minute or wanting. Petals deciduous, usually slightly oblique. [Tribe HERMANNIEAE.] 20
    Fertile stamens 10 or more, rarely (*Melhania*) 5, but then alternating with long staminodes. Filaments united at the base. Petals usually very oblique and persistent. [Tribe DOMBEYEAE.] 22

20. Filaments free, broadened at the base or above the middle. Ovary 5-celled, the cells alternating with the petals. Ovules 3 or more in each cell. Seeds reniform ; embryo curved. Herbs, undershrubs, or small shrubs. — Species 190. South and Central Africa. Some are used as ornamental plants. (Including *Mahernia* L.) [Subtribe HERMANNINAE.]
    Hermannia L.
    Filaments united below, not broadened above. Ovary 5-celled, the cells opposite to the petals, or 1-celled. Ovules 2 in each cell. Seeds elliptical ; embryo straight. [Subtribe MELOCHINAE]. 21

21. Ovary 1-celled. Style 1, simple ; stigma penicillate. — Species 2. Tropical and South Africa and Canary Islands. Used medicinally.
    Waltheria L.
    Ovary 5-celled. Styles or style-branches 5. — Species 5. Tropics ; one species only naturalized. They yield fibres, vegetables, and medicaments. (Including *Altheria* Thouars) . . . . . . **Melochia** L.

22. Staminodes wanting. Ovules 2 in each ovary-cell. Shrubs or trees. . 23
    Staminodes 2—8, usually 5. 24
23. Ovary-cells and styles 5. Anthers 20. Fruit with loculicidal dehiscence. —
    Species 1. Island of Mauritius. . . . . **Astiria** Lindl.
    Ovary-cells and styles 10. Anthers 20—30, associated in 5 bundles.
    Fruit with loculicidal and septicidal dehiscence. — Species 1. Island of
    Réunion. . . . . **Ruizia** Cav.
24. Fertile stamens 5. Ovary 5-celled. Bracteoles 3, persistent. Herbs,
    undershrubs, or low shrubs. — Species 30. Tropical and South Africa.
                                          Melhania Forsk.
    Fertile stamens 10 or more. Bracteoles deciduous or wanting. . . . 25
25. Ovary almost completely 2-celled with 1 ovule in each cell. Petals slightly
    oblique, deciduous. Bracteoles remote from the flower. Undershrubs.
    — Species 3. East Africa. . . . . **Harmsia** K. Schum.
    Ovary 3—10-, usually 5-celled, with 2 or more ovules in each cell. Trees
    or shrubs. 26
26. Ovules 2 in each ovary-cell. — Species 120. Tropical and South Africa.
    Some species yield timber, fibres, and medicaments, or serve as orna-
    mental plants. (Including *Assonia* Cav. and *Xeropetalum* Del.) (Plate
    94.) . . . . **Dombeya** Cav.
    Ovules 3 or more in each ovary-cell. Style simple 27
27. Bracteoles palmately cut. Petals falling off together with the staminal
    tube. Leaves linear. — Species 1. Madagascar and Mascarenes.
                                          Cheirolaena Benth.
    Bracteoles entire or wanting. Petals persistent. — Species 8. Madagascar
    and Mascarenes. . . . . **Trochetia** DC.

SUBORDER SCYTOPETALINEAE
FAMILY 145. SCYTOPETALACEAE

Trees or shrubs. Leaves alternate, undivided. Flowers in fascicles, racemes,
or panicles. Calyx entire or lobed. Petals 3—16, free or almost free, valvate
in bud, more rarely wholly united. Stamens numerous, slightly perigynous.
Anthers attached by the base. Ovary superior, rarely half-inferior, completely
or almost completely 3—8-celled. Ovules 2 or more in each cell, pendulous,
inverted, with dorsal raphe. Style simple. Seeds albuminous. — Genera 5,
species 40. West Africa. (*RHAPTOPETALACEAE*, under *OLACINEAE*.)
(Plate 95.)
1. Ovules 2 in each ovary-cell. Anthers usually opening by longitudinal
   slits. Corolla furrowed in the bud, subsequently separating into 5
   or more petals. Fruit one-seeded. Seeds usually without a crown of
   hairs. Flowers in axillary or terminal racemes or panicles. [Tribe
   OUBANGUIEAE.] 2
   Ovules 6 or more in each ovary-cell. Anthers usually opening by apical
   pores. Corolla not furrowed in the bud, sometimes subsequently

separating into 2—5 petals. Seeds usually with a crown of hairs.
Flowers in fascicles or cymes, usually on the old wood. [Tribe RHAP-
TOPETALEAE.].   3
2. Flowers in racemes. Stigma usually lobed. Fruit a drupe. Albumen
ruminate. — Species 9. West Africa. .   .   .   . **Scytopetalum** Pierre
Flowers in panicles. Stigma entire. Fruit a capsule. Albumen uniform.
— Species 10. West Africa. (Including *Egassea* Pierre)
Oubanguia Baill.
3. Ovary almost superior to half-superior. Fruit a one-seeded drupe. Albu-
men ruminate. — Species 5. West Africa. (Plate 95.)
Rhaptopetalum Oliv.
Ovary superior. Fruit a several-seeded capsule. Albumen uniform. .   4
4. Fruit long, with 2 fertile and 2 sterile cells. — Species 2. Equatorial
West Africa (Cameroons). .   .   .   . **Pierrina** Engl.
Fruit short, with 4—6 fertile cells. — Species 15. West Africa. (Including
Erythropyxis Pierre) .   .   .   . **Brazzeia** Baill.

ORDER PARIETALES

SUBORDER THEINEAE

FAMILY 146. DILLENIACEAE

Shrubs or trees. Leaves undivided. Sepals imbricate in bud, persistent in
fruit. Petals imbricate in bud. Stamens numerous, hypogynous. Anthers
adnate. Carpels 2 or more, free or united at the base of the ovarial portion.
Ovules erect, ascending or horizontal, inverted, with a ventral raphe. Fruit
dry. Seeds with an aril ; albumen abundant ; embryo minute, straight. —
Genera 3, species 25. Tropics. (Plate 96.)
1. Filaments much broadened at the top. Anther-halves short, diverging
below, opening lengthwise. Aril laciniate. Leaves hispid, penninerved
with parallel side-nerves, exstipulate. Flowers in panicles. — Species
20. Tropics. The stem of several species (especially *T. alnifolia* L.,
water-tree) secretes much watery juice when cut across. (Plate 96.)
[Tribe TETRACERAE.] .   .   .   .   **Tetracera** L.
Filaments not conspicuously broadened. Anther-halves long, parallel.   2
2. Stamens crowded at one side of the flower. Anthers opening by longitudinal slits. Carpels 2, free. Ovules 1—3. Leaves opposite, oblong,
one-nerved or faintly net-veined. Flowers in racemes. — Species 2.
Madagascar. .   .   .   . **Hibbertia** Andrz.
Stamens equally distributed all round. Anthers opening by apical pores
sometimes prolonged downwards into slits. Carpels 5 or more, united
at the base. Ovules numerous. Leaves penninerved, with parallel
side-nerves, usually stipulate. — Species 3. Madagascar and neighbouring islands. They yield timber. (*Wormia* Blume) .   .   **Dillenia** L.

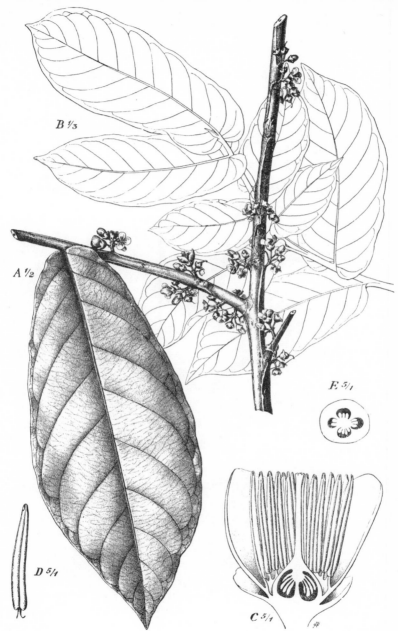

J. Fleischmann del.

Rhaptopetalum sessilifolium Engl.

A Part of flowering branch. *B* End of branch. *C* Flower cut lengthwise. *D* Stamen. *E* Cross-section of ovary.

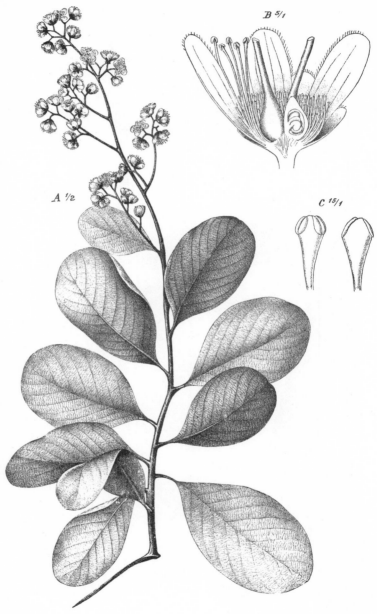

J. Fleischmann del.

Tetracera alnifolia Willd.

A Flowering branch.   B Flower cut lengthwise (most of the stamens cut off)   C Anther.

FAMILY 147. OCHNACEAE

Leaves alternate, undivided, usually stipulate. Flowers in racemes or panicles, rarely solitary, hermaphrodite. Sepals free or nearly so, imbricate in bud. Petals free, with imbricate or contorted aestivation. Stamens hypogynous or nearly so. Anthers adnate, 2-celled, usually opening by apical pores. Receptacle usually prolonged into a gynophore. Carpels almost free, but with a common style, or united. Style undivided or cleft. Ovules with a ventral raphe. Embryo of the seeds rather large. –– Genera 7, species 150. Tropical and South Africa. (Plate 97.)

1. Fertile stamens 5. Petals usually white or red. Seeds albuminous. Herbs or undershrubs. 2
   Fertile stamens 10 or more ; no staminodes. Petals usually yellow. Seeds exalbuminous.   Shrubs or trees. 4

2. Anthers opening by apical pores. Staminodes absent. Ovary 3-celled with 1 pendulous ovule in each cell. Leaves glandular. Flowers in racemes. — Species 2. South Africa (Cape Colony). **Roridula** L.
   Anthers opening by longitudinal slits. Staminodes present. Ovary 1-celled or 3-celled at the base, with numerous parietal ovules. [Tribe LUXEMBOURGIEAE.] 3

3. Staminodes in one row, 5, petal-like, adnate below to the fertile stamens. Flowers in cymes. — Species 2. West Africa. . . **Vausagesia** Baill.
   Staminodes in two rows, the 5 inner petal-like, free, but twisted into a tube, the outer numerous, thread-shaped. Flowers usually solitary. — Species 2. Tropical and South Africa. Used medicinally. **Sauvagesia** L.

4. Ovary 1, one-celled or two-celled at the base, with numerous basal ovules. Style 2-cleft. Stamens numerous, in 3—5 indistinct rows. Sepals enlarged and wing-like in fruit. Fruit a woody capsule. — Species 1 (*L. alata* Banks). Central Africa. Yields timber, oily seeds, and medicaments. (Tribe LOPHIREAE.) . . . . **Lophira** Banks
   Ovaries 3—15, free, with one ovule in each and with a common style. Stamens in 2—3 rows. Sepals not wing-like. Fruit a drupe or consisting of several drupes. [Tribe OURATEEAE.] 5

5. Stamens numerous, in 3 rows. Filaments as long as or longer than the anthers. — Species 80. Tropical and South Africa. Some species yield timber or dye-stuffs. (Plate 97.) . . . . . . **Ochna** L.
   Stamens 10, in 2 rows. Filaments shorter than the anthers or wanting.   6

6. Anthers borne upon distinct filaments, oblong, smooth, opening by longitudinal slits or by apical pores which later on are prolonged into slits. Ovules, seeds, and embryo curved. Flowers in few-flowered clusters. — Species 3. East Africa. . . . . **Brackenridgea** A. Gray
   Anthers subsessile, linear, wrinkled or warty, opening by apical pores. Flowers in many-flowered panicles or racemes. –– Species 60. Tropics. (*Gomphia* Schreb.) . . . . **Ouratea** Aubl.

FAMILY 148. THEACEAE

Shrubs or trees. Leaves alternate, undivided, without stipules. Sepals 5, free or united at the base, imbricate in bud. Petals 5, free or united below, with imbricate or contorted aestivation. Stamens 10 or more, rarely (*Thomassetia*) 5. Ovary superior or almost so, 2—5-celled, with 2 or more ovules in each cell. Fruit a capsule or a nut. Albumen scanty or wanting. — Genera 6, species 12. Tropics and Canary Islands. (*TERNSTROEMIACEAE*.) (Plate 98.)

1. Flowers in cymes or panicles. Fruit a capsule. [Tribe ASTEROPEI-
      EAE.] 2
   Flowers solitary or in pairs in the axils of the leaves. 4
2. Fertile stamens 5, alternating with staminodes which are united in
      5 bundles. Ovary 5-celled. Flowers in long-stalked, axillary clusters.
      — Species 1. Seychelles. . . . . **Thomassetia** L.
   Fertile stamens 10 or more. Flowers in panicles. 3
3. Stamens 10—15, united at the base. Anthers versatile, turned inwards.
      Ovary 3-celled. Sepals enlarged and wing-like in fruit. Low trees or
      climbing shrubs. — Species 6. Madagascar. (Including *Rhodoclada*
      Bak.) . . . . **Asteropeia** Thouars
   Stamens numerous. Ovary 5-celled. Fruit with 5 wing-like ribs. Tall
      trees. Inflorescence terminal, scantily branched. — Species 1. Mad-
      agascar. Yields timber. . . . . **Nesogordonia** Baill.
4. Anthers versatile, turned outwards. Stamens numerous, the outer ones
      united at the base. Ovules 4—6 in each ovary-cell. Fruit a capsule.
      Seeds wingless, exalbuminous; embryo straight. — Species 2. Culti-
      vated and occasionally naturalized in the tropics. One of them (*Th.
      sinensis* L.) is the tea-plant, the other (*Th. japonica* L., camellia) is an
      ornamental plant and yields wood and oily seeds. (Including *Camellia*
      L.) [Tribe THEEAE.] . . . . **Thea** L.
   Anthers adnate. Fruit a nut. Seeds albuminous; embryo curved.
      [Tribe TERNSTROEMIEAE.] 5
5. Ovules 2—3 in each cell, axile, descending. Styles 3. Fruit half-inferior.
      — Species 1. Canary Islands. It has edible fruits and is used in
      medicine and as an ornamental plant. (Plate 98.) . . **Visnea** L. f.
   Ovules many in each cell, attached to a pendulous placenta. Style 1,
      simple. — Species 1. West Africa. . . . . . **Adinandra** Jacks.

FAMILY 149. GUTTIFERAE

Leaves opposite, rarely whorled, undivided. Flowers regular. Petals with imbricate or contorted aestivation. Stamens numerous, hypogynous. Ovary superior. Seeds exalbuminous. — Genera 16, species 180. (Including *CLUSIACEAE* and *HYPERICINEAE*.) (Plate 99.)

1. Ovary-cells and styles numerous (17—24). Ovules 2 in each cell, one
      ascending, the other pendulous. Filaments free. Shrubs. — Species 1.
      Seychelles. . . . . **Medusagyne** Bak.
   Ovary-cells 1—12. Styles 1—5. 2

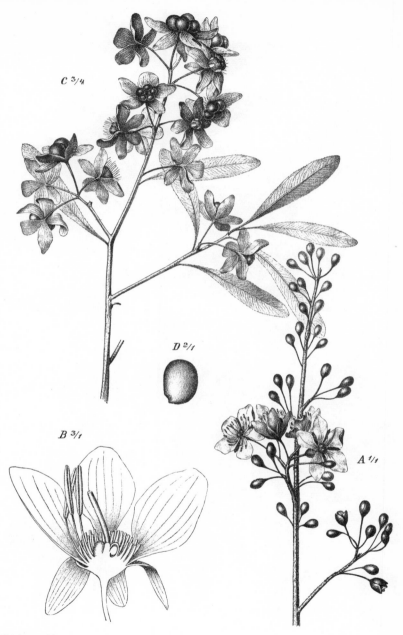

J. Fleischmann del.

Ochna Hoepfneri Engi. & Gilg

A Inflorescence.   *B* Flower cut lengthwise (most of the stamens cut off).   *C* Fruiting branch.   *D* Mericarp.

J. Fleischmann del.

Visnea Mocanera L. f.

A Flowering branch *B* Flower. *C* Flower cut lengthwise. *D* End of a fruiting branch. *E* Young fruit. *F* Young fruit cut lengthwise.

2. Styles 3—5, free or united below. Sepals 5. Embryo with distinct, not very thick cotyledons. [Subfamily **HYPERICOIDEAE**.] . . 3
Style 1, undivided or cleft at the top, or 1 sessile stigma. Shrubs or trees. 7

3. Fruit a berry or a drupe. Carpels 5. Seeds not winged ; cotyledons longer than the radicle. Petals usually woolly within. Stamens in 5 bundles. Shrubs or trees. [Tribe VISMIEAE.] 4
Fruit a capsule, rarely a berry, but then carpels 3. Petals glabrous within. 6

4. Fruit a drupe. Ovules 2—3 in each ovary-cell. Stamens in bundles of 3—5. — Species 1 (*H. paniculata* Lodd.). Tropics. Yields timber, dyes, edible fruit from which a drink is prepared, and medicaments. (*Harungana* Lam.) . . . . **Haronga** Thouars
Fruit a berry. Stamens in bundles of 4—20. 5

5. Ovules 1—2 in each ovary-cell. Embryo with usually twisted cotyledons. Flowers in terminal, umbel-like cymes. — Species 35. Tropics. Some are used medicinally. . . . . **Psorospermum** Spach
Ovules 3 or more in each ovary-cell. Embryo with semiterete cotyledons. Flowers in panicles. — Species 6. Central Africa. (*Caopia* Adans.)
Vismia Vell.

6. Fruit dehiscing septicidally and loculicidally. Seeds with a long wing. Embryo with a very short radicle and longer cotyledons. Ovary 3-celled, with 2 ovules in each cell. Stamens in 3 bundles. Petals with a basal appendage. Shrubs. — Species 2. Madagascar. [Tribe CRATOXYLEAE.] . . . . **Eliaea** Camb.
Fruit dehiscing septicidally, rarely indehiscent. Seeds without a distinct wing, but sometimes keeled. Embryo with the cotyledons usually shorter than the radicle. — Species 35. Some of them yield wood and medicaments, or serve as ornamental plants. (Including *Androsaemum* All. and *Triadenia* Spach). [Tribe HYPERICEAE.] **Hypericum** L.

7. (2.) Style very short or wanting. Fruit a berry. Seeds usually with an aril. Embryo undivided. [Subfamily **CLUSIOIDEAE,** tribe GARCINIEAE.] 8
Style distinctly developed. Seeds usually without an aril. 11

8. Ovary incompletely 5-celled with numerous parietal ovules in each cell. Flowers unisexual. Sepals 5. Petals 5. Stamens in 5 bundles. Anthers opening by longitudinal slits. Seeds with an aril. — Species 4. Central Africa. The seeds yield a fat. (Including *Stearodendron* Engl.) (Plate 99.) . . . . **Allanblackia** Oliv.
Ovary completely 2—12-celled with 1—2 axile ovules in each cell. Flowers hermaphrodite or polygamous. 9

9. Ovary with 2—3 two-ovuled cells, sometimes each cell subsequently divided into two incomplete, one-ovuled compartments. Sepals 2. Petals 4. Filaments united at the base. Seeds without an aril. Flowers in clusters, rarely solitary. — Species 12. Madagascar and West

Africa. They yield timber, dyes, and edible fruits. (*Calysaccion* Wight) . . . . **Ochrocarpus** Thouars

Ovary with one-ovuled cells. Seeds with an aril. 10

10. Sepals 2. Petals 4—7. Filaments free. — Species 4. Madagascar. (Including *Tsimatimia* Jum. et Perrier). . . . . . **Rheedia** L.

Sepals 4—5, rarely 2, but then filaments united in several bundles. Petals 4—5. — Species 60. Tropical and South Africa. Some species yield timber, gum-resin (gambodge); dyes, edible fruits, fat-containing seeds, and various medicaments, among which are the false cola-nuts. (Including *Xanthochymus* Roxb.) . . . . **Garcinia** L.

11. Ovary 5-celled, with several or many ovules in each cell. Style 5-cleft. Sepals 5. Petals 5. Stamens united in 5 bundles or in a tube. Fruit a berry. Embryo undivided. [Subfamily **MORONOBOIDEAE.**] 12

Ovary 1—4-celled with 1—2 ovules in each cell, surmounted by a simple style with an entire or 2—4-parted stigma, rarely (*Hypericum*) ovary 5-celled and style or stigma 5-cleft, but then fruit a capsule and embryo with distinct cotyledons. 13

12. Stamens in 5 bundles consisting of numerous stamens each. Sepals nearly equalling the petals. — Species 3. West Africa. The fruits of the tallow-tree (*P. butyracea* Sabine) yield a fat. . **Pentadesma** Sabine

Stamens united in a tube, the lobes of which bear 3—4 anthers each. Sepals much smaller than the petals. Disc cupular. — Species 15. Madagascar and West Africa. *S. globulifera* L. f. yields timber and a resin used industrially and medicinally; other species afford edible fruits, oily seeds, food for silkworms, and medicaments. (Including *Chrysopia* Thouars). . . . . **Symphonia** L. f.

13. Sepals 2—4. Stamens free or shortly united at the base. Ovary 1—4-celled with 1—2 ovules in each cell. Fruit a drupe. Embryo with a very short radicle and thick-fleshy cotyledons. [Subfamily **CALOPHYL-LOIDEAE.**] 14

Sepals 5. 15

14. Ovary 1-celled, with a single erect ovule. Fleshy mesocarp thin. Flowers in racemes or panicles. — Species 6. Madagascar and East Africa. They yield timber, resin, oil, fish-poison, and medicaments.

Calophyllum L.

Ovary 2—4-celled, with altogether 4 ovules. Flowers solitary or in clusters. — Species 2, one growing wild in West Africa, the other (*M. americana* L.) cultivated in the tropics and naturalized on the Cape Verde Islands. The latter species yields timber, resin, medicaments, and edible fruits (mammee-apples), which are also used for preparing drinks. **Mammea** L.

15. Ovary 1-celled, with a single pendulous ovule. Filaments united at the base in 5 bundles, further upwards in a tube. Fruit a drupe. Embryo with a very short radicle and thick cotyledons. — Species 1. West Africa. [Subfamily **ENDODESMIOIDEAE.**] **Endodesmia** Benth.

Ovary 2—5-celled. 16

GUTTIFERAE.

Pl. 99.

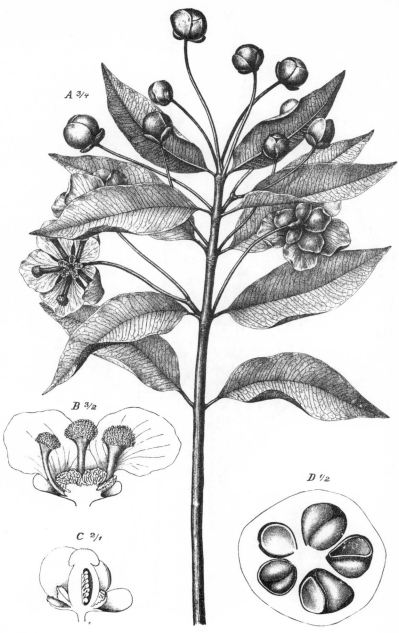

A ³/₄

B ³/₂

D ¹/₂

C ²/₁

J. Fleischmann del.

Allanblackia floribunda Oliv.

A Flowering branch. *B* Male flower cut lengthwise. *C* Female flower cut lengthwise. *D* Cross-section of fruit.

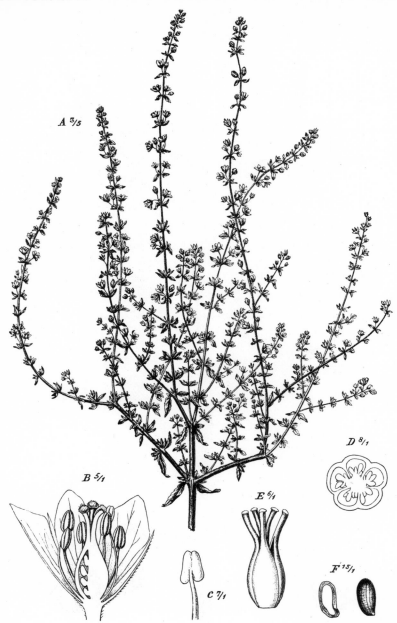

J. Fleischmann del.

Bergia suffruticosa (Del.) Fenzl

A Flowering branch.   *B* Flower cut lengthwise.   *C* Anther from behind   *D* Cross-section of ovary.   *E* Fruit.   *F* Seed

16. Flowers unisexual. Ovary 2-celled with 2 ovules in each cell. Fruit a berry. — Species 1. Madagascar.   . . . .   **Leioclusia** Baill.
Flowers hermaphrodite. Ovary 3—5-celled. Fruit a capsule. (See 6.)
Hypericum L.

FAMILY 150. DIPTEROCARPACEAE

Trees or shrubs. Leaves alternate, simple, entire, stipulate. Flowers in cymes or panicles, regular, hermaphrodite. Sepals 5, imbricate in bud, enlarged in fruit. Petals 5, with contorted aestivation. Stamens numerous, hypogynous or nearly so, with a prolonged connective. Ovary superior, 3-celled. Ovules 2 in each cell, descending, inverted. Style simple. Fruit a one-seeded nut. Seeds without albumen or with a very thin albumen. — Genera 2, species 15. Tropics.

Receptacle flat. Filaments short. Anthers linear, adnate. Ovary glabrous. Embryo with thick, fleshy cotyledons. Tall trees. — Species 1. Seychelles. Yields timber, resin, and fatty seeds. [Subfamily **DIPTEROCARPOIDEAE.**]   . . . .   **Vateria** L.
Receptacle raised. Filaments long. Anthers oval, versatile. Embryo with thin, leaf-like, twisted cotyledons. — Species 15. Central Africa. (Under *Vatica* L.) [Subfamily **MONOTOIDEAE.**]   **Monotes** A. DC.

SUBORDER TAMARICINEAE
FAMILY 151. ELATINACEAE

Herbs or undershrubs. Leaves opposite or whorled, undivided, stipulate. Flowers solitary or in cymes, regular, hermaphrodite. Sepals 3—5, free or united at the base, imbricate in bud. Petals 3—5, free, hypogynous, imbricate in bud, persistent in fruit. Stamens hypogynous, as many or twice as many as the petals. Anthers attached by the back, opening inwards by longitudinal slits. Ovary 3—5-celled. Ovules numerous, axile, inverted, with a short funicle. Styles 3—5, free. Fruit a septicidal capsule. Seeds exalbuminous. — Genera 2, species 15. (Plate 100.)

Flowers 3—4-merous. Sepals united below, with a faint midrib and without membranous margins. Ovary depressed at the top. Flowers solitary. — Species 3. North Africa. . . . . . .   **Elatine** L.
Flowers 5-merous. Sepals free or almost free, with a very projecting midrib and with membranous margins. Ovary narrowed at the top. Leaves serrate. — Species 12. Central and South Africa and Egypt. (Plate 100.)   . . . .   **Bergia** L.

FAMILY 152. FRANKENIACEAE

Herbs or undershrubs, rarely low shrubs. Stem jointed. Leaves opposite, undivided, stipulate. Flowers in cymes, bracteolate, regular, hermaphrodite. Calyx 4—5-lobed or -cleft, valvate in bud. Petals 4—5, hypogynous, free or united in the middle, clawed, usually with a scale-like appendage, persistent. Stamens 4—6, hypogynous. Filaments united at the base, broadened in the middle. Anthers versatile, opening outwards by longitudinal slits. Ovary 1-celled, with 2—3 parietal placentas bearing the ovules at their base. Style simple with 2—3 stigmas, or 2—3-cleft at the top. Ovules with a long ascending funicle, inverted. Fruit a loculicidal capsule. Seeds with a copious, mealy albumen and a straight, axile embryo. — Genera 2, species 10.

Stamens 5, equal. Carpels 2. Petals without a ligule. Small shrubs. — Species 1. Island of St. Helena. Used as a substitute for tea. (Under *Frankenia* L.) . . . . **Beatsonia** Roxb.

Stamens 4 or 6, the outer ones shorter. Carpels usually 3. Petals usually with a ligule. — Species 10. North Africa, northern Central Africa, and South Africa. . . . . **Frankenia** L.

FAMILY 153. TAMARICACEAE

Shrubs, undershrubs, or trees. Leaves alternate, undivided, exstipulate. Flowers terminal, solitary or in racemes, regular, 4—5-, rarely 6—7-merous. Petals hypogynous, free. Disc present. Anthers versatile, opening by longitudinal slits. Ovary superior, 1-celled, with basal or parietal placentas. Ovules numerous, ascending, inverted, with a very short funicle. Styles or sessile stigmas several, free or united at the base. Fruit a capsule. Seeds hairy; embryo straight. — Genera 3, species 25. (Plate 101.)

1. Flowers solitary. Petals 5, with an appendage on the inner face. Stamens numerous. Styles distinctly separated from the ovary, thread-shaped; stigmas small, simple. Placentas extending throughout the ovary, but bearing ovules at the base only, later on separating from the wall of the ovary. Seeds with a boss at the top, hairy all round, albuminous. — Species 3. North Africa. Used for making salt. [Tribe REAU-MURIEAE.] . . . . **Reaumuria** L.

   Flowers in racemes. Petals unappendaged. Stamens as many or twice as many as the petals. Ovary beaked. Styles short and thick or wanting; stigmas broadened. Placentas basal-subparietal, cushion-shaped. Seeds without a boss, but with a tuft of hairs at the top, exalbuminous. [Tribe TAMARICEAE.] 2

2. Anthers turned inwards. Stigmas sessile, cushion-shaped. Seeds with a stalked tuft of hairs. — Species 1. North West Africa (Algeria).
                                                                        Myricaria Desv.

   Anthers turned outwards. Filaments free or almost free. Stigmas borne upon a short style, more or less spatulate. Seeds with a sessile tuft of hairs. — Species 20. Some of them yield timber, tanning and dyeing materials, and medicaments, or serve as ornamental plants. (Plate 101.) " Tamarisk." . . . . **Tamarix** L.

TAMARICACEAE.

Pl. 101.

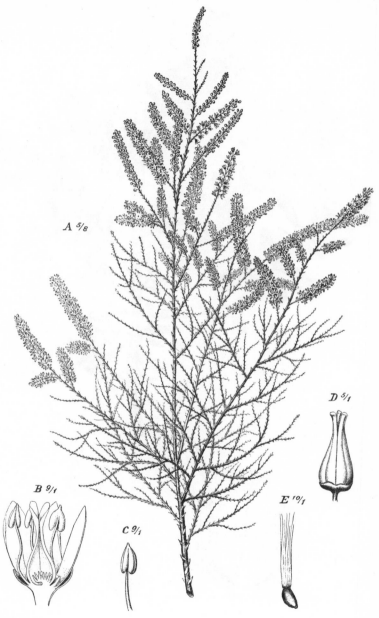

J. Fleischmann del.

Tamarix senegalensis DC.

A Flowering branch. *B* Flower cut lengthwise. *C* Stamen. *D* Fruit. *E* Seed,

A ¹/₂

B ⁵/₂

D ³/₂

C ⁵/₂

E ⁶/₁

J. Fleischmann del.

Cistus heterophyllus Desf.

A Flowering branch.   *B* Flower cut lengthwise (most of the stamens cut off).   *C* Transverse section of ovary.   *D* Fruit.   *E* Seed in longitudinal section.

SUBORDER CISTINEAE
FAMILY 154. CISTACEAE

Leaves simple, entire. Flowers regular, hermaphrodite. Sepals 3 or 5, with contorted aestivation. Petals 5, with contorted aestivation, deciduous. Stamens hypogynous, 7 or more, usually numerous, unequal. Anthers opening inwards or laterally. Ovary 1-celled with 3—10 parietal placentas, or more or less completely 3—10-celled. Style simple or wanting ; stigma large. Ovules numerous, usually· straight. Fruit a loculicidal capsule. Seeds albuminous ; embryo curved. — Genera 5, species 75. North Africa and Cape Verde Islands. (Plate 102.)

1. Stamens partly (the outer ones) sterile. Carpels 3. Ovules 6—12, inverted. Style long. Undershrubs. -- Species 5. North Africa. (Under *Helianthemum* L.) . . . . . : . . **Fumana** Spach
   Stamens all fertile. Ovules straight. 2
2. Carpels 5 or 10. Funicle thread-shaped. Petals white or red. Shrubs or undershrubs. Leaves opposite, without stipules. — Species 15. North Africa. Some are used as ornamental plants ; the resin of others (ladanum) is employed in medicine and perfumery and as a fumigant. (Plate 102.) . . . . **Cistus** L.
   Carpels 3. 3
3. Style long, usually kneed or sigmoid at the base. Funicle obconical. Embryo folded. Herbs or undershrubs. — Species 40. North Africa and Cape Verde Islands. Some are used as ornamental plants. " Rockrose." . . . . **Helianthemum** Adans.
   Style short and straight or wanting. Funicle thread-shaped or thickened in the middle. Embryo coiled or hooked. 4
4. Funicle thread-shaped. Embryo coiled. Leaves, at least the upper ones, alternate, without stipules. — Species 3. North Africa. (Under *Helianthemum* Tourn.) . . . . **Halimium** Willk.
   Funicle thickened in the middle. Embryo hooked. Herbs. — Species 10. North Africa. (Under *Helianthemum* Tourn.) **Tuberaria** Spach

FAMILY 155. BIXACEAE

Shrubs. Leaves alternate, entire or lobed, palminerved, stipulate. Flowers in terminal racemes, clothed with scales, regular, hermaphrodite. Sepals 5, free, glandular at the base, imbricate in bud. Petals 5, free, rosecoloured, with imbricate or contorted aestivation. Stamens numerous, hypogynous, free or slightly united at the base. Anthers curved, opening at the top by two short, transverse slits. Ovary superior, 1-celled, with 2 parietal placetas. Ovules numerous, inverted. Style simple ; stigma small, 2-lobed. Fruit 2-valved, usually prickly. Seed-coat red and fleshy outside, hard within. Albumen copious. ·

Genus 1, species 1 (*B. orellana* L.). Cultivated and naturalized in the tropics. Yields fibres, dyes (arnatto), and medicaments. . **Bixa** L.

SUBORDER COCHLOSPERMINEAE

FAMILY 156. COCHLOSPERMACEAE

Trees, shrubs, or undershrubs. Leaves undivided or palmately lobed or divided, stipulate. Flowers in racemes or panicles, glabrous or clothed with simple hairs, regular, hermaphrodite. Sepals 4—5, free, imbricate in bud. Petals 4—5, free, with imbricate or contorted aestivation. Stamens numerous, hypogynous, free or united at the base. Anthers straight, opening by two sometimes confluent slits or pores. Ovary superior, 1-celled with 3—5 more or less projecting parietal placentas, or 2—3-celled. Ovules several or many, inverted. Style simple. Fruit a capsule. Seeds with a curved embryo and copious albumen. — Genera 2, species 7. Tropics. (Under *BIXINEAE*.)

Petals large, yellow. Anthers long, attached by the base, opening at the top. Ovary 1-celled, sometimes incompletely 3—5-celled. Ovules numerous, parietal. Seeds covered with long hairs. Leaves palmately lobed or divided. Flowers in few-flowered racemes or panicles. --- Species 5. Central Africa. They yield fibre, gum, dyes, and medicaments. (*Maximilianea* Mart. & Schrank.) . . . . . **Cochlospermum** Kunth

Petals small. Anthers short, attached by the back, opening lengthwise. Ovary 2—3-celled. Ovules few, subbasal. Leaves undivided, penni-nerved. Flowers in compound cymes. — Species 2. Madagascar.

Sphaerosepalum Bak.

SUBORDER FLACOURTIINEAE

FAMILY 157. WINTERANACEAE

Trees. Leaves alternate, simple, entire, penninerved, gland-dotted, without stipules. Flowers solitary or in cymes, axillary, hermaphrodite. Sepals 3, imbricate in bud. Petals 4—10, free or united below, imbricate in bud. Stamens 7—18, hypogynous. Filaments wholly united. Anthers opening outwards by longitudinal slits. Ovary superior, 1-celled, with 3—5 parietal placentas. Ovules inverted. Style simple, short. Fruit a berry. Seeds with a minute embryo and copious albumen. — Genera 2, species 4. Tropics. (*CANELLACEAE*.)

Petals 4—6, united beyond the middle. Anthers 7—9, two-celled, or 14—18, 1-celled. Placentas 3—4. Stigma 1. Flowers solitary. — Species 2. Madagascar. Used medicinally. [Tribe CINNAMOSMEAE.]

Cinnamosma Baill

Petals 10, free. Anthers 10. Placentas 5. Stigmas 5. Flowers cymose. — Species 2. East Africa. Yielding an aromatic oil. [Tribe CINNA-MODENDREAE.] . . . . **Warburgia** Engl.

FAMILY 158. VIOLACEAE

Leaves simple. Flowers bracteolate, more or less irregular. Sepals 5, free or united at the base, with open or imbricate aestivation. Petals 5, free, hypogynous or nearly so, imbricate in bud. Stamens 5, alternating with

Rinorea gracilipes Engl.

A Flowering branch.   *B* Flower cut lengthwise.   *C* Stamen from front and back.   *D* Cross-section of ovary.   *E* Group of
fruits.   *F* Fruit.

J. Fleischmann del.

Flacourtia Ramontchi L'Hér.

A Flowering branch.   *B* Male flower cut lengthwise.   *C* Female flower.   *D* Female flower cut lengthwise.   *E* Cross-section of ovary.

the petals, hypogynous or nearly so. Filaments short. Anthers turned inwards ; connective usually prolonged. Ovary superior, sessile, 1-celled, with 3 parietal placentas. Ovules inverted. Style simple. Fruit a loculicidal capsule with an elastically seceding exocarp. Seeds albuminous. — Genera 4, species 100. (Plate 103.)

1. Flowers distinctly irregular. Lowest petal larger than the rest and furnished with a spur or boss at the base. Anterior filaments bearing a spur, a boss, or a gland. Style thickened and usually curved above. Ovules numerous. Herbs or undershrubs, rarely shrubs. [Tribe VIOLEAE.] 2

 Flowers nearly regular. Petals subequal, without spur or boss. Style straight, with a terminal stigma. Shrubs or trees. [Tribe RINOREEAE.] 3

2. Sepals produced at the base into two auricles. Filaments very short. Herbs or undershrubs. Leaves alternate. Flowers solitary or in pairs. — Species 20. Some of them yield perfumes and medicaments and serve as ornamental plants (violets and pansies). . . . **Viola** L.

 Sepals not auricled. Lowest petal saccate or gibbous. — Species 10. Tropical and South Africa Some are used medicinally. (*Calceolaria* Loefl., *Ionidium* Vent.) . . . . **Hybanthus** Jacq.

3. Flowers in clusters springing from the old wood. Petals connivent. Ovules 3. Seeds with an aril and with scanty albumen. — Species 1. West Africa (Cameroons). . . . . **Allexis** Pierre

 Flowers solitary or in terminal or axillary racemes or panicles. Seeds without an aril, with copious albumen. — Species 70. Tropical and South-east Africa. Some yield timber. (*Alsodeia* Thouars). (Plate 103.) . . . . **Rinorea** Aubl.

FAMILY 159. FLACOURTIACEAE

Shrubs or trees. Leaves undivided, usually stipulate. Flowers regular. Petals free, with imbricate or valvate, rarely (*Dioncophyllum*) with contorted aestivation, or wanting. Stamens as many as the sepals or more. Anthers 2-celled, very rarely 4-celled, opening by longitudinal slits, rarely (*Kiggelaria*) by apical pores. Ovary superior and sessile or nearly so, or half-inferior, rarely (*Bembicia*) inferior, one-celled or incompletely, rarely completely 2- or more-celled, with 2—8 parietal, rarely axile placentas bearing the ovules sometimes at the top only, rarely with a single placenta. Ovules 3 or more, rarely 2, inverted. Seeds nearly always albuminous and with a straight embryo. — Genera 46, species 250. Tropical and South Africa. (Including *SAMYDACEAE*, under *BIXINEAE*.] (Plate 104.)

1. Perianth-leaves spirally arranged ; sepals gradually passing into the petals. Ovary superior, 1-celled. Flowers in spikes or racemes. [Tribe ERYTHROSPERMEAE.] 2

 Perianth-leaves whorled ; sepals separated from the petals, or petals absent. 7

2. Inner perianth-leaves with small, scale-like appendages at the base.   .   3
   Inner perianth-leaves without appendages.   5
3. Outer perianth-leaves much smaller than the inner, free, leathery.   Style
   very short. — Species 4.   East and South-east Africa.
   Rawsonia Harv. & Sond.
   Outer perianth-leaves about as large as the inner.   4
4. Stamens 5. — Species 5. West Africa.   (Under *Dasylepis* Oliv.)
   Scottelia Oliv.
   Stamens numerous. — Species 3.   Central Africa.   .   .   **Dasylepis** Oliv.
5. Stamens 5—15, hypogynous.   Anthers broad-sagittate.   Style simple.
   with a 2—4-lobed stigma.   Leaves exstipulate.   Flowers in racemes,
   hermaphrodite. — Species 15.   Madagascar and neighbouring islands
   and East Africa. .   .   .   .   **Erythrospermum** Lam.
   Stamens 20 or more, perigynous.   Anthers oblong or linear.   Style 3—4-
   cleft or -parted.   6
6. Flowers hermaphrodite.   Style 3, free.   Fruit a few-seeded, loculicidal
   capsule.   Low trees.   Leaves stipulate.   Flowers in spikes. — Species 1.
   Equatorial West Africa. .   .   .   .   .   .   **Pyramidocarpus** Oliv.
   Flowers unisexual or polygamous.   Style 1, with 4 branches.   Fruit a
   many-seeded, septicidal capsule.   Tall trees.   Flowers in racemes. —
   Species 2.   Equatorial West Africa. (*Cerolepis* Pierre).
   Camptostylus Gilg
7. (1.) Petals present.   Ovary 1-celled.   8
   Petals absent.   Sepals 3—6, very rarely 7—8.   35
8. Petals more than sepals, unappendaged.   Stamens numerous.   Ovary
   superior.   9
   Petals as many as sepals.   17
9. Stamens collected in bundles opposite to the petals and alternating with
   8 glands inserted at the margin of the receptacle.   Calyx 4-partite.
   Petals 8.   Ovules few, suspended from the upper part of the placentas.
   Styles 3—4.   Flowers in axillary spikes. — Species 1.   West Africa.
   Dissomeria Benth.
   Stamens not in bundles.   Receptacle without glands.   Ovules numerous,
   parietal.   Style 1, simple cleft or 2-parted.   [Tribe ONCOBEAE.]   10
10. Sepals wholly or partly united, when young, with valvate aestivation.
    Style simple.   11
    Sepals free or nearly so, with imbricate aestivation.   12
11. Flowers hermaphrodite or polygamous, in few-flowered racemes.   Calyx
    hood-shaped.   Petals 5.   Filaments free, thread-shaped.   Placentas
    2—3.   Fruit a capsule. — Species 1.   Madagascar.   **Prockiopsis** Baill.
    Flowers dioecious, in fascicles or abbreviated spikes or racemes.   Calyx of 3
    sepals.   Petals 6—7.   Stamens in 2 rows, the outer longer and with
    broadened, incompletely united filaments.   Placentas 3—5. — Species 5.
    Central Africa. .   .   .   .   **Buchnerodendron** Guerke

12. Flowers hermaphrodite. Sepals 3. Petals 9—12. Anthers attached by the back. Ovary and fruit winged. Style long, 2-cleft at the top, with small stigmas. Shrubs. Leaves serrate, stipulate. Flowers in the axils of undeveloped leaves, towards the ends of the branches. — Species 3. West Africa. . . . . **Poggea** Guerke

Flowers polygamous or unisexual. Petals 4—12. 13

13. Style very short, with 2—4 recurved stigmas. Anthers attached by the back near the base. Sepals 3. Petals 5—7. Fruit winged. Shrubs. Leaves entire, stipulate. Flowers in spikes. — Species 1. East Africa.
Grandidiera Jaub.

Style thread-shaped, simple or 3—7-cleft. Anthers attached by the base. Fruit not winged. Flowers solitary or in fascicles or racemes. . . 14

14. Flowers rather small, in racemes. Stigma inconspicuous or slightly branched. Placentas 3. Seeds few. Leafstalk jointed. Branches without spines. — Species 6. Central Africa. (Under *Oncoba* Forsk.)
Lindaekeria Presl

Flowers large. Placentas 4 or more. 15

15. Stigma (or style-apex) not thickened, slightly notched or divided into several branches. Fruit dehiscing incompletely ; seeds numerous, minute. Leafstalk jointed. Branches without spines. — Species 15. Central Africa. Some have edible fruits or serve as ornamental or medicinal plants. (Under *Oncoba* Forsk.) . . . **Caloncoba** Gilg

Stigma thickened or divided into many branches. Leafstalk not jointed. Flowers solitary or 2—3 together. 16

16. Branches without spines. Fruit ovoid, beaked, dehiscing by 4—6 valves ; seeds few, large. — Species 10. Tropical and South-east Africa. Some species have edible fruits or serve as ornamental or medicinal plants. (Under *Oncoba* Forsk.) . . . . **Xylotheca** Hochst.

Branches spinous. Fruit globose, indehiscent, with many placentas and numerous seeds. — Species 2. Central Africa. Used medicinally ; the fruits are edible and used for making ornaments. **Oncoba** Forsk.

17. (8.) Petals 5, each with a scale-like appendage at the base. Sepals valvate in bud. Stamens 10—12. Anthers opening at the top. Ovary superior. Styles 2—5. Flowers dioecious, in axillary cymes. Shrubs. — Species 6. South and East Africa. [Tribe PANGIEAE.]
Kiggelaria L.

Petals without scales at the base. Anthers opening lengthwise. . . 18

18. Receptacle (flower-tube) bearing a cupular or filamentous corona at its margin. Petals 5. Ovary superior. Seeds with an aril. [Tribe PAROPSIEAE.] 19

Receptacle without a corona, but sometimes with glands. 25

19. Anthers peltate, 4-celled. Stamens numerous, perigynous. Corona short-tubular, entire. Ovules 6, apical. Styles 3, long. Stigmas not thickened. Low trees. Leaves entire, stipulate. Flowers in elongated axillary spikes or racemes. — Species 3. West Africa. **Soyauxia** Oliv.

2 A

Anthers cordate, 2-celled. Ovules parietal. Stigmas thickened. Flowers solitary or in fascicles or terminal panicles. 20

20. Ovules 2 on each placenta. Styles 3. Stamens 5. Filaments broadened and united below. Corona many-parted. Flowers in terminal panicles. Bracts with two large glands at the base. — Species 1. West Africa (Liberia). (Under *Paropsia* Nor.) . . . . . **Androsiphonia** Stapf
Ovules 3 or more on each placenta. 21

21. Style 1, simple. Stamens numerous. Corona double. Flowers sessile, in the axils of the leaves or by the side of them, enveloped by imbricate bracts. Fruit indehiscent. Branches with swellings inhabited by ants. Leaves stipulate. — Species 4. West Africa and region of the Great Lakes. . . . . **Barteria** Hook.
Styles 3—5, free or united at the base. Flowers stalked. 22

22. Corona double, the outer slit into narrow segments, the inner ring-shaped. Stamens 8—10. Leaves toothed. Flowers solitary, axillary. — Species 6. Equatorial West Africa. . . . . **Paropsiopsis** Engl.
Corona simple. Stamens 5 or many. 23

23. Flowers in panicles. Corona divided into thread-like segments. Stamens 5. Filaments flat. Styles 5. — Species 1. Madagascar.
Hounea Baill.
Flowers solitary or few together in the axils of the leaves. Filaments thin, thread-like. Fruit dehiscent. Leaves toothed. 24

24. Stamens 5. Flowers rather small. Leaves with glandular patches at the base of the blade. — Species 10. Tropics. Some have edible fruits.
Paropsia Nor.
Stamens numerous. Flowers large. Leaves with glands at the base of the stalk. — Species 4. West Africa. (Under *Paropsia* Nor.)
Smeathmannia Soland.

25. (18.) Inflorescences springing from the midrib of the leaves, cymose. Ovary superior, many-ovuled. [Tribe PHYLLOBOTRYEAE.] . 26
Inflorescences axillary or terminal. 28

26. Stamens 5. Anthers linear. Petals 5. Leaves toothed. — Species 1. Equatorial West Africa. . . . . **Moquerysia** Hua
Stamens numerous. Anthers oval or triangular. Petals 3—5. . . 27

27. Style 1, shortly 2-cleft. Anthers oval or elliptical. Flowers solitary or in pairs. Leaves large, serrate. — Species 1. Equatorial West Africa.
Phylloclinium Baill.
Styles 3, free or united below. Petals 3—4. Flowers in glomerules. Leaves very large. — Species 2. Equatorial West Africa.
Phyllobotryum Muell. Arg.

28. Stamens singly or in bundles opposite to the petals. Ovary half-inferior, more rarely superior. Fruit a capsule. [Tribe HOMALIEAE.] . 29
Stamens numerous, not collected in bundles. Ovary superior. Fruit a berry. [Tribe SCOLOPIEAE. 33

29. Flowers dioecious. Stamens 9—15. Ovary superior. Placentas 3, with 1—2 ovules each. Styles 3. Leaves palminerved. Flowers in spikes or spike-like panicles. — Species 4. East and South Africa.
Trimeria Harv.
Flowers hermaphrodite. 30

30. Style 1, simple, with a capitate stigma. Ovules 4. Stamens 5. Flowers in axillary cymes. — Species 1. South-east Africa. **Gerrardina** Oliv.
Styles 2—6, or style single and 2—6-cleft. 31

31. Ovary superior. Ovules numerous. Styles 3—6, free. Stamens 5—8, nearly hypogynous. Seeds woolly. Leaves stipulate. Flowers in panicles. — Species 5. Madagascar and East Africa. (Including *Bivinia* Tul.) . . . . **Calantica** Tul.
Ovary half-inferior. Seeds not woolly. 32

32. Style 1, thick, 4—6-cleft at the apex. Ovules numerous. Stamens 12—18. Petals scarcely larger than the sepals. Flowers in spike-like panicles. Leaves exstipulate. — Species 2. West Africa. . **Byrsanthus** Guill.
Styles 2—6, thread-shaped, free or united at the base, rarely beyond ; in the latter case stamens 4—8 or petals considerably larger than the sepals. Petals persistent. — Species 50. Tropical and South Africa. Some species yield timber. (Including *Blackwellia* Comm.) **Homalium** Jacq.

33. Sepals united below. Petals with contorted aestivation. Anthers attached by the base. Placentas 5—7. Ovules numerous. Styles 5—7, united at the base. Leaves ending in two tendrils. Flowers in cymose panicles. — Species 1. West Africa (Congo). . . . . **Dioncophyllum** Baill.
Sepals free. Anthers attached by the back. Placentas 2—4. Style 1, simple. Leaves stipulate, without tendrils. 34

34. Ovary stalked, incompletely 3-celled at the base, 6-ovuled. Connective not prolonged. Sepals 5, imbricate in bud. Petals larger than the sepals. Flowers in compound racemes or panicles. Leaves penninerved. — Species 1. Southern West Africa (Angola). **Marquesia** Gilg
Ovary sessile or nearly so, completely 1-celled. Connective usually prolonged. Sepals valvate or slightly imbricate in bud. Petals similar to the sepals. Flowers solitary or in racemes, rarely in panicles. Leaves 3—5-nerved at the base. — Species 12. Tropical and South Africa. Some species yield timber or serve as ornamental plants. (*Phoberos* Lour.) . . . . **Scolopia** Schreb.

35. (7.) Ovary inferior, 1-celled, with 2—3 parietal placentas. Styles 2—3. Stamens numerous. Sepals 7—8, petaloid. Inflorescences head-like. — Species 1. Madagascar. [Tribe BEMBICIEAE.] **Bembicia** Oliv.
Ovary superior. 36

36. Receptacle with thread- or strap-shaped, sometimes partly united appendages. Stamens 5 or more. Ovary 1-celled, with 2—4 parietal placentas. 37
Receptacle with separate glands or with a ring-shaped disc, but without thread- or strap-shaped appendages, or without any appendages . 39

37. Stamens 15—20. Styles 4. Sepals 4, unequal. Flowers unisexual, solitary, axillary. — Species 1. Equatorial West Africa (Cameroons).

Trichostephanus Gilg

Stamens 5—12. Style 1, simple or cleft at the top. Fruit a capsule. Seeds hairy or arillate. Leaves stipulate, usually gland-dotted. [Tribe CASEARIEAE.] 38

38. Flowers in terminal panicles, polygamous. Stamens 5—6. Seeds with a minute aril. — Species 1. Equatorial West Africa (Cameroons).

Ophiobotrys Gilg

Flowers solitary and axillary or in axillary fascicles or heads, hermaphrodite. Stamens 6—12. — Species 20. Tropics to Delagoa Bay. Some species yield timber or are used in medicine. (*Guidonia* Plum.)

Casearia Jacq.

39. Stamens collected in 5—8 bundles alternating with the sepals. Sepals glandular, valvate in bud. Placentas 3—6, parietal, with numerous ovules. Styles 3—6. Fruit a capsule. Seeds woolly. Leaves entire or crenate, stipulate. Flowers in racemes, hermaphrodite. (See 31.)

Calantica Tul.

Stamens not in bundles. 40

40. Anthers 10—15, linear, large, subsessile. Calyx very small, imbricate in bud. Placentas 2, parietal, bearing 2 ovules each. Styles 2. Fruit a nut. Seeds very large, arillate, exalbuminous. Embryo with a minute radicle and very unequal cotyledons. Shrubs. Leaves without stipules. Flowers in racemes or panicles, dioecious. — Species 2. Madagascar and neighbouring islands. Used medicinally.

Physena Thouars

Anthers short and broad, more or less oval. Seeds albuminous. . . 41

41. Ovary 2- or more-celled, with 2—4 subbasal ovules in each cell. Style 1, simple. Stamens numerous, surrounding a thick disc. Fruit a prickly nut. Seeds ruminate within. Stipules connate. Flowers in cymes, hermaphrodite. — Species 5. Madagascar. (*Ropalocarpus* Boj.)

Rhopalocarpus Boj.

Ovary 1-celled, sometimes incompletely, very rarely completely 2- or more-celled, with parietal or axile ovules; if ovary 2- or more-celled, then styles 2—8, free or united at the base, and fruit a berry or a drupe. Seeds not ruminate. [Tribe FLACOURTIEAE.] 42

42. Ovary incompletely, very rarely completely 2- or more-celled. Styles 2—8, free or united at the base. Receptacle bearing a disc or free glands . 43

Ovary completely 1-celled. Style usually 1. Stamens numerous. . . 44

43. Flowers dioecious. Stamens 10—25, alternating with glands. Placentas with 1—6 ovules each. Fruit a berry. Stipules minute, deciduous. — Species 17. Tropical and South Africa. Some have edible fruits. (*Dovyalis* Arn. & Mey., including *Aberia* Hochst.) **Doryalis** Arn. & Mey.

Flowers hermaphrodite or polygamous. Stamens numerous, surrounded by a ring-shaped disc. Placentas with several or many ovules each.

Fruit a drupe with several stones. Stipules wanting. — Species 7. Tropics to Delagoa Bay. They yield timber, edible fruits (Indian plums), and medicaments, and serve also as hedge-plants. (Plate 104.)
Flacourtia Juss.

44. Flowers dioecious or polygamous, in cymes. Receptacle expanded into a disc. Stamens with short filaments and introrse anthers. Style very short, simple or 2—6-cleft. Ovary with a single placenta and 2 ovules. Fruit a drupe. Stipules minute. — Species 1. Island of Réunion. Yields timber and condiments. . . . . **Guya** Frapp.

Flowers hermaphrodite. Receptacle unappendaged, rarely with a disc. but then style distinctly developed. 45

45. Receptacle expanded into a glandular-toothed disc. Sepals 5—6, oblong, imbricate in bud. Placentas 2—4. Style filiform, 2—4-cleft at the apex. Stipules none. — Species 2. East Africa (Sansibar), Madagascar and neighbouring islands. They yield timber and are used in medicine.
Ludia Lam.

Receptacle without a disc and without glands. Sepals 4—5, roundish, or 3. Styles 3 or 0. 46

46. Sepals 3, valvate in bud. Anthers attached by the base. Placentas 3. Styles 3, free, filiform ; stigmas not thickened. Stipules linear. Flowers in racemose inflorescences. — Species 6. Madagascar. . **Tisonia** Baill.

Sepals 4—5, imbricate in bud. Anthers attached by the back near the base. Placenta 1. Style none ; stigma peltate. Fruit a berry. Flowers solitary or in clusters. — Species 5. Madagascar and neighbouring islands, East and South-east Africa. Some species yield edible fruits, a substitute for tea, and medicaments. (*Aphloia* Benn.)
Neumannia Rich.

FAMILY 160. TURNERACEAE

Leaves alternate, simple. Flowers regular, hermaphrodite. Sepals 5, furnished with a gland or a callosity, imbricate in bud, deciduous. Petals 5, with contorted aestivation. Stamens 5, alternating with the petals. Filaments free. Anthers versatile, opening by longitudinal slits. Ovary superior, 1-celled with 3 parietal placentas. Ovules inverted. Styles 3, often divided. Fruit a loculicidal capsule. Seeds arillate, pitted, with a large embryo and copious albumen. — Genera 7, species 20. Tropical and South Africa. (Plate 105.)

1. Sepals free or nearly so. 2
   Sepals united below into a distinct tube. 3

2. Stigmas nearly entire. Sepals with ovate glands. Petals white. Fruit dehiscing throughout its whole length. Aril formed of long hairs. Trees with simple hairs. Leaves stipulate, with two glands on the stalk. Flowers pendulous, solitary or in clusters of 3, bracteolate. — Species 1. Mascarene Islands. . . . . . . **Mathurina** Balf. fil.

Stigmas many-cleft. Fruit dehiscing from the top to the middle. Aril one-sided, crenate. Leaves without glands at the base, but sometimes with small glands at the margin. Flowers erect, solitary or in cymes. Species 3. Madagascar and South Africa. (Including *Erblichia* Seem., under *Turnera* L.) . . . . **Piriqueta** Aubl.

3. Calyx-tube with very numerous and very thin nerves. Stamens inserted at the base of the tube. Stigmas entire or obscurely notched. Areas of the seed-coat without holes. Glandular shrubs. Stipules minute. Flowers solitary, erect, bracteolate. — Species 2. East Africa.

Loewia Urban

Calyx-tube with 10—15 nerves. Herbs or undershrubs, rarely shrubs or trees, but then stigmas divided. 4

4. Calyx-tube 10-nerved, with hemispherical callosities or without any appendage on the inside. Areas of the seed-coat with one hole in each or without a hole. Flowers solitary or in fascicles or heads. . . . 5

Calyx-tube 15-nerved, furnished with linear ledges within. Areas of the seed-coat with two holes in each. Flowers in one-sided racemes. Hairy herbs. Leaves without stipules. 6

5. Sepals thin-membranous, colourless. Petals inserted at the base of the calyx-tube. Stigmas many-cleft. Ovules 9. Fruit pendulous. Aril entire. Herbs. Leaves without glands. Flowers solitary. — Species 2. Madagascar. (Under *Turnera* L.) . . . . . . **Hyalocalyx** Rolfe

Sepals herbaceous, green. Petals inserted at the mouth of the calyx-tube. Fruit erect. Aril crenate or lobed. — Species 2, one a native of Madagascar, the other naturalized in the Mascarene Islands. **Turnera** L.

6. Petals inserted below the mouth of the calyx-tube, provided with a scale at their base. Stamens arising from the base of the tube. Fruit linear. Seeds in one row. — Species 8. Tropical and South-east Africa. (Plate 105.) . . . . **Wormskioldia** Schum. & Thonn.

Petals inserted at the mouth of the calyx-tube, unappendaged. Stamens adnate to the tube at their base. Fruit oblong or oval. Seeds in several rows. — Species 3. East Africa. (Under *Wormskioldia* Schum. & Thonn.) . . . . **Streptopetalum** Hochst.

FAMILY 161. PASSIFLORACEAE

Usually tendril-bearing plants. Leaves alternate. Flowers regular. Sepals 4—6, imbricate in bud. Petals as many, free, imbricate in bud, more rarely wanting. Receptacle produced into a corona which is sometimes divided into separate scales, rarely without any appendage. Stamens 4—10, as many as and alternate with the petals or twice as many. Anthers opening by two longitudinal slits. Ovary superior, 1-celled, with 3, rarely 4—5 parietal placentas and numerous inverted ovules. Seeds arillate, with a pitted or furrowed testa and a fleshy albumen. — Genera 8, species 75. (Plate 106.)

A ⁵⁄₈

B ⁵⁄₁

C

D ⁷⁄₁

E ⁷⁄₁

J. Fleischmann del.

Wormskioldia lobata Urb.

A Whole plant. B Flower cut lengthwise. C Cross-section of ovary. D Seed with aril. E Seed cut lengthwise.

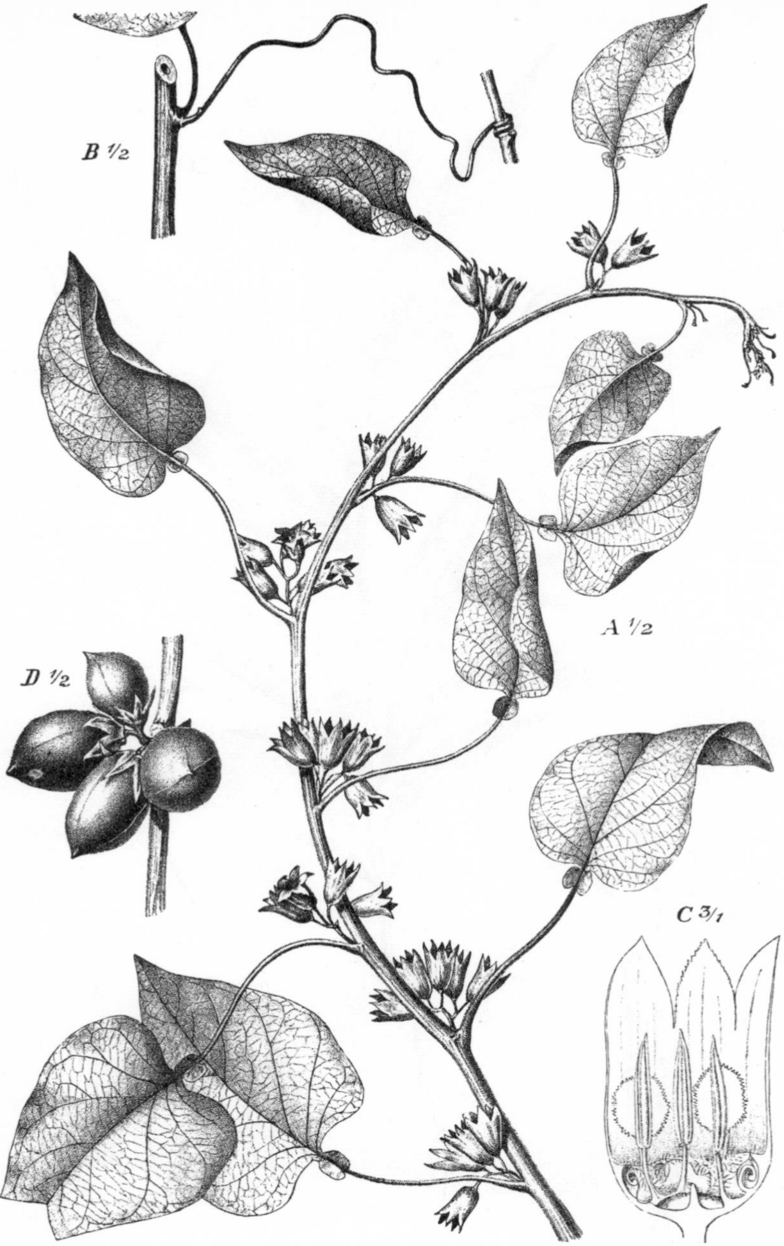

PASSIFLORACEAE.

Pl. 106.

B ½

A ½

D ½

C ³/₁

J. Fleischmann del.

Adenia lobata (Jacq.) Engl.

A Flowering branch. *B* Tendril. *C* Male flower cut lengthwise. *D* Cluster of fruits.

1. Leaves compound : 2—3-foliolate or pinnate. Shrubs. Flowers hermaphrodite. Stamens 5—10, free from the short gynophore. Anthers
   attached by the back. 2

   Leaves simple : entire, toothed, lobed, or cleft. 3

2. Corona formed of numerous threads springing from the base of the calyx.
   Petals 4—5, resembling the sepals. Stamens united at base. Style
   3—5-cleft. Ovules numerous. Fruit a capsule. Stem climbing.
   Leaflets in 1—2 pairs. Flowers in cymes. — Species 6. West Africa
   and Madagascar. . . . . **Deidamia** Thouars

   Corona none, but a disc within the stamens present. Petals 5, much
   exceeding the sepals. Fertile stamens 5, free, alternating with 5 staminodes. Style simple. Ovules 10—12. Leaflets in 4—5 pairs. Flowers
   in panicles. — Species 1. East Africa. . . . . **Donaldsonia** Bak.

3. Fertile stamens twice as many as the sepals or petals, 6—8. Corona
   formed of one row of threads. Ovary almost sessile, with 4 placentas
   and 4 subsessile stigmas. Shrubs. — Species 1. South-east Africa.

   Schlechterina Harms

   Fertile stamens as many as the sepals or petals. 4

4. Fertile stamens alternating with as many staminodes. Flowers hermaphrodite. Petals 5. Style simple. 5

   Fertile stamens not alternating with staminodes. 6

5. Calyx-tube saucer-shaped. Sepals ovate. Petals ovate, larger than the
   sepals. Corona formed of one row of threads. Staminodes tooth-
   shaped. Ovary seated in the centre of the disc. Stigma entire. Climbing, tendril-bearing shrubs. Leaves oblong. — Species 1. Northern
   West Africa. . . . . **Crossostemma** Planch.

   Calyx-tube bell- or funnel-shaped. Sepals oblong. Petals linear-oblong,
   much smaller than the sepals. Corona none. Staminodes awl-shaped.
   Anthers affixed by the back, near the base, and surmounted by a
   prolonged, awl-shaped connective. Stamens free from the short gynophore. Stigma 3-lobed. Fruit a berry. Erect herbs without tendrils.
   Leaves linear-lanceolate. — Species 1. Southern West Africa.

   Machadoa Welw.

6. Stamens adnate to the gynophore. Anthers affixed by the back, at first
   turned inwards, later on outwards. Styles 3 or style single and 3-cleft.
   Corona present. Flowers hermaphrodite. Fruit a berry. — Species
   8. One of them a native of Madagascar, the others cultivated and
   sometimes naturalized in the tropics and the Canary Islands. They
   yield edible fruits, drinks, and medicaments, and serve as ornamental
   plants. " Passion-flower." . . . . **Passiflora** L.

   Stamens free from the gynophore, or no gynophore present. Anthers
   affixed by the base or between its lobes, opening inwards or laterally.
   Fruit a capsule, rarely a berry. 7

7. Flowers hermaphrodite. Calyx-tube saucer-shaped. Corona triple. Style 3-cleft. Herbs or undershrubs. Flowers in 2—3-flowered cymes. — Species 15. Central and South Africa. (Including *Basananthe* Peyr.)

Tryphostemma Harv.

Flowers unisexual, rarely hermaphrodite or polygamous, but then without a corona. Petals 4—6. Corona simple, double, or wanting. Leaves with 1—3 glands at the base. — Species 40. Tropical and South Africa. Some are poisonous, others have edible fruits or are used in medicine. (*Modecca* Lam., including *Echinothamnus* Engl., *Jaeggia* Schinz, *Keramanthus* Hook. fil., *Ophiocaulon* Hook. fil., and *Paschanthus* Burch.) (Plate 106.) . . . . **Adenia** Forsk.

FAMILY 162. ACHARIACEAE

Herbs or undershrubs. Leaves alternate, undivided or lobed, without stipules. Flowers regular, 3—5-merous, monoecious, solitary or fascicled, axillary, the male sometimes in racemes. Sepals free, at least in the female flowers, imbricate or open in bud. Petals united below, imbricate in bud. Stamens as many as and alternating with the corolla-lobes, affixed to the corolla. Anthers adnate, opening inwards. Receptacle produced into a corona formed of 3—5 scales which are inserted at the base of the corolla and alternate with the stamens. Ovary superior, sessile or short-stalked, 1-celled, with 3—5 parietal placentas bearing 2 or more inverted ovules each. Style 3—10-cleft. Fruit a capsule. Seeds with a sometimes adnate aril, a pitted or wrinkled testa, a copious albumen, and a straight embryo. — Genera 3, species 3. South Africa. (Under *PASSIFLORACEAE*.)

1. Stem twining. Leaves 5—7-lobed. Flowers 4—5-merous, the male in racemes, the female solitary. Sepals of the male flowers linear. Stamens inserted at the base of the corolla. Anthers cohering. Corona formed of linear or oblong scales. Ovary short-stalked, oblong. Style-branches twice as many as placentas. Fruit linear. Aril adnate to the wrinkled testa. — Species 1. South Africa. . . . . . **Ceratiosicyos** Nees

Stem erect or underground. Leaves 3-lobed or undivided. Flowers solitary or fascicled. Stamens inserted in the tube or at the throat of the corolla. Aril free from the pitted testa. 2

2. Aboveground stem erect or ascending, woody at the base. Leaves 3-lobed. Flowers 3—4-merous. Sepals oblong or ovate, free. Anthers with a broad connective. Ovary sessile, subglobose. Ovules few, usually 6—8. Style-branches twice as many as placentas. — Species 1. Cape Colony. . . . . **Acharia** Thunb.

Aboveground stem wanting. Leaves undivided. Flowers solitary, 5-merous. Sepals linear, adnate to the corolla. Stamens inserted at the throat of the corolla. Anthers with a narrow connective. Ovary short-stalked, oblong. Ovules numerous. Style-branches as many as placentas. Fruit elliptical. — Species 1. Cape Colony.

Guthriea Bolus

SUBORDER PAPAYINEAE
FAMILY 163.   CARICACEAE

Trees with a milky juice. Leaves alternate, usually crowded at the top of the stem, palmately lobed or divided, without stipules. Flowers, at least the male ones, panicled, 5-merous, unisexual or polygamous. Petals united below, with contorted aestivation. Stamens 10, inserted in the tube of the corolla. Anthers turned inwards, with a prolonged connective. Ovary superior, 1- o ;-celled. Ovules numerous, parietal, inverted. Style simple with 5 stigmas, or 5- to many-cle* Fruit a berry. Seeds albuminous, with a double coat, succulent outside, woody within. — Genera 2, species 3.   Tropics. *PAPAYA AE*, under *PASSIFLORACEAE*.)

  Filaments free. Ovary 1-celled. Stigmas branched. Stem unarmed, simple or scantily branched. — Species 1 (*C. Papaya* L., papaw-tree). Cultivated and sometimes naturalized in the tropics. It yields edible fruits, medicaments, and substitutes for soap and tobacco. The juice of the stem is poisonous, that of the leaves is used for rendering meat tender. (*Papaya* Tourn.) . . . . **Carica** L.

  Filaments united below. Ovary 5-celled. Stigmas undivided. Stem branched, prickly. — Species 2. Central Africa. (Under *Jacaratia* Marcgr.) . . . . **Cylicomorpha** Urban

SUBORDER LOASINEAE
FAMILY 164.   LOASACEAE

Shrubs.   Leaves alternate, toothed or lobed, without stipules. Flowers in cymes, regular, 5-merous, hermaphrodite. Sepals open in bud, becoming wing-like after flowering. Petals shorter, free, concave, with imbricate or contorted aestivation. Stamens numerous, collected in 5 bundles opposite to the petals, alternating with glandular scales bearing each two staminodes on their inner surface. Ovary inferior, unequally 2-celled, the larger cell with two ovules, the smaller with one. Ovules descending, inverted. Style simple or 3-cleft. Fruit dry, indehiscent. Seeds exalbuminous ; embryo straight. Genus 1, species 1. South Africa. . . . . **Kissenia** R. Br.

SUBORDER BEGONIINEAE
FAMILY 165.   BEGONIACEAE

Leaves alternate, simple or palmately compound, usually oblique, stipulate. Flowers in cymes, monoecious. Perianth simple, of 2—5, very rarely 6—9 free segments. Stamens numerous. Anthers basifixed. Ovary inferior, completely or almost completely 2—6-celled, usually winged. Placentas attached to the inner angle of the cells or to the partitions. Ovules numerous, inverted. Styles 2—6, free or united at the base, usually cleft. Fruit a capsule, rarely a berry. Seeds very numerous, minute, with a striate or netted testa, exalbuminous. (Plate 107.)

Genus 1, species 110.   Tropical and South Africa.   Some species are used as ornamental or medicinal plants or as vegetables.   (Including *Mezierea* Gaud.) . . . .   **Begonia** L.

SUBORDER ANCISTROCLADINEAE
FAMILY 166.   ANCISTROCLADACEAE

Climbing, tendril-bearing shrubs.   Leaves alternate, undivided, with small, deciduous stipules.   Flowers in racemes or panicles, regular, hermaphrodite. Sepals unequal, imbricate in bud.   Petals 5, united at the base, with contorted aestivation.   Stamens 10, rarely 9.   Filaments united at the base, short.   Anthers basifixed, opening inwards by longitudinal slits.   Ovary inferior, 1-celled.   Ovule 1, basal, half-inverted.   Style simple with 3 stigmas or 3-cleft.   Fruit a nut surmounted by the enlarged, wing-like sepals.   Seeds with a thin testa, a repeatedly folded albumen, and a straight embryo.   (Under *DIPTEROCARPACEAE*.)

Genus 1, species 2.   West Africa.   . . . . .   **Ancistrocladus** Wall.

ORDER OPUNTIALES
FAMILY 167.   CACTACEAE

Succulent plants with a thickened, usually jointed and spiny stem.   Leaves mostly scale-like, often deciduous.   Flowers solitary or in clusters, hermaphrodite.   Perianth of 8 or more segments not distinctly differentiated into sepals and petals.   Stamens numerous.   Anthers opening inwards or laterally. Ovary inferior, 1-celled, with several parietal placentas.   Ovules inverted. Style simple, with several stigmas.   Fruit a berry.   Seeds albuminous; embryo curved. — Genera 5, species 13.

1. Leaves well-developed.   Stem not jointed.   Spines not barbed.   Perianth wheel-shaped.   Ovules few, not enveloped by the short funicle.   Cotyledons intertwisted. — Species 1.   Naturalized in the Mascarene Islands. A decorative and medicinal plant. [Subfamily **PEIRESKIOIDEAE,** tribe PEIRESKIEAE.] . . . .   **Peireskia** Plum.
   Leaves scale-like or absent.   Stem more or less copiously jointed.   Cotyledons not intertwisted.   2
2. Plants destitute of barbed spines.   Joints of the stem elongated.   Ovules not enveloped by the funicle.   [Subfamily **CEREOIDEAE.**] . . .   3
   Plants bearing barbed spines, at least upon the fruit.   Joints of the stem short, more or less ovoid.   Perianth regular, more or less wheel-shaped. Ovules enveloped by the funicle.   [Subfamily **OPUNTIOIDEAE,** tribe OPUNTIEAE.]   4
3. Perianth funnel- or salver-shaped, with obviously united segments.   Ovules numerous, on long funicles.   Terrestrial plants. — Species 1.   Cultivated and sometimes naturalized in various regions.   A decorative plant with edible fruits. [Tribe ECHINOCACTEAE.]
   Cereus Haw.

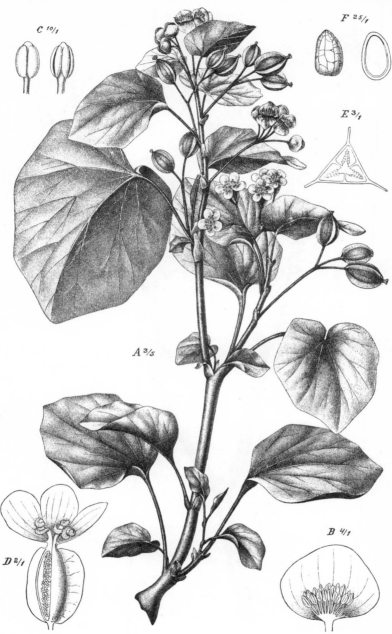

C $^{10}/_1$

F $^{25}/_1$

E $^{3}/_1$

A $^{3}/_5$

D $^{2}/_1$

B $^{4}/_1$

J. Fleischmann del.

Begonia Favargeri Rechinger

A Aboveground part of the plant.   B Male flower cut lengthwise.   C Anther from front and back.   D Female flower cut lengthwise.
E Cross-section of ovary.   F Seed.

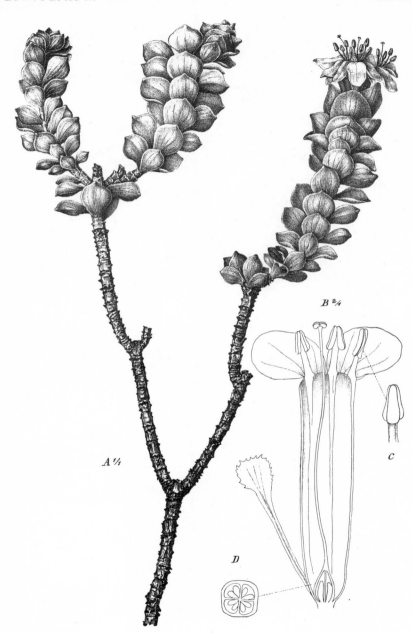

J. Fleischmann del.

Sarcocolla squamosa (L.) Kunth

A Flowering branch. *B* Flower in longitudinal section and bracteole. *C* Anther. *D* Transverse section of ovary.

Perianth wheel-shaped, of free or nearly free segments. Ovules few, on short funicles. Epiphytes. — Species 7. Tropical and South Africa. (Under *Hariota* Adans.)   [Tribe RHIPSALIDEAE.]   **Rhipsalis** Gaertn.

4. Stamens much exceeding the perianth. Seed-coat leathery. Stem without spines. Flowers red. — Species 1 (*N. coccinellifera* S. Dyck). Culti-vated and sometimes naturalized, especially in the Canary Islands. It is used for rearing the cochineal insect and as a vegetable. (Under *Opuntia* Haw.) . . . .   **Nopalea** S. Dyck

Stamens shorter than the perianth. Seed-coat hard. — Species 3. Culti-vated, especially in North Africa. They yield edible fruits (prickly pear) from which also dyes, drinks, medicaments, and sugar are prepared ; one species is used for rearing the cochineal insect. . . .   **Opuntia** Haw.

ORDER MYRTIFLORAE

SUBORDER THYMELAEINEAE

FAMILY 168. GEISSOLOMATACEAE

Shrubs of heath-like appearance. Leaves opposite, undivided, stipulate. Flowers solitary, axillary, regular, 4-merous, hermaphrodite, surrounded by 6—8 unequal bracteoles. Calyx-tube short. Sepals petal-like, imbricate in bud. Petals none. Stamens 8, perigynous, unequal. Anthers versatile, short, with a narrow connective, opening inwards by two longitudinal slits. Ovary superior, 4-celled. Ovules 2 in each cell, pendulous, inverted, the raphe turned outwards. Style 1. Stigmas 4. Fruit a loculicidal capsule. Seeds with a small outgrowth at the hilum, a smooth testa, a fleshy albumen, and a large straight embryo. (Under *PENAEACEAE*.)

Genus 1, species 2. South Africa. . . .   **Geissoloma** Lindl. & Kunth

FAMILY 169. PENAEACEAE

Shrubs or undershrubs of heath-like appearance. Leaves opposite, entire, with sometimes gland-like stipules. Flowers solitary or in pairs in the axils of the leaves or in terminal spikes or heads, with 2 or 4 bracteoles, regular, 4-merous, hermaphrodite. Calyx-tube long. Sepals petal-like, red or yellow, valvate in bud. Petals none. Stamens 4, perigynous, alternating with the sepals. Anthers adnate, with a thickened connective, opening inwards by two longitudinal slits. Ovary superior, sessile, 4-celled. Ovules 2 or 4 in each cell, all or the lower ones ascending, inverted, the raphe turned outwards. Style simple with a 4-lobed or 4-parted stigma, or 4-cleft. Fruit a loculicidal capsule. Seeds exalbuminous. Embryo with very small cotyledons. — Genera 5, species 35. South Africa. (Plate 108.)

1. Ovules 4 in each ovary-cell, two of them ascending, two descending. Ovary and style cylindrical. Style simple. [Tribe ENDONEMEAE.] .   2

Ovules 2, very rarely 4 in each ovary-cell, all ascending. Flowers in the axils of crowded leaves or bracts. Bracteoles 2. [Tribe PENAEEAE.] 3

2. Flowers in the axils of coloured bracts, crowded in terminal spikes or heads. Bracteoles 2. Filaments much shorter than the anthers. Anthers turned inwards in the bud ; cells equalling the connective. — Species 1. Cape Colony. (Under *Endonema* Juss.)

Glischrocolla A. DC.

Flöwers in the axils of foliage-leaves, not crowded. Bracteoles 4. Filaments nearly as long as or longer than the anthers. Anthers turned outwards in the bud ; cells much shorter than the connective. Seeds with an outgrowth at the top. — Species 2. Cape Colony.

Endonema A. Juss.

3. Ovary and style 4-angled or 4-winged. Ovules 2 in each cell. Stamens very short. — Species 20. Cape Colony. (Including *Stylapterus* Juss.)

Penaea L.

Ovary and style cylindrical. Style simple. 4

4. Calyx-tube short, oblong-oval, somewhat longer than the sepals. Stamens slightly exceeding the calyx-tube ; filaments short. Ovules 2 in each cell. — Species 6. Cape Colony. (Under *Sarcocolla* Kunth).

Brachysiphon A. Juss.

Calyx-tube long, cylindrical, much longer than the sepals. Stamens much exceeding the calyx-tube; filaments long. Anthers-cells almost equalling the connective. — Species 5. Cape Colony. Used as ornamental plants. (Plate 108.) . . . . **Sarcocolla** Kunth

FAMILY 170.   OLINIACEAE

Shrubs or trees. Leaves opposite, entire, without stipules. Flowers in terminal cymose inflorescences, regular, 4—5-merous. Calyx petaloid, white or red. Petals much smaller than the sepals, white, valvate in bud. Fertile stamens 4—5, opposite to the petals, usually alternating with scale-like staminodes. Anthers nearly sessile, with a large connective. Ovary inferior, 3—5-celled. Ovules 2—3 in the inner angle of each ovary-cell, inverted, the raphe turned outwards. Style simple ; stigma entire. Fruit a drupe. Seeds exalbuminous ; embryo with folded cotyledons. (Under *LYTRHACEAE*, *MELASTOMATACEAE*, or *RHAMNACEAE*.)

Genus 1, species 7. South and Central Africa. Some species yield timber.

Olinia Thunb.

FAMILY 171.   THYMELAEACEAE

Leaves entire, without stipules. Flowers 4—5-merous. Sepals petaloid. Petals usually present. Stamens as many as and opposite to the petals, 4, or twice as many, 8 or 10. Anthers opening by longitudinal slits. Ovary superior, 1—5-celled. Ovule 1 in each cell, pendulous, inverted, with a ventral raphe. Style simple ; stigma entire. Fruit a drupe or a nut. Embryo large, straight. — Genera 17, species 250. (Plate 109.)

1. Receptacle flat. Sepals free. Petals none, but 4—10 scales placed singly or in pairs opposite to the sepals. Stamens 8—10, hypogynous. Ovary

4—5-celled. Low trees. Leaves alternate, dotted beneath. Flowers solitary or fascicled. axillary, white. — Species 7. West Africa. (Including *Makokoa* Baill.) [Subfamily **OCTOLEPIDIOIDEAE**, tribe OCTOLEPIDEAE.] . . . . **Octolepis** Oliv.
Receptacle concave. Sepals united. Stamens perigynous. Ovary 1—2-celled. 2

2. Ovary 2-celled, surrounded by a disc. Petals none. Stamens 8—10. Fruit a drupe. Shrubs. Leaves alternate. Flowers in umbels, yellowish-green. — Species 10. Tropical and South Africa. [Subfamily **PHALERIOIDEAE,** tribe PEDDIEAE.] . . **Peddiea** Harv.
Ovary 1-celled. [Subfamily **THYMELAEOIDEAE.**] 3

3. Petals present, usually smaller than the sepals and 2-parted, sometimes united into a ring. 4
Petals none, but sometimes 8 or more scales present, inserted below the stamens, and usually alternating with them. Stamens 8—10. . . . 9

4. Calyx-tube constricted and jointed above the ovary, the upper part falling off after flowering. Fruit with a membranous exocarp. [Tribe GNIDIEAE.] 5
Calyx-tube not jointed, persisting in fruit or falling off as a whole. Fruit with a hard or fleshy exocarp. Stamens 8—10. [Tribe DICRANO-LEPIDEAE.] 6

5. Stamens 4, inserted in the upper part of the calyx-tube, nearly sessile, with a broadened connective. Petals thick-fleshy, surrounded by hairs. Shrubs or undershrubs. Leaves small, leathery. Flowers solitary or in pairs in the axils of the leaves. — Species 25. South and Central Africa. . . . . **Struthiola** L.
Stamens 8 or 10, in two whorls very distant from each other and inserted in the upper part of the calyx-tube and at the throat. Trees, shrubs, or undershrubs. Flowers in heads, more rarely arranged spike-like in the axils of the upper leaves. — Species 125. Southern and tropical Africa. Some species are used as ornamental, medicinal, or textile plants. (Including *Arthrosolen* Mey. and *Lasiosiphon* Frees) **Gnidia** L.

6. Petals united into a ring. Stamens 10. Shrubs. 7
Petals free, 2-partite. Leaves herbaceous. 8

7. Petals united into a nearly entire ring. Ovary short-stalked, surrounded at the base by a cup-shaped or slashed disc. Flowers in few-flowered axillary clusters or in short terminal racemes. — Species 6. Central Africa to Delagoa Bay. . . . . **Synaptolepis** Oliv.
Petals united into a slashed ring. Ovary sessile. Disc none. Flowers in long-stalked spikes or heads. —- Species 2. Madagascar and Comoro Islands. . . . . **Stephanodaphne** Baill.

8. Flowers 4-merous. Petals thickish, almost erect. Staminal whorls remote from each other. Anthers nearly sessile, slightly exserted. Disc none. Ovary sessile, hairy. Style included. Shrubs. Leaves op-

posite. Flowers in terminal umbels. — Species 1. East and South-east
Africa. . . . . **Englerodaphne** Gilg
Flowers 5-merous. Petals thin, spreading. Staminal whorls approximate.
Anthers more or less exserted. Disc cup-shaped. Ovary short-stalked.
Style long. Shrubs or trees. Leaves alternate. Flowers solitary or in
pairs, axillary. — Species 25. Central Africa. . **Dicranolepis** Planch.

 9. (3.) Stamens 10, inserted at or below the middle of the long, narrowly
funnel-shaped, not jointed calyx-tube at the same level. Filaments
short, unequal in length. Anthers included. Corona none. Disc
ring- or saucer-shaped. Ovary sessile. Style short. Twining shrubs.
Leaves opposite or nearly so, leathery. Flowers in axillary clusters,
greenish-yellow. — Species 2. West Africa. [Tribe CRATEROSI-
PHONEAE.] . . . . **Craterosiphon** Engl. & Gilg
Stamens inserted at the throat or the upper part of the calyx-tube ; in the
latter case calyx-tube wide or jointed. [Tribe DAPHNEAE.] . . 10

10. Calyx-tube bearing in its upper part a corona of 8 or more scales, jointed
above the ovary, the lower part persistent in fruit. Flowers 4-merous.
Filaments thread-like. Anthers exserted. Ovary sessile. Fruit dry.
Shrubs. Leaves small, leathery, sometimes needle-shaped. . . . 11
Calyx-tube without a corona, but sometimes the ovary surrounded at
the base by a disc or by several glands. 12

11. Flowers solitary, white or reddish. Sepals equal in length. Corona
inserted in the middle of the calyx-tube. — Species 5. South Africa.
Some are used as ornamental plants. . . . **Cryptadenia** Meissn.
Flowers in fascicles or heads. Corona inserted next to the throat of the
calyx, and formed of 8 scales which alternate with the stamens. — Species
20. South Africa. Some are used as ornamental plants. (Plate 109.)
Lachnaea L.

12. Calyx-tube constricted and jointed above the ovary, the upper part,
rarely the whole calyx, falling off after flowering. 13
Calyx-tube not jointed, persistent in fruit or falling off as a whole, the
segments sometimes falling off singly. Filaments and style short.
Flowers 4-merous. 16

13. Filaments very short. Staminal whorls widely separated. Disc minute or
wanting. (See 5.) . . . . **Gnidia** L.
Filaments long. Staminal whorls approximate, rarely somewhat distant,
but then disc distinctly developed. Shrubs. 14

14. Flowers 5-merous. Segments of the calyx much shorter than the tube.
Disc saucer-shaped, lobed. Ovary hairy. Fruit dry. Seeds without
albumen. Flowers in terminal heads. — Species 6. South Africa
and Madagascar. Some are used as ornamental plants. **Dais** L.
Flowers 4-merous. Segments of the calyx nearly as long as the tube.
Disc none. Ovary glabrous. Seeds with a copious albumen. Leaves
opposite. Flowers solitary and axillary, or in terminal spikes. . . 15

15. Fruit fleshy. Calyx-tube short, urn-shaped. — Species 1. South Africa.
Chymococca Meissn.

THYMELAEACEAE.

Pl. 109.

A ⁴/₅

B ⁵/₁

J. Fleischmann del.

Lachnaea filamentosa (L. fil.) Gilg

A Flowering branch.   *B* Flower cut lengthwise (the hairs are omitted).

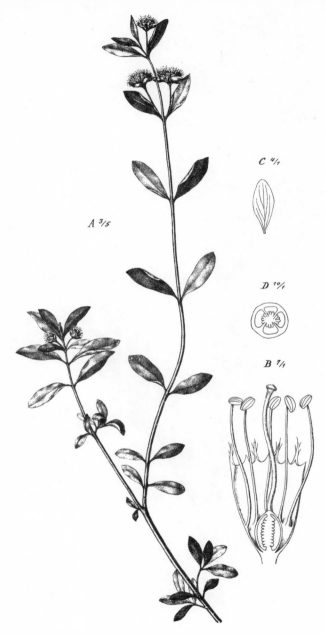

J. Fleischmann del.

Nesaea floribunda Sond.

A Flowering branch.   *B* Flower without the petals, cut lengthwise.   *C* Petal.   *D* Cross-section of ovary.

Fruit dry. — Species 7.   South Africa.   Some species yield dyes or serve as ornamental plants.   .   .   .   .   **Passerina** L.

16. Disc hypogynous, consisting of 1—4, usually 4, free or partly united, narrow, almost thread-shaped scales. Calyx-tube long ; segments deciduous. Ovary hairy. Shrubs or trees. Flowers in terminal racemes or spikes, hermaphrodite. — Species 1. Naturalized in the Mascarene Islands. Ornamental plant.   .   .   .   **Wikstroemia** Endl.

Disc minute and ring-shaped, or wanting.   17

17. Fruit a drupe. Flowers hermaphrodite. Calyx-tube long. Stigma large. Shrubs or trees. Flowers in heads, racemes, or panicles. — Species 4. North Africa. Poisonous plants yielding bast-fibres, tanning and dyeing materials, and medicaments ; they also serve as ornamental plants. .   .   .   .   **Daphne** L.

Fruit a nut. Disc none. Ovary short-stalked. Herbs, undershrubs, or shrubs. Leaves alternate. Flowers solitary or fascicled, axillary. — Species 10. North Africa. Some species are used as medicinal or fibre-plants.   .   .   .   .   **Thymelaea** Endl.

FAMILY 172.   ELAEAGNACEAE

Shrubs or trees, covered with scaly hairs. Leaves alternate, entire, without stipules. Flowers in axillary fascicles or racemes, 4-merous, very rarely 5—8-merous, hermaphrodite or polygamous. Calyx white or yellow within, valvate in bud. Petals none. Stamens perigynous, as many as and alternate with the sepals. Filaments very short. Anthers attached at the back, opening by longitudinal slits. Ovary superior, but tightly enclosed by the concave receptacle, 1-celled, with a single erect and inverted ovule. Style simple, long ; stigma entire, capitate. Fruit a nut enclosed by the succulent calyx-tube. Seed with a hard coat and scanty albumen or without albumen ; embryo straight, with a minute radicle and thick, fleshy cotyledons.

Genus 1, species 2. Naturalized in North Africa and the Island of Mauritius. Ornamental plants yielding timber and medicaments.   " Oleaster."

Elaeagnus L.

SUBORDER MYRTINEAE
FAMILY 173.   LYTHRACEAE

Leaves entire, usually stipulate. Flowers 3—8-merous, hermaphrodite. Sepals valvate in the bud. Petals inserted at the throat of the calyx, usually crumpled in the bud, sometimes absent. Stamens nearly always inserted below the petals. Anthers fixed by the back. Ovary superior, completely or incompletely 2—6-celled. Ovules numerous in each cell, attached at the inner angle, ascending, inverted, with ventral raphe. Style simple or wanting ; stigma entire or 2-lobed. Fruit dry. Seeds exalbuminous ; embryo straight. — Genera 12, species 90.   (Plate 110.)

1. Partitions of the ovary incomplete above ; placentas not continuing into the style. [Tribe LYTHREAE.]   2

Partitions of the ovary complete ; placentas continuing into the style. Flowers regular. [Tribe NESAEEAE.]   9

2. Flowers distinctly irregular. Sepals 6. Petals 6—7, unequal. Stamens 10—14, usually 11. Disc present. Placenta finally protruding from the bursting ovary and calyx-tube. Leaves opposite or whorled. — Species 1. Naturalized in the Mascarene Islands. Ornamental plant.
Cuphea P. Browne

Flowers regular or almost so.   3

3. Stem herbaceous or woody at the base only. Leaves not dotted. Seeds not winged.   4
Stem woody. Leaves opposite, marked with black dots, rarely without dots, but then seeds with a thick wing. Style long.   7

4. Fruit indehiscent, membranous, not striate. Seeds very numerous. Flowers 6-merous. Calyx-tube hemispherical or broad-campanulate, with appendages at the apex. Sepals herbaceous. Stamens as many as the sepals. Ovary 2-celled. Style very short. Flowers solitary, axillary, with whitish bracteoles. — Species 1. North Africa. Used as a vegetable. . . . .   **Peplis** L.
Fruit dehiscing by 2—4 valves or bursting transversely or irregularly ; in the latter cases flowers 4-merous and cymose.   5

5. Fruit bursting transversely or irregularly, membranous, not striate. Seeds very numerous. Flowers 4-merous. Sepals herbaceous. Stamens as many or twice as many as the sepals. Flowers in axillary cymes, with whitish bracteoles. — Species 15. Tropical and South Africa and Egypt. Some are used medicinally. . . . . . .   **Ammania** L.
Fruit dehiscing longitudinally in 2—4 valves.   6

6. Fruit marked with dense, sometimes very faint, tranverse veins. Sepals usually membranous. Stamens as many as the sepals or fewer. Glabrous plants. Flowers solitary or umbellate and axillary, or in terminal spikes or racemes, bracteolate. — Species 20. Tropical and South Africa. (Including *Quartinia* Endl., *Rhyacophila* Hochst., and *Suffrenia* Bellardi). . . . .   **Rotala** L.
Fruit without transverse veins. Calyx-tube tubular, rarely campanulate, with appendages at the top. Flowers solitary or paired in the leaf-axils, rarely in spikes or racemes of cymes (false whorls). — Species 8. North, East, and South Africa. Some are used as ornamental or medicinal plants. . . . .   **Lythrum** L.

7. Stamens 6. Calyx-tube top-shaped. Sepals membranous. Ovary nearly completely 2-celled. Flowers in panicles. — Species 1. South-east Africa. . . . .   **Galpinia** N. E. Brown
Stamens 12—18. Flowers solitary or in racemes.   8

8. Calyx-tube tubular. Petals small. Stamens 12. Ovary nearly completely 2-celled. Fruit bursting irregularly or remaining closed. Seeds not winged. Flowers in racemes. — Species 2. East Africa and

Madagascar. They yield tanning and dyeing materials and serve as ornamental plants. . . . . **Woodfordia** Salisb.

Calyx-tube campanulate or cupular. Ovary very incompletely 3—4-celled. Fruit opening transversely. Seeds with a thick wing. Flowers solitary or in pairs in the leaf-axils. — Species 2. Madagascar and East Africa. They serve as vegetables. . . . . **Pemphis** Forst.

9. (1.) Stamens 5—6, opposite to the petals and adnate to their base. Calyx-tube expanded. Sepals lanceolate. Ovary 2-celled. Ovules in a single row. Low trees. Flowers in panicles. — Species 1. South-east Africa (Natal). . . . . **Rhynchocalyx** Oliv.

Stamens 4—23, inserted below the petals, or petals wanting. Ovules in two or more rows. Herbs, undershrubs, or shrubs. 10

10. Calyx-tube top- or saucer-shaped, without appendages. Sepals 4. Stamens inserted near the petals, singly or in clusters of 2—3 opposite the sepals. Fruit bursting irregularly or remaining closed. Seed-coat with a spongy thickening at the top. Shrubs. Leaves opposite. Flowers in panicles. — Species 1 (*L. inermis* L.). Tropical and North Africa. Yields a dye (henna) and is used in perfumery and medicine. (Including *Rotantha* Bak.) . . . . **Lawsonia** L.

Calyx-tube bell-, urn-, or cup-shaped. Sepals 4—8. Stamens remote from the petals, or petals wanting. Fruit opening by 4 valves or by a lid. Seed-coat not specially thickened. Flowers in cymes or umbels. . 11

11. Calyx-tube winged. Sepals 4. Petals none. Stamens 4, alternating with the sepals. Anthers finally kidney-shaped. Fruit opening by 4 valves. Style persisting upon the placentas. Shrubs. Leaves opposite. Flowers in axillary, 2—4-flowered umbels. — Species 1. Island of Mauritius. . . . . **Tetrataxis** Hook. fil.

Calyx-tube not winged. Fruit at first opening by a small lid, later on splitting towards the base. Style persisting upon a valve or falling off. Herbs, undershrubs, or low shrubs. Flowers in sometimes head-like cymes. — Species 40. Tropical and South Africa. (Plate 110.)

Nesaea Comm.

FAMILY 174. SONNERATIACEAE

Trees or shrubs. Leaves opposite, entire, not dotted, without stipules Flowers solitary, without bracteoles, regular. Sepals 6—7, fleshy, valvate in bud. Petals 6—7, linear, occasionally wanting. Stamens numerous, peri-gynous. Filaments bent inwards in the bud. Anthers fixed by the back, kidney-shaped, opening inwards by longitudinal slits. Ovary almost superior, with 10—20 somewhat incomplete cells not reaching the top. Ovules very numerous, attached to the partitions, inverted. Style simple ; stigma entire. Fruit succulent, indehiscent or bursting irregularly. Seeds curved, exalbumin-ous, with a hard coat and a straight embryo. (*BLATTIACEAE*, under *LYTHRACEAE*.)

Genus 1, species 1. East Africa, Madagascar and neighbouring islands. Yields edible fruits, condiments, and medicaments. (*Blatti* Adans.) **Sonneratia** L. f.

2 B

FAMILY 175. PUNICACEAE

Trees or shrubs. Leaves undivided, without stipules. Flowers solitary
or in clusters of 2—5 at the ends of the branches, regular, hermaphrodite.
Sepals 5—8, red, fleshy, valvate in bud. Petals as many, red or yellow, imbricate and crumpled in the bud. Stamens numerous, curved inwards in the
bud. Anthers fixed by the back, opening inwards by longitudinal slits. Ovary
inferior or half-inferior, with several cells, which are usually arranged in 2—3
whorls placed one above the other. Ovules numerous, at first basal, afterwards
parietal, inverted. Style simple ; stigma 1. Fruit a berry. Seeds exalbuminous, with an outer fleshy and an inner horny coat ; embryo straight, with
twisted cotyledons. (*GRANATEAE*, under *LYTHRACEAE*.)

> Genus 1, species 2. One of them growing wild in the Island of Socotra,
> the other one (*P. Granatum* L., pomegranate) cultivated and naturalized
> in northern and tropical Africa. The latter serves as an ornamental
> plant and yields wood, tanning and dyeing materials, medicaments
> and edible fruits, from which also a drink is prepared. **Punica** L

FAMILY 176. LECYTHIDACEAE

Trees or shrubs. Leaves alternate, undivided, without stipules. Flowers
solitary or racemose, hermaphrodite. Sepals 2—5. Petals 4—6, adnate to
the staminal tube, imbricate in bud, or wanting. Stamens numerous, united
at the base, curved in the bud. Anthers versatile, usually basifixed, opening by
longitudinal slits. Disc within the stamens, ring-shaped. Ovary inferior,
2—20-celled, with 2 or more inverted ovules in each cell. Style simple. Fruit
indehiscent. Seeds exalbuminous. — Genera 4, species 15. Tropical and South-
east Africa. (Under *MYRTACEAE*.) (Plate 111.)

> 1. Petals and staminodes absent. Sepals 3—5, usually 4. Stamens almost
>   free. Disc obscure. Ovules numerous in each cell, inserted in a
>   vertical ring round a shield-shaped placenta, horizontal, the micropyle
>   turned outwards. Stigmas 4. Fruit a drupe. Leaves clustered.
>   Flowers solitary, axillary. — Species 4. Madagascar and Mascarenes.
>   Yielding timber. [Subfamily **FOETIDIOIDEAE**.]   **Foetidia** Comm.

> Petals or staminodes present. Stamens obviously united at the base.
> Disc distinct. Ovules inserted in rows on slightly thickened placentas,
> horizontal with the micropyle turned inwards, or ascending, or pendu-
> lous. Flowers racemose, rarely solitary, but then leaves scattered. . 2

> 2. Sepals 5. Petals 0. Stamens and staminodes united to different heights,
>   in 4 concentric rows, the inner row partly fertile, the rest barren. Anthers
>   1-celled. Disc thick. Ovary 5—20-celled. Style short ; stigmas 5.
>   Seeds 5 or more. Flowers solitary or 2—3 together, axillary. Leaves
>   scattered. — Species 5. Central Africa. They yield timber and edible
>   fruits. [Subfamily **NAPOLEONOIDEAE**.]   . .   **Napoleona** Beauv.

> Sepals 2—4. Petals 4—6. Stamens all fertile or the innermost barren,
> all united to the same height. Anthers 2-celled. Disc ring-shaped.

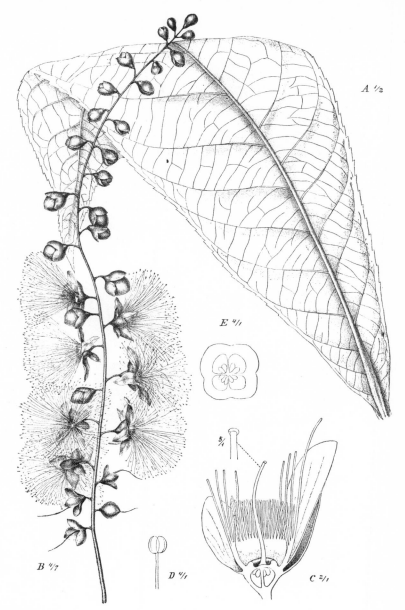

A ¹/₂

E ⁴/₁

5/₁

B ⁴/₇

D ⁴/₁

C ²/₁

J. Fleischmann del.

Barringtonia racemosa (L.) Blume

A Leaf.   *B* Inflorescence.   *C* Flower cut lengthwise (the stamens cut off near the middle).   *D* Anther.   *E* Cross-section of ovary.
(*A* from Curtis Botanical Magazine, pl. 3831.)

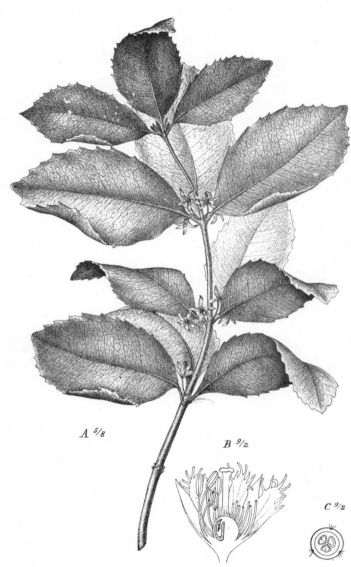

A ⁵/₈

B ⁹/₂

C ⁹/₂

J. Fleischmann del.

Weihea africana Benth.

A Flowering branch. *B* Flower cut lengthwise (some anthers cut off). *C* Cross-section of ovary.

Ovary 2—4-celled. Style long ; stigma 1, entire or 2—4-lobed. Seeds 1—4. Flowers in racemes. Leaves clustered. [Subfamily **PLAN-CHONIOIDEAE.**] 3

3. Ovary long, winged. Ovules inserted along the inner angle of the cells or in the middle of the partitions. Fruit a nut. Embryo with distinct cotyledons. Bracteoles in the middle of the long pedicels. — Species 2. West Africa. . . . . **Petersia** Welw.

Ovary short, ovate. Ovules suspended from the apex of the inner angle of the cells. Fruit a one-seeded drupe. Embryo undivided. Bracteoles at the base of the pedicels. — Species 5. Madagascar and neighbouring islands. East and South-east Africa. They yield timber, tanning bark, vegetables, oil, fish-poison, and medicaments, and serve also as ornamental plants. (Plate 111.) . . . **Barringtonia** Forst.

FAMILY 177. RHIZOPHORACEAE

Trees or shrubs. Leaves undivided. Flowers regular, hermaphrodite or polygamous. Sepals valvate in bud. Petals free, induplicate-valvate in bud, usually lobed or fringed. Stamens perigynous or epigynous, twice as many as the petals or more, rarely (*Anisophyllea*) some of them barren. Anthers opening inwards by longitudinal slits. Ovary completely or incompletely 2—6-celled. Ovules 1—2 in the inner angle of each cell, pendulous, inverted. Seeds usually germinating in the still attached fruit. — Genera 10, species 45. Tropical and South Africa. (Plate 112.)

1. Styles 3—4. Ovary inferior, with 1 ovule in each cell. Stamens 6—8, several of them sometimes barren. Flowers 3—4-merous, polygamous. Fruit a drupe. Seeds exalbuminous. Leaves alternate, exstipulate. [Subfamily **ANISOPHYLLOIDEAE.**] 2

Style 1. Ovary with 2 ovules in each cell. Fruit a berry or a capsule. Seeds albuminous. Leaves opposite or whorled, stipulate. [Subfamily **RHIZOPHOROIDEAE.**] 3

2. Flowers in few-flowered spikes or racemes. Fruit 1-seeded. — Species 7. Tropics. They yield timber and edible fruits. **Anisophyllea** R. Br.

Flowers in spikes arranged in racemes. Style ovate. Fruit 2—4-seeded. — Species 1. Equatorial West Africa (Gaboon). Yields edible, oily seeds.

Poga Pierre

3. Ovary inferior or half-inferior. Placentas usually passing into the style. Ovules without appendages. Petals yellow, brown, red, or greenish. Stamens twice as many as the petals. [Tribe GYNOTROCHEAE.] 4

Ovary superior or nearly so. Placentas not reaching to the base of the style. Ovules with appendages. Petals 4—6, toothed or split, usually white. [Tribe MACARISIEAE.] 7

4. Ovary inferior. Receptacle (flower-tube) deeply concave, bell- or funnel-shaped, distinctly prolonged above the ovary. Petals 5—14. Calyx crowning the fruit. 5

Ovary half-inferior. Receptacle slightly concave, saucer-shaped, scarcely prolonged above the ovary. Petals 4—6. Calyx at the base of the fruit. Seeds germinating in the still attached fruit. Plants with aerial roots. Flowers with an involucre of two bracteoles, arranged in cymes. . .   6

5. Receptacle funnel-shaped, prolonged above the ovary into a long tube. Flowers 8—14-merous. Petals red or brown, 2-lobed, with thread-like appendages. Antesepalous stamens curved sideways at the base, becoming opposite to the antepetalous. Disc obscurely lobed. Ovary 2—4-celled. Seeds germinating in the still attached fruit. Flowers solitary. — Species 1. Tropical and South-east Africa. Yields timber and bark used for tanning and dyeing.   . . . . **Bruguiera** Lam.

Receptacle bell-shaped, prolonged above the ovary into a short tube. Flowers 5—8-merous. Petals yellowish, irregularly lobed. Antesepalous stamens not opposite to the antepetalous. Disc usually double. Fruit 1- or 3—6-celled. Seeds germinating after the fruit has fallen. Flowers with an involucre of two bracteoles, arranged in cymes. — Species 2. Madagascar. . . . . . .   **Carallia** Roxb.

6. Flowers 4-merous. Petals entire, yellowish or green. Anthers with numerous cells (pollen-sacks). Disc obscurely lobed. Ovary 2-celled. Stigma 2-lobed. — Species 2. Tropical and South-east Africa. They yield timber, tanning and dyeing materials, and medicaments. " Mangrove." . . . . **Rhizophora** L,

Flowers 5—6-merous. Petals 2-lobed, brownish. Anthers with 4 cells. Disc deeply lobed. Ovary 3-celled above, 1-celled below. Stigma entire. — Species 1. Tropics. Yields timber and tanning bark.

Ceriops Arn.

7. Ovary 2—4-celled, adnate to the receptacle by the broad base. Leaves opposite. 8

Ovary 5-celled, sessile or short-stalked. Stamens 10. Flowers 5-merous, in few-flowered inflorescences. Seeds winged. 9

8. Disc distinctly 8—15-lobed. Stamens 10—15. Stigma entire. Placentas reaching the middle of the ovary only. Flowers in many-flowered inflorescences, frequently in glomerules. — Species 10. Tropical and South-east Africa. (Under *Cassipourea* Aubl.) **Dactylopetalum** Benth.

Disc not distinctly lobed. Stamens 10—30. Stigma 2—4-lobed. Placentas reaching the base of the style. Fruit fleshy. Seeds with an aril. Flowers with an involucre of two bracteoles, solitary or in few-flowered inflorescences. — Species 18. Tropical and South-east Africa. (Plate 112.) . . . . **Weihea** Spreng.

9. Ovary sessile. Tall trees. Leaves whorled. — Species 2. West Africa.

Anopyxis Pierre

Ovary short-stalked. Low trees. Leaves opposite. — Species 3. Madagascar. . . . . **Macarisia** Thouars

FAMILY 178. ALANGIACEAE

Trees or shrubs. Leaves alternate, undivided, without stipules. Flowers in axillary cymes, regular, hermaphrodite. Calyx 6—10-toothed. Petals 6—-10, free or slightly cohering at the base, narrow, valvate in bud. Stamens as many as the petals and alternate with them, or more. Filaments short, free or nearly so, hairy. Anthers long, adnate, opening inwards or laterally by two longitudinal slits. Disc cushion-shaped. Ovary inferior, 1-celled, rarely 2-celled. Ovule 1 in each cell, pendulous, inverted, with a ventral raphe. Style simple ; stigma lobed. Fruit a drupe. Seed with a large central embryo and fleshy albumen. (Under *CORNACEAE*.)

Genus 1, species 2. Tropics. Used medicinally. (Including *Marlea* Roxb. and *Stylidium* Lour.) . . . . **Alangium** Lam.

FAMILY 179. COMBRETACEAE

Trees or shrubs, rarely undershrubs. Leaves entire, without stipules. Flowers in spikes heads or panicles, regular or nearly so, 4—6-merous. Petals free or wanting. Stamens usually twice as many as the sepals. Anthers versatile. Ovary inferior, rarely half-inferior, 1-celled. Ovules 2—3, rarely 4—6, pendulous from the apex of the cavity, inverted. Style simple. Fruit a one-seeded drupe or nut, rarely incompletely dehiscent, usually angled or winged. Seeds exalbuminous. — Genera 12, species 330. Tropical and South Africa. (Plate 113.)

1. Ovary half-inferior. Petals 5. Stamens 10. Ovules 2, with a short funicle. Fruit dorsally compressed, dry, indehiscent. Embryo with very thick, almost hemispherical cotyledons. — Species 2. West Africa. [Subfamily **STREPHONEMATOIDEAE**.] . . **Strephonema** Hook. fil.
   Ovary inferior. Ovules usually with a long funicle. Fruit winged, angled, laterally compressed, or terete. Embryo with flat, folded, or twisted cotyledons. [Subfamily **COMBRETOIDEAE**.] 2

2. Flowers with bracteoles adnate to the ovary, arranged in spikes or racemes. Sepals persistent. Petals 5. Cotyledons twisted. [Tribe LAGUN-CULARIEAE.] 3
   Flowers without bracteoles. Sepals deciduous, rarely persistent, but then flowers in heads. 4

3. Leaves opposite. Flowers sessile. Stamens 10. Ovules 2 ; funicle short. —- Species 1. Coasts of West Africa. Yields timber, tanning and dyeing materials, and medicaments. . . . **Laguncularia** Gaertn.
   Leaves alternate. Flowers stalked. Ovules 4—6 ; funicle long. — Species 1. Coast of East Africa and Madagascar. . . **Lumnitzera** Willd.

4. Petals 4—5, rarely none ; in this case, as usually, leaves opposite. Flowers mostly hermaphrodite. Funicle usually tubercled. Cotyledons flat or folded, more rarely twisted. [Tribe COMBRETEAE.] . . . 5
   Petals none. Leaves alternate, rarely almost opposite. Flowers mostly polygamous. Sepals deciduous. Funicle usually smooth. Cotyledons twisted. Trees or erect shrubs. [Tribe TERMINALIEAE.] . . 10

5. Petals absent. Sepals 5. . . . . 6.
   Petals present, sometimes minute, rarely absent, but then sepals 4. . 7
6. Calyx campanulate, divided down to the ovary, wing-like in fruit. Cotyledons twisted. Climbing shrubs. Flowers in panicled spikes. — Species
   1. Madagascar. . . . . **Calycopteris** Lam.
   Calyx tubular-campanulate, lobed or cleft, net-veined, corolla-like, deciduous. Fruit woody. Cotyledons flat. Flowers in heads or short
   spikes. — Species 9. Madagascar. (Under *Combretum* L.)

   Calopyxis Tul.
7. Flowers ebracteate, arranged in heads which are subtended by 4 involucral
   bracts. Sepals persistent. Petals 5, strap-shaped. Stamens 10.
   Ovules 4—6. Fruit elongate, spindle-shaped, obscurely 5-angled, clothed
   with long hairs. Erect shrubs or trees. Leaves opposite, dotted.
   — Species 1. Central Africa. Used medicinally. **Guiera** Adans.
   Flowers bracteate, arranged in spikes or racemes. Sepals deciduous.
   Fruit winged or angled. 8
8. Flowers polygamous (hermaphrodite and male). Fruit 2-, rarely 3—4-
   winged, indehiscent. Trees or erect shrubs. — Species 5. Central
   Africa to Delagoa Bay. (Under *Combretum* L.) . **Pteleopsis** Engl.
   Flowers hermaphrodite. Fruit 4—5-winged or 4—5-angled. . . . 9
9. Calyx-tube above the ovary very long and thin, filiform ; style adnate to it.
   Ovules 3—4. Flowers 5-merous. Fruit dehiscing at the top along the
   5 angles. Climbing shrubs. Lower leaves alternate, upper opposite.
   — Species 3. Tropical and South-east Africa. Used as ornamental or
   medicinal plants. . . . . **Quisqualis** L.
   Calyx-tube not elongate-filiform. Ovules 2—3 ; funicles equal in length.
   Fruit indehiscent. Leaves opposite or whorled, sometimes intermixed
   with alternate ones. — Species 230. Tropical and South Africa. Some
   species yield timber, gum, tanning and dyeing materials, arrow-poison,
   medicaments, and fatty seeds ; several serve as ornamental plants.
   (Including *Cacoucia* Aubl., *Campylochiton* Welw., *Campylogyne* Welw.,
   and *Poivrea* Comm.) (Plate 113.) . . . . . **Combretum** L.
10. (4.) Flowers and fruits in globose heads. Receptacle (calyx-tube) pro-
    longed above the ovary into a stalk. Calyx-lobes 5, reflexed. Ovules 2.
    Fruits erect or spreading, flat, 2-winged, produced into a long beak ;
    pericarp corky. Shrubs. — Species 1. Central Africa. Yields timber,
    dyes, a substitute for soap, and medicaments. . . . **Anogeissus** Wall.
    Flowers and fruits in sometimes ovate, usually panicled spikes. Receptacle
    not much prolonged. Fruit not long-beaked but sometimes acuminate ;
    pericarp leathery or drupaceous. : 11
11. Fruits crowded in a cone, bent downwards, flat, 2-winged, acuminate ;
    pericarp leathery. Flowers in short panicled spikes, 5-merous. Calyx-
    lobes erect. Ovules 2. — Species 2. Central Africa. They yield
    timber, tanning materials, and medicaments. . . **Conocarpus** Gaertn.

J. Fleischmann del.

Combretum racemosum Beauv.

A Part of a flowering branch   *B* Flower cut lengthwise   *C* Fruit.   *D* Cross-section of fruit.

MYRTACEAE.

Pl. 114.

J. Fleischmann del.

Eugenia natalitia Sond.

A Flowering branch.   B Hermaphrodite flower cut lengthwise (most of the anthers having fallen off).   C Cross-section of ovary.
D Male flower cut lengthwise (most of the anthers having fallen off).   E Fruit.   F Seed cut lengthwise.

Fruits not crowded in a cone ; pericarp fleshy or leathery outside, bony within. Flowers in usually long, often panicled spikes. Funicle smooth. Leaves usually crowded at the ends of the branches. — Species 80. Tropical and South Africa. Some species yield timber, resin used for fumigating, tanning and dyeing materials, food for silk-worms, edible oily seeds, and medicaments ; others are used as ornamental plants.

Terminalia L.

FAMILY 180. MYRTACEAE

Trees or shrubs. Leaves undivided, gland-dotted, without stipules. Flowers regular, 4—5-merous. Calyx with imbricate, open, or closed aestivation. Petals free and imbricate in bud, or united into a hood. Stamens usually numerous. Anthers opening by longitudinal slits. Ovary usually inferior or half-inferior, 2—5-celled, the cells sometimes incomplete at the top. Ovules inverted. Style simple ; stigma entire, rarely (*Psiloxylon*) 3—4-parted. Seeds exalbuminous. — Genera 10, species 85. (Plate 114.)

1. Fruit a capsule or a nut. Embryo straight, with large cotyledons. Trees. [Subfamily **LEPTOSPERMOIDEAE,** tribe LEPTOSPERMEAE.] .   2
   Fruit a berry. Ovary inferior or half-inferior. Stamens numerous. Leaves opposite. [Subfamily **MYRTOIDEAE,** tribe MYRTEAE.] .   5
2. Calyx entire or nearly so. Petals united into a hood falling off as a whole. Stamens numerous. Ovary inferior. Leaves of older trees mostly alternate. — Species 3. Cultivated and naturalized in various regions. They yield timber, bark for tanning, an astringent resin (kino), and an ethereal oil used in perfumery and medicine. [Subtribe EUCALYPTINAE.] . . . . **Eucalyptus** L'Hér.
   Calyx with 5 lobes. Petals 5, free. 3
3. Stamens numerous. Ovary inferior or half-inferior. Leaves opposite. — Species 1. South Africa. [Tribe METROSIDERINAE.]
   Metrosideros Banks
   Stamens 5—10. Ovary superior. Leaves alternate. 4
4. Stamens 5—8. Stigma 1, entire. Flowers in terminal panicles. — Species 2. South Africa. . . . . **Heteropyxis** Harv.
   Stamens 10. Stigmas 3—4. Flowers in axillary clusters. — Species 1. Mascarene Islands. Yields timber. (*Tropicra* Hook. fil.)
   Psiloxylon Thouars
5. Embryo with a short radicle and large, fleshy cotyledons. Flowers usually 4-merous. Sepals separate or indistinct. Ovary 2-, rarely 3-celled. [Subtribe EUGENIINAE.] 6
   Embryo with a long, curved radicle and shorter or somewhat longer cotyledons. Flowers usually 5-merous. Petals free. [Subtribe MYRTINAE.] 8
6. Ovary in the centre of the receptacle. Calyx-tube contrasting distinctly with the pedicel, not or slightly prolonged above the ovary. Petals

free. — Species 40. Tropical and South Africa. Some species yield
timber, bark used for tanning, edible fruits, and medicaments. (Including *Chloromyrtus* Pierre). (Plate 114.) . . . . **Eugenia** L.
Ovary in the upper part of the receptacle. Calyx-tube gradually narrowed
   into the pedicel, usually much prolonged above the ovary. . . . 7

7. Petals free, falling singly. Stamens inserted upon a distinct disc. Sepals
   comparatively large. — Species 8, of which 6 are growing wild in Madagascar and the Mascarenes, the other two cultivated and sometimes
   naturalized in the tropics. They yield timber, bark used for tanning,
   spices (cloves from *J. caryophyllus* Nied.), medicaments, and edible
   fruits ; some are used as ornamental plants. (Including *Caryophyllus*
   L., under *Eugenia* L.) . . . . **Jambosa** DC.
   Petals more or less cohering, usually falling off together. Staminiferous
   disc none. Sepals usually small. — Species 25. Tropical and South
   Africa. They yield timber, tanning and dyeing materials, spices,
   medicaments, and edible fruits. (Including *Acmena* DC., under *Eugenia*
   L.) . . . . **Syzygium** Gaertn.

8. Placentas in the upper part of the ovary-cells, bearing 1—6 ovules each.
   Ovary 2-celled. Calyx divided already in the bud. Seeds 1—2, with
   a membranous coat ; embryo spirally twisted, with minute cotyledons. —
   Species 2. Cultivated and naturalized in the Mascarene Islands. They
   yield timber, an aromatic oil, spices (allspice), and medicaments, and
   serve also as ornamental plants. . . . . **Pimenta** Lindl.
   Placentas in the middle of the ovary-cells, bearing numerous ovules each.
   Ovary completely or incompletely 3—5-, rarely 2-celled. Seeds numerous, with a horny coat ; embryo curved, not spiral. 9

9. Calyx already divided into segments in the bud. Ovary and fruit completely or incompletely 2—3-celled. Embryo with rather large cotyledons. — Species 1 (*M. communis* L., myrtle). North Africa and
   Abyssinia, also naturalized in St. Helena. It is used as an ornamental
   plant and yields tanning bark and an oil employed in perfumery and
   medicine. . . . . **Myrtus** L.
   Calyx closed in the bud, bursting subsequently. Ovary and fruit usually
   4—5-celled. Embryo with minute cotyledons. — Species 2. Cultivated
   in the tropics. They yield timber, bast used for paper-making, tanning
   and dyeing materials, vegetables, edible fruits (guavas), and medicaments.
   Psidium L.

FAMILY 181. MELASTOMATACEAE

Leaves opposite or whorled, undivided, usually with 3—11 longitudinal
nerves, not dotted, without stipules. Flowers regular or nearly so. Petals
perigynous or epigynous, free, usually with contorted aestivation. Stamens
perigynous or epigynous, twice as many, rarely as many as the petals. Filaments inflexed in the bud. Anthers 2-celled, turned inwards, usually with an

enlarged connective and opening at the top by 1—2 pores or short slits. Ovary generally inferior or half-inferior. Ovules numerous. Style simple ; stigma entire. Seeds exalbuminous. — Genera 33, species 280. Tropical and South Africa. (Plate 115.)

1. Ovary 1-celled, inferior. Ovules 6—20, inserted upon a free central placenta. Fruit a berry. Seed 1, large. Calyx entire or 4-lobed. Petals white or blue. Stamens twice as many as the petals. Anthers short, with a posterior appendage, opening in front by two longitudinal slits. Shrubs or trees. Leaves penninerved or obscurely trinerved. [Subfamily **MEMECYLOIDEAE,** tribe MEMECYLEAE.] 2

 Ovary completely 2- or more-celled. Ovules numerous, inserted upon axile placentas. Seeds numerous, small. [Subfamily **MELASTOMA-TOIDEAE.**] 3

2. Connective of the stamens lengthened at the base. Petals reddish. Flowers in terminal fascicles. Stem and inflorescence bristly. — Species 1. East Africa. . . . . **Warneckea** Gilg

 Connective of the stamens not lengthened at the base, but spurred at the back. Petals white or blue. Flowers in axillary inflorescences, more rarely in terminal, many-flowered cymes. Stem and inflorescence glabrous. — Species 60. Tropical and South-east Africa. Some species yield timber, dyes, medicaments, and edible fruits. . . **Memecylon** L.

3. Seeds strongly curved or spirally coiled. Fruit usually a membranous, 4—5-valved capsule with a convex, usually bristly summit. Connective of the stamens unappendaged behind, but furnished with two spurs or gibbosities in front, rarely quite unappendaged. Calyx-lobes usually large and alternating with bristles or small teeth. [Tribe OSBECKIEAE.] 4

 Seeds straight or slightly curved, rarely strongly curved, but then fruit bursting irregularly or indehiscent and connective gibbous before and behind. Connective usually appendaged behind, or before and behind. 17

4. Stamens of two kinds, the larger with the connective distinctly lengthened at the base and furnished with two spurs or bosses, the smaller ones with a not or slightly lengthened connective. Shrubs or trees. . . . 5

 Stamens equal in shape, but sometimes unequal in length. 8

5. Connective of the smaller stamens unappendaged, of the larger with two bosses. Calyx-tube glabrous ; teeth very short. Fruit with a membranous skin, bursting irregularly. Low shrubs. Flowers in terminal panicles. — Species 2. West Africa. . . . . . **Dinophora** Benth.

 Connective of all stamens provided with 2 spurs or bosses. Calyx-tube usually hairy. Fruit with a membranous skin, but dehiscing in 4—5 valves, or with a leathery or fleshy skin. 6

6. Calyx without accessory teeth. Connective of all stamens lengthened at the base and provided with 2 awns. Fruit 4—5-valved. Rough-

hairy shrubs or trees.   Flowers in terminal panicles. — Species 20.
Madagascar. . . . .   **Dichaetanthera** Endl.
Calyx with accessory teeth outside the sepals. Connective of the smaller
    stamens not or scarcely lengthened.   7

7. Fruit bursting irregularly or remaining closed ; skin leathery or fleshy.
    Flowers 5—7-merous. Shrubs with rough branches and bristly leaves.
    — Species 1. Seychelles. . . . .   **Melastoma** Burm.
    Fruit opening by 4—5 valves ; skin membranous or leathery. Ovary
    adnate to the calyx-tube by 4—5 longitudinal partitions. Flowers 4—5-
    merous. Hairy, usually bristly herbs undershrubs or shrubs. — Species
    50. Central and South Africa ; one species also naturalized in the
    Mascarene Islands. An intoxicating drink is prepared from the roots
    of some species. (Including *Argyrella* Naud.) (Plate 115.) **Dissotis** Benth.

8. Connective with two spur-like appendages. Ovary half-inferior. Flowers
    in terminal cymes or panicles.   9
    Connective with two bosses or without any appendage.   12

9. Stamens unequal in length. Connective much lengthened at the base.
    Flowers 4-merous. Calyx-lobes broadly rounded. Ovary with 4 bristles
    at the top. Shrubs. — Species 1. Equatorial West Africa.
                              Barbeyastrum Cogn.
    Stamens equal in length. Connective not or slightly lengthened at the
    base.   10

10. Connective lengthened at the base. Flowers 4-merous. Calyx-tube
    pitcher-shaped, glabrous. Calyx-lobes 4, very short. Petals yellow.
    Shrubs. — Species 1. Madagascar. . . . . **Amphorocalyx** Bak.
    Connective not or scarcely lengthened at the base. Calyx-tube bell-shaped.
    Calyx-lobes rather large. Shrubs with pink petals, or herbs. . . 11

11. Flowers 4-merous. Calyx without accessory teeth. Shrubs. Leaves
    5—11-nerved. — Species 2. Madagascar. . . **Dionychia** Naud.
    Flowers 5-merous . Calyx with 5 bristle-like accessory teeth alternating
    with the sepals. Herbs. Leaves 3-nerved. — Species 4. Madagascar.
                               Rhodosepala Bak.

12. Calyx with accessory teeth or bristles alternating with the sepals. Stamens
    equal in length. Ovary with bristles at the top   13
    Calyx without accessory teeth or bristles. Petals red or white. Ovary
    more or less adnate to the calyx-tube.   15

13. Ovary free. Flowers 4-merous. Calyx-tube glabrous or scantily hairy.
    Petals yellow. Connective not lengthened at the base, obscurely
    tubercled. Erect herbs. Flowers terminal, solitary or ternate. —
    Species 1. West Africa. . . . . **Nerophila** Naud.
    Ovary more or less adnate to the calyx-tube. Calyx-tube usually hairy.
    Petals usually red.   14

14. Anthers smooth, oval-oblong. Connective more or less lengthened and
    provided with two bosses at the base. Herbs. Flowers in cymes. —
    Species 2. Tropics. (Under *Osbeckia* L.)   .   **Antherotoma** Hook. fil.

Anthers with a wavy surface, linear, rarely broader, but then connective not distinctly lengthened at the base. — Species 20. Tropical and Southeast Africa. Some species are used as ornamental or medicinal plants.

Osbeckia L.

15. Anthers linear. Connective not or scarcely lengthened at the base, provided with two bosses in front. Stamens usually unequal in length. Calyx-tube bristly. Shrubs. — Species 15. Tropics. Some species yield edible fruits and medicaments. . . . . **Tristemma** Juss.

Anthers ovoid. Connective lengthened at the base, unappendaged. Stamens equal in length. Ovary glabrous at the top. Herbs. Flowers solitary. 16

16. Flowers 4-merous. Calyx-tube hairy. Ovary inferior. Flowers terminal. — Species 1. West Africa. (Under *Guyonia* Naud.) **Afzeliella** Gilg

Flowers 5-merous. Calyx-tube glabrous. Ovary half-inferior. — Species 2. West Africa. . . . . **Guyonia** Naud.

17. (3.) Fruit bursting irregularly or remaining closed ; skin fleshy or leathery, rarely membranous. Connective furnished with appendages in front and behind, rarely only in front. [Tribe DISSOCHAETEAE.] . 18

Fruit opening by 3—6 valves ; skin membranous, rarely leathery. Connective usually furnished with appendages only behind. 25

18. Connective with two spurs in front, unappendaged behind. Stamens equal or nearly so. 19

Connective with two spurs or bosses in front and 1—2 behind. Calyx-lobes tooth-shaped, bristle-shaped, or wanting. Flowers in cymes, umbels, or panicles. 20

19. Calyx distinctly 5-lobed. Connective very shortly prolonged at the base. Fruit a berry. Herbs. Flowers solitary. — Species 1. West Africa (Cameroons) . . . . **Tetraphyllaster** Gilg

Calyx obscurely lobed. Connective much prolonged at the base. Fruit a capsule with a membranous skin. Shrubs or trees. Flowers in panicles. — Species 5. West Africa. . . . . **Sakersia** Hook. fil.

20. Stamens distinctly unequal, the connective of the longer ones lengthened at the base and furnished with 1 spur behind and 2 in front, that of the shorter ones also with one spur behind but none in front. Flowers 5-merous. Calyx-tube top- or urn-shaped ; lobes short, alternating with accessory teeth. Petals red. Ovary adnate up to the middle. Shrubs. Flowers in terminal, few-flowered cymes. — Species 3. West Africa.

Diceliandra Hook. fil.

Stamens equal or nearly so, rarely very unequal, but then the connective of all with 2 appendages in front and usually not lengthened at the base. 21

21. Stamens distinctly unequal. Flowers 4-merous. Calyx-tube constricted above the ovary, saucer-shaped at the top, entire or nearly so. Climbing shrubs. Lower leaves alternate, upper whorled. Flowers at the base

of the stem in many-flowered globose inflorescences composed of cymes.
— Species 1. Equatorial West Africa (Gaboon) **Myrianthemum** Gilg
Stamens equal or subequal, rarely (*Medinilla*) distinctly unequal, but
then calyx-tube not much constricted and inflorescence not many-
flowered and springing from the base of the stem. 22

22. Connective of the stamens lengthened at the base and furnished with a
spur in front and a boss behind. Flowers 5-merous. Ovary wholly
adnate. Shrubs. Flowers in terminal, few-flowered cymes. — Species 1.
Equatorial West Africa (Cameroons). . . . . . . **Preussiella** Gilg
Connective with 2 spurs or bosses in front and 1—2 behind. 23

23. Stem woody, shrubby. Flowers in cymes or panicles. Ovary adhering
to the calyx-tube entirely or by several dissepiments. — Species 25.
Tropics. Some are used as ornamental or medicinal plants.
Medinilla Gaud.
Stem herbaceous or woody at the base only. Leaves opposite ; side-
nerves nearly perpendicular to the main nerves. Flowers 5-merous, in
terminal umbels or panicles. Connective with 2 bosses in front and
one behind. 24

24. Flowers in panicles. Petals subacute. Ovary in its lower half adhering
to the calyx-tube by dissepiments. Style without scales at the base.
Fruit bursting irregularly. Seeds curved. — Species 1. Central Africa.
Phaeoneuron Gilg
Flowers in umbels. Petals acuminate. Ovary adhering to the calyx-tube
to above the middle. Style surrounded at the base by 5 scales. —
Species 1. East Africa. . . . . **Orthogoneuron** Gilg

25. (17.) Fruit and ovary cylindrical or angled, convex at the top. Stamens
equal ; connective appendaged behind only, more rarely without any
appendage. [Tribe OXYSPOREAE.] 26
Fruit and usually also the ovary angled or winged, broad and flat or concave
at the top, rarely (*Calvoa*) slightly convex, but then the connective
appendaged in front or in front and behind. [Tribe SONERILEAE.] 29

26. Stem herbaceous or half-shrubby, erect. Leaves large. Flowers in
umbels, large, red, 5-merous. Calyx-tube angled ; lobes long. Petals
produced into a thread-like point. Connective with a thick spur and two
glands. Ovary crowned by 5 scales. — Species 1. East Africa.
Petalonema Gilg
Stem shrubby, more rarely half-shrubby, but then decumbent and bearing
small leaves. Flowers in cymes or panicles. 27

27. Stem half-shrubby, decumbent. Connective shortly prolonged at the base,
tubercled or obscurely spurred behind. — Species 1. Madagascar.
Phornothamnus Bak.
Stem shrubby. Connective not prolonged. 28

28. Calyx-limb divided into 4 large lobes without accessory teeth. Connective
unappendaged. Ovary adhering below to the calyx-tube by several

D ²/₁

E ¹²/₁

A ⁵/₁₂

C ⁴/₁

B ²/₁

J. Fleischmann del.

Dissotis capitata (Vahl) Hook. fil.

A Flowering branch.   *B* Flower cut lengthwise.   *C* Cross-section of ovary.   *D* Fruit.   *E* Seed.

A ²/₃

B ²/₃

E ³/₂

F ³⁰/₁

D ¹⁰/₁

C ⁶/₁

J. Fleischmann del.

Jussieua linifolia Vahl

A Plant in flower. *B* Flowering branch of a taller specimen. *C* Flower cut lengthwise. *D* Cross-section of ovary. *E* Fruit. *F* Seed.

dissepiments and crowned by 4 bristle-like scales. — Species 1. Madagascar. . . . . **Rousseauxia** DC.
Calyx-limb entire or sinuate, provided with 5 accessory teeth. Ovary adhering to the calyx-tube all round. — Species 20. Madagascar.

Veprecella Naud.

29. Connective of the stamens appendaged behind only, not or shortly prolonged at the base. 30
Connective of the stamens appendaged in front or also behind, or unappendaged. Flowers 5-merous. 32

30. Stamens unequal in length. Herbs with a thickened root-stock. Leaves cordate, 9-nerved. — Species 2. Central Africa. **Cincinnobrys** Gilg
Stamens equal in length. Flowers 5-merous. 31

31. Calyx almost entire. Ovary crowned by 5 scales. Erect herbs with glandular hairs. Leaves lanceolate. Flowers in umbels. — Species 1. East Africa . . . . **Urotheca** Gilg
Calyx 5-toothed. Herbs with a very short stem and cymose flowers, or climbing shrubs. — Species 15. Madagascar. Some are used as ornamental plants. . . . . **Gravesia** Naud.

32. Stamens distinctly unequal; connective of the longer ones lengthened at the base, furnished with 1—2 bosses or spurs in front, spurred or unappendaged behind. — Species 8. West Africa. Some are used as ornamental plants. . . . . **Amphiblemma** Naud.
Stamens equal or nearly so; connective not or shortly lengthened at the base, usually provided with a scale in front, rarely also with a boss behind. — Species 9. Central Africa. . . . . . **Calvoa** Hook. fil.

FAMILY 182. OENOTHERACEAE

Leaves undivided or pinnately cleft. Flowers solitary or in spikes, heads, racemes, or panicles, 2—6-, rarely 4-merous. Sepals valvate in bud. Petals free, rarely (*Ludwigia*) absent. Stamens as many or twice as many as the sepals. Anthers opening inwards by longitudinal slits. Ovary inferior or half-inferior, completely or almost completely 2—6-celled. Ovules inverted. Style simple. Seeds exalbuminous. — Genera 10, species 40. (*ONAGRACEAE* including *HYDROCARYACEAE*.) (Plate 116.)

1. Ovary half-inferior, 2-celled, with one pendulous ovule in each cell. Flowers 4-merous. Fruit top-shaped, woody, indehiscent. Floating herbs, with filiform branched side-roots and broad radical leaves. — Species 2. The seeds are edible and are used for preparing meal and medicaments. "Water Chestnut." [Tribe TRAPEAE.] . . . . . **Trapa** L.
Ovary inferior, 2-celled with one ascending ovule in each cell, or more frequently 3—6-celled with numerous ovules. 2

2. Flowers 2-merous. Receptacle prolonged above the ovary in the shape of a stalk. Petals white or reddish. Stamens 2. Ovules and seeds
2. Fruit an ovoid nut with a leathery rind, covered with hooked

bristles. Herbs. Leaves opposite. Flowers in racemes. — Species 1. North Africa. [Tribe CIRCAEEAE.]   .   .   .   .   .   . **Circaea** L.
Flowers 3—6-merous. Stamens 3—12. Ovules and seeds numerous. Fruit a capsule or a berry.   3

3. Flowers with bracteoles, regular. Receptacle (calyx-tube) not prolonged beyond the ovary. Calyx persistent. Petals yellow or white, rarely absent. Fruit loculicidal and septicidal. Herbs or undershrubs. Stipules present, but usually minute and caducous. [Tribe JUSSIEU-EAE.]   4
Flowers without bracteoles, 4-merous. Receptacle more or less prolonged above the ovary; if obscurely prolonged, then flowers somewhat irregular with red petals. Calyx deciduous. Stamens 8. Fruit loculicidal or indehiscent. 5

4. Stamens 3—6. — Species 5. (Including *Isnardia* L.) .   . **Ludwigia** L.
Stamens 8—12. Petals 4—6. Epigynous disc pyramidal or cushion-shaped. — Species 10. Some of them are used medicinally and for dyeing. (Plate 116.)   .   .   .   . **Jussieua** L.

5. Stem woody. Leaves stipulate. Flowers regular. Calyx coloured, with a long tube. Petals red or violet. Stamens unequal. Fruit a berry. — Species 1. Naturalized in some tropical countries. An ornamental plant. [Tribe FUCHSIEAE.]   .   .   .   . **Fuchsia** L.
Stem herbaceous or woody at the base only. Leaves exstipulate. Fruit a capsule. 6

6. Calyx-tube short, bell-shaped. Petals usually red. Stamens unequal in length. Fruit linear with a membranous rind. Seeds with a tuft of hairs. [Tribe EPILOBIEAE.]   7
Calyx-tube long, funnel-shaped or cylindrical. Calyx-lobes reflexed. Flowers regular. Petals usually yellow. Stamens subequal. Stigma 4-partite. Seeds without a tuft of hairs. [Tribe OENOTHEREAE.]   8

7. Flowers somewhat irregular, large. Calyx-tube scarcely prolonged beyond the ovary. Petals red, spreading. Stamens in one row, bent down, broadened at the base. Style bent down, hairy at the base. Stigma 4-partite. — Species 1. Canary Islands. Yields tea and medicaments, and serves as a vegetable and as an ornamental plant. (Under *Epilob-ium* L.)   .   .   .   . **Chamaenerium** Spach
Flowers regular, usually small. Calyx-tube shortly bell-shaped above the ovary. Stamens in two rows, erect. Style erect, glabrous. — Species 15. Some of them are used as ornamental or medicinal plants. "Willow-herb."   .   .   .   . **Epilobium** L.

8. Calyx-tube funnel-shaped, rather short (as long as or shorter than the lobes). Petals red or white. Fruit club-shaped, stalked, keeled at the angles, with a more or less woody rind. Seeds with an elongated funicle. Leaves pinnatifid. — Species 2. Naturalized in North and South Africa. Ornamental plants. (Under *Oenothera* L.) .   . **Xylopleurum** Spach

Calyx-tube cylindrical, long. Petals yellow. Fruit obscurely angled, with a more or less membranous or leathery rind. 9

9. Seeds horizontal, sharply angled, with a thick coat. Leaves dentate. — Species 2. Naturalized in North and South Africa. Ornamental plants ; one species (*O. biennis* Scop.) has edible roots. (Under *Oenothera* L.)

Onagra Tourn.

Seeds ascending, rounded, egg-shaped, with an appendage at the top. Leaves sinuate-dentate or pinnatifid. — Species 2. Naturalized in North and South Africa and some tropical islands. Ornamental plants. "Evening primrose." . . . . **Oenothera** Spach

SUBORDER HALORRHAGINEAE

FAMILY 183. HALORRHAGACEAE

Herbs or undershrubs. Leaves undivided, lobed, or pinnately divided, without stipules. Flowers solitary or in fascicles spikes or panicles, small, regular, 2—4-merous. Petals free or in the female flowers wanting. Stamens 1—8. Anthers attached by the base, opening laterally by two longitudinal slits. Ovary inferior, 1-celled with a single ovule or with 4 ovules, or 4-celled with one-ovuled cells. Ovules pendulous, inverted. Styles or sessile stigmas 2 or 4. Fruit a nut, drupe, or schizocarp. Seeds albuminous ; embryo straight. — Genera 3, species 15. (Plate 117.)

1. Ovary 1-celled with a single ovule. Styles or sessile stigmas 2. Sepals 2. Petals 1—2, or more frequently wanting. Stamens 1—2. Fruit a drupe. Seed with a very short embryo. Terrestrial plants. Leaves radical, kidney-shaped, crenate. Flowers in spikes or panicles. — Species 1. East and South Africa and Madagascar. Used medicinally. [Subfamily **GUNNEROIDEAE.**] . . . . **Gunnera** L.

   Ovary 1-celled with 4 ovules, or 4-celled. Styles or sessile stigmas 4. Sepals 4, sometimes scarcely perceptible in the female flowers. Petals 4 or in the female flowers absent. Stamens 2—8. Seeds with a long embryo. [Subfamily **HALORRHAGOIDEAE.**] 2

2. Ovary 1-celled, sometimes incompletely 4-celled. Stamens 4. Fruit one-seeded, dry and indehiscent. Terrestrial plants. Leaves undivided. Flowers in axillary clusters. — Species 9. (*Serpicula* L.) (Plate 117.) [Tribe HALORRHAGEAE.] . . . . . . **Laurembergia** Berg

   Ovary 4-celled. Fruit 2—4-seeded, usually separating into mericarps. Aquatic plants. Leaves usually pinnately divided. Flowers solitary and axillary or in terminal spikes. — Species 5. North, South, and East Africa and Madagascar. [Tribe MYRIOPHYLLEAE.]

Myriophyllum L.

SUBORDER CYNOMORIINEAE
FAMILY 184. CYNOMORIACEAE

Reddish-brown, fleshy herbs, parasitic upon roots. Leaves scale-like. Flowers in terminal spadices, polygamous. Perianth of 1- 5 narrow segments. Stamen 1. Anther versatile, turned inwards, 2-celled. Ovary inferior, 1-celled. Ovule 1, pendulous, almost straight. Style simple ; stigma entire. Fruit a nut. ¯ Seed albuminous ; embryo small, without cotyledons.

Genus 1, species 1. North Africa. Used medicinally. **Cynomorium** Mich.

ORDER UMBELLIFLORAE
FAMILY 185. ARALIACEAE

Shrubs or trees. Leaves usually stipulate. Inflorescence composed of umbels, racemes, heads, or spikes. Flowers 4 16-merous. Calyx entire or shortly toothed, imbricate or open in bud. Petals free, valvate in bud, or united into a cap. Stamens as many as petals or more. Anthers versatile, opening by two longitudinal slits. Ovary inferior or half-inferior, crowned by a disc (stylopod), 2- or more-celled, rarely (*Polyscias*) 1-celled. Ovules solitary in each cell, pendulous, inverted, with ventral raphe. Fruit indehiscent. Seeds albuminous. — Genera 8, species 75. (Plate 118.)

1. Stem climbing by means of small aerial roots. Leaves entire or lobed, without stipules. Flowers in umbels. 5-merous ; pedicels not jointed. Stamens 5. Ovary 5-celled ; style simple. Fruit a berry ; endocarp membranous. Seeds with ruminate albumen. — Species 1 (*H. Helix* L., ivy). North Africa. Used as ornamental and medicinal plants ; the fruits are poisonous. . . . . **Hedera** L.

    Stem without adhesive roots. Leaves pinnate or digitate, rarely undivided or lobed, but then ovary 2—4-celled and style 2—4-parted. Fruit a drupe or a nut ; endocarp leathery, crustaceous, cartilaginous, or bony. 2

2. Leaves undivided, lobed, or digitate. Stipules usually distinctly developed. Pedicels not jointed. 3

    Leaves pinnate. Stipules indistinctly developed or wanting. Seeds with uniform albumen. 5

3. Ovary 2-, rarely 3—4-celled. Styles short, free or united below. Stylopod convex or conical. Petals 5, free. Stamens 5. Endocarp crustaceous. Albumen usually ruminate. Flowers in spikes or racemes, rarely in umbels. — Species 25. Tropical and South Africa. (Including *Secmannaralia* Viguier). (Plate 118.) . . . . **Cussonia** Thunb.

    Ovary 5—15-celled. Petals 5—15, usually united in the shape of a cap. Albumen uniform. Flowers in umbels or heads, rarely in racemes. Leaves digitate. 4

4. Stamens as many as the petals. — Species 13. Tropics. (Including *Astropanax* Seem., *Heptapleurum* Gaertn., and *Sciadophyllum* P. Browne) **Schefflera** Forst.

C $^{12}/_1$

D $^{5}/_1$

E $^{3}/_1$

B $^{6}/_1$

A $^{1}/_1$

J. Fleischmann del.

Laurembergia repens Berg

A Flowering branch.   *B* Male flower cut lengthwise.   *C* Female flower cut lengthwise.   *D* Young fruit,   *E* Young fruit cut lengthwise.

ARALIACEAE.

Pl. 118.

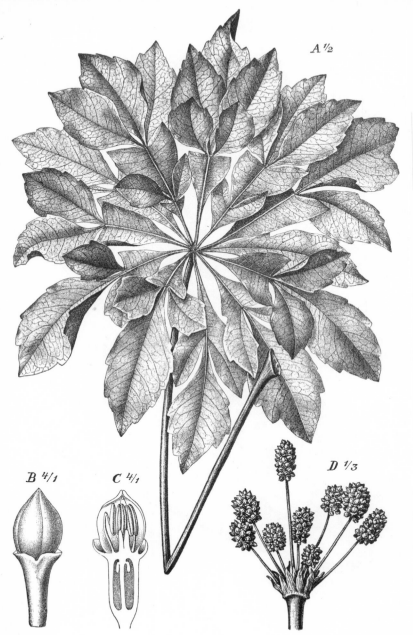

A ½

B ⁴/₁   C ⁴/₁   D ⅓

J. Fleischmann del.

Cussonia spicata Thunb.

A Leaf.   *B* Flower-bud.   *C* Flower-bud cut lengthwise.   *D* Inflorescence.

Stamens twice as many as the petals. Petals 5, cohering in the shape of a
cap. Ovary 8—10-celled. Flowers in spicately arranged heads. —
Species 1. Seychelles. . . . . **Geopanax** Hemsl.
5. Flowers in umbels or racemes with jointed pedicels, very rarely in spikes or
heads. Ovary-cells and styles or style-branches 1—10. Stamens as
many as the petals. 6
Flowers in umbels; pedicels not jointed. Ovary-cells and styles or
style-branches 10—15. Leaves unequally pinnate with entire leaflets . 7
6. Styles present, usually free and filiform. Seeds smooth or folded on the
surface. — Species 30. Tropics. (Including *Cuphocarpus* Decne. et
Planch. and *Tieghemopanax* Viguier, under *Panax* L.) **Polyscias** Forst.
Styles absent; stigmas 2, seated upon the conical stylopod. Ovary 2-celled.
Pericarp with 8 oil-channels. Seeds 4-lobed. Trees. Leaves unequally pinnate with entire leaflets. Flowers in panicled umbels. —
Species 1. Madagascar. (Under *Panax* L.) . **Sciadopanax** Seem.
7. Petals free or cohering at the tip. Stamens as many as the petals, 10—15;
filaments flattened. Styles awl-shaped. Trees. — Species 4. Madagas-
car and the neighbouring islands. . . . . . . **Gastonia** Comm.
Petals united throughout their whole length. Stamens numerous; filaments awl-shaped. Style none; stigma 2-cleft. Shrubs. — Species 1.
Seychelles. . . . . **Indokingia** Hemsl.

FAMILY 186. UMBELLIFERAE

Mostly herbs with a jointed stem. Leaves alternate, rarely (*Drusa*) opposite,
usually dissected and with a sheathing stalk. Flowers in umbels or heads,
rarely in spikes or in racemed false-whorls, regular or the outermost flowers
of the inflorescence somewhat irregular, usually hermaphrodite. Calyx-limb
usually faintly developed or wanting. Petals 5, free, usually bent inwards
at the tip and therefore apparently notched or 2-lobed, valvate or slightly
imbricate in bud. Stamens 5, alternating with the petals. Ovary inferior,
2-celled, rarely one cell only fertile, very rarely ovary 3-celled. Ovules
solitary in each cell, pendulous, inverted, with ventral raphe. Styles 2, free,
arising from a more or less distinctly 2-lobed disc (stylopod), rarely (*Lagoecia*)
style simple. Fruit dry, usually separating into 2 mericarps attached to the
2-parted, more rarely 2-cleft, simple, or obsolete carpophore. Pericarp ribbed
and usually traversed by oil-channels commonly situated in the furrows between
the primary ribs which as a rule enclose vascular bundles. Seeds with an adnate
testa, a horny albumen, and a small embryo with flat cotyledons. — Genera 92,
species 410. (*APIACEAE*.) (Plate 119.)
1. Fruit with a woody rind, without a free carpophore. Oil-channels wanting,
more rarely small and situated beneath the primary ribs. Seeds rather
flat on the inner face. Petals straight, rarely bent inwards at the point
and thread-shaped. Flowers in solitary or fascicled simple umbels or in
racemed false-whorls, rarely (*Hermas*) in compound umbels. Leaves undivided, lobed, or 3-parted. [Subfamily **HYDROCOTYLOIDEAE.**] . 2

2 C

Fruit with a membranous or leathery rind, rarely (tribe *Coriandreae*) with a woody one, but then oil-channels situated on the inner surface of the mericarps and seeds deeply grooved on this side. Flowers usually in compound umbels. 6

2. Fruit much compressed laterally, with a very narrow commissure and a much projecting dorsal angle. Oil-channels very narrow or wanting. Calyx-limb indistinct or shortly toothed. Petals with a straight point. [Tribe HYDROCOTYLEAE.] 3

Fruit compressed from front to back, with a broad commissure. [Tribe MULINEAE.] . . . . 4.

3. Mericarps with 5 ribs, the marginal ones contiguous. Flowers hermaphrodite. Petals valvate in bud. Leaves roundish, stipulate. — Species 15. Some are used medicinally. . . . . **Hydrocotyle** L.

Mericarps with 7—9 ribs connected by a network of veins, the marginal ribs divergent. Flowers polygamous. Petals imbricate in bud. Leaves exstipulate. — Species 20. Southern and tropical Africa. Some are used medicinally. (Under *Hydrocotyle* L.) . . . . **Centella** L.

4. Fruit slightly compressed, not winged, with faint ribs. Oil-channels more or less obvious. Calyx-teeth narrow. Petals elliptical or lanceolate, with a straight point. Herbs forming cushion-shaped tufts. Leaves 3-cleft or 3-parted, alternate. Flowers in terminal simple umbels. — Species 1. Island of Kerguelen. . . . . . . **Azorella** Lam.

Fruit much compressed, winged. Oil-channels obscure or absent. Calyx-teeth large or wanting. Leaves undivided or lobed 5

5. Wings of the fruit arising from the marginal ribs and covered with barbed prickles. Seeds not furrowed. Flowers hermaphrodite. Calyx-lobes wanting. Petals elliptical, with a straight point. Flowers in simple umbels arising at the forks of the stem. Leaves usually opposite, clothed with barbed bristles. — Species 1. Canary Islands. (Under *Bowlesia* Ruiz et Pav.) . . . . **Drusa** DC.

Wings of the fruit arising from the intermedial ribs. Fruit netted or wrinkled on the back. Seeds angular-furrowed. Flowers polygamous. Calyx-lobes broad-lanceolate, petal-like in the male flowers. Petals awl-shaped, with the point bent inwards. Flowers in compound umbels. Leaves alternate, tomentose beneath. — Species 5. South Africa (Cape Colony). . . . . **Hermas** L

6. (1.) Styles 2, surrounded by a ring-shaped disc, filiform and rather long, rarely a single style. Fruit covered with scales, prickles, or tubercles. Carpophore adnate or wanting. Oil-channels under the primary ribs, scattered, or wanting (none in the furrows). Calyx-lobes large. Petals with the point bent inwards. Flowers in umbels heads or spikes, which are simple or arranged in heads or cymes. [Subfamily **SANICULOID-EAE.**] 7

Styles 2, arising from the top of a more or less elevated disc (stylopod). Carpophore usually free. Oil-channels in general only in the furrows of the fruit. Flowers nearly always in compound umbels. [Subfamily **APIOIDEAE.**] 11

7. Ovary with 1 perfect and 1 imperfect cell, the latter empty or containing a rudimentary ovule ; in the latter case flowers dioecious and fruit with faint secondary ribs and without oil-channels. Oil-channels indistinct or wanting ; in the former case style single. [Tribe LAGOECIEAE.] 8

Ovary with 2 perfect cells and ovules. Styles 2. Flowers hermaphrodite or monoecious-polygamous. [Tribe SANICULEAE.] 9

8. Style 1. Oil-channels present. Flowers hermaphrodite, in simple umbels with pinnately divided involucral bracts. Leaves pinnatipartite. — Species 1. North-east Africa (Cyrenaica). . . . . **Lagoecia** L.

Styles 2. Oil-channels absent. Flowers dioecious, in compound umbels or in umbels arranged in heads, with undivided involucral bracts. Leaves lobed. — Species 3. South Africa (Cape Colony). Used medicinally.

Arctopus L.

9. Flowers polygamous, in umbels arranged in cymes. Ovary and fruit clothed with hooked prickles. Fruit more or less globose, without distinct ribs, but with many large and small oil-channels. — Species 2. North and South Africa and mountains of the tropics. Used medicinally.

Sanicula L.

Flowers hermaphrodite, in heads or spikes. Ovary and fruit clothed with scales or tubercles. Fruit ovoid, with several large and many small oil-channels or without distinct oil-channels. 10

10. Flowers in few-flowered heads with a 2-ranked involucre of usually 10 bracts, without bracteoles beneath the single flowers. Calyx-limb membranous. Fruit with thick and warty primary ribs. Oil-channels indistinct. Leaves undivided. — Species 8. South and Central Africa.

Alepidea Laroch.

Flowers in many-flowered heads or spikes with an involucre of several or many, usually prickly bracts, and with a bracteole under each flower. Calyx-teeth stiff. Fruit without distinct ribs, scaly. — Species 15. North and Central Africa. Some are used as vegetables or in medicine.

Eryngium L.

11. (6.) Secondary ribs between the primary ribs of the fruit distinctly developed, similar to, or larger than the primary ribs, more or less distinctly winged or beset with rows of prickles. 12

Secondary ribs slightly prominent or wanting. 23

12. Secondary ribs, at least some of them, winged and unarmed. [Tribe LASERPITIEAE.] 13

Secondary ribs not distinctly winged, but beset with prickles, more rarely with bristles or tubercles. 17

13. Fruit much compressed from front to back. Seeds flat or nearly so on the inner face. [Subtribe THAPSIINAE.] 14

Fruit scarcely or not at all compressed, broadly winged, glabrous. Oil-channels also under the primary ribs. Seeds deeply grooved on the inner face. [Subtribe ELAEOSELINAE.] 16

14. Secondary ribs with a narrow or indistinct wing. Oil-channels only under
     the secondary ribs, narrow. Petals white, slightly notched. — Species 3.
     Cape Verde Islands. Used medicinally. . . . . **Tornabenea** Parl.
   Secondary ribs with a broad wing. Petals entire. 15
15. Primary ribs very prominent. Oil-channels also under the primary ribs.
     Petals white or reddish. — Species 2. Island of Madeira. The roots
     are edible. (Including *Monizia* Lowe, under *Thapsia* L.)
                                                    Melanoselinum Hoffm.
   Primary ribs slightly prominent. Oil-channels only under the secondary
     ribs. Petals yellow. — Species 3. North Africa. Used medicinally.
                                                               Thapsia L.
16. Fruit with 4 wings, contracted at the commissure. Oil-channels distant.
     Petals narrow, yellow. — Species 5. North Africa. Used medicinally.
                                                        Elaeoselinum Koch
   Fruit with 8 wings and a broad commissure. Oil-channels nearly con-
     tiguous. Petals broad, white, — Species 1. North-west Africa (Algeria).
     (Under *Elaeoselinum* Koch) . . . . **Margotia** Boiss.
17. (12.) Albumen deeply grooved on the inner face of the seeds. [Tribe
     SCANDICINEAE, subtribe CAUCALINAE.] 18
   Albumen slightly grooved or flat on the inner face of the seeds. . . . 21
18. Albumen rolled in at the edge. Commissure narrowed. Primary ribs
     prickly. Secondary ribs with 1—3 rows of prickles. Oil-channels
     obvious. Umbels of 2—6 rays. — Species 5. North Africa and moun-
     tains of the tropics. Used medicinally . (Including *Turgenia* Hoffm.)
                                                              Caucalis L.
   Albumen flat at the edge. 19
19. Fruit with a broad commissure (plane of junction of the mericarps). Primary
     ribs covered with short bristles. Secondary ribs with 2—3 rows of
     prickles. Oil-channels large. Umbels of 5—8 rays. — Species 1.
     North Africa. (Under *Daucus* L.) . . . . . . **Orlaya** Hoffm.
   Fruit with a narrow commissure. 20
20. Secondary ribs prominent, rounded, warty. Oil-channels obscure. Umbels
     of many rays. — Species 2. North-west Africa. **Ammiopsis** Boiss.
   Secondary ribs scarcely prominent, prickly. Primary ribs ciliate. Oil-
     channels large. Umbels of 6—12 rays. — Species 9. North and South
     Africa and mountains of Central Africa. (Under *Caucalis* L.)
                                                            Torilis Adans.
21. Fruit somewhat flattened laterally and narrowed at the commissure.
     Secondary ribs clothed with bristles. Seeds slightly grooved on the
     inner face. Calyx-teeth long, awl-shaped, unequal. Petals oblong,
     white or pink. Umbels of 3—5-rays. — Species 1 (*C. Cyminum* L.).
     North Africa, also cultivated in East Africa. The fruits serve as a
     condiment and a medicament. . . . . **Cuminum** L.
   Fruit flattened from front to back. Calyx-teeth short. [Tribe
     DAUCEAE.] 22

22. Secondary ribs clothed with white bristles.   Primary ribs nearly glabrous.
     Petals white.   Umbels opposite to the leaves, with 2—4 rays. — Species
     1. North Africa.   The fruits serve as a condiment.   (Under *Daucus* L.)
     Ammodaucus Coss. & Dur
     Secondary ribs beset with one row of long prickles.   Primary ribs clothed
     with short bristles. — Species 20.   North Africa to Abyssinia ; one
     species naturalized in Tropical and South Africa.   Some species (especi-
     ally *D. Carota* L., carrot) yield vegetables, gum-resin, and medicaments.
     Daucus L.
23. (11.) Seeds very concave or marked with a deep furrow on the inner
     face.   24
     Seeds flat, slightly concave, or somewhat convex on the inner face. .   .   44
24. Flowers polygamous, the sessile hermaphrodite ones surrounded each by
     several stalked males.   Petals white.   Style long.   Fruit nearly always
     one-seeded.   Ribs indistinct.   Albumen rolled in at the edge.   [Tribe
     ECHINOPHOREAE.]   25
     Flowers of the primary umbels polygamous, but irregularly arranged, or
     hermaphrodite.   Fruit nearly always 2-seeded.   26
25. Ovary of the hermaphrodite flower adnate to the pedicels of the male,
     which subsequently form a woody cup around the fruit.   Oil-channels
     solitary in each furrow. — Species 1.   North Africa.   The root is edible.
     Echinophora L.
     Ovary of the hermaphrodite flower not adnate to the pedicels of the male ;
     no cup around the fruit.   Oil-channels 2—3 in each furrow. — Species 1.
     Abyssinia   .   .   .   .·   .   .   **Pycnocycla** Lindl.
26. Leaves undivided, entire.   Calyx not toothed.   Petals yellow or yellowish-
     green.   Fruit laterally compressed. — Species 25.   North and South
     Africa.   Some are used medicinally.   .   .   .   .   **Bupleurum** Tourn.
     Leaves, at least the lower ones, dissected.   27
27. Fruit linear or oblong.   [Tribe SCANDICINEAE, subtribe SCANDI-
     CINAE.]   28
     Fruit ovoid, globose, or biglobose.   35
28. Fruit beaked.   Oil-channels very narrow, situated in the furrows and
     under the primary ribs.   29
     Fruit not beaked.   Oil-channels usually broad.   Petals bent inwards
     and notched at the tip.   31
29. Fruit with a long beak.   Ribs obtuse.   Calyx not toothed.   Petals entire
     and not or shortly bent inwards at the tip.   Umbels of few rays. —
     Species 3.   North Africa.   Used medically. .   .   .   .   .   **Scandix** L.
     Fruit with a short beak.   30
30. Fruit cylindrical, broadened at the base, without ribs in the lower part.
     Calyx not toothed.   Petals narrow, entire and not or shortly bent
     inwards at the tip. — Species 3.   North and East Africa.   One of them,
     the chervil (*A. Cerefolium* Hoffm.) is grown as a pot-herb and also used
     medicinally.   .   .   .   .   **Anthriscus** Hoffm.

Fruit oblong, hispid, with broad and obtuse ribs.   Calyx toothed.   Petals broad, bent inwards and notched at the tip.   Involucral bracts numerous. — Species 2.   North-west Africa.   (Under *Athamantha* L.)

Tinguarra Parl.

31. Fruit without distinct ribs, oblong, somewhat flattened from front to back, clothed with long hairs.   Oil-channels solitary in the furrows, narrow ; besides two larger ones at the commissure.   Calyx-teeth awl-shaped. Petals minute, white. — Species 1.   North-west Africa.   (Under *Caucalis* L.) . . . .   **Chaetosciadium** Boiss.

Fruit with distinct ribs.   Calyx-teeth wanting. 32

32. Fruit with thread- or keel-shaped ribs.   Oil-channels thin or rather thin. Root tuberous. 33

Fruit with broad and rounded, roll-shaped ribs.   Oil-channels large, solitary in the furrows.   Root not tuberous. 34

33. Leaf-segments linear.   Umbels of 10—20 rays.   Involucre reduced to a single bract or wanting.   Involucels of many bractlets.   Oil-channels numerous. — Species 1.   North-west Africa.   (*Geocaryum* Coss. et Dur., under *Chaerophyllum* L.) . . . . .   **Conopodium** Koch

Leaf-segments lanceolate or ovate.   Umbels of 5—10 rays.   Involucre and involucels of 1—4 bracts. — Species 1.   North-west Africa.   (Including *Balansaea* Boiss. et Reut., under *Chaerophyllum* L. or *Bunium* Koch) . . . .   **Biasolettia** Koch

34. Fruit conical, clothed with bristles or short prickles.   Umbels few-flowered. — Species 1.   North-west Africa.   (Under *Chaerophyllum* L.)

Physocaulis Tausch.

Fruit cylindrical, glabrous. — Species 3.   North Africa.   One species is poisonous. . . . .   **Chaerophyllum** L.

35. (27.) Pericarp woody.   Ribs slightly prominent or obscure.   Oil-channels only at the commissure.   [Tribe CORIANDREAE.] 36

Pericarp not woody.   Oil-channels also on the back of the fruit, or all indistinct.   [Tribe SMYRNIEAE.] 37

36. Fruit biglobose, much broader than long, wrinkled, without distinct ribs. Commissure small, perforated.   Mericarps separating when ripe.   Calyx not toothed. — Species 2.   North Africa.   The fruits serve as a condiment. . . . .   **Bifora** Hoffm.

Fruit ovoid or globose, not broader than long, with wavy ribs.   Commissure large, not perforated.   Mericarps not separating.   Calyx toothed. — Species 1   (*C. sativum* L.).   North Africa, also cultivated and naturalized in Central Africa.   The fruits are used as a condiment and for preparing an aromatic oil. . . . .   **Coriandrum** L.

37. Pericarp much thickened : corky, spongy, or blistery.   Ribs broad, more or less roll-shaped, sometimes confluent. 38

Pericarp not much thickened.   Ribs narrow, thread-shaped, sometimes obscure.   Fruit laterally compressed, with a narrow commissure, more or less biglobose. 41

38. Ribs of the fruit confluent ; furrows hardly perceptible. Fruit ovoid, glabrous or hairy. Oil-channels numerous. Albumen rolled inwards. Calyx not toothed. Petals yellow. Leaf-segments linear. — Species 3. North-west Africa. . . . . **Cachrys** L.

Ribs of the fruit separated ; furrows distinctly visible. Calyx toothed. 39

39. Ribs of the fruit broad and rounded, roll-shaped ; furrows very narrow, each with several oil-channels. Fruit slightly or not compressed, hairy. Albumen curved. Petals white. Leaf-segments broad. — Species 2. North-west Africa. . . . . **Magydaris** Koch

Ribs of the fruit slender, more or less thread-shaped ; furrows not very narrow. Albumen rolled inwards. Leaf-segments narrow . . . 40

40. Fruit covered with blisters, broad-cordate, laterally much compressed. Oil-channels 1—3 to each furrow. Seeds loosely enclosed by the pericarp. Petals white. Leaf-segments oblong. — Species 1. East Africa.

Trachydium Link

Fruit smooth or covered with tubercles or hairs. Oil-channels numerous. Petals yellow. Leaf-segments linear. — Species 3. North-west Africa. Used medicinally. . . . . **Hippomarathrum** Lindl.

41. Oil-channels replaced by a continuous oil-layer. Fruit ovoid. Pericarp thick. Ribs thick, wavy or crenate. Albumen curved. Calyx not toothed. Petals white, shortly inflexed. — Species 2. North Africa, Abyssinia, and South Africa. Poisonous and used medicinally. " Hemlock " . . . . **Conium** L.

Oil-channels separated. Fruit cordate. Pericarp thin. Ribs thin. Petals long inflexed. 42

42. Oil-channels solitary in the furrows. Albumen curved. Calyx toothed. Petals white. — Species 1. North Africa. **Physospermum** Cuss.

Oil-channels 2 or more in each furrow. Root tuberous. 43

43. Oil-channels 2—3 in each furrow. Albumen curved. Calyx not toothed. Petals white. Involucre wanting. — Species 1. North-east Africa (Cyrenaica). (Under *Conopodium* Koch). . . . . **Scaligeria** DC.

Oil-channels numerous. Albumen rolled inwards. Petals yellow. — Species 2. North Africa. They yield vegetables and medicaments.

Smyrnium L.

44. (23.) Marginal ribs of the mericarps much more prominent than the dorsal and more or less distinctly winged. Mericarps and seeds much compressed from front to back. [Tribe PEUCEDANEAE.] 45

Marginal ribs of the mericarps similar to the dorsal. Mericarps and seeds slightly or not compressed. [Tribe AMMINEAE.] 57

45. Nerves (vascular bundles) of the marginal ribs next to the edge of the mericarps, distant from the seed. 46

Nerves of the marginal ribs situated at their base near the seed. . . 52

46. Marginal wings of the mericarps much thickened at the edge. . . . 47

Marginal wings of the mericarps slightly or not thickened at the edge or not distinctly developed. 50

47. Mericarps without dorsal ribs. Oil-channels only in the marginal ribs. Petals white. — Species 1. South Africa. (*Pappea* Sond. & Harv.)

                                           Choritaenia Benth. & Hook.

  Mericarps with filiform dorsal ribs. Oil-channels also on the back of the mericarps. 48

48. Thickened margin of the mericarps gibbous. Oil-channels very thin. Calyx toothed. Petals white, 2-cleft. — Species 2. North Africa. They yield vegetables and medicaments. . . . . **Tordylium** L.

  Thickened margin of the mericarps slightly uneven. Oil-channels distinctly developed. 49

49. Marginal wings of the mericarps traversed lengthwise by a broad oil-channel. Petals yellow, turned or rolled inwards at the top. — Species 7. East and North Africa. . . . . **Malabaila** Hoffm.

  Marginal wings of the mericarps not traversed by an oil-channel. Petals white, hairy. — Species 1. North-east Africa (Egypt). (Under *Heracleum* L.) . . . . **Zozimia** Hoffm.

50. Oil-channels not extending to the base of the mericarps, usually ending at the middle in a club-shaped swelling, solitary in the furrows. Dorsal ribs slightly prominent. Marginal wings membranous. Calyx toothed. Petals deeply emarginate, usually white. Involucels of many bractlets. — Species 2. North Africa and Abyssinia. They yield edible roots, fodder, and medicaments. . . . . **Heracleum** L.

  Oil-channels, at least some of them, extending to the base of the fruit. Calyx rarely toothed. Petals slightly or not emarginate, yellow greenish or reddish. 51

51. Leaves once pinnatisect. Flowers mostly hermaphrodite, only those of the uppermost lateral umbels male. Petals broad, much rolled in. Marginal wings of the mericarps membranous. Oil-channels solitary in the furrows, rarely in pairs. — Species 2. One growing wild in South Africa, the other cultivated in North Africa. Root edible. " Parsnip." (Under *Peucedanum* L.) . . . . **Pastinaca** L.

  Leaves repeatedly pinnatisect. Flowers polygamous, those of the lateral umbels male. Petals narrow, shortly bent inwards. Disc broad. Marginal wings of the mericarps thickish or indistinct. — Species 10. North and East Africa. Several species yield a gum-resin (African ammoniacum) used industrially and medicinally, others serve as vegetables or as ornamental plants. . . . . **Ferula** L.

52. (45.) Dorsal ribs of the mericarps very prominent. Marginal ribs more or less thickened. Oil-channels solitary in each rib and solitary or wanting in the furrows. Umbels opposite to the leaves, of few rays. Petals white. — Species 4. North and South Africa. Some have edible roots. (*Krubera* Hoffm., including *Sclerosciadium* Koch). **Capnophyllum** Gaertn.

  Dorsal ribs of the mericarps slightly prominent, more or less filiform. . 53

53. Marginal ribs of the mericarps thickened, corky. Oil-channels solitary in the furrows. Calyx toothed. 54
    Marginal ribs of the mericarps not thickened, closely contiguous. . . 55
54. Petals yellow. Leaf-segments broad. — Species 1. Canary Islands.
    Astydamia DC.
    Petals white. Leaf-segments narrow. — Species 1. Egypt. **Ducrosia** Boiss.
55. Oil-channels numerous. Marginal wings thick. Disc broad. Petals yellow, not or shortly bent inwards. Flowers polygamous, in the lateral umbels male. — Species 1. North Africa. (Under *Ferula* L.)
    Ferulago Koch
    Oil-channels 1—3 in each furrow. Petals much bent or rolled inwards. Flowers mostly hermaphrodite, only those of the uppermost lateral umbels sometimes male. 56
56. Fruit moderately compressed, with a narrow marginal wing. Oil-channels solitary in the furrows. Calyx not toothed. Petals broad and rolled inwards at the tip, yellow. Umbels without an involucre. — Species 1. (*A. graveolens* L., dill). North Africa, also cultivated and naturalized in Central and South Africa. Used as a pot-herb. (Under *Peucedanum* L.) . . . . **Anethum** Tourn.
    Fruit much compressed, with a membranous, usually broad marginal wing. Petals narrowed and much bent inwards at the tip. — Species 50. Some of them have edible roots or are used in medicine. (Including *Bubon* L., *Imperatoria* Tourn., and *Lefeburia* A. Rich.) . . . **Peucedanum** L.
57. (44.) Fruit compressed from front to back or not compressed ; commissure (plane of junction of the mericarps) broad. Ribs usually prominent : wing-like, keeled, or broad, more rarely filiform. [Subtribe SESELINAE.] 58
    Fruit compressed laterally ; commissure more or less narrowed. Ribs usually slender, filiform, rarely keel- or wing-like. [Subtribe CARINAE.] 73
58. Ribs of the fruit very prominent, keel- or wing-like. 59
    Ribs of the fruit slightly prominent, filiform or broad. 69
59. Ribs wing-like. 60
    Ribs keel- or ridge-like. 62
60. Oil-channels numerous. Leaves 2—5 times pinnately dissected. — Species 1. North Africa. " Lovage." (Under *Meum* Jacq.) **Ligusticum** L.
    Oil-channels solitary in the furrows. 61
61. Marginal wings of the fruit thin. Dorsal wings either corky or partly wing-like, partly filiform. Mericarps usually unequal. Calyx toothed. — Species 10. South Africa. Some of them have edible roots. (Including *Stenosemis* E. Mey.) (Plate 119.)
    Annesorrhiza Cham. & Schlechtd.
    Marginal wings of the fruit thick. All wings equal, membranous or spongy. Mericarps equal. Leaves 2—3 times pinnately dissected. — Species 2. South Africa. (Under *Selinum* L.) . . . . . . **Cnidium** Cuss.

62. Oil-channels numerous, crowded around the seed. Pericarp thickened, spongy. Fruit egg-shaped. Calyx toothed. Petals narrowed and rolled in at the tip, white. Undershrubs. Leaves fleshy, with narrow segments. Involucre and involucels of many bracts. — Species 1. North Africa. Used as a pot-herb. " Samphire." **Crithmum** Tourn.
Oil-channels solitary in the furrows, rarely (*Seseli*) accompanied by a second channel in each furrow or one under each rib. 63

63. Calyx toothed. Petals white or reddish. Involucel present . . . 64
Calyx not toothed. 67

64. Stem woody, shrubby. Petals elliptical, entire, with an inflexed point. Fruit oblong, not compressed, glabrous. Disc depressed. Leaves once or twice dissected. — Species 2. South Africa.
Polemannia Eckl. & Zeyh.
Stem herbaceous. 65

65. Petals lanceolate or elliptical. Disc biglobose. Fruit narrowly bottle-shaped, compressed from front to back, hairy. Involucre present. Leaves thrice dissected. — Species 2. Canary Islands. **Todaroa** Parl.
Petals broad-cordate. Disc conical or flattened. Fruit oblong or oval. 66

66. Seeds concave on the inner face. Fruit cylindrical, with warty or bristly ribs. Oil-channels solitary in the furrows. Disc conical. Styles long, with broad stigmas. Flowers hispid. Involucre present. Leaves twice pinnatisect, with broad leathery segments. — Species 3. Central Africa. . . . . **Physotrichia** Hiern
Seeds flat on the inner face. Leaves, as a rule, repeatedly pinnatisect and with narrow segments. — Species 7. North and South Africa. Some are used in medicine. (Including *Libanotis* Crantz) . . **Seseli** L.

67. Involucels and involucre wanting. Petals yellow. Disc conical. Pericarp not essentially thickened. Leaves with linear segments. — Species 2. North Africa and Abyssinia, one species also naturalized in other regions. They yield vegetables, condiments, perfumes, and medicaments, and serve also as ornamental plants. " Fennel ". . . **Foeniculum** L.
Involucels of a few bracts. Petals white or greenish-white. Pericarp thickened. Leaves with oblong, lanceolate, or elliptical segments. . 68

68. Involucre of a few bracts. Petals oblong, greenish-white. Disc conical. Fruit oblong; furrows narrow. — Species 1. Madagascar. Used medicinally. . . . . **Phellolophium** Bak.
Involucre absent. Petals obovate, white. Disc flattened. Fruit ovoid; furrows broad. — Species 1. North-west Africa. Poisonous and used medicinally. " Fools parsley." . . . . **Aethusa** L.

69. (58.) Ribs of the fruit broad and rounded. Carpophore none. Oil-channels solitary in the furrows. Calyx-teeth large. Petals obovate, white. Involucels of many bracts. — Species 10. North and South Africa. Some are poisonous or used in medicine. . . **Oenanthe** L.
Ribs of the fruit slender, filiform. Carpophore present. 70

70. Oil-channels numerous, scattered. Fruit linear-oblong. Pericarp not considerably thickened. Seeds somewhat grooved on the inner face. Calyx-teeth short. Petals yellow. Involucre and involucels of many bracts. Leaves with broad segments. — Species 1. North Africa. (*Brignolia* Bertol.) . . . . **Kundmannia** Scop.
Oil-channels solitary in the furrows, more rarely accompanied by a second in each furrow or one under each rib. Petals white or reddish. . . 71

71. Seeds flat on the inner face. Calyx toothed. Petals broad-cordate. Disc depressed. (See 66.) . . . . **Seseli** L.
Seeds grooved on the inner face. Fruit oblong, hairy. Disc conical. Involucre present. Leaves thrice dissected. 72

72. Oil-channels in the furrows and under the ribs of the fruit. Seeds with a keel in the middle of the groove on the inner face. Calyx toothed. — Species 4. North Africa. Used medicinally. . . **Athamanta** L.
Oil-channels only in the furrows. Calyx not toothed. Rays of the umbels thickened. — Species 2. East Africa. . . **Diplolophium** Turcz.

73. (57.) Leaves undivided, entire, rarely (*Heteromorpha*) toothed to dissected, and then some ribs of the fruit wing-like. 74
Leaves, at least some of them, toothed to dissected. Ribs of the fruit filiform, rarely keeled but not wing-like. 77

74. Flowers in heads. Calyx toothed. Petals greenish-white. Carpophore none ; mericarps closely cohering. Ribs thickened, corky. Oil-channels solitary in each furrow, faint or obscure. — Species 2. Northwest Africa. . . . . **Hohenackeria** Fisch. & Mey.
Flowers in compound umbels. Petals yellow or yellowish-green. Carpophore free. 75

75. Calyx toothed. Mericarps unequal, one 2-winged, the other 3-winged. Oil-channels solitary in the furrows. Shrubs or trees. — Species 3. Central and South Africa. (*Franchetella* O. Ktze.).
Heteromorpha Cham. et Schlechtd.
Calyx not toothed. Mericarps and ribs equal. 76

76. Petals much inflexed and 2-lobed at the tip. Disc conical, crenate. Fruit oblong, with thick and very prominent ribs. Oil-channels solitary in each furrow. Undershrubs. Leaves stalked, cordate-orbicular, leathery. Umbels of few rays, involucrate. — Species 1. Island of Socotra.
Nirarathamnus Balf.
Petals rolled in and entire or slightly notched at the tip. Disc flat, entire. Leaves usually sessile. (See 26.) . . . . . **Bupleurum** Tourn.

77. Oil-channels solitary under each rib, none in the furrows. Calyx toothed. Petals white, with a long inflexed point. Involucre and involucels of many bracts. — Species 7. South Africa. **Lichtensteinia** Cham. & Schlechtd.
Oil-channels in the furrows, sometimes also under the ribs. 78

78. Fruit linear or oblong, at least twice as long as broad. Ribs slender. Petals white or reddish. 79
Fruit ovoid, globose, or biglobose. 83

79. Fruit linear or linear-oblong. Oil-channels solitary in the furrows. Disc broadened at the base, with a wavy margin. Calyx-teeth distinctly developed. Petals white, 3—5-nerved, notched. Involucre and involucels present. — Species 1. North Africa. Used medicinally.
Falcaria Host.

Fruit oblong. Calyx-teeth minute or wanting. 80

80. Mericarps with 5 ribs at the back and near the margin and 2 smaller ones on the inner face. Oil-channels solitary in the furrows and under the ribs, very narrow. Disc reduced to a swelling of the base of the styles. Umbels panicled. Involucre wanting. Involucels of few bracts. — Species 1. West Africa (Cameroons). (*Lereschia* Boiss., under *Anthriscus* L.) . . . . **Cryptotaenia** DC.

Mericarps with 5 ribs only. Oil-channels only in the furrows. Disc broadened at the base, with a wavy margin. Umbels terminal and lateral. 81

81. Involucre of many large dissected bracts. Petals unequally 2-lobed. Oil-channels solitary in the furrows. — Species 5. North and Central Africa. Used medicinally ; one species has edible roots. . **Ammi** L.

Involucre of usually few entire bracts or wanting. Petals equally notched. 82

82. Root-stock tuberous. Oil-channels 1—3 in each furrow. Embryo with a single cotyledon. — Species 6. North Africa. The tubers are edible. (Including *Diaphycarpus* Calestani, partly under *Carum* L.) **Bunium** L.

Root-stock not tuberous. Oil-channels solitary in each furrow. Embryo with 2 cotyledons. — Species 7. North Africa, Abyssinia, Madagascar, and South Africa; one species (*C. Carvi* L., caraway) also cultivated elsewhere. The fruits of this species are used as a condiment and for preparing an aromatic oil ; eaten in large quantities they are poisonous. Other species yield edible roots or medicaments. (Including *Selinopsis* Coss. et Dur., partly under *Bunium* L.) . . . . **Carum** L.

83. Oil-channels numerous, narrow. Ribs filiform. Herbs or undershrubs. Leaves dissected or the lower lobed. 84

Oil-channels solitary in each furrow, rarely (*Rhyticarpus*) 3, large, but then shrubs and upper leaves undivided. 85

84. Calyx toothed. Petals white. Involucre and involucels large, persistent. — Species 7. Central and South Africa and Egypt. Some are used as vegetables. (Including *Berula* Koch) . . . . **Sium** L.

Calyx not toothed. Involucre and involucels usually wanting. — Species 25. The fruits of *P. anisum* L., anise, serve as a condiment ; other species are used in medicine. (Including *Reutera* Boiss.) **Pimpinella** L.

85. Pericarp densely bristly or warty. Ribs filiform. 86

Pericarp smooth or wrinkled, not hairy. 87

86. Calyx toothed. Petals deeply notched, white. Fruit tubercled upon the ribs, not hairy. Herbs. Leaves twice or thrice pinnately dissected with very narrow segments. — Species 7. South and North Africa and

Island of Socotra ; one species also naturalized in the Mascarene Islands. Some species yield condiments. (*Tragiopsis* Pomel, under *Carum* L. or *Ptychotis* L.) . . . . **Trachypermum** Link

Calyx entire. Petals not notched, white or greenish. Undershrubs. Radical leaves once or twice pinnately dissected, cauline reduced to the sheath. Umbels of few rays. — Species 10. North and South Africa. (*Deverra* DC.) . . . . **Pituranthos** Viv.

87. Carpophore entire or shortly cleft at the top. Ribs very prominent. Oil-channels large. Calyx not or obscurely toothed. Petals greenish-white, straight or shortly inflexed at the tip. Involucre of 1—3 bracts or wanting. — Species 7. One of them (*A. graveolens* L., celery) is used as a pot-herb, as a salad, or in medicine. (Including *Helosciadium* Koch) . . . . **Apium** L.
Carpophore split down to the middle or beyond. 88

88. Oil-channels extending down to the middle of the fruit and ending there in a club-shaped swelling. Calyx entire. Petals white, broadly inflexed and deeply notched at the tip. Leaves with broad segments. — Species 1. North Africa. Used medicinally. . . . . . **Sison** L.
Oil-channels extending down to the base of the fruit. Calyx toothed, more rarely entire, but then petals yellow and not notched. . . . 89

89. Calyx not or obscurely toothed. Petals yellow, yellowish-green, or somewhat reddish, much inflexed at the tip. 90
Calyx distinctly toothed. 91

90. Ribs of the fruit prominent, filiform. Oil-channels broad. Leaves 2—3 times pinnately dissected. — Species 2. North Africa ; also naturalized in tropical and South Africa. One species (*P. sativum* Hoffm., parsley) is used as a pot-herb. (Under *Apium* L. or *Carum* L.).

Petroselinum Hoffm.

Ribs of the fruit scarcely prominent or indistinct. Oil-channels narrow. Leaves 4-times pinnately dissected. — Species 1. North Africa and Abyssinia. (Under *Carum* L.) . . . . . **Ridolfia** Moris.

91. Ribs of the fruit very prominent. Oil-channels narrow. Petals shortly inflexed at the tip, white or greenish. Umbels involucrate. — Species 3. South Africa, St. Helena, and Canary Islands. One species is used for preparing an intoxicating drink. (*Glia* Sond., under *Lichtensteinia* Cham. & Schlechtd.) . . . . **Ruthea** Bolle
Ribs of the fruit slightly prominent. Petals much inflexed at the tip, rarely shortly inflexed, but then red. 92

92. Mericarp with 9 faint ribs. Petals dark-red, oblong, shortly inflexed at the tip. — Species 1. Madagascar. . . . . . **Anisopoda** Bak.
Mericarps with 5 filiform ribs. Petals white or yellow, much inflexed at the tip. 93

93. Petals white, notched, the terminal point proceeding from a transverse fold beneath the notch. Herbs. Umbels without an involucre. —

Species 4. North and South Africa. (Under *Carum* L., *Petroselinum* Hoffm., or *Seseli* L.) . . . . **Ptychotis** Koch

Petals yellow, entire. Undershrubs or shrubs. — Species 3. South Africa (Cape Colony). . . . . **Rhyticarpus** Sond.

FAMILY 187. CORNACEAE

Shrubs or trees. Leaves undivided, without stipules. Flowers regular. Calyx entire or toothed. Petals 4-5, free or cohering at the base. Stamens as many as the petals. Ovary inferior, 2—4-celled, with 1 pendulous ovule in each cell. Fruit a drupe. Seeds albuminous; embryo long. — Genera 4, species 6. Tropical and South Africa.

1. Ovary 4-celled. Micropyle turned outwards. Style simple; stigma 4-parted. Anthers oval. Petals broad. Flowers 4-merous, hermaphrodite, in cymose panicles. Leaves opposite, toothed. — Species 1. South Africa. Yields timber. [Subfamily **CURTISIOIDEAE**.]
   Curtisia Ait.

   Ovary 2—3-celled. Micropyle turned inwards. Style and stigma simple, or styles 2—3. Flowers 4-merous, but unisexual, or 5-merous. [Subfamily **CORNOIDEAE**.] 2

2. Petals imbricate in bud. Filaments short, thread-shaped. Flowers hermaphrodite, 5-merous, in racemes sometimes arranged in panicles. — Species 3. Madagascar. [Tribe GRISELINIEAE.]
   Melanophylla Bak.

   Petals valvate in bud. Flowers unisexual, 4-merous. [Tribe CORNEAE.] 3

3. Style simple. Filaments thread-shaped. Anthers ovate. Petals ovate. Fruit with a 2-celled stone. Flowers in umbel-like cymes. Leaves opposite. — Species 1. Equatorial East Africa (Kilimandjaro).
   Cornus L.

   Styles or sessile stigmas 2. Filaments very short, rather thick. Anthers oblong. Petals oblong. Fruit with two 1-celled stones. Flowers in panicles. Leaves alternate. — Species 1. Madagascar.
   Kaliphora Hook. fil.

SUBCLASS METACHLAMYDEAE

(*SYMPETALAE*)

ORDER ERICALES

FAMILY 188. CLETHRACEAE

Low trees. Leaves alternate, undivided. Flowers in terminal racemes or panicles, without bracteoles, regular, hermaphrodite. Calyx 5-parted, imbricate in bud, persistent. Petals 5, free, hypogynous, deciduous. Stamens 10, hypogynous. Anthers turned inwards, shortly beaked at the base, opening by

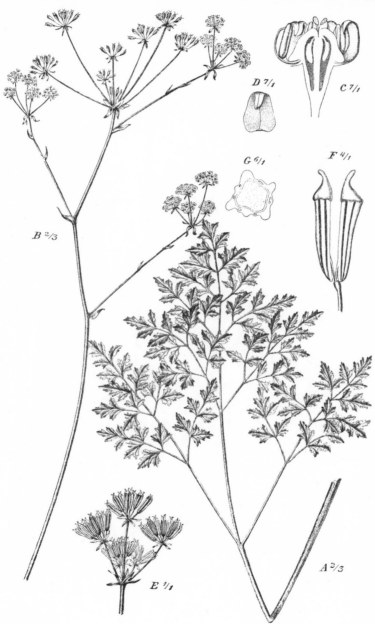

J. Fleischmann del.

Annesorrhiza capensis Cham. & Schlechtd.

A Leaf. *B* Inflorescence. *C* Flower cut lengthwise. *D* Petal. *E* Group of fruits. *F* Fruit. *G* Cross-section of a mericarp.

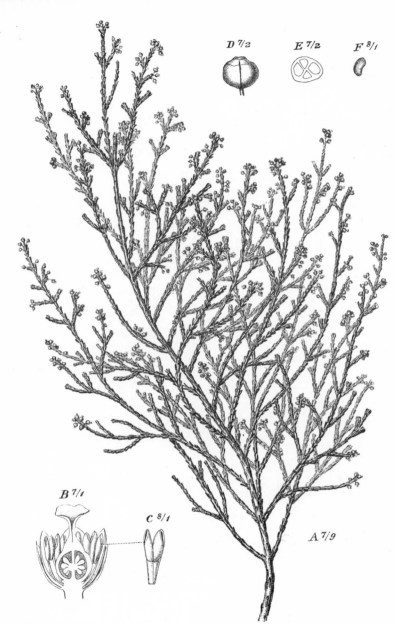

J. Fleischmann del

Philippia Chamissonis Klotzsch

A Flowering branch. *B* Flower cut lengthwise. *C* Anther. *D* Fruit. *E* Fruit cut across. *F* Seed.

two short slits at the top ; pollen-grains separate. Disc none. Ovary superior, 3-celled. Ovules numerous, axile, inverted. Style 3-cleft at the top. Fruit a loculicidal capsule. Seeds with a lax testa, a fleshy albumen, and a short embryo. (Under *ERICACEAE*.)

Genus 1, species 1. Island of Madeira. Yields wood especially used for making walking-sticks, and serves as an ornamental plant.

Clethra L.

FAMILY 189. ERICACEAE

Undershrubs, shrubs, or trees. Leaves undivided, usually narrow. Flowers solitary or in umbels racemes or panicles, regular or nearly so, hermaphrodite. Calyx 4—5-cleft or -parted, persistent. Petals united below, with imbricate or contorted aestivation. Stamens 3—15, usually twice as many as the petals, free from the corolla or almost so, rarely (*Ficalhoa*) distinctly inserted on the corolla-tube. Anthers turned inwards, usually opening towards the top ; pollen-grains united in groups of four. Disc more or less distinctly developed. Ovary usually superior, 1—5-celled. Ovules axile or solitary, inverted or almost so. Style simple. Seeds with copious albumen. — Genera 17, species 720. (Including *VACCINIACEAE*.) (Plate 120.)

1. Ovary inferior, adnate to the calyx-tube. Corolla deciduous. Stamens 8—10. Fruit a many-seeded berry. — Species 8. Azores, Madeira, East Africa to Transvaal, and Madagascar. Some have edible fruits. [Subfamily **VACCINIOIDEAE,** tribe VACCINIEAE.]   **Vaccinium** L.
   Ovary superior, free from the calyx, but sometimes (*Salaxis*) adnate to the corolla-tube at the base.   2
2. Flowers 5-merous, rarely 6-merous. Corolla deciduous. Stamens 10—15 inserted at the base of the corolla. Ovules numerous in each ovary-cell. Fruit a capsule without a persistent central column, or a berry. Trees or tall shrubs. Leaves alternate or subopposite, oblong or lanceolate. Flowers in racemes or panicles. [Subfamily **ARBUTOIDEAE.**]   3
   Flowers 4-merous, rarely 2—3-merous, very rarely (*Erica*) 5-merous, but then low shrubs with fascicled flowers. Corolla usually persistent. Stamens 3—8, rarely 10—12. Fruit a capsule, usually with a persistent central column, or an achene. Undershrubs or mostly low shrubs, very rarely trees.   5
3. Anthers attached below the apex, provided with two spur-like appendages. Filaments broadened at the base. Disc distinctly developed. Ovules axile. Fruit a mealy berry with a warty skin. — Species 2. North Africa. They yield tanning materials, medicaments, and edible fruits, and serve as ornamental plants. " Strawberry-tree." [Tribe ARBUTEAE.] . . . .   **Arbutus** L.
   Anthers attached above the base, without appendages. Disc indistinct. Ovules subbasal. Fruit a loculicidal capsule. [Tribe ANDROMEDEAE.]   4

4. Corolla shortly urn-shaped, deeply 5-lobed. Stamens 15, in groups of three, inserted in the corolla-tube. Filaments glabrous. Stigma finally 5-parted. Seeds ovoid. Trees. Leaves serrate. — Species 1. Southern West Africa (Angola). . . . . . **Ficalhoa** Hiern

    Corolla tubular or funnel-shaped, 5—6-toothed. Stamens 10—12, inserted singly at the base of the corolla-tube. Filaments hairy. Stigma entire. Seeds oblong. Leaves entire. — Species 7. Tropics. Some of them are poisonous or yield wood and medicaments. . . . **Agauria** DC.

5. Fruit dehiscing septicidally, many-seeded. Corolla shortly toothed, deciduous. Stamens 8. Anthers longer than the filaments, without appendages, opening by terminal pores. Ovary-cells many-ovuled. Small shrubs. Leaves alternate, elliptical. Flowers in terminal racemes. — Species 1. Azores. Used as an ornamental plant. [Subfamily **RHODODENDROIDEAE**, tribe PHYLLODOCEAE.]
                                                    Daboecia Don

    Fruit dehiscing loculicidally or indehiscent, rarely septicidal, but then few-seeded and enveloped by the persistent corolla. Corolla usually persistent after the time of flowering. Leaves usually whorled and linear. [Subfamily **ERICOIDEAE**.] 6

6. Ovary with a single ovule in each cell, rarely with several ovules, but then 1—2-celled. [Tribe SALAXIDEAE.] 7
    Ovary with 2 or more ovules in each of its 3—8 cells. [Tribe ERICEAE.] 12

7. Stigma large, cupular or discoid. Bracteoles rudimentary or wanting. Corolla-lobes 4 8
    Stigma small, capitate or truncate. Bracts and bracteoles usually 3. . 10

8. Style short, included in the corolla-tube. Stamens 6—8. Calyx unequally 4-cleft or 4-parted. — Species 15. South Africa. (Including *Coccosperma* Klotzsch, *Lagenocarpus* Klotzsch, and *Lepterica* N. E. Brown).
                                                Salaxis Salisb.

    Style long, exserted. Stamens 3—5. Calyx 3—4-toothed or -cleft. . 9

9. Anthers much exserted. Calyx 4-toothed. Bract 1. — Species 1. South Africa. (Under *Syndesmanthus* Klotzsch). . **Codonostigma** Klotzsch
    Anthers included or slightly exserted. Bracts none. — Species 20. South Africa. (Including *Coilostigma* Klotzsch). . . **Scyphogyne** Brongn.

10. Corolla 2-lobed. Calyx 2-lobed or 4-toothed. Stamens 4. — Species 9. South Africa. (Including *Aniserica* N. E. Brown)
                                      Sympieza Lichtenst.

    Corolla 4-lobed. Calyx 4-toothed to 4-parted. 11

11. Calyx shortly toothed, usually thickened. Stamens 3—4. Ovary 1—2-celled. — Species 50. South Africa. (Including *Anomalanthus* Klotzsch and *Syndesmanthus* Klotzsch) . . **Simochilus** Hook. & Benth.
    Calyx divided to the middle or beyond. Stamens 4—8. — Species 40. South Africa. (Including *Acrostemon* Klotzsch, *Eremiopsis* N. E. Brown, *Grisebachia* Klotzsch, *Hexastemon* Klotzsch, *Platycalyx* N. E. Brown, *Thamnus* Klotzsch, and *Thoracosperma* Klotzsch). . **Eremia** Don

12. (6.) Stamens 4. Fruit few-seeded, loculicidal. 13
    Stamens 8, very rarely 6, 7, 10, or 12. 14
13. Calyx-lobes unequal, one of them somewhat larger than the others. Disc
    distinctly developed. Bracts and bracteoles none. — Species 6. Tropi-
    cal and South Africa. . . . .   **Ericinella** Klotzsch
    Calyx-lobes equal. Disc rudimentary. Bracts and bracteoles 3. — Species
    30. Tropical and South Africa. . . . . . .   **Blaeria** L.
14. Flowers with 4 bracts and bracteoles. Calyx corolla-like, 4-parted neaɪly
    to the base, slightly exceeding the deeply 4-cleft corolla. Anthers
    spurred, opening by longitudinal slits. Fruit dehiscing septicidally,
    few-seeded. — Species 1 (C. *vulgaris* Salisb., ling). North-west
    Africa (Morocco and Azores). Yields tanning and dyeing materials,
    medicaments, and food for bees. . . . . . .   **Calluna** Salisb.
    Flowers with 1—3 bracts and bracteoles or without any. Fruit dehiscing
    loculicidally, usually many-seeded. 15
15. Calyx-lobes unequal, the lowest larger than the others. Bracts and
    bracteoles none. Disc rudimentary. Stigma broad. Flowers terminal.
    — Species 45. Tropical and South Africa. Some are used medicinally.
    (Plate 120.) . . . .   **Philippia** Klotzsch
    Calyx-lobes equal. Bracts and bracteoles nearly always present. Disc
    usually distinctly developed. 16
16. Calyx much longer than the corolla, two of the segments including the
    other two. Anthers opening by loculicidal slits. — Species 1. South
    Africa (Cape Colony). (Under *Erica* L.). . . . **Macnabia** Benth.
    Calyx not much longer, usually shorter than the corolla. — Species 480.
    South Africa, East Africa to Comoro Islands, and North Africa. Many
    species are used as ornamental plants, some yield wood or dyes. (In-
    cluding *Pentapera* Klotzsch). " Heath." . . . . . . **Erica** L.

ORDER PRIMULALES

FAMILY 190. MYRSINACEAE

Trees or shrubs, rarely (*Afrardisia*) herbs. Leaves alternate, undivided,
gland-dotted, without stipules. Flowers in racemes panicles umbels or heads,
regular, 4—5-, very rarely 6—7-merous. Petals white or red, rarely yellow or
green, usually united below. Stamens as many as the petals, opposite to them,
inserted on the corolla. Anthers opening inwards, more rarely near the apex.
Ovary superior, rarely (*Maesa*) half-inferior, 1-celled, with a free central, usually
globular placenta. Ovules several or many, inverted or half-inverted. Style
simple or wanting ; stigma entire or lobed. Fruit a berry, a drupe, or a nut.
Seeds with copious albumen. Embryo with a long radicle and small cotyledons.
— Genera 10, species 130. (Plate 121.)

1. Ovary inferior or half-inferior. Ovules seated upon the surface of the
   placenta. Fruit several-seeded. Petals united below, white. Stigma
   broadened. Shrubs. Flowers in racemes or panicles. — Species 10.

2 D

Tropical and South Africa. Some are used medicinally. (Plate 121.)
[Subfamily **MAESOIDEAE**.] . . . . **Maesa** Forsk.
Ovary superior. Ovules sunk into the placenta. Fruit one-seeded.
[Subfamily **MYRSINOIDEAE**.] 2

2. Ovules in several rows. Petals free, pink. Flowers hermaphrodite,
   5-merous, in short racemes. Stigma punctiform. Filaments long. —
   Species 1. Madeira and Canary Islands. (Under *Ardisia* Swartz or
   Myrsine L.) [Tribe ARDISIEAE.] . . . . **Heberdenia** Banks
   Ovules in a single row. Petals united below, more rarely free, but then
   flowers dioecious and stigma peltate. [Tribe MYRSINEAE.] . . 3

3. Ovules numerous, about ten. Anthers opening by a single pore at the
   apex. Sepals unequal-sided. Petals united below. Filaments short.
   Stigma punctiform. Trees. Flowers in panicles, dioecious, 5-merous.
   — Species 6. Madagascar. (Under *Ardisia* Swartz). **Monoporus** A.DC.
   Ovules few. Anthers opening by two slits or pores. . . . . . . 4.

4. Stigma punctiform. Style thin. Flowers hermaphrodite, 5—7-merous.
   Petals united below. Filaments short, free or nearly so. 5
   Stigma more or less dilated. Style thick. 6

5. Sepals and petals with imbricate, not contorted aestivation ; petals white,
   equal-sided. Trees or tall shrubs. Leaves entire. Flowers sessile
   or nearly so, in heads or umbels arising from lateral dwarf-shoots. —
   Species 1. Madeira and Canary Islands. (Under *Myrsine* L.)
                                           Pleiomeris A. DC.

   Sepals and petals with contorted aestivation ; petals red, unequal-sided.
   Herbs, undershrubs, or shrubs. Flowers in axillary umbels or racemes,
   5-merous. — Species 10. West Africa. (Under *Ardisia* Swartz).
                                           Afrardisia Mez

6. Petals free or nearly so. Filaments usually free. Flowers unisexual. —
   Species 25. Tropical and South-east Africa. Some are used medicinally.
   (*Samara* L., *Pattara* Adans.) . . . . . . **Embelia** Burm.
   Petals obviously united below. 7

7. Filaments wanting. 8
   Filaments distinctly developed, more or less united. Style present. . 9

8. Style wanting. Flowers in umbels upon sometimes imperceptible dwarf-
   shoots. — Species 10. Tropical and South Africa. (Under *Myrsine* L.)
                                           Rapanea Aubl.

   Style present. Flowers in axillary racemes or panicles. — Species 10.
   Mascarene Islands and Madagascar. (Under *Ardisia* Swartz or *Icacorea*
   Aubl.) . . . . **Badula** Juss.

9. Flowers dioecious, in umbels arising from dwarf-shoots. Petals imbricate
   in bud. Anthers free. — Species 2. Tropical and South Africa and
   Azores. They yield timber and are used as ornamental, medicinal, or
   fodder plants. . . . . **Myrsine** L.
   Flowers hermaphrodite, in axillary umbels racemes or panicles. — Species
   55. Madagascar and neighbouring islands. . **Oncostemon** A. Juss.

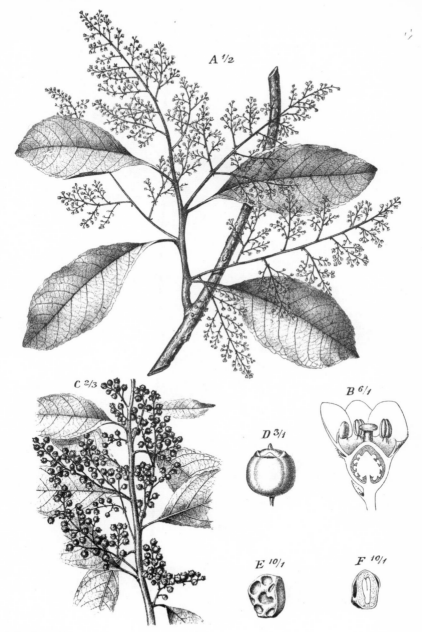

A ½

C ⅔

D ³/₁

B ⁶/₁

E ¹⁰/₁

F ¹⁰/₁

J. Fleischmann del.

Maesa lanceolata Forsk.

A Flowering branch.　*B* Flower cut lengthwise.　*C* Fruiting branch.　*D* Fruit.　*E* Seed.　*F* Seed cut lengthwise.

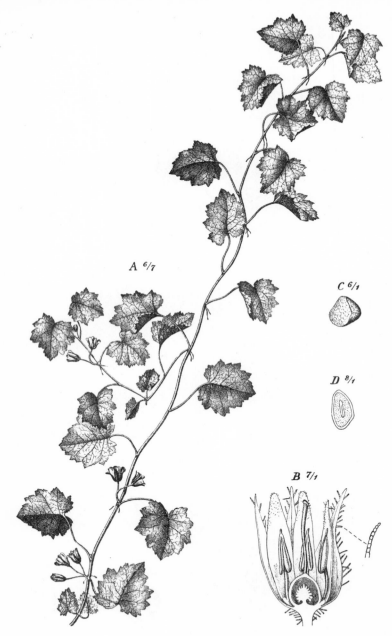

A 6/7

C 6/1

D 8/1

B 7/1

J. Fleischmann del.

Ardisiandra Sibthorpioides Hook.

A Flowering branch. *B* Flower cut lengthwise. *C* Seed *D* Seed cut lengthwise.

FAMILY 191.   PRIMULACEAE

Herbs or undershrubs.   Leaves undivided or lobed, without stipules.   Flowers solitary or in umbels racemes or panicles, without bracteoles, 3—7-merous, hermaphrodite.   Petals usually united below, with imbricate or contorted aestivation.   Fertile stamens as many as the petals and opposite to them. Ovary usually superior, 1-celled, with a free central placenta.   Ovules several or many, half-inverted.   Style simple ; stigma entire.   Fruit a capsule.   Seeds with ventral hilum ; albumen fleshy ; embryo small, axile. — Genera 11, species 45.   (Plate 122.)

1. Ovary inferior or half-inferior.   Corolla white, 5-cleft, regular, imbricate in bud, with 5 scales at the throat.   Ovules numerous.   Flowers in terminal racemes or panicles.   Leaves alternate. — Species 2.   Used as vegetables.   [Tribe SAMOLEAE.] . . . . . . **Samolus** L.
Ovary superior. 2

2. Corolla irregular, red.   Calyx prickly.   Ovules 5.   Flowers in terminal racemes.   Leaves alternate, linear, prickly toothed. — Species 1. North Africa.   Used medicinally.   [Tribe CORIDEAE.] . **Coris** L.
Corolla regular.   Calyx not prickly. 3

3. Corolla-lobes bent back, with contorted aestivation, red or white.   Ovules numerous.   Stem tuberous.   Leaves radical, stalked, broad.   Flowers solitary, radical. — Species 4.   North Africa.   Used as ornamental or medicinal plants ; the tubers are poisonous.   [Tribe CYCLAMINEAE.]
Cyclamen L.
Corolla-lobes erect or spreading.   Stem not tuberous. 4

4. Corolla with contorted aestivation.   [Tribe LYSIMACHIEAE.] . . 5
Corolla with imbricate, not contorted aestivation. [Tribe ANDROSACEAE.] 9

5. Corolla smaller than the calyx.   Flowers solitary in the axils of the leaves. 6
Corolla larger than the calyx ; petals united below. 8

6. Petals 3, free.   Fruit 2-seeded, opening in 3 valves.   Leaves opposite. — Species 1.   Naturalized in the Canary Islands.   (Under *Asterolinum* Link & Hoffmsg.) . . . . **Pelletiera** St. Hil.
Petals 4—5, united below.   Fruit many-seeded. 7

7. Corolla-tube short.   Fruit opening by a lid.   Leaves alternate, at least the upper ones. — Species 1.   North and East Africa.   **Centunculus** L.
Corolla-tube long.   Fruit opening by 4—5 valves.   Leaves opposite. — Species 2.   North and East Africa. . . **Asterolinum** Link & Hoffmsg.

8. Fruit opening by a lid.   Corolla red or blue.   Flowers solitary, axillary. — Species 20.   Some of them yield a fish-poison or medicaments, or serve as ornamental plants.   " Pimpernel." . . . **Anagallis** L.
Fruit opening by valves.   Corolla usually yellow or white. — Species 12. North, South, and East Africa and Madagascar.   Some are used as ornamental or medicinal plants.   (Including *Lubinia* Vent.)
Lysimachia L.

9. Stamens with an acuminate connective, inserted at the base of the corolla. Corolla white, about as long as the calyx, bell-shaped, deeply cleft, ciliate. Flowers solitary or 2—3 together in the axils of the leaves. Leaves alternate, stalked, cordate, lobed. Stem creeping. — Species 1. Mountains of Central Africa. (Plate 122.) . . **Ardisiandra** Hook.
  Stamens with an obtuse connective, inserted in the tube of the corolla. Flowers terminal, solitary or in umbels or whorls. Leaves radical. Stem erect, sometimes very short. 10
10. Corolla smaller than the calyx, bell-shaped, with a short tube, whitish or reddish. Flowers in umbels. Leaves elliptical, subsessile. — Species 1. North Africa. Used medicinally. . · . . . . **Androsace** L.
  Corolla larger than the calyx, salver-shaped, with a long tube. Leaves spatulate. — Species 2. North Africa and Abyssinia. Used as ornamental or medicinal plants. " Primrose." . . . **Primula** L.

FAMILY 192. **PLUMBAGINACEAE**

Herbs, undershrubs, or shrubs. Leaves undivided. Flowers in spike-head- or panicle-like inflorescences, regular or nearly so, 5-merous, herma-phrodite, bracteolate. Calyx with valvate or open aestivation, usually folded. Petals more or less clearly united, with contorted aestivation. Stamens as many as the petals and opposite to them. Anthers turned inwards. Ovary superior, 1-celled. Ovule 1, suspended from the basal funicle, inverted, with superior micropyle. Style or style-branches 5. Seeds with a straight embryo and mealy albumen. — Genera 7, species 90. (Plate 123.)

1. Styles united high up. Stamens generally free from the corolla. Inflorescence usually simple ; each flower with 2 bracteoles, which usually bear no flowers in their axils. [Tribe PLUMBAGINEAE.] . . . 2
  Styles free or united at the base only. Stamens attached to the corolla. Inflorescence composed of cymes ; each flower with 1—2 bracteoles, one of which bears a flower in its axil. [Tribe STATICEAE.] . . . 4
2. Sepals glandular, evidently united below. Corolla salver-shaped. Stamens free from the corolla. Undershrubs. — Species 9. Some of them yield arrow-poison, tanning materials, or medicaments, or serve as ornamental plants. . . . . **Plumbago** L.
  Sepals without glands, free or nearly so. Shrubs. 3
3. Stamens inserted in the middle of the corolla-tube. Corolla salver-shaped, pink or violet. Inflorescence capitate. — Species 2. Abyssinia.
     Ceratostigma Bunge
  Stamens free from the corolla. Corolla funnel-shaped. Inflorescence spicate-paniculate. — Species 3. Central and South Africa. (*Vogelia* Lam.) (Plate 123.) . . . . **Dyerophyton** O. Ktze.
4. Stamens inserted in the middle of the corolla-tube. Styles united nearly halfway up. Corolla blue, with a long tube. Undershrubs. — Species 3. North Africa. (*Bubania* Gir.) . . . . . **Limoniastrum** Moench
  Stamens inserted at the base of the corolla. 5

PLUMBAGINACEAE.

Pl. 123.

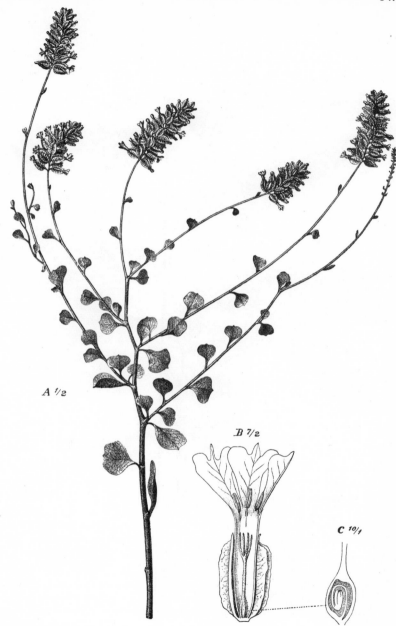

A ¹/₂

B ⁷/₂

C ¹⁰/₁

J. Fleischmann del.

Dyerophyton africanum (Lam.) O. Ktze.

A Flowering branch. *B* Flower cut lengthwise. *C* Ovary cut lengthwise.

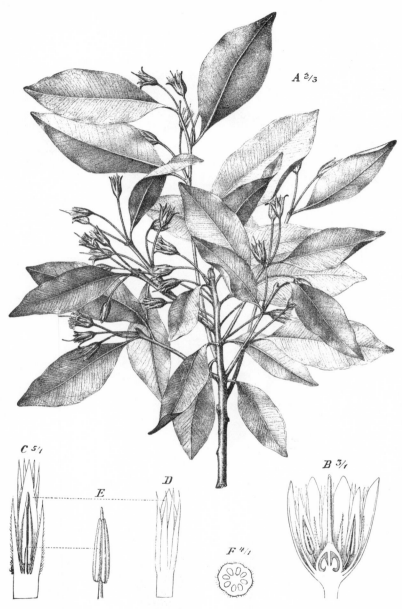

A ²/₃

C ⁵/₁

E

D

B ³/₁

F ⁴/₁

J. Fleischmann del.

Mimusops Kummel Bruce

A Flowering branch.   *B* Flower cut lengthwise.   *C* Petal, stamen, and staminodes.   *D* Petal from outside.   *E* Anther from outside.
F Cross-section of ovary.

5. Stigmas capitate. Styles tubercled. Fruit opening by a lid. Inflorescence
panicu ate. Herbs. — Species 1 North Africa. Yields tanning and
dyeing materials and medicaments, and serves as an ornamental plant.
Goniolimon Boiss.
Stigmas cylindrical or filiform. 6
6. Styles hairy.' Petals almost free. Fruit bursting all round at the base.
Inflorescence capitate. Leaves usually linear. — Species 10. North
Africa. Some are used as ornamental or medicinal plants. " Thrift."
Armeria Willd.
Styles glabrous. Fruit opening with a lid, or bursting irregularly, or
remaining closed. Inflorescence paniculate. — Species 60. North
Africa, northern Central Africa, and South Africa. Some species are
used for tanning or as ornamental or medicinal plants. (*Limonium*
Boiss.) . . . . **Statice** L.

ORDER EBENALES

SUBORDER SAPOTINEAE

FAMILY 193. SAPOTACEAE

Trees, rarely shrubs. Leaves entire. Flowers solitary or in clusters in the
leaf-axils or on the trunk. Calyx imbricate in bud. Petals united below,
imbricate in bud. Stamens as many as the petals and opposite to them, or more.
Anthers opening lengthwise. Ovary superior, completely or almost completely 2- or more-celled. Ovules solitary in each cell, more or less curved,
the micropyle turned downwards. Style simple. Fruit a berry. — Genera 19,
species 150. (Plate 124.)
1. Petals with two sometimes laciniate or minute dorsal appendages, rarely
with one only. [Tribe MIMUSOPEAE.] 2
Petals without dorsal appendages. [Tribe PALAQUIEAE.] . . . 4
2. Fertile stamens as many as the petals, 6 ; staminodes none. Appendages
of the petals small, toothed. Flowers hermaphrodite. Seeds exalbuminous, affixed by a broad, lateral hilum. — Species 1. Seychelles.
Northea Hook. fil.
Fertile stamens as many as the petals, 6--8, but alternating with as many
staminodes, or more. 3
3. Fertile stamens more than twice as many as the petals. Fruit 1-seeded. —
Species 3. Madagascar and Mascarenes. Yielding timber.
Labourdonnesia Boj.
Fertile stamens as many, rarely twice as many as the petals. — Species 60.
Tropical and South Africa. Some species yield timber, tanning-bark,
a resin (balata) similar to guttapercha, edible fruits, fat-containing seeds,
fish-poison, and medicaments. (Including *Baillonella* Pierre, *Dumoria*
A. Chev., *Imbricaria* Commers., *Labramia* A.DC., and *Tieghemella*
Pierre). (Plate 124.) . . . . **Mimusops** L.

4. Fertile stamens as many as petals. [Subtribe SIDEROXYLINAE.]   .   5
   Fertile stamens more than petals.   17
5. Staminodes none, rarely 1—4, small.   6
   Staminodes 5 or more.   11
6. Filaments with a leaf-like appendage. Leaves crowded at the top of the
   branches ; stipules linear. Flowers in clusters springing from older
   branches. — Species 1. Madagascar. . . **Cryptogyne** Hook. fil.
   Filaments without a leaf-like appendage.   7
7. Anthers converging around the style, oblong. Filaments adnate to the
   long corolla-tube at their base. Sepals free. Endocarp separating and
   enveloping the 5 seeds. Seeds exalbuminous. Shrubs with long, reddish
   brown, undivided hairs. Leaves lanceolate, with 2 pouch-shaped
   auricles at the base of the blade ; side-nerves numerous, somewhat
   distant, connected by numerous transverse veins. — Species 1. Equatorial West Africa (Gaboon) . . . . **Delpydora** Pierre
   Anthers not converging. Leaves not auricled. Hairs usually 2-parted.   8
8. Seeds albuminous. Primary side-nerves of the leaves usually approximate.
   — Species 20. Central and South Africa. Some species yield timber
   or edible fruits. . . . . **Chrysophyllum** L.
   Seeds exalbuminous, solitary. Stigma 5-lobed. Primary side-nerves
   of the leaves somewhat distant. Trees.   9
9. Sepals free or nearly so. Tube of the corolla longer than the segments.
   Anthers opening inwards or laterally. Leaves oblong or ovate ; primary
   side-nerves straight and connected by numerous transverse veins. —
   Species 6. Central Africa. They yield timber. . **Malacantha** Pierre
   Sepals obviously united at the base. Tube of the corolla as long as or
   shorter than the segments. Anthers opening outwards. Leaves
   lanceolate or elliptical ; primary side-nerves arched, connected by a network of veins.   10
10. Corolla-tube as long as the segments. Ovules attached below the middle. —
   Species 6. Central Africa. Some have edible fruits. (Under *Sideroxylon* L.) . . . . **Sersalisia** R. Br.
   Corolla-tube shorter than the segments. Ovules attached by the middle
   or above it. Leaves lanceolate ; stipules linear. — Species 4. Central
   Africa. They yield timber, edible fruits, and oily seeds.
                                        Pachystela Pierre
11. (5.) Ovary 2—6-celled.   12
   Ovary 8—12-celled.   16
12. Filaments much longer than the anthers. Staminodes linear. Style long.
   Ovules attached above the middle. Corolla with a short tube and
   narrow segments. Seed 1, with a very scanty albumen. Trees. Leaves
   lanceolate, stipulate. — Species 4. West Africa. (Under *Sideroxylon*
   L.) . . . . **Bakerisideroxylon** Engl.
   Filaments about as long as or slightly longer than the anthers. Ovules
   attached by the middle or below it.   13

13. Sepals united to above the middle. Anthers opening inwards. Staminodes lanceolate or ovate. Styles very long, with a very small stigma. Seeds exalbuminous. Trees. Leaves lanceolate. — Species 3. Central Africa. (Including *Stironeurum* Radlk.) . . . **Synsepalum** A. DC. Sepals free or united at the base. Anthers opening outwards. . . . 14

14. Staminodes awl-shaped. Ovary 2—4-celled. Seeds 2—4, connate, albuminous. Spiny trees. Leaves lanceolate. — Species 1. Morocco. Yields timber (iron-wood) and oil. . . **Argania** Roem. & Schult. Staminodes more or less petal-like, or short and broad. Ovary usually 5-celled. Seeds separate or solitary. 15

15. Staminodes more or less petal-like. Seeds albuminous, with leaf-like cotyledons. — Species 20. Tropical and South Africa, Canary Islands, and Madeira. Some species yield timber, edible fruits, or medicaments. (Including *Calvaria* Commers. and *Sapota* A.DC.) . . **Sideroxylon** L. Staminodes small, broad. Seeds exalbuminous, with thick cotyledons. (See 10.) . . . . **Sersalisia** R. Br.

16. Calyx 5—6-parted. Corolla 5—6-lobed. Ovary 10—12-celled. Ovules attached by the base. Fruit 4—12-seeded. Seeds ovoid, compressed, with a narrow hilum, albuminous. Flowers solitary. — Species 1 (*A. Sapota* L., sapodilla-plum). Cultivated in the tropics. Yields a guttapercha-like resin, edible fruits, and medicaments. (Under *Sapota* Plum.) . . . . **Achras** L. Calyx 8—10-parted. Corolla 8—10-cleft or -parted. Ovary 8—10-celled. Ovules attached by the middle. Fruit 1—4-seeded. Seeds globular, with a broad hilum, exalbuminous. Flowers in clusters, clothed with rusty-brown hairs. — Species 1 (*B. Parkii* Kotschy). Central Africa. Yields timber, a guttapercha-like resin, edible fruits, and a fat (shea-butter) from the seeds. (*Bassia* L.) . . . **Butyrospermum** Kotschy

17. (4.) Sepals 5, unequal, spirally arranged. Fertile stamens 15, 20, or more; staminodes 5 or more. Ovary 9—30-celled. Style cone- or club-shaped. [Subtribe OMPHALOCARPINAE.] . . . . 18 Sepals 4 or 6, nearly equal, whorled. Stamens 12 or 16, all fertile. Anthers opening outwards. Style awl-shaped. [Subtribe ILLIPINAE.] . . 19

18. Stamens 15, united in 5 bundles. Anthers opening outwards. Ovary 10-celled. Style club-shaped. Petals 5, white. Sepals red. Flowers solitary or few together in the axils of the lower, sometimes fallen leaves. — Species 1 . Equatorial West Africa (Cameroons). **Tridesmostemon** Engl. Stamens 20 or more, free. Anthers opening inwards. Style cone-shaped. Flowers springing from the old wood. — Species 13. West Africa. They yield timber and a sort of guttapercha. **Omphalocarpum** Beauv.

19. Sepals 4. Petals 8. Stamens 16. Ovary 10—12-celled. Seeds albuminous. — Species 1. Cultivated in the tropics. Yields guttapercha.
Payena A.DC.
Sepals 6. Petals 6. Stamens 12 Ovary 6-celled. Seeds exalbuminous. — Species 2. Cultivated in the tropics. Yielding guttapercha
Palaquium Blanco

SUBORDER DIOSPYRINEAE
FAMILY 194. HOPLESTIGMATACEAE

Trees. Leaves alternate, undivided, without stipules. Flowers in terminal panicles. Calyx closed in the bud, subsequently cleft into 2—4 lobes. Corolla with a short tube and 11—14 imbricate segments. Stamens 23—34, inserted in the tube of the corolla. Anthers opening lengthwise. Ovary 1-celled with 2 much projecting placentas. Ovules 4, pendulous inverted. Styles 2, united at the base, with roundish stigmas. Fruit a drupe with 2 empty cavities. Seeds with a large embryo and scanty albumen. (Under *FLA-COURTIACEAE*.)

Genus 1, species 2. Equatorial West Africa. . . **Hoplestigma** Pierre

FAMILY 195. EBENACEAE

Trees or shrubs. Leaves entire, without stipules. Flowers solitary or in cymes in the leaf-axils, regular. Petals united below, with contorted, rarely valvate aestivation. Stamens as many as the petals and opposite to them, or more numerous, inserted at the base of the corolla-tube. Filaments free or united in bundles. Anthers basifixed, 2-celled. Ovary superior, sessile, 2—16-celled. Ovules 1—2 in each cell, pendulous, inverted. Styles 2—8, free or united at the base. Seeds with a copious, cartilaginous albumen and an axile embryo. — Genera 6, species 150. Tropical and South Africa. (Plate 125.)

1. Corolla with valvate aestivation. Stamens about 30. Flowers 4-merous, dioecious, the male in cymes, the female solitary. — Species 1. Madagascar. . . . . **Tetraclis** Hiern

   Corolla with contorted aestivation. 2

2. Stamens 2—3, with hairy filaments and linear anthers. Corolla 3—4-lobed. Flowers dioecious. Fruit oblong or ovoid. Leaves oblique at the base. — Species 1. West Africa. . . . **Rhaphidanthe** Hiern

   Stamens 4 or more, very rarely 3, but then filaments glabrous and anthers oblong or lanceolate. 3

3. Stamens in a single row, 4—14, usually 10. Flowers usually hermaphrodite, 5-, rarely 4-, 6-, or 7-merous. Ovary 4—10-celled with 1 ovule in each cell. Pericarp leathery. — Species 20. South and Central Africa. Some species yield timber. . . . . . . **Royena** L.

   Stamens in 2 or more rows, very rarely in a single row, but then only 3. Flowers unisexual, rarely polygamous. Pericarp usually fleshy. . 4

4. Ovary 3-celled with 2 ovules, or 6-celled with 1 ovule in each cell; in the latter case female flowers with staminodes. Flowers 3-merous, more rarely 4—6-merous. Stamens usually 9, glabrous. Leaves alternate. — Species 20. Tropical and South-east Africa. Some species yield timber, edible fruits, and medicaments. (Plate 125.) **Maba** Forst.

   Ovary 4- or 8—16-celled, rarely 2- or 6-celled; in the latter case female flowers without staminodes. Flowers 4—7-, very rarely 3-merous. Stamens usually 12—20. 5

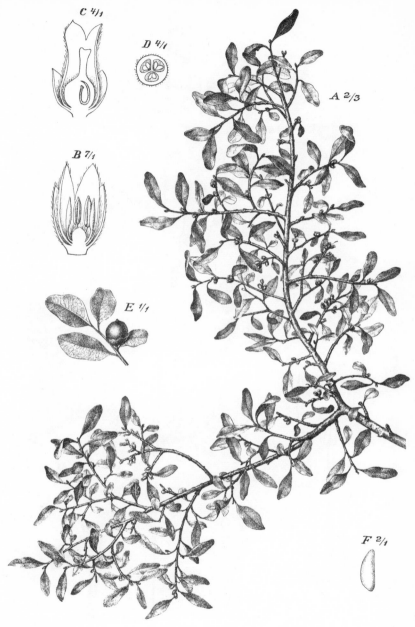

C ⁴/₁

D ⁴/₁

B ⁷/₁

E ¹/₁

A ²/₃

F ²/₁

J. Fleischmann del.

Maba buxifolia (Rottb.) Pers.

A Flowering branch.   *B* Male flower cut lengthwise.   *C* Female flower cut lengthwise.   *D* Cross-section of ovary.   *E* Fruit.   *F* Seed

J. Fleischmann del.

Schrebera alata Welw.

A Flowering branch.   *B* Flower cut lengthwise.   *C* Group of fruits.   *D* Fruit cut lengthwise.   *E* Fruit cut across.

5. Staminodes usually absent in the female flowers.   Ovary 2-celled with 2 ovules, or 4—6-celled with one ovule in each cell.   Calyx not enlarged after flowering.   Fruit fleshy.   Stamens 10—30. — Species 35.   Central and South Africa.   Some species yield timber or edible fruits. **Euclea L.**
Staminodes usually present in the female flowers.   Ovary 4—16-, usually 8-celled, with 1 ovule in each cell.   Calyx most frequently enlarged after flowering.   Stamens usually 16. — Species 75.   Tropical and South-east ·Africa.   They yield timber (ebony), tanning and dyeing materials, mucilage, edible fruits (date-plums), fish-poison, and medicaments.   (Including *Thespesocarpus* Pierre).   .   . **Diospyros** Dalech.

FAMILY 196. STYRACACEAE

Trees.   Leaves alternate, undivided, without stipules.   Flowers solitary or in pairs in the leaf-axils, clothed with stellate hairs, hermaphrodite.   Calyx closed in the bud, splitting subsequently into 2 or 3 segments.   Petals 5, free, fleshy, whitish-yellow.   Stamens 10, free.   Anthers basifixed, pointed, opening by 2 longitudinal slits.   Ovary superior, 1-celled.   Ovules 6, basal, inverted.   Style simple.   Fruit dry, indehiscent.   Seed 1, with a crusty-woody testa and a copious, horny albumen.   Embryo axile, large, straight, with a short radicle and thin cotyledons.
Genus 1, species 1.   Equatorial West Africa (Cameroons).

Afrostyrax Perkins & Gilg

ORDER CONTORTAE
SUBORDER OLEINEAE
FAMILY 197. OLEACEAE

Shrubs or trees, rarely undershrubs.   Leaves exstipulate, usually opposite. Flowers regular.   Stamens 2, alternating with the carpels, rarely 3—4, inserted on the corolla, if the latter is present.   Disc none.   Ovary superior, rarely (*Fraxinus*) naked, 2-celled, rarely 3—4-celled.   Ovules 1—4, usually 2, in each cell, inverted.   Style simple ; stigmas 1—2.   Seeds with a straight embryo. — Genera 11, species 120.   (Including *JASMINEAE*.)   (Plate 126.)
  1. Seeds erect or ascending, the radicle turned downwards.   Fruit 2-parted, but sometimes one half only developed.   Corolla conspicuous, white or yellow, with 5—6, more rarely 7—12 or 4 imbricate segments ; in the latter case anthers opening inside.   Shrubs or undershrubs.   [Subfamily **JASMINOIDEAE,** tribe JASMINEAE.]   2
  Seeds pendulous or descending, the radicle turned upwards.   Fruit not 2-parted.   Petals 4 or 0, rarely 5—8 ; in this case petals valvate in bud or stem tree-like.   Anthers opening laterally, very rarely inside, but then petals valvate in bud.   [Subfamily **OLEOIDEAE.**]   3
  2. Fruit a capsule.   Sepals linear.   Corolla bell- or wheel-shaped, with a short tube and 5—6 segments.   Anthers opening laterally.   Ovules 2—4 in each ovary-cell.   Undershrubs.   Leaves simple, undivided or pinnatifid. — Species 3.   South Africa. **Menodora** Humb. & Bonpl.

Fruit a berry. Corolla salver-shaped. Anthers opening inside. Shrubs. Leaves compound, with 1—7 leaflets. — Species 60. Some of them are used in perfumery and medicine or as ornamental plants (jessamine).

Jasminum L.

3. Fruit a linear or lanceolate winged nut. Seeds with fleshy albumen. Ovules 2 in each ovary-cell. Corolla absent. Flowers unisexual or polygamous. Leaves pinnate. Trees. — Species 4. North-west Africa. They yield timber, tanning and dyeing materials, and medicaments. " Ash." [Tribe FRAXINEAE.] . . . . . **Fraxinus** L.

Fruit a capsule, a berry, or a drupe. Corolla present. 4

4. Fruit a capsule. Albumen very scanty or absent. Ovules 4 in each ovary-cell. Corolla with a long tube and 4—8 imbricate lobes. Flowers in panicles. Trees. — Species 15. Central and South Africa. (*Nathusia* Hochst.) (Plate 126.) [Tribe SYRINGEAE.] . **Schrebera** Roxb.

Fruit a berry or a drupe. Ovules 2 in each ovary-cell. Corolla with a short tube or without a tube, and with valvate, rarely imbricate segments; in the latter case shrubs with spicate or racemose flowers. Leaves undivided. [Tribe OLEINEAE.] 5

5. Petals free or united in pairs, with valvate aestivation. 6

Petals all united at the base. 7

6. Flowers in axillary and terminal simple racemes. Embryo with a long radicle. — Species 1. Canary Islands and Madeira. Yields timber. (*Picconia* DC.) . . . . **Notelaea** Vent.

Flowers in axillary or terminal compound racemes. Embryo with a short radicle. — Species 10. Tropical and South-east Africa. Some species yield timber. (*Mayepea* Aubl.) . . . . . **Linociera** Swartz

7. Corolla with imbricate aestivation. Flowers in axillary simple spikes or racemes. Shrubs. — Species 4. North Africa. They yield timber and medicaments, and serve also as ornamental plants. . **Phillyrea** L.

Corolla with induplicate-valvate aestivation 8

8. Corolla globular. Seeds exalbuminous, with thick cotyledons. Flowers in axillary and terminal simple racemes, more rarely solitary or in clusters. Trees. — Species 6. Madagascar and Mascarenes. Some have edible fruits. . . . . **Noronhia** Stadtmann

Corolla not globular. Seeds with a fleshy albumen and flat cotyledons. Flowers in compound racemes or in clusters. 9

9. Corolla-tube very short ; segments narrow, bent inwards at the margins. Sepals free or nearly so. Anthers opening outwards. Flowers in clusters. Low trees. — Species 1. Southern Central Africa. . **Dekindtia** Gilg

Corolla-tube not very short. Sepals united high up. Anthers opening inwards or laterally. Flowers in compound racemes. 10

10. Fruit a berry with a membranous or crustaceous endocarp, 2 cells, and 2—4 seeds. Inflorescences terminal. Shrubs. — Species 1. Naturalized in North Africa. Serves as an ornamental or hedge plant ; also the wood is used ; the berries are poisonous. " Privet." **Ligustrum** L.

Fruit a drupe with a bony, woody, or crustaceous endocarp and 1, rarely 2 seeds. Inflorescences usually axillary. — Species 15. Some of them, especially the olive (*O. europaea* L.), yield timber, edible fruits, oil, and medicaments, or serve as ornamental plants. . . . . . **Olea** L.

SUBORDER GENTIANINEAE

FAMILY 198. LOGANIACEAE

Shrubs or trees. Juice not milky. Leaves opposite or whorled, entire, rarely toothed or lobed; stipules well developed or reduced to a transverse ridge or line connecting the leaf-stalks. Calyx-lobes 4—5. Petals 4—16, united below. Stamens as many as or fewer than the petals, inserted on the corolla. Ovary superior, completely or incompletely 2-, rarely 4-celled, with 2 or more inverted ovules in each cell. Style simple or 4-cleft. Seeds albuminous. — Genera 14, species 240. Tropical and South Africa. (Plate 127.)

1. Glandular hairs present. Corolla-lobes 4, imbricate in bud. Stamens 4. Style simple. [Subfamily **BUDDLEIOIDEAE**.] 2
   Glandular hairs absent. [Subfamily **LOGANIOIDEAE**.] 8

2. Anther-halves cohering above, divergent below. Anthers projecting beyond the corolla-tube. Filaments inserted at the throat of the corolla. Style long; stigma small. Ovary incompletely 2-celled. Fruit a capsule. Flowers in terminal panicles. Stipules reduced to a transverse line. Capitate tips of the glandular hairs consisting of several cells. — Species 30. Tropical and South Africa. Some species yield timber. (Plate 127.) . . . . **Nuxia** Lam.
   Anther-halves separate. Style short with a thick stigma, rarely rather long, but then flowers in racemes. Capitate tips of the glandular hairs consisting of 2 cells. 3

3. Anthers distinctly projecting beyond the corolla-tube. Filaments inserted at the base of the corolla-tube. Ovary 2-celled. Fruit a capsule. Flowers in many-flowered, terminal panicles. Stipules reduced to a transverse line. Trees. — Species 4. South Africa and Madagascar.
   Chilianthus Burch.
   Anthers concealed within the corolla-tube or scarcely projecting. . . 4

4. Style long. Ovary 2-celled. Fruit a capsule. Flowers in terminal simple racemes. Stipules reduced to a transverse line. Shrubs. — Species 2. South Africa and southern Central Africa. . **Gomphostigma** Turcz.
   Style short. Flowers in capitate, racemose, or panicled inflorescences composed of cymes. 5

5. Ovary completely or incompletely 4-celled. Corolla salver-shaped. Fruit a globular drupe. Flowers in terminal panicles. Stipules reduced to a transverse line. — Species 2. Madagascar. (Under *Buddleia* L.)
   Adenoplea Radlk.
   Ovary completely or incompletely 2-celled. 6

6. Fruit a globular drupe. Seeds with a small embryo. Ovary completely 2-celled. Corolla salver-shaped. Inflorescences lateral, racemiform. Leaves toothed, with foliaceous stipules. — Species 2. Madagascar.

Adenoplusia Radlk.

Fruit an oblong berry or an oblong or ovate capsule. 7

7. Fruit a berry. Seeds with a comparatively large embryo. Ovary incompletely 2-celled. Corolla salver-shaped. Inflorescences capitate. Shrubs. — Species 7. Madagascar and the neighbouring islands.

Nicodemia Ten.

Fruit a capsule. Seeds with a small embryo. — Species 18. Tropical and South Africa. Some species yield timber, dye-stuffs, a substitute for soap, and medicaments, or serve as ornamental plants. **Buddleia** L.

8. (1.) Style 4-cleft. Ovary 2-celled with 2 ovules in each cell. Corolla funnel-shaped, 4—5-lobed, imbricate in bud. Stamens 4—5. Fruit a capsule. Leaves entire. Stipules triangular or united into a sheath. [Tribe GELSEMIEAE.] 9

Style simple. Ovules with several or many ovules in each cell, rarely with 2, but then corolla valvate in bud. 10

9. Flowers in few-flowered cymes enclosed by two large involucral bracts united at the base. Stamens unequal in length. — Species 6. Central Africa. (Under *Mostuea* Didr.) . . . . **Coinochlamys** Anders.

Flowers without an involucre. — Species 25. Tropics. **Mostuea** Didr.

10. Corolla with imbricate or contorted aestivation ; segments 5-16. Stamens the same in number. 11

Corolla with valvate aestivation ; segments 4—5. Stamens the same in number or fewer. Stipules reduced to a transverse line. Inflorescences terminal and lateral 12

11. Calyx with 4, corolla with 10—16 segments. Anthers long and narrow. Disc present. Ovary 4-celled below, 2-celled above. Fruit a berry. Inflorescences terminal. — Species 20. Tropical and South Africa. Some species have edible fruits or are used in medicine. [Tribe FRAGRAEEAE.] . . . . **Anthocleista** Afz.

Calyx and corolla with 5 segments each. Anthers short. Ovary 2-celled. Fruit a capsule. Inflorescences lateral. — Species 10 Madagascar and Mascarenes. Some species yield timber. [Tribe LOGANIEAE.] . . . . **Geniostoma** Forst.

12. Calyx-segments very unequal, one of them much larger than the others and petal-like. Corolla salver-shaped, 4-lobed. Stamen 1. Ovary 2-celled with numerous ovules. Fruit a capsule. Seeds winged. Climbing shrubs. — Species 1. West Africa. [Tribe ANTONIEAE.]

Usteria Willd.

Calyx-segments nearly equal. Stamens 4—5. 13

13. Corolla tubular, red. Ovules 2—3 in each ovary-cell. Fruit a capsule. Leaves whorled, linear. Flowers few, terminal or arising in the upper leaf-axils. Shrubs. — Species 1. South Africa. . **Retzia** Thunb.

A ²/₃

C ⁶/₁

B ⁴/₁

D ¹⁰/₁

J. Fleischmann del.

Nuxia Autunesii Gilg

A Flowering branch.   B Flower (from which the anthers have fallen off excepting one).   C Flower cut lengthwise.   D Ovary cut lengthwise.

J. Fleischmann del.

Chironia transvaalensis Gilg

A Flowering branch.   *B* Flower cut lengthwise.   *C* Stamen.   *D* Cross-section of ovary.   *E* Fruit.   *F* Seed.

Corolla salver-, bell-, or wheel-shaped, usually white. Ovules several or many in each ovary-cell. Fruit a berry. Leaves opposite, 3—5-nerved — Species 110. Tropical and South Africa. Some species yield timber, poisons, and medicaments·; some have poisonous, others edible fruits and seeds, which are also used for preparing alcohol. (Including *Brehmia* Harv. and *Ignatia* L. f.)   [Tribe STRYCHNEAE.]

Strychnos L.

FAMILY 199. GENTIANACEAE

Herbs or undershrubs, rarely shrubs. Leaves undivided, sometimes reduced to scales ; stipules absent or replaced by a transverse ridge or line connecting the leaf-stalks. Flowers regular, rarely (*Canscora*) somewhat irregular. Petals united below. Stamens as many as the petals, and alternating with them, 3—8, sometimes one only fertile. Ovary superior, 1-celled with 2 or 4 parietal placentas, or 2-celled with axile placentas. Ovules numerous. Style simple with 1—2 stigmas rarely (*Erythraea*) 2-cleft. Fruit a capsule, rarely a nut or (*Chironia*) a berry. Seeds minute, albuminous. — Genera 23, species 250. (Plate 128.)

1. Corolla with induplicate-valvate aestivation, 5-partite, white or yellow. Pollen-grains compressed from one side. Ovary 1-celled, with little intruding placentas. Stigma 2-partite. Leaves alternate or all radical, broad-cordate. [Subfamily **MENYANTHOIDEAE**.]   2
   Corolla with contorted or imbricate aestivation. Pollen-grains not compressed from one side. Leaves opposite or whorled or nearly so. [Subfamily **GENTIANOIDEAE.**]   3
2. Stem erect. Leaves slightly cordate at the base, ovate, radical. Flowers panicled. Fruit opening by 4 valves at the top. — Species 1. South Africa (Cape Colony). Used medicinally.   .   .   .   . **Villarsia** Vent.
   Stem floating or creeping. Leaves deeply cordate at the base. Flowers fascicled. Fruit bursting irregularly or remaining closed. — Species 9. Tropical and South Africa. Some have edible roots or serve as ornamental or medicinal plants.   .   .   .   . **Limnanthemum** Gmel.
3. Stem and leaves reddish. Leaves reduced to scales. Flowers solitary, terminal. Corolla salver-shaped, 5-lobed, yellow or blue. Anthers included. Pollen-grains with a single pore. Ovary 1-celled. Stigma entire. Ovules straight. Seeds with a very scanty albumen. — Species 2. West Africa. (Under *Voyria* Aubl.) [Tribe LEIPHAIMEAE.]   .   .   .   . **Leiphaimos** Cham. & Schlechtd.
   Stem and leaves green. Leaves well developed, rarely very small, but then flowers in cymes. Pollen-grains with 3 pores. Ovules inverted. Seeds with copious albumen. 4
4. Pollen-grains connected in groups of four, tubercled on the surface. Calyx 4-toothed, with a winged tube. Corolla funnel-shaped, 4-lobed. Filaments inserted on the upper part of the corolla-tube, winged at the base.

Ovary 1-celled. Stigma 2-partite. — Species 1. West Africa. Used medicinally. [Tribe HELIEAE.] . . . . . **Schultesia** Mart.
Pollen-grains separate. [Tribe GENTIANEAE.] 5
5. Ovary completely 2-celled. Pollen-grains very small. 6
Ovary 1-celled, sometimes incompletely 2-celled. Pollen-grains rather large. 9
6. Anthers opening by terminal pores which are sometimes produced into slits, without glands, exserted. Filaments inserted at the throat of the corolla or somewhat lower. Corolla violet, pink, or white, with a short and wide tube. Calyx winged. — Species 12. Tropics. Used as ornamental plants. . . . . **Exacum** L.
Anthers opening by longitudinal slits, nearly always with 1—4 small glands at the base or the apex. Corolla yellow, with a more or less elongated tube. 7
7. Anthers projecting beyond the corolla-tube. Filaments inserted in the sinuses between the corolla-lobes. — Species 80. South Africa and tropics. Some are used medicinally. . . . . . **Sebaea** R. Br.
Anthers concealed within the corolla-tube. Filaments inserted in the corolla-tube. Flowers 5-merous. 8
8. Filaments inserted in the lower part of the corolla-tube. Calyx not winged. Small plants with small flowers. — Species 1. South Africa (Cape Colony). (Under *Sebaea* R. Br.) . . . . . **Lagenias** E. Mey.
Filaments inserted in the middle or the upper part of the corolla-tube, Calyx winged. Flowers rather large. — Species 30. Tropical and South Africa. (*Parasia* Rafin., including *Exochaenium* Griseb., under *Sebaea* R. Br.) . . . . **Belmontia** E. Mey.
9. Ovary divided into incomplete cells by the intrusion of the placentas. Stigma more or less distinctly 2-lobed. Stamens 5. 10
Ovary completely one-celled with little intruding placentas. 12
10. Anthers more or less twisted after flowering. Pollen-grains smooth. — Species 6. North Africa and northern Central Africa. Used as medicinal or ornamental plants. . . . . **Erythraea** L. C. Rich.
Anthers erect or bent back after flowering. Pollen-grains tubercled or netted. Calyx with small scales on the inside. 11
11. Corolla yellow ; tube short, glabrous within. Anthers exserted. Pollen-grains tubercled. Leaves stem-clasping. Flowers in many-flowered panicles with large bracts. — Species 1. Canary Islands.
Ixanthus Griseb.
Corolla white or red ; tube long, with 5 small scales on the inside. Anthers included. Pollen-grains netted. Flowers solitary or in few-flowered cymes. — Species 9. Madagascar. Some are poisonous or are used in medicine. . . . . **Tachiadenus** Griseb.
12. Corolla with 1—2 glandular nectaries at the base of each segment ; tube very short. Stamens 4—5. Pollen-grains tubercled. — Species 35. Tropical and South Africa. Some are used medicinally. **Sweertia** L.

Corolla without nectaries, but sometimes with scales at the insertion of the stamens. Pollen-grains smooth or dotted. 13

13. Corolla with distinctly unequal segments and imbricate, more rarely contorted aestivation, white or red. Stamens 4, inserted at different heights on the corolla-tube, usually one only perfect. Pollen-grains smooth. Stigma 2-lobed. — Species 3. Tropics. Used medicinally.

Canscora Lam.

Corolla with equal or subequal segments and contorted aestivation. . 14

14. Fertile stamen 1, staminodes 3 ; all inserted in the sinuses between the corolla-lobes. Pollen-grains smooth. Corolla yellow, with a short tube. Stigma 2-lobed. Stem 4-angled or winged. Leaves very small, decurrent along the stem. · Flowers in dense cymes. - Species 1. Southern West Africa (Angola). (Under *Canscora* Lam.)

Schinziella Gilg

Fertile stamens 3—8, rarely more. 15

15. Flowers 6—8-merous, rarely polymerous. Corolla yellow, with a short tube. Pollen-grains smooth. Stigma 2-parted with deeply notched branches. Flowers in lax cymes. — Species 2. North-west Africa. Used as ornamental or medicinal plants. . . . . . **Chlora** L.

Flowers 3—5-merous. Stigma entire or 2-parted with entire branches. 16

16. Flowers 3-merous. Sepals very unequal. Corolla with a long tube, usually blue. Stamens inserted at the throat ; filaments with a swelling at the base. Stigma 2-parted. Flowers crowded in heads. — Species 3. Southern Central Africa. . . . . . . **Pycnosphaera** Gilg

Flowers 4—5-merous. Sepals not very unequal. 17

17. Flowers 4-merous. Anthers ovate, rarely oblong. Pollen-grains smooth. Herbs. 18

Flowers 5-merous. Anthers oblong or linear. 21

18. Stamens inserted below the middle of the corolla-tube. Calyx 8-—12-ribbed. Corolla with a narrow tube. Stigma 2-lobed. Dwarf herbs. Flowers solitary or paired in the leaf-axils, sometimes forming racemes or corymbs. — Species 8. Central Africa. . . **Neurotheca** Salisb.

Stamens inserted at the throat of the corolla. Anthers ovate Flowers small. 19

19. Flowers in dense fascicles. Calyx divided to the middle or below the middle. Corolla with 4 scales at the throat. — Species 10. Central and South Africa. Some are used medicinally. . . **Faroa** Welw.

Flowers in lax cymes. Corolla without scales at the throat. Dwarf herbs. 20

20. Stem much branched. Calyx deeply divided. Corolla with a long tube and broad lobes. Stigma 2-parted. — Species 1. North-west Africa (Algeria). . . . . **Cicendia** Adans.

Stem not or scantily branched. Calyx shortly toothed. Corolla with a rather long tube and narrow segments. Stigma entire or notched. — Species 1. North-west Africa. . . . **Microcala** Link & Hoffmsg

21. Filaments with a double scale at the base, inserted at the middle of the
      corolla-tube.   Anthers included, not twisted.   Pollen-grains smooth.
      Corolla-tube long.   Stigma entire.   Flowers small, in axillary fascicles.
      Herbs. — Species 3.   Tropical and South-east Africa.   Used medicinal-
      ly. (*Hippion* Spreng.) . . . .   **Enicostemma** Blume
    Filaments without a scale at the base.   Anthers usually exserted and
      twisted after flowering.   Flowers in usually lax cymes or solitary . 22
22. Stigma 2-lobed or 2-parted.   Pollen-grains medium-sized, smooth.   Herbs.
      (See 10.) . . . .   **Erythraea** L. C. Rich.
    Stigma entire.   Pollen-grains very large, dotted.   Corolla-tube rather
      short. 23
23. Calyx with blunt, not keeled segments.   Glands between calyx and corolla
      present.   Corolla red.   Stamens inserted at the throat of the corolla.
      Hairy shrubs.   Flowers large, in terminal cymes. — Species 1.   South
      Africa (Cape Colony).   Used as an ornamental plant.   **Orphium** E. Mey.
    Calyx with pointed, usually keeled segments.   Glands between calyx and
      corolla absent. — Species 40.   South Africa, southern Central Africa,
      and Malagasy Islands.   Some species serve as ornamental plants.   (In-
      cluding *Plocandra* E. Mey.) (Plate 128.) . . .   **Chironia** L.

FAMILY 200. APOCYNACEAE

Usually woody plants.   Juice milky.   Leaves entire, usually penninerved with closely arranged, parallel primary side-nerves, generally opposite.
Flowers with bracteoles, usually panicled, regular or nearly so, 5-, very rarely
4-merous, hermaphrodite.   Calyx imbricate in bud, usually deeply divided.
Petals united below, with contorted aestivation.   Stamens as many as the
petals, inserted in the tube or at the throat of the corolla.   Filaments free, short.
Anthers opening inwards by two longitudinal slits, sometimes adhering to the
stigma.   Pollen granular.   Ovary superior, more rarely half-inferior, 1—2-
celled, or 2, rarely (*Pleiocarpa*) 3—5 separate ovaries.   Ovules 2 or more in
each cell, rarely solitary, pendulous, inverted.   Style simple or divided at the
base, thickened at the apex, bearing the stigmas on the under-surface of the
thickened part (stigmatic or stylar head), and sometimes two-lobed above it.
Seeds usually albuminous and provided with a wing or a tuft of hairs. — Genera
61, species 450.   (Plate 129.)

  1. Stamens closely connected with the stigmatic head.   Anthers prolonged
       at the base into empty tails.   Corolla-lobes usually overlapping to the
       right.   Fruit dry, dehiscent.   Seeds usually with a tuft of hairs.   [Sub-
       family **ECHITIDOIDEAE.**]   2
     Stamens free or loosely cohering with the stigmatic head.   Anthers without
       tails, full of pollen to the base, more rarely prolonged into tails, but then
       fruit fleshy and most frequently indehiscent.   Corolla-lobes usually over-
       lapping to the left.   Seeds usually without a tuft of hairs.   [Subfamily
       PLUMIEROIDEAE.] 22

2. Anthers projecting beyond the mouth of the corolla-tube. [Tribe PAR-
   SONSIEAE.)] 3
   Anthers ,entirely or for the greatest part, concealed within the corolla-tube.
   [Tribe ECHITIDEAE.] 7
3. Calyx without glands ; segments blunt. Corolla with a very short tube
   without scales ; segments overlapping to the right. Filaments twisted
   around the style. Disc cupular, irregularly crenate. Twining shrubs. —
   Species 1. West Africa (Congo). . . . . . **Dewevrella** De Wild.
   Calyx with glands on the inside. Disc 5-lobed or wanting. 4
4. Disc 5-lobed. Calyx with 5—10 glands. Corolla white, with 5—10
   confluent scales at the throat ; segments overlapping to the right.
   Seeds glabrous. Trees or erect shrubs, glabrous. — Species 1. Northern
   West Africa. . . . . **Malouetia** A. DC.
   Disc absent. Seeds hairy. 5
5. Calyx with pointed segments and 10—20 glands. Corolla glabrous at the
   throat ; segments unequal-sided, overlapping to the right. Seeds with
   a terminal and a smaller basal tuft of hairs. Twining shrubs. — Species
   3. West Africa. . . . . **Isonema** R. Br.
   Calyx with blunt segments and 5—10 glands. Corolla nearly always with
   scales at the throat ; segments overlapping to the left. Erect shrubs
   or trees. 6
6. Flowers small. Seeds covered all over with long hairs densest at the
   base. — Species 5. West Africa. (Under *Wrightia* R. Br.)
   Pleioceras Baill.
   Flowers rather large. Seeds provided at the base with a deciduous tuft
   of hairs. — Species 3. South-east Africa and Madagascar. **Wrightia** R. Br.
7. Leaves alternate. Stem succulent. Flowers subsessile. Calyx without
   glands, with subulate or lanceolate segments. Corolla usually funnel-
   shaped ; segments overlapping to the right. Ovary superior. . . 8
   Leaves opposite or whorled. Stem woody. 9
8. Leaves with 2 or more spines at their base or in their axils. Disc 5-lobed or
   replaced by 2—5 glands. Seeds with a tuft of hairs at the apex. —
   Species 15. Madagascar, South Africa, and Angola. **Pachypodium** Lindl.
   Leaves and stem without spines. Corolla red. Disc none. Seeds with
   a tuft of hairs at either end. Flowers large, in few-flowered cymes. —
   Species 13. Central and South Africa. Some species yield an arrow-
   poison. (*Idaneum* O. Ktze.) . . . **Adenium** Roem. & Schult.
9. Corolla with separate or confluent scales at the throat. 10
   Corolla naked at the throat, but sometimes with scales or swellings lower
   down in the tube. 13
10. Scales at the throat of the corolla united into a tubular, 15-crenate corona.
    Corolla salver-shaped, the segments overlapping to the left. Calyx with-
    out glands. Ovary superior. Seeds with a basal tuft of hairs. Erect
    shrubs. Flowers small. — Species 1. East Africa.
    Stephanostema K. Schum.

Scales at the throat of the corolla free or slightly united at the base. Corolla-segments nearly always overlapping to the right. Ovary almost superior or half-inferior. 11

11. Corolla salver-shaped with 5 entire scales at the throat. Calyx without glands, rarely with 5 small glands within. Filaments inserted on the lower part of the corolla-tube. Disc cup-shaped, 5-lobed or 5-parted. Twining shrubs. Leaves opposite, without axillary glands. Flowers small. — Species 12. Tropical and South-east Africa. **Oncinotis** Benth.

Corolla funnel-shaped, with 5 divided scales at the throat. Calyx with usually numerous glands within. Disc none. 12

12. Corolla with laciniate scales at the throat, and with broad, not tailed segments, white or red. Anthers with a tailed connective. Mericarps at first cohering, subsequently divergent. Seeds with an apical tuft of hairs. Erect shrubs or low trees. Leaves whorled, narrow, densely veined. Flowers large. — Species 1 (*N. Oleander* L.). North Africa. A poisonous plant yielding wood and medicaments and used as an ornamental plant. . . . . **Nerium** L.

Corolla with bipartite scales at the throat, and with usually tailed segments. Mericarps divaricate, ultimately spreading horizontally. Seeds with a basal tuft of hairs and a long apical awn. Leaves usually opposite, with axillary glands. — Species 35. Tropical and South Africa. Some species yield vegetable silk, poisons, and medicaments, or serve as ornamental plants. (Including *Roupellia* Baill. and *Zygonerion* Baill.)

Strophanthus P. DC.

13. Corolla bell-, pitcher-, or funnel-shaped, usually small and with scales in the tube. Calyx-segments with 3—5 glands or without glands at the base. Twining shrubs. 14

Corolla salver-shaped and more or less constricted at the mouth, usually large and without scales in the tube. 18

14. Calyx and corolla very large ; corolla white, with a glabrous tube, the segments short and overlapping to the right. Filaments thickened above. Anthers acuminate. Disc cupular, lobed. Stigmatic head conical. Leaves with distant nerves and axillary glands. Flowers in terminal cymes. — Species 1. Naturalized in Madagascar.

Beaumontia Wall.

Calyx and corolla small or medium-sized ; in the latter case corolla-segments long. Leaves with distant nerves but without glands, or with closely set nerves and with axillary glands. 15

15. Corolla-segments overlapping to the left ; tube very short, with 10 longitudinal ridges. Anthers very shortly tailed. Disc none Ovules 4 in each carpel. Leaves closely nerved with small, axillary glands. — Species 2. Equatorial West Africa. . . . **Pycnobotrya** Benth.

Corolla-segments overlapping to the right. Disc cupular. Ovules numerous in each carpel. Leaves remotely nerved, without axillary glands. 16

16. Anthers with blunt, reflexed tails at the base and a small, feathery mucro at the apex. Corolla white or yellow ; tube with 5 longitudinal ridges inside, without scales or swellings. Stigmatic head spindle-shaped, with 2 narrow lobes. Seeds with an apical tuft of hairs. — Species 5. West Africa and equatorial Lake-region. One species yields rubber.

                                              Motandra A. DC.

    Anthers with pointed, almost straight tails at the base and without an apical mucro. Corolla-tube usually with scales or swellings above the insertion of the stamens. 17

17. Flowers in dense axillary cymes, inconspicuous. Corolla-lobes as long as or shorter than the tube, broad. Stigmatic head conical, crowned by a 2-cleft point. — Species 5. Central Africa. . . . **Zygodia** Benth.

    Flowers in terminal and axillary panicles or corymbs, more rarely in few-flowered cymes. Corolla-lobes as long as or longer than the tube, usually narrow. Stigmatic head campanulate. Seeds with an apical tuft of hairs. — Species 20. West Africa and Madagascar. One species yields rubber. (Including *Codonura* K. Schum., *Guerkea* K. Schum., and *Perinerion* Baill.) . . . . **Baissea** A. DC.

18. Calyx with 5 glands inside the base. Disc none. Twining shrubs. Stipules usually present. 19

    Calyx with numerous glands inside the base. Erect shrubs or trees. Stipules absent. 20

19. Ovary 1, entire, more or less completely 2-celled — Species 1. West Africa. (Under *Alafia* Thouars). . . . . **Holalafia** Stapf

    Ovaries 2, free. — Species 15. Tropics. (Including *Ectinocladus* Benth.)

                                            Alafia Thouars

20. Corolla-lobes overlapping to the left. Calyx with unequal segments. Disc absent. Ovary 1, two-celled. — Species 1. Madagascar.

                                    Ochronerium Baill.

    Corolla-lobes overlapping to the right. Disc present. Ovaries 2, free.   21

21. Flowers in many-flowered, axillary cymes. Corolla fleshy, white or yellowish ; segments not folded in the bud. Stigmatic head ovoid. Mericarps oblong or spindle-shaped. Seeds with a feathery, basal awn. — Species 3. Central Africa. One of them (*F. elastica* Stapf, Ireh-tree) yields rubber (Lagos-rubber). (Under *Kickxia* Blume)

                                      Funtumia Stapf

    Flowers solitary or in few-flowered fascicles. Corolla not fleshy, usually red ; segments folded lengthwise in the bud. Stigmatic head oblong. Mericarps linear. Seeds with an apical tuft of hairs. — Species 30. Madagascar and East Africa. Some of the species yield timber and rubber. . . . . **Mascarenhasia** A. DC.

22. (1.) Carpels united throughout their whole length. [Tribe ARDUI-NEAE.] 23

    Carpels only partly united ; ovaries wholly free or in their upper part only, styles usually free at the base. [Tribe PLUMIEREAE.] . . . 33

23. Ovary 1-celled, sometimes incompletely 2-celled. [Subtribe LANDOL-
PHIINAE.] 24

     Ovary completely 2-celled. [Subtribe MELODININAE.] 29

24. Corolla funnel-shaped, large, yellow ; tube cylindric below, much widened
above. Disc ring-shaped. Calyx without glands. Stamens inserted
somewhat below the mouth of the corolla-tube. Fruit a woody, spinous,
2-valved capsule. Seeds winged, with fleshy albumen. Erect shrubs. —
Species 1. Naturalized in the tropics. An ornamental and medicinal
plant. . . . . **Allamanda** L.

     Corolla salver-shaped ; tube more or less cylindric. Disc none. Fruit
a berry. 25

25. Anthers tailed at the base. Stamens inserted in the middle of the corolla-
tube. Calyx small, with 5 small glands within. Ovary incompletely
2-celled. Style short. Seeds with fleshy, ruminate albumen. Erect
shrubs or trees. — Species 5. West Africa. Used medicinally. (*Iboga*
Schum.) . . . . **Tabernanthe** Baill.

     Anthers not tailed. Calyx small and without glands inside, or large and
with numerous glands within. Seeds with horny albumen. Twining
shrubs, more rarely erect shrubs or undershrubs. 26

26. Stamens inserted near the mouth of the corolla-tube. Style long, usually
hairy. Calyx without glands. — Species 35. Central Africa. Some
species yield rubber and edible fruits. (Including *Sclerodictyon* Pierre)

                                         Carpodinus R. Br.

     Stamens inserted near the base or the middle of the corolla-tube. Style
short or rather short, usually glabrous. 27

27. Calyx large, with numerous filiform glands within, spreading or bent back
in the fruit. Corolla fleshy. Placentas much projecting. Pericarp
woody. Flowers in terminal panicles. — Species 1. West Africa
(Congo). (Under *Landolphia* Beauv.) . . . **Vahadenia** Stapf

     Calyx small, without glands on the inside. 28

28. Flowers in axillary, or axillary and terminal cymes. Ovules 12—16 ;
placentas much projecting. Glabrous plants. — Species 25. Central
Africa. Several species yield rubber. (Including *Aphanostylis* Pierre
and *Cylindropsis* Pierre). (Plate 129.) . . **Clitandra** Benth.

     Flowers in terminal panicles or corymbs sometimes overtopped by barren
shoots and then apparently lateral. — Species 45. Tropical and South
Africa. Several species yield rubber, dyes, and edible fruits, from
which drinks are prepared. (*Pacourea* Aubl., including *Ancylobothrys*
Pierre and *Vahea* Lam.) . . . . **Landolphia** Beauv.

29. (23.) Carpels cohering along the ventral suture only. Ovules numerous,
in several rows. Stigmatic head glabrous. Stamens inserted in the
upper half of the corolla-tube. Fruit usually of 2 spreading berries.
Trees. Leaves opposite, with numerous axillary glands. Flowers in

terminal false umbels. — Species 1. West Africa. (Under *Taber-naemontana* L.) . . . . **Picralima** Pierre

Carpels wholly connate. Fruit entire. 30

30. Ovules numerous in each cell, in several rows. Disc none. Stamens inserted in the lower half of the corolla-tube. Calyx without glands. Fruit a capsule. Seeds ciliate. Erect shrubs. Leaves whorled. — Species 1. Madagascar. . . . . . . **Craspidosperma** Boj.

Ovules 1—10 in each cell, in one or two rows. 31

31. Stamens inserted in the lower half of the corolla-tube. Anthers linear. Calyx-tube with many glands inside. Disc ring-shaped. Stigmatic head cylindrical. Unarmed, climbing shrubs. — Species 1. West Africa (Congo). . . . . **Cyclocotyla** Stapf

Stamens inserted in the upper half of the corolla-tube. Stigmatic head crowned by a hairy point. Fruit a berry. Leaves opposite, with a few axillary glands or without glands. 32

32. Stem unarmed, erect, woody. Bark bitter, poisonous. Inflorescences axillary. Ovules 1—2 in each ovary-cell. — Species 4. Tropical and South Africa. They yield arrow-poison and are used as ornamental plants. (*Toxicophloea* Harv.) . . . . . **Acocanthera** Don

Stem spinous. Bark not bitter nor poisonous. Inflorescences terminal or pseudo-axillary. — Species 12. Tropical and South Africa. Some species yield timber, edible fruits, and medicaments, or serve as hedge plants. (*Arduina* Mill., *Carandas* Adans.) . . . . **Carissa** L.

33. (22.) Ovules 2—6 in each carpel. 34

Ovules 8 or more in each carpel. 42

34. Placentas much projecting. Fruit drupaceous. Trees or shrubs. [Sub-tribe CERBERINAE.] 35

Placentas little projecting. Corolla-lobes overlapping to the left. Leaves opposite or whorled. [Subtribe RAUWOLFIINAE.] 38

35. Corolla without scales at the throat; segments overlapping to the right. Calyx-segments blunt, imbricate in bud. Anthers pointed. Leaves opposite or whorled. — Species 1. Madagascar and neighbouring islands. Yields timber, dyes, and medicaments. . **Ochrosia** Juss.

Corolla with scales at the throat; segments overlapping to the left. Calyx-segments pointed. Leaves alternate. 36

36. Calyx with many glands. Corolla yellow. Disc present. Ovules 2 in a carpel. — Species 1 (*Th. neriifolia* Juss.). Cultivated in the tropics. The seeds yield oil. . . . . **Thevetia** L.

Calyx without glands. Corolla white or reddish. Disc absent. Ovules 4 in a carpel. 37

37. Calyx-segments broadened at the base, imbricate in bud, persistent. Corolla-tube slightly widened at the throat. Anthers blunt. Pericarp not fibrous. — Species 1. Madagascar. Yields timber and poison.

Tanghinia Thouars

Calyx-segments narrowed at the base, open in bud, deciduous.   Corolla-
tube constricted at the throat.   Anthers pointed.   Pericarp fibrous. —
Species 1.   Madagascar and neighbouring islands.   Yields oil, poison,
and medicaments. . . . .   **Cerbera** L.

38. Ovules 4—6 in a carpel, in two rows.   Disc and glands of the calyx obscure
    or wanting.   Seeds with ruminate albumen.   Leaves remotely-nerved,
    usually whorled. — Species 4.   Madagascar.   (*Gynopogon* Forst.)
    Alyxia R. Br.
    Ovules 2—4 in a carpel, in one row.   Seeds with uniform albumen or
    without albumen.   Leaves usually closely-nerved.   39

39. Disc distinctly developed, cup-shaped.   Calyx without glands at the base.
    Stigmatic head short-cylindrical with a membranous margin at the base.
    Fruit drupaceous.   Seeds with a fleshy albumen.   Leaves with numerous
    axillary glands, usually whorled. — Species 25.   Tropical and South
    Africa.   Some species yield timber and medicaments.   **Rauwolfia** L.
    Disc obscure or wanting.   Anthers pointed.   Leaves with hardly per-
    ceptible axillary glands or without glands.   40

40. Calyx with glands at the base.   Stigmatic head elliptical, ending in a 2-
    cleft point.   Fruit berry- or nut-like.   Seeds with a cartilaginous albu-
    men.   Trees.   Leaves opposite.   Flowers in terminal panicles. —
    Species 2.   Central Africa. . . . .   **Hunteria** Roxb.
    Calyx without basal glands.   41

41. Stigmatic head depressed-capitate, ending in a 2-cleft point.   Carpels 2.
    Mericarps leathery or woody, dehiscent.   Seeds winged, exalbuminous ;
    embryo with kidney-shaped cotyledons and a short radicle.   Leaves
    opposite.   Flowers in terminal panicles. — Species 5.   Central Africa.
    One species yields a kind of rubber or resin used as a varnish.
    Diplorrhynchus Welw.
    Stigmatic head oblong-ellipsoid, without a distinct point.   Carpels 2—5.
    Mericarps berry-like.   Seeds not winged, with cartilaginous albumen ;
    embryo with oblong cotyledons and a long radicle.   Flowers in axillary,
    rarely pseudo-terminal fascicles or panicles. — Species 13.   Central
    Africa.   One species yields a kind of rubber, another a poison.
    Pleiocarpa Benth.

42. (33.) Calyx with glands at the base.   Fruit succulent, usually indehiscent.
    [Subtribe TABERNAEMONTANINAE.]   43
    Calyx without basal glands, rarely (*Holarrhena*) the inner sepals with glands,
    the outer without.   Fruit dry, usually dehiscent.   [Subtribe ALSTON-
    IINAE.]   52

43. Stigmatic head with a usually ring-shaped appendage at the base.   Anthers
    more or less sagittate.   44
    Stigmatic head without a basal appendage.   Anthers shortly 2-lobed
    at the base.   Sepals free or nearly so.   Corolla-lobes overlapping to
    the left.   48

44. Sepals united high up, obtuse, usually deciduous. Stamens inserted above the middle of the corolla-tube. Anthers deeply sagittate. Disc usually distinctly developed. Inflorescences terminal. — Species 15. Tropical and South-east Africa. (*Orchipeda* Blume, *Piptolaena* Harv., under *Tabernaemontana* L.) . . . . **Voacanga** Thouars
    Sepals free or nearly so. 45

45. Corolla-lobes overlapping to the right. Stamens inserted in the middle of the corolla-tube. Anther-halves pointed at the base. Disc adnate to the ovary for the greatest part. Ovules about 9 in a cell, in two rows. Mericarps striped, dehiscent. Shrubs. Leaves exstipulate. Flowers small. — Species 1. East Africa. Used medicinally.
    Schizozygia Baill.
    Corolla-lobes overlapping to the left. Disc free or wanting. Leaves stipulate. 46

46. Corolla-tube slightly widened above the insertion of the stamens. Anthers obtusely 2-lobed at the base. Disc ring-shaped. Shrubs. Flowers large, white. — Species 6. West Africa. (Under *Tabernaemontana* L.)
    Callichilia Stapf
    Corolla-tube gradually narrowed above the insertion of the stamens. Anthers distinctly sagittate. Disc wanting. 47

47. Corolla-tube slender or widened at the base ; stamens inserted near its base. Climbing shrubs. Leaves without axillary glands. — Species 8. West Africa to the Great Lakes. (Under *Tabernaemontana* L.)
    Gabunia K. Schum.
    Corolla-tube widened and bearing the stamens at the middle. Trees or erect shrubs. Leaves usually with numerous axillary glands. — Species 35. Tropical and South Africa. Some species yield timber, fibres, rubber edible fruits, or medicaments, or serve as ornamental plants ; some are poisonous. (Under *Tabernaemontana* L.) **Conopharyngia** Don

48. Corolla bell- or funnel-shaped ; tips of the lobes not bent inwards in the bud. Disc ring-shaped, adnate to the ovary. 49
    Corolla salver-shaped ; tips of the lobes bent inwards in the bud. Disc none. 50

49. Narrow part of the corolla-tube short. Bracts small, not forming an involucre. Undershrubs with a creeping root-stock. — Species 1. Equatorial West Africa (Cameroons) . . . **Calocrater** K. Schum.
    Narrow part of the corolla-tube long. Bracts large, forming an involucre. Erect or twining shrubs. — Species 2. Equatorial West Africa (Gaboon).
    Crioceras Pierre

50. Stigmatic head globose, entire, without an apical point. Mericarps 3-winged, not or tardily dehiscent. Erect shrubs. Axillary glands and stipules present. Flowers small, in terminal few-flowered cymes. — Species 1. Equatorial West Africa. (Under *Tabernaemontana* L.)
    Pterotaberna Stapf
    Stigmatic head oblong, crowned by a 2-cleft point. 51

51. Anthers linear, on short but distinct filaments. Axillary glands and stipules present. — Species 2, one a native of Madagascar, the other naturalized in the tropics. Ornamental plants. (Under *Tabernae-montana* L.) . . . . **Ervatamia** Stapf

Anthers oblong or ovate, sessile. Axillary glands and stipules absent. — Species 2. West Africa. (Under *Carpodinus* R. Br. or *Picralima* Pierre) . . . . **Polyadoa** Stapf

52. (42.) Disc reduced to two glands alternating with the carpels. Ovules in two rows. Herbs or undershrubs. Flowers solitary, axillary. . . 53

Disc ring-shaped or wanting. Shrubs or trees. 54

53. Stamens inserted at the middle of the corolla-tube; filament inflexed; connective broadened, hairy. Stigmatic head with 5 tufts of hairs. Corolla blue. — Species 2, one a native of North-west Africa, the other naturalized there and in the Islands of St. Helena and Ascension. Used as ornamental and medicinal plants. " Periwinkle." . . **Vinca** L.

Stamens inserted in the upper part of the corolla-tube; filament very short, oblong; connective glabrous, not broadened. Stigmatic head glabrous. Corolla white or pink. — Species 3; two natives of Madagascar, the other one naturalized in Tropical and South Africa. They are used as ornamental and medicinal plants. (Under *Vinca* L.)

Lochnera Reichb.

54. Disc distinct, wavy, adnate to the ovary. Corolla funnel-shaped. Stamens inserted below the middle of the corolla-tube. Anthers with long, curved tails. Erect shrubs. Leaves opposite. — Species 2. East Africa. . . . . **Carvalhoa** K. Schum.

Disc obscure or absent. Corolla salver-shaped. Anthers with short tails or without tails. 55

55. Ovary half-inferior. Style very short. Calyx-lobes broad. Stamens inserted in the lower part of the corolla-tube. Seeds winged. Leaves alternate, exstipulate, without axillary glands. Erect shrubs or trees. — Species 3. Cultivated and sometimes naturalized in the tropics. They yield timber, perfumes, medicaments, and edible fruits, and serve also as ornamental plants. (*Plumeria* Willd.) . . . . **Plumiera** L.

Ovary superior. Leaves opposite or whorled. 56

56. Corolla with a short ventricose tube and with 5 scales at the throat. Ovules in two rows. Mericarps keeled or winged, long cohering. Twining shrubs. Leaves opposite. — Species 5. Madagascar. Some are poisonous or yield rubber and medicaments. **Plectaneia** Thouars

Corolla with a long, cylindric tube slightly widened at the insertion of the stamens, without scales, but sometimes with hairs or with a continuous ring at the throat. Ovules usually in three or more rows. 57

57. Corolla with a tubercled ring at the throat. Stamens inserted in the upper part of the corolla-tube. Stigmatic head conical, with a membranous

A ⁴/₁

B ³/₁

C ⁴/₁

D ⁶/₁

J. Fleischmann del.

Clitandra Arnoldiana De Wild.

A Flowering branch. *B* Flower. *C* Flower cut lengthwise. *D* Cross-section of ovary.

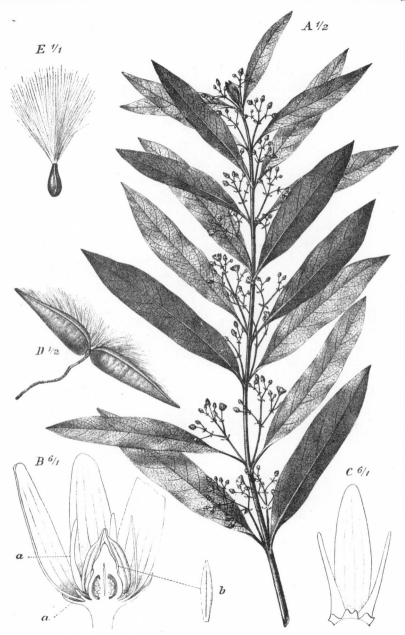

E 1/1

A 1/2

D 1/2

B 6/1

a

a

b

C 6/1

J. Fleischmann del.

Tacazzea venosa (Hochst.) Decne.

A Flowering branch   *B* Flower cut lengthwise (*a* corona-lobe, *b* pollen-carrier).   *C* Corolla-segment and corona-lobes.   *D* Fruit.
E Seed.

margin at the base. Small trees. Leaves opposite. Flowers in terminal, many-flowered panicles. — Species 1. Madagascar.

Stephanostegia Baill.
Corolla without a ring, but sometimes with a crown of hairs at the throat. 58

58. Corolla-lobes overlapping to the right. Calyx-segments narrow. Stamens inserted in the lower part of the corolla-tube. Seeds with an apical tuft of hairs. Trees or erect shrubs. Leaves opposite, herbaceous, exstipulate. — Species 6. Tropics. Some of them yield timber or medicaments. .   .   .   .   **Holarrhena** R.Br.
Corolla-lobes overlapping to the left 59

59. Stamens inserted at the base of the corolla-tube. Anthers with short, pointed tails at the base. Twining shrubs. Leaves opposite, stipulate. without axillary glands. (See 46.) .   .   .   .   **Gabunia** K. Schum,
Stamens inserted at the middle or in the upper part of the corolla-tube. Anthers not tailed.   60

60. Stamens inserted about the middle of the corolla-tube. Anthers acuminate. Stigmatic head elliptical. Seeds winged. Twining shrubs. Leaves opposite. Flowers in lateral, few-flowered cymes. — Species 2. Madagascar and Comoro Islands. .   .   .   .   .   **Ellertonia** Wight
Stamens inserted in the upper part of the corolla-tube. Erect shrubs. Leaves whorled. Flowers in terminal cymes or panicles. 61

61. Ovules in two rows. Corolla yellow, glabrous at the throat ; lobes auricled at the base. Seeds winged. Leaves with few or obscure side-nerves. Flowers in few-flowered cymes. — Species 1. South Africa. Yields timber and an aromatic oil. .   .   .   .   .   .   **Gonioma** E. Mey.
Ovules in 3 or more rows. Seeds hairy. Leaves with numerous side-nerves. Flowers in many-flowered, whorled panicles. — Species 1. Central Africa. Poisonous and yielding cork-wood, a guttapercha-like resin, and medicaments. .   .   .   .   .   .   **Alstonia** R. Br.

FAMILY 201. ASCLEPIADACEAE

Stem usually twining and woody at the base. Juice mostly milky. Leaves simple, without stipules, usually opposite, sometimes reduced to scales. Flowers with bracts and bracteoles, regular, hermaphrodite, 5-merous. Sepals free or nearly so, imbricate in bud. Petals united below, with contorted or valvate aestivation. Stamens 5, usually adnate to the style. Filaments short or wanting. Pollen-grains united in waxy masses or in granules of 3—5 grains. Corona formed of appendages of the petals or stamens, rarely wanting. Disc none. Ovaries 2, free, superior, rarely half-inferior, with many pendulous inverted ovules on a ventral placenta, very rarely (*Emicocarpus*) with 1—2 ovules. Styles 2, united above into a thickened, sometimes 2-parted head bearing on its under surface 5 stigmatic dots and on its flanks between the anthers 5 small, usually horny bodies (" pollen-carriers ") to which the pollen is

attached. Fruit of one or two follicles. Seeds usually with a tuft of hairs and
scanty albumen. Embryo with flat cotyledons and a short radicle. — Genera
118, species 1100. (Including *PERIPLOCACEAE*). (Plate 130.)

1. Pollen in loosely cohering granules formed of 3—5 grains each. Pollen-
   carriers spoon- or trumpet-shaped, consisting of the concave blade
   holding the pollen, the stalk, and the adhesive gland at its base. Filaments usually free. [Subfamily **PERIPLOCOIDEAE**, tribe PERI-
   PLOCEAE.] 2

   Pollen of each anther-half closely united into 1—2 waxy masses. Pollen-
   carriers not spoon- or trumpet-shaped, consisting of a central body and
   two lateral, rarely obsolete arms (" caudicles ") to which the pollen-
   masses are attached. Filaments nearly always united or wanting.
   [Subfamily **CYNANCHOIDEAE**.] 29

2. Corona inserted on the stamens or at their base. 3
   Corona inserted on the corolla remote from the stamens, but sometimes
   decurrent nearly to the insertion of the stamens. 16

3. Corona consisting of free scales or threads. 4
   Corona consisting of scales or threads united at their base. 9

4. Corona indistinct, consisting of minute scales. 5
   Corona distinctly developed. 6

5. Corona adnate to the filaments. Corolla-lobes oval. Anthers ovate-
   oblong. Leaves lanceolate. Flowers in dense, long-stalked cymes or
   panicles. — Species 2. East Africa. (Including *Macropelma* Schum.
   and *Sacleuxia* Baill.) . . . . **Gymnolaema** Benth.

   Corona free from the filaments. Corolla-lobes linear-oblong. Anthers
   linear-oblong. Leaves orbicular. Flowers in lax cymes. — Species
   1. Equatorial East Africa. . . **Baseonema** Schlecht. & Rendle

6. Corolla with valvate or almost valvate aestivation, divided nearly to the
   base. Calyx without glands. Corona-lobes broad, contiguous, usually
   with a linear, 2-cleft dorsal appendage. Stem twining. Leaves cordate,
   connected by a toothed stipular sheath. Inflorescences axillary. —
   Species 2. Central and South-east Africa. Used medicinally.
   Chlorocodon Hook. fil.

   Corolla with distinctly contorted aestivation. Sepals alternating with
   glands, very rarely without, but then stem erect. ; 7

7. Anthers hairy. Corona-lobes thread-like, sometimes broadened at the base
   or cleft at the top. — Species 5. Some of them yield fibre, rubber,
   poison, or medicaments. (Including *Parquetina* Baill. and *Socotora*
   Balf. fil.) . . . . **Periploca** L.

   Anthers glabrous. 8

8. Stem woody, twining. Leaves linear. Inflorescences axillary or on
   axillary dwarf-shoots. Corolla white, rotate, divided nearly to the
   base. Corona-lobes thread-like, 3-cleft. — Species 1. Equatorial East
   Africa. (*Pleurostelma* Schlecht., under *Tacazzea* Decne.)
   Schlechterella K. Schum.

Stem herbaceous or woody at the base only, usually erect ; underground
part tuberous. Corolla with a distinct tube, rarely divided nearly to
the base, but then inflorescences terminal. — Species 30. Central and
South Africa. Several species yield rubber. (*Raphionacme* Harv.,
including *Gonocrypta* Baill., *Kompitsia* Cost. et Gall., and *Mafekingia*
Baill.) . ᛭ . . . . **Raphiacme** Harv.

9. (3.) Corona indistinct, consisting of minute scales. Corolla dark purple.
Seeds hairy all round. Leaves oblong-cordate, connected by a large
toothed stipular sheath. Flowers in axillary panicles. — Species 1.
Equatorial West Africa. (Including *Perithrix* Pierre).

Batesanthus N. E. Brown

Corona distinctly developed. 10

10. Corolla with valvate or almost valvate aestivation. 11
Corolla with distinctly contorted aestivation 13

11. Corona-lobes united high up, usually 10. Anthers with a leaf-like appendage at the top. Pollen-carriers at first hooded, subsequently spreading
reniform. Flowers in axillary cymes. — Species 7. Madagascar and
Mascarenes. Used medicinally. (Including *Baroniella* Cost. et Gall.)

Camptocarpus Decne.

Corona-lobes united at the base only, lanceolate, 5. Anthers with a small
appendage or without any. Pollen-carriers spatulate or spoon-shaped.
Leaves lanceolate. 12

12. Corona-lobes rather blunt. Anthers ending in a membranous, trigonous
appendage. Stigmatic head 5-angled. Flowers in few-flowered axillary
cymes. — Species 1. Island of Rodrigues.   . **Tanulepis** Balf. fil.
Corona-lobes tailed. Anthers without an appendage. Stigmatic head
conical. Flowers solitary or 2—3 together. — Species 1. Madagascar.

Symphytonema Schlecht.

13. Anthers hairy. (See 7.) . . . . **Periploca** L.
Anthers glabrous. Corona-lobes 5, filiform or linear. 14

14. Stigmatic head flat, 5-lobed. Corona-lobes shortly and unequally two-
cleft at the top. Corolla yellow. Flowers small, in axillary panicles.
Leaves lanceolate. — Species 1. Madagascar. **Harpanema** Decne.
Stigmatic head short-conical. Corona-lobes entire or divided into 2—3
filiform branches. 15

15. Corona-lobes provided with 2 lateral teeth at the base ; no lobules within
them. Pollen-carriers with an oval, entire blade. Corolla greenish.
Flowers large, in terminal cymes. Leaves oblong-obovate. — Species 1.
South-east Africa. (Under *Raphionacme* Harv,) . **Chlorocyathus** Oliv.
Corona-lobes without basal teeth ; 5 small lobules within them. Pollen-
carriers with a notched blade. Flowers small, in axillary cymes or
panicles. — Species 15. Central and South-east Africa. Some species
are used medicinally, one of them produces a kind of rubber. (Including
Leptopaetia Harv.) (Plate 130.) . . . . . . **Tacazzea** Decne.

16. (2.) Corolla-tube as long as or longer than the segments. Corona-lobes awl-shaped. 17
Corolla-tube shorter than the segments. 18

17. Sepals linear, without basal glands. Corolla salver-shaped, with scales at the throat. Anthers hairy, with a tailed connective. Ovary superior. Mericarps cylindrical, smooth. Leaves linear or lanceolate. — Species 2. South Africa. . . . . **Ectadium** E. Mey.
Sepals oval, with numerous basal glands. Corolla funnel-shaped, red or violet, with scales in the tube. Anthers with an acute appendage. Ovary half-inferior. Mericarps ribbed lengthwise or winged. Leaves oblong to ovate. — Species 2. Madagascar and Mascarenes ; also cultivated in Central Africa. They yield rubber, poison, and medicaments, and serve as ornamental plants. . . . . **Cryptostegia** R. Br.

18. Corona double, the outer of 5 triangular, the inner of 5 obcordate scales. Filaments rather long. Anthers with a bristle-like point. — Species 1. Central Africa. . . . . **Omphalogonus** Baill.
Corona simple. 19

19. Corona-lobes 2-cleft, short and thick. Corolla bell-shaped. Sepals acuminate, with toothed glands at the base. Anthers ending in a long, awl-shaped appendage. Leaves broad-ovate. Flowers in many-flowered panicles. — Species 1. Island of Socotra. (*Socotranthus* O. Ktze.) . . . . **Cochlanthus** Balf. fil.
Corona-lobes entire or 3-cleft. 20

20. Corona-lobes three-cleft or broadened at the base. 21
Corona-lobes entire, not broadened at the base. 23

21. Filaments united below. Stigmatic head flat. Corona-lobes thread-shaped. Erect shrubs or undershrubs. Leaves whorled or alternate, linear. Flowers in axillary cymes. — Species 1. Southern West Africa (Angola). (Under *Tacazzea* Decne.) . **Aechmolepis** Decne.
Filaments free. Stigmatic head short-conical. 22

22. Sepals blunt, with basal glands. Corolla bell-shaped, with narrow segments. Corona-lobes thread- or spindle-shaped. Erect shrubs. Leaves in clusters, linear. Flowers solitary. — Species 1. Island of Socotra.
Mitolepis Balf. fil.
Sepals pointed. Corona-lobes usually 3-cleft. Herbs or undershrubs ; underground part of the stem tuberous. Flowers in cymes. (See 8.)
Raphiacme Harv.

23. Corona-lobes short and broad, arising from the very short corolla-tube opposite the segments. Stem twining. — Species 1. Madagascar (Under *Pentopetia* Decne.) . . . . **Pentopetiopsis** Cost. & Gall.
Corona-lobes long and narrow 24

24. Corona-lobes thread-shaped. Sepals pointed. Flowers in cymes. . 25
Corona-lobes club-shaped. Corolla bell- or wheel-shaped. 26

25. Corolla wheel-shaped. Anthers with a short mucro. Erect tuberous shrubs. Leaves whorled. — Species 1. Madagascar.
Ischnolepis Jum. & Perr.

Corolla funnel-shaped. Anthers with a long ciliate process. Twining shrubs.— Species 10. Madagascar. Used medicinally; one species yields rubber. (Under *Tacazzea* Decne.) . . . **Pentopetia** Decne.

26. Corona-lobes arising from the sinuses between the corolla-segments. Corolla bell-shaped, with oblong segments. Leaves opposite. Flowers in terminal and axillary cymes. — Species 1. South-east Africa to Lake Ngami. (Under *Cryptolepis* R. Br.) . **Stomatostemma** N. E. Brown
Corona-lobes arising from the corolla-tube below the sinuses. . . . 27

27. Sepals pointed, lanceolate. Corolla bell-shaped with long and narrow segments. Filaments united at the base. Pollen-carriers with an orbicular blade. Erect shrubs. Leaves in clusters. Flowers solitary or in pairs. — Species 1. South-west Africa to Angola. (Under *Cryptolepis* R. Br.)
Curroria Planch.
Sepals blunt. Corolla wheel-shaped. Pollen-carriers with a linear or oblong blade. Leaves scattered. Flowers in sometimes few-flowered cymes or panicles. 28

28. Corolla with long and narrow segments, beaked in bud. Filaments united at the base. Anthers almost erect. Pollen-carriers linear. Stem twining. Inflorescences lax. — Species 15. Tropical and South Africa. One species yields a dye. (Including *Acustelma* Baill.).
Cryptolepis R. Br.
Corolla with oblong, rather short segments, hence not beaked in bud. Filaments free. Anthers inflexed. Pollen-carriers with an oblong blade. Stem usually erect. Inflorescences dense. — Species 10. Central and South Africa. (Under *Cryptolepis* R. Br.) . . . **Ectadiopsis** Benth.

29. (1.) Pollen-masses contained in the lower part of the anthers, pendulous from the arms of the pollen-carriers. [Tribe ASCLEPIADEAE.] . 30
Pollen-masses contained in the upper part of the anthers and attached to the pollen-carriers in an erect, ascending, or horizontal, rarely (*Tylophora*) an almost pendulous position. 75

30. Corona obscure or wanting. [Subtribe ASTEPHANINAE.] 31
Corona distinctly developed. 34

31. Corolla shortly lobed, urceolate, hairy within. Calyx without glands. Corona arising from the corolla-tube or wanting. Filaments short. Stigmatic head conical, notched. Mericarps thin or rather thin. Twining shrubs. Leaves narrow. Flowers of medium size, in usually many-flowered cymes or umbels. — Species 10. South Africa.
Microloma R. Br.
Corolla deeply divided. Corona arising from the staminal tube or wanting; in the latter case filaments none and flowers small. 32

32. Anthers sessile or nearly so. Corona-lobes alternating with the anthers or wanting. Corolla campanulate or urceolate, glabrous or tubercled within. Stigmatic head more or less conical. Mericarps thick or rather thick. Shrubs or undershrubs. Flowers small, in usually few-flowered

cymes. — Species 10. Southern and tropical Africa. (Including *Haemax*
E. Mey. and *Microstephanus* N. E. Brown) . . **Astephanus** R. Br.
Anthers stalked. Corona-lobes opposite to the anthers. Leaves oval. 33

33. Stigmatic head beaked. Calyx glandular. Corolla campanulate. Small
shrubs. Flowers in few-flowered, sessile cymes or fascicles. — Species 1.
Northern East Africa. . . . . **Podostelma** K. Schum.

Stigmatic head truncate or slightly convex. Corolla campanulate or
rotate. Twining herbs or undershrubs. Flowers in racemosely arranged,
umbel-like cymes. — Species 1. East Africa. (Under *Tylophora* R. Br.)
Tylophoropsis N. E. Brown

34. (30.) Corona inserted on the corolla, free from the staminal tube, but
sometimes approximate to it. [Subtribe GLOSSONEMATINAE.] . . 35
Corona, at least the inner, inserted on the staminal tube. 43

35. Corona double, the outer ring-shaped, the inner of 5 lanceolate scales.
Anthers sessile. Calyx glandular within. Corolla rotate or widely
campanulate, glabrous within, with valvate aestivation. Twining herbs or
undershrubs. Flowers conspicuous, in umbels or racemes. — Species 2.
Central Africa and Egypt. Used as vegetables, as ornamental plants,
and in medicine. . . . . **Oxystelma** R. Br.
Corona simple. Corolla with contorted aestivation. 36

36. Corona-lobes united about to the middle. 37
Corona-lobes free or united at the base only. Staminal tube short or
wanting. 38

37. Sepals blunt. Corolla rotate, yellowish ; segments velvety within, with
distinctly contorted aestivation. Corona of 10 lobes, the alternating
2-cleft. Anthers without an apical appendage. Stigmatic head with
5 small points at the angles. Twining shrubs. Leaves wanting.
Flowers small, in few-flowered umbels. — Species 2. Madagascar.
Vohemaria Buchen.

Sepals pointed, with numerous glands within. Corolla almost campanulate ; segments glabrous within, with subvalvate aestivation. Corona
of 5 lobes. Staminal column long. Stigmatic head flat or slightly
concave, 5-lobed. Mericarps short and thick. Erect shrubs. Leaves
lanceolate. Flowers in many-flowered cymes. — Species 1. Nile-lands
and Sahara. Used medicinally, (Under *Cynanchum* L.)
Solenostemma Hayne

38. Corona inserted at the base of the corolla. Flowers in few-flowered
cymes. 39
Corona inserted below the sinuses of the corolla. Calyx with 5 glands
at the base. Flowers in umbel-like inflorescences. Erect herbs. . 41

39. Corolla-tube longer than the segments. Calyx without glands inside.
Corona-lobes strap-shaped, gibbous outside. Twining shrubs. —
Species 1. Naturalized in the island of Madeira. **Araujia** Brot.
Corolla-tube shorter than the segments. Herbs or undershrubs. . . 40

40. Calyx without glands inside. Corona-lobes petal-like. Twining under-shrubs. — Species 2. West Africa. . . . **Prosopostelma** Baill.
Calyx with 5 glands inside. Corona-lobes not petal-like. Mericarps thick, prickly. Erect or procumbent, downy or cottony plants. — Species 7. Central Africa, Sahara, and Egypt. **Glossonema** Decne.

41. Corona-lobes bristle-like, curved. Corolla with linear divisions. Stigmatic head elongate-conical. Leaves linear. Flowers solitary. — Species 1. Northern East Africa. (Under *Glossonema* Decne.) **Conomitra** Fenzl
Corona-lobes broad. Corolla with lanceolate or ovate divisions. Leaves lanceolate or oblong. 42

42. Stigmatic head elongate-conical, 2-cleft, projecting beyond the anther-appendages. — Species 1. South Africa. (Under *Parapodium* E. Mey.) **Rhombonema** Schlecht.
Stigmatic head obtuse-subconical, not projecting beyond the anther-appendages. — Species 2. South Africa. . . . **Parapodium** E. Mey.

43. (34.) Corona-lobes united more or less, usually high up. Corolla with contorted, rarely with valvate aestivation. [Subtribe CYNANCHINAE.] 44
Corona-lobes free or nearly so. Corolla with valvate or almost valvate aestivation. Erect or procumbent herbs or undershrubs, rarely twining or shrubby. [Subtribe ASCLEPIADINAE] 60

44. Corona double. 45
Corona simple, but sometimes with small accessory teeth between or within the lobes. 51

45. Leaves reduced to scales or absent. Flowers in umbels or fascicles. Twining or procumbent shrubs. 46
Leaves well developed. 49

46. Corolla shortly lobed or cleft to the middle, with valvate aestivation. Outer corona cupular, entire or lobed. 47
Corolla divided beyond the middle, with contorted aestivation, small, white or yellow. 48

47. Corolla shortly lobed, large, red. Outer corona entire or obscurely lobed. Stigmatic head 2-lobed. — Species 1. Madagascar. **Platykeleba** N. E. Brown
Corolla cleft to the middle. Outer corona distinctly lobed. Stigmatic head entire. — Species 1. Madagascar. **Decanemopsis** Cost. & Gall.

48. Outer corona of 5 long lobes united below, awl-shaped above. Corolla yellow. Mericarps very long. — Species 2. Madagascar and Mauritius. Used medicinally. . . . . **Decanema** Decne.
Outer corona short, ring- or cup-shaped, entire or shortly lobed. — Species 8. Tropical and South Africa. The stem and the milky juice of some species are edible or used medicinally ; they also yield resin. (Including *Sarcocyphula* Harv.) . . . . **Sarcostemma** R. Br.

49. Outer corona lobed ; lobes of the inner spurred. Sepals lanceolate, with glands at the base. Corolla white or greenish, woolly. Twining shrubs.

Leaves broad-cordate. Flowers in many-flowered panicles. — Species
  5. Used as medicinal and fibre-plants. (*Pergularia* L.) **Daemia** R. Br.
Outer corona nearly entire. Leaves linear, oblong, or ovate. Flowers
  in few-flowered umbels or fascicles. 50

50. Sepals lanceolate, without glands. Stigmatic head with a boss at the top
  and surrounded by a short 5-lobed cup. Erect shrubs. Leaves linear. —
  Species 1. East Africa. . . . . . .   **Diplostigma** K. Schum.
Sepals elliptical, with minute glands at the base. Stigmatic head without a
  distinct boss. Twining herbs or undershrubs. — Species 4. Tropics.
  Used medicinally. . . . . -   **Pentatropis** Wight & Arn.

51. (44.) Corona much lower than the stamens. 52
Corona equalling or exceeding the stamens. 54

52. Corona fleshy, crenate. Stigmatic head capitate, papillose. Mericarps
  linear. Erect herbs with a tuberous root-stock. Flowers in terminal
  panicles. — Species 1. West Africa (Congo). . .   **Nanostelma** Baill.
Corona membranous, lobed. Stigmatic head with a boss or beak. Twining
  or procumbent undershrubs or shrubs. 53

53. Corolla campanulate. Corona-lobes alternating with the anthers. Stigmatic head with a long, 2-lobed beak. Twining undershrubs. Leaves
  small. Flowers axillary, solitary or in few-flowered cymes. — Species 1.
  Madagascar. . . . .   **Pleurostelma** Baill.
Corolla rotate. Stigmatic head with a boss or a short beak. Twining or
  procumbent shrubs. Leaves none. Flowers in umbels. (See 48.)
                            Sarcostemma R. Br.

54. Corona very large, campanulate, corolla-like. Stigmatic head conical.
  Corolla campanulate ; lobes rolled back at the edge. Twining shrubs.
  Flowers in axillary umbels. — Species 3. Central Africa. (Under
  Cynanchum L.) . . . .   **Perianthostelma** Baill.
Corona not corolla-like. 55

55. Corona with concave or laterally compressed lobes. Herbs or undershrubs. 56
Corona with flat, but sometimes appendaged lobes, or entire. . . . 58

56. Corona-lobes obviously united below, concave, 10. Stigmatic head
  pyramidal. Sepals blunt, without glands. Flowers solitary or in pairs.
  Leaves linear. — Species 1. South Africa. (Under *Cynanchum* L.)
                            Flanagania Schlecht.
Corona-lobes nearly free. Stigmatic head rounded or produced into a
  boss at the top. Sepals pointed, with small glands at the base. Flowers
  in umbels or racemes. Stem twining. 57

57. Corolla with broad divisions. Corona-lobes with an inflexed apical appendage. Leaves broad. Flowers in racemes or panicles. — Species 5.
  South and Central Africa. Some have edible fruits. **Pentarrhinum** E. Mey.
Corolla with narrow divisions. Corona-lobes laterally compressed. Flowers
  in few-flowered umbels. (See 50.) . .   **Pentatropis** Wight & Arn.

58. Staminal column long. Corona-lobes 10—15. Sepals lanceolate-oblong, with basal glands. Corolla rotate. Erect shrubs. Leaves cordate-ovate. Flowers in racemes. — Species 2. East Africa. (Under *Cynanchum* L. or *Vincetoxicum* Moench). **Schizostephanus** Hochst.
   Staminal column short or wanting. 59
59. Sepals subulate, with solitary glands at the base. Corolla campanulate or urceolate ; lobes pointed, fleshy at the sinuses. Corona entire or 5-lobed. Stigmatic head lengthened, mushroom-shaped. Erect herbs. Leaves linear. Flowers small, in umbel-like inflorescences. — Species 2. Madagascar. . . . . **Pycnoneurum** Decne.
   Sepals lanceolate or ovate. Flowers in umbel- or raceme- like inflorescences. — Species 40. Some of them yield fibre, poison, or medicaments. (Including *Cynoctonum* E. Mey., *Endotropis* Endl., and *Vincetoxicum* Moench) . . . . **Cynanchum** L.
60. (43.) Corona-lobes distinctly concave, more or less hood-shaped. Erect plants. 61
   Corona-lobes flat or rather flat, sometimes keeled. 66
61. Pollen-carriers with very large, broad and concave arms. Stigmatic head more or less ruminate. Sepals pointed, with numerous basal glands. Corolla rotate. Corona-lobes not spurred. Herbs. Leaves narrow. Inflorescences umbel-like. — Species 10. Central and South Africa. (Under *Asclepias* L.) . . . . **Stathmostelma** K. Schum.
   Pollen-carriers with narrow and flat arms. Stigmatic head not ruminate. 62
62. Corona-lobes with a recurved spur at the base and two teeth at the apex. Anthers stalked. Stigmatic head depressed. Sepals pointed, with many glands at the base. Corolla green outside, red within. Mericarps inflated. Leaves broad. Flowers large, in panicles. — Species 2. Central and North Africa. They yield a kind of rubber, bast-fibre, vegetable silk, poison, and medicaments, and serve as ornamental plants.
   Calotropis R. Br.
   Corona-lobes not spurred. 63
63. Corona lobes with a more or less horn-like appendage arising from the cavity. Sepals pointed, with solitary or paired glands at the base. Corolla rotate. Mericarps thick. Herbs or undershrubs. Inflorescences umbel-like. — Species 40. Central and South Africa ; besides one species naturalized in the tropics. Some species yield rubber, fibre from the bark, vegetable silk from the hairy seeds, or medicaments ; several serve as ornamental plants. . . . . **Asclepias** L.
   Corona-lobes without an appendage in the cavity, but sometimes with scale- or tooth-like appendages at the base. 64
64. Corona-lobes without appendages or alternating with small teeth. Sepals pointed, with basal glands. Stigmatic head usually flat. — Species 110. Some of them yield vegetable silk or medicaments, or serve as ornamental plants. (Including *Krebsia* Harv. and *Pachycarpus* E. Mey., under *Asclepias* L.) . . . . **Gomphocarpus** L.

Corona-lobes with rather large scale-like appendages at the base. Sepals without basal glands. Herbs. Flowers small, in umbel-like inflorescences. 65

65. Corona-lobes curved inwards, attached to the stamens only by their basal appendages. Stigmatic head with a boss at the top. Leaves ovate. — Species 3. South and Central Africa. . . . **Woodia** Schlecht.

Corona-lobes erect-connivent, inserted on the stamens. Stigmatic head elevate-conical, 2-lobed. Sepals blunt. Corolla campanulate; segments with recurved tips. Leaves linear. — Species 1. South Africa. (Under *Schizoglossum* E. Mey.) . . . . **Stenostelma** Schlecht.

66. (60.) Corona of 3 rows of 5 lobes each; those of the middle row 3-lobed or 3-parted. Corolla rotate; segments narrowly overlapping in the bud. Sepals with basal glands. Flowers in few-flowered umbels or corymbs. Erect or more frequently procumbent herbs or undershrubs. . . . 67

Corona simple. 68

67. Ovules 1—2 in each carpel. Mericarps triangular, ending in three spines. Seeds glabrous. Branches long. Leaves palmately 5—7-lobed. — Species 1. South-east Africa (Delagoa Bay). (*Lobostephanus* N. E. Brown). . . . . **Emicocarpus** K. Schum. & Schlecht.

Ovules 3 or more in each carpel. Branches short. Leaves linear-filiform or linear-hastate. — Species 5. South Africa.. . **Eustegia** R. Br.

68. Corona-lobes petal-like, coloured, larger than the corolla-lobes, spatulate. Divisions of the corolla usually rolled back. Sepals with many glands at the base. Stigmatic head flat or short-conical. Erect herbs with a tuberous root-stock. Leaves narrow. Flowers in umbels. — Species 6. Central Africa. . . . . **Margaretta** Oliv.

Corona-lobes not petal-like. 69

69. Corona-lobes very thick and fleshy, more rarely moderately fleshy, and then without an appendage and without a keel or with a single keel on the inner face, but sometimes alternating with small teeth. Stigmatic head low. Erect plants. 70

Corona-lobes thin, rarely somewhat fleshy, but then with 2 keels or 1—2 appendages on the inner face. Herbs or undershrubs. 71

70. Stem woody. Leaves narrow, with minute bristles in their axils. Flowers in sometimes very short racemes. Sepals with basal glands. Corolla campanulate, cleft to the middle or beyond; segments woolly within. — Species 1. Central Africa. Used medicinally. . **Kanahia** R. Br.

Stem herbaceous or woody at the base, tuberous under ground. Flowers in umbels. Corolla divided nearly to the base. — Species 45. Central and South Africa. Some species have edible tubers or are used in medicine. (Including *Glossostelma* Schlecht.) . **Xysmalobium** R. Br.

71. Corolla shortly lobed or cleft half-way down. Sepals with glands at the base. Corona-lobes gibbous within. Stigmatic head truncate or umbon-

ate. Stem twining. Flowers large, in axillary umbels or racemes. (See 34.) . . . . **Oxystelma** R. Br.
Corolla deeply divided. 72

72. Stigmatic head produced much beyond the anthers into a long beak 2-lobed at the apex. Corona-lobes linear. Corolla-segments narrow.. Sepals awl-shaped, without glands. Flowers in lateral cymes or racemes. Leaves linear. Twining herbs or undershrubs. — Species 1. South Africa. (*Oncinema* Arn.). . . . . . . **Glossostephanus** E. Mey.
Stigmatic head not or slightly projecting beyond the anthers. Sepals with glands at the base. Flowers in umbels. Stem erect, rarely procumbent. 73

73. Stigmatic head club-shaped. Corona-lobes somewhat fleshy, with a transverse ridge or a short scale on the inner face. Sepals lanceolate, with solitary glands. Inflorescences many-flowered. Leaves linear. — Species 5. South Africa and Southern East Africa. (Including *Periglossum* Decne.). . . . . **Cordylogyne** E. Mey.
Stigmatic head truncate or depressed and usually umbonate. . . . 74

74. Inflorescences terminal. Sepals with many glands at the base. Corolla white, with long hairs on the edges of the segments. Connective fringed. Corona-lobes purple, with two linear appendages at the base, but without keels. Leaves narrow. — Species 1. South Africa. Used as an ornamental plant. . . . . **Fanninia** Harv.
Inflorescences lateral or terminal and lateral. Corona-lobes usually with 2 keels on the inner face. — Species 120. South and Central Africa (Including *Aspidoglossum* E. Mey., *Lagarinthus* E. Mey., and *Mackenia* Harv.). . . . . **Schizoglossum** E. Mey.

75. (29.) Pollen-masses 2 in each anther-half (4 on each pollen-carrier), very small. Pollen-carriers very small, broad, pale, rather soft. Anthers with a more or less fringed appendage at the top. Corona, at least the inner, arising from the stamens. Flowers small, in axillary cymes or terminal panicles. [Tribe SECAMONEAE.] 76
Pollen-masses solitary in each anther-half (2 on each pollen-carrier). Pollen-carriers hard, horny, usually of a dark colour. [Tribe TYLOPHOREAE.] 78

76. Pollen-carriers with well developed, narrow arms. Corolla yellow, urceolate, with short triangular lobes. Sepals oval. — Species 1. Madagascar. Yields rubber. . . . . **Secamonopsis** Jum.
Pollen-carriers with short and broad or indistinct arms. Corolla rotate. 77

77. Stem erect, shrubby. Flowers in few-flowered cymes. Corolla adnate to the ovary at the base ; segments very long, spatulate. Corona-lobes 5, filiform. Pollen-carriers without distinct arms. — Species 1. Madagascar. Poisonous. . . . . **Menabea** Baill.
Stem twining or procumbent, shrubby or half-shrubby. — Species 45. Tropical and South Africa. Some are used medicinally. (Including *Toxocarpus* Wight et Arn.) . . . . **Secamone** R. Br.

78. Anthers with a distinct, membranous, flat or inflated appendage at the apex. Corolla usually with contorted aestivation. [Subtribe MARSDE-NIINAE.] 79
    Anthers with a very short appendage or a small point, or without any appendage at the apex. Corolla nearly always with valvate aestivation. [Subtribe CEROPEGIINAE.] 93
79. Corona absent. Sepals blunt, with solitary glands. Shrubs. . . . 80
    Corona present. 81
80. Inflorescence 1—3-flowered. Corolla campanulate, woolly within; segments overlapping to the right. Stigmatic head obtuse-conical. Mericarps short, thick, covered with longitudinal ridges. Branches erect or procumbent, downy. Leaves fleshy, linear. — Species 1. South Africa (Cape Colony) . . . . **Rhyssolobium** E. Mey.
    Inflorescence many-flowered. Sepals unequal. Corolla-segments overlapping to the left. Apical appendages of the anthers ciliate-laciniate. Stigmatic head hemispheric or conical. Mericarps long, smooth. Branches twining, glabrous. — Species 1. Madagascar and Mascarenes.
    Trichosandra Decne.
81. Corona arising from the corolla below its sinuses and consisting of 5 scales. Sepals blunt. Corolla campanulate. Twining, hairy shrubs. Leaves ovate. Flowers small, in umbels. — Species 1. Tropical and South Africa. Yields fibre. . . . . **Gymnema** R. Br.
    Corona, at least the inner, arising from the stamens. 82
82. Corona double. Twining shrubs. Leaves herbaceous. 83
    Corona simple ; lobes in one row, but sometimes furnished with appendages on the inner face. 85
83. Outer and inner corona arising from the staminal column and consisting of 5 scales each. Sepals linear-lanceolate. Flowers in few-flowered umbel-like cymes. — Species 1. Southern East Africa. **Swynnertonia** S. Moore
    Outer corona arising from the corolla, the inner from the stamens. . 84
84. Sepals lanceolate. Corolla with contorted aestivation. Inner corona ring-shaped, slightly lobed. Pollen-masses horizontal. Flowers in panicles. — Species 1. Equatorial West Africa. **Oncostemma** K. Schum.
    Sepals ovate or subulate. Corolla with valvate or almost valvate aestivation. Inner corona of oblong lobes. Pollen-masses erect. Flowers in globose, axillary, partly stalked, partly sessile umbels. — Species 2. West Africa. . . . . **Anisopus** N. E. Brown
85. Corona-lobes united high up, usually numerous. Anthers with a large inflated appendage. Pollen-masses flat and thin. Pollen-carriers very small, without distinct arms. Sepals lanceolate, with small solitary glands. Corolla rotate. Herbs with a tuberous root-stock. Leaves narrow. Flowers solitary or in fascicle- or corymb-like cymes. — Species 10. Southern and Central Africa. Some have edible tubers.
    Fockea Endl.
    Corona-lobes free or united at the base, 5, but sometimes appendaged. 86

86. Corona-lobes with a narrow appendage on the inner face. Sepals lanceolate, with solitary glands. Corolla salver-shaped. Mericarps thick. Twining shrubs. Flowers in dense umbels or racemes. — Species 3. Tropical and South Africa. (*Prageluria* N. E. Brown, under *Pergularia* L.) . . . . **Telosma** Coville
Corona-lobes without an appendage on the inner face, but sometimes with a small, usually tubercle-like appendage at the base of the back. 87

87. Corona-lobes united at the base, linear, erect. Sepals lanceolate, without glands. Corolla with linear segments recurved from the base. Stigmatic head truncate. Mericarps slender. Erect herbs with a tuberous rootstock. Leaves linear. Flowers in fascicles. — Species 1. Southeast Africa to Rhodesia. The tubers are edible. **Macropetalum** Burch.
Corona-lobes free or nearly so. Twining plants, rarely erect shrubs or herbs without a tuberous rootstock. 88

88. Corona-lobes spreading, linear. Sepals lanceolate, without glands. Corolla rotate. Stigmatic head flat or umbonate. Mericarps thick, villous. Twining, tomentose shrubs. Leaves elliptical. Flowers in cymes. — Species 1. Madagascar. . . . . . . **Pervillaea** Decne.
Corona-lobes spreading and tubercle-shaped, or erect, or converging. . 89

89. Pollen-masses very small, disc-shaped. Corona-lobes short, usually tubercle-like. Sepals pointed, with solitary glands. Corolla rotate. Stigmatic head more or less flattened and usually provided with a central boss at the top. Mericarps slender. — Species 25. Tropical and South Africa. Some are used medicinally. **Tylophora** R. Br.
Pollen-masses large or rather large, usually pear-shaped. Mericarps usually thick. 90

90. Filaments united at the base, free above. Stigmatic head produced into a long beak. Ovary glabrous. Sepals oblong or ovate, with solitary glands. Corolla campanulate. Twining shrubs or undershrubs. Leaves leathery. Flowers in racemes or panicles. — Species 3. West Africa. (Under *Secamone* R. Br. or *Toxocarpus* Wight et Arn.)
Rhynchostigma Benth.
Filaments united up to the anthers. 91

91. Anther-appendages cohering into a long tube. Stigmatic head beaked. Ovary hairy. Sepals elliptical, with solitary glands. Corolla campanulate, with linear segments. Twining shrubs. Leaves elliptical, herbaceous. Flowers in panicles. — Species 1. East Africa. (Under *Marsdenia* R. Br.) . . . . **Traunia** K. Schum.
Anther-appendages not cohering into a tube. 92

92. Sepals large, without glands. Corolla funnel- or salver-shaped; tube widened below. Stigmatic head conical. Twining shrubs. Leaves leathery. Flowers large, in umbels. — Species 5. Madagascar. They are used as ornamental plants, and the hairs of the seeds as vegetable silk. . . . . **Stephanotis** Thouars

Sepals small, usually with glands. Leaves herbaceous. Flowers small or
of moderate size. — Species 17. Tropical and South Africa. Some
species yield rubber or serve as vegetables. (Including *Dregea* E. Mey.
and *Pterygocarpus* Hochst.) . . . . . .   **Marsdenia** R. Br.

93. (78.) Stem cactus-like, thick and fleshy, with 4 or more angles or rows of
tubercles, usually low. Leaves more or less rudimentary or wanting.
Flowers solitary or in fascicles, fleshy. Sepals pointed, with solitary
glands. Corolla-segments very rarely coherent at the tip. Stigmatic
head flat or ending in a small boss. 94
Stem herbaceous or woody, rarely (*Ceropegia*) fleshy, but then leafy or
obscurely 3-angled and corolla-segments cohering at the tip, at least
when young. 106

94. Branches divided by longitudinal and transverse furrows into several-
ranked areas, not spiny nor bristly. Corolla rotate or campanulate,
cleft to the middle. Corona-lobes 5 or 10, united at the base. —
Species 7. East Africa. . . . .   **Echidnopsis** Hook. fil.
Branches angled or tubercled, but not divided into areas, usually spiny
or bristly. 95

95. Branches with more than 6 angles or rows of tubercles, rarely with 6 ;
in this case with 3-parted spines. 96
Branches with 4, more rarely with 5 or 6 angles or rows of tubercles. Spines
or other appendages of the tubercles simple. 98

96. Spines 3-parted. Flowers solitary or in pairs, large. Corolla tube- or
funnel-shaped, shortly lobed. Corona double, the outer divided into 10
filiform segments terminating in knobs. — Species 2. South Africa and
southern West Africa. (*Tavaresia* Welw.) . .   **Decabelone** Decne.
Spines simple or absent. Corolla saucer- or cup-shaped. Outer corona
of 5 two-lobed or two-parted pointed lobes or indistinct. 97

97. Tubercles of the stem united into continuous angles, spiny. Flowers large.
Corolla slightly lobed.—Species 10. South and Central Africa. **Hoodia** Sweet
Tubercles of the stem not confluent. Flowers rather small. Corolla
lobed to about halfway. — Species 12. South Africa and southern
Central Africa. . . . .   **Trichocaulon** N. E. Brown

98. Corolla-segments cohering at the tip. Corona double. — Species 5. South
Africa. Used as vegetables. . . . .   **Pectinaria** Haw.
Corolla-segments free at the tip. 99

99. Corona simple, of 5 lobes. 100
Corona double or triple. 101

100. Sepals large. Corolla campanulate, divided half-way down, hairy, inside
red mottled with yellow. Corona-lobes thick, without a dorsal crest :—
Species 1. South Africa to Damaraland. (*Huerniopsis* N. E. Brown).
Heurniopsis N. E. Brown
Sepals small. Corolla rotate or campanulate, divided to beyond the
middle. Corona-lobes with a dorsal transverse crest at the base. —
Species 10. South Africa. . . . .   **Piaranthus** R. Br.

101. Third (outermost) corona corolla-like, arising from the base of the corolla-tube. Corolla campanulate, hairy. — Species 1. South Africa (Cape Colony). . . . . **Diplocyathus** N. E. Brown
Third (outermost) corona not corolla-like, arising from the throat of the corolla, or wanting. 102

102. Second (intermediate) corona disc-shaped, entire; third (outermost) ring-shaped. Corolla rotate. — Species 20. South Africa to Lake Ngami. Some are used as ornamental plants. . . . . . . **Duvalia** Haw.
Second (intermediate or outer) corona ring- or cup-shaped and more or less deeply divided. 103

103. Corolla with accessory teeth between the lobes, campanulate, more or less distinctly lobed or cleft. — Species 30. South and Central Africa. Some are used as ornamental plants. (*Huernia* R. Br.) **Heurnia** R. Br.
Corolla without accessory teeth between the lobes. 104

104. Corolla campanulate with broad lobes or rotate; in the latter case (as usually) outer corona divided to the base. Stem with soft spines or teeth, or without any. Flowers usually large, solitary or in pairs, more rarely in clusters. — Species 100. South and Central Africa. Some are used as ornamental or medicinal plants. (Including *Podanthes* Decne.)
Stapelia L.
Corolla campanulate with narrow lobes or rotate; in the latter case outer corona nearly entire or more or less deeply divided, but not to the base. 105

105. Inner corona-lobes bent inwards and broadened at the tip, beset with short spines on the back; outer short, united at the base. Corolla purple-brown, rotate, cleft half-way down, bearing club-shaped hairs. Flowers very large, solitary or in pairs. Stem with hard, usually brown spines. — Species 2. Northern East Africa. **Edithcolea** N. E. Brown
Inner corona-lobes not broadened at the tip. Flowers of moderate size. Stem with soft, green spines or teeth. — Species 30. Some of them are used as ornamental plants, or as vegetables, others are poisonous. (Including *Apteranthes* Mik. and *Boucerosia* Wight et Arn.)
Caralluma R. Br.

106. (93.) Corolla tubular, rarely funnel- or salver-shaped; tube long and narrow, usually widened at the base; lobes usually cohering at the tip, at least when young. Flowers large or of moderate size, very rarely small. Herbs or undershrubs. 107
Corolla rotate or campanulate; tube short or rather long but wide; lobes rarely cohering at the tip. 109

107. Calyx without glands at the base. Corona of 5 lobes. Anthers with a small appendage at the apex. Flowers in few-flowered umbel-like cymes. Species 3. South Africa and southern Central Africa. (*Barrowia* Decne.) . . . . **Orthanthera** Wight
Calyx with glands at the base. Corolla more or less tubular; lobes cohering at the tip, at least in bud. Corona double, rarely simple, but then anthers without an apical appendage. 108

108. Corona double, the inner with short lobes. Anthers with a small appendage at the apex. Mericarps constricted between the seeds. Twining plants with a tuberous rootstock. Leaves heart-shaped. Flowers long-stalked, in fascicles arranged in racemes or panicles. — Species 8. South and East Africa. . . . . **Riocreuxia** Decne.

Corona double, the inner with long lobes, or simple. Anthers without an apical appendage. Mericarps not constricted. Flowers solitary or in fascicles, umbels, or racemes ; if in fascicles arranged in racemes or panicles, then short-stalked. — Species 90. Tropical and South Africa and Canary Islands. Some species have edible tubers or stems, or serve as ornamental plants. . . . . **Ceropegia** L.

109. Corona of 5 lobes inserted on the corolla beneath the sinuses, sometimes with an inconspicuous fleshy ring at the base of the staminal column. Anthers sometimes with a short apical appendage. Corolla hairy. Sepals ovate, without glands. Shrubs, sometimes leafless. Flowers small. — Species 6. Tropics, Sahara, and Egypt. Some species yield fibre. . . . . **Leptadenia** R. Br.

Corona inserted on the stamens. 110

110. Corona simple. 111
Corona double or triple. 114

111. Corona of 10 lobes united below. Sepals with glands at the base. Corolla almost rotate, deeply divided. Stigmatic head depressed. Erect herbs. Leaves broad. Flowers very small. — Species 1. South-east Africa (Natal). (Under *Brachystelma* R. Br.) . **Aulostephanus** Schlecht.

Corona of 5 free lobes. 112

112. Corolla rotate. Sepals with glands at the base. Pollen-masses minute, orbicular. Stigmatic head with a boss at the top. Twining plants. (See 89.) . . . . **Tylophora** R. Br.

Corolla campanulate or almost urceolate. Erect herbs or undershrubs. 113

113. Sepals lanceolate, with glands at the base. Corolla with contorted aestivation. Stigmatic head flat. Leaves oblong or elliptic. — Species 4. Central and South Africa. . . . . . . **Sphaerocodon** Benth.

Sepals without glands. Corolla with valvate aestivation. Leaves linear. — Species 10. South Africa . . . . . . **Sisyranthus** E. Mey.

114. Corona 3-ranked, the outermost lobes reflexed, the others erect, the innermost the largest. Corolla campanulate, deeply divided. Twining plants. Flowers in racemes, on long pedicels. — Species 1. Equatorial West Africa (Cameroons). . . . . . **Neoschumannia** Schlecht.

Corona 2-ranked. Erect or procumbent herbs or undershrubs, rarely twining, but then flowers in fascicles. 115

115. Inner corona-lobes broad, shorter than the outer. 116
Inner corona-lobes narrow, longer than the outer. 118

116. Outer corona cupular, entire ; inner of 5 small lobes. Corolla campanulate, blackish-red, hairy within, with valvate aestivation. Flowers solitary,

small. Leaves linear. — Species 1. Southern West Africa (Amboland).
Craterostemma K. Schum.

Outer corona divided into 10 lobes. Flowers usually fascicled. . . . 117

117. Corolla rotate, with valvate aestivation. Stem branched. Flowers small. — Species 2. South Africa. (Under *Anisotome* Fenzl or *Brachystelma* R. Br.) . . . . **Decaceras** Harv.

Corolla rotate-campanulate, with contorted aestivation. Stem simple. — Species 5. South and East Africa. (Under *Brachystelma* R. Br. or *Tenaris* E. Mey.) . . . . **Lasiostelma** Benth.

118. Outer corona-lobes 5, entire or 2-cleft. 119

Outer corona-lobes 10, free from each other or nearly so. Pollen-masses disciform. Flowers solitary, fascicled, or umbellate. 123

119. Corolla campanulate. Roots spindle-shaped. Stem erect. Flowers solitary or fascicled. — Species 6. South Africa. (Under *Brachystelma* R. Br., *Dichaelia* Harv., or *Lasiostelma* Benth.) **Brachystelmaria** Schlecht.

Corolla rotate. Roots fibrous, somewhat fleshy. 120

120. Stem erect, arising from a tuber. Leaves linear. Flowers usually in racemes or panicles, rather large. Corolla-segments linear. Anthers usually with a short appendage at the apex. — Species 5. Central and South Africa. . . . . **Tenaris** E. Mey.

Stem prostrate or twining. Leaves oblong or ovate. Flowers solitary or in fascicles or pseudo-umbels. Anthers without an appendage. . 121

121. Leaves ovate. Flowers solitary or in pairs, small. Corolla yellow, with ovate segments. Stem prostrate, springing from a tuber. — Species 1. South Africa. (Under *Brachystelma* R. Br.) **Tapeinostelma** Schlecht.

Leaves cordate. Flowers in fascicles or pseudo-umbels. 122

122. Stem prostrate. Flowers small. Corolla-segments oblong-linear. Inner corona-lobes subulate. — Species 2. South Africa. (*Lophostephus* Harv.) . . . . **Anisotome** Fenzl

Stem twining. Inner corona-lobes oblong or linear-oblong. — Species 2. South Africa. . . . . **Emplectanthus** N. E. Brown

123. Outer corona-lobes erect. Corolla-segments cohering at the tip. — Species 15. South Africa. (Under *Brachystelma* R. Br.) **Dichaelia** Harv.

Outer corona-lobes spreading. Corolla-segments free at the tip. — Species 35. South and Central Africa. Some have edible tubers. (Including *Micraster* Harv.) . . . . . **Brachystelma** R. Br. —

ORDER TUBIFLORAE

SUBORDER CONVOLVULINEAE

FAMILY 202. CONVOLVULACEAE

Leaves alternate, simple, sometimes dissected or reduced to scales, exstipulate, rarely (*Ipomoea*) stipulate. Flowers regular, rarely slightly irregular, usually hermaphrodite. Sepals 5, rarely 4, persistent. Petals united into a 5-angled, 5-lobed, or 5-cleft, rarely a 4-lobed corolla, usually with plicate-valvate aestivation. Stamens as many as and alternating with the corolla-lobes, inserted on the corolla. Anthers 2-celled, opening inwards or laterally by longitudinal slits. Disc within the stamens, sometimes indistinct. Ovary superior, 1—4-celled, sometimes deeply divided. Ovules 1—4 in each cell, rarely (*Humbertia*) more, erect, inverted. Styles 1—2, sometimes 2-cleft. Seeds albuminous ; embryo with folded cotyledons. — Genera 34, species 450. (Plate 131.)

1. Plants without green colour, parasitic. Stem herbaceous, twining. Leaves reduced to scales or wanting. Flowers small, in fascicles. Corolla imbricate in bud, usually with scales at the throat. Ovary completely or incompletely 2-celled, with 4 ovules. Embryo twisted, without cotyledons. — Species 25. Some of them are noxious weeds, several are used medicinally. " Dodder." [Tribe CUSCUTEAE.]

Cuscuta L.

Plants of green colour. Corolla plicate or valvate in bud, rarely (*Cressa*) imbricate, but then stem shrubby. Embryo straight or slightly curved, with 2 cotyledons. 2

2. Calyx minute. Ovary 1-celled with 2 ovules. Styles 2. Fruit 1-seeded, ripening underground. Creeping herbs. Leaves kidney-shaped. Flowers solitary. — Species 1. Abyssinia. (*Nephrophyllum* A. Rich.)

Hygrocharis Hochst.

Calyx distinctly developed. 3

3. Ovary lobed or divided. Ovules 4. Styles 2, inserted between the lobes of the ovary. Sepals more or less united below. Flowers solitary. Creeping or prostrate herbs. [Tribe DICHONDREAE.] . . . 4
Ovary entire. Sepals free, rarely (*Rapona*) united below, but then ovules 2, style 2-cleft, flowers in panicles, and stem twining. 5

4. Ovary and fruit 2-lobed. Corolla deeply cleft, yellow. Sepals nearly free. Leaves kidney-shaped. — Species 1. Tropical and South Africa, also naturalized in the Island of Madeira. . . . . **Dichondra** Forst.
Ovary and fruit 4-parted. Corolla slightly lobed. Sepals evidently united below. — Species 4. South Africa and Abyssinia. . **Falkia** L. f.

5. Styles 2, free or united below. 6
Style 1, undivided; stigmas 2, continuous at the base, or a single stigma. 16

6. Flowers in axillary or terminal and axillary racemes or panicles. Twining shrubs. [Tribe PORANEAE.] 7
Flowers solitary ,in axillary cymes, or in terminal spikes or heads. Ovules 4. [Tribe DICRANOSTYLEAE.] 10

7. Sepals united below, not enlarged in the fruit. Corolla entire, with plicate aestivation. Filaments broadened and hairy at the base. Disc large, cup-shaped. Ovary incompletely 2-celled, with 1 ovule in each cell. Style 2-cleft at the top, with capitate stigmas. — Species 1. Madagascar.

Rapona Baill.

Sepals free. Corolla more' or less lobed. Disc small. Ovary 1—2-celled, with 2 ovules in each cell. Style deeply 2-cleft or divided to the base. 8

8. Sepals unequal, the two outer ones much enlarged in the fruit. Corolla deeply lobed. Disc cup-shaped. Ovary 1-celled. Ovules 2. Style 2-cleft; stigmas linear or oblong. — Species 1. Equatorial West Africa (Cameroons). . . . . **Dipteropeltis** Hallier

Sepals about equal. Disc ring-shaped or indistinct. Ovary completely or incompletely 2-celled. Ovules 4. Style divided to the base; stigmas capitate or peltate. 9

9. Inflorescence composed of racemes. Bracts surrounding the fruit much enlarged. Corolla deeply lobed, induplicate-valvate in bud. Ovary incompletely septate. Stigmas peltate. — Species 2. West Africa.

Neuropeltis Wall.

Inflorescence composed of fascicles. Bracts not much enlarged in the fruit. Stigmas capitate. — Species 2. East Africa. . . **Porana** Burm.

10. Flowers dioecious. Sepals enlarged in the fruit. Corolla deeply cleft. Stigmas horse-shoe-shaped. Shrubs with small leaves. 11

Flowers hermaphrodite. 12

11. Sepals of the female flowers distinctly unequal, the outer much larger than the inner. Flowers usually 4-merous. — Species 4. Northern East Africa. . . . . **Hildebrandtia** Vatke

Sepals nearly equal. Flowers 5-merous. Styles united at the base. Seeds 2. Branches stiff. — Species 2. Northern East Africa.

Cladostigma Radlk.

12. Stigmas filiform, 2-parted. Erect herbs or undershrubs. Leaves small. — Species 4. Tropical and South Africa. . . . . **Evolvulus** L.

Stigmas globose or peltate, usually entire. Shrubs. 13

13. Anthers and stigmas projecting beyond the corolla-tube. Sepals subequal. Corolla small, cleft to the middle, imbricate in bud. Fruit 1-seeded. Prostrate or ascending small shrubs. Leaves small. Flowers in terminal spikes. — Species 1. Tropical and North Africa. Used medicinally. . . . . **Cressa** L.

Anthers and stigmas concealed within the corolla-tube. Corolla folded in bud. 14

14. Corolla small, funnel-shaped. Sepals subequal. Filaments glabrous, broadened at the base and usually toothed on each side. Stigmas more or less peltate. Fruit 4-seeded. Erect or procumbent, small shrubs. Leaves small. — Species 20. Tropical and South Africa. (Under *Breweria* R. Br.) . . . . **Seddera** Hochst.

Corolla large or medium-sized. Filaments not toothed, but usually hairy at the base. Stigmas more or less globose. Twining shrubs. Leaves large or of moderate size. Flowers solitary or in axillary cymes or terminal panicles. 15

15. Sepals herbaceous or leathery, subequal, or the inner somewhat smaller, not enlarged after flowering. Corolla funnel-shaped. Fruit 4-seeded. — Species 10. Tropics. (Under *Breweria* R. Br.) . **Bonamia** Thouars

Sepals membranous or scarious, the inner much smaller than the outer, enlarged after flowering. Corolla bell- or pitcher-shaped. Fruit 1-seeded. — Species 12. Tropics. (Under *Breweria* R. Br.)

Prevostea Choisy

16. (5.) Flowers in axillary racemes. Outer sepals much larger than the inner, together with the 3 bracteoles much enlarged in the fruit. Corolla small, deeply lobed. Anthers exserted. Disc cushion-shaped. Ovary 1-celled. Ovules 2. Stigma 1. Twining herbs. Leaves cordate. — Species 2. Madagascar. . . . . **Cardiochlamys** Oliv.

Flowers solitary or in axillary, sometimes raceme-like cymes, rarely in terminal spikes or panicles. Ovules 4 or more. 17

17. Ovules numerous. Stigmas 2. Filaments curved; anthers much exserted. Corolla entire. Flowers solitary. Trees. — Species 1. Madagascar. Yields timber. . . . . **Humbertia** Lam.

Ovules 4—6. Herbs, undershrubs, or shrubs. 18

18. Pollen-grains smooth. Corolla usually gradually widened from below upwards and without well defined midpetaline areas. Anthers included. Ovules 4. [Tribe CONVOLVULEAE.] 19

Pollen-grains spinous. Corolla irregularly widened, with 5 longitudinal midpetaline areas limited by prominent nerves. 26

19. Ovary 1-celled, sometimes with an incomplete partition. 20

Ovary 2-celled, rarely (*Merremia*) 4-celled 22

20. Stigmas globose. Sepals lanceolate, unequal, not enlarged after flowering. Corolla bell-shaped, shortly lobed. Stamens unequal. Fruit one-seeded, indehiscent. Prostrate herbs. Leaves lobed. — Species 1. East Africa (Somaliland). . . . . . **Hyalocystis** Hallier

Stigmas ovate or oblong, flattened. Fruit 4-seeded, 4-valved. . . . 21

21. Sepals unequal. Corolla bell-shaped, entire. Twining herbs. Leaves ovate-cordate. Bracts small. — Species 1. Tropical and South-east Africa. (*Shutereia* Choisy). . . . . . **Hewittia** Wight & Arn.

Sepals about equal. Corolla slightly lobed. Twining or prostrate herbs. Leaves sagittate or hastate. Bracts large, leaf-like. — Species 5. North, South, and East Africa. Some of them have edible rootstocks or serve as ornamental or medicinal plants. (Under *Convolvulus* L.) . . . . **Calystegia** R. Br.

22. Stigmas filiform. Disc present. Corolla funnel-shaped without well-defined midpetaline areas. — Species 70. Some of them yield an essential oil used in perfumery or serve as ornamental or medicinal plants. "Bind-weed." (Including *Rhodorrhiza* Webb et Berth.)

Convolvulus L.

Stigmas elliptic, disciform, or globose. 23

23. Stigmas elliptic or disciform. Disc indistinct or wanting. Corolla with well-defined midpetaline areas, blue, more rarely white or reddish. Sepals not decurrent on the pedicel, usually subequal. Herbs or under-

shrubs. — Species 5. Tropical and South Africa. Some are used as vegetables. (Plate 131.) . . . . . **Jacquemontia** Choisy
Stigmas more or less globose. Corolla white or yellow. 24
24. Sepals very unequal, the outer much larger than the inner and decurrent on the pedicel, herbaceous. Corolla tubular-funnel-shaped, entire, hairy outside, with well-defined midpetaline areas. Disc obscure. Twining herbs. Leaves oblong. — Species 1. Tropical and South-east Africa. (Under *Ipomoea* L.) . . . . **Aniseia** Choisy
Sepals nearly equal, usually leathery or parchment-like. 25
25. Fruit opening by a lid. Flowers large. Sepals much enlarged in the fruit. Corolla without sharply limited midpetaline areas and without dark lines. Twining herbs. Stem usually winged. Leaves broad. — Species 6. Tropics. Some are used medicinally. (Under *Merremia* Dennst. or *Ipomoea* L.) . . . . **Operculina** Manso
Fruit opening by 4 valves. Corolla bell-shaped; midpetaline areas usually marked with 5 dark-violet lines. Stem rarely winged. — Species 25. Tropical and South Africa. Some species yield fodder and a substitute for coffee. (Under *Convolvulus* L. or *Ipomoea* L.) **Merremia** Dennst.
26. (18.) Fruit fleshy, mealy, or dry, and then with a woody or crusty rind, indehiscent. Ovary 2—4-celled. Stigmas globose or elliptical. Disc cupular. Shrubs. [Tribe ARGYREIEAE.] 27
Fruit dry, with a membranous leathery or parchment-like rind, dehiscing by 4—6 valves, rarely (*Ipomoea*) indehiscent. [Tribe IPOMOEEAE.] 29
27. Fruit fleshy or mealy. Corolla more or less bell-shaped. Stigmas 1—2, globose. Stem twining. Leaves cordate. — Species 2. Naturalized in the Mascarene Islands. Ornamental plants. . . . **Argyreia** Lour.
Fruit dry. Corolla funnel- or salver-shaped. Stigmas 2, globose or elliptical. 28
28. Fruit with a woody rind, 1-celled, usually 1-seeded. Seeds glabrous. — Species 10. Central and South Africa and Canary Islands. (Including *Legendrea* Webb, under *Ipomoea* L.) . . . . . **Rivea** Choisy
Fruit with a crustaceous rind, 4-celled, 4-seeded, enveloped by the adnate sepals. Seeds large, brown-velvety. Ovary 4-celled. Corolla funnel-shaped. Stem twining. Leaves cordate. — Species 4. Tropics. (Under *Argyreia* Lour., *Rivea* Choisy, or *Ipomoea* L.) . **Stictocardia** Hallier
29. Filaments with a large scale at the base within. Corolla shortly lobed. Disc cupular. Ovary 2-celled. Ovules 4. Stigma capitate, 2-lobed. Twining herbs. Leaves usually lobed. Flowers in axillary cymes. 30
Filaments without a scale at the base. 31
30. Sepals distinctly unequal. Corolla bell-shaped. Fruit 2-valved. Seed-coat granular. Flowers medium-sized. — Species 1. East Africa.
Lepistemonopsis Dammer
Sepals nearly equal. Corolla pitcher-shaped. Fruit 4-valved. Seed-coat smooth. Flowers small. — Species 2. Central Africa. Noxious to cattle. . . . . **Lepistemon** Blume

31. Stigmas 2, oblong or linear. Corolla funnel-shaped, white red or violet. Seeds hairy. Plants with star-shaped hairs. — Species 20. Central and South-east Africa. . . . . Plants without star-shaped hairs. **Astrochlaena** Hallier
    Stigmas 1—3, more or less capitate. Plants without star-shaped hairs. 32
32. Pedicels club-shaped, becoming large and fleshy in the fruit. Sepals cartilaginous, pointed or awned. Corolla very large, regular, salver-shaped, white or violet. Ovary 2-celled. Stigma biglobose. Seeds glabrous. Twining herbs. Leaves cordate or lobed. — Species 2. Naturalized in the tropics. Ornamental and medicinal plants ; the young seeds are edible. (Under *Ipomoea* L.) . **Calonyction** Choisy
    Pedicels not much thickened in the fruit. 33
33. Anthers and stigmas projecting beyond the corolla-tube. Ovary 4-celled. Corolla scarlet, medium-sized, salver-shaped, usually somewhat irregular. Sepals herbaceous, ending in a short point. Seeds glabrous or downy. Twining herbs. Leaves cordate, lobed, or pinnately dissected. Flowers in cymes. — Species 2. Naturalized in the tropics and in South Africa. Ornamental plants. (Under *Ipomoea* L.) . . **Quamoclit** Tourn.
    Anthers and stigmas usually concealed within the corolla-tube. Ovary 1—3-celled, rarely 4-celled, but then corolla not scarlet and salver-shaped. Corolla regular. — Species 220. Some of them (especially the sweet potato, *I. Batatas* Lam.) yield edible tubers from which also starch and brandy are prepared, besides vegetables, fodder, and medicaments, others are used in preparing rubber, for fixing sand-dunes, or as ornamental plants. (Including *Batatas* Choisy and *Pharbitis* Choisy).

Ipomoea L.

SUBORDER BORRAGININEAE
FAMILY 203. HYDROPHYLLACEAE

Erect herbs or undershrubs. Juice not milky. Leaves alternate, herbaceous, undivided, without stipules. Flowers solitary or in cymes or panicles, regular, hermaphrodite. Sepals united at the base, narrow, imbricate in bud. Corolla more or less bell-shaped, 5—12-cleft, imbricate in bud. Stamens as many as and alternating with the corolla-lobes, inserted on the lower part of the corolla-tube, equal or subequal in length. Anthers attached at the back, opening inwards by two longitudinal slits. Disc none. Ovary superior, completely or almost completely 2-celled, with numerous descending, inverted ovules in each cell. Styles 2, free or partly united. Fruit a capsule opening by 2—4 valves or irregularly. Seeds with a small, straight embryo and copious albumen. — Genera 2, species 8. Tropical and South Africa.

Flowers 5-merous. Corolla blue. Styles free. Placentas free from the pericarp. Seed-coat wrinkled. Glandular-hairy or glabrous plants. — Species 6. Tropics. [Tribe HYDROLEEAE.] . . . **Hydrolea** L.
Flowers 8—12-merous. Corolla white or yellow. Styles united below. Placentas attached to the valves of the fruit. Seed-coat bladdery. Spinous plants. — Species 2. South Africa to Damaraland. [Tribe PHACELIEAE.] . . . . **Codon** L.

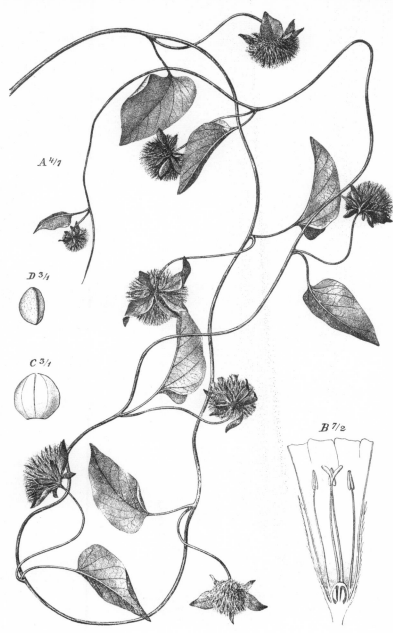

Jacquemontia capitata Don

A Flowering branch.   *B* Flower cut lengthwise.   *C* Fruit (without the calyx).   *D* Seed.

8. Style 1, two -cleft. Shrubs or trees. — Species 30. Tropical and South
Africa. Some species yield timber, edible fruits, or medicaments.

Ehretia L.

Styles 2, free or nearly so. Anthers included. Prostrate herbs. Flowers
solitary, axillary. — Species 1. Central Africa. Used medicinally.

Coldenia L.

9. (1.) Ovary 2-celled, 2-ovuled. Nutlets 2, adnate to the columnar re-
ceptacle by the ventral face. — Species 1. North-west Africa. [Tribe
HARPAGONELLEAE.] . . . . **Rochelia** Reichb.
Ovary 4-celled, 4-ovuled.. 10

10. Flowers more or less irregular. Corolla funnel-shaped, with an oblique
limb and more or less unequal lobes. Stamens usually unequal in
length. [Tribe ECHIEAE.] 11
Flowers regular. 14

11. Calyx-segments 5, distinctly unequal, or 4. Stamens concealed in the tube
of the corolla. Low shrubs or undershrubs. 12
Calyx-segments 5, equal or subequal. Stamens protruding beyond the
corolla. Nutlets seated upon a flat receptacle.. 13

12. Calyx-segments 5, one of which is very small, or 4. Corolla 2-lipped.
Nutlets laterally attached to the conical receptacle. Stems and leaves
clothed with white bristles. — Species 1. North Africa to Nubia.

Echiochilon Desf.

Calyx-segments 5, one or two of them smaller than the others. Corolla
almost regular. Nutlets seated upon the flat receptacle. — Species 3.
Central Africa. (Under *Lobostemon* Lehm.) . **Leurocline** S. Moore

13. Style entire with an entire or shortly lobed stigma. Filaments usually
with a hairy scale at the base. Corolla almost regular. — Species 50.
South Africa. . . . . **Lobostemon** Lehm.
Style 2-cleft at the apex. Filaments without a scale at the base. — Species
45. North Africa and northern Central Africa, one species also naturalized in South Africa. Some of them are used as ornamental, medicinal,
or dye-plants. " Bugloss." . . . . **Echium** L.

14. (10.) Nutlets inserted on a flat or very slightly convex receptacle (gynobase). 15
Nutlets inserted on an elevated, more or less conical or columnar receptacle
(gynobase). 26

15. Surface of attachment of the nutlets flat or slightly convex, rarely somewhat concave and then small. [Tribe LITHOSPERMEAE.] . . 16
Surface of attachment of the nutlets concave and large, usually with a
prominent ring-like margin. [Tribe ANCHUSEAE.] 22

16. Ovary 2-lobed. Nutlets 2, two-celled. Glabrous or papillose plants.
Corolla yellow. Anthers acuminate.— Species 3. North-west Africa.
Used as ornamental or medicinal plants. . . . . **Cerinthe** L.
Ovary 4-lobed. Nutlets 1—4, one-celled. 17

17. Corolla with contorted aestivation, blue red or white. Inflorescence with bracts at the base or without bracts. — Species 15. North and South Africa and mountains of Central Africa. Used as ornamental or medicinal plants. "Forget-me-not." . . . . **Myosotis** L.
Corolla with quincuncially imbricate aestivation. 18
18. Anthers ending in a long point. Stigma entire. 19
Anthers blunt or shortly pointed. 20
19. Anthers oblong, with a very long point. Filaments with a pouch-shaped appendage at the back. Corolla-lobes long. — Species 1. Island of Socotra. . . . . **Cystistemon** Balf. fil.
Anthers linear-sagittate. Filaments without an appendage at the back. Corolla-lobes very short. Corolla yellow, white, or red. — Species 4. North Africa. Used as ornamental, medicinal, and dye-plants. (Including *Podonosma* Guerke) . . . . **Onosma** L.
20. Corolla-tube with a glandular ring at the base. Corolla yellow or violet. Style 2—4-cleft. — Species 5. North Africa and northern Central Africa. Some species are used as ornamental or dye-plants.
Arnebia Forsk.
Corolla-tube without a glandular ring. 21
21. Corolla with long and dense hairs, but without scales at the throat. Filaments as long as the anthers. Stigma 1, almost entire. Low shrubs or undershrubs. — Species 2. East Africa (Somaliland).
Sericostoma Stocks
Corolla with hollow scales, folds, or thin hairs at the throat. Stigmas 2, more or less distinct. — Species 15. South, North, and East Africa. Used for dyeing and in medicine. "Gromwell." **Lithospermum** L.
22. (15.) Calyx shortly lobed or cleft half-way down, enlarged in the fruit. Corolla-tube cylindrical, with scales on the inside. Style simple with a 2-parted stigma, or 2-cleft. — Species 5. North Africa.
Nonnea Medik.
Calyx deeply divided. Stigma usually entire. 23
23. Corolla rotate ; tube short, bearing hollow scales on the inner face. Filaments appendaged on the back. — Species 2. North Africa. They are used as pot-herbs or as ornamental or medicinal plants. "Borage."
Borrago L.
Corolla more or less tubular. Filaments unappendaged on the back. . 24
24. Corolla without hollow scales at the throat, but sometimes with small scales in the lower part of the tube. — Species 2. North Africa. They yield a dye and medicaments. . . . . . . **Alkanna** Tausch.
Corolla with hollow scales at the throat. 25
25. Corolla with long narrow scales at the throat ; lobes very short. — Species 2. Naturalized in North Africa. They serve as vegetables or as medicinal or dye-plants. "Comfrey." . . . . **Symphytum** L.
Corolla with short scales at the throat. — Species 15. North Africa to Abyssinia and South Africa. Some species serve as vegetables or as

ornamental or medicinal plants. " Alkanet." (Including *Stomotechium* Lehm.) . . . . **Anchusa** L.

26. (14.) Tips of the nutlets considerably projecting above their surface of attachment. [Tribe ERITRICHIEAE.] 27

Tips of the nutlets scarcely or not projecting above their surface of attachment. [Tribe CYNOGLOSSEAE.] 31

27. Surface of attachment of the nutlets at least half as large as their ventral surface. 28

Surface of attachment of the nutlets occupying less than half their ventral surface. Prostrate herbs. 29

28. Nutlets beset with hooked bristles, usually margined. — Species 7. North and South Africa. Some are used medicinally. (*Echinospermum* Swartz) . . . . **Lappula** Moench

Nutlets without hooked bristles, not margined. — Species 1. North-west Africa. (*Megastoma* Coss. et Durieu) . . . . **Eritrichium** Schrad.

29. Surface of attachment of the nutlets not margined ; nutlets keeled on the back. Calyx much enlarged in fruit. — Species 1. North-west Africa. Used for dyeing and in medicine. . . . . . . **Asperugo** L.

Surface of attachment of the nutlets surrounded by a prominent margin. Calyx slightly enlarged in fruit. 30

30. Surface of attachment of the nutlets shallow-concave, with a slightly projecting margin. — Species 1. Naturalized in the Mascarene Islands.

Bothriospermum Bunge

Surface of attachment of the nutlets deep-concave, with a toothed margin. — Species 1. Egypt.. . . . . **Gastrocotyle** Bunge

31. (26.) Nutlets attached to the receptacle towards their apex, saccate at the base. Calyx slightly enlarged in the fruit. 32

Nutlets attached to the receptacle by almost their whole inner surface. 34

32. Corolla-segments erect, blue or red. Anthers projecting beyond the corolla-tube. Stigma capitate. Inflorescence compact. — Species 2. North Africa. . . . . **Solenanthus** Ledeb.

Corolla-segments spreading ; tube short. Anthers concealed within the corolla-tube. 33

33. Nutlets distinctly concave on the back, with an inflexed margin. Corolla white or blue, with a very short tube. — Species 1. Naturalized in North Africa. An ornamental plant, also used in medicine.

Omphalodes Moench

Nutlets nearly flat on the back. Stigma broadened. — Species 20. Some of them are poisonous or used medicinally. " Houndstongue."

Cynoglossum L.

34. Calyx much enlarged after flowering, enclosing the fruit. Corolla without distinct scales within. Anthers prolonged at the apex into a long, usually twisted appendage. Inflorescence bracteate. Lower leaves opposite. — Species 20. Tropical and South Africa, Sahara, and Egypt. Some are used medicinally. (*Borraginoides* Boerh., *Pollichia* Medik.)

Trichodesma R. Br.

Calyx not or slightly enlarged after flowering. Corolla with scales inside.
Anthers unappendaged. Leaves alternate. 35

35. Corolla wheel-shaped, with 10 scales or swellings at the base of the tube,
white or yellowish. Anthers short, blunt, projecting beyond the corolla-
tube. Nutlets 1—3. — Species 1. South Africa. **Tysonia** Bolus
Corolla funnel-shaped, without scales or swellings at the base of the tube. 36

36. Anthers projecting beyond the corolla-tube, oblong or linear. Style long.
Corolla yellowish-red. Nutlets smooth, with an entire margin. —
Species 1. North-west Africa. (*Mattia* Schult.)   . **Rindera** Pall.
Anthers concealed within the corolla-tube. Style short. Corolla blue or
violet. — Species 3. Egypt. . . . . . .   **Paracaryum** Boiss.

SUBORDER VERBENINEAE

FAMILY 205. VERBENACEAE

Leaves opposite or whorled, very rarely alternate, simple or compound with
1—7 leaflets, without stipules. Flowers nearly always more or less irregular,
hermaphrodite or polygamous. Sepals more or less united below. Petals 4—8,
usually 5, united below, imbricate in bud, the foremost inside. Stamens 4,
usually in two pairs of unequal length, alternating with the corolla-lobes,
rarely 2 or (*Tectona*) 5—6. Filaments free. Anthers opening inwards by two
longitudinal slits. Disc more or less distinctly developed. Ovary superior,
sessile, entire or slightly lobed, completely or incompletely 2- or 4-celled, rarely
(*Duranta*) 8-celled, sometimes only 1 cell fertile. Ovules solitary in each
complete or incomplete cell ; micropyle turned downwards. Style terminal
or nearly so, simple or 2—4-cleft. Seeds with straight embryo. — Genera 27,
species 340. (Plate 133.)

1. Flowers in racemose (centripetal) spikes racemes or heads. Ovules basal,
inverted. 2
Flowers in cymose inflorescences or solitary. Ovules attached laterally
or at the apex, straight or half-inverted. 15

2. Seeds albuminous. Fruit dry. Ovary 2-celled ; one cell sometimes
rudimentary. Stamens 4. Leaves whorled, densely crowded, linear.
Low shrubs. [Subfamily **STILBOIDEAE**.] 3
Seeds exalbuminous. Leaves usually opposite. [Subfamily **VERBENOI-
DEAE**.] 7

3. Corolla two-lipped, 5-lobed. 4
Corolla regular or nearly so. 5

4. Calyx slightly two-lipped. Upper lip of the corolla flat. Anther-halves
parallel, free. Leaves in whorls of three. — Species 1. South Africa.
Xeroplana Briq.
Calyx regular. Upper lip of the corolla slightly convex. Anther-halves
divergent below, confluent at the apex. Leaves in whorls of four. —
Species 1. South Africa (Cape Colony).   . **Eurylobium** Hochst.

5. Calyx two-lipped. Anther-halves divergent below, confluent at the apex. Stigma entire. Corolla 5-lobed. — Species 1. South Africa (Cape Colony) . . . . **Euthystachys** A. DC.
Calyx regular or nearly so. Anther-halves parallel. 6

6. Corolla 4-lobed, with a wide tube. Calyx 5-parted. Stigma 2-lobed. Fruit dehiscing by 4 valves. — Species 1. South Africa.
Campylostachys Kunth
Corolla 5-lobed, with a narrow tube. Fruit indehiscent. — Species 5. South Africa. . . . . **Stilbe** Berg

7. Flowers in racemes. Corolla unequally 5-lobed. Stamens 4. Fruit fleshy. Shrubs. [Tribe CITHAREXYLEAE.] 8
Flowers in spikes or heads. Stamens 4 with more or less parallel anther-halves, or 2. Ovary 2- or 4-celled. 9

8. Racemes few-flowered. Anther-halves divergent. Ovary 4-celled. Style-apex 2-cleft. Fruit with 2 stones. — Species 2. Islands of Madagascar and Socotra. . . . . **Coelocarpus** Balf. fil.
Racemes many-flowered. Anther-halves parallel. Ovary 8-celled. Style-apex 4-cleft. Fruit with 4 stones. — Species 1. Naturalized in various regions. An ornamental and hedge-plant with edible fruits.
Duranta L.

9. Ovary 2-celled. Ovules 2. Fruit two-celled or separating into 2 one-celled mericarps. Seeds 2, very rarely 1. [Tribe LANTANEAE.] . 10
Ovary 4-celled. Ovules 4. Fruit separating into 2 usually two-celled, or into 4 one-celled mericarps. Seeds 4, very rarely 2. Calyx 5-toothed. Corolla unequally 5-lobed. Stamens 4. Herbs or undershrubs. . 14

10. Perfect stamens 2. Anther-halves spreading horizontally. Calyx 5-ribbed and 5-toothed. 11
Perfect stamens 4. Anther-halves parallel. 12

11. Ovary and fruit with an anticous and a posticous cell or stone. Corolla 2-lipped. Shrubs. — Species 1. Cape Verde Islands. **Ubochea** Baill.
Ovary and fruit with two lateral cells or stones. — Species 6, one of them only naturalized. Tropics. Used as ornamental or medicinal plants. (*Valerianodes* Medik.) . . . . **Stachytarpheta** Vahl

12. Calyx long, tubular, 5-ribbed, 5-toothed. Corolla 5-lobed. Fruit dry. Herbs or undershrubs. — Species 20. South and Central Africa.
Bouchea Cham.
Calyx short, 2—4-ribbed or without ribs. Corolla unequally 4—5-lobed. 13

13. Calyx 2—4-lobed, two-ribbed. Corolla 4-lobed. Fruit dry. — Species 17. Some are used as ornamental or medicinal plants ; one of them (*L. citriodora* Kunth) yields also an aromatic oil and serves as a substitute for tea. (Including *Zapania* Scop.) . . . . **Lippia** L.
Calyx entire or toothed. Fruit fleshy. — Species 10, 7 natives of Central and South Africa, 3 naturalized there and on the Canary Islands. Some of them are used as ornamental or medicinal plants. . . **Lantana** L.

14. Fruit separating into 2 usually two-celled mericarps, enveloped by the enlarged and more or less inflated calyx. — Species 1. East and South Africa. [Tribe PRIVEAE.] . . . . **Priva** Adans.

Fruit separating into 4 one-celled mericarps, surrounded by the not or scarcely enlarged calyx. — Species 4, two of them natives of North and East Africa and naturalized in other regions, the others naturalized in various countries. They are used as ornamental and medicinal plants and for preparing an aromatic oil. " Vervain." [Tribe EUVERBEN-EAE.] . . . . **Verbena** L.

5. (1.) Ovules pendulous from the top of a free, central, 4-winged placenta, straight. Calyx 5-parted. Corolla white or yellow, nearly equally 4-cleft. Stamens 4. Anthers exserted. Fruit dehiscing by 2 valves, one-seeded. Shrubs or trees. — Species 2. Shores of tropical and South-east Africa and Egypt. They yield timber, tanning material, and medicaments. [Subfamily **AVICENNIOIDEAE.**] **Avicennia** L.

Ovules parietal or axile, laterally attached, half-inverted. Fruit dehiscing by 4 valves or indehiscent, usually separating into mericarps. . . 16

16. Fruit a 4-valved capsule. Ovary incompletely 4-celled. Style divided into 2 awl-shaped branches. Stamens 4. Anther-halves spreading horizontally. Shrubs or trees. Leaves with 7 leaflets. — Species 1. Madagascar. [Subfamily **CARYOPTERIDOIDEAE.**] **Varangevillea** Baill.

Fruit a drupe, a nut, or a schizocarp, indehiscent or separating into meri-carps. 17

17. Ovary completely or incompletely 2-celled. Ovules 2. Stamens 4. Anther-halves parallel, with an appendage at the base. Calyx 10-ribbed, 5-toothed. Fruit 1—2-celled, indehiscent, 1—2-seeded. Seeds albuminous. Herbs. Flowers solitary or in false spikes. [Subfamily **CHLOANTHOIDEAE,** tribe ACHARITEAE.] 18

Ovary completely or incompletely 4-celled. Ovules 4. Fruit 2—4-celled or separating into 2—4 mericarps. Seeds exalbuminous. Shrubs or trees. [Subfamily **VITICOIDEAE.**] 19

18. Calyx distinctly enlarged in the fruit. Corolla 4-lobed ; tube included. Anthers included. Stigma entire. Fruit with a thin rind, 1-celled or unequally 2-celled. Flowers in false spikes, 1—3 in each bract. — Species 2. Madagascar. . . . . **Acharitea** Benth.

Calyx scarcely or not enlarged in the fruit. Corolla 5-lobed ; tube exserted. Anthers slightly exserted. Fruit with a somewhat fleshy rind, incom-pletely 2-celled. Flowers solitary or in clusters of 2—5 in the axils of the leaves. — Species 1. Island of Rodrigues. . **Nesogenes** A. DC.

19. Flowers regular. Stamens 4—6, equal. Fruit a drupe. Leaves undivided. 20

Flowers more or less irregular. Stamens 4, in two pairs of unequal length. 21

20. Flowers 4-merous. Calyx shortly toothed, unchanged in fruit. Stamens inserted on the upper part of the corolla-tube. Fruit with 3—4 stones. Shrubs. Leaves toothed. Cymes axillary. — Species 1. Island of Réunion. [Tribe CALLICARPEAE.] . . . **Callicarpa** L.

Flowers 5—6-merous. Calyx cleft halfway down, inflated in fruit. Stamens inserted on the lower part of the corolla-tube. Fruit with a 4-celled stone. Tall trees. Leaves entire. Cymes arranged in a terminal panicle. — Species 1 (*T. grandis* L., teak).   Cultivated in the tropics. Yields valuable timber, tanning bark, oil, and medicaments. [Tribe TECTONEAE.] . . . . **Tectona** L.f.

21. Flowers solitary, axillary. Leaves undivided. 22
Flowers in cymes or inflorescences composed of cymes. Style-apex or stigma 2-cleft. 23

22. Calyx 2-parted. Anthers included. Stigma entire. — Species 2. East Africa. (Under *Holmskioldia* Retz). . . .   **Cyclocheilon** Oliv.
Calyx 5-cleft. Anthers exserted. Stigma 2-parted. Pedicels partly transformed into spines. — Species 1. Central and South Africa. (Under *Clerodendron* L.) . . . .   **Kalaharia** Baill.

23. Fruit with 2 two-celled or 4 one-celled stones. Anthers exserted. Corolla 5-lobed. Leaves undivided or lobed. [Tribe CLERODENDREAE.] 24
Fruit with a single, 2—4-celled stone. [Tribe VITICEAE.] . . . 25

24. Calyx rotate ; tube very short, enclosing the fruit ; limb spreading, entire or obscurely lobed, coloured, much enlarged in fruit. Corolla with a curved tube and an oblique limb. — Species 4. East Africa and Madagascar. Used as ornamental plants. (Under *Clerodendron* L. or *Cyclonema* Hochst.) . . . .   **Holmskioldia** Retz
Calyx campanulate or tubular, not much enlarged in fruit. — Species 130. Tropical and South Africa and Egypt. Some species are used as ornamental or medicinal plants. (Including *Cyclonema* Hochst. and *Siphonantha* L.) (Plate 133.) . . . .   **Clerodendron** L.

25. Corolla 4-lobed, small, white blue or greenish. Leaves undivided. — Species 20. Tropics. Some of them yield timber, condiments, or medicaments. . . . .   **Premna** L.
Corolla 5-lobed. Calyx 5-toothed or 5-cleft. 26

26. Seeds with a membranous border. Fruit incompletely septate. Leaves undivided. — Species 1. Madagascar . . . . .   **Adelosa** Baill.
Seeds without a membranous border. Fruit completely septate. Leaves usually compound with 3—7 leaflets. — Species 100. Some of them yield timber, vegetables, edible fruits, or medicaments. **Vitex** L.

FAMILY 206. LABIATAE

Stem usually 4-angled. Branches and leaves opposite or whorled, very rarely alternate. Leaves simple, without stipules. Flowers in cymose false-whorls, usually more or less irregular. Calyx with open aestivation. Corolla more or less distinctly two-lipped and 2—6-lobed, more rarely regularly 4-cleft, imbricate in bud, the foremost lobe inside. Stamens 4, usually in two pairs of unequal length, or 2, inserted on the corolla. Filaments usually free. Anthers opening inwards by slits. Disc present. Ovary superior, 4-lobed or 4-parted, 4-celled. Ovules solitary in each cell, basal, inverted, rarely lateral and half-

VERBENACEAE.

Pl. 133.

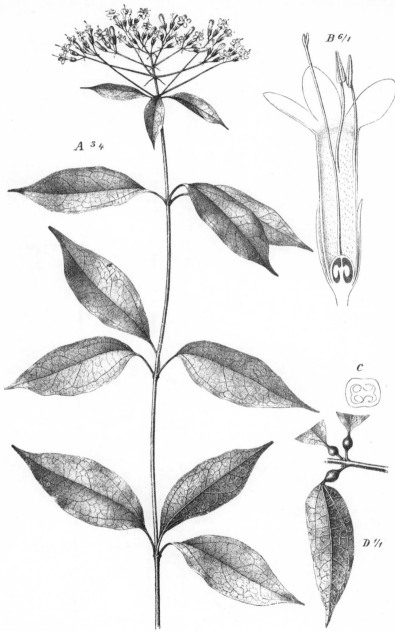

$A\ ^3\!4$

$B\ ^6\!/_1$

c

$D\ ^7\!/_1$

J. Fleischmann del.

Clerodendron formicarum Guerke

A Flowering branch.   *B* Flower cut lengthwise.   *C* Cross-section of ovary.   *D* Leaves with swellings inhabited by ants.

D 5/1   *E* 8/1   *B* 5/1   *C* 5/1   *A* 4/5

J. Fleischmann del.

Plectranthus madagascariensis Benth.

A Flowering branch. *B* Flower. *C* Flower cut lengthwise. *D* Fruit. *E* Seed.

inverted or curved ; micropyle turned downwards. Style inserted between the lobes of the ovary, simple or 2-cleft, rarely (*Cleonia*) 4-cleft. Fruit separating into 4 nutlets, rarely (*Prasium*) drupe-like. Seeds without albumen or with a very scanty albumen. — Genera 70, species 1200. (Plate 134.)

1. Nutlets with a large, lateral surface of attachment. Ovary slightly lobed, rarely to the middle ; style more or less terminal. Stamens ascending. Corolla 2-lipped, with a 3-lobed lower lip, or 1-lipped. [Subfamily **AJUGOIDEAE.**] 2

Nutlets with a small, basal or subbasal surface of attachment. Ovary deeply lobed or divided ; style springing from between the lobes. . 5

2. Nutlets smooth. Ovary deeply lobed ; style springing from between the lobes. Disc equal-sided. Stamens 2. Anthers 1-celled. Calyx 2-lipped, 11-nerved. Corolla blue or white, 2-lipped ; tube glabrous within ; lower lip with a strongly concave middle lobe. Shrubs. Leaves linear. — Species 1. North Africa and Cape Verde Islands. Yields an aromatic oil which is also used medicinally, and serves as an ornamental plant. " Rosemary." [Tribe ROSMARINEAE.] **Rosmarinus** L.

Nutlets wrinkled. Ovary slightly lobed ; style terminal. Stamens 4. Anthers 2-celled ; cells divergent or divaricate, sometimes confluent at the top. [Tribe AJUGEAE.] 3

3. Calyx 2-lipped, with entire lips, inflated in fruit. Corolla red or violet, 2-lipped, with a short erect upper lip. Nutlets oblong, furnished with a large shield-shaped wing on the back. Leaves entire. — Species 20. Central Africa to Transvaal. Some are used medicinally.

Tinnea Peyr. & Kotschy

Calyx equally or somewhat unequally 5-toothed. Nutlets rounded on the back, wingless. 4

4. Corolla 1-lipped, all its lobes being placed below the stamens. — Species 35. North, East, and South Africa. Some species are used as ornamental or medicinal plants. " Germander." . . . . . . **Teucrium** L.

Corolla 2-lipped, with a short upper lip. — Species 9. North Africa, northern Central Africa, Madagascar, and South Africa. Some species are used as ornamental or medicinal plants. " Bugle." . . **Ajuga** L.

5. Nutlets drupe-like, with a fleshy mesocarp and a crustaceous endocarp. Calyx subequally 5-cleft. Corolla white or pink, 2-lipped ; upper lip entire, lower 3-cleft ; tube included, hairy within. Stamens 4, ascending. Style-branches subequal. Shrubs. False whorls two-flowered. — Species 1. North Africa. [Subfamily **PRASIOIDEAE.**] **Prasium** L.

Nutlets dry, but the fruiting calyx sometimes succulent, berry-like. . 6

6. Seeds more or less horizontal ; radicle curved. Nutlets more or less depressed-globose. Calyx 2-lipped ; lips entire, one of them bearing on its back a scale-like appendage and falling after flowering. Corolla 2-lipped ; lower lip usually entire ; tube exserted. Stamens 4, usually ascending, the anticous with 1-celled, the posticous with 2-celled anthers. Disc prolonged into a stalk-like gynobase. Style-branches unequal. —

only naturalized. Tropical and South-east Africa. Used medicinally ;
the seeds of one species yield oil. (*Maesosphaerum* P. Br.) [Subtribe
HYPTIDINAE.] . . . .   **Hyptis** Jacq.
Lower lip of the corolla not abruptly bent downwards, entire, exceeding the
upper lip. Upper lip 3—4-lobed or entire. [Subtribe PLECTRAN-
THINAE.] 21

21. Fertile stamens 2. Corolla whitish or violet. Fruiting calyx berry-like·
Shrubs. False whorls 2—4-flowered. -- Species 1. Tropical and
South-east Africa. The fruits are edible. . . .   **Hoslundia** Vahl
Fertile stamens 4. Fruiting calyx dry. 22

22. Filaments free. 23
Filaments united at the base into a closed tube or a sheath split behind. 27

23. Fruiting calyx bursting by a circular slit near the base. — Species 50.
Central and South Africa. Some species are used as ornamental plants.
(Including *Icomum* Hua). . . . .   **Aeolanthus** Mart.
Fruiting calyx not bursting by a circular slit near the base. 24

24. Fruiting calyx tubular-elongate and curved or coiled, expanded at the base,
constricted at the middle, subequally 5-toothed. Disc one-sided. Herbs
or undershrubs. — Species 3. Madagascar and South Africa. (Under
Plectranthus L'Hér.) . . . .   **Burnatastrum** Briq.
Fruiting calyx not tubular-elongate and curved. 25

25. Fruiting calyx bladdery-inflated, membranous, net-veined. Corolla pink ;
upper lip almost entire. Disc equal-sided. False whorls many-flowered,
arranged in racemes. Shrubs. — Species 1. Central Africa.
Alvesia Welw.
Fruiting calyx not inflated. 26

26. Fruiting calyx with 5 subequal, subulate, rigid, almost spinous teeth. Disc
almost equal-sided. Corolla blue or violet. False whorls arranged in
spikes. Herbs. — Species 40. Tropical and South-east Africa.
Pycnostachys Hook.
Fruiting calyx with subequal but not rigid-subulate teeth, or two-lipped.
Disc one-sided. — Species 160. Tropical and South Africa. Some
species have edible tubers or serve as ornamental or medicinal plants or
for keeping off insects. (Including *Germanea* Lam. and *Symphostemon*
Welw.) (Plate 134.) . . . .   **Plectranthus** L'Hér.

27. Staminal tube slit open behind. Herbs or undershrubs. 28
Staminal tube closed. 31

28. Calyx-lobes orbicular, much enlarged in the fruit, membranous, net-veined.
Corolla-tube abruptly bent downwards ; upper lip entire. Disc almost
equal-sided. Style-apex 2-cleft. Stem ascending. Leaves fleshy.
False whorls 6-flowered, aggregated in panicled racemes. — Species 1.
East Africa. . . . .   **Capitanya** Schweinf.
Calyx-lobes ovate or oblong, slightly enlarged in the fruit. Upper lip of the
corolla 4-toothed or 4-lobed. Stem erect. False whorls in lax racemes. 29

29. Calyx distinctly 2-lipped. Corolla-tube abruptly bent downwards. Disc one-sided. Style-apex 2-cleft. False whorls of 6 or more flowers. — Species 5. Central Africa. (Under *Plectranthus* L'Hér.)

Solenostemon Schum. & Thonn.

Calyx subequally 5-toothed. Corolla-tube straight or slightly curved. 30

30. Corolla-tube curved, gibbous at the base. Disc nearly equal-sided. Style-apex notched. Leaves alternate, sometimes almost opposite or whorled. False whorls in terminal racemes. (See 26.) . . **Plectranthus** L'Hér.

Corolla-tube straight, not gibbous at the base. Disc one-sided. Style-apex two-cleft. Leaves opposite. False whorls 1—2-flowered, in axillary racemes. — Species 2. Central Africa. . . . . **Englerastrum** Briq.

31. Calyx with an ovate, not much prolonged upper lip and narrower, acuminate lower teeth, little changed in fruit. — Species 110. Tropical and South Africa. Some have edible tubers or serve as ornamental or medicinal plants. . . . . **Coleus** Lour.

Calyx with a much prolonged upper lip. Herbs or undershrubs. . . 32

32. Filaments shortly united at the base. Fruiting calyx not bursting; lower teeth suborbicular. Leaves oblong-lanceolate. Inflorescence dense, paniculate. — Species 1. West Africa. **Anisochilus** Wall.

Filaments united halfway up. Lower calyx-teeth acute. Leaves cordate at the base. 33

33. Inflorescence lax, panicle- or corymb-like. Leaves ovate. Fruiting calyx much enlarged, ventricose, bursting at the base. — Species 3. West Africa. . . . . **Neomuellera** Briq.

Inflorescence dense, raceme-like. Leaves oblong-lyrate. Calyx-teeth narrow. — Species 1. West Africa. . . . . . . **Leocus** A. Chev.

34. (8.) Anther-halves linear, usually separated by an enlarged connective. Stamens usually 2. 35

Anther-halves oblong, ovate, or globose. Stamens usually 4. . . . 37

35. Fertile stamens 4, the lower pair longer. Anthers with a very small connective and separate halves divergent below. Corolla obscurely 2-lipped; tube slightly exserted, hairy at the base within. Calyx 13—15-nerved, with 5 subequal acuminate teeth. Shrubs. False whorls few-flowered. — Species 1. Naturalized in the Island of Réunion. (*Mahya* Cordem.) [Tribe HORMINEAE.] . . . **Sphacele** Benth.

Fertile stamens 2, with a lengthened connective. Calyx 2-lipped. . . 36

36. Anthers with both halves fertile, parallel, and attached to a short connective. Disc equal-sided. Corolla almost regular, 4-lobed. Shrubs. False whorls many-flowered. — Species 1. Abyssinia. Yields condiments and medicaments. [Tribe MERIANDREAE.]

Meriandra Benth.

Anthers with one half only fertile and attached to one branch of the long connective, the other half abortive or wanting. Disc more or less one-sided. Corolla 2-lipped. — Species 80. Some of them yield condiments, medicaments, and a substitute for tea, or serve as ornamental plants. " Sage." [Tribe SALVIEAE.] . . . . . . **Salvia** L.

37. Anther-halves globose or ovate, spreading horizontally and usually confluent at the apex, flat after opening. Stamens 4. Calyx subequally 5-toothed. [Tribe POGOSTEMONEAE.]. 38

Anther-halves oblong or ovate, not flat after opening. 40

38. Filaments unequal, the lower pair longer, glabrous. Anther-halves tardily confluent. Disc one-sided. Corolla slightly 2-lipped, the upper lip somewhat concave and notched, the lower 3-lobed. Herbs or undershrubs. False whorls many-flowered. — Species 3. East Africa.

Elsholtzia Willd.

Filaments equal. Anther-halves confluent at an early stage. Disc almost equal-sided. Corolla subequally 4—5-lobed. 39

39. Filaments bearded. Disc columnar, truncate. Calyx-teeth equal. Corolla-lobes 4. Herbs. — Species 1. Southern East Africa.

Pogostemon Desf.

Filaments glabrous. Disc with 4 glands. Calyx-teeth unequal. Corolla-lobes 5. Shrubs or trees. False whorls 6—10-flowered, in paniculately arranged spikes. — Species 3. Madagascar. . **Tetradenia** Benth.

40. Stamens 4, the upper (posticous) pair longer than the lower, all parallel and ascending under the upper lip of the corolla. Calyx 13—15-nerved, subequally 5-toothed. Herbs. [Tribe NEPETEAE.] 41

Stamens 4, the lower longer than the upper, or all equal, or only 2 present.

42

41. Anther-halves parallel or nearly so. Disc almost equal-sided. Corolla white, with a much projecting tube. Leaves 3-partite. — Species 1. Madeira and Canary Islands ; naturalized in South Africa. Used as an ornamental plant. . . . . **Cedronella** Moench

Anther-halves spreading. — Species 15. North and Central Africa. Some are used as ornamental or medicinal plants. . . . . **Nepeta** L.

42. Stamens and styles enclosed in the corolla-tube. Stamens 4, in two unequal pairs, the lower sometimes with rudimentary anthers. Anther-halves spreading. Style-apex entire or shortly and obtusely lobed. Calyx 5—10-nerved, subequally 5—10-toothed. Corolla 2-lipped ; tube not or slightly projecting beyond the calyx. [Tribe MARRUBI-EAE.] 43

Stamens and styles of the hermaphrodite flowers projecting beyond the corolla-tube, very rarely enclosed in it, but then anther-halves more or less parallel or calyx distinctly two-lipped. Corolla-tube usually projecting beyond the calyx. 45

43. Nutlets truncate at the apex. Calyx 10—11-nerved. Upper lip of the corolla slightly convex. Anthers all fertile, those of the lower stamens larger ; halves confluent. Disc equal-sided. Herbs or undershrubs. — Species 6. South Africa and southern Central Africa.

Acrotome Benth.

Nutlets rounded at the apex. 44

44. Anthers all fertile, the halves early confluent at the apex. False whorls of
flowers axillary. Herbs. — Species 9. North Africa and Cape Verde
Islands. Some are used medicinally. " Hore-hound."

Marrubium L.

Anthers of the upper stamens 2-celled, those of the lower nearly always
abortive or rudimentary. Disc equal-sided. Calyx 5-toothed. Upper
lip of the corolla nearly flat. Leaves undivided. — Species 20. North
Africa. Some are used medicinally. (Including *Leucophae* Webb et
Berth.) . . . . **Sideritis** L.

45. Corolla distinctly two-lipped with a convex, more or less helmet-shaped
upper lip. Stamens 4, in two pairs of unequal length, ascending under
the upper lip of the corolla. [Tribe STACHYEAE.] 46

Corolla two-lipped with a rather flat upper lip, or more or less regular.
Leaves undivided. [Tribe SATUREIEAE.] 59

46. Calyx compressed from front to back, 10-nerved, distinctly 2-lipped ; upper
lip 3-toothed, lower 2-cleft, bent towards the upper and closing the
mouth of the calyx after flowering. Corolla blue, violet, red, or white ;
tube exserted, widened above ; upper lip entire, lower 3-lobed. Filaments with an appendage at the apex. Anther-halves separate, divergent. Herbs. False whorls 6-flowered, in dense racemes, with imbricate bracts. [Subtribe BRUNELLINAE.] 47

Calyx more or less equally 5—10-toothed, rarely two-lipped, but
the lower lip not closing the mouth of the calyx. [Subtribe
LAMIINAE.] 48

47. Corolla-tube narrow below, widened at the throat, glabrous within ; limb
blue or violet ; midlobe of the lower lip two-cleft. Disc one-sided.
Style-apex 4-cleft. Nutlets very slimy when wet. Bracts narrow,
awned. — Species 1. North-west Africa. . . . . . . **Cleonia** L.

Corolla-tube wide, narrow at the throat, with a ring of hairs or scales within ;
midlobe of the lower lip concave, toothed. Disc equal-sided. Style-
apex 2-cleft. Nutlets not or slightly slimy when wet. Bracts broad. —
Species 2. North Africa and Cape Verde Islands ; one species also
naturalized in the Mascarene Islands. Used medicinally. (*Prunella* L.)

Brunella L.

48. Style-branches very unequal, the posterior much shorter than the anterior.
Anther-halves spreading, finally confluent at the apex. Corolla white,
yellow, or red ; upper lip very hairy. Herbs or undershrubs. . . 49

Style-branches equal or nearly equal, rarely distinctly unequal, but then
the upper lip of the corolla almost glabrous. 51

49. Upper lip of the corolla much longer than the lower one. Calyx with
8—10 unequal, usually stiff teeth. Disc equal-sided. Leaves toothed.
— Species 30. Tropical and South Africa. Some are used as ornamental
or medicinal plants. . . . . **Leonotis** Pers.

Upper lip of the corolla as long as or shorter than the lower one. . . 50

50. Upper lip of the corolla laterally compressed ; tube with a ring of hairs inside. Corolla red or yellow. Calyx 5-toothed. Disc equal-sided. False whorls 6- or more-flowered, axillary. — Species 4. North Africa. Used as ornamental or medicinal plants. . . . . . **Phlomis** L.

   Upper lip of the corolla not laterally compressed ; tube included. Corolla white or red. — Species 90. Tropical and South Africa and Egypt. Several species are used medicinally ; others are noxious weeds. (Including *Lasiocorys* Benth.) . . . . **Leucas** R. Br.

51. Nutlets 3-angled, with a truncate apex. Leaves toothed or divided. . 52

   Nutlets more or less egg-shaped, with a rounded apex. 55

52. Style-branches very unequal. Calyx two-lipped with entire lips. Corolla red, with a much exserted tube. Small shrubs. — Species 1. East Africa (Somaliland). (Under *Tinnaea* Peyr. et Kotschy).

                                         Renschia Vatke

   Style-branches almost equal. Calyx 2-lipped with spiny-toothed lips, or subequally 5-toothed. Upper lip of the corolla hairy. Herbs. . . 53

53. Calyx-limb broadened, two-lipped, with 5—10 spiny teeth. Corolla white ; tube included, furnished with a ring of hairs inside, slightly widened above. Anther-halves spreading. Disc equal-sided. — Species 1. North Africa (Tunisia). . . . . **Moluccella** L.

   Calyx-limb not broadened, subequally 5-toothed. Corolla white or red. 54

54. Calyx-teeth spinous. Corolla-tube slightly widened above. Disc equal-sided. — Species 2. One a native of North Africa, the other naturalized in the Mascarene Islands. Used medicinally. . . . **Leonurus** L.

   Calyx-teeth unarmed. Corolla-tube ventricose above. Anther-halves finally spreading. — Species 8. North Africa and Abyssinia. Some species are used medicinally. " Deadnettle." . . . **Lamium** L.

55. Nutlets densely clothed with scales at the apex. Corolla-tube glabrous within ; upper lip short, slightly concave, notched or two-lobed, glabrous or downy. Anther-halves usually confluent at an early stage. Disc equal-sided. Herbs. Leaves toothed. — Species 15. Tropics.

                                   Achyrospermum Wall.

   Nutlets not scaly. Anther-halves not or tardily confluent. 56

56. Anthers of the posterior stamens with one half, of the anterior with both halves developed ; halves placed transversely. Disc equal-sided. Corolla-tube with a ring of hairs inside ; upper lip short, slightly concave, entire, glabrous or very scantily hairy. Calyx equally 5-toothed. Herbs. — Species 2. Mascarene Islands. Used medicinally.

                                   Anisomeles R. Br.

   Anthers all with both halves developed. Upper lip of the corolla more or less hairy. 57

57. Calyx funnel-shaped, 10-nerved, 2-lipped ; upper lip entire or 3-toothed, lower much larger, entire or 4-toothed. Corolla-tube with a ring of hairs inside ; upper entire, densely hairy. Anther-halves finally

spreading. Disc equal-sided. False whorls many-flowered. Shrubs or undershrubs. — Species 8. Central Africa and Egypt. **Otostegia** Benth.
Calyx equally or subequally toothed, very rarely two-lipped with a 3-toothed upper and a 2-cleft lower lip. 58
58. Calyx funnel-shaped, 10-nerved, subequally toothed. Corolla white or red ; tube with a ring of hairs inside ; upper lip notched, densely hairy. Anther-halves finally spreading. Leaves toothed. — Species 7. North, East, and South Africa. Some species are used medicinally. **Ballota** L.
Calyx tube- or bell-shaped, 5—10-nerved. — Species 80. Some of them are used as ornamental or medicinal plants, others are poisonous for cattle. (Including *Betonica* L.) . . . . **Stachys** L.
59. (45.) Stamens ascending under the upper lip of the corolla, more or less arched. Corolla two-lipped. Herbs or undershrubs. [Subtribe MELISSINAE.] 60
Stamens projecting straight forwards, divergent. 63
60. Stamens 2. Anthers with 2 confluent halves, or with a fertile and a rudimentary half, or one half only developed. Style-apex unequally two-cleft. Calyx 13-nerved, two-lipped. Corolla-tube shortly exserted, glabrous within. False whorls few-flowered. — Species 3. North Africa.
Ziziphora L.
Stamens 4. 61
61. Corolla-tube ascending-reflexed at the middle, glabrous within. Corolla white or yellowish. Calyx 13-nerved, two-lipped. Style-apex cleft into two subequal, awl-shaped branches. Leaves toothed. False whorls few-flowered. — Species 1. North Africa. Used as an ornamental and medicinal plant. "Balm." . . . . **Melissa** L.
Corolla-tube straight or slightly curved. 62
62. Calyx inflated in the fruit, 15—20-nerved, subequally 5-toothed. Corolla red ; tube included, glabrous within. Style-apex cleft into two equal, awl-shaped branches. Undershrubs. Leaves entire. False whorls 4--6-flowered. — Species 1. North-west Africa (Algeria). (Under *Satureia* L.) . . . . **Saccocalyx** Coss.
Calyx not inflated, 10—15-nerved. Corolla-tube exserted. — Species 45. Some of them are used as pot-herbs (savory), as a substitute for tea, or as medicinal or ornamental plants. (Including *Calamintha* Moench, *Clinopodium* L., and *Micromeria* Benth.) . . . . . . **Satureia** L.
63. Calyx 15-nerved, equally 5-toothed. Corolla blue, rarely reddish or white, 2-lipped, with an included tube. Stamens 4, in two pairs of unequal length, ascending at the base, divergent and projecting straight forwards towards the apex. Shrubs. Leaves entire, narrow. False whorls 6- or more-flowered. — Species 1. North-west Africa (Morocco). Used as an ornamental plant and for preparing perfumes and medicaments. [Subtribe HYSSOPINAE.] . . . . **Hyssopus** L.
Calyx 10—13-nerved. Stamens divergent and projecting straight forwards from the base. 64

64. Corolla two-lipped; upper lip notched or 2-cleft, lower 3-cleft. Stamens 4, in two pairs of more or less unequal length. [Subtribe THYMINAE.] 65 Corolla equally or subequally 4-cleft; tube included. Stamens 4, about equal in length, with parallel halves, rarely only 2. Herbs. [Subtribe MENTHINAE.] 69

65. Calyx more or less distinctly 2-lipped. Leaves entire. . . . . 66 Calyx equally 5-toothed. 68

66. Upper lip of the calyx entire or obscurely 3-toothed; lower lip slightly 2-toothed, almost entire, or rudimentary. Anther-halves spreading. Herbs. Bracts suborbicular. — Species 1 (*M. hortensis* Moench). Cultivated and sometimes naturalized in North Africa. Used as a pot-herb, for the preparation of an essential oil and a kind of snuff, and in medicine. " Marjoram." (Under *Origanum* L.) . . . . **Majorana** Moench Upper lip of the calyx 3-toothed, lower 2-cleft. 67

67. Calyx-tube much compressed from above, 13-nerved. Corolla pink; tube exserted; upper lip 2-cleft. Anthers with a small connective and spreading halves. Style-apex unequally 2-cleft. Shrubs. False whorls 6-flowered, in heads. — Species 1. North Africa. (Under *Thymus* L.)

Coridothymus Reichb. fil.

Calyx-tube more or less cylindric, not or slightly compressed. Anthers with a thick connective. Style-apex equally or subequally 2-cleft. — Species 20. North Africa and Abyssinia. Some species yield condiments, medicaments, and an essential oil, or serve as ornamental plants. " Thyme." . . . . **Thymus** L.

68. Corolla-tube more or less projecting beyond the calyx. Anthers exserted, with spreading halves. Style-apex unequally 2-cleft. Herbs. — Species 5. North Africa. They yield condiments, medicaments, and an essential oil. . . . . **Origanum** L. Corolla-tube not projecting beyond the calyx. Anthers with parallel halves. Shrubs. — Species 9. Madeira and Canary Islands. **Bystropogon** L'Hér.

69. Stamens 2. Anther-halves finally spreading. Calyx equally 5-toothed, glabrous within. Nutlets truncate at the apex. Leaves toothed. False whorls many-flowered, axillary. Bracteoles small. — Species 1. North Africa. Used medicinally. . . . . . . **Lycopus** L. Stamens 4. Nutlets round at the apex. 70

70. Calyx equally 4-toothed, hairy within; teeth with an awn-like process on the back. Stem decumbent. Leaves linear. False whorls axillary, many-flowered. Bracteoles large, as long as the flowers. — Species 1. North-West Africa. Used medicinally. . . . . . **Preslia** Opiz Calyx equally or subequally 5-toothed; teeth without an awn-like process on the back. Bracteoles small. — Species 9. North Africa, northern Central Africa, and South Africa, also naturalized in Madagascar, its neighbouring islands, and St. Helena. Some species (especially *M. piperita* L., peppermint) yield condiments, medicaments, insectifuges, and an essential oil used as an aromatic or for medicinal purposes; several serve as ornamental plants. " Mint." . . . **Mentha** L.

SUBORDER SOLANINEAE

FAMILY 207. SOLANACEAE

Leaves alternate, sometimes in pairs, simple, but sometimes (*Solanum*) dissected.   Flowers solitary or in cymose inflorescences, 5-merous, very rarely 4- or pleio-merous.ˈ Corolla of united petals, usually regular or nearly so, mostly folded lengthwise in the bud.   Stamens as many as the divisions of the corolla and alternating with them, rarely some of them rudimentary.   Anthers turned inwards.   Disc usually distinct.   Ovary superior, 2—4-, rarely 5- or more-celled, usually 2-celled with the partition oblique to the median plane of the flower, rarely (*Capsicum*) incompletely septate.   Ovules axile, usually numerous, inverted.   Style simple ; stigma usually 2-lobed.   Fruit a berry or a capsule. Seeds albuminous. — Genera 16, species 220.   (Including *ATROPACEAE*.) (Plate 135.)

1. Fertile stamens fewer than the corolla-lobes, 2, rarely 4.   Corolla violet or yellow, tube- or funnel-shaped ; lobes 5, club-shaped, alternating with entire or 2-lobed appendages.   Ovary 2-celled.   Fruit a capsule.   Seeds with straight embryo.   Herbs.   Leaves undivided.   Flowers panicled. — Species 2.   Central Africa.   They yield fish-poison.   [Tribe SAL-PIGLOSSIDEAE.] . . . . **Schwenkia** L.
    Fertile stamens as many as the corolla-lobes, 5, rarely 4. 2

2. Ovary 3—5-celled.   Embryo much curved.   Leaves entire, toothed, or lobed.   Flowers solitary, large. 3
    Ovary 2-celled, rarely incompletely 2-celled or many-celled by cultivation.   4

3. Ovary-cells and placentas unequal.   Calyx 5-partite with obcordate segments, enlarged after flowering and enveloping the fruit.   Corolla blue, regular, bell-shaped.   Fruit a berry.   Herbs. — Species 1.   Naturalized in various regions.   An ornamental and medicinal plant.   (*Pentagonia* Heist.)   [Tribe NICANDREAE.] . . . **Nicandra** Adams
    Ovary-cells and placentas equal, 4.   Calyx tubular, 5-lobed, deciduous excepting the base.   Corolla funnel-shaped, with a long tube. — Species 5, one of them only naturalized.   They yield poisons, dyes, intoxicants, and medicaments, and serve as ornamental plants.   " Thorn-apple." (Including *Brugmansia* Pers.)   [Tribe DATUREAE.] . **Datura** L.

4. Seeds with a straight or slightly curved embryo, usually thick.   Corolla with a long tube and a comparatively narrow limb.   Flowers in cymes or cymose panicles.   Leaves undivided.   [Tribe CESTREAE.] . 5
    Seeds with a strongly curved embryo, flat.   [Tribe SOLANEAE.] . . 6

5. Fruit a berry with one or few large seeds.   Ovules few in each ovary-cell. Stamens inserted at or below the middle of the corolla-tube.   Flowers in cymes.   Trees or shrubs. — Species 2.   Naturalized in several islands. Ornamental and medicinal plants.   [Subtribe CESTRINAE.]

Cestrum L.

2 H

Fruit a capsule with many small seeds.   Ovules many in each ovary-cell. Stamens inserted in the lower part of the corolla-tube.   Flowers in cymose, raceme- or panicle-like inflorescences. Herbs or undershrubs. — Species 5.   Cultivated and sometimes naturalized in various regions. They yield tobacco (especially from *N. tabacum* L. and *rustica* L.), lamp-oil, vermin-poison, and medicaments, and serve as ornamental plants. [Subtribe NICOTIANINAE.] . . . . **Nicotiana** L.

6. Fruit a capsule opening by a lid. Calyx enlarged in the fruit. Corolla widely funnel-shaped, 5-lobed, imbricate in bud, white or yellow with red or violet veins. Herbs. Leaves alternate, undivided or lobed. Flowers solitary, axillary. — Species 8. North and Central Africa. They are poisonous and yield oil and medicaments. " Henbane." [Subtribe HYOSCYAMINAE.] . . . . **Hyoscyamus** L.

Fruit a berry, indehiscent or at length bursting irregularly. Corolla tubular, campanulate, or rotate. 7

7. Anthers attached at the middle of the back. Corolla campanulate, 5-cleft. Root thick. Stem very short. Leaves radical, undivided. Flowers solitary, axillary. — Species 2. North Africa. Poisonous and used in medicine and magic. " Mandrake." [Subtribe MAN-DRAGORINAE.] . . . . **Mandragora** Juss.

Anthers attached at the base or the lower part of the back. Stem well developed. Leaves alternate. 8

8. Corolla tubular or campanulate ; limb narrow in proportion to the tube. Calyx not or slightly enlarged in the fruit. Flowers solitary or in clusters. Leaves undivided. [Subtribe LYCIINAE.] 9

Corolla rotate or campanulate ; limb broad. [Subtribe SOLANINAE.] . 12

9. Corolla irregular, with an oblique limb, violet, folded in the bud. Stamens inserted at the base of the corolla-tube ; filaments short, as long as or shorter than the anthers. Fruit almost dry. Herbs. Leaves lobed. Flowers in pairs in the leaf-axils. — Species 1. North-west Africa (Algeria). Used medicinally. . . . . **Triguera** Cav.

Corolla regular. Fruit succulent. 10

10. Corolla-tube narrow ; lobes imbricate in bud. Stamens inserted at or below the middle of the corolla-tube. Shrubs or trees. — Species 25. Some of them are poisonous ; several species are used as hedge-plants or in medicine. . . . . **Lycium** L.

Corolla-tube wide. Fruit globose. 11

11. Calyx 5-lobed. Corolla brownish-green, urceolate, valvate in bud. Stamens inserted above the middle of the corolla-tube. Shrubs. Flowers in clusters. — Species 1. Mountains of Central Africa. (Plate 135.) . . . . **Discopodium** Hochst.

Calyx 5-cleft. Corolla brownish-violet or dull-red, campanulate, imbricate in bud. Stamens inserted at the base of the corolla-tube ; filaments long. Herbs. Flowers solitary. — Species 1 (*A. Belladonna* L., dwale). North-west Africa (Algeria). Poisonous and yielding oil and medicaments. . . . . **Atropa** L.

A ½

B ⁵/₂

D ⁵/₁

C ⁵/₁

J. Fleischmann del.

Discopodium penninervium Hochst.

A Flowering branch. *B* Flower. *C* Flower cut lengthwise. *D* Cross-section of ovary.

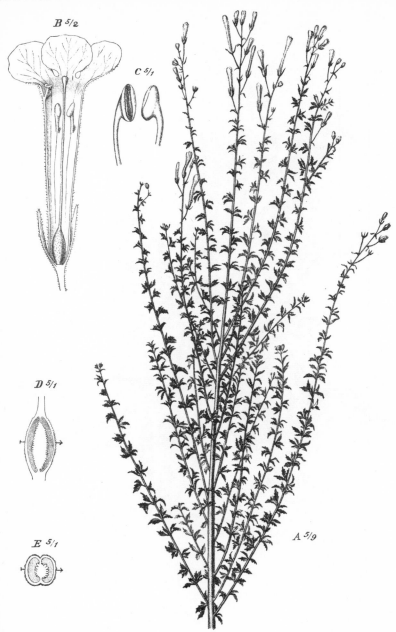

B 5/2

C 5/1

D 5/1

E 5/1

A 5/9

J. Fleischmann del.

Chaenostoma Burkeanum (Benth.) Wettst.

A Flowering branch.   *B* Flower cut lengthwise.   *C* Stamens.   *D* Ovary cut lengthwise.   *E* Ovary cut across.

12. Anthers cohering or opening by apical pores. Corolla rotate or widely campanulate. Calyx not or slightly enlarged in the fruit. Flowers usually in cymose, umbel-, raceme-, or panicle-like inflorescences. — Species 150 ; three of them (*S. tuberosum* L., potato, *S. Melongena* L., egg-plant, and *S. Lycopericum* L., tomato) only cultivated. Several species yield edible fruits or tubers, from which starch sugar and alcohol are prepared, also tanning and dyeing materials, a substitute for soap, a means to coagulate milk, and various medicaments ; others serve as vegetables or as ornamental or hedge-plants ; some are poisonous. (Including *Lycopersicum* Mill. and *Normania* Lowe).   **Solanum** L.
Anthers free, opening by longitudinal slits. Leaves entire, toothed, or lobed. 13

13. Corolla narrowly campanulate, white. Calyx much enlarged and inflated in the fruit. Flowers in clusters. Leaves undivided. Shrubs. — Species 6. Poisonous and used medicinally ; the sap coagulates milk. (*Physaloides* Moench) . . . .   **Withania** Pauq.
Corolla rotate or very widely campanulate. Flowers solitary. . . . 14

14. Calyx entire or with 5 small teeth, usually but slightly enlarged in the fruit. Corolla white. Filaments longer than the anthers. Fruit slightly fleshy. Herbs or undershrubs. — Species 6. Cultivated and sometimes naturalized in various regions. The fruits (chillies) serve as condiments or medicaments. " Cayenne pepper." . . **Capsicum** L.
Calyx 5-lobed, much enlarged in the fruit. 15

15. Calyx spreading under the fruit. Corolla white. Shrubs. Leaves undivided, covered with dense hairs. — Species 1. Island of St. Helena.
Melissea Hook.
Calyx inflated and enclosing the fruit. Corolla white, yellow, or violet. Herbs. — Species 6 ; three of them natives of Central and South Africa, the others cultivated and sometimes naturalized in various regions. They yield edible fruits and medicaments. " Winter-cherry."
Physalis L.

FAMILY 208. SCROPHULARIACEAE

Leaves without stipules. Flowers hermaphrodite, usually irregular. Petals 4—5, united below, imbricate, not folded in the bud. Stamens 2—5, usually 4. Disc present. Ovary superior, 2-celled, the partition placed transversely to the median plane of the flower, rarely 1-celled or (*Bowkeria*) 3-celled. Ovules inverted or half-inverted. Style simple or 2-cleft. Seeds albuminous with a straight or slightly curved embryo, rarely (*Dintera*) exalbuminous. — Genera 107, species 1150. (Including *SELAGINEAE*.) (Plate 136.)

1. Posterior lobes or upper lip of the corolla overlapped in the bud by one or both of the lateral lobes. [Subfamily **RHINANTHOIDEAE**.] . . 2
Posterior lobes or upper lip of the corolla overlapping the lateral lobes in the bud. 45

2. Corolla 2-lipped with a helmet-shaped upper lip and a 3-lobed lower lip.
   Stamens 4. Anther-halves separate. Fruit capsular, loculicidal. Herbs.
   Leaves well developed. Flowers in leafy spikes or racemes. [Tribe
   RHINANTHEAE.] 3
   Corolla 2-lipped with a flat upper lip, or 1-lipped with only 3 distinct lobes,
   or subequally 4—5-lobed. 8

3. Upper lip of the corolla with reflexed margins. Calyx 4-lobed. Seeds
   numerous, ribbed. Leaves undivided. — Species 1. Azores. " Eyebright." . . . .   **Euphrasia** L.
   Upper lip of the corolla with straight margins. 4

4. Calyx 5-lobed, slit in front. Corolla yellow. Capsule oblique, narrow·
   Leaves pinnately divided. — Species 1. North-west Africa (Algeria)·
   " Lousewort." . . . .   **Pedicularis** L·
   Calyx 4-lobed. Capsule straight. Leaves entire, toothed, or lobed. . 5

5. Ovules few, pendulous. Corolla yellow or red. Capsule broad. Seeds
   ribbed. — Species 10. North Africa. Some are used medicinally.
   (Under *Bartsia* L.) . . . .   **Odontites** Pers.
   Ovules many, horizontal. 6

6. Placentas thin. Seeds few, large, with wing-like ribs. Capsule broad.
   Corolla blue or red. — Species 8. Central and North-west Africa.
   (*Bartsia* L.) . . . .   **Bartschia** L.
   Placentas thick. Seeds numerous, small. Corolla yellow or red. . . 7

7. Seeds ribbed. Capsule broad. — Species 2. North and South Africa,
   Abyssinia, and Island of Réunion. (*Trixago* Stev., under *Bartsia* L.)
                                                     Bellardia All.
   Seeds smooth. Capsule narrow. — Species 3. North Africa. (*Eufragia*
   Griseb., under *Bartsia* L.) . . . .   **Parentucellia** Viv.

8. (2.) Anther-halves separate, sometimes one of them rudimentary or one
   only developed. Stamens 4, more or less unequal, rarely (*Strigina*)
   2 only fertile. Corolla with a distinct, usually long tube. Calyx-teeth
   about as long as or shorter than the tube. [Tribe GERARDIEAE.]   9
   Anther-halves confluent at the apex, more rarely separate, but then corolla-
   tube very short and stamens nearly equal or reduced to two, or calyx-
   teeth much longer than the tube. [Tribe DIGITALEAE.] . . 36

9. Anthers 1-celled (with one half only developed) in all stamens. . . . 10
   Anthers 2-celled (with both halves developed), at least in two of the stamens,
   but one cell (or half) sometimes smaller than the other and barren. . 17

10. Corolla almost 1-lipped, with only 3 distinct lobes ; tube curved ; limb
    narrow, convex. Calyx 5-cleft. Red-coloured, fleshy, parasitic herbs.
    Leaves reduced to scales. Flowers in terminal spikes. — Species 5.
    South Africa. . . . .   **Hyobanche** Thunb.
    Corolla regular or 2-lipped, distinctly 4—5-lobed. Green herbs with well
    developed leaves. 11

11. Corolla subequally 5-lobed, blue red or white ; tube straight or slightly
curved. Calyx tubular, 4—5-toothed. Capsule straight, oblong or
ovate. Leaves undivided. 12
Corolla more or less distinctly 2-lipped ; lobes unequal. 14

12. Calyx 2-lipped, 4-lobed, 5-nerved. Stamens inserted in the lower
part of the corolla-tube. Lower leaves opposite, upper alternate. —
Species 1. Southern East Africa. . . . . . . **Eylesia** S Moore
Calyx subequally 4—5-toothed, 7—10-nerved. 13

13. Calyx 7—9-nerved, 4-toothed. Stamens inserted in the upper part of the
corolla-tube. Leaves all opposite. — Species 3. West Africa. (Under
Buchnera L.) . . . . **Stellularia** Benth.
Calyx 10-nerved, usually 5-toothed. — Species 60. Tropical and South
Africa. (*Buchnera* L.) . . . . **Buechnera** L.

14. Corolla-tube abruptly curved at or above the middle. Calyx tubular.
Capsule straight, oblong or ovate. Leaves undivided. 15
Corolla-tube straight or gradually curved. 16

15. Placentas thin. Ovules few, large. Stem prostrate. — Species 3. East
Africa. . . . . **Cycniopsis** Engl.
Placentas thick. Ovules numerous, small. Stem erect. — Species 30.
Tropical and South Africa and Egypt. Some are noxious weeds.
Striga Lour.

16. Calyx tubular, 5-toothed. Capsule ellipsoid, straight, not beaked. —
Species 12. Central and South Africa. . . . **Cycnium** E. Mey.
Calyx campanulate, 5-cleft. Capsule usually oblique and beaked, rarely
globose and not beaked. — Species 25. Tropical and South Africa.
Rhamphicarpa Benth.

17. (9.) Anther-halves (anther-cells) very unequal, one of them fertile, the
other barren (without pollen) or almost so. 18
Anther-halves equal or subequal, both of them fertile. 27

18. Leaves scale-like, yellow or reddish. 19
Leaves well developed, green. 20

19. Corolla with a narrow limb, red. Barren anther-cell very small. — Species 1.
Madagascar. . . . . **Tetraspidium** Bak.
Corolla with a broad limb. Barren anther-cell usually long. — Species 30.
Southern and tropical Africa. (*Aulaya* Harv.) . . **Harveya** Hook.

20. Fertile stamens 2, inserted at the throat of the corolla ; barren ones filiform.
Corolla with a long curved tube and a 2-lipped limb. Leaves undivided.
— Species 1. East Africa. . . . . **Strigina** Engl.
Fertile stamens 4. 21

21. Anthers partly with, partly (two of them) without a barren cell. Corolla-
tube long, inflated. Stem erect. Leaves undivided. 22
Anthers all with a barren cell, which in two is sometimes very small ; in
this case stem climbing. Herbs or undershrubs. 23

22. Anthers of the lower (anterior) stamens 1-celled, those of the upper stamens with a fertile cell opening by a longitudinal slit and a spur-like sterile cell. Corolla nearly regular. Mostly shrubs. — Species 1. East Africa (Somaliland). . . . . . . **Ghikaea** Schweinf. & Volk.

Anthers of the lower stamens with a cleft connective bearing at one end a fertile cell, which opens by an apical pore, and at the other a disc-like appendage; those of the upper stamens 1-celled. Corolla 2-lipped. Herbs or undershrubs. — Species 7. East Africa.
Pseudosopubia Engl.

23. Anthers with a minute, nearly imperceptible barren cell. Corolla violet; tube slightly exceeding the calyx. Calyx enlarged in the fruit. Stem erect, with spreading branches. Leaves undivided. — Species 1. Southern West Africa. . . . . **Hiernia** S. Moore

Anthers, at least those of the shorter stamens, with a distinctly developed barren cell. 24

24. Barren anther-cells of the longer stamens minute, nearly imperceptible, of the shorter awn- or worm-shaped. Corolla pink or violet; tube exceeding the calyx. Calyx enlarged and inflated in the fruit. Climbing undershrubs. — Species 2. Central and South-east Africa.
Buttonia Mac Ken

Barren anther-cells distinctly developed in all stamens, but sometimes unequal in length. Calyx scarcely changed in fruit. Herbs. . . 25

25. Anthers cohering all together or in pairs. Corolla funnel-shaped, with a broad limb. Stem erect. — Species 25. Tropical and South Africa.
Sopubia Hamilt.

Anthers free. Corolla more or less bell-shaped, with a rather narrow limb. 26

26. Corolla-tube exceeding the calyx. Stem climbing. Leaves undivided, broad, coarsely toothed. — Species 1. West Africa.
Thunbergianthus Engl.

Corolla-tube equalling the calyx. Stem erect. Leaves pinnately divided. — Species 1. Southern West Africa (Angola). **Baumia** Engl. & Gilg

27. (17.) Corolla-tube short, about equalling the calyx. 28

Corolla-tube long, distinctly exceeding the calyx. 30

28. Calyx becoming woody in the fruit. Anthers exserted, with unequal halves. Undershrubs. — Species 1. Island of Socotra.
Xylocalyx Balf.

Calyx not woody in the fruit. Herbs. 29

29. Calyx scarcely changed in the fruit. Capsule 4-valved. Non-parasitic plants. Stem thin. Leaves linear. Inflorescence lax. — Species 3. Tropics. (Including *Gerardianella* Klotzsch). . **Micrargeria** Benth.

Calyx more or less enlarged and inflated in the fruit; if but slightly changed, then parasitic plants with thick stems and usually broad or scale-like leaves. — Species 30. Tropical and South Africa. (Including *Alectra* Thunb. and *Velvitsia* Hiern) . . . . **Melasma** Berg

30. Anther-halves unequal, one of them somewhat shorter or narrower. . 31
Anther-halves equal. 33
31. Anther-halves nearly equal, one of them somewhat shorter than the other.
Filaments very unequal. Ovules numerous. Stem herbaceous. Flowers
without bracteoles. — Species 1. Southern Central Africa and Transvaal.

Gerardiina Engl.

Anther-halves distinctly unequal, one of them narrower. Stem woody,
at least at the base. 32
32. Corolla with a very long tube and a very narrow limb, white. Ovules
2—4 in a cell. Shrubs. — Species 1. Madagascar.

Leucosalpa Scott Elliot

Corolla with a rather broad limb. Ovules numerous. — Species 3. South
Africa and island of Socotra. (*Bopusia* Presl) . **Graderia** Benth.
33. Stamens nearly equal in length. Corolla-tube rather short. Stem her-
baceous. 34
Stamens distinctly unequal. Stem woody. 35
34. Flowers solitary or in clusters, axillary. Calyx 5-cleft. Corolla blue.
Capsule 4-valved. — Species 1. South Africa. **Charadrophila** Marloth
Flowers in spikes or racemes. Corolla yellow. Capsule 2-valved. —
Species 1. Madagascar. . . . . **Seymeria** Pursh
35. Calyx-teeth very short. Corolla bell-shaped. Glabrous shrubs. — Species 1.
Madagascar. (*Raphispermum* Benth.) . . **Rhaphispermum** Benth.
Calyx-teeth distinctly developed, pointed. Corolla funnel-shaped. Hairy
shrubs. — Species 2. Madagascar and neighbouring islands.

Radamaea Benth.

36. (8.) Stamens 2. 37
Stamens 4—8. 38
37. Corolla-tube long, thin, curved. Corolla white. Stamens included ;
anther-halves confluent. Capsule loculicidal and septicidal, many-
seeded. Shrubs. Leaves alternate, linear. — Species 3. Canary and
Cape Verde Islands and Socotra. . . . . . **Campylanthus** Roth
Corolla-tube short or rather short. Stamens long. — Species 30. Some of
them yield salad, a substitute for tea, and medicaments, or serve as
ornamental plants. " Speedwell." . . . . . . **Veronica** L.
38. Corolla-tube very short. Stamens 4—8, nearly equal in length. . . 39
Corolla-tube long. Stamens 4, unequal. 41
39. Anther-halves confluent at the apex. Stamens 4—5. Corolla 5-parted,
white. Calyx 5-parted. Capsule loculicidal, many-seeded. Erect
undershrubs. Leaves alternate, narrow. — Species 1. Naturalized in
West Africa and in the Seychelles. Used medicinally and as a substitute for tea. . . . . **Capraria** L.
Anther-halves separate. 40
40. Calyx 4-parted. Corolla white, with 4 segments. Stamens 4. Capsule
septicidal ; seeds numerous. Erect undershrubs. Leaves opposite

or whorled, subsessile, narrow. — Species 1. Naturalized in the tropics.
Used medicinally . . . . **Scoparia** L.
Calyx 4—8-cleft. Corolla yellow or red, with 4—8, usually 5, segments.
Capsule loculicidal; seeds not numerous. Creeping herbs. Leaves
alternate, stalked, broad. — Species 3. Azores and Canary Islands,
Mauritius, and high mountains of Central Africa. Used as ornamental
plants. . . . . **Sibthorpia** L.

41. Anther-halves separate. Corolla with a long cylindrical tube and a two-
lipped limb. Leaves opposite. Flowers in spikes or racemes. —
Species 1. Sahara. . . . . **Lafuentea** Lag.
Anther-halves confluent at the apex. Leaves alternate. 42

42. Corolla with a cylindrical tube and a broad, slightly 2-lipped limb, blue or
violet. Capsule 4-valved. Low herbs. Flowers in terminal racemes. —
Species 1. Algeria. Used as an ornamental plant. . **Erinus** L.
Corolla with a funnel- or bell-shaped tube more or less widened above.
Tall herbs, undershrubs, or shrubs. 43

43. Stigma 2-lobed. Corolla yellow or red, 2-lipped. Flowers in terminal
racemes. — Species 6. North Africa ; one of them also naturalized
in the island of Réunion. Poisonous plants used medicinally and as
ornamental plants. " Foxglove." (Including *Callianassa* Webb et
Berth.) . . . . **Digitalis** L.
Stigma entire. Flowers in terminal heads or in axillary fascicles. Leaves
broad. Undershrubs. 44

44. Anthers protruding beyond the corolla-tube. Corolla 2-lipped. Calyx-
segments glume-like, fringed or ciliate. Flowers in terminal heads. —
Species 1. South Africa. . . . . **Glumicalyx** Hiern
Anthers concealed within the corolla-tube. Flowers in axillary fascicles. —
Species 1. Island of Socotra. . . . . . . **Camptoloma** Benth.

45. (1.) Leaves all alternate. Corolla almost regular. Anther-halves confluent
at the apex. Ovules many in each cell of the ovary. Fruit a septicidal,
many-seeded capsule. [Subfamily **PSEUDOSOLANEAE**.] . . . 46
Leaves, at least the lower, opposite or whorled ; more rarely all radical or
alternate ; in the latter case corolla distinctly irregular or ovules and
seeds solitary in each cell. [Subfamily **ANTIRRHINOIDEAE**.] . . 50

46. Corolla with a long tube, funnel-shaped, blue or red. Stamens 2 or 4.
Flowers solitary, axillary, sometimes forming leafy racemes. Leaves
undivided. [Tribe APTOSIMEAE.] 47
Corolla with a short or very short tube, bell- or wheel-shaped. Stamens 4
or 5. Flowers in spikes, racemes, or panicles. [Tribe VERBASC-
EAE.] 49

47. Stamens 2. Fruit pointed. Low herbs with glandular hairs. — Species 10.
Central and South Africa, Sahara, and Egypt. Some are used medicin-
ally. (Including *Doratanthera* Benth. and *Gerardiopsis* Engl.)
Anticharis Endl.
Stamens 4, but two of them sometimes sterile. 48

48. Fruit pointed. Stamens all fertile. Herbs or undershrubs. — Species 5.
South and Central Africa. . . . . . . **Peliostomum** E. Mey.
Fruit blunt. Shrubs. — Species 25. Central and South Africa.
Aptosimum Burch.

49. Stamens 4. — Species 18. Central and North Africa. Some are used as
ornamental or medicinal plants. . . . . **Celsia** L.
Stamens 5. — Species 17. North Africa and northern East Africa ; two
of the species also naturalized in South Africa and in the Mascarene
Islands. They yield fish-poison and medicaments, and serve as ornamental plants. " Mullein." . . . . **Verbascum** L.

50. (45.) Ovules and seeds solitary in each cell of the ovary and fruit. Fruit
indehiscent. Stamens 2 or 4. Anther-halves confluent. Flowers in
spikes, more rarely in heads or panicles or solitary. Leaves entire,
toothed, or lobed. [Tribe SELAGINEAE.] 51
Ovules and seeds two or more in each cell, usually numerous. . . . 56

51. Corolla 4-lobed, deeply slit in front. Calyx entire or 2-parted. Stamens 4.
Flowers in spikes. 52
Corolla 5-lobed, not slit at one side. Calyx with 3 or 5, rarely with 2
segments. 53

52. Calyx slit open in front, entire or notched behind. — Species 30. South
and Central Africa. . . . . **Hebenstreitia** L.
Calyx divided into two narrow entire segments. — Species 10. South
Africa. . . . . **Dischisma** Choisy

53. Fertile stamens 2. Corolla-lobes subequal. Calyx 5-lobed. Fruit 1-
seeded. Shrubs. Flowers in spikes. 54
Fertile stamens 4. Corolla-lobes more or less unequal. 55

54. Sterile stamens present. — Species 1. South Africa. **Gosela** Choisy
Sterile stamens absent. — Species 3. South Africa. **Agathelpis** Choisy

55. Calyx subequally 5-toothed, adnate at the base to the bract. Fruit 1-
seeded. — Species 5. South Africa. . . . . . **Microdon** Choisy
Calyx with 5 segments, free from the bract, or with 2—3 segments. Fruit
2-seeded. — Species 160. Southern and tropical Africa. Some are used
as ornamental plants. (Including *Walafrida* E. Mey.) . **Selago** L.

56. (50.) Corolla two-lipped with concave, bladdery-inflated lips and a very
short tube. Stamens 2. — Species 1. Naturalized in the Canary Islands.
An ornamental plant. [Tribe CALCEOLARIEAE.] **Calceolaria** L.
Corolla two-lipped with flat or convex lips, or nearly regular. . . . 57

57. Corolla spurred or saccate, two-lipped. Calyx 5-parted. Fruit a capsule. 58
Corolla neither spurred nor saccate, rarely slightly gibbous, but then calyx
5-lobed or 3-parted. 71

58. Corolla without a distinct tube. Capsule opening by 2 or 4 valves. Herbs.
[Tribe HEMIMERIDEAE.] 59
Corolla with a distinctly developed tube. Stamens 4. [Tribe ANTIR-
RHINEAE.] 62

59. Corolla yellow, 4-cleft, usually with two pouches and two teeth at the base of the lower lip. Stamens 2. Flowers solitary, axillary. — Species 4. South Africa. . . . . **Hemimeris** Thunb.
    Corolla red or blue, 5-lobed. Stamens 4, but two of them sometimes sterile. 60
60. Flowers turned upside down by the twisting of the pedicel. Corolla scarlet, with two shallow pits at the base. Stamens subequal, all fertile, glabrous. Anther-halves confluent at the apex. Flowers solitary, axillary. — Species 1. South Africa. Used as an ornamental plant.
    Alonsoa Ruiz & Pav.
    Flowers very rarely turned upside down ; if so, then anthers hairy. Corolla with 1—2 pits, pouches, or spurs at the base. Stamens unequal. . 61
61. Lower lip of the corolla ventricose and gibbous at the base. Stamens all fertile. Anther-halves separate, spreading. — Species 2. Naturalized in Madagascar. . . . . **Angelonia** Humb. & Bonpl.
    Lower lip of the corolla with 2 pits, pouches, or spurs, very rarely with one only. Anther-halves confluent at the apex. — Species 45. South Africa. . . . . **Diascia** Link & Otto
62. Throat of the corolla closed by a projecting palate. Herbs or under-shrubs. 63
    Throat of the corolla open. 67
63. Corolla spurred at the base. Anther-halves separate. 64
    Corolla ventricose, but not spurred at the base. 66
64. Corolla with a long spur. Cells of the capsule opening by 2—5 teeth or valves. Leaves pinnately nerved. Flowers in terminal spikes or racemes. — Species 40. North Africa ; one of the species also naturalized in South Africa. Some yield vermin-poison or medicaments, or serve as ornamental plants. " Toadflax." . . . . . . **Linaria** Juss.
    Corolla with a short spur. Flowers solitary, axillary. 65
65. Corolla violet. Cells of the capsule opening by 3 teeth or valves. Seeds oblong. Creeping herbs. Leaves palmately nerved. — Species 1. North Africa. Used as an ornamental and medicinal plant. (Under *Linaria* Juss.) . . . . **Cymbalaria** Baumg.
    Corolla white, yellow, or two-coloured. Cells of the capsule opening by lids. Seeds ovoid. Leaves pinnately nerved. — Species 17. North Africa and northern Central Africa ; one of the species also naturalized in South Africa. (Under *Linaria* L.) . . . . **Elatinoides** Wettst.
66. Anther-halves separate. Capsule opening by 2 or 3 toothed pores. — Species 6. North Africa and northern Central Africa ; one of the species also naturalized in South Africa and Mauritius. Some are used as ornamental or medicinal plants. " Snap-dragon." **Antirrhinum** L.
    Anther-halves confluent at the apex. A fifth, sterile stamen present. Capsule with unequal cells, opening irregularly. Seeds ribbed. Flowers small, axillary. — Species 3. Northern East Africa and Comoro Islands.
    Schweinfurthia A. Braun

67. Corolla-tube with 2 pits or pouches at the base ; lobes subequal. Anther-halves confluent. Capsule 4-valved. Shrubs. Leaves alternate, broad. Flowers solitary, axillary, yellow. — Species 1. South Africa.

Colpias E. Mey.

Corolla-tube with 1 pit, pouch, or spur. Herbs or undershrubs. Leaves opposite. 68

68. Anther-halves separate. Corolla-tube long. Capsule with unequal cells. Flowers solitary, axillary. — Species 4. North Africa. (Under *Linaria* Juss.) . . . . **Chaenorrhinum** (DC.) Lange

Anther-halves confluent at the apex. 69

69. Corolla-tube long. Capsule opening by two apical pores. Flowers in racemes. Radical leaves rosulate. — Species 5. North Africa and Abyssinia. (*Simbuleta* Forsk.) . . . . . **Anarrhinum** Desf.

Corolla-tube short. Capsule opening by 2 or 4 longitudinal valves. . 70

70. Corolla with a 2-lobed upper and a 3-lobed lower lip. Capsule globose, 4-valved. Seeds with a tight testa. — Species 7. Tropical and South Africa. . . . . **Diclis** Benth.

Corolla with a 4-lobed upper and an entire lower lip. Capsule compressed, 2-valved. Seeds with a loose testa, girt with a membranous wing. — Species 50. South Africa and southern Central Africa. Some are used as ornamental plants. . . . . **Nemesia** Vent.

71. (57.) Flowers in cymes or in cymose panicles or fascicles ; occasionally solitary with two bracteoles on the pedicel ; in this case shrubs or trees. Anther-halves usually confluent. Fruit a septicidal capsule or a berry. [Tribe CHELONEAE.] 72

Flowers solitary or in heads, spikes, racemes, or racemose panicles. Stamens 2 or 4. Fruit a capsule. Herbs or undershrubs. 81

72. Stem herbaceous or woody at the base only. Corolla with a ventricose tube and a narrow limb. Fertile stamens 4 ; a fifth, sterile stamen distinctly developed, usually scale-like. Anther-halves confluent. Fruit a capsule. — Species 20. North Africa and northern Central Africa. Some are used medicinally. . . . . **Scrophularia** L.

Stem woody throughout. The fifth stamen minute or wanting, rarely fertile. 73

73. Corolla-tube short and wide. Stamens 2 or 4. Anther-halves confluent at the apex. Fruit a capsule. 74

Corolla-tube long and narrow. Stamens 4 or 5. 76

74. Calyx 3-parted, the posterior segment 3-toothed. Corolla yellow or white. Fertile stamens 2. Anther-halves divergent. Capsule 4-valved, many-seeded. Leaves whorled. Flowers solitary or 2—3 together in the leaf-axils. — Species 1. South Africa. . . . . **Ixianthes** Benth.

Calyx 5-lobed or 5-parted, with nearly equal segments. Fertile stamens 4. 75

75. Calyx 5-lobed, valvate in bud. Corolla yellow, with a 2-parted upper lip. Capsule 4-valved, few-seeded. Leaves opposite, tomentose beneath.

Flowers in axillary and terminal, many-flowered cymes. — Species 1.
South Africa. Yields timber. . . . . . . **Anastrabe** E. Mey.
Calyx 5-parted, imbricate in bud. Corolla with a 2-toothed upper lip.
Anther-halves nearly parallel. Capsule 2—3-valved, many-seeded.
Leaves nearly always whorled. — Species 6. South Africa.

Bowkeria Harv.

76. Fertile stamens 5. Corolla-lobes equal. Fruit a berry. Epiphytic
shrubs. Flowers in axillary clusters. — Species 1. South-east Africa.

Dermatobotrys Bolus

Fertile stamens 4. 77
77. Anther-halves divergent. Corolla red. Leaves glabrous. 78
Anther-halves parallel or nearly so, separate. 79
78. Leaves scale-like. Fruit a capsule. — Species 1. Naturalized in the
Seychelles. Ornamental plant. . . . . . . **Russelia** Jacq.
Leaves well developed. Fruit a berry. — Species 5. Tropical and South
Africa. The fruits are edible. . . . . **Halleria** L.
79. Anthers protruding beyond the corolla-tube. Corolla red. Fruit a two-
valved capsule. — Species 2. South Africa. Used as ornamental
plants. . . . . **Phygelius** E. Mey.
Anthers concealed within the corolla-tube. Fruit a 4-valved capsule or a
berry. 80
80. Corolla red, slightly exceeding the calyx. Fruit a berry. — Species 2.
South Africa. . . . . **Teedia** Rudolphi
Corolla yellow or violet. Fruit a capsule. — Species 2. South Africa.

Freylinia Pangelli

81. (71.) Anther-halves completely confluent ; hence anthers apparently
1-celled. Calyx 5-parted or 2-lipped. [Tribe MANULEAE.] . . 82
Anther-halves separate or confluent at the apex only, rarely completely
confluent, but then calyx subequally 5-lobed. [Tribe GRATIOLEAE.]
91
82. Calyx 2-lipped or 2-parted. 83
Calyx subequally 5-parted. Stamens 4. 84
83. Anthers 4, unequal, or 2. — Species 30. South Africa.

Zaluzianskia Schmidt

Anthers 4, equal. — Species 20. South Africa to Damaraland.

Polycarena Benth.

84. Corolla-tube very short. 85
Corolla-tube distinctly developed, usually long. 86
85. Corolla 2-lipped. Capsule 2-cleft. Flowers solitary. Leaves all radical.
(See 61.) . . . . **Diascia** Link & Otto
Corolla nearly regular. Capsule 4-cleft. Flowers in racemes. Leaves
opposite. — Species 2. South Africa. (Under *Sutera* Roth)

Sphenandra Benth.

86. Corolla more or less distinctly 2-lipped. Capsule opening by pores or
transverse slits. 87

Corolla nearly regular or slightly 2-lipped. Capsule opening lengthwise, septicidal. 88

87. Flowers solitary. Stem climbing. — Species 1. Naturalized in the island of St. Helena. An ornamental plant. (*Lophospermum* Don)
Maurandia Ort.

Flowers in racemes. Stem erect. (See 69.) . . **Anarrhinum** Desf.

88. Stigma 2-lobed. Corolla-tube curved. Leaves cleft or dissected. — Species 1. Egypt and Nubia. (*Jamesbrittenia* O. Ktze.) **Sutera** Roth

Stigma entire. Leaves entire or toothed. 89

89. Bracts adnate to the pedicels. — Species 20. South Africa.
Phyllopodium Benth.

Bracts free from the pedicels. 90

90. Calyx open or nearly open in the bud, surrounded by narrow bracts or without bracts. Corolla-tube nearly always straight. Flowers in compound, rarely in simple racemes. — Species 35. South Africa to Angola. (*Nemia* Berg). . . . . **Manulea** L.

Calyx imbricate in the bud or surrounded by broad bracts. Flowers solitary or in usually simple spikes, racemes, or heads, — Species 120. South and Central Africa and Canary Islands. Some are used as ornamental, medicinal, or dye-plants. (Including *Lyperia* Benth., under *Sutera* Roth). (Plate 136.) . . . . **Chaenostoma** Benth.

91. (81.) Fertile stamens 2. 92

Fertile stamens 4, rarely 3. 97

92. Staminodes none. Flowers minute, solitary. 93

Staminodes 2. Ovary 2-celled. Corolla 2-lipped, 5-lobed. 95

93. Ovary 1-celled. Style very short. Stamens inserted in the upper part of the corolla-tube. Corolla 2-lipped, 5-lobed. Calyx 5-parted. Leaves ovate. Aquatic herbs. — Species 1. Southern West Africa (Damaraland) . . . . **Dintera** Stapf

Ovary 2-celled. Style distinctly developed, curved. Corolla 4-lobed or sub-equally 5-lobed. 94

94. Calyx 5-parted. Corolla 4-lobed. Stamens inserted in the lower part of the corolla-tube. Leaves linear or oblong. — Species 1. Mascarene Islands. . . . . **Bryodes** Benth.

Calyx 5-toothed. Corolla 5-lobed. Leaves ovate. — Species 1. Egypt.
Peplidium Del.

95. Staminodes inserted at the throat of the corolla. Anther-halves spreading. — Species 20. Tropical and South Africa. (Including *Bonnaya* Link et Otto) . . . . **Ilysanthes** Rafin.

Staminodes inserted in the tube of the corolla. Anther-halves parallel or nearly so. 96

96. Leaves lobed or dissected. Flowers in racemes. Lower lip of the corolla with a 2-cleft middle-lobe. Aquatic herbs. — Species 1. Madagascar.
Hydrotriche Zucc.

Leaves entire. — Species 10. Central Africa. . . **Dopatrium** Hamilt.

97. (91.) Stamens inserted at the throat of the corolla. Anther-halves parallel. Corolla white, unequally 3—5-lobed. Creeping herbs. Leaves broad, palmately nerved, gland-dotted. Flowers solitary. — Species 1. West Africa. . . . . **Hydranthelium** H. B. & Kunth

Stamens, all or two of them, inserted in the tube of the corolla. . . . 98

98. Stamens inserted in the tube and at the throat of the corolla. . . . 99

Stamens inserted in the tube of the corolla. 102

99. Sepals free, broad. Corolla slightly irregular, white. The fifth, sterile stamen filiform. Prostrate herbs. Leaves very small. Flowers solitary. — Species 1. Island of Réunion. . . . **Allocalyx** Cordem.

Sepals united below. Corolla 2-lipped. Lower stamens with a tooth- or bristle-like appendage at the base. 100

100. Calyx without wings or prominent angles, but sometimes striped; segments subequal. — Species 17. Tropics. Some are used medicinally. (*Vandellia* L.) . . . . **Lindernia** All.

Calyx winged or with very prominent angles. 101

101. Calyx subequally toothed. Anterior stamens sharply bent at the base. Stem usually leafless. — Species 15. Central and South Africa.
Craterostigma Hochst.

Calyx 2-lipped. Anterior stamens not sharply bent at the base. Stem leafy. — Species 8. Tropical and South Africa. Some are used as ornamental or medicinal plants. . . . . **Torenia** L.

102. Anther-halves separate, not contiguous. Corolla 2-lipped. 103

Anther-halves contiguous or confluent. 105

103. Sepals united high up. Fruit 2-valved. Stem procumbent or ascending. — Species 8. Northern East Africa and Egypt. **Lindenbergia** Lehm.

Sepals united at the base only. Fruit 4-valved. 104

104. Placentas winged and connate in the fruit. Glabrous water- or marsh- plants. — Species 6. Central Africa. Some are used medicinally. (*Ambulia* Lam., *Stemodiacra* P. Browne) . . . **Limnophila** R. Br.

Placentas not winged, usually separate. Corolla blue. Glandular- pubescent land-plants. — Species 1. Central Africa. **Stemodia** L.

105. Sepals united high up. 106

Sepals united at the base only 107

106. Corolla 2-lipped. Anther-halves separate or confluent at the top. Ovary completely septate. Leaves opposite. — Species 3. Two of them indigenous in tropical and South Africa, the third naturalized in the Azores. Used as ornamental plants . . . . . **Mimulus** L.

Corolla nearly regular. Anther-halves completely confluent. Ovary septate at the base only. Leaves all radical. Flowers axillary. — Species 5. Southern and tropical Africa and Egypt. **Limosella** L.

107. Sepals very unequal. Anther-halves separate. — Species 10. Tropics, South Africa, and Egypt. Some are used as ornamental or medicinal plants. (*Moniera* P. Browne, including *Herpestis* Gaertn. and *Bramia* Lam.) . . . . **Bacopa** Aubl.

Sepals nearly equal. Anther-halves confluent at the top. Corolla 2-
lipped. 108
108. Sepals broad. Corolla red or violet. Stamens, at least the anterior
exserted ; filaments with an appendage at the base. Flowers in
racemes, rather large. — Species 1. Central Africa. **Artanema** Don
Sepals narrow. Stamens included ; filaments without an appendage.
Flowers solitary, very small. — Species 4. East Africa.

Stemodiopsis Engl.

FAMILY 209. BIGNONIACEAE

Shrubs or trees. Leaves usually opposite and compound, without stipules.
Flowers usually large and panicled, more or less irregular, hermaphrodite.
Sepals united below. Petals united below, imbricate in bud. Stamens inserted
on the lower part of the corolla, 4, in two pairs of unequal length, the fifth
sterile, rarely all 5 fertile. Anthers opening by two longitudinal slits, rarely
(*Colea*) by one. Disc present. Ovary superior, 1—2-celled. Ovules numerous,
in two or more rows, inverted. Style simple ; stigmas 2. Fruit a capsule with
the valves usually separating from the partition, or a nut or berry. Seeds
usually placed transversely and margined or winged, exalbuminous. — Genera
21, species 90. Tropical and South Africa. (Plate 137.)

1. Fruit a capsule. Seeds winged. Ovary completely 2-celled. [Tribe
TECOMEAE.] 2
Fruit a berry or nut. Seeds not winged, but often margined. Ovary
cylindric, 1-celled or incompletely, rarely (*Colea*) completely 2-celled.
Fertile stamens 4. Stem erect. [Tribe CRESCENTIEAE.] . . 14
2. Fertile stamens 5. Anthers exserted, with parallel halves. Calyx 5-
toothed. Ovules few, in two rows. Erect, spiny shrubs. Leaves
fascicled. Flowers solitary or in clusters. 3
Fertile stamens 4. Leaves pinnate, very rarely (*Stenolobium*) unifoliolate. 4
3. Calyx tubular, slit on one side, with linear teeth. Corolla white, with a
long tube. Capsule slightly compressed, with prickly warts. Leaves
undivided. — Species 1. South Africa and southern Central Africa.

Catophractes G. Don
Calyx bell-shaped. Capsule much compressed, smooth. — Species 9.
Tropical and South Africa. . . . . **Rhigozum** Burch.
4. Stamens projecting beyond the corolla-tube. Anther-halves divergent or
divaricate. Flowers in racemes or panicles. 5
Stamens concealed within the corolla-tube. 6
5. Calyx spathe-like, slit on one side. Seeds with a broad wing. Trees. Leaflets
entire. — Species 3. Central Africa. They yield timber, edible seeds,
and medicaments, and serve as ornamental plants. " African tulip-
tree." . . . . **Spathodea** Beauv.
Calyx bell-shaped, equally 5-toothed. Seeds with a narrow wing. Twining
shrubs. Leaflets serrate. — Species 3. Central and South Africa.
Used as ornamental plants. (Under *Tecoma* Juss.) **Tecomaria** Fenzl

6. Anther-halves parallel. Calyx spathe-like, split down one side. Trees. Flowers panicled. **7**

Anther-halves divergent or divaricate. **8**

7. Basal (cylindric) part of the corolla-tube short. Ovules of each cell in 2 rows. Fruit 2-celled; valves boat-shaped. — Species 1. West Africa. Yields timber and medicaments. . . **Newbouldia** Seem.

Basal part of the corolla-tube long. Ovules of each cell in more than two rows. Fruit 4-celled; valves flat. Leaflets entire. — Species 1. Madagascar. . . . . **Dolichandrone** Fenzl

8. Inflorescences lateral, usually springing from the old wood. Anther-halves usually divergent. **9**

Inflorescences terminal. Anther-halves usually divaricate. **11**

9. Flowers solitary or in cymes. Calyx tubular, 5-toothed. Corolla distinctly 2-lipped; tube curved. Disc conical. Ovules of each cell in two rows. Climbing shrubs. — Species 1. Madagascar.
Perichlaena Baill.

Flowers in panicles. Calyx bell-shaped, unequally 3—5-cleft. Corolla not distinctly 2-lipped. Ovules of each cell in several rows. Trees. **10**

10. Calyx-tube narrow, leathery. Corolla campanulate-funnel-shaped. Disc saucer-shaped. Fruit with leathery, keeled valves. Leaves glabrous, crowded at the end of the branches. — Species 2. Madagascar.
Kigelianthe Baill.

Calyx-tube wide. Corolla ventricose-campanulate, curved. Disc cushion-shaped. Fruit cylindric, twisted. Leaves tomentose beneath. — Species 2. Central Africa. (*Ferdinandia* Seem., under *Heterophragma* DC.) . . . . **Fernandia** Baill.

11. Flowers in racemes or umbels. Calyx narrowly bell-shaped, 5-toothed. Connective of the stamens broadened, leaf-like. Ovules of each cell in two rows. Erect shrubs. Leaflets serrate. — Species 1. Naturalized in Central Africa. An ornamental plant. (Under *Tecoma* Juss.)
Stenolobium D. Don

Flowers in panicles. Connective not leaf-like. **12**

12. Ovules arranged in 2 rows in each cell. Calyx bell-shaped or tubular, truncate or unequally 2—5-lobed. Fruit with a spongy partition. Trees. — Species 6. Tropics. They yield timber, gum, and medicaments. . . . . **Stereospermum** Cham.

Ovules arranged in 4—8 rows in each cell. **13**

13. Ovules in 4 rows in each cell. Calyx spathe-like, split down one side. Fruit with a winged partition. Trees. — Species 10. Central Africa. Some species yield timber. (Under *Dolichandrone* Fenzl)
Markhamia Seem.

Ovules in 8 rows in each cell. Calyx bell-shaped, inflated, equally 5-toothed. Climbing shrubs. — Species 2. Central and South-east Africa. (Under *Pandorea* Endl. or *Tecoma* Juss.) . . . . . **Podranea** Sprague

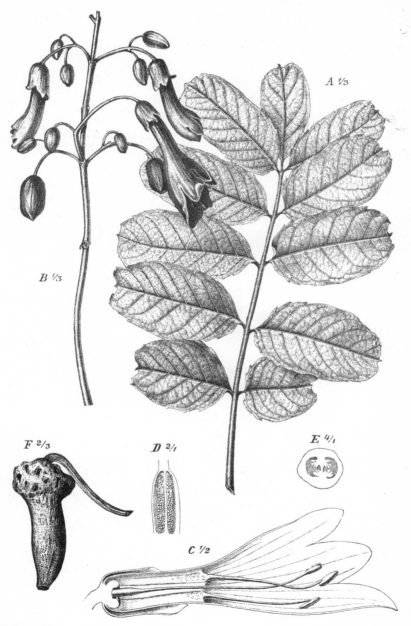

J. Fleischmann del.

Kigelia aethiopica Decne.

A Leaf.   *B* Inflorescence.   *C* Flower cut lengthwise.   *D* Ovary cut lengthwise.   *E* Ovary cut across.   *F* Fruit.

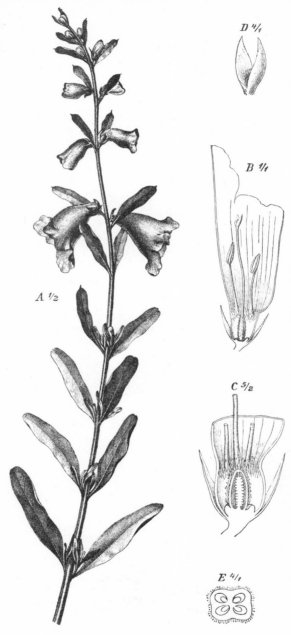

J. Fleischmann del.

Sesamum angolense Welw.

A Flowering plant.   *B* Flower cut lengthwise.   *C* Lower part of the flower cut lengthwise.   *D* Stigma.   *E* Cross-section of ovary.

14. (1.) Ovary completely 1-celled. Calyx bell-shaped, bursting irregularly. Corolla red or orange, ventricose-campanulate, irregular. Anther-halves parallel or divergent. Fruit with a thick rind. Trees. Leaves pinnate. — Species 12. Tropical and South Africa. Some species yield timber or medicaments. (*Kigelkeia* Rafin.). (Plate 137.)

Kigelia DC.

Ovary completely or incompletely 2-celled. 15

15. Leaves simple, undivided. Ovary 2-celled nearly to the apex. . . . 16
Leaves pinnately compound or reduced to the winged leaf-stalk. Flowers panicled. 18

16. Leaves with a pair of spines at their base. Flowers solitary or in clusters, axillary or springing from the old wood. Calyx pouch-shaped, unequally 2—5-lobed. Corolla regular, long funnel-shaped. Anther-halves divaricate. — Species 2. Madagascar. . . . . . . **Paracolea** Baill.
Leaves without spines at the base, but the leaf-stalk sometimes becoming spine-like. Flowers in terminal racemes or panicles. Calyx bell-shaped, 5-toothed. Corolla more or less irregular, bell- or bell-funnel-shaped. 17

17. Leaves herbaceous; leaf-stalk hardening into a spine. Flowers in panicles. Corolla irregular. Anther-halves divaricate. — Species 1. Madagascar.

Phylloctenium Baill.

Leaves leathery, resinous; leaf-stalk not hardening into a spine. Flowers in racemes. Corolla almost regular. Anther-halves divergent, pendulous. — Species 1. Madagascar. (Under *Tabebuia* Gomez).

Zaa Baill.

18. Leaves reduced to the jointed and winged leaf-stalk bearing sometimes 1—3 terminal leaflets. Calyx 5-toothed. Corolla slightly irregular. Anther-halves divaricate. Disc saucer-shaped. Ovary septate at the base. Fruit succulent. — Species 7. Madagascar and neighbouring islands. Some species yield timber and edible fruits or serve as ornamental plants. (*Arthrophyllum* Boj.) . . . . **Phyllarthron** DC.
Leaves pinnate, opposite or whorled. 19

19. Calyx long tubular, 5-toothed. Corolla funnel-shaped, nearly regular. Anther-halves divergent. Disc ring-shaped Ovary 2-celled nearly to the apex. Inflorescences terminal. — Species 3. Madagascar.

Siphocolea Baill.

Calyx bell-shaped. 20

20. Calyx subequally 5-cleft. Corolla regular, almost barrel-shaped, red. Anther-halves divaricate. Disc saucer-shaped, crenate. Trees. Inflorescences terminal. — Species 1. Madagascar. **Rhodocolea** Baill.
Calyx 5-toothed or unequally cleft. Corolla more or less irregular, bell-funnel-shaped. Fruit dry. — Species 25. Madagascar and neighbouring islands. Some species have edible fruits. . . . . . **Colea** Boj.

21

FAMILY 210. PEDALIACEAE

Plants with glandular hairs. Leaves opposite, at least the lower ones, simple. Flowers irregular, hermaphrodite. Calyx 5-partite. Petals 5, united below, imbricate in bud. Stamens inserted on the lower part of the corolla-tube, the 4 fertile in pairs of unequal length, the fifth sterile, small, awl-shaped. Ovary superior, 2—8-celled with 2 or more axile ovules in each cell, rarely (*Linariopsis*) 1-celled with 2 basal ovules. Style 1, long, with 2 stigmas or stigmatic lobes. Fruit a capsule or a nut. Seeds with a straight embryo and thin albumen. — Genera 14, species 65. (Plate 138.)

1. Flowers in terminal, raceme- or umbel-like cymes. Shrubs or small trees. Ovary 2—4-celled with numerous ovules in each cell. Fruit a capsule. 2

   Flowers solitary or in fascicles in the axils of the leaves, with glands at the base of the pedicels. Herbs, rarely (*Pretreothamnus*) shrubs, but then ovules 3 in each ovary-cell. 4

2. Inflorescences umbel- or fascicle-like. Glands at the base of the pedicels none. Corolla-tube moderately long, funnel-shaped, neither spurred nor curved. Anthers included ; halves divergent, pendulous. Disc slightly one-sided. Ovary-cells not or very incompletely chambered. Fruit beset with hooked bristles. Seeds narrowly winged. Leaves large, broad, long-stalked, lobed. Spines none. — Species 6. Madagascar. (Under *Harpagophytum* DC.) . . . . . **Uncarina** (Baill.) Stapf

   Inflorescences raceme-like. Glands at the base of the pedicels presente Corolla-tube very long, cylindrical, spurred or curved. Ovary-cell. nearly completely chambered. Leaves small, partly replaced by spines. 3

3. Corolla spurred. Anthers scarcely exserted, with parallel halves. Disc one-sided. Stem much thickened at the base. — Species 6. Central Africa. . . . . **Sesamothamnus** Welw.

   Corolla not spurred, with an S-shaped tube, yellow. Anthers exserted, with divergent halves. Disc equal-sided. Stem not much thickened. Species 1. Southern West Africa (Damaraland). **Sigmatosiphon** Engl.

4. Ovary and fruit 1-celled. Ovules 2, erect. Seed 1. Calyx-lobes very unequal. Corolla violet ; tube widened from the base, almost straight. Anther-halves parallel. Disc equal-sided. Stem prostrate, hairy. Leaves undivided. Flowers solitary. — Species 1. Southern West Africa (Angola). Used medicinally. . . . . **Linariopsis** Welw.

   Ovary and fruit 2—4-celled. Ovules 2 or more in each cell. 5

5. Ovary and fruit 2-celled, with undivided cells. Ovules descending or horizontal. Leaves toothed, lobed, or divided. Flowers solitary. . 6

   Ovary and fruit 2—4-celled, each cell completely or incompletely divided into two chambers. 10

6. Ovules 2 in each cell of the ovary. 7
 Ovules 8 or more in each cell of the ovary. Anthers opening by long slits.
 Disc one-sided. Succulent, prostrate herbs. 9
7. Fruit 4-winged, without spines. Anther-halves divergent, opening by
 short slits. Disc one-sided. Corolla yellow or red. Stem tuberous
 at the base. — Species 15. Central and South Africa.
 Pterodiscus Hook.
 Fruit wingless, bearing spines or tubercles. Corolla yellow. Succulent
 herbs. 8
8. Fruit with a large spine at the base of each angle. — Species 1. East
 Africa and Madagascar. Yields vegetables and is used in medicine.
 Pedalium Royen
 Fruit without large spines at the base, but with small spines or tubercles
 on the flanks. Seeds winged. — Species 1. East Africa. (Under
 Pedalium Royen) . . . . **Pedaliophytum** Engl.
9. Ovules 8 in each cell of the ovary. Corolla yellow ; tube deeply saccate
 at the base. — Species 1. South-east Africa. . **Holubia** Oliv.
 Ovules numerous in each cell of the ovary. Corolla red ; tube not or slightly
 saccate at the base. Fruit with several rows of recurved spines. —
 Species 3. South and Central Africa. Noxious weeds. " Grapple
 plant." (*Uncaria* Burch.) . . . . . . **Harpagophytum** DC.
10. Ovules 2—3 in each chamber of the ovary, ascending, or one ascending,
 the other descending. Fruit a nut. 11
 Ovules numerous in each chamber, at least in the larger ones, descending or
 horizontal. Fruit a capsule. 12
11. Ovules 2 in each of the 4 chambers of the ovary. Fruit with 2 spines
 in the middle. Corolla red. Trailing herbs. Leaves lobed. — Species 1.
 Tropical and South Africa. . . . . **Pretrea** J. Gay
 Ovules 3 in each chamber Shrubs. — Species 1. Northern East Africa
 (Somaliland). . . . . **Pretreothamnus** Engl.
12. Cells of the ovary and fruit unequal in size and containing an unequal
 number of ovules or seeds. Corolla violet or white. Fruit with 2—8
 spines or tubercles at the base ; only the larger cell dehiscent. Erect
 herbs. Leaves toothed or lobed. Flowers usually in cymes. —Species
 3. Central Africa to Namaland. . . . . . . **Rogeria** J. Gay
 Cells of the ovary and fruit equal. Flowers solitary. 13
13. Fruit with two horns or spines at the apex. Corolla red, violet, or yellow. —
 Species 5. Central and South Africa. Some are used as ornamental or
 medicinal plants. . . . . **Ceratotheca** Endl.
 Fruit without horns nor spines. Corolla red or white. — Species 20.
 Central and South Africa ; one species (*S. indicum* L.) also cultivated in
 Egypt and Madagascar. The seeds of this and a second species are used
 as food or as a condiment and for preparing meal and oil ; some species
 yield dyes or medicaments or serve as ornamental plants. (Plate 138.)
 Sesamum L.

FAMILY 211. MARTYNIACEAE

Erect, hairy herbs. Leaves broad, undivided. Flowers in racemes, with large bracteoles, irregular, hermaphrodite. Calyx unequally 5-lobed, slit in front. Corolla obliquely campanulate, two-lipped, 5-lobed, red. Fertile stamens 2, inserted on the lower part of the corolla-tube, included ; staminodes 3. Disc regular. Ovary superior, 1-celled, with 2 two-cleft parietal placentas. Ovules 4—16, descending, inverted. Style 1, long, with 2 stigmas or stigma-lobes. Fruit ending in two horns, 8-ribbed, 4-chambered and 4-seeded, opening loculicidally at the apex ; exocarp leathery, endocarp hard. Seeds with a straight embryo and thin albumen. (Under *PEDALINEAE*.)

Genus 1, species 1. Naturalized in Madagascar and Mauritius. An ornamental and medicinal plant. . . . . **Martynia** L.

FAMILY 212. OROBANCHACEAE

Parasitic herbs destitute of green colour. Leaves reduced to scales. Flowers in terminal spikes or racemes, irregular, hermaphrodite. Calyx 2—5-toothed or consisting of two entire or 2-toothed segments or sepals. Corolla 4—5-lobed, imbricate in bud. Stamens inserted on the tube of the corolla, 4, in two pairs of unequal length. Anthers opening lengthwise. Ovary superior, 1-celled, with 4 parietal placentas. Ovules numerous, inverted. Style simple. Fruit a loculicidal capsule. Seeds with a pitted testa, a copious albumen, and an undivided embryo. — Genera 2, species 30. North and Central Africa. (Plate 139.)

Calyx 5-lobed, with blunt or rounded, nearly equal lobes. Corolla almost equally 5-lobed. Bracteoles adnate to the calyx. — Species 6. North and Central Africa. (Under *Phelipaea* E. Mey.) (Plate 139.)

Cistanche Hoffm. & Link

Calyx 2—5-toothed with pointed teeth, or consisting of two entire or 2-toothed segments or sepals. — Species 25. North and East Africa ; two species also naturalized in South Africa. Some are used as vegetables or as medicinal or ornamental plants, others are noxious weeds. " Broomrape." (Including *Phelipaea* E. Mey.)

Orobanche (Tournef.) G. Beck

FAMILY 213. GESNERACEAE

Herbs or undershrubs. Leaves undivided, without stipules. Flowers irregular, hermaphrodite. Sepals united below. Petals united below, imbricate in bud. Fertile stamens 2. Disc present. Ovary superior, 1-celled, with parietal placentas, sometimes incompletely 2—4-celled. Ovules numerous, inverted. Style simple. Fruit a capsule. Seeds exalbuminous ; embryo straight. — Genera 6, species 65. Tropical and South Africa. (*CRYTAND-REAE*.) (Plate 140.)

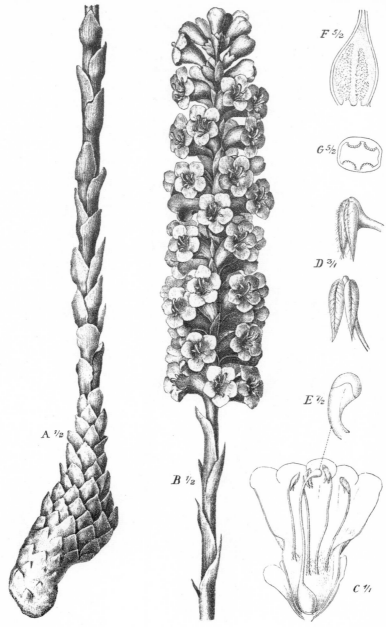

F 5/2

G 5/2

D 3/1

E 1/2

A 1/2

B 1/2

C 1/1

J. Fleischmann del.

Cistanche lutea Link & Hoffmsg.

A Stem.   *B* Inflorescence.   *C* Flower laid open.   *D* Anther.   *E* Stigma.   *F* Ovary cut lengthwise.   *G* Ovary cut across

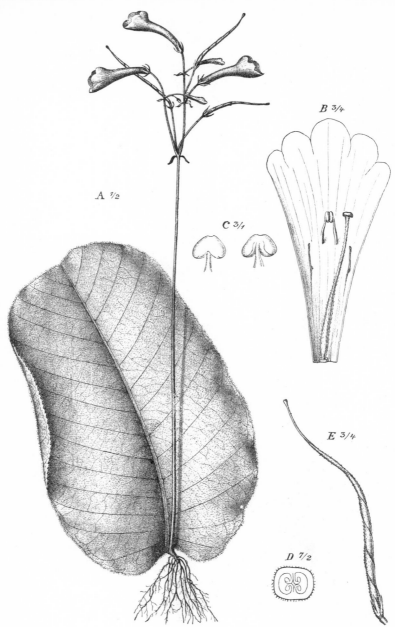

A ½

B ¾

C ³⁄₁

E ¾

D ⁷⁄₂

J. Fleischmann del.

Streptocarpus Cooperi Clarke

A Whole plant. *B* Flower laid open. *C* Anther (from front and back). *D* Cross-section of ovary. *E* Fruit.

1. Fruit linear, loculicidal or follicular. Disc equal-sided, sometimes indistinct. 2
   Fruit oblong, ovate, or globose. Disc one-sided, rarely (*Saintpaulia*) equal-sided. 3
2. Fruit twisted. — Species 50. Tropical and South Africa. Some are used as ornamental plants. (Plate 140.) (Tribe STREPTOCARPEAE.] . . . . **Streptocarpus** Lindl.
   Fruit not twisted. — Species 5. West Africa and Madagascar. (*Roettlera* Vahl, including *Trachystigma* C. B. Clarke) [Tribe DIDYMOCARPEAE.] . . . . **Didymocarpus** Wall.
3. Fruit globose, opening transversely. Calyx shortly toothed. Corolla blue or white. Posterior stamens fertile. Inflorescence capitate. Leaves few. — Species 2. West Africa. [Tribe BESLERIEAE.]
   Epithema Blume
   Fruit ovate or oblong, opening lengthwise. 4
4. Fruit loculicidal or follicular. Leaf single. — Species 2. West Africa. (Including *Carolofritschia* Engl.) [Tribe KLUGIEAE.]
   Acanthonema Hook. fil.
   Fruit septicidal. Leaves several. [Tribe RAMONDIEAE.] . . . 5
5. Corolla white, lobed. Disc one-sided. Anthers oblong. Ovary completely 1-celled, glandular-hairy. Stigma entire. Stem creeping. Leaves alternate. — Species 1. East Africa. . . . . . **Linnaeopsis** Engl.
   Corolla blue or violet, cleft. Disc equal-sided. Anthers ovoid or subglobose. Ovary incompletely 2—4-celled, hairy. Stigma 2-lobed. Stem erect or ascending. Leaves opposite or all radical. — Species 4. East Africa. Some are used as ornamental plants.
   Saintpaulia Wendl.

FAMILY 214. LENTIBULARIACEAE

Rootless herbs with pitcher-leaves. Flowers solitary or in spikes or racemes, irregular, hermaphrodite. Calyx 2- or 5-parted. Corolla of united petals, 2-lipped, spurred or saccate. Stamens 2, attached to the base of the corolla. Anthers 1-celled. Ovary superior, 1-celled, with a free central placenta. Ovules several or many, inverted. Stigma sessile, entire or unequally 2-lobed. Fruit a 3—many-seeded capsule. Seeds exalbuminous. — Genera 2, species 65. (Plate 141.)

Calyx subequally 5-partite. Land- or marsh-plants. Pitcher-leaves tubular with two spirally twisted arms. Flowers in few-flowered racemes, with 2 bracteoles each. — Species 3. South Africa and southern Central Africa. . . . . **Genlisea** St. Hil.
Calyx 2-partite or of 2 free sepals. Pitcher-leaves bladder-like, ovoid or globose. — Species 60. Some of them are used as ornamental, medicinal, or dye-plants. " Bladderwort." (Plate 141.) . . . **Utricularia** L.

FAMILY 215. GOBULARIACEAE

Shrubs. Leaves alternate, undivided, without stipules. Flowers in heads or spikes, irregular, hermaphrodite. Calyx 5-cleft. Corolla 2-lipped, 5-lobed, usually blue. Stamens 4, in two pairs of unequal length, attached to the corolla. Staminodes none. Anthers turned inwards, 2-celled, opening by a transverse slit. Disc present, usually gland-like. Ovary superior, 1-celled. Ovule 1, pendulous, inverted. Style simple ; stigma entire or 2-lobed. Fruit dry, indehiscent. Seed albuminous ; embryo straight, the radicle turned upwards. — Genera 3, species 6. North Africa, Cape Verde Islands, and Socotra. (Under *SELAGINEAE*.)

1. Flowers in spikes. Corolla scarcely exceeding the calyx ; lobes of the upper lip similar to those of the lower. — Species 1. Island of Socotra.

    Cockburnia Balf.

    Flowers in heads. Corolla distinctly exceeding the calyx ; lobes of the upper lip much shorter than those of the lower. 2

2. Heads axillary. Corolla-tube slit open between the lobes of the upper lip. — Species 2. Madeira, Canaries, and Cape Verde Islands. (Under *Globularia* L.) . . . . **Lytanthus** Wettst.

    Heads terminal. Corolla-tube not slit. — Species 3. North Africa. Used medicinally. . . . . **Globularia** L.

SUBORDER ACANTHINEAE

FAMILY 216. ACANTHACEAE

Leaves opposite or whorled, simple, without stipules, usually dotted with cystoliths. Flowers more or less irregular, 4—5-merous, hermaphrodite. Petals united below. Fertile stamens 2 or 4. Disc usually present. Style simple. Stigma entire or 2-lobed, rarely 4-lobed. Ovary superior, 2-celled, rarely (*Afromendoncia*) 1-celled. Fruit a loculicidal capsule, the valves bearing the split dissepiments, more rarely a drupe. Seeds 2 or more, mostly exalbuminous ; funicle usually with a hook-like outgrowth. — Genera 106, species 1100. (Plate 142.)

1. Fruit a 1—2-celled, 1—2-seeded drupe. Funicles small, without an outgrowth. Ovary 1—2-celled, with 2 ovules in each cell. Stamens 4, with 2-celled anthers. Corolla with contorted aestivation. Calyx minute, enveloped by two large bracteoles. Flowers solitary or in clusters in the leaf-axils, rarely in terminal racemes. Leaves not dotted with cystoliths. Climbing shrubs. [Subfamily **MENDONCIOID-EAE.**] 2

    Fruit a 2-celled, 2- or more-seeded capsule. Funicles with a tubercle- or hook-shaped outgrowth, or thickened throughout their length. Ovary 2-celled. 4

2. Ovary 1-celled. Fruit oblong or ovate. Flowers in axillary clusters. — Species 6. Tropics. (Including *Liraya* Pierre, under *Mendoncia* Vell.) . . . . **Afromendoncia** Gilg

    Ovary 2-celled, at least when young. 3

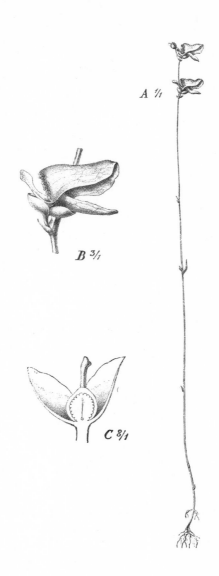

J. Fleischmann del.

Utricularia livida E. Mey.

A Plant in flower.   *B* Flower.   *C* Pistil and calyx cut lengthwise.

J. Fleischmann del.

Justicia matammensis (Schweinf.) Lindau

A Plant in flower (most of the corollas having fallen off). *B* Flower. *C* Flower cut lengthwise. *D* Stamen. *E* Fruit cut lengthwise (without the seeds).

3. Flowers solitary, axillary. Leaves ovate. Corolla-tube curved, gibbous below. Fruit globose. — Species 1. West Africa (Congo).

Gilletiella De Wild. & Dur.

Flowers in axillary clusters or in terminal racemes. Leaves oblong. — Species 2. Madagascar. . . . . **Monachochlamys** Bak.

4. Funicles short and thick, without a distinct outgrowth. Seeds and ovules 2 in each cell. Seeds globular, with a lateral hilum. Fruit beaked at the apex. Stamens 4; anthers 2-celled. Corolla nearly regular, with contorted aestivation. Calyx enclosed by two large bracteoles. Leaves not dotted with cystoliths. Shrubs or climbing herbs. [Subfamily **THUNBERGIOIDEAE**.] 5

Funicles with a large hook-shaped or a small tubercle-shaped outgrowth; in the latter case seeds and ovules 6 or more in each cell. 6

5. Anthers opening by pores. Stigma two-lobed. Calyx truncate. Corolla slightly two-lipped. Flowers in racemes. Climbing shrubs. — Species 2. Madagascar and southern East Africa. (Under *Thunbergia* L. f.)

Pseudocalyx Radlk.

Anthers opening by longitudinal slits. — Species 100. Tropical and South Africa. Some are used as ornamental plants. (Including *Hexacentris* Nees) . . . . **Thunbergia** L. f.

6. Funicles small, with a minute wart-like outgrowth. Seeds and ovules 6 or more in each cell. Seeds globose, with a lateral hilum, albuminous. Fruit beaked, rarely only pointed at the apex. Calyx unequally 4—5-parted. Corolla obscurely 2-lipped, with imbricate, not contorted aestivation. Anthers 2-celled. Disc indistinct. Herbs. Leaves not dotted with cystoliths. Flowers in spikes. [Subfamily **NELSONIOIDEAE**.] 7

Funicles with a distinct hook-shaped outgrowth, rarely (*Synnema*) thickened with an obscure outgrowth, but then corolla with contorted aestivation and leaves dotted with cystoliths. Seeds with a basal or subbasal hilum, exalbuminous, usually flat. Fruit usually prolonged into a stalk at the base, rarely beaked at the top. [Subfamily **ACANTHOIDEAE**.] 9

7. Sepals 5, unequal, almost free. Stamens 4. Ovules in each cell numerous, in 3—4 rows. Fruit not distinctly beaked. — Species 1. Central Africa. (*Ebermaiera* Nees, *Zenkerina* Engl.) . . . **Staurogyne** Wall.

Sepals 5, two of them united nearly to the top. Stamens 2. Ovules in each cell 6—10, in two rows. Fruit beaked. 8

8. Flowers with bracteoles. Stalk of the inflorescence covered with imbricate bracts. Leaves radical or alternate. Stem erect, usually very short. — Species 1. Central Africa. (*Tubiflora* Gmel.)

Elytraria Vahl

Flowers without bracteoles. Stalk of the inflorescence without bracts or wanting. Leaves opposite. Stem procumbent or ascending. — Species 1. Tropics. . . . . **Nelsonia** R. Br.

9. Corolla with contorted aestivation. Anthers 2-celled. Seeds usually
   hairy. 10
   Corolla with imbricate, not contorted aestivation. Seeds usually glabrous. 40

10. Corolla distinctly 1- or 2-lipped. 11
    Corolla nearly regular. 17

11. Fertile stamens 2. Corolla-tube long and thin. Fruit contracted into a
    stalk. Seeds 2 in each cell. Flowers in panicles. — Species 1. Equator-
    ial East Africa (Uganda). . . . . **Eranthemum** L.
    Fertile stamens 4, rarely 2, but then, as usually, seeds more than 2 in
    each cell of the fruit. Ovules 4 or more in each ovary-cell. [Tribe
    HYGROPHILEAE.] 12

12. Corolla 1-lipped, 5-lobed; tube cylindrical. Calyx equally 5-toothed.
    Stamens 4. Anthers not spurred. Ovules 4—8 in each cell of the ovary.
    Shrubs. Flowers in panicles. — Species 5. Central Africa. Some
    of them yield fish-poison or serve as ornamental plants. (Including
    Eremomastax Lindau). . . . . **Paulowilhelmia** Hochst.
    Corolla 2-lipped. 13

13. Fertile stamens 2; the anterior stamens sterile. Calyx 5-partite. Corolla
    red or violet; tube short, with a transverse fold. Ovules numerous.
    Herbs or undershrubs. Flowers in panicles, racemes, or spikes. —
    Species 20. Tropics. Some are used as ornamental plants.
    　　　　　　　　　　　　　　　　Brillantaisia Beauv.
    Fertile stamens 4, rarely 2, but then the posterior stamens sterile or want-
    ing. 14

14. Funicles of the seeds with an indistinct, cushion-shaped outgrowth. Ovules
    numerous. Stamens 2—4. Calyx 5-partite. Flowers solitary or in
    axillary cymes. Herbs. — Species 6. Central Africa. (*Cardanthera*
    Ham.) . . . . **Synnema** Benth.
    Funicles of the seeds with a distinct, hook-shaped outgrowth. Stamens 4,
    approximate in pairs, each decurrent upon a common fold. . . . 15

15. Stem woody. Flowers in axillary cymes. Calyx equally 5-partite.
    Anthers spurred, rarely only pointed at the base. Ovules 4—6 in each
    cell of the ovary. — Species 4. East Africa. **Mellera** S. Moore
    Stem herbaceous. Anthers not spurred. 16

16. Flowers in axillary clusters, intermixed with spines. Calyx 4-partite.
    Ovules 4—6 in each ovary-cell. — Species 2. Central Africa. Used for
    making salt. (Under *Hygrophila* R. Br.) . . **Asteracantha** Nees
    Flowers solitary or in spineless clusters or panicles. — Species 20. Tropical
    and South Africa. Some are used medicinally. (Including *Nomaphila*
    Blume) . . . . **Hygrophila** R. Br.

17. (10) Fruit distinctly compressed from front to back, contracted into a
    short stalk, 2—4-seeded. Ovules 1—2 in each ovary-cell. Stamens 4,
    united in pairs and decurrent at the base. [Tribe PETALIDIEAE.] 18

Fruit more or less terete or 4-angled. [Tribes RUELLIEAE and STROB-
ILANTHEAE.] 22

18. Ovary-cells 1-ovuled. Stigmas 2. Calyx 5-cleft or 4-parted. Flowers
in axillary clusters. Bracts oblong, about as long as the calyx ; bracteoles smaller. — Species 8. Central Africa. **Disperma** C. B. Clarke
Ovary-cells 2-ovuled. Bracts or bracteoles large. 19

19. Calyx-segments 4 owing to the complete or nearly complete union of the
two anticous segments. Flowers solitary or in short lateral inflorescences. — Species 18. Tropics. (Under *Petalidium* Nees).
Pseudobarleria T. Anders.
Calyx-segments 5, almost free. 20

20. Calyx-segments very unequal, the posticous much larger, bract-like.
Inflorescences spike-like, composed of cymes. — Species 15. Tropical
and South Africa. Some are used medicinally. (*Aetheilema* R. Br.,
Micranthus Wendl., *Phaylopsis* Willd.) . . . . . **Phaulopsis** Willd.
Calyx-segments nearly equal 21

21. Stigma entire, capitate. Anther-halves blunt. Flowers in terminal false
umbels. — Species 1. Madagascar. . . . . . **Zygoruellia** Baill.
Stigma unequally 2-lobed, filiform. Anther-halves pointed or tailed below.
Flowers solitary or in cymes. — Species 5. West and South Africa.
Petalidium Nees

22. (17.) Ovules 2 in each ovary-cell. Fruit contracted into a stalk, 2—4-
seeded. 23
Ovules 3 or more in each ovary-cell. 30

23. Fertile stamens 2. Corolla-tube long and narrow throughout its length. 24
Fertile stamens 4. 25

24. Calyx divided nearly to the base. Corolla orange. Stigma capitate
or oblong, more or less 2-lobed. Fruit ellipsoid, contracted into a
short stalk, usually 2-seeded. Flowers in heads, spikes, or panicles.
Bracteoles nearly as long as the calyx. — Species 5. Central Africa.
Used as ornamental plants. . . . . **Lankesteria** Lindl.
Calyx divided to the middle or somewhat beyond. Corolla white. Stigma
entire, oblong-linear. Fruit linear, contracted into a long stalk, usually
4-seeded. Flowers solitary or few together in the leaf-axils. Bracteoles
much shorter than the calyx. — Species 4. South and East Africa.
(Under *Calophanes* Don). . . . . . . **Chaetacanthus** Nees

25. Filaments free from the base. 26
Filaments united in pairs at the base and decurrent in the form of two
ridges. 27

26. Calyx shortly toothed. Corolla blue, with a long tube. Disc very small.
Flowers solitary, axillary. Bracteoles very small and narrow. —
Species 2. Northern East Africa. . . . . **Satanocrater** Schweinf.
Calyx deeply divided. Flowers in racemes or panicles. Bracteoles large,
membranous. — Species 15. Central Africa. (Including *Stylarthropus*
Baill.) . . . . **Whitfieldia** Hook.

27. Staminal ridges confluent, hence all stamens inserted upon a common
    fold. Anther-halves blunt. Fruit oblong ovoid or globose, 3—4-
    seeded. Flowers solitary or in spikes. — Species 4. Madagascar.
                                         Strobilanthes Blume
    Staminal ridges separate. Flowers solitary or in cymes. 28
28. Calyx 5-cleft. Anther-halves usually tailed. Fruit linear, 4-seeded. —
    Species 30. Tropical and South Africa. (*Calophanes* Don, including
    Phillipsia Rolfe). . . . . **Dyschoriste** Nees
    Calyx 5-parted. Anthers blunt. Fruit oblong or elliptical 29
29. Fruit 2-seeded. Pollen-grains ovoid, with longitudinal ribs. Under-
    shrubs. — Species 1. Southern East Africa. **Strobilanthopsis** S. Moore
    Fruit 4-seeded. Pollen-grains globular, prickly. — Species 8. Tropics.
    (Under *Dischistocalyx* T. Anders.) . . . **Acanthopale** C. B. Clarke
30. (22.) Fertile stamens 2. 31
    Fertile stamens 4. 32
31. Ovules 3—6 in each ovary-cell. Staminodes present. Corolla nearly
    2-lipped ; tube short, wide, funnel-shaped. Flowers several together
    in the leaf-axils. Shrubs. — Species 2. Madagascar. (Under *Ruttya*
    Harv.) . . . . **Forsythiopsis** Bak.
    Ovules 10 in each ovary-cell. Flowers solitary. Herbs. — Species 1.
    Madagascar. . . . . **Ruelliola** Baill.
32. Filaments free from the base. Anthers with a fertile and a rudimentary
    half. Calyx 5-lobed. Corolla white. Ovules 3—4 in each ovary-cell.
    Flowers in spikes or heads. — Species 3. West Africa. (*Physacanthus*
    Benth.) . . . . **Haselhoffia** Lindau
    Filaments united in pairs at the base, decurrent in the form of two ridges.
    Anthers with both halves fertile. Calyx 5-cleft or 5-parted. . . . 33
33. Staminal ridges confluent. Anthers not tailed. 34
    Staminal ridges separate. 35
34. Corolla long funnel-shaped. Flowers in loose panicles. — Species 1.
    Island of St. Thomas. (Under *Paulowilhelmia* Hochst.)
                                         Heteradelphia Lindau
    Corolla tubular. Flowers in spike- or head-like inflorescences. — Species
    5. Central Africa. . . . . **Hemigraphis** Nees
35. Anther-halves of the anterior stamens, at least one of them, tailed at the
    base. Calyx-segments subequal. Corolla funnel-shaped, with a short
    and wide tube. Flowers in panicles. — Species 15. Tropics. (Includ-
    ing *Epiclastopelma* Lindau) . . . . . **Mimulopsis** Schweinf.
    Anther-halves without an appendage at the base, rarely (*Ruelliopsis*)
    all tailed, and then calyx-segments unequal and flowers solitary. . 36
36. Stigma 2-lobed. Ovules 3—4 in each ovary-cell. Disc cup-shaped,
    toothed. Anthers exserted. Corolla red. Flowers solitary. Leaves
    crowded at the end of the branches. Glabrous shrubs. — Species 1.
    Madagascar. . . . . **Camarotea** Elliot
    Stigma entire or provided with a small tooth. 37

37. Flowers in spike- or head-like inflorescences. Calyx-segments usually
    very unequal. Bracteoles very small. — Species 9. Central Africa.
    (*Dischistocalyx* T. Anders.) . . . . . **Distichocalyx** T. Anders.
    Flowers solitary or in neither spike- nor head-like cymes or panicles. . 38
38. Leaves one-sided (with unequal halves) and usually very unequal in size,
    entire. Flowers solitary. Bracteoles very small. Calyx-segments
    subequal, very long. Corolla red or blue, with a long cylindrical tube.
    Anthers included. — Species 2. Equatorial West Africa.
    Endosiphon T. Anders.
    Leaves equal-sided or nearly so, about equal in size. 39
39. Pollen-grains with many longitudinal ribs. Anthers usually tailed. Calyx-
    segments unequal. Corolla funnel-shaped. Flowers solitary. Bract-
    eoles small. Leaves linear, entire. Shrubs. — Species 3. East and
    South Africa. . . . . **Ruelliopsis** C. B. Clarke
    Pollen-grains netted or pitted. Anthers not tailed. — Species 30. Tropical
    and South Africa. Some are used as ornamental or medicinal plants.
    (Including *Dipteracanthus* Nees) . . . . **Ruellia** L.
40. (9.) Corolla with imbricate, not ascending aestivation, 2-lipped or nearly
    regular. Filaments free. Anthers, at least those of the anterior
    stamens, 2-celled. Ovules 1—2 in each cell, rarely(*Crabbea*) 3—4.
    Fruit not distinctly contracted into a stalk. [Tribe BARLERIEAE.] 41
    Corolla with imbricate, ascending aestivation. 48
41. Calyx 4-parted, one of the segments sometimes shortly toothed. Stamens
    2, more rarely 4, exserted. Disc cup-shaped. Stigma-lobes 2, subequal,
    sometimes nearly confluent. Flowers in cymes, spikes, racemes, or
    heads. — Species 120. Tropical and South Africa and Egypt. Some
    are used as ornamental or medicinal plants. (Including *Somalia* Oliv.)
    Barleria L.
    Calyx 2- or 5-parted. Stamens 4, included. Disc ring-shaped or indistinct.
    42
42. Calyx 2-lipped or 2-parted. Corolla folded in the bud, nearly regular, with
    short triangular lobes. Anthers of the posterior stamens 1-celled.
    Disc indistinct. Stigma entire. Inflorescence spike- or head-like. —
    Species 12. Tropics. (Including *Leucobarleria* Lindau)
    Neuracanthus Nees
    Calyx 5-parted. Corolla not folded. Anthers 2-celled, rarely those
    of the posterior stamens 1-celled, but then corolla 2-lipped. Disc
    ring-shaped. 43
43. Flowers surrounded by 4 united bracts, solitary, with narrow bracteoles.
    Corolla-lobes spreading, pink. Anthers 2-celled. — Species 1. Mada-
    gascar. (*Periblema* DC.) . . . . **Boutonia** DC.
    Flowers not surrounded by united bracts, solitary but without bracteoles,
    or in spike- or head-like inflorescences. Corolla two-lipped. . . . 44
44. Bracteoles surrounding the flowers 4, large, exceeding the calyx. Flowers
    in head-like cymes, very small, stalked, intermixed with bracts. Corolla

white. Anthers with equal halves. Ovary hairy above. Ovules 2 in each cell. Stigma unequally 2-lobed. — Species 1. Madagascar.

Warpuria Stapf

Bracteoles minute or absent. 45

45. Flowers solitary, axillary. Stamens approximate in pairs. Anthers all 2-celled. Stigma with two almost equal lobes. — Species 2. South Africa. . . . . **Glossochilus** Nees

Flowers in spike- or head-like inflorescences. Stigma entire or very unequally 2-lobed, rarely almost equally 2-lobed, but then anthers partly 1-celled. 46

46. Stamens approximate in pairs. Anther-halves unappendaged, inserted nearly at the same level. Calyx-teeth pointed. Ovary and style glabrous. Ovules 2—4 in each ovary-cell. Fruit narrow-oblong, 4—8-seeded. Inflorescence capitate. — Species 10. South and Central Africa. . . . . **Crabbea** Harv.

Stamens not approximate in pairs. Anthers all with one half inserted lower than the other, or the posterior with one half only developed. Ovules 1—2 in each ovary-cell. Fruit 2—4-seeded. 47

47. Anterior calyx-segments united halfway up. Corolla violet. Anthers of the anterior stamens with unappendaged halves inserted at the same level; those of the posterior stamens with one half only developed. Stigma with 2 minute, subequal lobes. Flowers in few-flowered spikes. — Species 1. Northern East Africa (Somaliland). **Lindauea** Rendle

Anterior calyx-segments nearly free. Anthers of all or only the anterior stamens with one half inserted lower than the other. Stigma entire. — Species 30. Central Africa. (Including *Volkensiophyton* Lindau).

Lepidagathis Willd.

48. (40.) Corolla 1-lipped, 3—5-lobed; in place of the upper lip a slit. Stamens 4. Anthers 1-celled. Ovules 1—2 in each ovary-cell. Flowers in spikes. [Tribe ACANTHEAE.] 49

Corolla 2-lipped or nearly regular. 55

49. Calyx 4-parted. Corolla white or blue, rarely yellow; tube short. Leaves usually prickly. 50

Calyx 5-parted. Leaves undivided. 53

50. Corolla-tube of moderate length. Sepals free. Filaments very short. Bracts small; bracteoles much larger. Leaves undivided. — Species 1. Equatorial East Africa (Uganda). . . . **Crossandrella** C. B. Clarke

Corolla-tube very short. Bracts large, imbricate, usually prickly; bract-eoles small and narrow or wanting. 51

51. Anterior filaments with a process near the top. Ovary with two glandular pits at the apex. Stigma-lobes 2, equal. Corolla-tube nearly globular. Fruit more or less contracted at the base. Seeds hairy. — Species 60. Tropical and South Africa and Egypt. Some are used as vegetables or in medicine; others are noxious weeds. . . . . **Blepharis** Juss.

Anterior filaments without an apical process. Ovary without glandular pits at the top. Corolla-tube short-cylindrical. Fruit not or scarcely contracted at the base. 52

52. Stigma with 2 almost equal lobes. Disc oblique. Seeds 3—4, glabrous. Spikes stalked. — Species 15. Some of them are used as ornamental or medicinal plants. . . . . **Acanthus** L.

Stigma with very unequal lobes or entire. Disc indistinct. Seeds bristly, usually 2. Spikes sessile. Bracts ending in 3—5 spines. — Species 7. South Africa. . . . . **Acanthopsis** Harv.

53. Calyx-segments unequal, the posterior much broader than the anterior, 2-nerved, often toothed. Corolla red or yellow; tube very long. Anthers included. Seeds hairy. Bracteoles usually as long as the calyx. — Species 17. Tropical and South Africa. Some are used as ornamental plants. . . . . **Crossandra** Salisb.

Calyx-segments subequal, the posterior as broad as or a little broader than the anterior, one-nerved, rarely many-nerved and then sometimes toothed. Anthers more or less exserted. Seeds not hairy. Bracteoles shorter than the calyx. 54

54. Corolla-tube long. Anthers blunt. Disc thick. Fruit not contracted at the base. — Species 8. Tropics. (Including *Butayea* De Wild. and *Pleuroblepharis* Baill., under *Sclerochiton* Harv.) **Pseudoblepharis** Baill.

Corolla-tube short. Anthers pointed. Disc small. Fruit slightly contracted at the base. — Species 4. Central and South Africa.

Sclerochiton Harv.

55. (48.) Corolla nearly regular, often obscurely two-lipped. Ovules 2 in each ovary-cell. Flowers in spikes, racemes, or panicles. . . . 56

Corolla distinctly 2-lipped. 64

56. Fertile stamens 2. Staminodes usually present. Calyx 5-parted. [Tribe PSEUDERANTHEMEAE.] 57

Fertile stamens 4. 59

57. Anthers 1-celled. Calyx-segments subulate. Corolla-tube cylindrical, not widened above. Seeds 1—2, nearly smooth. Shrubs. Flowers in panicles. — Species 1. Northern East Africa (Somaliland).

Ruspolia Lindau

Anthers 2-celled. Seeds 4, rarely fewer. 58

58. Corolla-tube funnel-shaped, much widened above. Seeds nearly smooth. Flowers in racemes, white. Shrubs. — Species 1. Natal. Used as an ornamental plant. (Under *Asystasia* Blume). . . **Mackaya** Harv

Corolla-tube cylindrical, scarcely widened above. Seeds wrinkled. — Species 12. Tropics. Some are used as ornamental plants. (Under *Eranthemum* L.) . . . . **Pseuderanthemum** Radlk.

59. Anthers 1-celled, cohering. Fruit not contracted into a stalk. Flowers in spikes. — Species 1. Madagascar. . . **Stenandriopsis** S. Moore

Anthers 2-celled. Fruit contracted at the base into a long stalk. [Tribe ASYSTASIEAE.] 60

60. Calyx 5-lobed, with broad segments. Sterile stamen present. Stigma-
lobes unequal. Shrubs. Flowers in racemes. Bracteoles none. —
Species 4. West Africa. (*Scytanthus* T. Anders.) **Thomandersia** Baill.
Calyx 5-parted, with narrow segments. Sterile stamen absent. Stigma-
lobes subequal. Seeds 4. Bracteoles present. 61

61. Anther-halves of the longer stamens elliptical, one inserted much lower
than the other ; those of the shorter stamens suborbicular and divergent.
Flowers in panicles. — Species 1. Equatorial West Africa.
Filetia Miq.
Anther-halves oblong, nearly parallel and inserted at about the same
level. 62

62. Disc laterally 2-lobed. Bracts long. Flowers in spikes. — Species 2.
East Africa. (Under *Asystasia* Blume). . . . **Parasystasia** Baill.
Disc not 2-lobed. Bracts short. 63

63. Pollen-grains prickly, not striped. Anther-halves shortly spurred at the
base. Flowers in panicles. — Species 1. East Africa.
Asystasiella Lindau
Pollen-grain striped, not prickly. — Species 20. Tropical and South
Africa. Some of them are used as vegetables or as ornamental or
medicinal plants. . . . . **Asystasia** Blume

64. (55.) Ovules 3—6 in each ovary-cell. Fertile stamens 2, staminodes none.
Anthers 2-celled. Herbs. Flowers in panicles. — Species 1. Natural-
ized in the Mascarene Islands. Used medicinally. [Tribe AND-
ROGRAPHIDEAE.] . . . . **Andrographis** Nees
Ovules 1—2 in each ovary-cell. [Tribes GRAPTOPHYLLEAE, ODON-
TONEMEAE, ISOGLOSSEAE, and JUSTICIEAE.] 65

65. Fertile stamens 4. Anthers 2-celled. 66
Fertile stamens 2. 70

66. Corolla-tube long, cylindrical. Anther-halves pointed at the base. Leaves
ovate or elliptical. Flowers in terminal cymes or panicles. . . . 67
Corolla-tube rather short and wide. Leaves oblong or lanceolate. . . 68

67. Stigma entire. Stamens inserted a little below the throat of the corolla.
Bracteoles small. — Species 1. Central Africa. (*Styasasia* S. Moore,
under *Asystasia* Blume) . . . . **Isochoriste** Miq.
Stigma 2-lobed. Stamens inserted in the middle of the corolla-tube.
Bracteoles large. — Species 2. Madagascar. . . **Forcipella** Baill.

68. Anther-halves blunt at the base. Stamens inserted at the throat of the
corolla. Posterior stigma-lobe tubercle-shaped. Calyx-segments un-
equal. Seeds oblong. Flowers crowded in the axils of the leaves.
Bracts and bracteoles narrow, clothed with red hairs. — Species 1.
Madagascar. . . . . **Synchoriste** Baill.
Anther-halves pointed at the base. Bracts and bracteoles broad. . 69

69. Inflorescences axillary, cymose, borne on a long stalk. Bracts incised. —
Species 1. Madagascar. . . . . **Podorungia** Baill.

Inflorescences terminal, racemose, the lower flowers solitary in the leaf-axils. Pedicels 4-winged. Seeds 2, roundish. — Species 1. Madagascar.

Chlamydacanthus Lindau

70. (65.) Staminodes 2. Fruit contracted into a long stalk. Bracts and bracteoles small. 71

Staminodes none, rarely (*Duvernoya*) solitary. 73

71. Anthers projecting far beyond the corolla-tube; halves at equal heights, pointed at the base. Calyx short. Corolla red; tube long, funnel-shaped. Shrubs. Flowers panicled. — Species 1. Naturalized in West Africa. An ornamental and medicinal plant. **Graptophyllum** Nees

Anthers slightly projecting, with one half only developed . . . 72

72. Anthers pointed. Corolla red; tube short and wide. Flowers in cymes or panicles. — Species 5. East and South Africa and Madagascar.

Ruttya Harv.

Anthers blunt. Corolla yellow; tube long, ventricose. Flowers solitary or in cymes. Shrubs. — Species 4. Island of Socotra.

Ballochia Balf. fil.

73. Anthers 1-celled, blunt. 74

Anthers 2-celled. 80

74. Stigma entire. 75

Stigma 2-lobed. 76

75. Flowers in cymes surrounded by united bracts and collected in heads or fascicles. Bracteoles exceeding the calyx. Calyx scarious. Woolly shrubs. — Species 2. Madagascar. . . . . . **Lasiocladus** Boj.

Flowers in spikes or panicles, with free bracts. Corolla-tube very long and narrow. — Species 9. Tropics. . . . . . **Brachystephanus** Nees

76. Corolla-tube very short, bell-shaped. Stamens inserted in the lower part of it. Fruit contracted into a long stalk. Flowers in panicles. — Species 1. Equatorial West Africa (Cameroons). **Oreacanthus** Benth.

Corolla-tube not very short, cylindrical or funnel-shaped. Stamens inserted in its upper part or at the throat. 77

77. Flowers in spikes. Bracteoles equalling the calyx. Corolla funnel-shaped. Fruit contracted into a long stalk. — Species 2. Central Africa.

Monothecium Hochst.

Flowers in cymes, heads, or panicles. Bracts usually united. Bracteoles exceeding the calyx. Calyx scarious. Fruit contracted into a short stalk or not contracted. 78

78. Calyx deeply two-lipped, shortly 5-toothed. Corolla funnel-shaped. Fruit without a stalk. Flowers panicled. — Species 1. Madagascar.

Amphiestes S. Moore

Calyx regular or nearly so, 4—5-lobed or -parted. 79

79. Calyx 4-parted. Flowers in umbellately arranged cymes. — Species 2. Madagascar and Comoro Islands. . . . . . . **Periestes** Baill.

Calyx 5-lobed to 5-parted. — Species 70. Tropical and South Africa. Some are used in medicine. . . . . **Hypoëstes** R. Br.

80. (73.) Anther-halves inserted at unequal heights. 81
Anther-halves inserted at the same level, unappendaged at the base. . 101
81. Anther-halves, both or the lower one, prolonged at the base into a spur- or
tail-like appendage. 82
Anther-halves blunt or pointed, sometimes bearing a short mucro, but
neither spurred nor tailed. 92
82. Corolla-tube barrel-shaped, widened from the base ; lips short. Calyx-
segments very long and narrow. Stamens inserted in the middle of the
corolla-tube. Upper anther-half without a spur. Disc cup-shaped.
Fruit contracted into a long stalk. Shrubs. Flowers panicled, red.
Bracts and bracteoles small. — Species 2. Island of Socotra.
Trichocalyx Balf. fil.

Corolla-tube cylindrical or narrowly funnel-shaped. 83
83. Corolla-tube very long, much longer than the limb. Herbs or undershrubs. Flowers solitary or 2—3 together in the axils of the leaves.
Bracts narrow. 84
Corolla-tube short or rather short. 85
84. Corolla very large, red. Stamens inserted in the upper part of the corolla-
tube. Leaves lanceolate. — Species 1. South-east Africa. (Under
Siphonoglossa Oerst.) . . . . **Aulojusticia** Lindau
Corolla medium-sized. Stamens inserted in the lower part of the corolla-
tube. Leaves elliptical to orbicular. — Species 3. South and East
Africa. (Under *Justicia* L.) . . . . . **Siphonoglossa** Oerst.
85. Disc cup-shaped. Stamens inserted at the throat of the corolla. Pollen-
grains with several longitudinal rows of tubercles sometimes replaced
by patches. Partition of the fruit not separating from the valves at
maturity. — Species 160. Tropical and South Africa and Canary
Islands. Some of the species are used as ornamental, medicinal, or
dye-plants. (Including *Adhatoda* Nees, *Dianthera* L., *Gendarussa* Nees,
Monechma Hochst., and *Rhytiglossa* Nees). (Plate 142.) **Justicia** L.
Disc ring-shaped. Pollen-grains usually without tubercles. . . . 86
86. Calyx-segments 4. 87
Calyx-segments 5. 88
87. Flowers in spikes arranged in false umbels at the ends of the branches.
Fruit contracted into a short stalk. Shrubs. — Species 1. Madagascar.
Corymbostachys Lindau

Flowers in axillary spikes. Fruit contracted into a rather long stalk.
Herbs. — Species 5. Madagascar and West Africa. (Under *Justicia* L.)
Anisostachya Nees

88. Flowers in panicles. 89
Flowers in spikes. 90
89. Stem woody, shrubby Inflorescences scantily branched. Bracts very
narrow. Corolla blue. ' Anther-halves both spurred. Fruit contracted
into a short stalk. — Species 1. Equatorial West Africa (Cameroons).
(Under *Justicia* L.) . . . . **Salviacanthus** Lindau

Stem herbaceous. Inflorescences abundantly branched. Bracts broad. Lower anther-half spurred, the upper not. Fruit contracted into a long stalk. — Species 6. Tropical and South Africa. (Under *Justicia* L.)

Rhaphidospora Nees

90. Stem woody, shrubby. Calyx 5-cleft, scarious. Corolla large, red. — Species 4. East Africa and Madagascar. (Under *Macrorungia* C. B. Clarke) . . . . **Symplectochilus** Lindau

Stem herbaceous. 91

91. Stamens inserted at the throat of the corolla. Calyx membranous. Partition of the fruit separating from the valves at maturity. Flowers small. Bracts broad, in 4 ranks, whereof two enclose no flowers. Bracteoles large. — Species 9. Tropics. . . . . **Rungia** Nees

Stamens inserted in the lower part of the corolla-tube. Partition of the fruit not separating from the valves. — Species 10. Central Africa. Some are used as ornamental plants. (Under *Justicia* L.)

Nicoteba Lindau

92. (81.) Corolla-tube bell- or funnel-shaped, wide throughout or much widened above. 93

Corolla-tube cylindrical, narrow and not or slightly widened above. . 95

93. Anther-halves inserted at slightly unequal heights. Corolla-tube somewhat shorter than the limb. Pollen-grains ovoid, with several rows of patches. Disc lobed. Fruit oblong or club-shaped. Flowers in spikes or panicles. — Species 18. Tropical and South Africa. (Under *Adhatoda* Nees or *Justicia* L.) . . . . . . **Duvernoya** E. Mey.

Anther-halves inserted at very unequal heights, more rarely at slightly unequal ones, but then corolla-tube as long as or longer than the limb. Pollen-grains more or less globose, nearly smooth. Herbs or undershrubs. 94

94. Flowers in cymes. Corolla-tube long. Stamens inserted at its middle. Anther-halves inserted at slightly unequal heights. Stigma 2-lobed. Fruit oblong, without a distinct stalk. Seeds 2 fertile and 2 sterile. Leaves sessile, lanceolate. — Species 1. Madagascar.

Melittacanthus S. Moore

Flowers in racemes or panicles. Fruit contracted into a stalk. — Species 40. Tropical and South Africa. . . . . . . **Isoglossa** Oerst.

95. Corolla-tube short, much shorter than the lips. Anther-halves inserted at slightly unequal heights. Shrubs. 96

Corolla-tube long or rather long; upper lip entire or shortly toothed. Disc cup-shaped. 98

96. Upper lip of the corolla deeply cleft. Anther-halves pointed. Disc cup-shaped. Leaves broad, unequal-sided. Flowers in panicles. — Species 1. Madagascar. . . . . **Populina** Baill.

Upper lip of the corolla entire or shortly toothed. Disc ring-shaped. Flowers in spikes or fascicles. 97

2 K

97. Bracts very small, shorter than the calyx. Calyx-segments nearly free, 3-nerved. Stamens inserted at the throat of the corolla. Partition of the fruit not separating from the valves. — Species 5. Central Africa. . . . . **Anisotes** Nees

Bracts large, as long as or longer than the calyx. Stamens inserted in the corolla-tube. Partition of the fruit separating from the valves at maturity. — Species 5. Tropical Africa to Transvaal. (*Macrorungia* C. B. Clarke). . . . . **Himantochilus** T. Anders.

98. Bracts small. Anther-halves inserted at slightly unequal heights. Fruit oblong, narrowed into a long stalk. Shrubs, usually climbing. Flowers in panicles. — Species 6. Tropical and South Africa. Some are used as ornamental or medicinal plants. . . . . . **Rhinacanthus** Nees

Bracts large. Fruit narrowed into a short stalk. Herbs. 99

99. Bracts not opposite in pairs. Corolla small. Anther-halves inserted at slightly unequal heights. Pollen-grains globose, with 6 pores and several longitudinal rows of raised dots. — Species 3. Equatorial West Africa. . . . . **Chlamydocardia** Lindau

Bracts opposite in pairs and usually united at the base, enclosing 1—2 flowers. Pollen-grains ovoid, smooth, with 3 pores and 3 bands. . 100

100. Stamens inserted at the throat of the corolla. Fruit oblong ; partition not separating from the valves. — Species 10. Tropical and South Africa. Some are used as ornamental or medicinal plants.

Peristrophe Nees

Stamens inserted in the corolla-tube. Fruit ovate ; partition separating from the valves at maturity. — Species 30. Tropical and South Africa. (*Diapedium* Koenig). . . . . **Dicliptera** Juss.

101. (80.) Corolla-tube much widened above, long, curved ; lower lip rolled in. Stamens inserted at the throat of the corolla. Shrubs. Flowers in long terminal spikes or racemes, reddish-yellow. Bracts and bracteoles very small. — Species 1. Island of Socotra. (*Ancalanthus* Balf. fil.) . . . . **Angkalanthus** Balf. fil.

Corolla-tube not or slightly widened above. Stamens inserted in the corolla-tube. Bracts not very small. 102

102. Corolla-tube rather short, about equalling the limb. Seeds usually 2. Inflorescence spike-like. Bracts large. Bracteoles small or wanting. 103

Corolla-tube long. Fruit contracted into a long stalk. 104

103. Flowers solitary in the axil of each bract. Bracteoles linear. Fruit subglobose, contracted into a short stalk. — Species 5. Central Africa. (Under *Ecbolium* Kurz) . . . . **Schwabea** Endl.

Flowers 2—3 in the axil of each bract. Bracteoles bristle-like or wanting. Shrubs. — Species 3. Central Africa. (Under *Dicliptera* Juss.)

Megalochlamys Lindau

104. Bracts broad. Bracteoles long. Fruit flat. Seeds 2. Shrubs. Flowers in spikes. — Species 15. Tropical and South Africa. Some are used

medicinally. . . . . **Ecbolium** Kurz
  Bracts narrow. Seeds 4. 105
105. Flowers in one-sided spikes. Bracts small. Shrubs. — Species 1.
    Naturalized in the Canary Islands. . . . **Anisacanthus** Nees
  Flowers in panicles. Bracts long. Herbs. — Species 1. Equatorial
    West Africa. . . . . **Schaueria** Nees

SUBORDER MYOPORINEAE
FAMILY 217. MYOPORACEAE

Shrubs. Leaves alternate, at least the upper ones, undivided, without stipules. Flowers solitary or in pairs in the leaf-axils, without bracteoles, regular or nearly so, hermaphrodite. Sepals 5, united at the base, imbricate or open in the bud. Petals 5, united below, white, imbricate in the bud. Stamens 4, inserted on the corolla tube, in two pairs of slightly unequal length. Anthers 2-celled, the cells confluent at the top, opening inwards by longitudinal slits. Ovary superior, 2—4-celled. Ovules 1—6 in each cell, pendulous from the apex of the partition, inverted, with a thick funicle. Style simple ; stigma entire or 2—4-lobed. Fruit a drupe. Seeds albuminous ; radicle of the embryo superior. — Genera 3, species 4. Southern and tropical Africa.
  1. Corolla salver-shaped. Ovary 2-celled. Ovules in each cell 4—6, in
    pairs placed one above the other. Stigma oblong, oblique. Fruit
    with a 1—2-celled stone. — Species 2. South Africa. . **Oftia** Adans.
  Corolla bell-shaped. Ovules in each ovary-cell solitary or two side by
    side. 2
  2. Calyx-segments linear. Corolla slightly irregular. Ovary 2-celled. Stigma
    capitate. Fruit with 4 stones. — Species 1. West Africa.
                                        Zombiana Baill.
  Calyx-segments lanceolate. Corolla regular. Fruit with a 2—4-celled
    stone. — Species 1. Mascarene Islands. . . **Myoporum** Banks & Sol.

ORDER PLANTAGINALES
FAMILY 218. PLANTAGINACEAE

Herbs, undershrubs, or shrubs ; in the latter case leaves opposite. Leaves sessile, entire toothed lobed or pinnately cleft, without stipules. Flowers solitary or in spikes or heads, with broad bracts, without bracteoles, small, regular, 4-merous. Calyx of united sepals. Corolla scarious, of united petals, with imbricate aestivation, sometimes 2-toothed. Stamens 4, inserted on the tube of the corolla and alternating with its lobes. Filaments long, bent inwards in the bud. Anthers large, versatile, opening by two longitudinal slits. Ovary superior, 2—4-celled, sometimes one cell only fertile. Ovules axile, half-inverted. Style simple ; stigma entire, filiform. Fruit dry, opening by a lid or remaining closed. Seeds with a fleshy albumen ; embryo straight or nearly so. — Genera 2, species 40. (Plate 143.)

Flowers monoecious, the male solitary, the female at their base, solitary
or several together ; the latter with a bag-shaped, 2—4-toothed corolla.
Ovule 1.   Fruit indehiscent, 1-seeded. — Species 1.   Azores.

Litorella L.

Flowers hermaphrodite or polygamous, in 2- or more-flowered spikes
or heads, all with a 4-lobed corolla.   Ovules 2 or more.   Fruit dehiscent,
2- or more-seeded. — Species 40.   Some of them yield food for cattle
and birds, vegetables, medicaments, soda, and a mucilage. " Plantain."
(Plate 143.)   .   .   .   .   **Plantago** L.

ORDER RUBIALES

FAMILY 219.   RUBIACEAE

Leaves opposite or whorled, entire, provided with sometimes leaf-like stipules.   Flowers regular or nearly so, but sometimes with a curved corolla-
tube.   Petals united below.   Stamens as many as the corolla-lobes, inserted
on the corolla, free.   Anthers opening by two longitudinal slits, rarely (*Argostema*) by 1—2 apical pores.   Ovary inferior, rarely (*Gaertnera*) superior, usually
2- or more-celled.   Ovules inverted.   Style 1, or several styles united at the
base. — Genera 150, species 1900.   (Plate 144.)

1. Ovules solitary in each ovary-cell.   [Subfamily **COFFEOIDEAE**.] .   .   2
   Ovules two or more in each ovary-cell.   [Subfamily **CINCHONOIDEAE**.] 81

2. Ovules pendulous or descending ; micropyle superior.   Radicle of the
   embryo superior.   3
   Ovules ascending ; micropyle inferior.   Radicle of the embryo inferior.   30

3. Corolla with imbricate, sometimes contorted aestivation.   Shrubs or
   trees.   4
   Corolla with valvate aestivation.   18

4. Corolla with contorted aestivation.   Ovary 2-celled.   Seeds with copious
   albumen.   Flowers in fascicles or panicles, rarely solitary.   [Tribe
   ALBERTEAE.]   5
   Corolla with imbricate, not contorted aestivation.   16

5. Corolla curved, tubular, hairy within.   Calyx 5-partite ; 1—4 of the
   segments much enlarged after flowering.   Anthers hairy.   Style much
   exserted.   Flowers in terminal panicles.   6
   Corolla straight.   Calyx-segments not enlarged, rarely all enlarged after
   flowering.   7

6. Calyx with 1 enlarged segment.   Corolla hairy at the base and at the
   throat.   Stamens inserted at the throat of the corolla.   Anthers
   bearded at the base.   Style-apex 2-cleft. — Species 1.   Madagascar.

Nematostylis Hook. fil.

   Calyx with 2—4 enlarged segments.   Stamens inserted in the corolla-
   tube.   Style-apex entire. — Species 5.   Madagascar and Natal.   (*Ern-
   estimeyera* O. Ktze.) .   .   .   .   **Alberta** E. Mey.

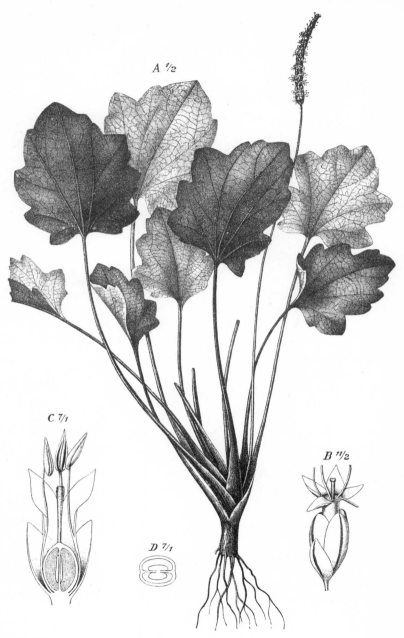

J. Fleischmann del.

Plantago palmata Hook. fil.

A Plant in flower.   *B* Flower with a bracteole (without the anthers).   *C* Flower cut lengthwise.   *D* Cross-section of ovary.

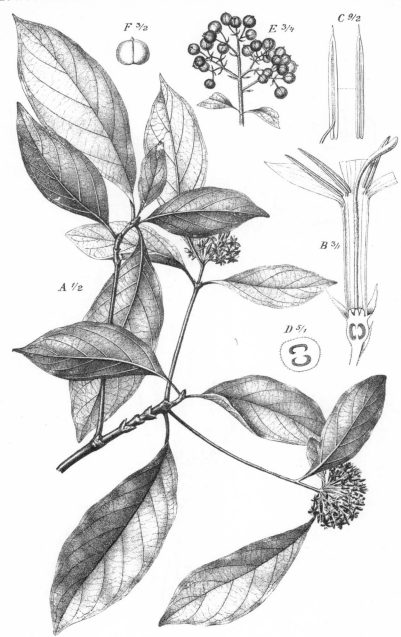

J. Fleischmann del.

Pavetta lasiorrhachis K. Schum.

A Flowering branch. *B* Flower cut lengthwise (two corolla-lobes cut off). *C* Anther. *D* Cross-section of ovary. *E* Group of fruits. *F* Fruit.

7. Flowers solitary or in pairs. Calyx-segments enlarged in the fruit. Corolla glabrous at the throat. Anthers included. Style long, glabrous, two-cleft at the apex. — Species 6. Central Africa. **Psilanthus** Hook. fil.
Flowers in fascicles or panicles. Calyx-segments not enlarged in the fruit. 8

8. Flowers in terminal panicles. Corolla hairy at the throat. Anthers exserted. Style downy above. Shrubs. 9
Flowers in axillary fascicles or panicles. 10

9. Calyx shortly lobed. Corolla white, funnel-shaped, 6—7-cleft. Style-apex 2-cleft. — Species 1. East Africa. . **Lamprothamnus** Hiern
Calyx deeply divided. Corolla yellow, salver-shaped, 4-cleft. Style-apex entire. — Species 1. Equatorial West Africa (Cameroons).
Exechostylus K. Schum.

10. Style hairy. 11
Style glabrous. 12

11. Calyx 4-toothed or truncate. Style-apex 2-cleft. Albumen of the seeds ruminated. Bracteoles 4, one pair united into a cup. — Species 10. Tropics. . . . . **Polysphaeria** Hook. fil.
Calyx 5-toothed or 5-cleft. Anthers exserted. Style-apex entire. Albumen of the seeds uniform. Bracteoles free. — Species 13. Tropics.
Cremaspora Benth.

12. Style short, with 2 long stigmas. Sepals free above the ovary. Corolla salver-shaped, glabrous at the throat. Anthers included. Trees. Flowers subtended by 2—3 pairs of bracteoles. — Species 1. Island of St. Thomas. . . . . **Belonophora** Hook. fil.
Style long, with 2 short stigmas or with a single stigma. 13

13. Style-apex 2-lobed. Corolla glabrous at the throat, but sometimes hairy below. 14
Style-apex entire, spindle-shaped, 10-ribbed. Flowers 5-merous. Anthers more or less exserted. 15

14. Flowers 4-merous. Sepals free above the ovary. Corolla salver-shaped. Anthers included. Flowers surrounded by 4 pairs of bracteoles. — Species 1. West Africa (Togoland). . . . **Kerstingia** K. Schum.
Flowers 5-merous. Sepals united above the ovary. Corolla funnel-shaped. Anthers exserted. — Species 4. West Africa.
Aulacocalyx Hook. fil.

15. Corolla bell-funnel-shaped, glabrous at the throat. Stipules very narrow. Species 2. East Africa. . . . . **Heinsenia** K. Schum.
Corolla bell-wheel-shaped, hairy at the throat. Stipules broad. — Species 3. East and South-east Africa. . . . **Rhabdostigma** Hook. fil.

16. (4.) Flowers in heads. Calyx 4-toothed. Ovary 2-celled. Fruit separating into two leathery nutlets. Seeds with a thick aril and copious albumen. — Species 3. West Africa, Madagascar, Natal.
Cephalanthus L.

Flowers in forked cymes. Ovules with a thickened funicle. Fruit a drupe. Seeds with scanty albumen or without albumen. [Tribe GUETTARDEAE.] 17

17. Calyx deciduous. Corolla salver-shaped. Anthers included. Ovary 4—9-celled. Fruit globose; cells of the stone curved. — Species 1. East Africa, Madagascar and neighbouring islands. Used as an ornamental plant and in medicine. . . . . **Guettarda** Blume

Calyx persistent. Corolla funnel-shaped. Anthers somewhat exserted. Ovary 2—8-celled. Fruit oblong. — Species 5. Madagascar and neighbouring islands. They yield timber and medicaments. (Under *Guettarda* Blume) . . . . **Antirrhoea** Comm.

18. (3.) Flowers in terminal or terminal and lateral heads. Ovary 1—2-celled. Fruit dry, of 1—2 nutlets. Herbs. Stipules united. [Tribe KNOXIEAE.] 19

Flowers in lateral cymes, fascicles, or panicles. Ovary 2—many-celled. Fruit fleshy, drupe-like. Shrubs or trees, rarely (*Pachystigma*) herbs, but then ovary 3—5-celled. 22

19. Ovary 1-celled. Sepals 1—2. Corolla bluish, funnel-shaped, 5-lobed. Anthers included. Leaves whorled. Flowers connate in pairs, without bracteoles. Stipules undivided. — Species 1. Southern West Africa (Angola) . . . . **Calanda** K. Schum.

Ovary 2-celled. Leaves opposite. Stipules lacerated or bristle-like. 20

20. Calyx with awl-shaped, not enlarged segments. Corolla violet, salver-shaped, with 4 lobes bearded at the apex. Anthers exserted. Disc tubular. Stigma 2-lobed. Mericarps dehiscing lengthwise. — Species 1. Equatorial West Africa (Cameroons). **Paragophyton** K. Schum.

Calyx with some of the segments enlarged and leaf-like. Corolla with long hairs at the throat. Mericarps dehiscing transversely or indehiscent. 21

21. Mericarps separating from a central column, dehiscing transversely. Calyx-segments 4, one of them enlarged. Corolla-lobes 4. Anthers included. Stigma 2-lobed. Heads in panicles. — Species 1. West Africa (Togo). . . . . **Baumannia** K. Schum.

Mericarp without a central column, indehiscent. — Species 15. Tropical and South Africa. (Including *Holocarpa* Bak.) . **Pentanisia** Harv.

22. Ovary-cells and fruit-stones 20—30. Flowers polygamous-dioecious, 4-merous. Corolla white or yellowish, glabrous within. Anthers included or nearly so. Seeds with scanty albumen. Shrubs. — Species 1. Madagascar and Seychelles. . . . . . **Timonius** Rumph.

Ovary-cells 2—10. Fruit-stones 1—10. Seeds with copious albumen. [Tribe VANGUERIEAE.] 23

23. Stem herbaceous. Leaves whorled. Ovary 3—5-celled. Stigma lobed. — Species 20. Central and South-east Africa. (*Fadogia* Schweinf.)

Pachystigma Hochst.

Stem woody. Leaves opposite. 24

24. Inflorescences fascicle-like or reduced to a single flower, surrounded by an involucre of two bracts united at the base. Calyx truncate or shortly toothed. Corolla hairy at the throat. 25
Inflorescences without an involucre. 26

25. Style deeply 4—5-cleft. Flowers in 6—12-flowered fascicles or heads. Trees. — Species 1. Island of Rodrigues. . **Scyphochlamys** Balf. fil.
Style simple, with a capitate stigma. — Species 10. Mascarene Islands and Madagascar. They yield timber. . . . . **Pyrostria** Comm.

26. Corolla curved, tubular. Calyx-segments 5, narrow. Anthers sessile. Ovary 5-celled. Stigma 5-lobed. — Species 6. Central Africa to Delagoa Bay. . . . . **Ancylanthus** Desf.
Corolla straight. Stigma entire or 2-lobed. 27

27. Ovary 2-celled. Flowers small. Calyx truncate or shortly toothed. . 28
Ovary 3—6-celled. 29

28. Stigma peltate, 2-toothed or 2-cleft. Corolla white, hairy at the throat. Shrubs. Leaves stiff-leathery. Stipules united at the base. Flowers in clusters. — Species 10. Central Africa and Seychelles. Some species yield dye-stuffs. . . . . **Craterispermum** Benth.
Stigma capitate, entire. — Species 120. Tropical and South Africa. Some of them have edible fruits and are used in medicine. (*Canthium* Lam.) . . . . **Plectronia** l

29. Flowers large, in many-flowered panicles, polygamous. Calyx deeply divided, exceeding the corolla. Anthers exserted. Ovules with a broadened funicle. Stigma hemispherical or mushroom-shaped. — Species 10. Central Africa to Delagoa Bay. . . . **Cuviera** DC.
Flowers small. Stigma capitate, cylindrical, or truncate. — Species 70. Tropical and South Africa. Some have edible fruits or are used in medicine. . . . . **Vangueria** Juss.

30. (2.) Ovules inserted on the partitions of the ovary, but sometimes near their base. 31
Ovules inserted at the base of the ovary-cells. Corolla with valvate aestivation. Stipules unlike the leaves. 54

31. Corolla with contorted aestivation. Fruit succulent. Shrubs or trees. Stipules small. Flowers solitary or in cymes. [Tribe IXOREAE.] 32
Corolla with valvate aestivation. 38

32. Ovules attached to placentas arising near the base of the partition of the ovary. Ovary 2-celled. Stigma spindle-shaped. Corolla glabrous at the throat. Flowers 5-merous, in head-like cymes. Seeds with ruminated albumen. Climbing shrubs. — Species 20. Tropics.
Rutidea DC.
Ovules attached to placentas arising near the middle of the partition. 33

33. Corolla with a curved tube, 5—7-lobed. Calyx-teeth indistinct. Anthers included. Ovary 2-celled. Style with two unequal stigmas. Flowers

terminal, solitary or in groups of 3, surrounded by an involucre. Trees.
— Species 1. Madagascar. . . . . . .   **Pleurocoffea** Baill.

Corolla with a straight tube. 34

34. Flowers with an epicalyx. Style 2—6-cleft. 35
Flowers without an epicalyx, hermaphrodite. Style 2-cleft or simple.
Ovary 2-celled. 36

35. Flowers in terminal corymbs, 4-merous. polygamous. Epicalyx 2-partite.
Corolla glabrous at the throat. Fruit globose. — Species 5. Mascarene
Islands. They yield timber, and are used in medicine. **Myonima** Comm.
Flowers in axillary fascicles, 5—8-merous, hermaphrodite. Ovary 2-
celled. — Species 50. Tropics ; one species also cultivated in Madeira.
Several species (especially *C. arabica* L. and *C. liberica* L.) yield coffee,
oil, medicaments, a substitute for tea, and timber ; some are used as
ornamental plants. (Including *Solenixora* Baill.) . . . **Coffea** L.

36. Calyx entire. Corolla-tube short, glabrous at the mouth. Stamens 5.
Style-branches 2, linear, ending in a cone. Shrubs. Stipules united.
Flowers in axillary, few-flowered cymes. — Species 1. Madagascar.
(*Buseria* Dur.) . . . .   **Leiochilus** Hook. fil.
Calyx toothed. Corolla-tube long. Stamens 4, rarely 5. Flowers in
usually terminal and many-flowered cymose corymbs. 37

37. Bracts at the base of the lowest branches of the inflorescence connate
into a sheath. Style-apex entire or shortly 2-toothed. — Species 120.
Tropical and South Africa. Some have edible fruits or serve as ornamental or medicinal plants. (Plate 144.) . . . . . . **Pavetta** L.
Bracts at the base of the branches of the inflorescence not connate into
a sheath. Style-apex 2-cleft. Leaves leathery. Stipules not united.
— Species 60. Tropics. Some are used as ornamental plants or in
medicine. . . . . **Ixora** L.

38. (31.) Stem woody. Stipules small, undivided, combined into a sheath.
Flowers in heads, connate by their ovaries. Calyx truncate or with
small teeth. Ovary 4-celled. Ovules inserted in the inner angle near
the base. Style 2-cleft. Fruit formed of connate drupes. — Species
6. Tropics. They yield timber, dyes, mucilage, condiments, and
medicaments. [Tribe MORINDEAE.] . . . . . **Morinda** L.
Stem herbaceous or woody at the base, rarely (*Gaillonia*) throughout, but
then flowers solitary or in cymes or spikes. Stipules more or less
lacerated or leaf-like. Ovary 2—3-celled. 39

39. Stipules similar to the leaves ; hence leaves apparently whorled. Style
2-cleft or 2-parted, with head- or club-shaped stigmas. Fruit indehiscent ; seed adnate to the pericarp. [Tribe GALIEAE.] 40
Stipules unlike the leaves, toothed slashed or crowned by bristles, united
at the base. Ovules inserted near the middle of the partitions of the
ovary. [Tribe SPERMACOCEAE.] 46

40. Corolla funnel-shaped. 41
Corolla wheel- or bell-shaped. Calyx-limb indistinct or wanting. . . 43

41. Calyx-limb distinctly developed, 4—6-cleft. Corolla pink or lilac. Stamens 4. Flowers in heads. Stem prostrate. — Species 1. North Africa. Yields a dye-stuff. . . . . **Sherardia** Dill.

Calyx-limb indistinct or wanting, rarely of 4 free minute teeth. . . . 42

42. Flowers in spikes. Corolla-lobes with an inflexed appendage. Stamens 4—5. Ovules attached at the base of the partition of the ovary. — Species 7. North Africa. Used medicinally. . . **Crucianella** L.

Flowers in sometimes head-like cymes. Stamens 4. Ovules attached near the middle of the partition. — Species 5. North-west Africa. They (especially *A. odorata* L., woodruff) yield dyes, vermin-poison, condiments, and medicaments, or serve as ornamental plants.

Asperula L.

43. Flowers subtended by a large involucral bract, in few-flowered, axillary cymes. Stamens 3—4. Ovary with a fertile and a sterile cell. — Species 2. North Africa. . . . . **Callipeltis** Stev.

Flowers without an involucral bract. 44

44. Pedicels connate in threes, thick, spinous, enclosing the fruit. Flowers axillary, polygamous-monoecious. Corolla 3-lobed in the male flowers, 4-lobed in the female and hermaphrodite. Fruit dry, one-seeded. — Species 2. North Africa and northern East Africa. **Vaillantia** L.

Pedicels not connate and either not spinous or not enclosing the fruit. . 45

45. Fruit fleshy. Stamens 5, rarely 4. — Species 10. Some of them yield dyes and medicaments. " Madder." . . . . . . **Rubia** L.

Fruit dry. Stamens 4, rarely 3. — Species 60. Some of them yield dyes, condiments, or medicaments. (Including *Aspera* Moench)

Galium Tourn.

46. (39.) Ovary 3-celled. Style 3-cleft. Fruit separating into 3 nutlets. Calyx-limb 5—6-partite. Corolla-lobes 4—5. Flowers in terminal heads. — Species 1. Naturalized in East and South Africa. Used in medicine. (*Richardia* Bartl.) . . . . **Richardsonia** L.

Ovary 2-celled. 47

47. Fruit indehiscent, not separating into mericarps. Flowers solitary or three together in the axils of the leaves. 48

Fruit dehiscent or separating into mericarps. 49

48. Pericarp corky. Flowers rather large. Calyx-lobes 4. Corolla broadly funnel-shaped, 4-lobed, hairy at the throat. — Species 2. South Africa and Madagascar. They yield dye-stuffs. . . . **Hydrophylax** L. f.

Pericarp bony. Flowers small. Calyx-lobes 7—8. Corolla salver-shaped, 5-lobed. Style 2-cleft. — Species 1. Madagascar. **Gomphocalyx** Bak.

49. Fruit separating into indehiscent mericarps. 50

Fruit dehiscent. Inflorescences head-like. 51

50. Pericarp very thin, adnate to the seed. Low shrubs. Leaves linear or subulate, stiff. Flowers solitary or in cymes or spikes. — Species 6. North Africa and northern Central Africa. . . **Gaillonia** A. Rich.

Pericarp thick or rather thick, not adnate to the seed. Herbs or undershrubs. — Species 12. Tropical and South Africa. **Diodia** Gronov.

51. Fruit opening by a lid. Calyx-lobes 4. — Species 2. Central and South
Africa. Used medicinally. . . . .   **Mitracarpus** Zucc.
Fruit opening lengthwise. 52

52. Fruit splitting upwards from the base, remaining entire at the apex. Calyx-
lobes 4. Corolla long funnel-shaped. Stamens inserted on the limb
of the corolla. Style-apex capitate, shortly 2-lobed. — Species 2. East
Africa. (Under *Spermacoce* Dill.) . . .   **Hypodematium** A. Rich.
Fruit splitting downwards from the apex, remaining entire at the base. 53

53. Fruit with only one valve opening, the other remaining attached to the
partition. Calyx-lobes 4. Corolla shortly funnel-shaped. Stamens
inserted at the base of the corolla-tube. — Species 1. Comoro Islands.
(*Spermacoceoides* O. Ktze.) . . . .   **Spermacoce** Dill.
Fruit with both valves opening and splitting at the apex. — Species 45.
Tropical and South-east Africa. Some are used medicinally. (*Tardavel*
Adans., including *Octodon* Thonn., under *Spermacoce* Dill.)
                                           Borreria G. W. Mey.

54. (30.) Stamens inserted at the base or on the lower part of the corolla-tube ;
filaments long ; anthers versatile. Flowers usually unisexual. Seeds
with fleshy albumen. Leaves having a bad smell when rubbed. [Tribe
ANTHOSPERMEAE.] 55
Stamens inserted at the mouth or on the upper part of the corolla-tube.
Flowers usually hermaphrodite. 61

55. Style and stigma entire. Flowers solitary, axillary, 5-merous, polygamous.
Fruit a nut or separating into two nutlets. — Species 3. South Africa.
                                           Carpacoce Sond.

Style 2-cleft or 2-parted. 56

56. Style shortly 2-cleft. Flowers axillary, hermaphrodite. Corolla-lobes
3-lobed. Anthers included. Fruit a drupe. Shrubs. — Species 1.
Naturalized in the Mascarene Islands. A medicinal and ornamental
plant. . . . .   **Serissa** Comm.
Style deeply 2-parted. Anthers exserted. 57

57. Ovary and fruit with empty cavities between the two fertile cells ; hence
apparently 3—5-celled. Fruit separating into nutlets. Flowers axillary,
dioecious. — Species 6. South Africa. (*Ambraria* Cruse). **Nenax** Gaertn.
Ovary and fruit 2-celled without conspicuous empty cavities. . . . 58

58. Stem herbaceous, prostrate. Flowers axillary. Corolla-lobes erect. Fruit
a drupe. — Species 2. Island of Tristan da Cunha. Used as ornamental plants. . . . .   **Nertera** Banks & Sol.
Stem woody, at least at the base. Fruit capsular or separating into
mericarps. 59

59. Flowers axillary, solitary or in clusters, rarely in terminal panicles ; in this
case undershrubs with entire stipules and dioecious, 4-merous flowers. —
Species 35. Southern and tropical Africa. . . . .   **Anthospermum** L.

Flowers in terminal or terminal and lateral cymes or panicles. Under-shrubs with 3—6-parted stipules, or shrubs with undivided stipules and monoecious flowers. 60

60. Calyx 4-toothed. Fruit warty. Stipules 3—6-parted. Undershrubs. — Species 2. South Africa. . . . . **Galopina** Thunb.

Calyx 5-toothed in the male flowers, 2-toothed in the female. Flowers polygamous-monoecious. Fruit smooth. Stipules entire. Shrubs. — Species 1. Madeira amd Canary Islands. . . . . . **Phyllis** L.

61. (54.) Style deeply 2-parted. Fruit a capsule or a schizocarp. Leaves fetid when rubbed. 62

Style cleft, toothed, or entire. Fruit a drupe, rarely a berry or a schizo-carp. 64

62. Stem climbing, woody. Stipules entire. Flowers in terminal and lateral cymes. Anthers included. Style-branches twisted. Fruit with a fragile rind. — Species 10. Tropics. Some are used medicinally. (Including *Lecontea* A. Rich. and *Siphomeris* Boj.) [Tribe PAED-ERIEAE.] . . . . **Paederia** L.

Stem erect or prostrate. Stipules toothed or slit, connate. Flowers in terminal fascicles or spikes, rarely axillary, 5-merous. Anthers exserted. Fruit separating into two nutlets. 63

63. Flowers polygamous. Calyx-lobes nearly equal. Corolla-lobes recurved. Ovary and style hairy. Shrubs. Stipules toothed. Flowers in terminal, head-like fascicles. — Species 1. South Africa. (Under *Anthospermum* L.) . . . . **Crocyllis** E. Mey.

Flowers hermaphrodite. Calyx-teeth very unequal, some of them leaf-like. Corolla-lobes spreading. Ovary and style glabrous. Stipules slit. Flowers axillary or in terminal spikes or heads. — Species 9. Tropical and South Africa. . . . . **Otiophora** Zucc.

64. Fruit dry, separating into two mericarps. 65

Fruit succulent, berry- or drupe-like. 66

65. Filaments rather long. Mericarps without a carpophore. Flowers solitary. — Species 1. Seychelles. . . . . . . **Neoschimpera** Hemsl.

Filaments none. Mericarps suspended from a cleft carpophore. Flowers in cymes. — Species 1. Comoro Islands. . . **Cremocarpus** Boiv.

66. Seeds with fleshy albumen. Flowers hermaphrodite. Corolla funnel-shaped. Ovary 2—3-celled. Style 2—3-toothed. Shrubs, having a bad smell when rubbed. Flowers in terminal or terminal and lateral cymes. 67

Seeds with horny albumen. Plants without a strong smell, rarely exhaling a bad smell when rubbed ; in this case inflorescences axillary and style 4—12-cleft. [Tribe PSYCHOTRIEAE.] 68

67. Flowers in terminal fascicles, 4-merous. Corolla with a long tube and spreading lobes, glabrous at the throat. Anthers distinctly exserted. Style-apex thread-shaped, 2-cleft. Fruit a drupe. — Species 3. North-west Africa. Used medicinally. . . . . **Putoria** Pers.

Flowers in terminal and lateral cymes, 5—7-merous. Corolla with a rather short tube and erect lobes, hairy at the throat. Anthers scarcely exserted. Style-apex thickened, 2—3-lobed. Fruit a berry. Leaves linear. — Species 1. Canary Islands. . . . . . **Plocama** Ait.

68. Ovary superior. Style 2-cleft at the apex. Stamens 5, inserted on the corolla-tube. Anthers included. Shrubs or trees. Flowers in terminal panicles or heads. — Species 25. Tropics. Some yield timber or are used in medicine. . . . . **Gaertnera** Lam.
    Ovary inferior. 69

69. Flowers axillary, solitary or in usually few-flowered cymes or heads. Shrubs or small trees. 70
    Flowers in terminal or terminal and lateral, many-flowered inflorescences, hermaphrodite. 74

70. Ovary-cells and style-branches or stigmas 2. 71
    Ovary-cells and style-branches or stigmas 4—12. 73

71. Anthers exserted. Calyx 5-partite. Corolla hairy within above the base, glabrous at the throat. Seeds with ruminated albumen. Flowers in heads surrounded by an involucre. — Species 1. Equatorial West Africa (Gaboon) . . . . **Peripeplus** Pierre
    Anthers included. Calyx 4-partite or nearly entire. Flowers solitary or in glomerules. 72

72. Calyx with 4 segments alternating with small teeth. Corolla funnel-shaped. Anthers with a short appendage at the apex. Flowers solitary, — Species 2. Madagascar. . . . . . . **Hymenocnemis** Hook.fil.
    Calyx nearly entire. Corolla bell-shaped. Anthers unappendaged. Fruit with a single stone. Flowers in clusters. — Species 3. Madagascar.
                                                    Saldinia A. Rich.

73. Leaves at first decussate, subsequently spreading in one plane, with many thin transverse veins. Stamens inserted at the throat or on the limb of the corolla. — Species 15. Tropics. . . . . **Lasianthus** Jack.
    Leaves always decussate, without conspicuous tranverse veins. Stamens inserted in the tube of the corolla. Flowers hermaphrodite. — Species 7. Madagascar and neighbouring islands. Used medicinally.
                                                    Psathura Comm.

74. Inflorescences capitate, surrounded by an involucre. Ovary-cells and style-branches 2—4. 75
    Inflorescences without an involucre. 77

75. Corolla with a curved tube, 6-lobed, white. Calyx irregularly lobed. Ovary-cells and style-branches 3. Shrubs. — Species 1. East Africa.
                                                Megalopus K. Schum.
    Corolla with a straight tube. 76

76. Seeds grooved on the ventral face. — Species 18. Central Africa. (Under *Uragoga* L.) . . . . **Cephaëlis** Swartz
    Seeds flat on the ventral face. Creeping herbs. Leaves long-stalked, heart- or kidney-shaped. — Species 13. Tropics. . . . **Geophila** Don

77. Corolla-tube curved. Anthers included. Ovary-cells and style-branches
    2. Seeds convex-concave. Shrubs or trees. — Species 20. Tropics.
    (Under *Psychotria* L.) .   .   .   .   **Chasalia** Blume
    Corolla-tube straight.   78
78. Fruit with a 5—7-celled stone. Ovary-cells and style-branches 5—7.
    Corolla salver-shaped, hairy at the throat. Anthers half-exserted.
    Shrubs or trees. Stipules 3-pointed. Flowers in corymbs. — Species
    2. East Africa and Madagascar. .   .   .   .   **Triainolepis** Hook. fil.
    Fruit with 2—5 stones. Ovary-cells and style-branches or stigma-lobes
    2, rarely 3—5.   79
79. Seeds flat on the ventral face. Calyx elongate. Corolla funnel-shaped,
    hairy at the throat. Anthers included. Herbs. Inflorescences capit-
    ate. — Species 12. Central Africa.   . **Trichostachys** Benth. & Hook.
    Seeds grooved on the ventral face.   80
80. Seeds with a ruminate albumen. Corolla salver-shaped, hairy at the
    throat. Anthers half-exserted. Shrubs. — Species 50. Tropical and
    South Africa. (Under *Psychotria* L.).   .   .   .   .   **Grumilea** Gaertn.
    Seeds with a uniform albumen. — Species 200. Tropical and South Africa.
    (*Myrstiphyllum* P. Br., including *Uragoga* L. partly). . . **Psychotria** L.
81. (1.) Corolla with imbricate, sometimes contorted aestivation. Shrubs or
    trees.   82
    Corolla with valvate aestivation.   124
82. Corolla with imbricate, not contorted aestivation. Ovary 2-celled.
    Style simple. Inflorescences head-like. [Tribe NAUCLEEAE.] . 83
    Corolla with contorted aestivation.   88
83. Ovaries of each head connate. Fruits fleshy, connate.   84
    Ovaries separate. Fruits dry, separate, opening by two valves or breaking
    up into two mericarps.   85
84. Inflorescences surrounded by two at first united involucral bracts. —
    Species 10. Madagascar and Mascarene Islands.   **Breonia** A. Rich.
    Inflorescences without involucral bracts. — Species 3. Tropics. They
    yield timber, edible fruits (negro-peaches), arrow-poison, and medica-
    ments. .   .   .   .   **Sarcocephalus** Afzel.
85. Ovules 2—3 in each ovary-cell. Calyx 4-toothed. Fruit separating
    into two nutlets. (See 16.) .   .   .   .   **Cephalanthus** L.
    Ovules 6 or more in each ovary-cell. Calyx 5-lobed or 5-parted. .   .   86
86. Ovules 6—8 in each ovary-cell. Flowers bracteolate, in glomerules col-
    lected in heads. Stem erect. — Species 1. Madagascar.
                                              Paracephaëlis Baill.
    Ovules numerous in each ovary-cell. Flowers ebracteolate, in heads. . 87
87. Fruit separating into two 2-valved mericarps. — Species 2. Madagascar.
    They yield timber, dye-stuffs, edible fruits, and medicaments.
                                                          Nauclea L.
    Fruit opening by two valves. Stem climbing by hooks. — Species 2.
    Tropics. (*Ourouparia* Aubl.) .   .   .   .   **Uncaria** Schreb.

88. (82.) Fruit opening by 4 valves, leathery. Corolla salver-shaped ; tube glabrous within. Style much exserted, 2-lobed at the top. Flowers in panicles. — Species 2. Central Africa. They yield timber and are used in medicine. . . . . **Crossopteryx** Fenzl
Fruit bursting irregularly or remaining closed, usually berry-like. [Tribe GARDENIEAE.] 89

89. Ovary 1-celled, sometimes incompletely 2- or more-celled. Anthers included or slightly exserted. 90
Ovary completely 2—5-celled. 93

90. Ovary 1-celled throughout its whole length, but the placentas sometimes much projecting and approximate in the centre. Style simple and entire or two-toothed at the apex. Flowers 5—11-merous. . . . 91
Ovary 2-celled in its lower or upper half. Style 2-cleft. Flowers 4—5-merous, axillary. 92

91. Stipules glume-like, imbricate. Stem climbing. Flowers in terminal cymes. Calyx 5-parted, with awl-shaped segments. Corolla salver-shaped, glabrous within. Style very long. Stigma 2-lobed. Fruit globose. — Species 3. Central Africa. Used as ornamental plants.
Macrosphyra Hook. fil.
Stipules not glume-like. — Species 45. Tropical and South Africa. Some species yield timber, dyes, edible fruits, or medicaments, or serve as ornamental plants. (Including *Genipa* L. partly.) . . **Gardenia** Ellis

92. Calyx 4-parted, with an epicalyx. Corolla salver-shaped. Stamens inserted in the corolla-tube. Seed-coat leathery. Flowers solitary or in pairs. — Species 4. Mascarene Islands. . . **Fernelia** Comm.
Calyx 5-toothed, without an epicalyx. Corolla funnel-shaped. Stamens inserted at the throat of the corolla. Seed-coat fibrous. Flowers in panicles. — Species 5. West Africa. . . . . **Pouchetia** A. Rich.

93. (89.) Ovary 2—3-celled. 94
Ovary 4—5-celled. 122

94. Ovules 2—3 in each ovary-cell. 95
Ovules 4 or more in each ovary-cell. 102

95. Ovules attached to thick, fleshy placentas, and more or less sunk in them. 96
Ovules attached to thin placentas, not sunk in them. 99

96. Style entire or shortly toothed at the apex, far exserted. Flowers in terminal corymbs. — Species 40. Tropical and South Africa. (*Chomelia* L., *Webera* Schreb., including *Coptosperma* Hook. fil.) **Tarenna** Gaertn.
Style more or less deeply cleft. Anthers exserted. 97

97. Flowers in terminal and lateral panicles. Corolla salver-shaped. Placentas ascending from the base of the ovary-cells. — Species 1. Madagascar. Yields an essential oil used in perfumery and medicine. **Santalina** Baill.
Flowers axillary, solitary or clustered. Corolla funnel-shaped. . . . 98

98. Flowers solitary or 2—3 together, without an epicalyx. Calyx deeply lobed. — Species 3. East and South Africa. . **Empogona** Hook. fil.

Flowers fascicled, with an epicalyx of 2—6 bracteoles united at the base. — Species 60. Tropical and South Africa. (Including *Bunburya* Meissn., *Diplocrater* Benth. & Hook., *Diplospora* DC., and *Kraussia* Harv.)
Tricalysia A. Rich.

99. Style entire or shortly toothed at the apex. Corolla funnel-shaped. . 100
Style cleft at the apex or further. Anthers exserted. Inflorescences lateral. 101

100. Flowers in terminal corymbs. Anthers included. Seeds solitary. — Species 1. East Africa. . . . . **Enterospermum** Hiern
Flowers in axillary fascicles. Anthers exserted. — Species 1. East Africa. . . . . **Zygoon** Hiern

101. Flowers solitary or fascicled on dwarf shoots, appearing before the leaves. Calyx-teeth awl-shaped. Corolla funnel-shaped. Seeds without an aril; albumen uniform. — Species 3. Central Africa. **Feretia** Del.
Flowers in cymes, appearing with the leaves. Calyx-teeth minute. Corolla wheel-shaped. Seeds with an aril; albumen ruminate. — Species 1. East Africa. . . . . **Galiniera** Del.

102. (94.) Style entire or shortly lobed or toothed at the apex. 103
Style more or less deeply cleft. 113

103. Calyx-segments large and broad, with imbricate, sometimes contorted aestivation. Corolla hairy within. Anthers included. Flowers hermaphrodite. 104
Calyx-segments small or narrow, with open aestivation. 105

104. Flowers solitary or in pairs in the leaf-axils. Corolla bell-shaped, hairy within the base, glabrous at the throat. — Species 5. Central Africa. (*Sherbournia* Don) . . . . **Amaralia** Welw.
Flowers in terminal cymes. Corolla salver-shaped. — Species 25. Central and South-east Africa. . . . . **Leptactinia** Hook. fil.

105. Flowers unisexual. 106
Flowers hermaphrodite. 108

106. Flowers in terminal cymes. Calyx entire or minutely toothed. Stamens inserted at the throat of the corolla. Trees. — Species 1. Madagascar.
Byrsophyllum Hook. fil.
Flowers solitary or paired in the leaf-axils, or in axillary panicles. Calyx lobed or divided. Shrubs. 107

107. Flowers in panicles. Calyx shortly lobed. Stamens inserted at the base of the corolla-tube; connective with a leaf-like appendage. Stem climbing. — Species 2. West Africa. . . . . **Atractogyne** Pierre
Flowers solitary or in pairs. Calyx deeply divided. Stamens inserted at the throat of the corolla, without an appendage. Stem erect; branches thickened and hollow at the nodes. — Species 1. Equatorial West Africa (Cameroons). . . . . . . **Epitaberna** K. Schum.

108. Inflorescences terminal or terminal and lateral. 109
Inflorescences lateral. 111

109. Style much projecting beyond the corolla-tube. Flowers in cymose
     corymbs. (See 96.) . . . . **Tarenna** Gaertn.
     Style not or slightly projecting beyond the corolla-tube. 110

110. Corolla-tube as long as or slightly longer than the limb. Calyx-segments
     awl-shaped. Anthers included. Style hairy. Flowers in clusters,
     yellowish-red. — Species 1. South Africa. Yields timber.
                                                        Burchellia R. Br.

     Corolla-tube considerably longer than the limb. — Species 85. Tropical
     and South Africa. Some species yield timber, poison, a substitute for
     soap, dyes, or medicaments, or serve as ornamental plants. (Including
     Genipa L. partly, *Mitriostigma* Hochst., and *Stylocoryne* Cav.)
                                                           Randia Houst.

111. Seed-coat membranous or leathery. (See 110.) . . .   **Randia** Houst.
     Seed-coat fibrous. . . . . 112.

112. Corolla-tube slightly longer than the limb. Stamens inserted in the
     tube, included. Fruit with a leathery rind. Flowers in fascicles. —
     Species 2. Madagascar. (Including *Tamatavia* Hook. fil.)
                                                        Chapeliera A. Rich

     Corolla-tube considerably longer than the limb. Stamens inserted at the
     throat, exserted. Fruit a berry. Flowers in corymbs. — Species 35.
     Central and South Africa. Some have edible fruits or serve as orna-
     mental plants. . . . . **Oxyanthus** DC.

113. (102.) Inflorescences lateral. Ovules 4—8 in each ovary-cell. . . 114
     Inflorescences terminal or terminal and lateral. Ovules numerous in
     each ovary-cell. 119

114. Placentas thick. 115
     Placentas thin. 117

115. Flowers without an epicalyx. Calyx with awl-shaped segments. Stamens
     inserted in the corolla-tube. — Species 1. Madagascar.
                                                         Flagenium Baill.

     Flowers with an epicalyx. 116

116. Inflorescences borne upon a broadened, leaf-like stalk. Calyx 5-toothed.
     Corolla glabrous at the throat. Anthers included. — Species 3. Mada-
     gascar. . . . . **Canephora** Juss.
     Inflorescences sessile or borne upon a not broadened stalk. Anthers
     exserted. (See 98.) . . . . **Tricalysia** A. Rich.

117. Flowers large, with an epicalyx of partly leaf-like bracts. Corolla salver-
     shaped, hairy at the throat. Anthers far exserted. — Species 1. West
     Africa. . . . . **Probletostemon** K. Schum.
     Flowers small, without an epicalyx. 118

118. Style-branches hairy. Seeds 1—2. Shrubs. Stipules long. — Species
     4. Madagascar. . . . . **Hypobathrum** Blume
     Style-branches glabrous. Seeds 3 or more. Trees. Stipules short. —
     Species 1. Madagascar. . . . . **Paragenipa** Baill.

119. (113.) Calyx shortly toothed. Anthers included or nearly so. Seed-coat pitted. Stipules united at the base. — Species 25. Tropics.
Bertiera Aubl.
Calyx deeply divided, with leaf-like segments. 120

120. Anthers projecting beyond the corolla-tube, with several-chambered halves. Corolla funnel-shaped. Fruit fleshy. Seed-coat smooth. — Species 2. West Africa. . . . . **Dictyandra** Welw.
Anthers included within the corolla-tube or nearly so, with 2-chambered halves. Corolla salver-shaped. 121

121. Fruit fleshy. Seed-coat smooth. (See 104.) **Leptactinia** Hook. fil.
Fruit dry or nearly so. Seed-coat pitted. — Species 7. Central Africa.
Heinsia DC.

122. (93.) Ovules 2—4 in each ovary-cell. Calyx 5-toothed. Corolla funnel-shaped. Anthers exserted. Style simple. Flowers in axillary clusters. — Species 1. Central Africa. Yields fish-poison. (Under *Randia* Houst.) . . . . **Morelia** A. Rich.
Ovules numerous in each ovary-cell. 123

123. Flowers in lateral inflorescences. Disc cushion-shaped. Fruit clothed with long hairs. Seeds with a fleshy aril. — Species 1. Southern West Africa (Angola). . . . . **Chalazocarpus** Hiern
Flowers in terminal clusters. Disc rather flat. Calyx irregularly toothed. Corolla yellow, 8-lobed. Style 4-cleft at the top. Leaves very large. — Species 1. Equatorial West Africa (Cameroons). (*Tetrastigma* K. Schum.) . . . . **Schumanniophyton** Harms

124. (81.) Fruit a berry or a nut with a leathery skin. Seeds numerous, small; testa netted or dotted. [Tribe MUSSAENDEAE.] . . . 125
Fruit a capsule or a schizocarp, rarely (*Oldenlandia*) an achene or nut with a membranous or crustaceous skin. Ovary 2-celled, rarely (*Penta-carpaea*) 5-celled. Flowers small. 133

125. Corolla-tube short. Style entire or toothed at the apex. Shrubs or trees. Inflorescences without an involucre. 126
Corolla-tube long. Style more or less deeply cleft. 128

126. Flowers in terminal clusters. Calyx 5-parted. Ovary 2-celled. Twining shrubs. — Species 1. Southern West Africa (Angola). **Justenia** Hiern
Flowers in axillary inflorescences. Calyx 4—7-toothed. 127

127. Corolla urn-shaped. Anthers slightly exserted. Ovary 2-celled. Flowers solitary or in pairs. — Species 2. West Africa. **Pauridiantha** Hook. fil.
Corolla wheel- or funnel-shaped. Anthers included. Ovary 4—7-celled. Flowers in panicles or heads. — Species 20. Tropics. Some species yield dyes. . . . . **Urophyllum** Wall.

128. Flowers in terminal panicles. Calyx 5-toothed or 5-lobed; one of the segments in several flowers of each inflorescence leaf-like enlarged and brightly coloured. Stamens inserted at the throat of the corolla. Ovary

2-celled. Shrubs or undershrubs. — Species 30. Tropics. Some are used as ornamental, medicinal, or dye-plants. (Including *Spallanzania* DC.)
Mussaenda L.

Flowers in axillary inflorescences. 129

129. Inflorescences head-like and surrounded by a large, more or less bell-shaped involucre of united bracts. Stamens inserted in the corolla-tube. 130
Inflorescences with an involucre of free bracts or without an involucre. 131

130. Calyx deeply divided ; segments at first awl-shaped, subsequently some or all broadened and leaf-like. Ovary-cells and style-branches 5. Fruit globose. Erect herbs. — Species 1. Equatorial West Africa.
Temnopteryx Hook. fil.
Calyx cleft about halfway down ; segments ovate. Fruit ovate or oblong. Shrubs. — Species 4. Central Africa. . . . . . **Stipularia** Beauv.

131. Stamens inserted in the middle of the corolla-tube. Calyx deeply divided ; segments enlarged, leaf-like. Ovary 5-celled. Decumbent herbs. — Species 1. West Africa. . . . . . . **Pentaloncha** Hook. fil.
Stamens inserted at the mouth of the corolla-tube or somewhat below it. Shrubs. 132

132. Corolla funnel-shaped. Calyx deeply divided. Disc cup-shaped. Ovary-cells and style-branches 2. Flowers in clusters springing from the base of the stem. Erect, glabrous plants. — Species 1. Equatorial West Africa (Cameroons). . . . . **Ecpoma** K. Schum.
Corolla tube- or salver-shaped. Hairy, usually twining plants. — Species 35. Tropics. . . . . **Sabicea** Aubl.

133. (124.) Seeds winged, numerous. Fruit a capsule. Trees or shrubs. Stipules entire or toothed. 134
Seeds wingless. Herbs, undershrubs, or shrubs. [Tribe OLDEN-LANDIEAE.] 143

134. Flowers in heads, 5-merous. 135
Flowers in panicles. [Tribe CINCHONEAE.] 137

135. Calyx 5-cleft with leaf-like segments imbricate in the bud. Corolla tubular. Stamens concealed in the corolla-tube. Placentas ascending. Style 2-cleft. — Species 1. Madagascar. . . . . **Payera** Baill.
Calyx with small and narrow segments, open in the bud, or entire. Corolla long funnel-shaped. Stamens inserted at the throat of the corolla. Placentas pendulous or adnate to the partition of the ovary. Style simple, far exserted. Fruit a septicidal capsule. 136

136. Calyx entire or shortly toothed. Stigma hood-shaped. — Species 4. Central Africa. They yield timber, dyes, and medicaments. (*Mamboga* Blanco, *Stephegyne* Korth., under *Nauclea* L.) . . . **Mitragyne** Korth.
Calyx cleft about to the middle. Stigma head- or club-shaped. — Species 4. Central and South Africa. Yielding timber. . . . **Adina** Salisb.

137. Placentas shortly adnate to the partition of the ovary and more or less distinctly stalked. 138

Placentas adnate to the partition of the ovary throughout their whole length or almost so. 141

138. Flowers unisexual or polygamous, 5-merous. Corolla-lobes unappendaged. Fruit globose. Shrubs. — Species 20. Madagascar and neighbouring islands. Some species yield dyes or medicaments; several are poisonous.
Danais Comm.

Flowers hermaphrodite. Corolla-lobes usually with a thread- or club-shaped appendage on the back. Fruit oblong or linear. Trees. . 139

139. Anthers concealed within the corolla-tube. Flowers 4-merous. Corolla urn-shaped. Fruit loculicidal. Leaves opposite. — Species 1. West Africa. Used medicinally. . . . . . **Pseudocinchona** A. Chev.

Anthers projecting at least partly beyond the corolla-tube. Corolla-lobes appendaged. Flowers usually 5-merous. 140

140. Fruit loculicidal. Corolla usually funnel-shaped. — Species 3. West Africa. . . . . **Corynanthe** Welw.

Fruit septicidal. Corolla urn- or bell-shaped. Leaves whorled. — Species 3. West Africa. They yield timber and medicaments. (Under *Corynanthe* Welw.) . . . . **Pausinystalia** Pierre

141. Fruit loculicidal. Calyx-segments subulate, deciduous. Corolla-lobes erect. Style shortly lobed. Trees. Leaves herbaceous. Stipules glandular-toothed. Bracts partly petal-like. — Species 8. Tropics.
Hymenodictyon Wall.

Fruit septicidal. 142

142. Fruit splitting downwards from the apex. Calyx-segments lanceolate, leaf-like, deciduous. Corolla violet. — Species 4. Madagascar.
Schismatoclada Bak.

Fruit splitting upwards from the base. Calyx-segments persistent. Corolla pink or yellowish. Stamens of the long-styled flowers inserted in the middle of the corolla-tube, those of the short-styled at its mouth. Placentas thick. — Species 3. Cultivated in the tropics. They yield medicaments (especially quinine). . . . . **Cinchona** L.

143. (133.) Ovary 5-celled. Stigmas 5. Stamens 5, inserted a little above the base of the corolla-tube. Corolla salver-shaped, with a long tube. Calyx-segments unequal. Flowers in panicles. Herbs. — Species 1. Southern West Africa (Angola). . . . . . **Pentacarpaea** Hiern

Ovary 2-celled. Stigmas 1—2. 144

144. Placentas club-shaped, ascending from the base of the ovary-cells, few-ovuled. Shrubs or undershrubs. Flowers in terminal cymes, 4-merous. 145

Placentas attached to the partition of the ovary. 147

145. Calyx-segments distinctly unequal, one or several of them considerably enlarged. Corolla tubular or funnel-shaped. Stamens inserted in the corolla-tube. Fruit bursting irregularly. Stipules lacerated. — Species 15. Tropics. (Under *Carphalea* Juss.) . . . **Dirichletia** Klotzsch

Calyx-segments equal. 146

146. Calyx inversely umbrella-shaped, membranous at the base of the segments.
Corolla salver-shaped. Stamens inserted at the throat of the corolla.
Fruit opening loculicidally. Leaves linear. — Species 1. Madagascar.
                                                    Carphalea Juss.
Calyx not inversely umbrella-shaped, with 4 lobes alternating with small
teeth. Corolla tubular. Stamens inserted in the corolla-tube. Leaves
ovate. — Species 1. Island of Socotra.   . . . **Placopoda** Balf.

147. Calyx-segments distinctly unequal, usually one of them much enlarged. 148
Calyx-segments equal or nearly so. 151

148. Corolla glabrous at the throat. Style 2-lobed. Fruit loculicidal, with a
persistent and a deciduous valve. Herbs. Flowers in cymes. —
Species 10. Central Africa. . . . . **Virecta** Afzel.
Corolla hairy at the throat. Style 2-cleft. 149

149. Flowers in spikes. Fruit with septicidal and loculicidal dehiscence.
Undershrubs. — Species 12. Tropics. . . . . . **Otomeria** Benth.
Flowers in fascicles, cymes, or panicles. Fruit with loculicidal dehiscence.
                                                 150

150. Corolla red or violet. Stamens inserted in the upper part of the corolla-
tube. Herbs or undershrubs. Stipules divided into awl-shaped or
bristle-like segments. — Species 35. Tropical and South Africa. Some
are used as ornamental plants. (*Neurocarpaea* R. Br.) **Pentas** Benth.
Corolla yellow or white. Stamens inserted at the throat of the corolla.
Shrubs or trees. (See 128.) . . . . **Mussaenda** L.

151. Stamens inserted in the lower part of the corolla-tube. Anthers converging above or cohering into a tube, opening at the top. Corolla
rotate. Style simple, with a capitate stigma. Fruit opening with a
lid or irregularly. Herbs. Stipules undivided. Flowers in spike- or
umbel-like cymes. — Species 2. Central Africa. . . **Argostema** Wall.
Stamens inserted in the upper part of the corolla-tube or at its mouth.
Anthers neither converging nor cohering, opening lengthwise. . . 152

152. Flowers in racemes, 5-merous. Calyx-segments linear. Corolla white,
funnel-shaped; tube rather short. Anthers included. Placentas
spindle-shaped. Style 2-cleft. Creeping herbs. — Species 1. East
Africa. . . . . **Dolichometra** K. Schum.
Flowers solitary or in sometimes capitate or scorpioid cymes, often
collected in false racemes or panicles. 153

153. Flowers in one-sided cymose inflorescences, 5-merous. Stamens inserted
in the corolla-tube, included. Placentas filiform. Style-branches
spatulate. Fruit narrow, compressed, few-seeded, with septicidal and
loculicidal dehiscence. Climbing herbs. Stipules lanceolate. — Species
1. Central Africa. . . . . **Hekistocarpa** Hook. fil.
Flowers in head-like or lax, not one-sided cymes, or solitary. . . . 154

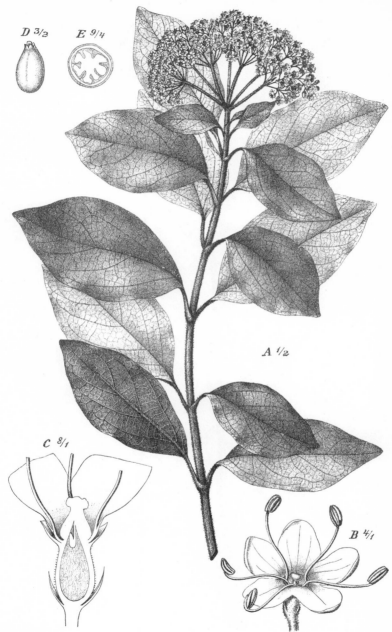

D 3/2   *E* 9/4

A 1/2

C 8/1

B 4/1

J. Fleischmann del.

Viburnum rugosum Pers.

A Flowering branch.   *B* Flower.   *C* Lower part of the flower cut lengthwise.   *D* Fruit.   *E* Cross-section of fruit.

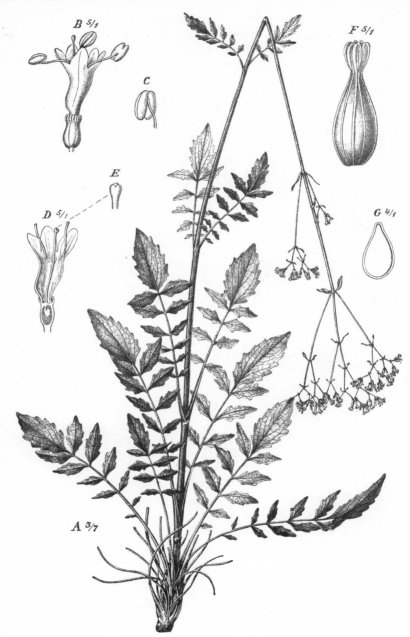

J. Fleischmann del.

Valeriana capensis Vahl

A Aboveground part of the plant.   *B* Flower.   *C* Anther.   *D* Flower cut lengthwise (without the anthers).   *E* Stigma.   *F* Fruit.
G Seed cut lengthwise.

154. Flowers 5-merous. Corolla shortly funnel-shaped. Anthers included. Style 2-cleft. Fruit opening loculicidally at the apex. Herbs. Stipules entire or toothed. Flowers in lax cymes. — Species 1. Tropical and South-east Africa. (Under *Oldenlandia* Plum.) **Pentodon** Hochst.
Flowers 4-merous, very rarely 5-merous, but then solitary or in pairs or style simple. 155
155. Fruit opening by a lid, few-seeded. Flowers 4-merous. Corolla rotate. Placentas globose, with 3—4 ovules. Undershrubs. Flowers in terminal fascicles. — Species 1. Northern East Africa (Somaliland).
Mitratheca K. Schum.
Fruit opening lengthwise or remaining closed. — Species 120. Some of them yield vegetables, dyes, or medicaments. (Including *Hedyotis* L. and *Pentanopsis* Rendle). . . . . **Oldenlandia** Plum.

FAMILY 220. CAPRIFOLIACEAE

Leaves opposite. Flowers hermaphrodite. Sepals 5, united below. Petals 5, united below. Stamens 5, inserted on the corolla. Ovary inferior. Ovules axile, pendulous. Fruit a berry or a drupe. Seeds with a straight embryo and fleshy albumen. — Genera 4, species 15. North and East Africa. (Plate 145.)
1. Ovary 1-celled when fully developed. Ovule 1. Style very short, 3-parted. Anthers turned inwards. Flowers in corymbs, regular, at least the inner ones. Fruit a drupe with a 1-seeded stone. Shrubs or trees. Leaves entire, toothed, or lobed. — Species 4. North Africa. They yield timber and medicaments or serve as ornamental plants, so especially the guelder-rose (*V. Opulus* L.) and the laurustinus (*V. tinus* L.) ; the latter has posionous fruits. (Plate 145.) [Tribe VIBUR-NEAE.] . . . . **Viburnum** L.
Ovary 2—5-celled. Ovules 2 or more. Fruit a drupe with 3—5 stones or a several-seeded berry. 2
2. Ovary with 1 ovule in each cell. Style very short, 3—5-parted. Anthers turned outwards. Corolla rotate. Flowers regular, in panicles or corymbs. Fruit a drupe. Leaves pinnately dissected. — Species 4. North and East Africa ; one species (*S. nigra* L.) only naturalized. The latter yields wood, pith, oil, edible fruits, and medicaments ; another species is poisonous. " Elder." [Tribe SAMBUCEAE.] **Sambucus** L.
Ovary with 2 or more ovules in each cell. Style long. Anthers turned inwards. Flowers more or less irregular. Fruit a berry. Leaves entire, toothed, or lobed. Shrubs. [Tribe LONICEREAE.] . . 3
3. Ovary 2—3-celled. — Species 6. North-west Africa. Some are used as ornamental or medicinal plants. " Honeysuckle." . . **Lonicera** L.
Ovary 5-celled. Fruit many-seeded. — Species 1. Naturalized in the Azores. An ornamental plant. . . . . **Leycesteria** Wall.

FAMILY 221. VALERIANACEAE

Herbs or undershrubs. Leaves opposite or all radical, without stipules. Inflorescence cymose. Calyx not distinctly developed at the time of flowering. Petals 5, united below. Stamens 1—3, attached to the corolla-tube. Anthers turned inwards. Ovary inferior, with 3 cells, two of which are empty and sometimes rudimentary. Ovule 1, pendulous, inverted. Style simple ; stigma entire or 3-parted. Seed exalbuminous ; embryo straight. — Genera 4, species 35. (Plate 146.)

1. Stamen 1. Corolla spurred. Calyx-limb developing into a feathery pappus crowning the fruit. Fruit 1-celled. — Species 5. North Africa. Used as ornamental plants. . . . . **Centranthus** DC.
   Stamens 2—3. Corolla not spurred, but sometimes gibbous. . . . 2

2. Stamens 2, more rarely 3, two of which are united. Corolla 2-lipped ; tube long, with a minute gibbosity near the base. Calyx-limb toothed. Branches of the inflorescence thickened. — Species 4. North-west Africa. . . . . **Fedia** Moench
   Stamens 3, free. Corolla not 2-lipped. 3

3. Calyx-limb rolled inwards at the time of flowering, developing afterwards into a pappus of feathery bristles. Fruit 1-celled. Corolla-tube usually gibbous. Perennial herbs or undershrubs. Leaves divided. — Species 5. North-west, East, and South Africa. Used as medicinal or orna- mental plants. (Plate 146.) . . . . **Valeriana** L.
   Calyx-limb entire or toothed. Corolla-tube without a distinct gibbosity. Annual herbs. — Species 20. North and South Africa and northern East Africa. Some species, especially *V. olitoria* Poll., are used as salad. " Cornsalad." . . . . **Valerianella** Haller

FAMILY 222. DIPSACACEAE

Herbs or undershrubs. Leaves opposite, without stipules. Flowers in heads ; each flower with an epicalyx embracing the ovary. Petals 4—5, united below. Stamens 2—4. Anthers turned inwards. Ovary inferior, 1-celled. Ovule 1, pendulous, inverted. Style simple ; stigma entire or 2-parted. Fruit enclosed by the epicalyx, dry, indehiscent. Seed albuminous ; embryo straight. — Genera 7, species 50. (Plate 147.)

1. Involucral bracts in many rows, imbricate, usually stiff and smaller than the scales of the receptacle. Calyx-teeth numerous. Corolla-lobes 4. Stigma entire. — Species 15. (Plate 147.) . . **Cephalaria** Schrad.
   Involucral bracts in 1—3 rows. 2

2. Involucral bracts united. Epicalyx with 8 pits near the apex. Calyx- teeth 5. Stigma entire. — Species 2. North-west Africa. (Under *Scabiosa* L.) . . . . **Pycnocomon** Hoffmsg. & Link
   Involucral bracts free. 3

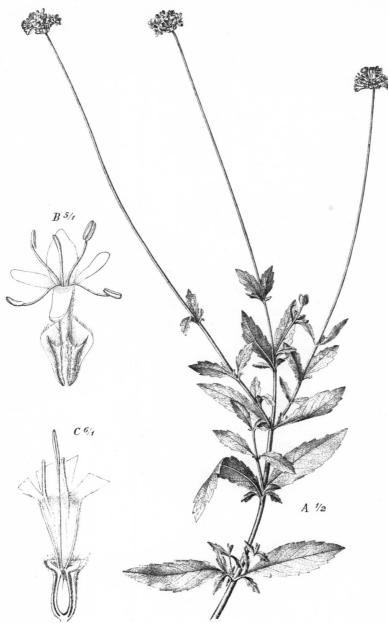

B ⁵/₁

C ⁶/₁

A ½

J. Fleischmann del.

Cephalaria rigida (Spreng.) Schrad.

A Flowering branch.   *B* Flower with epicalyx and bract.   *C* Lower part of the flower cut lengthwise.

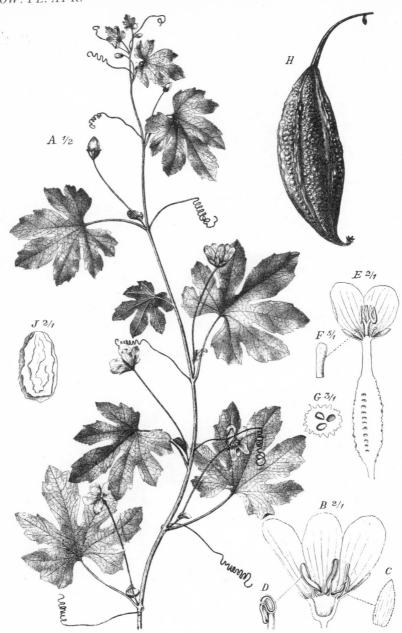

J. Fleischmann del.

Momordica Charantia L.

A Flowering branch. *B* Male flower cut lengthwise. *C* Sepal. *D* Anther. *E* Female flower cut lengthwise. *F* Staminode.
G Cross-section of ovary. *H* Fruit. *I* Seed. (*H* from Curtis' Botanical Magazine, plate 2455.)

3. Scales of the receptacle stiff and pointed. Calyx-teeth usually 4. Stem prickly or bristly. — Species 5. North and East Africa. Several species are used in the manufacture of cloth and in medicine. "Teasel."

Dipsacus L.

Scales of the receptacle herbaceous or replaced by hairs. Stem glabrous or hairy, rarely bristly. 4

4. Scales of the receptacle nearly as large as the flowers. Epicalyx with 8 longitudinal furrows. Calyx-teeth 5. Stigma entire. — Species 2. North-west Africa and Cameroons. They yield dyes and medicaments. (Under *Scabiosa* L.) . . . . **Succisa** Coult.

Scales of the receptacle much smaller than the flowers or replaced by hairs. 5

5. Calyx-teeth 4—6. Stigma 2-parted. Epicalyx with 8 longitudinal furrows or ribs and a saucer-shaped limb. Receptacle scaly. — Species 18. Some of them are used as ornamental or medicinal plants.

Scabiosa L.

Calyx-teeth 8—24. 6

6. Calyx-teeth 8. Epicalyx without distinct furrows or ribs, and with a narrow, toothed limb. Receptacle hairy. — Species 2. North-west Africa. Used as ornamental or medicinal plants. (Under *Scabiosa* L.)

Knautia Coult.

Calyx-teeth 12—24. Epicalyx with 8 longitudinal furrows and a saucer-shaped limb. — Species 6. North Africa and Abyssinia. (Under *Scabiosa* L.) . . . . **Pterocephalus** Vaill.

ORDER CAMPANULATAE

SUBORDER CUCURBITINEAE

FAMILY 223. CUCURBITACEAE

Nearly always prostrate or climbing and tendril-bearing plants. Leaves broad, usually with pedate nervation. Flowers unisexual or polygamous, regular or nearly so, 5-merous. Calyx of united sepals. Stamens 4—5, four of them united in pairs, rarely all united or all free. Anthers usually opening outwards. Ovary inferior. Ovules inverted. Style undivided or cleft. Fruit berry-like, but sometimes dehiscent, more rarely dry and indehiscent. Seeds with a leathery or woody testa and a straight embryo, without albumen. — Genera 42, species 270. (Plate 148.)

1. Filaments all united into a column. [Tribe SICYOIDEAE.] . . . 2
   Filaments free or united at the base or in pairs. 5

2. Anthers 2—3, horizontal, straight or slightly curved. Staminal column very short. Male flowers in panicles, yellowish. Tendrils 2-cleft. — Species 1. East Africa. (Under *Gerrardanthus* Harv.)

Cyclantheropsis Harms

Anthers 3—5, erect and much curved or twisted. 3

3. Flowers usually dioecious, the female with staminodes. Ovules numerous, horizontal. Herbs. Tendrils simple or 2-cleft. Female flowers solitary. — Species 30. Central and South Africa. Some species have edible fruits or serve as ornamental or medicinal plants. (*Cephalandra* Schrad.)
Coccinia Wight & Arn.

Flowers monoecious, the female without staminodes. Ovule 1, pendulous. Tendrils 3—5-cleft. Male flowers in racemes or panicles. 4

4. Female flowers solitary or in pairs. Anthers free. Fruit large, fleshy. Shrubs. Flowers whitish. — Species 1 (*S. edule* Swartz). Cultivated and sometimes naturalized in North Africa, the island of St. Thomas, and the Mascarenes. The stem yields fibres, the roots and fruits are edible and contain starch. . . . . **Sechium** P. Browne

Female flowers crowded in heads. Fruit small, with a leathery rind. Herbs. Flowers greenish. — Species 1. Central Africa ; also cultivated in the Mascarene Islands. Yields starch and medicaments. **Sicyos** L.

5. Stamens 5, one of them sterile ; filaments free ; anthers more or less cohering, 2-celled. Petals unequal, undivided. Ovary incompletely 3-celled ; ovules few in each cell, pendulous. Styles 3 ; stigmas 2-lobed. Fruit 3-valved at the apex. Seeds winged. Shrubs. Tendrils 2-cleft. Flowers dioecious, the male in racemes, the female solitary. — Species 4. Central and South Africa. Used medicinally. (Including *Atheranthera* Mast.) [Tribe FEVILLEAE.] . . **Gerrardanthus** Harv.

Stamens 4—5, united in pairs, hence apparently only 2—3, rarely stamens 5, free and all fertile. 6

6. Anther-cells straight or slightly curved, rarely shortly inflexed at the base or apex. [Tribe MELOTHRIEAE.] 7

Anther-cells much curved or twisted, U- or S-shaped. [Tribe CUCURBITEAE.] 19

7. Anther-cells (pollen-sacs) 4. Flowers large, rose-coloured, the male without a rudimentary pistil. Calyx-segments toothed. Petals ciliate. Ovary oblong, 3—5-celled. Ovules numerous. Style 1. Fruit very large. Leaves compound. Tendrils 2-cleft. — Species 2. Tropics. They yield edible oily seeds and medicaments. (Including *Ampelosicyos* Thouars). [Subtribe TELFAIRIINAE.] . . . . . **Telfairia** Hook.

Anther-cells 2, rarely (*Melothria*) 4, but then flowers small, white or yellow, the male with a rudimentary pistil, fruit small, and leaves simple. . 8

8. Disc at the base of the style distinctly developed. [Subtribe MELOTHRIINAE.] 9

Disc at the base of the style indistinct or wanting. [Subtribe ANGURIINAE.] 10

9. Calyx with a cylindrical tube and long, awl-shaped segments. Anthers sessile, attached by the back. Male flowers solitary or 2—3 together, female solitary. — Species 3. Central Africa. **Oreosyce** Hook. fil.

Calyx with a campanulate tube and short segments. Anthers attached by the base. — Species 30. Tropical and South Africa. They yield vegetables and medicaments, or serve as ornamental plants. (Including *Mukia* Arn., *Pilogyne* Schrad., and *Zehneria* Endl.) **Melothria** L.

10. Stamens inserted at the throat of the calyx. 11
    Stamens inserted in the calyx-tube. Climbing or prostrate herbs. . 12

11. Stem erect, woody, tree-like. Leaves more or less deeply divided. Flowers monoecious, the male in panicles, without a pistil. Stigma 1, 3-lobed. — Species 1. Island of Socotra. . . . . . **Dendrosicyos** Balf. fil.
    Stem prostrate or climbing, herbaceous. Stigmas 3. — Species 30. Central and South Africa, one species also cultivated in North Africa and the Mascarene Islands. Some species yield edible fruits and medicaments, or serve as ornamental plants. (Plate 148.) . . **Momordica** L.

12. Anther-cells inflexed at the apex. Connective broad. Flowers small, yellow, monoecious, the male with a rudimentary pistil. Stigmas 3. — Species 2. West Africa. They yield edible fruits, oily seeds, and medicaments. (Including *Cladosicyos* Hook., under *Zehneria* Endl.)
    Cucumeropsis Naud.
    Anther-cells straight, slightly curved, or inflexed at the base. . . . 13

13. Calyx-tube long, cylindrical. Flowers dioecious, the male in panicles, the female in racemes. Ovules numerous. Stigmas 2, 2-cleft. — Species 1. Madagascar. . . . . **Trochomeriopsis** Cogn.
    Calyx-tube short, campanulate. Flowers nearly always monoecious. . 14

14. Male flowers solitary or in fascicles or heads. Stamens with a lengthened or broadened connective. 15
    Male flowers in racemes. 16

15. Stigma 1, lobed. Ovules few in each ovary-cell. Staminodes of the female flowers minute or wanting. Flowers small, yellowish-green. Fruit opening by a lid. — Species 20. Tropical and South Africa.
    Corallocarpus Welw.
    Stigmas 3—5. Ovules numerous. Staminodes hair-like or strap-shaped. — Species 30. Some of them (especially the cucumber, *C. sativus* L., and the melon, *C. Melo* L.) yield edible fruits, oily seeds, and medicaments, or serve as ornamental plants. . . . . . **Cucumis** L.

16. Leaf-stalk with a small, fringed, stipule-like leaf at the base. Calyx-segments awl-shaped. Male flowers without a rudimentary pistil, female without staminodes. Connective not prolonged. Ovules 2—3 in each cell. — Species 2. Central and South-west Africa. (*Ctenolepis* Hook.)
    Blastania Kotschy & Peyr.
    Leaf-stalk without a stipule-like leaf at its base. 17

17. Stem short. Flowers appearing before the leaves, the male with a rudimentary pistil, the female with linear staminodes. Calyx-segments narrow. Connective narrow, not prolonged. Stigmas 3. Ovules numerous. Leaves lobed. — Species 1. South Africa.
    Pisosperma Sond. & Harv.
    Stem long. Flowers appearing with the leaves. 18

18. Staminodes in the female flowers thread-like, curved. Connective not prolonged at the apex. Male flowers without a rudimentary pistil. Stigmas 1—2. Ovules numerous. Calyx-segments broad. Fruit bottle-shaped. Seeds globose. Leaves toothed or lobed. — Species 3. South Africa to Ngamiland. . . . . **Toxanthera** Hook.

Staminodes in the female flowers small or wanting. Connective prolonged at the apex, very rarely not prolonged, but then fruit oblong, without a beak, and leaves deeply divided. Ovules usually few. — Species 15. Central and South Africa. Some are used as ornamental or medicinal plants. (Including *Coniandra* Schrad. and *Rhynchocarpa* Schrad.) . . . . **Kedrostis** Medik.

19. (6.) Ovules solitary in each ovary-cell, erect. Style surrounded at the base by a disc. Staminodes present in the female flowers. Anthers cohering. Petals undivided. — Species 1. West Africa and Canary Islands. (Including *Trianosperma* Mart.) [Subtribe ABOBRINAE.]

                                       Cayaponia Manso

Ovules 2 or more in each ovary-cell or upon each placenta, horizontal, rarely ovary 1-celled with 2 ovules, one erect, the other pendulous.   20

20. Petals slit at the edge, free or nearly so. Calyx-tube long. Stem climbing. Leaves cleft or compound. Tendrils 2—3-cleft. Male flowers in racemes. [Subtribe TRICHOSANTHINAE.] 21

Petals not slit. 22

21. Stamens combined into 3, projecting beyond the calyx-tube. Male flowers with a rudimentary pistil. Fruit snake-shaped. Leaves 3—7-lobed. Tendrils 3-cleft. Flowers white. — Species 1. Cultivated and naturalized in Madagascar and the neighbouring islands. Used as a vegetable or as an ornamental or medicinal plant. "Snake-gourd."

                                         Trichosanthes L.

Stamens 5, free, seated in the calyx-tube. Male flowers without a rudimentary pistil. Fruit pear-shaped. Leaves ternately compound. Tendrils 2-cleft. — Species 1. Madagascar. . . . **Delognaea** Cogn.

22. Corolla distinctly campanulate, lobed or cleft. Ovules numerous. Flowers large or medium-sized, the male without a rudimentary pistil. Leaves entire, toothed, or lobed. [Subtribe CUCURBITINAE.] 23

Corolla more or less rotate. [Subtribe CUCUMERINAE.] 26

23. Calyx-segments pinnately dissected. Female flowers without staminodes. Style long, inserted on the disc. Stigmas 3. 3—5-lobed. Fruit dry. Tendrils simple. — Species 4. Tropics. (*Raphidiocystis* Hook.)

                                     Rhaphidiocystis Hook.

Calyx-segments undivided. Female flowers provided with staminodes.   24

24. Flowers monoecious. Style short and thick. Stigmas 3—5, 2-lobed. Tendrils 2- or more-cleft. — Species 4. Cultivated and sometimes naturalized. They yield edible fruits, oil, and medicaments, and serve as ornamental plants. "Pumpkin." . . . . . . **Cucurbita** L.

Flowers dioecious. Style long. Stigma 1, 3-lobed or 3-partite. Tendrils simple or 2-cleft. 25

25. Anthers cohering. Staminodes of the female flowers from subulate to oblong. Fruit small. (See 3.) . . . **Coccinia** Wight & Arn.
Anthers free. Staminodes of the female flowers conical or globose. Fruit rather large. — Species 6. Central Africa. (Including *Staphylosyce* Hook.) . . . . **Physedra** Hook.

26. (22.) Calyx-tube of the male flowers long, cylinder- or funnel-shaped. . 27
Calyx-tube of the male flowers short, top- or bell-shaped. 32

27. Anthers connate. Female flowers without staminodes. Flowers large, white or yellow. 28
Anthers free or loosely cohering. Female flowers provided with staminodes. 29

28. Flowers monoecious. Anthers folded lengthwise. Ovary oblong. Leafstalk without glands at the apex. — Species 20. Tropical and South Africa. (*Peponia* Naud.) . . . . **Peponium** Naud.
Flowers dioecious. Anthers twisted transversely. Ovary globose. — Species 9. Tropics. Used medicinally. . . . . **Adenopus** Benth.

29. Flowers small or medium-sized, yellow or red. Anthers cohering. Rudimentary pistil of the male flowers conical. Stigma 1, 3-lobed. Seeds flattened. Root tuberous. — Species 15. Tropical and South Africa. Some species have edible roots also used in medicine. (Including *Heterosicyos* Welw.) . . . . **Trochomeria** Hook.
Flowers large. Rudimentary pistil of the male flowers gland-like or wanting Stigmas 3. Climbing herbs. 30

30. Flowers monoecious, white, solitary. Style very short. Stigmas 2-lobed. Fruit with a woody rind. Seeds flattened. Leaves undivided ; stalk with 2 glands at the apex. Tendrils 2-cleft. — Species 1 (*L. vulgaris* Ser., bottle-gourd). Tropics ; also cultivated and naturalized in extratropical countries. It yields edible fruits, also used for making bottles and other utensils, and serves as an ornamental and medicinal plant. . . . . **Lagenaria** Ser.
Flowers dioecious. Tendrils simple. 31

31. Male flowers in racemes. Leaves undivided. — Species 5. West Africa.
Cogniauxia Baill.
Male flowers solitary or in clusters. Corolla yellow. Stamens with a broad connective. Staminodes bearded at the base. Stigmas heart-shaped. Fruit fleshy. Seeds nearly globose. Leaves lobed ; stalk without glands. — Species 4. Central Africa. (*Euryandra* Hook.)
Eureiandra Hook.

32. (26.) Anthers connate. Flowers dioecious, the male in clusters and without a rudimentary pistil, the female without staminodes. Leaves undivided. 33
Anthers free or loosely cohering ; in the latter case flowers monoecious. 34

33. Stem herbaceous, without tendrils. Leaves linear. Anthers with a
scale at the base. — Species 1. Abyssinia. . . **Eulenburgia** Pax
Stem woody, climbing, bearing tendrils. Leaves broad. — Species 3.
West Africa. They yield oily seeds. . . . **Dimorphochlamys** Hook.
34. Anthers cohering ; cells horse-shoe-shaped. Flowers monoecious, the male
in umbels and with a rudimentary pistil, the female solitary and without
staminodes. Stigma subcapitate. Herbs. Leaves lobed, with a stipule-
like leaf at the base. Tendrils simple. Flowers white. Fruit small.
— Species 1. West Africa. (Under *Bryonia* L.) **Dactyliandra** Hook. fil.
Anthers free, at least when fully developed. 35
35. Stamens inserted at the throat of the calyx. 36
Stamens inserted in the tube of the calyx. 39
36. Calyx without scales at the base. Flowers dioecious, yellow or green,
the male solitary or in clusters, the female solitary, with 5 staminodes.
Ovary globose. Placentas and stigmas 5. Fruits large. Leafless,
nearly erect, spiny shrubs. — Species 1. German South-west Africa
and Angola. Yields edible fruits and seeds and medicaments.
Acanthosicyos Welw.
Calyx with 2—3 scales at the base. Ovary bottle-shaped. Placentas and
stigmas 1—3. Climbing or prostrate herbs. 37
37. Ovules 2. Stigma 1, capitate. Flowers large, yellow, monoecious, the
male 2—3 together at the base of the leaf-blade, without a rudimentary
pistil, the female solitary or in pairs, without staminodes. Fruits small.
Leaves slightly lobed. Tendrils simple. — Species 3. Central Africa.
(*Raphanocarpus* Hook.) . . . . **Rhaphanocarpus** Hook.
Ovules 3 or more. Stigmas 3. 38
38. Ovules few. Fruit constricted between the seeds. — Species 1. East
Africa. (*Raphanistrocarpus* Baill.) . . **Rhaphanistrocarpus** Baill.
Ovules numerous. (See 11.) . . . . **Momordica** L.
39. Male flowers in racemes. 40
Male flowers solitary or in clusters, yellow. 43
40. Female flowers in racemes or clusters, small. Ovules few. Male flowers
without a rudimentary pistil. Fruit more or less globular. Tendrils
simple. — Species 4. North Africa. Poisonous and used medicinally.
Bryonia L.
Female flowers solitary. Ovules numerous. 41
41. Flowers dioecious large, white, the male without a rudimentary pistil.
Stigma 1, 3-lobed. Fruit large, globose. Leafstalk with two glands
at the apex. Tendrils 2-cleft, rarely simple. — Species 1. Tropical and
South Africa. . . . . **Sphaerosicyos** Hook.
Flowers monoecious. Stigmas 3, 2-lobed. Leaf-stalk without glands. 42
42. Tendrils cleft. Leaves lobed. Fruit dry, opening by a lid. — Species 7.
Tropical and South Africa ; one species also cultivated in North Africa.
They are used as vegetables and medicinal plants ; some have edible,

others poisonous fruits ; the fibres of the fruit are employed for making sponges, hats, and various utensils ; the seeds are oily. **Luffa** L. Tendrils absent. Leaves undivided. Flowers yellow, the male without a rudimentary pistil. Fruit fleshy, ejecting the seeds when ripe. — Species 1. North Africa. A poisonous and medicinal plant. " Squirting cucumber." . . . . **Ecballium** A. Rich.

43. Male flowers without a rudimentary pistil. Ovules few. Stem climbing. Tendrils two-cleft. Flowers in clusters, small, yellowish-green, monoecious. Fruit small, globular. — Species 1. Tropics. Used as an ornamental and medicinal plant. . . . . . . **Bryonopsis** Arn.
Male flowers with a rudimentary pistil. Ovules numerous. 44

44. Connective of the stamens with a 2-cleft appendage at the apex. Tendrils simple, rarely wanting. (See 15.) . . . . . . **Cucumis** L.
Connective of the stamens not prolonged at the apex. Tendrils 2—3-cleft. Stem prostrate. Leaves lobed or divided. Flowers large, monoecious.

45

45. Calyx-segments leaf-like, serrate, recurved. Flowers solitary. — Species 1 (*B. hispida* Cogn.). Cultivated in various regions. The fruits are eaten and used in medicine. . . . . **Benincasa** Savi
Calyx-segments awl-shaped, entire. — Species 4. They yield edible fruits (chiefly from *C. vulgaris* Neck., water-melon), edible oily seeds, and medicaments ; some are poisonous. (*Colocynthis* L.)

Citrullus Neck.

SUBORDER CAMPANULINEAE

FAMILY 224. CAMPANULACEAE

Leaves entire toothed or lobed, without stipules. Petals usually united below. Stamens as many as the petals. Anthers turned inwards. Ovary inferior or half-inferior, rarely (*Lightfootia*) superior, 2—10-celled, rarely (*Merciera*) 1-celled. Ovules inverted, numerous and axile, rarely few and apical or basal. Style simple. Fruit a capsule, rarely a nut or (*Canarina*) a berry. Seeds with fleshy albumen ; embryo straight. — Genera 26, species 400. (Including *LOBELIACEAE* and *SPHENOCLEACEAE*.) (Plate 149.)

1. Anthers connate. Flowers more or less irregular, solitary or in racemes or panicles. [Subfamily **LOBELIOIDEAE.**] 2
Anthers free, rarely (*Jasione*) cohering at the base, but then flowers regular and in heads. 7

2. Petals free. Flowers nearly regular, small, greenish-yellow, in many-flowered terminal and lateral racemes. — Species 2. Madagascar.

Dialypetalum Benth.

Petals united below 3

3. Corolla-tube slit down to the base or nearly so, at least on one side. Stamens free from the corolla or nearly so. 4
Corolla-tube not or but shortly slit. 6

4. Fruit linear. All anthers hairy at the apex. — Species 1. South Africa.
(Under *Lobelia* L.) . . . . **Grammatotheca** Presl
Fruit roundish. 5

5. Anthers and stigmas ripe at the same time. All anthers hairy at the apex.
Odd sepal in front. — Species 12. South and East Africa and Comoro
Islands. Some are used as ornamental plants. (Including *Dobrowskya*
Presl and *Parastranthus* Don, under *Lobelia* L.) **Monopsis** Salisb.
Anthers ripe before the stigmas. Odd sepal usually behind. — Species 120.
Southern and tropical Africa, Madeira, and Azores. Some are poisonous
or are used as ornamental or medicinal plants. (Including *Isolobus* A.
DC. and *Metzleria* Presl) . . . . **Lobelia** L.

6. Filaments adnate to the corolla on one side to beyond the middle. Corolla
white. — Species 1. Naturalized in the Island of Réunion. A poisonous
and medicinal plant. . . . . **Isotoma** Lindl.
Filaments free from the corolla or shortly adnate to it. Corolla blue or
white. –– Species 10. South and North-west Africa. (Including
Enchysia Presl) . . . . **Laurentia** Neck.

7. (1.) Flowers distinctly irregular. Ovary 2-celled. Fruit opening loculicidally and septicidally. — Species 30. South and Central Africa. Several
species have edible tubers. [Subfamily **CYPHIOIDEAE**.] **Cyphia** Berg
Flowers regular or nearly so. [Subfamily **CAMPANULOIDEAE**.] . . 8

8. Corolla imbricate in the bud. Style very short, without collecting hairs.
Ovary 2-celled ; placentas thick, suspended from the top of the partition.
Fruit opening by a lid. Flowers in spikes, small, greenish or yellowish.
— Species 1. Tropics and Egypt. [Tribe SPHENOCLEEAE.]
Sphenoclea Gaertn.
Corolla valvate in the bud. Style with hairs or viscid glands for collecting
the pollen. [Tribe CAMPANULEAE.] 9

9. Carpels 5, as many as the sepals or stamens, and alternating with them. 10
Carpels as many as the sepals or stamens, but opposite to them, or fewer. 11

10. Corolla rotate or broadly campanulate, deeply cleft, yellow or red. Filaments broadened at the base. Fruit opening laterally by many transverse slits. Large herbs or undershrubs. Leaves elliptical. Flowers
large, in panicles. –– Species 2. Madeira. Used as ornamental plants.
Musschia Dumort.
Corolla tubular or narrowly campanulate. Filaments not broadened.
Fruit opening loculicidally by 5 apical valves. Seeds few. Small
herbs. Leaves linear. Flowers small, solitary or in clusters. — Species
4. South Africa. . . . . **Microcodon** A. DC.

11. Filaments adnate to the corolla halfway or higher up. Fruit opening
by an apical lid. 12
Filaments free from the corolla or nearly so. 13

12. Ovules 2 in each ovary-cell, suspended from the top of the cell. Flowers
blue, in raceme- or panicle-like cymose inflorescences. Leaves linear.
Herbs or undershrubs. . . . . **Siphocodon** Turcz.

Ovules many in each cell, attached to the inner angle. Flowers red, in heads. Leaves ovate. Shrubs. — Species 1. South Africa.

Rhigiophyllum Hochst.

13. Anthers cohering at the base. Petals free or nearly so. Ovary 2-celled. Fruit opening loculicidally at the top. Flowers in heads surrounded by an involucre. — Species 4. North Africa. . . . . . **Jasione** L.
Anthers free. 14

14. Ovules 4, basal. Ovary 1-celled, sometimes incompletely 2-celled. Corolla tubular-funnel-shaped. Fruit dry, indehiscent, 1-, rarely 2—4-seeded. Undershrubs. Flowers solitary, axillary. — Species 4. South Africa.

Merciera A. DC.

Ovules axile, usually numerous. Ovary 2—10-celled. 15

15. Fruit a roundish berry. Flowers solitary, terminal, large, nearly always 6-merous. Corolla bell-shaped, yellow or red. Filaments broadened at the base. Leaves opposite, the lower whorled. — Species 3. East Africa and Canary Islands. They yield edible roots and fruits and serve as ornamental plants. . . . . **Canarina** L.
Fruit a capsule, rarely a nut. Flowers usually 5-merous. 16

16. Fruit narrow, opening by an apical lid and sometimes also by lateral slits, more rarely remaining closed. Ovary 2-celled. 17
Fruit opening by apical valves or by lateral valves, slits, or pores. . . 18

17. Flowers in terminal heads. Corolla tubular. Ovary ovoid. — Species 1. South Africa. (*Leptocodon* Sond.) . . . . . **Treichelia** Vatke
Flowers terminal and solitary, or in lateral glomerules. Ovary oblong. — Species 15. South Africa. Some are used as ornamental plants.

Roëlla L.

18. Fruit opening by lateral, but sometimes nearly apical valves, slits, or pores. 19
Fruit opening loculicidally at the apex, usually broad. 22

19. Fruit narrow, opening by pores or slits. 20
Fruit broad, opening by valves. 21

20. Fruit opening by long slits. Ovary 2-celled. Corolla funnel-shaped or narrowly bell-shaped. — Species 20. South Africa.

Prismatocarpus L'Hér.

Fruit opening by short slits or pores. Ovary 3-celled. Corolla wheel-shaped or broadly bell-shaped. — Species 4. North Africa. They serve as ornamental plants; the root is edible. " Venus's looking-glass." . . . . **Specularia** Heist.

21. Corolla tubular. Ovary 2—3-celled. Style projecting far beyond the corolla. Flowers in panicles. — Species 1. North-west Africa. Used as an ornamental plant; the root is edible. . . **Trachelium** L.
Corolla bell- or funnel-shaped. Ovary 3—5-celled. Style not or slightly projecting beyond the corolla. — Species 25 North Africa and northern Central Africa. Several species are used as vegetables or as medicinal or ornamental plants. . . . . **Campanula** L.

22. Stigma-lobes 2—10, narrow. 23
    Stigma-lobes 2—3, broad, sometimes very small. 24
23. Petals free or nearly so, narrow. — Species 50. Southern and tropical
    Africa. (Plate 149.) . . . .   **Lightfootia** L'Hér.
    Petals obviously united below, or broad. — Species 80. Some of them
    serve as ornamental plants. (Including *Cervicina* Del.)
                                                Wahlenbergia Schra'd.
24. Petals free or nearly so, narrow, blue. Herbs. — Species 6. Central and
    South-west Africa. . . . .   **Cephalostigma** A. DC.
    Petals obviously united below. 25
25. Corolla bell-shaped, deeply cleft, yellow. Style equalling the corolla.
    Fruit opening at the top and laterally. Seeds numerous. Stem woody.
    Species 1. Mascarene Islands. (Under *Wahlenbergia* Schrad.)
                                                Heterochaenia A. DC.
    Corolla narrowly funnel-shaped, shortly lobed. Style much exceeding the
    corolla. Fruit opening at the top only. Seeds about ten. Stem
    herbaceous. — Species 1. Morocco. (Under *Trachelium* L.)
                                                Feeria Buser

FAMILY 225. GOODENIACEAE

Shrubs or trees. Juice not milky. Leaves alternate, undivided, without
stipules. Flowers in axillary cymes, irregular, hermaphrodite. Calyx truncate
or 5-toothed. Corolla 5-lobed, slit open behind, with folded aestivation.
Stamens 5, alternating with the corolla-lobes, free from the corolla. Anthers
free, turned inwards. Ovary inferior, 2-celled. Ovules solitary in each cell,
erect. Style simple. Stigma capitate, surrounded by a fringed cup. Fruit a
drupe. Seeds with fleshy albumen ; embryo straight.
    Genus 1, species 2. Tropical and South Africa. They yield wood for
    carpenters' work, pith used in the manufacture of paper, vegetables,
    and medicaments. . . . .   **Scaevola** L.

FAMILY 226. COMPOSITAE

Leaves simple and exstipulate, but sometimes dissected or provided with
stipule-like auricles. Flowers seated upon a dilated or elevated receptacle
and arranged in sometimes spike-like or one-flowered heads which are surrounded
by an involucre. Heads either containing only hermaphrodite flowers, several
of which are sometimes sterile (male), or consisting of hermaphrodite or male
central (disc-) flowers and female or neuter marginal (ray-) flowers, more
rarely heads unisexual or reduced to a single flower. Calyx-limb (pappus)
formed of sometimes connate scales or hairs, fully developed only in fruit,
or wanting. Corolla of united petals, in the hermaphrodite and male flowers
3—5-lobed with valvate aestivation, regular (tube-, funnel-, or bell-shaped)
or 2-lipped or 1-lipped (strap-shaped), in the female flowers sometimes
wanting. Stamens as many as the corolla-lobes and alternate with them,
inserted in the corolla-tube. Anthers connate, rarely free, opening inwards by

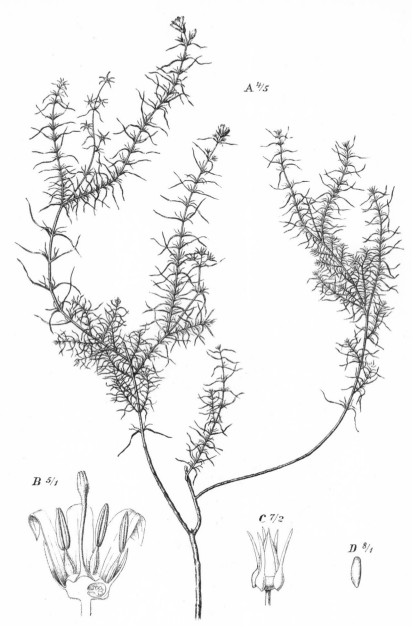

A ⁴/₅

B ⁵/₁

C ⁷/₂

D ⁸/₁

J. Fleischmann del.

Lightfootia subulata L'Hér.

A Flowering branch. *B* Flower cut lengthwise. *C* Fruit. *D* Seed.

J. Fleischmann del.

Vernonia Baumii O. Hoffm.

A Flowering branch. *B* Flower. *C* Flower cut lengthwise and pappus-bristle. *D* Anther from front and back.

two longitudinal slits. Ovary inferior, 1-celled. Ovule 1, erect, inverted. Style of the fertile hermaphrodite flowers cleft into two branches, which bear stigmatic papillae on the inner face or the margins, and hairs on the outer face, on both sides, or at the top; style of the sterile flowers usually entire. Fruit indehiscent, mostly dry. Seed solitary, with a thin coat usually adnate to the pericarp, exalbuminous. Embryo straight; radicle short, inferior. — Genera 327, species 4200. (Including *AMBROSIACEAE*.) (Plate 150.)

1. Corolla of all flowers strap-shaped (ligulate). Juice milky. [Tribe CICHORIEAE.] 2
   Corolla of the hermaphrodite and male flowers not strap-shaped. Juice not milky. 31

2. Scales on the receptacle enclosing the fruits. Thistle-like herbs. — Species 3. North Africa and northern East Africa. Used as vegetables and in medicine. [Subtribe SCOLYMINAE.] . . . . . . **Scolymus** L.
   Scales on the receptacle not enclosing the fruits or wanting. Not thistle-like plants. 3

3. Pappus of all or of the inner fruits consisting of feathery bristles which are sometimes broadened at the base or surrounded by simple bristles or by a small crown. [Subtribe LEONTODONTINAE.] 4
   Pappus consisting of simple, smooth or rough, in some cases shortly ciliate bristles, or of such bristles and scales, or only of scales sometimes ending in a not feathery, in some cases shortly ciliate awn, or of scales united into a small crown, or wanting altogether. 10

4. Pappus-bristles, at least on the inner fruits, with interwoven pinnae. Receptacle without scales. 5
   Pappus-bristles with not interwoven pinnae, in 1 or 2 rows. Flowers yellow. 7

5. Pappus-bristles and involucral bracts in one row. Flower-heads terminal, solitary, large or rather large. Leaves linear. — Species 3. North Africa; one of the species also naturalized in St. Helena. Used as vegetables or in medicine. "Salsify." (Including *Geropogon* L.)
   Tragopogon L.
   Pappus-bristles and involucral bracts in several rows. 6

6. Fruits obliquely truncate at the top; hence pappus lateral. Flower-heads terminal, solitary; flowers yellow. Leaves radical. — Species 1. North-west Africa (Algeria) . . . . **Tourneuxia** Coss.
   Fruits straight at the top. — Species 7. North and Central Africa; one species only cultivated. They yield edible roots, food for silkworms, and medicaments. (Including *Podospermum* DC.) **Scorzonera** L.

7. Receptacle with scales between the flowers. Involucral bracts in several rows. — Species 6. North Africa; two of the species also naturalized in South Africa, St. Helena, and the Mascarenes. Used in medicine. (Including *Seriola* L.) . . . . **Hypochoeris** L.
   Receptacle without scales. 8

8. Involucral bracts in one row. Fruits with a hollow beak. Pappus-bristles
in two rows. Flower-heads solitary. — Species 2. North Africa and
Cape Verde Islands ; naturalized in South Africa. **Urospermum** Scop.
Involucral bracts in several rows. 9

9. Leaves all radical. Stem simple or scantily branched. Pappus per-
sistent. — Species 20. North Africa. (Including *Asterothrix* Coss.,
Fidelia Schultz, *Kalbfussia* Schultz, *Microderis* DC., *Millina* Cass., and
Thrincia Roth). . . . . **Leontodon** L..
Leaves cauline or cauline and radical. Stem branched, hairy. — Species
20. North and Central Africa. Several species are used as vegetables.
(Including *Deckera* Schultz, *Helminthia* Juss., *Spitzelia* Schultz, *Viraea*
Vahl, and *Vigineixia* Pomel). . . . . **Picris** L.

10. (3.) Pappus, at least on the inner fruits, consisting of bristles. [Subtribe
CREPIDINAE.] 11
Pappus consisting of scales and bristles, or of scales sometimes prolonged
into an awn or united in a small crown, or wanting. [Subtribe
CICHORINAE.] 24

11. Receptacle beset with bristles. Fruits not beaked. 12
Receptacle glabrous or shortly ciliate. 13

12. Receptacle bristly throughout. Fruits linear. — Species 1. North-east
Africa (Egypt). (*Lagoseris* M. Bieb.) . . . . **Pterotheca** Cass.
Receptacle pitted ; only the edges of the pits beset with bristles. Fruits
oblong. — Species 10. North Africa. . . . . . **Andryala** L.

13. Fruits ending in a beak. 14
Fruits without a beak, but sometimes narrowed at the apex. . . . 18

14. Fruits tubercled at the base of the beak. 15
Fruits not tubercled at the base of the beak. 17

15. Outer fruits not beaked, with a rudimentary pappus or without a pappus.
Flower-heads subequal, in corymbs. — Species 1. North-east Africa
(Egypt). . . . . **Heteroderis** Boiss.
Outer fruits similar to the inner. 16

16. Heads rather small, 7—15-flowered. Leaves radical and cauline. —
Species 1. North Africa. Used as a salad and in medicine.
Chondrilla L.

Heads rather large, many-flowered. Leaves all radical. — Species 8.
Some of them are used as salad or in medicine. " Dandelion."
Taraxacum Hall.

17. Fruits compressed. — Species 40, one of them (*L. sativa* L.) only cultivated.
They are used as salad and fodder and in medicine ; some are poisonous.
" Lettuce." (Including *Cicerbita* Wallr.) . . . . . **Lactuca** L.
Fruits, at least the inner, terete or angular, many-ribbed. — Species 35.
(Including *Anisorhamphus* DC. and *Barkhousia* Moench). . **Crepis** L.

18. Fruits much narrowed at the top. 19
Fruits, at least the inner, not or slightly narrowed and truncate at the top. 20

19. Stem reduced to a rootstock sometimes prolonged into a short scape. Flowers yellow. — Species 2. East Africa. . . **Dianthoseris** Schultz
Stem well developed, not scape-like. (See 17.) . . . . **Crepis** L.
20. Fruits of two kinds, the inner differing from the outer. Involucral bracts in many rows, with scarious margins. 21
Fruits all alike. 22
21. Outer fruits transversely wrinkled or hairy, inner smooth and glabrous. — Species 20. Some of them are used medicinally. (Including *Heterachaena* Fres., *Microrhynchus* Less., *Rhabdotheca* Cass., and *Zollikoferia* DC.) . . . . **Launaea** Cass.
Outer and inner fruits 3—5-furrowed, with crenate ribs, the inner less deeply furrowed. Pappus-bristles falling away together. — Species 5. North and East Africa. Some are used as vegetables. (*Picridium* Desf.) . . . . **Reichardia** Roth
22. Fruits obscurely ribbed, not or slightly compressed, angular. Flowers red, violet, or white. Heads in racemes or panicles. — Species 2. Canary Islands and Socotra. . . . . **Prenanthes** L.
Fruits distinctly ribbed. Flowers usually yellow. 23
23. Fruits compressed. — Species 40. Some of them are used as vegetables or in medicine. "Sowthistle." . . . . . . **Sonchus** L.
Fruits terete or angular. — Species 7. North and South Africa and Madagascar. Some are used in medicine. "Hawkweed."

Hieracium L.

24. (10.) Pappus present. 25
Pappus absent. Receptacle glabrous or shortly ciliate. Flowers yellow. 29
25. Receptacle entirely beset with long bristles. Pappus consisting of toothed or awned scales. Involucral bracts with a scarious appendage. — Species 5. North Africa. Some are used as ornamental plants.

Catananche L.

Receptacle glabrous or shortly ciliate, sometimes with some long bristles in the centre. 26
26. Involucral bracts hardened at the time of maturity. Flower-heads terminal, solitary; flowers yellow. 27
Involucral bracts not hardened at maturity. 28
27. Fruits compressed, some of them winged. — Species 3. North Africa.

Hyoseris L.

Fruits terete, not winged. — Species 2. North Africa. (Under *Leontodon* L.) . . . . **Hedypnois** Schreb.
28. Flowers yellow. Involucral bracts subequal in length. Fruits 6—8-ribbed. Pappus of the inner fruits consisting of scales and bristles. — Species 12. North and Central Africa. Some are used as ornamental plants. . . . . **Tolpis** Bivona
Flowers blue, red, or white. Involucral bracts unequal in length. Fruits 5-angled. Pappus consisting of short scales. — Species 6. North and Central Africa; one of the species also naturalized elsewhere, two of them

only cultivated. The latter yield vegetables, salad, fodder for cattle, medicaments, and a substitute for coffee. " Chicory." **Cichorium** L.

29. Involucral bracts hardened later on and enclosing the outer fruits. Fruits linear, the outer spreading. — Species 2. North Africa. Used as salad. . . . . **Rhagadiolus** Juss.
   Involucral bracts neither hardened nor enclosing the fruits. 30

30. Fruits linear, incurved at the top, spreading, the ribs beset with short prickles. — Species 1. North-west Africa (Algeria). **Koelpinia** Pall.
   Fruits oblong-ovate, rounded at the top, compressed, many-streaked, glabrous. — Species 1. North Africa, also naturalized in the Mascarene Islands. Yields salad and is used in medicine. (*Lampsana* Juss.)
   Lapsana L.

31. (1.) Styles of the hermaphrodite flowers, at or somewhat below the point of division, thickened or provided with a ring of rather long hairs. Involucral bracts in several rows. [Tribes CYNAREAE and ARCTO-TIDEAE.] 32
   Styles of the hermaphrodite flowers neither thickened nor provided with a ring of long hairs at or below the point of division. 67

32. Outer (ray-) flowers strap-shaped. Anthers not tailed. 33
   Outer flowers not strap-shaped. Anthers usually more or less distinctly tailed. 41

33. Involucral bracts free, the inner scarious at the apex. Flower-heads solitary. 34
   Involucral bracts united below. [Subtribe GORTERINAE.] 35

34. Pappus formed of feathery bristles. Outer involucral bracts leaf-like and usually prickly. Leaves prickly. — Species 12. North Africa. One of the species yields gum and is used in medicine. . . **Atractylis** L.
   Pappus formed of scales sometimes united into a small crown, or wanting. — Species 85. South and Central Africa. Some are used as ornamental plants. (Including *Arctotheca* Wendl., *Cryptostemma* R. Br., *Damatris* Cass., *Haplocarpha* Less., *Landtia* Less., *Microstephium* Less., and *Venidium* Less.) . . . . **Arctotis** L.

35. Involucral bracts united at the base only. Receptacle with deep pits enclosing the fruits. 36
   Involucral bracts united to the middle or beyond. Receptacle with more or less shallow pits not enclosing the fruits. 38

36. Involucral bracts in two rows, the outer leaf-like and longer than the inner. Pappus of feathery-fringed scales. Flower-heads solitary. Leaves entire or prickly-toothed, often ciliate. — Species 5. South Africa.
   Didelta L'Hér.
   Involucral bracts in 3 or more rows, prickly. Leaves prickly. . . . 37

37. Pappus formed of scales. — Species 80. South and Central Africa. Some are used medicinally, others are noxious weeds. (*Crocodiloides* Adans., including *Stephanocoma* Less. and *Stobaea* Thunb.) **Berkheya** Ehrh.

Pappus wanting. Flower-heads solitary. Leaves undivided. — Species
15. South Africa. . . . . **Cullumia** R. Br.

38. Involucral bracts united at the base or up to halfway. Fruits clothed
with long hairs. 39
Involucral bracts united high up. Receptacle with shallow pits. Herbs.
40

39. Receptacle with deep pits. Pappus of two unequally long rows of scales.
Herbs. — Species 7. South and Central Africa. **Berkheyopsis** O. Hoffm.
Receptacle with shallow pits. Pappus a small crown of bristles or wanting.
Shrubs. — Species 3. South Africa. . . . . . **Hirpicium** Cass.

40. Involucral bracts hardened and prickly at the time of maturity. Pappus
formed of one-ranked scales or wanting. Fruits nearly glabrous. —
Species 4. South Africa. . . . . **Gorteria** L.
Involucral bracts unchanged at maturity. Pappus formed of usually
two-ranked scales. Fruits clothed with long hairs. — Species 35.
South Africa and southern Central Africa. Some are used as ornamental
plants. (*Meridiana* Hill). . . . . **Gazania** Gaertn.

41. (32.) Receptacle with scales between the flowers. Flower-heads collected
in clusters. Flowers red or violet. Corolla-tube short. Leaves
pinnately divided. [Subtribe GUNDELINAE.] 42
Receptacle rarely with scales between the flowers, and then flower-heads
not in clusters. 43

42. Involucral bracts united below. Pappus crown-shaped. Leaves cauline,
prickly. — Species 1. North Africa. . . . . . . **Gundelia** L.
Involucral bracts free. Pappus of unequal scales. Leaves radical. —
Species 3. South and Central Africa. . . . . **Platycarpha** Less.

43. Heads 1-flowered, collected in globose secondary heads. Partial involucres of many bracts and bristles. Flowers blue or white. Anthers
tailed. Pappus present. Leaves toothed or divided. — Species 20.
Central and North Africa. Some are used as ornamental plants. " Globe-
thistle." (*Sphaerocephalus* L.) . . . . **Echinops** L.
Heads several-flowered, rarely 1-flowered but not arranged in heads. . 44

44. Fruits with a lateral or at least distinctly oblique point of attachment.
[Subtribe CENTAUREINAE.] 45
Fruits with a basal, straight or nearly straight point of attachment. . 51

45. Heads surrounded outside the calyx-like involucre by an involucre of
leaves. Leaves prickly. 46
Heads without an outer involucre of leaves, rarely (*Centaurea*) surrounded
by some unarmed leaves. 48

46. Pappus double, of two unequally long rows of bristles. Fruits ribbed.
Heads containing hermaphrodite and male flowers. Flowers yellow. —
Species 1. North Africa, also naturalized in South Africa. Used
medicinally. (*Carbenia* Adans.) . . . . . . **Cnicus** Gaertn.
Pappus simple or wanting. 47

47. Pappus of feathery bristles. Flowers blue, all hermaphrodite. — Species
    13.   North Africa and northern East Africa. . .   **Carduncellus** Juss.
    Pappus of not feathery bristles or scales, or wanting — Species 15   North
    Africa and northern East Africa ; two of the species also naturalized
    in South Africa.   Some species (chiefly the safflower, *C. tinctorius* L.)
    yield dyes, oil, and medicaments.   (Including *Kentrophyllum* Neck.)
                                                          Carthamus L.
48. Fruits with a threefold border towards the top.   Pappus of scales and
    bristles.   Heads containing hermaphrodite and neuter flowers.   Flowers
    white or yellow.   Involucral bracts appendaged.   Leaves undivided. —
    Species 1.   North-east Africa (Egypt). . . . . . .   **Zoegea** L.
    Fruits with a simple border at the top.   49
49. Fruits with a crenate ring within the pappus, hairy ; pappus of scales and
    bristles.   Heads containing hermaphrodite and neuter flowers.   Flowers
    red.   Involucral bracts unappendaged.   Leaves pinnately divided into
    narrow segments. — Species 1.   North Africa. . .   **Crupina** Cass.
    Fruits without a crenate ring within the pappus, or without any pappus.   50
50. Involucral bracts with a scarious or prickly appendage, rarely without an
    appendage, and then pappus consisting of unequally long scales or
    double. — Species 90.   North and Central Africa ; two of the species
    naturalized in South Africa.   Several species yield edible roots or medica-
    ments or serve as ornamental plants.   (Including *Aegialophila* Boiss. &
    Heldr., *Amberboa* DC., *Leuzea* DC., *Melanoloma* Cass., *Microlonchus*
    Cass., *Phaeopappus* Boiss., *Rhaponticum* Lam., and *Volutarella* Cass.)
                                                          Centaurea L.
    Involucral bracts without a scarious or prickly appendage, but sometimes
    with a small point.   Pappus of unequally long bristles. — Species 4.
    North Africa.   They yield dyes and medicaments.   " Sawwort."
                                                          Serratula L.
51. (44.) Fruits, at least the central ones, clothed with silky hairs, not margined
    at the apex.   [Subtribe CARLININAE.]   52
    Fruits glabrous, usually margined at the apex.   [Subtribe CAR-
    DUINAE.]   56
52. Pappus formed of feathery scales or bristles.   Outer bracts of the involucre
    leaf-like, usually prickly, inner scarious at the apex.   Leaves prickly.   53
    Pappus formed of not feathery scales.   54
53. Inner involucral bracts spreading horizontally, petal-like.   Flower-heads
    large. — Species 7.   North Africa.   Some are used medicinally.
                                                          Carlina L.
    Inner involucral bracts not spreading horizontally.   Herbs.   (See 34.)
                                                          Atractylis L.
54. Heads solitary, containing fertile hermaphrodite disc-flowers with a regular
    corolla and sterile female ray-flowers with a two-lipped corolla.   Inner
    involucral bracts long, usually petal-like.   Leaves entire, not prickly.
    — Species 2.   North Africa.   Used as ornamental plants.
                                                          Xeranthemum L.

Heads containing only fertile hermaphrodite flowers. Involucral bracts prickly. Leaves toothed or divided, prickly. 55

55. Receptacle deeply pitted. Anthers not tailed. (See 37.) **Berkheya** Ehrh.
Receptacle not pitted. Anthers tailed. Heads arranged in cymes. — Species 1. North Africa. Used medicinally. (*Broteroa* Willd.)

Cardopatium Juss.

56. (51.) Filaments united. Flowers red. Leaves white-stained, prickly. 57
Filaments free. 58

57. Heads panicled; the central flowers hermaphrodite, the outer neuter. Pappus-bristles feathery. — Species 3. North Africa. (*Lupsia* Neck.)

Galactites Neck.

Heads solitary; all flowers hermaphrodite. Pappus-bristles not feathery. — Species 2. North Africa; one of the species also naturalized in South Africa. Used as vegetables and in medicine. **Silybum** Gaertn.

58. Filaments warty or hairy. Leaves usually prickly. 59
Filaments glabrous. 62

59. Receptacle deeply pitted, without bristles. — Species 9. North Africa.

Onopordon L.

Receptacle slightly or not pitted, bristly. 60

60. Receptacle fleshy. Flower-heads large, solitary. Leaves divided. — Species 6. North Africa; one species (*C. Scolymus* L., artichoke) only cultivated. They are used as vegetables and in medicine. (Including *Cynaropsis* O. Ktze.) . . . . **Cynara** L.
Receptacle not fleshy. 61

61. Pappus-bristles feathery. — Species 17. North and Central Africa. Some are used as vegetables and in medicine. (*Cnicus* L., including *Chamaepeuce* DC., *Notobasis* Cass., and *Picnomon* DC.) . . . **Cirsium** Scop.
Pappus-bristles not feathery. — Species 20. North and East Africa.

Carduus L.

62. Receptacle deeply pitted, ciliate only at the edges of the pits. Pappus of scales. Involucral bracts united at the base. Flowers yellow. Anthers not tailed. 63
Receptacle not or slightly pitted, bristly. Pappus of bristles. . . . 64

63. Involucral bracts in two rows, the outer the longer. (See 36.)

Didelta L'Hér.

Involucral bracts in 3 or more rows, prickly. Leaves prickly. (See 37.) . . . . **Berkheya** Ehrh.

64. Involucral bracts ending in hooked awns. Heads in racemes. Leaves undivided, unarmed. Herbs. — Species 1. North Africa. Yields oil and medicaments. "Burdock." (*Lappa* Juss.) . . **Arctium** L.
Involucral bracts without hooked awns. 65

65. Pappus-bristles in one row, not feathery, united below. Flowers red. Heads narrow, in corymbs. Leaves undivided, unarmed. Undershrubs. — Species 1. North-west Africa. Used medicinally. **Staehelina** L
Pappus-bristles in several rows, rough or feathery. 66

66. Pappus-bristles rough. Leaves unarmed. Flowers red. — Species 1. North Africa. . . . . **Jurinea** Cass.

Pappus-bristles feathery. Leaves prickly. (See 61.) . . **Cirsium** Scop.

67. (31.) Anthers tailed, i.e., produced at the base into two acuminate, awned, or ciliate appendages. 68

Anthers not tailed : entire, auricled, or sagittate, rarely shortly mucronate at the base. 200

68. Corolla of the hermaphrodite flowers irregular, more or less 2-lipped. 69

Corolla of the hermaphrodite flowers, at least of the inner ones, regular. 71

69. Style-branches hairy at the top only. Pappus of scales and bristles. Heads containing only hermaphrodite flowers. Herbs. — Species 3. Central and South Africa. . . . . **Pegolettia** Cass.

Style-branches hairy far down or throughout their whole length. Pappus of bristles. Flower-heads solitary. [Tribe MUTISIEAE, subtribe MUTISINAE.] 70

70. Heads with all the flowers hermaphrodite. Trees. — Species 1. Madagascar. . . . . **Cloiselia** S. Moore

Heads with the inner flowers hermaphrodite and the outer female. Herbs. — Species 30. Southern and tropical Africa. Some are used as ornamental plants. (Including *Perdicium* L.) . . . **Gerbera** Gronov.

71. Corolla-limb of the hermaphrodite flowers deeply divided. [Tribe MUTISIEAE, subtribe GOCHNATINAE.] 72

Corolla-limb of the hermaphrodite flowers toothed or cleft, more rarely flowers unisexual. [Tribes INULEAE and CALENDULEAE.] . 78

72. Style hairy in the upper part, unappendaged. Fruits clothed with long silky hairs. Pappus of several rows of bristles. Heads solitary, large ; all flowers hermaphrodite. Shrubs. Leaves pinnately cleft. — Species 1. North Africa. . . . . **Warionia** Benth. & Coss.

Style appendaged above the hairy part or without hairs. 73

73. Pappus none. Fruits with 5 ribs thickened above, hairy. Receptacle with scales between the flowers. Heads with hermaphrodite and male flowers. Anthers with an appendage at the apex. Herbs. — Species 2. East Africa. . . . . **Achyrothalamus** O. Hoffm.

Pappus consisting of bristles or scales. 74

74. Receptacle with scales between the flowers. Flowers all hermaphrodite, but the corollas sometimes of two kinds. Fruits glabrous. Pappus of 4—5 deciduous scales. Herbs. Flower-heads solitary. — Species 10. Central Africa. . . . . **Erythrocephalum** Benth.

Receptacle without scales. 75

75. Receptacle pitted, with toothed edges to the pits. Corolla of the marginal flowers strap-shaped. Fruits hairy. Pappus of several rows of scales. Herbs. Flower-heads solitary. — Species 2. Central Africa. (*Phyllactinia* Benth.) . . . . **Pasaccardoa** O. Ktze.

Receptacle without pits toothed at the edges. 76

76. Involucral bracts blunt. Flowers all hermaphrodite. Pappus of several rows of bristles. — Species 13. Central Africa. . . **Pleiotaxis** Steetz

Involucral bracts pointed. 77

77. Heads with all the flowers hermaphrodite, but the marginal flowers with a 2-lipped corolla. Fruits hairy. Pappus of feathery bristles. Shrubs with thick branches. Leaves leathery. Heads very large, red-flowered. — Species 3. South Africa. . . . . . **Oldenburgia** Less.

Heads either with all the flowers hermaphrodite and equal-shaped, or with neuter marginal flowers. Leaves herbaceous. — Species 35. Tropical and South Africa. Some species are used medicinally. (Including *Brachyachaenium* Bak. and *Hochstetteria* DC.) . . . **Dicoma** Cass.

78. (71.) Receptacle bearing chaffy scales between the flowers, at least towards the margin. 79

Receptacle without scales between the flowers, glabrous or hairy. . . 114

79. Heads with all the flowers hermaphrodite. 80

Heads with the central flowers hermaphrodite or male, the marginal female or neuter. 85

80. Pappus of 3—4 minute teeth or ring-shaped or wanting. 81

Pappus of bristles or lacerated scales. 82

81. Fruits slightly flattened. Involucral bracts scarious. Flower-heads collected in compound heads. — Species 3. East Africa. . **Polycline** Oliv.

Fruits 4-angled. Involucral bracts united below, hardening after the time of flowering. Flower-heads solitary, terminal. — Species 3. North Africa. . . . . **Anvillea** DC.

82. Pappus of 5 lacerated scales. Heads in corymbs. Leaves mostly 3-lobed. — Species 1. Southern West Africa (Damaraland).

Eenia Hiern & Moore

Pappus of bristles. 83

83. Pappus-bristles in two rows, not feathery. Fruits hairy. Involucral bracts pungent. Heath-like shrubs. — Species 1. South Africa.

Lachnospermum Willd.

Pappus-bristles in one row. Involucral bracts scarious. Not heath-like plants. 84

84. Pappus-bristles feathery from the base. — Species 15. South Africa. Some are used as ornamental plants. . . . . **Helipterum** DC.

Pappus-bristles feathery only at the tip or not feathery. — Species 300. Some of them are used as medicinal or ornamental plants (" everlastings "). (*Elichrysum* Gaertn., including *Aphelexis* Don).

Helichrysum Gaertn.

85. (79.) Corolla of the marginal flowers strap-shaped. 86

Corolla of the marginal flowers thread-shaped. 102

86. Style-branches of the hermaphrodite flowers blunt or rounded, with the marginal rows of stigmatic papillae confluent at the tip. Disc-flowers hermaphrodite, fertile, yellow ; ray-flowers yellow or white. [Tribe INULEAE, subtribe BUPHTHALMINAE.] 87

Style-branches of the hermaphrodite flowers usually truncate ; marginal
　　rows of stigmatic papillae not confluent at the tip. 97
87. Pappus absent. 88
　　Pappus present, at least upon the inner fruits. 89
88. Involucral bracts united at the base. Scales on the receptacle broad.
　　(See 81.) . . . . **Anvillea** DC.
　　Involucral bracts free. Scales of the receptacle very narrow. — Species 2.
　　Central Africa. . . . . **Astephania** Oliv.
89. Pappus cup-shaped minutely toothed. — Species 12. **Sphacophyllum** Boj.
　　Pappus of scales or bristles. 90
90. Inner fruits with a pappus of feathery bristles, outer without a pappus.
　　Receptacle bearing scales at the margin only. — Species 3. North Africa.
　　　　　　　　　　　　　　　　　　　　Rhanterium Desf.
　　Inner and outer fruits with a pappus of scales or of scales and bristles. 91
91. Pappus of the central fruits consisting of outer scales and inner bristles.
　　Receptacle bearing scales at the margin only. Fruits 10-ribbed. Shrubs.
　　— Species 1. South-west Africa (Kalahari). **Philyrophyllum** O. Hoffm.
　　Pappus of all fruits consisting of scales, rarely (*Anisopappus*) of scales
　　intermingled with some bristles. 92
92. Involucral bracts with a large scarious appendage. Heads solitary. —
　　Species 1. German South-west Africa. . . . . **Ondetia** Benth.
　　Involucral bracts without a scarious appendage. 93
93. Involucral bracts leathery. Corolla of the hermaphrodite flowers deeply
　　5-cleft. Heads in cymes. — Species 20. South and Central Africa.
　　　　　　　　　　　　　　　　　　Geigeria Griesselich
　　Involucral bracts herbaceous or membranous. Corolla of the hermaphrodite
　　flowers 5-toothed. 94
94. Corolla-tube of the hermaphrodite flowers thickened, broader than the
　　limb, corky. Marginal fruits winged. Flower-heads solitary, with an
　　outer involucre of mucronate leaves. — Species 1. North Africa.
　　　　　　　　　　　　　　　　　　　　Pallenis Cass.
　　Corolla-tube of the hermaphrodite flowers not thickened, narrower than the
　　limb. 95
95. Outer and inner fruits alike, many-ribbed. Pappus-scales unequal.
　　Heads in leafy corymbs. Herbs. — Species 6. Central Africa.
　　　　　　　　　　　　　　　　　Anisopappus Hook. & Arn.
　　Outer and inner fruits dissimilar. Heads solitary, terminal. . . . 96
96. Inner fruits conspicuously compressed. Pappus of a few very unequal
　　scales. Herbs. — Species 5. South Africa. . . . **Callilepis** DC.
　　Inner fruits scarcely compressed. Pappus of many subequal scales. —
　　— Species 13. North and Central Africa. *O. pygmaeum* O. Hoffm.
　　is one of the hygroscopic plants called " rose of Jericho." (*Asteriscus*
　　Moench) . . . . **Odontospermum** Neck.
97. (86.) Pappus wanting. Shrubs. 98
　　Pappus present. 99

98. Scales between the flowers bristle-like. Leaves small, pungent, nearly glabrous. — Species 1. South Africa. . . . . **Arrowsmithia** DC.
Scales between the flowers not bristle-like. Leaves glandular-hairy. — Species 2. South Africa. Used medicinally. **Osmitopsis** Cass.

99. Pappus of the inner fruits formed of scales sometimes united into a small crown. 100
Pappus of the inner fruits formed of bristles or of scales and bristles 101

100. Involucral bracts in few rows. Style-branches truncate. Undershrubs. — Species 8. South Africa. Some are used medicinally. . . **Osmites** L.
Involucral bracts in many rows, — Species 20. South Africa.

Relhania L'Hér.

101. Pappus of the inner fruits consisting of many scales and two awns. Shrubs. — Species 2. South Africa. . . . . **Rosenia** Thunb.
Pappus of the inner fruits consisting of feathery bristles sometimes intermingled with scales. Herbs or undershrubs. — Species 7. South, North, and East Africa. Some are used medicinally. **Leyssera** L.

102. (85.) Heads collected in glomerules, heads, or spikes. Female marginal flowers usually numerous. [Tribe INULEAE, subtribe FILAGININAE.]

103

Heads solitary or in cymes, corymbs, or panicles. Female marginal flowers few. Involucral bracts scarious or ending in a coloured append-age. Pappus of the central fruits formed of bristles. 110

103. Marginal or all fruits without a pappus. Herbs. 104
Marginal fruits, at least the inner ones, or all fruits provided with a pappus.

106

104. Scales on the receptacle tightly enclosing the marginal fruits. Corolla of the female flowers inserted laterally upon the ovary. Herbs. — Species 2. North Africa. . . . . **Micropus** L.
Scales on the receptacle not enclosing the fruits. 105

105. Central fruits without a pappus. Heads in compound heads. Herbs. — Species 7. North Africa. (Including *Evacidium* Pomel)

Evax Gaertn.

Central fruits with a pappus of feathery bristles. Heads in glomerules or in spikes. Leaves linear. — Species 10. South and North Africa. (Including *Trichogyne* Less.) . . . . **Ifloga** Cass.

106. Pappus of the central fruits consisting of scales, that of the marginal ones of scales and bristles. Heads in glomerules. Glabrous herbs. — Species 1. North Africa. . . . . . . **Gymnarrhena** Desf.
Pappus of all fruits consisting of bristles. 107

107. Stem herbaceous, woolly or cottony. 108
Stem woody, at least at the base. 109

108. Stem winged. Pappus of all fruits formed of one or two rows of bristles. — Species 1. Madagascar and Mauritius. (*Monenteles* Labill.)

Pterocaulon Ell.

Stem not winged. — Species 13. North Africa, Abyssinia, and Cape Verde Islands. (Including *Logfia* Boiss. and *Xerotium* Bluff & Fing.)
Filago L.

109. Leaves hairy. Heads in glomerules. Female flowers in several rows. Shrubs. — Species 1. Island of Mauritius. . . **Cylindrocline** Cass.
Leaves glabrous. Heads in compound heads or in spikes. Female flowers few. — Species 7. Central Africa. . **Blepharispermum** Wight

110. (102.) Heads containing 3—6 female and 1—2 fertile hermaphrodite flowers and collected in dense cymes arranged in panicles. Undershrubs. — Species 9. Tropical and South-east Africa. . . **Achyrocline** Less.
Heads containing fewer female than hermaphrodite flowers. . . . III

111. Hermaphrodite flowers sterile, the inner not subtended by scales. Shrubs.
112

Hermaphrodite flowers fertile. 113

112. Female flowers in the axils of the outer involucral bracts and separated from the hermaphrodite flowers by two rows of inner involucral bracts. — Species 1. South Africa. . . . . . **Petalactella** N. E. Brown
Female flowers in the axils of the inner involucral bracts. Pappus-bristles thickened or penicillate at the apex. — Species 1. South Africa.
Petalacte Don

113. Scales between the flowers long, deciduous. Shrubs. — Species 3. Tropical and South-east Africa. (Including *Rhynea* DC.) **Cassinia** R. Br.
Scales between the flowers short, persistent. (See 84.) **Helichrysum** Gaertn.

114. (78.) Flowers dioecious. Trees or shrubs. [Tribe INULEAE, subtribe TARCHONANTHINAE.] 115
Flowers hermaphrodite, polygamous, or monoecious, rarely (*Anaphalis*) subdioecious, but then herbs. 117

115. Involucral bracts of the male heads in one row, united below, of the female in two rows. Pappus none. — Species 3. South and Central Africa. They yield timber and medicaments. **Tarchonanthus** L.
Involucral bracts in several rows. Pappus of bristles. 116

116. Pappus-bristles in one row. Heads in fascicles. — Species 3. Madagascar. . . . . **Synchodendron** Boj.
Pappus-bristles in two rows. Heads in racemes or panicles. — Species 10. Southern and Tropical Africa. Some species yield timber.
Brachylaena R. Br.

117. Inner flowers hermaphrodite but sterile (male). 118
Inner flowers hermaphrodite and fertile. 134

118. Corolla of the outer flowers strap-shaped. 119
Corolla of the outer flowers thread-shaped. 125

119. Pappus consisting of bristles. Shrubs. — Species 3. South Africa.
Macowania Oliv.

Pappus wanting. 120

120. Receptacle beset with many long bristles. Outer fruits compressed. **Shrubs**. Leaves pungent. (See 98.) . . . . **Arrowsmithia** DC.

Receptacle glabrous, rarely bearing some bristles; in this case fruits turgid. [Tribe CALENDULEAE.] 121

121. Marginal fruits of several kinds. Heads solitary, yellow-flowered. Herbs or undershrubs. 122

Marginal fruits all alike. 123

122. Fruits curved. Heads medium-sized. — Species 15. North and South Africa and Cape Verde Islands, some also naturalized in St. Helena, and one species naturalized in the extratropical regions. Some are used as ornamental plants (marigold) or yield medicaments and a substitute for saffron. . . . . **Calendula** L.

Fruits straight. Heads small. — Species 3. South Africa. (Including *Xenisma* DC.) . . . . **Oligocarpus** Less.

123. Fruits with 3 wings and a cupular apical appendage. Involucral bracts in one row. — Species 35. South and Central Africa. **Tripteris** Less.

Fruits without distinct wings or other appendages. 124

124. Involucral bracts in one row or nearly so. Fruits 3-angled, usually tubercled. Heads solitary. Herbs or undershrubs. — Species 20. South Africa to Angola. Some are used as ornamental plants.

Dimorphotheca Moench

Involucral bracts in 2 or more rows. Marginal flowers yellow. Fruits thick and hard, smooth or indistinctly ribbed. — Species 60. South and Central Africa. (Including *Gibbaria* Cass.) . **Osteospermum** L.

125. (118.) Heads of two kinds; one kind with nearly all the flowers male, the other with nearly all female. Pappus of free bristles. Woolly or cottony herbs. Heads in corymbs. — Species 1. Madagascar.

Anaphalis DC.

Heads all alike. 126

126. Female flowers in one row. Involucral bracts scarious, all or the inner petal-like. Pappus of bristles. Cottony shrubs or undershrubs. . 127

Female flowers in several rows. 128

127. Heads large, solitary. — Species 1. South Africa. Used as an ornamental plant. . . . . **Phaenocoma** Don

Heads small, in dense cymes. — Species 7. South Africa. **Anaxeton** Cass

128. Pappus consisting of bristles. 129

Pappus wanting, at least in the marginal fruits. 131

129. Heads in glomerules arranged in corymbs. Shrubs. — Species 3. Madagascar and Mascarenes. . . . . **Monarrhenus** Cass.

Heads solitary or in panicles or corymbs. 130

130. Involucral bracts narrow. Herbs. — Species 15. Tropical and South Africa. Some species yield camphor and medicaments. (*Placus* Lour.)

Blumea DC.

Involucral bracts broad. Shrubs or undershrubs, rarely herbs. — Species 15. Tropics. Some are used medicinally. (Including *Tecmarsis* DC.)

Pluchea Cass.

131. Inner fruits with a pappus of feathery bristles, outer without a
pappus. 132
Inner and outer fruits without a pappus. 133

132. Heads in glomerules. Involucral bracts scarious. Corolla-limb of the
female flowers shortly toothed. Pappus-bristles 2—6. — Species 6.
Tropical and South Africa. (Including *Demidium* DC.) **Amphidoxa** DC.
Heads in corymbs. Involucral bracts scarious only at the edges, subequal.
Corolla-limb of the female flowers two-cleft. Pappus-bristles 1—2. —
Species 2. South and Central Africa. . . . . **Denekia** Thunb.

133. Heads arranged in cymes. — Species 3. Central and South Africa.
(Including *Litogyne* Harv.) . . . . **Epaltes** Cass.
Heads collected in compound heads. — Species 25. Tropical and South
Africa and Egypt. Some species are used medicinally **Sphaeranthus** L.

134. (117.) Style-branches of the hermaphrodite flowers stigmatose within,
hairy outside from the tips downwards to below the point of division. 135
Style-branches of the hermaphrodite flowers stigmatose at the edges,
hairy only in their upper part. 149

135. Heads with all the flowers hermaphrodite. 136
Heads with the inner flowers hermaphrodite or male, the outer female. 138

136. Pappus wanting; fruits with an indistinctly cupular margin at the apex.
Heads small, 1—4-flowered, arranged in corymbs. Shrubs. —
Species 2. Madagascar. . . . . **Apodocephala** Bak.
Pappus present. Heads medium-sized. 137

137. Fruits hairy. Pappus of scales. Receptacle bristly. Heads sessile.
Undershrubs. — Species 1. Southern West Africa (Angola). (Under
Geigeria Griesselich). . . . . **Thysanurus** O. Hoffm.
Fruits glabrous. Pappus of bristles. Receptacle glabrous. Heads
stalked. Shrubs. — Species 5. Madagascar. . . . **Centauropsis** Boj.

138. Corolla of the female (marginal) flowers strap-shaped. Receptacle
pitted. Outer involucral bracts mucronate. Fruits hairy. Pappus
of several rows of bristles. Shrubs. Heads solitary, yellow-flowered. —
Species 1. South-west Africa (Namaland). **Eremothamnus** O. Hoffm.
Corolla of the female (marginal) flowers thread-shaped. [Tribe INULEAE,
subtribe PLUCHEINAE.] 139

139. Pappus wanting. 140
Pappus present, at least in the hermaphrodite (central) flowers. . . 141

140. Heads arranged in cymes. (See 133.) . . . . **Epaltes** Cass.
Heads collected in compound heads. (See 133.). . . **Sphaeranthus** L.

141. Inner fruits with a pappus of 1—5 bristles, outer without a pappus. 142
Inner and outer fruits provided with a pappus. 143

142. Pappus of 1—2 bristles feathery at the tip. Corolla-limb of the female
flowers 2-cleft. Heads in corymbs. (See 132.) **Denekia** Thunb.
Pappus of 3—5 simple bristles. Corolla-limb of the female flowers
4—5-cleft. Heads solitary. — Species 1. East Africa.
Delamerea S. Moore

143. Pappus of scales united into a small crown. Heads in compound heads collected in heads of the third order. — Species 1. East Africa.

Triplocephalum O. Hoffm.

Pappus of bristles or of scales and bristles. 144

144. Pappus of scales and bristles. Fruits hairy. Heads in leafy panicles, red-flowered. — Species 2. Central Africa. . **Porphyrostemma** Grant

Pappus of bristles. 145

145. Female flowers in one row. Inner involucral bracts membranous. Heads in leafy panicles. Undershrubs. — Species 1. Southern West Africa (Damaraland). (Under *Pluchea* Cass.) **Pechuel-Loeschea** O. Hoffm.

Female flowers in several rows. 146

146. Fruits compressed. Pappus of 3 bristles. Heads solitary or few together. Undershrubs. — Species 4. Central Africa.

Nicolasia S. Moore

Fruits terete or angular. 147

147. Heads in glomerules arranged in corymbs. Shrubs. (See 129.)

Monarrhenus Cass.

Heads solitary or in panicles or corymbs. 148

148. Involucral bracts narrow. Herbs. (See 130.) . . . **Blumea** DC.

Involucral bracts broad. Shrubs or undershrubs, rarely herbs. (See 130.) . . . . **Pluchea** Cass.

149. (134.) Style-branches of the hermaphrodite flowers blunt or rounded; marginal rows of stigmatic papillae confluent at the apex. Female (marginal) flowers with a strap-shaped corolla, rarely with a tubular one or wanting. [Tribe INULEAE, subtribe INULINAE.] . . . 150

Style-branches of the hermaphrodite flowers usually truncate; marginal rows of stigmatic papillae not confluent at the apex. 166

150. Pappus ring-shaped. Heads solitary. Herbs. — Species 3. West Africa. . . . . **Mollera** O. Hoffm.

Pappus of scales or bristles or of both. 151

151. Pappus of scales. 152

Pappus of bristles or of scales and bristles. 153

152. Pappus-scales 3—5. Heads with all the flowers hermaphrodite, arranged in panicles. Climbing shrubs. — Species 1. South Africa.

Anisochaeta DC.

Pappus-scales 10. Heads in leafy panicles. Herbs. — Species 4. Central and South-west Africa. . . . . . . **Calostephane** Benth.

153. Pappus of sometimes feathery bristles. 154

Pappus of scales and bristles. 161

154. Ray-flowers white, blue, or red. Pappus-bristles in several rows. Shrubs. — Species 7. South Africa. Some are used medicinally. **Printzia** Cass.

Ray-flowers yellow or wanting. 155

155. Ray-flowers sterile. Receptacle pitted. Pappus-bristles in several rows. Undershrubs. — Species 1. South Africa. . . **Cypselodontia** DC.

Ray-flowers fertile. 156

156. Pappus of two or more rows of bristles, the outer of which are shorter. **157**
    Pappus of subequal bristles sometimes intermingled with a few shorter
    ones. **159**

157. Pappus-bristles in 3 or more rows. Heads without ray-flowers. — Species
    10.   Tropical and South Africa and Egypt. . . . . **Iphiona** Cass.
    Pappus-bristles in 2 rows **158**

158. Pappus of 5 inner and 10 outer bristles. Heads without ray-flowers.
    Shrubs. — Species 1. South Africa. . . . **Anisothrix** O. Hoffm.
    Pappus of 10 inner and 10 outer bristles. Heads with ray-flowers. Under-
    shrubs. — Species 1. South Africa. . . . . **Minurothamnus** DC.

159. Heads few-flowered, without ray-flowers, arranged in panicles or corymbs.
    Involucre of few bracts. — Species 2. Egypt. (Under *Iphiona* Cass.)
                                    Varthemia DC.

    Heads many-flowered. Involucre of many bracts. **160**

160. Involucral bracts leathery, the outer sticky at the tip. Heads with ray-
    flowers, solitary. Pappus-bristles in one row. Glandular-hairy shrubs.
    — Species 1. South Africa. . . . . . . **Homochaete** Benth.
    Involucral bracts herbaceous or the inner scarious. — Species 30. Some of
    them yield vermin-poison or are used in medicine. (Including *Bojeria*
    DC., *Pentatrichia* Klatt, *Schizogyne* Cass., and *Vicoa* Cass.) **Inula** L.

161. Pappus-scales united below. **162**
    Pappus-scales free. **163**

162. Pappus-bristles about 5. Female marginal flowers wanting. Heads in
    corymbs. Shrubs. — Species 2. Canary Islands. **Allagopappus** Cass.
    Pappus-bristles 7 or more. Female marginal flowers present. Heads
    solitary at the ends of the branches. Herbs. — Species 30. Some of
    them yield vermin-poison or are used in medicine. (Including *Fran-
    coeuria* Cass.) . . . . **Pulicaria** Gaertn.

163. Pappus-scales rather broad, fringed. Fruits 10-ribbed. Heads without
    ray-flowers. Herbs. (See 69.) . . . . . . **Pegolettia** Cass.
    Pappus-scales very narrow. **164**

164. Fruits constricted into a short neck, 10-ribbed. Heads without ray-
    flowers. Shrubs. Leaves pinnately divided. — Species 3. North
    Africa. (Under *Grantia* Boiss.) . . . . . **Perralderia** Coss.
    Fruits not constricted above. Heads with ray-flowers. **165**

165. Fruits 4—5-ribbed. Pappus-bristles 5—10. Shrubs. — Species 1. Ca-
    nary Islands. . . . . **Viraea** Webb
    Fruits many-ribbed. Pappus-bristles numerous. Undershrubs. —
    Species 1. North-west Africa. . . . . **Jasonia** Cass.

166. (149.) Female or neuter marginal flowers with a strap-shaped corolla. **167**
    Female or neuter marginal flowers with a thread-shaped corolla or wanting.
    [Tribe INULEAE, subtribes GNAPHALINAE and RELHANINAE.] . **176**

167. Leaves grooved or rolled inwards on the upper side, small. Heath-like
    plants. [Tribe INULEAE, subtribe RELHANINAE.] **168**
    Leaves flat or rolled back from the margins. Not heath-like plants. . **172**

168. Heads one-flowered, some hermaphrodite, the others female, or 2-flowered with a hermaphrodite and a female or neuter flower. Pappus of feathery bristles united at the base. Shrubs. — Species 8. South Africa.

Disparago Gaertn.

Heads many-flowered. 169

169. Pappus wanting. Shrubs. — Species 2. South Africa. **Anaglypha** DC.
Pappus present. 170

170. Pappus of numerous scales sometimes united below. — Species 13. South Africa . . . . **Nestlera** Spreng.
Pappus of bristles. 171

171. Pappus-bristles feathery. Shrubs. — Species 5. South Africa.

Amphiglossa DC.

Pappus-bristles simple. Herbs. Flowers red. — Species 1. South Africa. . . . . **Bryomorphe** Harv.

172. Pappus wanting. Inner fruits compressed. Heads solitary. Herbs or undershrubs. (See 124.) . . . . **Dimorphotheca** Moench
Pappus present. [Tribe INULEAE, subtribe ATHRIXINAE.] . . . 173

173. Pappus of the outer fruits consisting of scales, of the inner of bristles or of scales and bristles. Fruits glabrous. Herbs or undershrubs. (See 101.) . . . . **Leyssera** L.
Pappus consisting of bristles. 174

174. Involucral bracts narrow, acuminate. Herbs or undershrubs. — Species 15. Southern and tropical Africa. . . . . . . **Athrixia** Ker
Involucral bracts blunt, scarious at the apex. Pappus-bristles in two rows. Shrubs. 175

175. Fruits hairy. Pappus-bristles thick and stiff. Involucre hemispherical. — Species 3. South Africa. . . . . **Heterolepis** Cass.
Fruits glabrous, but with a hairy swelling at the base. Pappus-bristles thin. Involucre narrow-campanulate. — Species 3. Central and South Africa. . . . . **Antithrixia** DC.

176. (166.) Hermaphrodite flowers fewer than the female. 177
Hermaphrodite flowers as many as or more than the female, or all flowers hermaphrodite. 184

177. Fruits without a pappus. Heads small, in dense cymes. Tall herbs. — Species 1. East Africa. . . . . **Chiliocephalum** Benth.
Fruits, at least the inner, crowned by a pappus. 178

178. Inner fruits with a pappus of feathery bristles, outer without a pappus. Heads small, in glomerules. Low herbs. (See 132.) **Amphidoxa** DC.
Inner and outer fruits crowned by a pappus. 179

179. Pappus of the inner fruits of bristles and united scales, that of the outer only of scales united below. Heads solitary. Herbs. — Species 1. East Africa. . . . . **Artemisiopsis** S. Moore
Pappus of all fruits formed of bristles. 180

2 N

180. Pappus-bristles feathery. Heads in glomerules. Herbs. — Species 2. South and North Africa. . . . . **Lasiopogon** Cass.
Pappus-bristles not feathery. 181

181. Fruits with a long beak. Herbs. Leaves radical or opposite. Heads solitary. — Species 1. Island of Tristan da Cunha. **Chevreulia** Cass.
Fruits without a beak. 182

182. Heads 4—8-flowered, cylindrical, in dense cymes arranged in panicles. Undershrubs. (See 110.) . . . . **Achyrocline** Less.
Heads many-flowered, hemispherical ovoid or campanulate. . . .183

183. Anthers very shortly tailed. Shrubs or undershrubs. Heads solitary or in long-stalked glomerules. — Species 15. North and Central Africa.
Phagnalon Cass.
Anthers distinctly tailed. Herbs. — Species 50. "Cudweed."
Gnaphalium L.

184. (176.) Heads 1-flowered. 185
Heads 2- or more -flowered. 188

185. Flowers partly hermaphrodite, partly female. Pappus of feathery bristles. Heads in glomerules. Shrubs. (See 168.) **Disparago** Gaertn.
Flowers all hermaphrodite. 186

186. Pappus wanting. Heads in glomerules. Shrubs. — Species 2. South Africa. . . . . **Perotriche** Cass.
Pappus formed of bristles. 187

187. Pappus-bristles feathery. Inner involucral bracts scarious. Heath-like shrubs. — Species 35. Southern and tropical Africa. . . **Stoebe** L.
Pappus-bristles feathery only at the apex or not feathery. Involucral bracts scarious, coloured. Heads in panicled cymes. Herbs. — Species 12. Madagascar, Mauritius, and South Africa to Damaraland. Some are used medicinally. . . . . . . **Stenocline** DC.

188. Pappus wanting. Heads 2—3-flowered, in leafy corymbs. 189
Pappus formed of bristles. 190

189. Leaves small. Undershrubs. — Species 1. Madagascar. **Syncephalum** DC.
Leaves rather large. Shrubs. Involucre woolly at the base. — Species 1. Madagascar. . . . . **Astephanocarpa** Bak.

190. Pappus-bristles feathery from the base. 191
Pappus-bristles feathery at the tip only or not feathery. 192

191. Heads 2—10-flowered. Heath-like shrubs. — Species 3. South Africa.
Pterothrix DC.
Heads many-flowered. Involucral bracts scarious, coloured. Not heath-like plants. (See 84.) . . . . **Helipterum** DC.

192. Pappus-bristles in 1 row. 193
Pappus-bristles in 2 or more rows. 197

193. Pappus-bristles with bladdery inflated cells at the tip. Heads small, in glomerules. Prostrate herbs. — Species 1. South Africa.
Eriosphaera Less.
Pappus-bristles without bladdery inflated cells. 194

194. Habit heath-like. Shrubs. Leaves small, **grooved** or rolled inwards
on the upper face. Flowers all hermaphrodite. 195
Habit not heath-like. 196

195. Pappus-bristles feathery at the tip, united at the base and surrounded by
a ring- or cup-shaped rim. Heads few-flowered. — Species 7. South
Africa. Some are used medicinally. . . . . **Elytropappus** Cass.
Pappus-bristles simple or thickened at the tip. Inner involucral bracts
coloured above. — Species 25. South Africa. . . **Metalasia** R. Br.

196. Fruits large, with 8—10 prominent ribs, glabrous or short-haired. Heads
2—6-flowered, in panicled cymes. Herbs. (See 187.) **Stenocline** DC.
Fruits small, not prominently 8—10-ribbed. (See 84.)

                                                        Helichrysum Gaertn.

197. Pappus-bristles in 2 rows. Heath-like shrubs. 198
Pappus-bristles in 3 or more rows. Not heath-like herbs or undershrubs. 199

198. Heads few-flowered. Involucre oblong, of oblong bracts. Receptacle
glabrous. Fruits ribbed. Leaves oblong. — Species 1. Madagascar.

                                                Cullumiopsis Drake
Heads many-flowered. Involucre top-shaped, of linear bracts. Recep-
tacle bristly at the margin. Fruits angular, hairy. Leaves linear.
(See 83.) . . . . **Lachnospermum** Willd.

199. Fruits beaked, hairy. Heads few-flowered. Inner involucral bracts
yellow. — Species 1. South Africa. . . . . **Pachyrhynchus** DC.
Fruits not beaked, glabrous. Heads in cymes. — Species 8. South
Africa. . . . . **Leontonyx** Cass.

200. (67.) Hermaphrodite disc-flowers sterile, their style without a stigma
and usually entire or shortly toothed. 201
Hermaphrodite flowers, at least some of them, fertile. 238

201. Anthers arrow-shaped, with acuminate halves. Corolla of the marginal
flowers strap-shaped. Fruits glabrous, usually large. Pappus wanting,
rarely cup-shaped. Receptacle glabrous, rarely bristly. [Tribe CAL-
ENDULEAE.] 202
Anthers entire or shortly auricled at the base, rarely (*Adelostigma*)
distinctly arrow-shaped, but then corolla of the marginal flowers
thread-shaped, fruits hairy, and pappus bristly. 207

202. Outer fruits of several kinds. Heads solitary, yellow-flowered. Herbs
or undershrubs. 203
Outer fruits all alike. 204

203. Fruits curved. Heads middle-sized. (See 122.) . . . **Calendula** L.
Fruits straight. Heads small. (See 122.) . . . . **Oligocarpus** Less.

204. Fruits with 3 wings and a cup-shaped apical appendage. Involucral
bracts in one row. (See 123.) . . . . **Tripteris** Less.
Fruits without distinct wings or other appendages. 205

205. Fruits very hard, smooth or indistinctly ribbed. Involucral bracts in two
or more rows. Ray-flowers yellow. (See 124.) • **Osteospermum** L.

Fruits not very hard, 3-angled, usually tubercled. Herbs or undershrubs. Heads solitary. 206

206. Involucral bracts in one row or in two indistinct rows. (See 124.)
Dimorphotheca Moench
Involucral bracts in several rows. Ray-flowers blue or white. Leaves
pinnately divided. — Species 6. South Africa. Some are used medicinally. . . . . **Garuleum** Cass.

207. (201.) Receptacle covered with chaffy scales. 208
Receptacle glabrous or hairy, without scales between the flowers. . . 213

208. Heads with the inner flowers male (apparently hermaphrodite), the
outer female and provided with a more or less strap-shaped, rarely a
thread-shaped corolla. 209
Heads unisexual, some with all the flowers male (apparently hermaphrodite), the others with all the flowers female and provided with a tubular
corolla or without a corolla. 211

209. Involucral bracts in one row, united below when young. Outer fruits
hairy, without a pappus, the inner with a pappus of numerous one-
ranked bearded bristles. Heads solitary. Shrubs. — Species 1.
South Africa. (Under *Eriocephalus* L.) . . . . **Lasiocoma** Bolus
Involucral bracts in two or more rows. Pappus of 2—3 bristles or wanting. 210

210. Involucral bracts all alike. Corolla of the female flowers 2-toothed.
Pappus of the outer fruits of 2—3 bristles. Heads in panicles. —
Species 1. Naturalized in tropical and South Africa. Used medicinally.
Parthenium L.
Involucral bracts of two kinds, the inner united below. Corolla of the
female flowers entire or 3-toothed. Pappus none. Heads in racemes
or umbels, or solitary. — Species 20. South Africa to Damaraland.
Some are used medicinally. . . . . **Eriocephalus** L.

211. Heads dioecious, many-flowered. Involucral bracts in 3 rows. Corolla
4-toothed, yellow. Anthers cohering, auricled at the base. Style cleft.
Fruits hairy. Pappus of 2—3 bristles. Trees. Leaves opposite.
Heads in leafy panicles. — Species 2. Island of St. Helena.
Petrobium R. Br.
Heads monoecious, the male many-flowered with a 5-toothed corolla,
the female 1—2-flowered with an involucre of partly united bracts and
without a corolla. Anthers free or slightly cohering, entire at the base.
Style of the male flowers undivided. Pappus none. Herbs or under-
shrubs. [Tribe HELIANTHEAE, subtribe AMBROSINAE.] . . 212

212. Involucral bracts of the male heads free. Filaments united. Female heads
2-flowered. Heads solitary or in glomerules in the axils of the leaves. —
Species 4. North and Central Africa and Mascarene Islands ; naturalized in South Africa. They yield dyes and medicaments and are noxious
to pasturing cattle. . . . . **Xanthium** L.

Involucral bracts of the male heads united **below. Filaments free** or nearly so. Female heads 1-flowered. Male heads in spikes or racemes. — Species 2. Northern and tropical Africa; naturalized in South Africa. Used medicinally. . . . . **Ambrosia L.**

213. (207.) Pappus of the outer fruits ring-, crown-, or ear-shaped, sometimes produced into two small points, or wanting. 214
Pappus of the outer fruits consisting of bristles. 223

214. Pappus of the inner fruits of bristles, of the outer of 1—2 small points or wanting. Involucral bracts in few rows. Receptacle pitted. Corolla of the female flowers strap-shaped. Style cleft, with lanceolate appendages. Fruits flattened. Shrubs or undershrubs. Leaves entire. — Species 8. South Africa. (*Heteractis* DC.) **Gymnostephium** Less.
Pappus of all fruits alike or wanting. 215

215. Outer flowers with a strap-shaped corolla. 216
Outer flowers with a tubular corolla or without a corolla. 220

216. Corolla of the outer flowers very shortly strap-shaped, of the inner 4-toothed, yellow in all flowers. Involucral bracts in two rows. — Species 40. Some of them are used as ornamental or medicinal plants. (Including *Brocchia* Vis. and *Cenia* Juss.) . . . . . **Cotula L.**
Corolla of the outer flowers distinctly strap-shaped. Involucral bracts rarely in two rows, and then corolla of the inner flowers 5-toothed. . 217

217. Involucral bracts in one row and united at the base. Corolla-limb of the hermaphrodite (male) central flowers bell-shaped, 5-cleft. Style-branches of the same ending in a blunt appendage. Fruits flattened, without ribs. Branching herbs. Leaves pinnately divided. Heads solitary. — Species 4. South Africa. . . . . . **Steirodiscus** Less.
Involucral bracts in two or more rows. 218

218. Involucral bracts in two rows. Corolla of the marginal flowers red, of the central yellow, the latter 5-toothed. Style-branches of the hermaphrodite (male) flowers pointed. Fruits beaked, without ribs. Herbs. Leaves undivided, radical. Heads solitary. — Species 1. Island of Tristan da Cunha. . . . . **Lagenophora** Cass.
Involucral bracts in 3 or more rows. Corolla of the marginal flowers white, yellow, or blue, more rarely red, but then style-branches of the hermaphrodite (male) flowers truncate and fruits ribbed. 219

219. Style of the hermaphrodite (male) flowers with pointed branches or undivided. Corolla of the marginal flowers blue, rarely white. Fruits wrinkled or smooth. Branching herbs or undershrubs. Leaves pinnately divided. (See 206.) . . . . **Garuleum** Cass.
Style of the hermaphrodite (male) flowers with truncate branches. Corolla of the marginal flowers white, yellow, or red. Fruits 5—10-ribbed. — Species 50. North Africa, Abyssinia, Madagascar, and South Africa. Some species yield condiments, medicaments, or insect-poison, or serve as ornamental plants. (Including *Argyranthemum* Webb, *Ismelia* Cass.,

Leucanthemum DC., *Monoptera* Schultz, *Myconia* Neck., *Pinardia* Cass., *Plagius* L'Hér., *Preauxia* Schultz, *Prolongoa* Boiss., *Pyrethrum* Gaertn., and *Tanacetum* L.) . . . . **Chrysanthemum** L.

220. Corolla of the hermaphrodite (male) flowers 2—4-toothed, of the female 2—3-toothed, entire, or wanting. Involucral bracts in two rows. Herbs. Flowers yellow. 221
Corolla of the hermaphrodite (male) flowers 5-toothed, of the female 2—4-toothed. 222

221. Heads sessile between the leaves. Female flowers in several rows, without a corolla. Outer fruits winged, with a persistent style. Leaves divided. — Species 1. Naturalized in the Island of Madeira. **Soliva** Ruiz & Pav.
Heads stalked, at the ends of the branches. (See 216.) **Cotula** L.

222. Heads in corymbs. Involucral bracts in two rows. Fruits with marginal ribs or wings. Herbs or undershrubs. — Species 4. South Africa. Used medicinally. . . . . **Hippia** L.
Heads not in corymbs. Involucral bracts in several rows. Fruits without strong ribs. — Species 20. Some of them (especially A. *Absinthium* L., wormwood) are used as ornamental or medicinal plants, as pot-herbs, or for preparing liquors and vinegar. . . . . . . **Artemisia** L.

223. (213.) Pappus of 1 or 2 rows of bristles. 224
Pappus, at least that of the outer fruits, of 3 or more rows of bristles. 233

224. Pappus-bristles feathery. 225
Pappus-bristles not feathery. 226

225. Corolla of all flowers yellow. Small shrubs. — Species 1. South Africa.
Homochroma DC.
Corolla of the marginal flowers white or red, of the central ones yellow. Herbs or undershrubs. — Species 13. South Africa. Used as ornamental plants. . . . . **Mairia** Nees

226. Involucral bracts in one row, sometimes surrounded by some much shorter ones. Herbs or undershrubs. Heads in corymbs or panicles. 227
Involucral bracts in two rows and all nearly of the same size, or in 3 or more rows. 228

227. Involucral bracts united at the base. Style of the hermaphrodite (male) flowers undivided. Inner fruits without a pappus. — Species 3. South Africa. . . . . **Gymnodiscus** Less.
Involucral bracts free. Style cleft. — Species 45. Southern and tropical Africa. . . . . **Cineraria** L.

228. Corolla of the female marginal flowers thread-shaped. Herbs. Heads solitary on the ends of the branches. Style of the central flowers entire or shortly toothed. 229
Corolla of the female marginal flowers, at least of the outer ones, strap-shaped, rarely (*Psiadia*) thread-shaped, but then shrubs, heads in corymbs, and style of the central flowers 2-cleft. 230

229. Involucral bracts in two rows. Corolla of the hermaphrodite (male) flowers 4-toothed. Anthers entire at the base. Fruits compressed, glabrous. (See 216.) . . . . **Cotula** L.
Involucral bracts in 3 or more rows. Corolla of the hermaphrodite (male) flowers 5-toothed. Anthers arrow-shaped. Fruits nearly terete, hairy. — Species 2. Central Africa . . . . **Adelostigma** Steetz

230. Corolla of the female marginal flowers yellow, thread- or shortly strap-shaped. Fruits scarcely compressed, 3—6-ribbed. Shrubs. Heads in corymbs. — Species 40. Tropics. Some are used as pot-herbs.

Psiadia Jacq.

Corolla of the female marginal flowers white red or blue, strap-shaped. Fruits compressed. 231

231. Stem woody, at least at the base. Marginal flowers in 1—2 rows. Pappus-bristles usually in one row. — Species 65. South and Central Africa. Some are used as ornamental plants. (Including *Asterosperma* Less., *Detris* Adans., and *Diplopappus* DC., under *Aster* L.) **Felicia** Cass.
Stem herbaceous. 232

232. Involucral bracts in 2 rows, membranous. Marginal flowers usually in several rows, with a linear corolla. Style-branches with a mostly short triangular appendage. Pappus-bristles usually in one row. — Species 13, one of them only naturalized. Several species are used medicinally.

Erigeron L.

Involucral bracts in 3 or more rows. Marginal flowers in 1—2 rows, with a usually oblong corolla. Style-branches with a lanceolate appendage. Pappus-bristles in two rows. — Species 10. South and North Africa. Some are used as ornamental or medicinal plants. (Including *Linosyris* Cass.) . . . . **Aster** L.

233. (223.) Involucral bracts in several rows. (See 232.) . . . **Aster** L.
Involucral bracts in one row, but sometimes surrounded by some much smaller ones. 234

234. Heads of two kinds, some with most of the flowers hermaphrodite (male), the others with most of them female. Corolla red or white; limb shortly strap-shaped in the female flowers. Herbs. Leaves radical, broad. Heads in racemes or corymbs. — Species 1. North Africa. Used as an ornamental plant. . . . . **Petasites** Gaertn.
Heads all alike. 235

235. Female marginal flowers in several rows. Corolla yellow; limb long strap-shaped in the female flowers. Herbs. Leaves radical, broad. Heads solitary. — Species 1. North Africa. Used medicinally. "Colts-foot." . . . . **Tussilago** L.
Female marginal flowers in one row. 236

236. Inner fruits without a pappus, outer with a pappus of interwoven hairs. Style 2-cleft. Herbs. Leaves pinnately divided. Heads solitary. — Species 3. South Africa. . . . . **Ruckeria** DC.
Inner and outer fruits with a pappus of bristles. 237

237. Style of the central flowers 2-cleft. Involucral bracts finally free. Undershrubs. — Species 7. South and North Africa. Some are used as ornamental plants. (*Othonnopsis* Jaub. et Spach) . . **Hertia** Less. Style of the central flowers undivided. Involucral bracts more or less united. — Species 110. South Africa and southern Central Africa. Some are used as ornamental plants. (Including *Doria* Less.)

Othonna L.

238. (200.) Style-branches of the hermaphrodite flowers rather long, semi-cylindrical, covered with stigmatic papillae on the inner surface, with hairs on the outer ; hairs also clothing the upper part of the style below the point of division. Anthers more or less arrow-shaped. . . . 239
Style-branches of the hermaphrodite flowers with marginal rows of stigmatic papillae, hairy only in their upper part, more rarely down to the point of division ; no hairs on the upper part of the style below that point. 262

239. Heads with inner hermaphrodite and outer female flowers. 240
Heads with all the flowers hermaphrodite, rarely (*Vernonia*) subdioecious by incomplete development of one sex. 242

240. Female marginal flowers with a thread-shaped corolla. Style-branches blunt. Pappus of bristles. Herbs. — Species 17. Tropical and South Africa and Egypt. . . . . **Laggera** Schultz
Female marginal flowers with a strap-shaped corolla. Flowers yellow. Receptacle pitted. 241

241. Pappus of scales. Involucral bracts united at the base. Leaves prickly. (See 37.) . . . . **Berkheya** Ehrh.
Pappus of bristles. Involucral bracts free. Shrubs. Heads solitary. (See 138.) . . . . **Eremothamnus** O. Hoffm.

242. Flowers yellow. 243
Flowers white, red, or blue. 244

243. Pappus of scales. Involucral bracts united at the base. Leaves prickly. (See 37.) . . . . **Berkheya** Ehrh.
Pappus of bristles. Involucral bracts free. — Species 7. Central Africa. (Including *Autunesia* O. Hoffm. and *Newtonia* O. Hoffm , under *Vernonia* Schreb.) . . . . **Gongrothamnus** Steetz

244. Receptacle with scales between the flowers. Leaves linear or lanceo-late. 245
Receptacle glabrous, rarely ciliate, bristly, or with toothed borders to the pits, without scales between the flowers. Style-branches rather long and pointed. [Tribe VERNONIEAE.] 247

245. Heads solitary. Scales between the flowers membranous. Style-branches rather long and pointed. Pappus of unequally broad scales. — — Species 1. West Africa (Congo). . . **Dewildemania** O. Hoffm.
Heads in corymbs. Scales between the flowers with a coloured appendage. Style-branches short; blunt or somewhat pointed. Pappus of scales united into a toothed cup. 246

246. Outer involucral bracts longer than the inner. Corolla slightly irregular. Leaves linear, sessile, glabrous. — Species 1. Southern West Africa (Angola). . . . . **Omphalopappus** O. Hoffm.
Outer involucral bracts shorter than the inner. Corolla regular. Leaves lanceolate, short-stalked, short-haired. — Species 1. Southern West Africa (Angola). . . . . **Gossweilera** S. Moore

247. Heads in dense glomerules or heads, few-flowered. Involucral bracts in several rows of two bracts each. Corolla 5-cleft. Fruits 10-ribbed. Pappus of 1—2 rows of bristles or narrow scales. Herbs. — Species 5. Tropics. Used medicinally. . . . . **Elephantopus** L.
Heads not in dense glomerules or heads. [Subtribe VERNONINAE.] 248

248. Pappus wanting. 249
Pappus present. 251

249. Heads 1—4-flowered, in corymbs. Involucre oblong. Fruits with an indistinctly cup-shaped border at the top. Shrubs. (See 136.)
Apodocephala Bak.
Heads many-flowered. Involucre campanulate or hemispherical. Herbs.
250

250. Fruits truncate at the top, 4—5-ribbed. — Species 5. Tropical and South Africa and Egypt. . . . . **Ethulia** L.
Fruits rounded at the top. — Species 10. Central Africa.
Gutenbergia Schultz

251. Pappus ear- or cup-shaped, entire or nearly so. Herbs. . . . 252
Pappus formed of scales or bristles. 253

252. Pappus auricle-like. Heads in cymes. Leaves linear. — Species 1. East Africa. . . . . **Hoehnelia** Schweinf.
Pappus cup-shaped. Heads solitary or in facsicles. — Species 1. Tropics.
Sparganophorus Vaill.

253. Pappus of one row of scales and sometimes some bristles within them. 254
Pappus only of bristles or of several rows of bristles with some small scales outside them. 257

254. Pappus-scales 5, long and narrow. Fruits 5-ribbed. Corolla white. Involucral bracts in two rows. Heads in panicles. Shrubs. — Species 1. West Africa (Congo). . . . . **Msuata** O. Hoffm.
Pappus-scales short. Herbs. 255

255. Pappus-scales 5. Fruits 4-ribbed, glabrous. Corolla violet. Receptacle pitted; pits with toothed borders. Heads many-flowered, in glomerules. — Species 3. Central Africa. . . . . . **Ageratina** O. Hoffm.
Pappus-scales more than 5. Receptacle not pitted. 256

256. Heads one-flowered, in corymbs. Involucral bracts in two rows. Fruits cylindrical, hairy. Pappus-scales united below. Leaves linear, with parallel veins. — Species 10. South Africa. . . **Corymbium** L.
Heads several-flowered. Involucral bracts in several rows. Fruits 3—5-angled, glandular. Pappus-scales free or nearly so. — Species 4. Central Africa. . . . . **Herderia** Cass.

257. Pappus of caducous, usually one-ranked bristles. 258
Pappus of persistent, several-ranked bristles or of bristles and scales. 260

258. Pappus surrounded by a wavy ring. Fruits 5-ribbed. Heads 4—5-flowered, in corymbs. Shrubs. — Species 1. East Africa.
Volkensia O. Hoffm.
Pappus not surrounded by a wavy ring. Herbs or undershrubs. . 259

259. Outer involucral bracts leaf-like, much larger than the inner. Fruits blunt, 8—10-ribbed. — Species 1. West Africa (Congo).
Centratherum Cass.
Outer involucral bracts, like the inner, scale-like. Fruits 4—5-angled. — Species 30. Central and South Africa. (Including *Bothriocline* Oliv. and *Stephanolepis* S. Moore) . . . . **Erlangea** Schultz

260. Leaves unarmed. — Species 330. Tropical and South Africa. Some of the species yield wood or medicaments. (Including *Bechium* DC., *Cyanopis* Blume, and *Decaneurum* DC.) (Plate 150.)
Vernonia Schreb.
Leaves prickly 261

261. Heads axillary. Stem branched, woody at the base. Fruits hairy. — Species 2. South Africa. . . . . **Hoplophyllum** DC.
Heads terminal. Stem not branched, herbaceous throughout. Fruits many-ribbed. — Species 2. West Africa. . . **Aedesia** O. Hoffm.

262. (238.) Style-branches of the hermaphrodite flowers rather long, semi-cylindrical, usually blunt ; the lower part bearing scarcely projecting and not recurved marginal rows of stigmatic papillae, the upper part subequally clothed with hairs on both sides. Flowers all hermaphrodite, red blue or whitish. [Tribe EUPATORIEAE.] 263
Style-branches of the hermaphrodite flowers rather flat, bearing conspicuous marginal rows of stigmatic papillae sometimes confluent in the middle, and above them either a crown of rather long hairs, with or without shorter ones, or an appendage clothed with dense hairs on the outer face, scantily haired or not hairy on the inner ; more rarely style-branches almost uniformly clothed with hairs, but then rows of stigmatic papillae curved outwards or confluent in the middle, or flowers yellow or partly female. 266

263. Anthers without an apical appendage. Fruits angular, glandular, without prominent ribs. Pappus of 3—5 bristles. Herbs. Leaves opposite. Heads in panicles. — Species 2. Tropical and South Africa. Used medicinally. . . . . **Adenostemma** Forst.
Anthers with an apical appendage. Pappus of numerous bristles or of scales. [Subtribe AGERATINAE.] 264

264. Pappus of 5—10 scales. Herbs. Leaves opposite. Heads in panicles. — Species 1. Used as an ornamental or medicinal plant. **Ageratum** L.
Pappus of numerous bristles. 265

265. Involucral bracts 4—5. Heads few-flowered, in panicles. Leaves opposite. — Species 10. Tropical and South Africa. Some are used medicinally. (*Willugbaeya* Neck.) . . . . **Mikania** Willd.

Involucral bracts 6 or more. — Species 6. Four species indigenous to North and Central Africa, the other two naturalized in Madagascar and the Mascarenes. Some are used as ornamental or medicinal plants.

Eupatorium L.

266. (262.) Style-branches of the hermaphrodite flowers bearing in the lower part marginal, finally reflexed rows of stigmatic papillae, in the upper part on the outer, more rarely also the inner surface, short subequal hairs. [Tribe ASTEREAE.] 267

Style-branches of the hermaphrodite flowers stigmatose at the margins or on the inner surface, bearing in the upper part or at the top only a crown of rather long hairs sometimes joined above or below or in both directions by shorter ones. 301

267. Female or neuter marginal flowers with a bell-, tube-, thread-, or very shortly strap-shaped corolla not overtopping the involucre. . . . 268

Female or neuter marginal flowers with a distinctly strap-shaped corolla overtopping the involucre, or wanting. 276

268. Pappus of scales or few short bristles, or wanting. Corolla of the marginal flowers bell-, tube-, or thread-shaped. Herbs. [Subtribe GRANGEINAE.]

269

Pappus of long bristles. Corolla of the marginal flowers thread- or strap-shaped. [Subtribe CONYZINAE.] 272

269. Pappus wanting, rarely some minute bristles on the central fruits. Fruits compressed. — Species 6. Tropical and South Africa. Some species yield condiments and medicaments. . . . . **Dichrocephala** DC.

Pappus present. 270

270. Pappus formed of bristles. Fruits subterete. — Species 1. Central Africa. . . . . **Microtrichia** DC.

Pappus cup-shaped or consisting of scales. 271

271. Receptacle with scales between the flowers. — Species 1. Central Africa and Egypt.. . . . . **Ceruana** Forsk.

Receptacle without scales between the flowers. — Species 3. Tropics to Egypt. Used medicinally. . . . . **Grangea** Adans.

272. Fruits turgid. Involucral bracts in many rows, membranous. Heads in panicles. Shrubs. — Species 13. Tropical and South Africa. Some species are used as vegetables or salad. . . . . **Microglossa** DC.

Fruits compressed. 273

273. Female flowers in one row. Pappus-bristles deciduous. Shrubs or undershrubs. Leaves linear. Heads solitary at the ends of the branches. — Species 6. South and North Africa. (*Leptothamnus* DC.)

Nolletia Cass.

Female flowers in two or more rows. 274

274. Corolla of the marginal flowers strap-shaped, but shorter than the style, or thread-shaped, yellowish or whitish. — Species 80. Some of them yield condiments, medicaments, or insect-poison. (*Marsea* Adans., including *Webbia* Schultz). . . . . **Conyza** Less.

Corolla of the marginal flowers strap-shaped, longer than the style. Involucral bracts in two rows. Herbs or undershrubs. 275

275. Ray-flowers yellow. Heads in corymbs. — Species 35. Southern and tropical Africa. . . . . **Nidorella** Cass.

Ray-flowers red or white. (See 232.) . . . . . . **Erigeron** L.

276. (267.) Ray-flowers yellow, sometimes reddish when old, or wanting. Pappus of bristles. [Subtribe SOLIDAGININAE.] 277

Ray-flowers white, blue, or red. 289

277. Heads with all the flowers hermaphrodite ; the inner flowers sometimes sterile. 278

Heads with the inner flowers hermaphrodite and surrounded by one row of female or neuter marginal flowers. 286

278. Involucral bracts in one row or in two very unequal rows (the outer of much smaller bracts). Fruits 5—10-ribbed. Herbs. 279

Involucral bracts in two subequal rows or in 3 or more rows. . . . 280

279. Hairy appendages of the style-branches short. Pappus of bristles. Leaves radical. — Species 1. West Africa. . . **Psednotrichia** Hiern

Hairy appendages of the style-branches long. Pappus of hairs. Leaves alternate. — Species 20. Tropical and South-west Africa. (Including *Crassocephalum* Moench, under *Senecio* L.) . . . . **Gynura** Cass.

280. Pappus-bristles in 1 row. Shrubs. Leaves linear. Heads in leafy corymbs. 281

Pappus-bristles in 2 or more rows. 282

281. Fruits turgid, 5-ribbed. — Species 1. South Africa (Orange River Colony). **Pentheriella** O. Hoffm. & Muschler

Fruits compressed. — Species 15. South Africa. Some are used as ornamental plants. . . . . **Chrysocoma** L.

282. Pappus-bristles in 2 very unequal rows, the outer of very short, sometimes scale-like bristles. Fruits compressed. 283

Pappus-bristles in 2 subequal rows or in 3 or more rows. . . . 284

283. Outer pappus-bristles scale-like. Hairy appendages of the style-branches linear, obtuse. Herbs. Leaves opposite. — Species 2. Southern West Africa. (*Adenogonum* Welw.) . . . . **Engleria** O. Hoffm.

Outer pappus-bristles hair-like. Hairy appendages of the style-branches lanceolate. Shrubs. — Species 5. South Africa. . . . **Fresenia** DC.

284. Stem woody, shrubby. — Species 55. South Africa to Damaraland. **Pteronia** L.

Stem herbaceous. Fruits compressed. Pappus-bristles in 2 or 3 rows. 285

285. Leaves decurrent. Flowers yellow. Heads in corymbs. — Species 2. South Africa. (Under *Chrysocoma* L.) . . . **Heteromma** Benth.

Leaves not decurrent. (See 232.) . . . . **Aster** L.

286. (277.) Marginal rows of stigmatic papillae confluent at the rounded apex of the style-branches. Flower-heads large. Involucre broad, of many rows of bracts. Pappus-bristles in 2—3 rows. Herbs. — Species 2. South Africa. . . . . **Alciope** DC.
Marginal rows of stigmatic papillae not confluent at the apex of the style-branches. Heads small or middle-sized. Involucre oblong or campanulate. 287

287. Involucral bracts subequal, in 2 rows. Pappus-bristles numerous, unequal. Heads in panicles. Shrubs. Leaves marked with pellucid dots. — Species 1. Madagascar. . . . . . . **Glycideras** Cass.
Involucral bracts unequal, in 3 or more rows. 288

288. Involucre broad-campanulate. Fruits 4—5-ribbed. Pappus-bristles in one row, intermixed with some shorter ones. Shrubs. — Species 3. Madagascar . . . . **Rochonia** DC.
Involucre narrow-campanulate or oblong. Fruits 8—12-ribbed. Herbs. Species 2. North Africa. Used as ornamental or medicinal plants. "Goldenrod." . . . . **Solidago** L.

289. (276.) Pappus indistinct or wanting. Herbs. 290
Pappus of the central fruits formed of bristles or of scales and bristles. [Subtribe ASTERINAE.] 292

290. Receptacle with scales between the flowers. Appendages of the style-branches linear, hairy all round. Involucral bracts membranous. Leaves dissected. — Species 1. Tropics. . **Chrysanthellum** Rich.
Receptacle glabrous. Appendages of the style-branches triangular or lanceolate, hairy on the outer face only. [Subtribe BELLIDINAE.] . 291

291. Involucral bracts scarious at the margin. — Species 2. Central Africa.
Brachycome Cass.
Involucral bracts herbaceous throughout. Leaves undivided. — Species 5. North Africa. Some are used as ornamental or medicinal plants. " Daisy." . . . . **Bellis** L.

292. Inner fruits with a pappus of one-ranked feathery bristles, outer without a pappus. Ray-flowers blue. Herbs. — Species 1. South Africa. Used as an ornamental plant. . . . . **Charieis** Cass.
Inner and outer fruits provided with a pappus. 293

293. Pappus of the inner fruits consisting of scales and bristles, that of the outer of scales only. Receptacle usually scaly. Heads solitary, terminating the branches. Herbs. — Species 12. South Africa.
Amellus L.
Pappus of all fruits consisting of bristles or of scales and bristles. . . 294

294. Pappus of 3—5 bristles intermixed with as many minute scales. Ray-flowers white. Heads solitary on leafless scapes. Herbs. — Species 1. North Africa. . . . . **Bellium** L.
Pappus of many bristles sometimes surrounded by some minute scales. 295

295. Pappus-bristles feathery. Herbs or undershrubs. (See 225.) **Mairia** Nees
Pappus-bristles not feathery. 296

296. Fruits compressed. 297
    Fruits not compressed. Heads in corymbs. 300

297. Fruits with 3—4 nerves on each side. Gummiferous shrubs or trees.
    — Species 4. Island of St. Helena. . . . . **Commidendron** DC.
    Fruits with 1—2 nerves on each side or without nerves. Herbs, under-
    shrubs, or non-gummiferous shrubs. 298

298. Stem woody, at least at the base, rarely herbaceous throughout and then
    much branched at the base. Involucral bracts scarious at the edge,
    usually in several rows. Marginal flowers in 1—2 rows, with a strap-
    shaped corolla. Hairy appendages of the style-branches lanceolate.
    Pappus-bristles in one row, rarely surrounded by a second of much shorter
    bristles. (See 231.) . . . . **Felicia** Cass.
    Stem herbaceous, not much branched at the base. 299

299. Involucral bracts membranous, in 2 rows. Marginal flowers usually in
    several rows, the outer with a narrow-linear corolla, the inner sometimes
    with a tubular one. Hairy appendages of the style-branches usually
    short, triangular. Pappus-bristles in 1 row, rarely in 2 rows. (See
    232.) . . . . **Erigeron** L.
    Involucral bracts herbaceous or scarious at the edges, in 3 or more rows.
    Marginal flowers in 1—2 rows, with a more or less strap-shaped, usually
    oblong corolla. Hairy appendages of the style-branches lanceolate.
    Pappus-bristles in 2 or 3 rows. (See 232.) . . . . . **Aster** L.

300. Involucral bracts in 2 rows. Receptacle convex. Marginal flowers in 1
    row, with a white, 3-toothed corolla. Fruits hairy. Pappus-bristles
    in one row. Downy undershrubs. — Species 1. Madagascar.
                                        Henricia Cass.
    Involucral bracts in 3 or more rows. Receptacle flat. Marginal flowers
    in 2 rows, with an entire corolla. Fruits glabrous. Pappus-bristles in
    2 rows. Trees with blackish hairs. — Species 1. Island of St. Helena.
                                  Melanodendron DC.

301. (266.) Pappus consisting of thin, hair-like, simple or toothed, but not
    feathery bristles, rarely outer fruits without a pappus. Receptacle
    without scales between the flowers. [Tribe SENECIONEAE.] . 302
    Pappus consisting of strong, awn-like or feathery bristles, or of scales
    sometimes united into a crown, or wanting. 316

302. Involucral bracts united below, one-ranked. [Subtribe OTHONNINAE.] 303
    Involucral bracts free, at least at and after the time of flowering. [Sub-
    tribe SENECIONINAE.] 306

303. Involucral bracts slightly united at the base. Inner disc-flowers sterile.
    Marginal flowers with a strap-shaped corolla. Fruits hairy. Inner
    disc-fruits without a pappus, the other fruits with a pappus of numerous
    interwoven hairs. Perennial, nearly stem-less herbs. Leaves pinnately
    dissected. Heads solitary on a long scape. (See 236.) **Ruckeria** DC.
    Involucral bracts obviously united below. Disc-flowers all fertile.
    Pappus on all fruits. Heads on a short scape or a branched stem. . 304

304. Stem woody, at least at the base. Heads stalked. Marginal flowers with a strap-shaped corolla. Fruits 10-ribbed. Pappus of several rows of caducous bristles. — Species 40. South and Central Africa. Some species yield a resin. . . . . **Euryops** Cass.
Stem herbaceous throughout. 305

305. Stem annual, branched. Heads small. Corolla-lobes with a strong midnerve. Fruit 5-ribbed. Pappus of few caducous bristles. — Species 3. Central and South Africa. . . . . **Oligothrix** DC.
Stem perennial, short and scape-like or branched; in the latter case pappus-bristles persistent. Heads medium-sized, solitary. Corolla-lobes without a strong midnerve. — Species 2. East Africa.
Werneria H. B. & Kunth

306. Female marginal flowers with a tubular or filiform corolla. 307
Female marginal flowers with a strap-shaped corolla or wanting. . . 311

307. Involucral bracts in 3 or more rows, imbricate, with scarious borders Female marginal flowers in several rows. Fruits without ribs. Heads solitary or in glomerules, yellow-flowered. (See 183.) **Phagnalon** Cass.
Involucral bracts in 1—2 rows. 308

308. Female marginal flowers in 2 or more rows. Fruits 5-angled or 10-ribbed. Herbs. Leaves scattered. Heads in corymbs, narrow. — Species 1. Naturalized in the Mascarene Islands. . . . . **Erechthites** Raf.
Female marginal flowers in 1 row. 309

309. Stem herbaceous. Leaves nearly all radical, orbicular-cordate. Outer fruits without a pappus. — Species 1. South Africa. **Stilpnogyne** DC.
Stem woody, shrubby. Leaves mostly cauline. 310

310. Leaves densely crowded, small. Heads solitary, terminating the branches. Involucral bracts leaf-like. — Species 1. Island of Réunion.
Eriothrix Cass.
Leaves scattered. Heads in corymbs. — Species 4. Madagascar and Mascarenes. . . . . **Faujasia** Cass.

311. Receptacle hemispherical. Involucral bracts in 2—3 rows, subequal. Ray-flowers yellow. Fruits 10-ribbed. Herbs. Heads solitary or several together, on long stalks. — Species 7. North Africa.
Doronicum L.
Receptacle flat or slightly convex. 312

312. Involucral bracts with a leaf-like appendage along the median nerve, 1-nerved. Receptacle pitted. Ray-flowers none. Style-branches with a crown of longer hairs in the middle of the hairy part. Fruits many-nerved. Shrubs or undershrubs. Leaves entire. — Species 8. South Africa. . . . . **Lopholaena** DC.
Involucral bracts without an appendage. 313

313. Involucral bracts in 3 or more rows. Ray-flowers present. Style-branches rounded, almost uniformly clothed with hairs. Herbs. (See 286.). . . . . **Alciope** DC.

Involucral bracts in 1—2 rows, rarely (*Senecio*) indistinctly arranged in 3 or more rows, but then style-branches with a crown of longer hairs. 314

314. Style-branches with an awl-shaped hairy appendage, without a distinct crown of longer hairs. Ray-flowers wanting. Herbs. (See 279.)

Gynura Cass.

Style-branches truncate with a terminal tuft of hairs or with a hairy appendage overtopping a crown of longer hairs. 315

315. Fruits, at least the outer, distinctly compressed. Style-branches truncate, ending in a tuft of hairs. Herbs or undershrubs. Heads in corymbs. (See 227.) . . . . **Cineraria** L.

Fruits not distinctly compressed, 5—10-ribbed. — Species 500. Some of them are used as vegetables, as food for birds, or as ornamental or medicinal plants. (Including *Brachyrhynchos* Less., *Cacalia* L. partly, *Emilia* Cass., *Kleinia* DC., *Lachanodes* DC., *Mesogramma* DC., *Notonia* DC., and *Pladaroxylon* Hook. fil.) . . . . **Senecio** L.

316. (301.) Involucral bracts, at least the inner, scarious at the tip and the edges. Pappus of minute scales, crown- or ear-shaped or wanting. Style-branches of the hermaphrodite flowers truncate, with a terminal crown of hairs. 317

Involucral bracts rarely scarious at the edges, and then pappus of rather large scales or bristles, or style-branches of the hermaphrodite flowers ending in a hairy appendage. 356

317. Anthers arrow-shaped; halves pointed at the base. Involucral bracts in 1—2 rows. Receptacle glabrous. Female marginal flowers in one row, with a strap-shaped corolla. Inner fruits flattened, outer 3-edged. Pappus none. Herbs or undershrubs. Heads long-stalked. (See 124.)

Dimorphotheca Moench

Anthers not arrow-shaped; halves blunt or rounded at the base. [Tribe ANTHEMIDEAE.] 318

318. Receptacle with scales between the flowers. [Subtribe ANTHEMID-INAE.] 319

Receptacle glabrous or hairy, without scales between the flowers. [Subtribe CHRYSANTHEMINAE.] 331

319. Receptacle-scales hairy in the middle, glabrous at the base and apex. Ray-flowers yellow. Fruits cylindrical, without a pappus. Herbs. Leaves pinnately divided. Heads seated between 2—6 (usually 5) branches of the much-branched cyme. — Species 1. North-west Africa. Used as an ornamental plant. . . . . **Cladanthus** Cass.

Receptacle-scales hairy throughout their whole length or at the top only, or glabrous. Heads solitary or in glomerules, corymbs, or panicles. 320

320. Corolla-tube with a basal appendage adnate to the ovary. Corolla persistent. Ray-flowers none. Pappus wanting. Herbs. Leaves entire. Heads in corymbs. — Species 1. North Africa. Used medicinally.

Diotis Desf.

Corolla-tube with appendages which are free frcm the ovary, or without any appendages. 321

321. Fruits clothed with long wool, 8—10-ribbed. Ray-flowers white or violet. Herbs. Leaves pinnately divided. Heads solitary, terminating the branches. — Species 3. South Africa. . **Lasiospermum** Lag.
Fruits not woolly. 322

322. Fruits much compressed. Herbs or undershrubs. 323
Fruits not or scarcely compressed. 325

323. Fruits, at least the outer, broadly winged. Leaves alternate, pinnately divided. — Species 10. North Africa. Some are used medicinally.

Anacyclus L.

Fruits not or indistinctly winged, without a pappus. 324

324. Leaves alternate, toothed or pinnately divided. — Species 7. North Africa ; one species also naturalized in South Africa. Some are used as ornamental or medicinal plants. . . . . **Achillea** L.

Leaves opposite, at least the lower, entire. Ray-flowers neuter, white.— Species 2. North-west Africa. (*Fradinia* Pomel, under *Cladanthus* Cass.) . . . . **Mecomischus** Benth. & Hook.

325. Leaves opposite or whorled, entire. Shrubs. Ray-flowers present. 326
Leaves alternate. 327

326. Heads collected in compound heads. Pappus of the inner fruits consisting of scales sometimes united into a small crown. — Species 4. South Africa. . . . . **Oedera** L.
Heads solitary at the ends of the branches. Pappus wanting. — Species 4. South Africa. . . . . **Eumorphia** DC.

327. Stem herbaceous. Leaves toothed or pinnately divided. 328
Stem woody, at least at the base. 329

328. Heads without ray-flowers. Corolla-tube regular. Pappus crown-shaped. Leaves toothed. Heads in dense corymbs. — Species 1. North Africa.

Lonas Adans.

Heads with ray-flowers, more rarely without, but then pappus auricle-shaped or wanting. Corolla-tube compressed, often with appendages. Heads stalked, terminating the branches. — Species 30. North and Central Africa ; one species naturalized in South Africa. Some are used as medicinal plants (camomile). (Including *Chamaemelum* Cass., *Ormenis* Cass., *Perideraea* Webb, and *Rhetinolepis* Cass.) **Anthemis** L.

329. Ribs of the fruits produced into unequal scales or strong awns. Shrubs. Leaves pinnatifid. Heads in corymbs. — Species 4. Canary Islands. (Including *Hymenolepis* Schultz and *Lugoa* DC.) **Gonospermum** Less.

Ribs of the fruits not produced into scales or awns. Heads without ray-flowers. 330

330. Corolla-tube with a more or less distinct appendage at the base, usually compressed. Pappus wanting. Heads long-stalked. Under-shrubs.

20

Leaves pinnatipartite. — Species 6. Central and North-west Africa. Some of the species are used as ornamental or medicinal plants.

Santolina L.

Corolla-tube without an appendage, not compressed. Fruits 5-angled. Heads in usually dense corymbs. — Species 55. Southern and tropical Africa. (Including *Bembycodium* Kunze and *Oligodora* DC.)

Athanasia L.

331. (318.) Heads with all the flowers hermaphrodite. 332
Heads with the inner flowers hermaphrodite, the outer female or neuter. 343
332. Flowers 4-merous. 333
Flowers 5-merous. 336
333. Involucral bracts in several rows, the outer shorter. Fruits 4-angled, glabrous. Herbs or undershrubs. Leaves dissected. Heads rather small. — Species 6. South and East Africa. (Under *Tanacetum* L.)

Schistostephium Less.

Involucral bracts in 1—3 rows, nearly equal. 334
334. Pappus ring- or crown-shaped. Herbs. Leaves pinnately divided. — Species 20. Some of them are used as ornamental or medicinal plants (camomile). (Including *Chamaemelum* Vis., *Chlamydophora* Ehrenb., *Courrantia* Schultz, and *Otospermum* Willk.) . . . . **Matricaria** L.
Pappus wanting. 335
335. Stem herbaceous. Heads solitary at the ends of the branches. (See 216.). . . . . **Cotula** L.
Stem woody, shrubby. Leaves entire. Heads in corymbs. Fruits compressed, glabrous. — Species 1. South Africa. . . **Peyrousea** DC.
336. Heads in leafy racemes or spikes sometimes arranged in elongated (not corymb-like) panicles. Pappus wanting. (See 222.) **Artemisia** L.
Heads solitary or in corymbs. 337
337. Involucral bracts in 1—3 rows, nearly equal. Herbs. Leaves pinnately divided. (See 334.) . . . . **Matricaria** L.
Involucral bracts in several rows, the outer ones shorter. 338
338. Stem herbaceous. Leaves alternate. (See 219.) . **Chrysanthemum** L.
Stem woody, shrubby. 339
339. Leaves opposite. Pappus wanting. 340
Leaves alternate. 341
340. Heads in corymbs. Involucral bracts in few rows. Fruits with 12—15 ribs. Leaves usually forked. — Species 2. South Africa.

Gymnopentzia Benth.

Heads solitary, seated between lateral tufts of leaves. Involucral bracts in many rows. Fruits 3—4-ribbed. Leaves entire, connate in pairs at the base. — Species 1. South Africa. . . . . **Asaemia** Harv.
341. Leaves toothed, lobed, or divided. Fruits 5-ribbed. — Species 20. South Africa and southern Central Africa. Some are used medicinally.

Pentzia Thunb.

Leaves entire. 342

342. Heads in corymbs. Central flowers sterile. Pappus none. — Species 3. South Africa. . . . . **Stilpnophytum** Less.
Heads few together at the` ends of the branches. Flowers all fertile. — Species 3. South Africa. (Including *Adenosolen* DC. and *Brachymeris* DC.) . . . . **Marasmodes** DC.

343. (331.) Female or neutral marginal flowers with a thread-shaped corolla or without a corolla. 344
Female or neuter marginal flowers with a strap-shaped corolla. . . 350

344. Hermaphrodite flowers 4-merous. Herbs or undershrubs. . . . 345
Hermaphrodite flowers 5-merous. Marginal flowers with a corolla. . 349

345. Involucral bracts of two kinds, the outer four broad and membranous, the inner numerous, longer and narrower, scarious. Marginal flowers in one row, without a corolla. Corolla of the central flowers with a large appendage enclosing the fruit. Pappus none. Leaves opposite. Heads stalked, solitary, terminating the branches. — Species 2. South Africa. . . . . **Otochlamys** DC.
Involucral bracts equal or nearly so. 346

346. Involucral bracts in 3—4 rows, the outer shorter. Marginal flowers with a corolla. Outer fruits compressed and hairy, the inner 4-angled, glabrous. Leaves fan-shaped or pinnately divided. (See 333.)

Schistostephium Less.

Involucral bracts in 1—2 rows, about equal. 347

347. Heads stalked, solitary, terminating the branches. (See 216.) **Cotula** L.
Heads sessile or arranged in racemes or corymbs. Marginal flowers with a corolla. Leaves undivided. 348

348. Female flowers in one row. — Species 1. Island of Rodrigues.

Abrotanella Cass.

Female flowers in several rows. Pappus wanting. — Species 1. Tropics. (*Myriogyne* Less.) . . . . **Centipeda** Lour.

349. Heads in racemes or spikes sometimes arranged in elongated (not corymb-like) panicles. Involucral bracts in few rows. Marginal flowers in one row. Fruits without ribs and without a pappus. (See 222.)

Artemisia L.

Heads solitary or in corymbs. (See 219.) . . . **Chrysanthemum** L.

350. (343.) Involucral bracts in many rows, imbricate, the outer much shorter. 351
Involucral bracts in few rows, about equal in length. 352

351. Leaves decurrent, undivided. Herbs. Heads in corymbs. Hermaphrodite flowers 5-merous. Fruits glandular-hairy. Pappus of scales. — Species 1. South Africa. . . . . . . **Lepidostephium** Oliv.
Leaves not decurrent. (See 219.) . . . . . **Chrysanthemum** L.

352. Involucral bracts broad. Herbs. Leaves dissected. 353
Involucral bracts narrow. Shrubs or undershrubs. Leaves entire, toothed, lobed, or cleft. Corolla-limb of the ray-flowers elongate, entire. 354

353. Corolla of the ray-flowers yellow, very shortly strap-shaped. Fruits compressed, 1—2-ribbed, without a pappus. Heads solitary on long stalks thickened above. (See 216.) . . . . **Cotula** L.
Corolla of the ray-flowers white, usually long strap-shaped. Fruits usually several-ribbed and provided with a pappus. (See 334.)
Matricaria L.

354. Ray-flowers fertile. Disc-flowers 5-merous. Fruits 8—10-ribbed, glandular-warted. Leaves linear or divided into 3 linear segments. — Species 7. South Africa. (Including *Adenachaena* DC. and *Iocaste* E. Mey.)
Phymaspermum Less.

Ray-flowers sterile. Disc-flowers 4-merous. 355

355. Corolla-lobes of the disc-flowers acuminate. Involucre campanulate. Heads short-stalked. Leaves linear, entire. Shrubs. — Species 2. South Africa. . . . . **Thaminophyllum** Harv.
Corolla-lobes of the disc-flowers not acuminate. Involucre hemispherical. Heads long-stalked. Leaves lobed or cleft. Undershrubs. — Species 3. South Africa. . . . . **Lidbeckia** Berg

356. (316.) Receptacle with scales between the flowers. 357
Receptacle glabrous, rarely hairy, without scales between the flowers. 383

357. Pappus of 5—6 large scales sometimes intermixed with bristles. Fruits 10-ribbed, not compressed. Involucral bracts in several rows, scarious at the edges. Ray-flowers in one row, neuter, with a yellow, strap-shaped corolla. Style-branches truncate, with a terminal crown of hairs. Herbs or undershrubs. Leaves alternate, usually toothed or pinnately divided. Heads solitary or in lax panicles. — Species 65. South Africa and Abyssinia. (Including *Sphenogyne* R. Br.) . . **Ursinia** Gaertn.
Pappus wanting or crown-shaped or consisting of bristles or minute scales, rarely of 1—2 or 8—16 larger scales. Involucral bracts rarely scarious at the edges. Leaves usually opposite. [Tribe HELIANTH-EAE.] 358

358. Pappus of feathery bristles. Fruits hairy, angular. Involucral bracts subequal, in 2—3 rows. Ray-flowers yellow, with a strap-shaped corolla. Prostrate herbs. Leaves opposite, broad, toothed. Heads on long stalks. — Species 1. Naturalized in South Africa, Madagascar, and the neighbouring islands. . . . . **Tridax** L.
Pappus of simple (not feathery) bristles or of scales sometimes united into a crown, or wanting. 359

359. Pappus, at least on the inner fruits, formed of 8—16 rather large, fringed scales. Fruits angular. Receptacle conical. Marginal flowers in one row, white, fertile, rarely wanting. Involucral bracts in 1—2 rows. embracing the outer fruits. Heads small, hemispherical. — Species 1, Naturalized in East Africa. . . . . . **Galinsoga** Ruiz & Pav.
Pappus formed of minute scales or of 1—2 larger scales or of bristles, or crown-shaped, or wanting. 360

360. Female or neuter marginal flowers persisting in the fruit, with a strap-shaped corolla. Receptacle conical. Herbs. Leaves opposite. Heads on long stalks. — Species 1. Naturalized in various regions. Ornamental plants. . . . . **Zinnia** L.
Female or neuter marginal flowers falling off before maturity or wanting.

361

361. Inner fruits compressed from front to back. Scales on the receptacle between the flowers flat or convex, not keeled. Female or neuter marginal flowers with a strap-shaped corolla or wanting. [Subtribe COREOPSIDINAE.] 362
Inner fruits not or laterally compressed. [Subtribe VERBESININAE.] . 368

362. Pappus formed of 2—6 barbed bristles (which are armed with minute reflexed prickles). Herbs. Leaves opposite, toothed or divided. . 363
Pappus formed of bristles which are not barbed, at least on the inner fruits, or ring-shaped, or wanting. 364

363. Fruits beaked. Ray-flowers red. — Species 1. Naturalized in Madagascar and the Mascarene Islands. . . . . **Cosmos** Cav.
Fruits not beaked. Ray-flowers, if present, yellow or white. — Species 20. Some of them are used medicinally, others are noxious weeds. (Including *Kerneria* Moench). . . . . **Bidens** L.

364. Involucral bracts 3—6. Marginal flowers female. Corolla glabrous at the base. Pappus of the inner fruits of 2—3 awns. Herbs. Leaves opposite. 365
Involucral bracts numerous, in two rows. 366

365. Involucral bracts partly herbaceous, partly membranous. Outer fruits winged. Heads several together in the leaf-axils. — Species 1. Naturalized in Central Africa. . . . . **Synedrella** Gaertn.
Involucral bracts herbaceous. Fruits all similar, not winged. Heads solitary. — Species 1. West Africa (Congo). **Calyptrocarpus** Less.

366. Involucral bracts free, the outer herbaceous, the inner membranous. Ray-flowers female. Corolla hairy at the base. Pappus none. Herbs. Leaves, at least the lower, opposite. Heads solitary or in cymes, stalked. — Species 8. Central Africa. One of the species yields oil from the seeds (ramtil-oil). . . . . **Guizotia** Cass.
Involucral bracts more or less united. Corolla glabrous at the base. 367

367. Ray-flowers female. Fruits oblong, many-ribbed, hairy. Pappus a minutely toothed crown. Herbs. Leaves opposite, divided. Heads in panicles. — Species 1. Abyssinia. . . . . . **Microlecane** Schultz
Ray-flowers neuter or wanting. Pappus of two teeth or awns, or ring-shaped, or wanting. — Species 50. Central Africa. Some are used as ornamental plants. . . . . **Coreopsis** L.

368. (361.) Inner fruits much compressed laterally. Pappus of two awns or wanting. Receptacle convex, conical, or cylindrical. Herbs. . . 369
Inner fruits slightly or not compressed. 370

369. Fruits winged. Receptacle convex. Involucre as long as the disc.
Heads in lax corymbs. Leaves alternate, at least the upper ones. —
Species 1. Naturalized in the tropics and in Egypt. Used medicinally.
(*Ximenesia* Cass.) . . . . **Verbesina** L.
Fruits not winged. Receptacle elongated. Involucre much shorter
than the disc. Heads solitary. Leaves opposite. — Species 1. Tropical
and South-east Africa. Yields condiments and medicaments.

Spilanthes L.

370. Inner involucral bracts embracing the outer fruits. Pappus wanting.
Herbs. Leaves opposite. 371
Inner involucral bracts not embracing the outer fruits. 372

371. Female marginal flowers in one row. Heads in panicles. — Species 5.
Tropical and South Africa and Canary Islands. Some are used medicin-
ally. . . . . **Siegesbeckia** L.
Female marginal flowers in several rows, with a strap-shaped corolla.
Heads solitary, sessile. Marsh plants. — Species 1. Central Africa.

Enydra Lour.

372. Receptacle-scales wholly enclosing the fruits. Pappus ring-shaped or
wanting. Flowers all hermaphrodite with a tubular corolla or the
marginal neuter with a strap-shaped corolla. Receptacle convex or
conical. Herbs. — Species 2. Central Africa. **Sclerocarpus** Jacq.
Receptacle-scales partly or not enclosing the fruits. 373

373. Receptacle-scales very narrow, nearly bristle-like. Pappus wanting.
Marginal flowers in two rows, with a strap-shaped corolla. Herbs.
Leaves opposite. Heads solitary or in pairs. — Species 2. They yield
dye-stuffs, salad, and medicaments. . . . . **Eclipta** L.
Receptacle-scales broad or rather broad, convex or keeled. 374

374. Pappus wanting. Heads containing hermaphrodite and female flowers.
Herbs. Leaves opposite. 375
Pappus present. 376

375. Inner flowers 4-merous, outer with a very shortly strap-shaped corolla-
limb. Fruits 4-angled. Leaves oblong. Heads in groups of three. —
Species 1. Madagascar. . . . . **Micractis** DC.
Inner flowers 5-merous, outer with a rather long strap-shaped corolla-limb.
Fruits 2—3-angled. Leaves ovate. — Species 15. Tropical and
South Africa. . . . . **Wedelia** Jacq.

376. Pappus ring-shaped. Fruits 4-angled. Receptacle flat. Receptacle-
scales slit. Heads in corymbs; all flowers hermaphrodite. Shrubs.
Leaves alternate. — Species 1. Madagascar. . . **Temnolepis** Bak.
Pappus cup-shaped or formed of scales and bristles. Herbs or undershrubs. 377

377. Pappus of free, caducous bristles or scales. 378
Pappus of bristles united at the base, or cup-shaped with or without free
bristles. 379

378. Pappus-bristles 1—4, more or less broadened below. Heads large. Ray-flowers neuter. — Species 3. Cultivated and sometimes naturalized. Used as ornamental plants (sunflower) and yielding edible tubers, dye-stuffs, and oily seeds from which bread may be prepared.

Helianthus L.

Pappus-þristles thin, usually numerous. Heads middle-sized. Receptacle convex. Receptacle-scales acuminate. Leaves opposite. — Species 17. Tropical and South-east Africa. (Including *Lipotriche* R. Br.)

Melanthera Rohr

379. Heads with all the flowers hermaphrodite, arranged in corymbs. Receptacle convex. Receptacle-scales with a coloured appendage. Anthers arrow-shaped. Fruits 5-ribbed. Pappus a toothed cup. Leaves alternate, linear. (See 246.) . . . . **Omphalopappus** O. Hoffm.

Heads with the inner flowers hermaphrodite, the outer female or neuter. 380

380. Marginal flowers neuter, with a strap-shaped corolla. Leaves opposite. — Species 40. Tropics. Some are used medicinally. **Aspilia** Thouars

Marginal flowers female. 381

381. Marginal flowers with a tubular or shortly strap-shaped corolla. Pappus of 2—5 unequal bristles united at the base. Leaves, at least the lower, opposite. — Species 4. Central Africa. . . . . **Blainvillea** Cass.

Marginal flowers with a distinctly strap-shaped corolla. Pappus cup-shaped, with or without awns. Heads stalked. 382

382. Leaves alternate. Fruits 4—5-angled, many-ribbed. — Species 6. Madagascar. . . . . **Epallage** DC.

Leaves opposite. Fruits 2—3-angled, with indistinct angles. (See 375.)

Wedelia Jacq.

383. (356.) Female marginal flowers in several rows, with a yellow, thread-shaped, 2—3-toothed corolla. Involucral bracts in several rows, imbricate, with scarious edges. Fruits without ribs. Pappus of one row of bristles. Leaves alternate, undivided. Heads solitary or in glomerules. (See 183.) . . . . **Phagnalon** Cass.

Female or neuter marginal flowers in one row, with a strap-shaped, rarely a tubular but 4-toothed corolla, or wanting. [Tribe HELENIEAE.] 384

384. Female marginal flowers with a tubular, 4-toothed corolla. Involucral bracts in 4—5 rows. Receptacle pitted. Pappus of scales. Herbs. Leaves alternate. Heads in panicles. — Species 1. Southern West Africa (Angola). . . . . **Welwitschiella** O. Hoffm.

Female or neuter marginal flowers with a strap-shaped corolla or wanting. Heads solitary or in glomerules. 385

385. Receptacle bristly. Involucral bracts in 3—4 rows. Anthers arrow-shaped, the halves pointed at the base. Pappus of scales. Herbs. Leaves alternate or radical. Heads solitary. — Species 1. Naturalized in Central Africa. An ornamental plant. . . . **Gaillardia** Foug.

Receptacle glabrous, rarely (*Tagetes*) ciliate at the edges of the pits. . 386

386. Involucral bracts in 3—4 rows.   Herbs or undershrubs.   Leaves opposite,
     entire.   Heads solitary. — Species 9.   Central Africa.   (Including
     Hypericophyllum Steetz) . . . . **Jaumea** Pers.
     Involucral bracts in 1—2 rows. 387
387. Involucral bracts free. 388
     Involucral bracts united below.   Heads solitary.   Anthers entire at the
     base or with blunt halves. 390
388. Involucral bracts numerous.   Heads many-flowered.   Female marginal
     flowers numerous.   Anthers arrow-shaped, the halves pointed at the
     base.   Pappus none.   Herbs or undershrubs.   Leaves alternate or
     all radical.   Heads solitary.   (See 124.) . . **Dimorphotheca** Moench
     Involucral bracts 2—6.   Heads few-flowered.   Female marginal flowers
     solitary or wanting.   Anthers entire at the base or with blunt halves.
     Heads in glomerules. 389
389. Pappus wanting.   Herbs.   Leaves opposite. — Species 2.   Naturalized
     in Egypt and Eritrea.   They yield dyes and medicaments.
                                                Flaveria Juss.

     Pappus of slit scales.   Small shrubs.   Leaves alternate. — Species 1.
     South Africa. . . . . **Phaeocephalus** S. Moore
390. Pappus wanting.   Fruits 5—10-ribbed.   Leaves alternate. — Species 15.
     South Africa.   Some are used as ornamental plants. **Gamolepis** Less.
     Pappus of scales or bristles.   Herbs. 391
391. Pappus of 3—6 scales.   Fruits scarcely ribbed.   Leaves opposite, pinnate-
     ly divided. — Species 3.   Naturalized.   Ornamental plants, also
     yielding dyes and medicaments. . . . . **Tagetes** L.
     Pappus of numerous bristles or slit scales.   Fruit 10—12-ribbed.   Leaves
     alternate, undivided. — Species 1.   South Africa. **Cadiscus** E. Mey.

STATISTICAL TABLE

showing the number of Genera and Species and the Geographical
Distribution of each Family.

	Whole Earth		Africa (in all)		Africa (indigenous)		North Africa		Central Africa		Malagasy Islands		South Africa	
Cycadaceae · · · ·	9	85	3	25	3	25	—	—	1	8	1	1	2	15
Ginkgoaceae · · ·	1	1	—	—	—	—	—	—	—	—	—	—	—	—
Taxaceae · · · ·	11	100	2	9	2	9	1	1	1	5	1	1	1	3
Pinaceae · · · ·	26	260	6	25	5	25	5	15	2	4	1	1	1	3
Gnetaceae · · · ·	3	45	3	8	3	8	1	5	3	5	—	—	—	—
Gymnospermae · ·	50	500	14	65	13	65	7	20	7	20	3	3	4	20
Typhaceae · · · ·	1	9	1	4	1	4	1	4	1	3	1	2	1	2
Pandanaceae · · ·	3	240	1	65	1	65	—	—	1	15	1	50	—	—
Sparganiaceae · ·	1	15	1	2	1	2	1	2	—	—	—	—	—	—
Potamogetonaceae	9	100	8	35	8	35	8	20	4	20	6	20	4	5
Naiadaceae · · ·	1	30	1	10	1	10	1	4	1	7	1	5	1	1
Aponogetonaceae ·	1	20	1	20	1	20	—	—	1	8	1	6	1	9
Scheuchzeriaceae ·	5	15	1	4	1	4	1	4	1	2	—	—	1	3
Alismataceae · · ·	12	75	9	15	9	15	4	5	8	10	4	4	—	—
Butomaceae · · ·	4	7	2	2	2	2	1	1	1	1	—	—	—	—
Hydrocharitaceae ·	15	65	10	40	10	40	4	4	9	35	8	10	1	1
Triuridaceae · · ·	2	25	1	3	1	3	—	—	1	2	1	1	1	1
Gramineae · · · ·	373	3700	205	1600	199	1600	108	380	130	850	66	200	80	460
Cyperaceae · · ·	77	3000	40	880	40	880	9	90	25	490	26	270	28	350
Palmae · · · · ·	169	1200	36	100	33	100	3	4	13	40	24	60	2	2
Cyclanthaceae · ·	6	45	—	—	—	—	—	—	—	—	—	—	—	—
Araceae · · · ·	115	1100	33	150	28	140	6	10	21	120	6	6	3	10
Lemnaceae · · ·	3	25	3	12	3	12	3	7	3	10	2	4	3	5
Flagellariaceae · ·	3	7	1	1	1	1	—	—	1	1	1	1	1	1
Restionaceae · · ·	23	250	12	230	12	230	—	—	1	1	—	—	12	230
Centrolepidaceae ·	7	40	—	—	—	—	—	—	1	1	—	—	—	—
Mayacaceae · · ·	1	7	1	1	1	1	—	—	1	1	—	—	—	—
Xyridaceae · · ·	2	55	1	40	1	40	—	—	1	30	1	6	1	8
Eriocaulaceae · · ·	9	570	4	80	4	80	—	—	4	60	3	15	2	10
Thurniaceae · · ·	1	2	—	—	—	—	—	—	—	—	—	—	—	—
Rapateaceae · · ·	7	25	1	1	1	1	—	—	1	1	—	—	—	—
Bromeliaceae · · ·	57	920	1	1	1	1	—	—	—	—	—	—	—	—
Commelinaceae · ·	29	320	12	160	12	160	1	5	12	140	6	25	5	20
Pontederiaceae · ·	6	20	3	5	3	5	—	—	3	5	1	1	—	—
Cyanastraceae · ·	1	5	1	5	1	5	—	—	1	5	—	—	—	—
Philydraceae · · ·	3	4	—	—	—	—	—	—	—	—	—	—	—	—
Juncaceae · · · ·	8	280	3	55	3	55	2	30	2	15	1	1	3	30
Stemonaceae · · ·	3	8	—	—	—	—	—	—	—	—	—	—	—	—
Liliaceae · · · ·	228	2600	79	1450	75	1450	27	130	37	600	22	65	52	880
Haemodoraceae · ·	9	30	4	6	4	6	—	—	—	—	—	—	4	6
Amaryllidaceae · ·	83	950	33	310	29	300	6	20	16	110	5	15	19	190
Velloziaceae · · ·	2	70	1	25	1	25	—	—	1	15	1	5	1	9
Taccaceae · · · ·	2	10	1	2	1	2	—	—	1	1	1	5	—	—
Dioscoreaceae · ·	10	240	2	45	2	45	1	3	1	20	1	8	1	15
Iridaceae · · · · ·	60	1100	39	600	37	600	5	30	13	120	6	10	32	500
Musaceae · · · ·	6	85	4	25	3	20	—	—	1	15	2	2	1	4
Zingiberaceae · · ·	41	900	11	120	7	110	—	—	4	110	4	6	1	3
Cannaceae · · · ·	1	40	1	5	—	—	—	—	—	—	—	—	—	—

	Whole Earth		Africa (in all)		Africa (indigenous)		North Africa		Central Africa		Malagasy Islands		South Africa	
Marantaceae · · ·	27	290	12	60	11	55	—	—	11	55	2	2	—	—
Burmanniaceae · ·	18	60	4	15	4	15	—	—	4	10	1	4	1	1
Orchidaceae · · ·	500	7400	97	1600	97	1600	14	50	55	900	56	370	37	430
Monocotyledonae ·	1944	26000	681	7800	650	7750	206	800	381	3850	261	1200	298	3200
Casuarinaceae · ·	1	30	1	2	1	2	—	—	—	—	1	2	—	—
Saururaceae · · ·	3	5	—	—	—	—	—	—	—	—	—	—	—	—
Piperaceae · · · ·	9	1100	3	80	3	80	—	—	3	40	2	40	2	7
Chloranthaceae · ·	4	35	—	—	—	—	—	—	—	—	—	—	—	—
Lacistemaceae · ·	1	15	—	—	—	—	—	—	—	—	—	—	—	—
Salicaceae · · · ·	2	200	2	20	2	20	2	12	2	6	1	1	1	3
Garryaceae · · · ·	1	15	—	—	—	—	—	—	—	—	—	—	—	—
Myricaceae · · · ·	1	55	1	25	1	25	1	1	1	6	1	6	1	15
Balanopsidaceae ·	2	9	—	—	—	—	—	—	—	—	—	—	—	—
Leitneriaceae · · ·	1	2	—	—	—	—	—	—	—	—	—	—	—	—
Juglandaceae · ·	6	40	1	2	—	—	—	—	—	—	—	—	—	—
Batidaceae · · ·	1	1	—	—	—	—	—	—	—	—	—	—	—	—
Julianiaceae · · ·	2	5	—	—	—	—	—	—	—	—	—	—	—	—
Betulaceae · · · ·	6	90	2	2	1	1	1	1	—	—	—	—	—	—
Fagaceae · · · ·	5	370	2	9	2	9	2	9	—	—	—	—	—	—
Ulmaceae · · · ·	15	120	5	35	5	35	2	2	4	20	3	10	3	7
Moraceae · · · ·	70	1000	26	260	19	250	1	5	15	200	9	65	1	12
Urticaceae · · · ·	43	580	20	150	19	150	4	13	17	75	11	55	9	20
Proteaceae · · ·	55	1000	13	400	13	400	—	—	3	50	2	2	12	360
Myzodendraceae ·	1	10	—	—	—	—	—	—	—	—	—	—	—	—
Santalaceae · · ·	26	250	6	140	6	140	2	5	3	55	2	3	5	90
Opiliaceae · · · ·	7	25	2	15	2	15	—	—	2	15	—	—	1	1
Grubbiaceae · · ·	1	4	1	4	1	4	—	—	—	—	—	—	1	4
Olacaceae · · · ·	27	160	11	70	11	70	—	—	9	55	4	13	1	2
Octoknemataceae ·	1	3	1	3	1	3	—	—	1	3	—	—	—	—
Loranthaceae · · ·	26	900	4	300	4	300	2	2	2	240	3	45	2	40
Balanophoraceae ·	14	50	4	6	4	6	—	—	2	3	2	2	2	3
Aristolochiaceae ·	6	200	1	30	1	30	1	6	1	20	1	6	1	1
Rafflesiaceae · · ·	7	25	2	4	2	4	1	1	1	1	1	1	1	2
Hydnoraceae · · ·	2	10	1	8	1	8	—	—	1	6	1	1	1	2
Polygonaceae · · ·	34	800	9	120	8	120	5	50	5	45	2	20	4	45
Chenopodiaceae · ·	76	450	26	120	25	120	24	75	12	40	3	6	9	40
Amarantaceae · ·	56	500	32	200	32	200	8	17	28	140	12	35	18	50
Nyctaginaceae · ·	20	170	5	30	3	30	1	6	3	12	3	15	3	6
Cynocrambaceae ·	1	2	1	1	1	1	1	1	—	—	—	—	—	—
Phytolaccaceae · ·	22	120	5	15	4	10	1	2	4	8	3	4	2	8
Aizoaceae · · · ·	24	600	20	480	20	480	6	10	14	45	6	12	20	440
Portulacaceae · ·	18	210	6	35	6	35	1	2	2	13	2	5	5	20
Basellaceae · · ·	5	15	2	4	1	2	—	—	1	1	1	1	—	—
Caryophyllaceae ·	79	1500	45	280	45	280	37	200	22	60	7	8	15	40
Nymphaeaceae · ·	8	60	3	20	3	20	2	4	2	20	1	2	1	2
Ceratophyllaceae ·	1	3	1	3	1	3	1	2	1	2	1	1	1	1
Trochodendraceae ·	2	5	—	—	—	—	—	—	—	—	—	—	—	—
Cercidiphyllaceae ·	1	2	—	—	—	—	—	—	—	—	—	—	—	—
Renunculaceae · ·	32	1200	11	140	11	140	11	70	5	50	2	13	4	25
Lardizabalaceae · ·	7	20	—	—	—	—	—	—	—	—	—	—	—	—
Berberidaceae · ·	9	150	3	6	3	6	3	4	1	1	—	—	—	—

	Whole Earth		Africa (in all)		Africa (indigenous)		North Africa		Central Africa		Malagasy Islands		South Africa	
Menispermaceae · ·	63	360	27	100	27	100	1	1	20	75	10	25	6	15
Magnoliaceae · · ·	13	110	—	—	—	—	—	—	—	—	—	—	—	—
Calycanthaceae · ·	1	5	—	—	—	—	—	—	—	—	—	—	—	—
Lactoridaceae · ·	1	1	—	—	—	—	—	—	—	—	—	—	—	—
Anonaceae · · ·	76	900	27	240	26	230	—	—	25	200	11	30	5	8
Myristicaceae · · ·	16	250	9	25	7	20	—	—	5	15	2	5	—	—
Gomortegaceae · ·	1	1	—	—	—	—	—	—	—	—	—	—	—	—
Monimiaceae · · ·	30	250	6	30	6	30	—	—	3	6	4	25	1	1
Lauraceae · · · ·	48	1100	15	75	12	70	4	5	6	30	7	35	3	10
Hernandiaceae · ·	4	25	3	7	3	7	—	—	3	4	2	4	—	—
Papaveraceae · ·	31	400	11	50	9	50	7	40	4	7	—	—	4	10
Capparidaceae · ·	43	450	20	260	20	260	7	15	19	200	7	35	8	40
Cruciferae · · ·	232	1900	88	420	87	410	75	270	28	85	4	8	21	110
Tovariaceae · · ·	1	4	—	—	—	—	—	—	—	—	—	—	—	—
Resedaceae · · ·	6	55	6	45	6	45	6	30	5	10	—	—	1	5
Moringaceae · · ·	1	6	1	6	1	5	1	1	1	5	1	1	—	—
Sarraceniaceae · ·	3	9	—	—	—	—	—	—	—	—	—	—	—	—
Nepenthaceae · ·	1	60	1	2	1	2	—	—	—	—	1	2	—	—
Droseraceae · · ·	4	85	3	15	3	15	1	1	2	6	1	2	1	10
Podostemonaceae ·	30	130	9	25	9	25	—	—	8	20	3	6	2	2
Hydrostachyaceae ·	1	15	1	15	1	15	—	—	1	4	1	12	1	1
Crassulaceae · · ·	18	550	10	400	10	400	5	110	6	60	5	50	6	200
Cephalotaceae · ·	1	1	—	—	—	—	—	—	—	—	—	—	—	—
Saxifragaceae · · ·	78	650	11	25	10	25	3	10	4	7	6	7	3	4
Pittosporaceae · ·	9	110	1	35	1	35	1	2	1	15	1	15	1	2
Brunelliaceae · · ·	1	10	—	—	—	—	—	—	—	—	—	—	—	—
Cunoniaceae · · ·	21	130	3	17	3	17	—	—	—	—	1	15	2	2
Myrothamnaceae · ·	1	2	1	2	1	2	—	—	1	1	1	1	1	1
Bruniaceae · · · ·	12	55	12	55	12	55	—	—	—	—	—	—	12	55
Hamamelidaceae · ·	20	50	3	20	3	20	—	—	1	2	2	15	1	2
Eucommiaceae · ·	1	1	—	—	—	—	—	—	—	—	—	—	—	—
Platanaceae · · ·	1	6	1	2	—	—	—	—	—	—	—	—	—	—
Crossosomataceae ·	1	3	—	—	—	—	—	—	—	—	—	—	—	—
Rosaceae · · · · ·	102	1700	32	230	30	220	18	65	13	85	5	20	12	65
Connaraceae · · ·	20	180	12	140	12	140	—	—	12	130	3	8	1	1
Leguminosae · · ·	522	11500	261	3300	253	3300	54	550	182	1650	82	440	88	1000
Pandaceae · · · ·	1	1	1	1	1	1	—	—	1	1	—	—	—	—
Geraniaceae · · ·	11	500	6	350	6	350	3	50	6	25	2	2	5	280
Oxalidaceae · · ·	7	300	3	160	2	160	1	4	2	15	2	25	1	120
Tropaeolaceae · ·	1	50	1	1	—	—	—	—	—	—	—	—	—	—
Linaceae · · · ·	13	130	7	60	6	60	2	20	6	30	2	8	1	5
Humiriaceae · · ·	3	20	1	1	1	1	—	—	1	1	—	—	—	—
Erythroxylaceae · ·	2	200	2	40	2	40	—	—	2	5	1	35	1	4
Zygophyllaceae · ·	28	170	12	90	12	90	9	35	6	18	2	3	7	50
Cneoraceae · · ·	1	10	1	1	1	1	1	1	—	—	—	—	—	—
Rutaceae · · · ·	125	950	33	320	30	310	1	8	17	80	7	35	17	210
Simarubaceae · · ·	32	150	16	40	16	40	—	—	13	35	4	5	1	1
Burseraceae · · ·	18	350	7	160	7	160	—	—	6	120	3	20	1	20
Meliaceae · · ·	49	800	23	150	23	150	—	—	18	100	8	45	5	15
Malpighiaceae · ·	65	700	16	80	16	80	—	—	10	45	10	30	4	13
Trigoniaceae · · ·	3	30	—	—	—	—	—	—	—	—	—	—	—	—
Vochysiaceae · · ·	5	100	—	—	—	—	—	—	—	—	—	—	—	—
Tremandraceae · ·	3	25	—	—	—	—	—	—	—	—	—	—	—	—

	Whole Earth		Africa (in all)		Africa (indigenous)		North Africa		Central Africa		Malagasy Islands		South Africa	
Polygalaceae · · ·	11	700	6	240	6	240	1	10	5	90	1	20	4	140
Dichapetalaceae ·	3	100	2	75	2	75	—	—	2	65	1	12	1	1
Euphorbiaceae · ·	278	4500	122	1200	117	1150	5	70	95	600	47	360	31	220
Callitrichaceae · ·	1	25	1	6	1	6	1	5	1	1	—	—	1	1
Buxaceae · · · ·	7	30	3	8	3	8	1	1	2	4	1	1	2	2
Empetraceae · · ·	3	4	2	2	2	2	1	1	—	—	—	—	1	1
Coriariaceae · · ·	1	8	1	1	1	1	1	1	—	—	—	—	—	—
Limnanthaceae · ·	2	5	—		—									
Anacardiaceae · ·	69	480	29	250	26	240	2	6	16	130	12	30	9	95
Cyrillaceae · · · ·	3	6	—											
Pentaphylacaceae ·	1	1	—											
Corynocarpaceae ·	1	1	—											
Aquifoliaceae · ·	4	280	1	5	1	5	1	4	1	1	1	1	1	1
Celastraceae · · ·	51	500	15	160	15	160	2	4	5	50	9	35	11	90
Hippocrateaceae ·	3	200	3	110	3	110	—	—	3	100	2	12	2	5
Salvadoraceae · ·	3	9	3	6	3	6	1	1	3	6	1	1	2	2
Stackhousiaceae · ·	2	15	—											
Staphyleaceae · ·	6	20	—											
Icacinaceae · · · ·	48	200	19	90	19	90	—	—	15	65	10	20	3	5
Aceraceae · · · ·	2	110	1	4	1	4	1	4	—	—	—	—	—	—
Hippocastanaceae ·	3	15	—											
Sapindaceae · · ·	128	1100	51	200	47	200	—	—	29	120	23	60	8	15
Sabiaceae · · · ·	3	70											3	10
Melianthaceae · ·	3	30	3	30	3	30	—	—	1	18	—	—	3	10
Balsaminaceae · ·	2	350	1	100	1	100	—	—	1	85	1	25	1	2
Rhamnaceae · · ·	52	500	18	140	18	140	3	15	14	25	9	20	8	90
Vitaceae · · · · ·	12	500	5	200	5	200	2	2	4	160	3	30	2	18
Elaeocarpaceae · ·	8	130	1	15	1	15	—	—	1	1	1	15	—	—
Chlaenaceae · · ·	7	25	7	25	7	25	—	—	—	—	7	25	—	—
Gonystilaceae · · ·	1	7	—											
Tiliaceae · · · ·	45	350	18	260	18	260	2	4	17	180	8	70	4	20
Malvaceae · · · ·	50	900	21	300	21	300	7	40	16	140	13	85	13	85
Bombacaceae · ·	22	140	3	13	3	13	—	—	3	9	1	4	—	—
Sterculiaceae · · ·	57	820	28	470	26	470	1	1	19	190	14	120	6	190
Scytopetalaceae ·	5	40	5	40	5	40	—	—	5	40	—	—	—	—
Dilleniaceae · · ·	14	320	3	25	3	25	—	—	1	18	3	8	—	—
Eucryphiaceae · ·	1	4	—											
Ochnaceae · · · ·	22	250	7	150	7	150	—	—	6	120	3	35	3	8
Caryocaraceae · ·	2	15	—											
Marcgraviaceae · ·	5	50	—											
Quiinaceae · · · ·	2	20	—											
Theaceae · · · · ·	20	200	6	12	5	10	1	1	1	1	3	8	—	—
Guttiferae · · · ·	50	850	16	180	16	180	1	25	12	85	11	80	2	6
Dipterocarpaceae ·	19	340	2	15	2	15	—	—	1	15	1	1	—	—
Elatinaceae · · ·	2	35	2	15	2	15	2	6	1	8	—	—	1	5
Frankeniaceae · ·	5	60	2	10	2	10	1	9	2	3	—	—	1	3
Tamaricaceae · ·	4	90	3	25	3	25	3	20	1	3	—	—	1	2
Fouquieriaceae · ·	1	4	—											
Cistaceae · · · ·	7	140	5	75	5	75	5	75	1	1	—	—	—	—
Bixaceae · · · ·	1	1	1	1	—	—								
Cochlospermaceae ·	3	20	2	7	2	7	—	—	1	5	1	2	—	—
Koeberliniaceae ·	1	1	—											
Winteranaceae · ·	4	8	2	4	2	4	—	—	1	2	1	2	—	—

	Whole Earth		Africa (in all)		Africa (indigenous)		North Africa		Central Africa		Malagasy Islands		South Africa	
Violaceae · · ·	17	450	4	100	4	100	1	15	4	55	3	30	3	8
Flacourtiaceae · ·	84	650	46	250	46	250	—	—	39	150	18	95	11	25
Stachyuraceae · ·	1	2	—	—	—	—	—	—	—	—	—	—	—	—
Turneraceae · · ·	7	100	7	20	7	20	—	—	3	12	5	6	2	2
Malesherbiaceae· ·	1	25	—	—	—	—	—	—	—	—	—	—	—	—
Passifloraceae· ·	13	380	8	75	8	70	—	—	6	45	3	15	3	12
Achariaceae · · ·	3	3	3	3	3	3	—	—	—	—	—	—	3	3
Caricaceae · · ·	3	30	2	3	1	2	—	—	1	2	—	—	—	—
Loasaceae · · · ·	13	230	1	1	1	1	—	—	—	—	—	—	—	—
Datiscaceae · · ·	3	5	—	—	—	—	—	—	—	—	1	1	1	1
Begoniaceae · · ·	5	450	1	110	1	110	—	—	1	90	1	20	1	7
Ancistrocladaceae ·	1	10	1	2	1	2	—	—	1	2	—	—	—	—
Cactaceae · · · ·	23	1500	5	13	1	7	—	—	1	3	1	4	1	1
Geissolomataceae ·	1	2	1	2	1	2	—	—	—	—	—	—	1	2
Penaeaceae · · ·	5	35	5	35	5	35	—	—	—	—	—	—	5	35
Oliniaceae · · · ·	1	7	1	7	1	7	—	—	1	3	—	—	1	4
Thymelaeaceae · ·	41	450	17	250	16	250	2	15	8	95	4	17	10	130
Elaeagnaceae · ·	3	30	1	2	—	—	—	—	—	—	—	—	—	—
Lythraceae · · · ·	25	500	12	90	11	90	4	15	7	65	7	17	6	25
Sonneratiaceae · ·	4	15	1	1	1	1	—	—	1	1	1	1	—	—
Punicaceae · · ·	1	2	1	2	1	1	—	—	1	1	—	—	—	—
Lecythidaceae · ·	19	250	4	15	4	15	—	—	3	8	2	9	1	1
Rhizophoraceae· ·	18	60	10	45	10	45	—	—	8	30	8	20	4	5
Nyssaceae · · · ·	3	8	—	—	—	—	—	—	—	—	—	—	—	—
Alangiaceae · · ·	1	20	1	2	1	2	—	—	1	1	1	1	—	—
Combretaceae· · ·	17	450	12	330	12	330	—	—	10	280	6	40	4	25
Myrtaceae · · · ·	76	2900	10	85	7	75	1	1	3	35	4	35	4	10
Melastomataceae ·	169	2800	33	280	33	280	—	—	24	160	14	110	3	9
Oenotheraceae · ·	39	500	10	40	6	35	6	12	4	20	3	12	3	9
Halorrhagaceae· ·	7	150	3	15	3	15	2	4	3	5	3	7	3	3
Hippuridaceae · ·	1	1	—	—	—	—	—	—	—	—	—	—	—	—
Cynomoriaceae · ·	1	1	1	1	1	1	1	1	—	—	—	—	—	—
Araliaceae · · · ·	55	660	8	75	8	75	1	1	3	25	7	45	1	10
Umbelliferae · · ·	270	2500	92	410	92	410	71	210	29	80	8	20	30	120
Cornaceae · · · ·	10	100	4	6	4	6	—	—	1	1	2	4	1	1
Archichlamydeae ·	4512	67500	1703	16700	1632	16600	454	2300	1054	7800	577	2950	573	5000
Clethraceae· · · ·	1	30	1	1	1	1	1	1	—	—	—	—	—	—
Pirolaceae · · · ·	10	30	—	—	—	—	1	1	—	—	—	—	—	—
Lennoaceae· · · ·	3	5	—	—	—	—	—	—	—	—	—	—	—	—
Ericaceae · · · ·	77	1550	17	720	17	720	5	12	7	40	6	45	12	630
Epacridaceae · ·	23	340	—	—	—	—	—	—	—	—	—	—	—	—
Diapensiaceae · ·	6	9	—	—	—	—	—	—	—	—	—	—	—	—
Theophrastaceae ·	4	70	—	—	—	—	—	—	—	—	—	—	—	—
Myrsinaceae · · ·	32	1000	10	130	10	130	3	3	5	35	7	95	4	8
Primulaceae · · ·	22	560	11	45	10	45	9	20	7	20	2	6	4	8
Plumbaginaceae ·	10	280	7	90	7	90	5	60	4	18	1	3	3	8
Sapotaceae · · ·	51	650	19	150	16	140	2	2	12	110	5	30	3	15
Hoplestigmataceae	1	2	1	2	1	2	—	—	1	2	—	—	—	—
Ebenaceae · · ·	7	350	6	150	6	150	—	—	5	80	3	35	4	35
Symplocaceae· ·	1	300	—	—	—	—	—	—	—	—	—	—	—	—
Styracaceae · · ·	7	110	1	1	1	1	—	—	1	1	—	—	—	—

	Whole Earth		Africa (in all)		Africa (indigenous)		North Africa		Central Africa		Malagasy Islands		South Africa	
Oleaceae · · · · ·	25	420	11	120	10	120	5	15	5	70	4	20	5	20
Loganiaceae · · ·	33	550	14	240	14	240	—	—	8	170	10	50	8	25
Gentianaceae · · ·	71	900	23	250	23	250	5	10	15	110	9	35	8	110
Apocynaceae · · ·	165	1300	61	450	57	440	2	2	42	330	25	95	12	30
Asclepiadaceae · ·	267	2200	118	1100	116	1100	11	18	75	470	33	75	65	610
Convolvulaceae · ·	45	1150	34	450	31	440	6	60	28	290	17	80	14	95
Polemoniaceae · ·	13	280	—											
Hydrophyllaceae ·	17	180	2	8	2	8	—	—	2	7	1	2	1	2
Borraginaceae · ·	97	1500	37	370	34	370	23	130	19	160	6	20	12	95
Verbenaceae · ·	80	900	27	340	25	320	5	7	15	230	13	60	13	55
Labiatae · · · ·	170	3400	70	1200	68	1200	34	250	48	700	22	95	26	230
Nolanaceae · · ·	3	50	—											
Solanaceae · · · ·	83	2100	16	220	12	200	8	30	9	120	4	30	5	55
Scrophulariaceae ·	210	3000	107	1150	101	1150	29	160	62	380	28	50	50	630
Bignoniaceae · · ·	109	670	21	90	20	90	—	—	10	40	13	50	5	8
Pedaliaceae · · ·	17	70	14	65	14	65	—	—	13	55	3	8	7	.11
Martyniaceae · ·	3	10	1	1	—									
Orobanchaceae · ·	13	130	2	30	2	30	2	30	2	7	—	—	—	—
Gesneraceae · · ·	97	1150	6	65	6	65	—	—	6	35	2	13	1	25
Columelliaceae · ·	1	2	—											
Lentibulariaceae ·	6	260	2	65	2	65	1	4	2	40	1	12	2	20
Globulariaceae · ·	3	20	3	6	3	6	2	4	2	2	—	—	—	—
Acanthaceae · · ·	214	2400	106	1100	103	1100	4	5	79	800	52	190	32	210
Myoporaceae · · ·	5	90	3	4	3	4	—	—	1	1	1	1	1	2
Phrymaceae · · ·	1	1	—											
Plantaginaceae · ·	3	200	2	40	2	40	2	30	1	10	1	1	1	8
Rubiaceae · · · ·	407	5500	150	1900	147	1900	12	65	102	1400	73	320	36	150
Caprifoliaceae · ·	11	370	4	15	3	13	3	13	1	1	—	—	—	—
Adoxaceae · · · ·	1	1	—											
Valerianaceae · · ·	12	310	4	35	4	35	4	30	2	5	—	—	2	2
Dipsacaceae · · ·	9	160	7	50	7	50	7	30	5	10	—	—	2	9
Cucurbitaceae · · ·	97	750	42	270	38	260	5	8	32	190	14	20	16	65
Campanulaceae · ·	67	1200	26	400	25	400	11	40	9	120	7	20	15	250
Goodeniaceae · · ·	14	210	1	2	1	2	—	—	1	1	1	2	1	1
Stylidiaceae · · ·	6	120	—											
Calyceraceae · · ·	4	25	—											
Compositae · · · ·	915	13500	327	4200	314	4150	111	690	155	1250	69	430	157	1900
Metachlamydeae ·	3549	50400	1314	15500	1256	15300	317	1750	793	7300	433	1900	526	5350
Dicotyledoneae · ·	8061	118000	3017	32200	2888	31900	771	4050	1847	15100	1010	4850	1099	10400
Angiospermae · ·	10005	144000	3698	40000	3538	39700	977	4850	2228	19000	1271	6050	1397	13600
Phanerogamae · ·	10055	144500	3712	40100	3551	39800	984	4900	2235	19000	1274	6100	1401	13600

GLOSSARY OF BOTANICAL TERMS

ABORTIVE (*abortivus*). Imperfectly developed.

ACCRESCENT (*accrescens*). Increasing in size with age.

ACCUMBENT (*accumbens*). Placed along the edge, especially of the cotyledons.

ACHENE (*achaenium*). A dry and indehiscent fruit, expecially one with a thin pericarp.

ACUMINATE (*acuminatus*). Narrowed at the top and drawn out into a point.

ACUTE (*acutus*). Sharply pointed, but not drawn out.

ADELPHOUS (*adelphus*). United in bundles, e.g., diadelphous = united in two bundles.

ADHERENT (*adhaerens*). Slightly united to an organ of another kind, usually to a part of another whorl.

ADNATE (*adnatus*). Closely united with an organ of another kind, usually with a part of another whorl. Adnate anthers have their halves attached through their whole length to the filament.

AËRIAL (*aëreus*). Growing above the surface of the earth or water.

AESTIVATION (*aestivatio*). Praefloration, i.e., the arrangement of the perianth-leaves in the bud.

ALBUMEN (*albumen*). The nutritive tissue (endosperm or perisperm) in which the embryo is more or less immersed.

ALTERNATE (*alternus*). Placed between two parts ; or inserted one on each node.

ANDROGYNOUS (*androgynus*). Containing both male and female flowers.

ANDROPHORE (*androphorum*). An elongation of the receptacle below the stamens.

ANNUAL (*annuus*). Terminating its whole cycle of life within one year.

ANNULAR (*annularis*). Ring-shaped.

ANTERIOR (*anticus*). Placed in front ; or turned away from the axis upon which the organ is inserted.

ANTHER (*anthera*). The thickened upper part of the stamen, which encloses the pollen. It usually consists of two halves (cells) containing two pollen-sacs each and opening by a common slit or pore.

APPRESSED (*appressus*). Pressed close.

AREOLE (*areola*). A space marked out on a surface.

ARIL (*arillus*). An expansion of the funicle or the adjoining part of the testa, more or less enveloping the seed.

ASCENDING (*ascendens*). Directed upwards. An ascending stem is more or less prostrate at the base, then erect ; an ascending ovule is attached somewhat above the base.

ASYMMETRICAL (*asymmetricus*). Which cannot be divided into two or more similar parts.

AURICLE (*auriculus*). An earlet, i.e., a small roundish lateral appendage of a leaf or leaf-like organ.

AWN (*arista*). A strong bristle-like appendage.

AXIL (*axilla*). The upper angle between a leaf and the stem from which it springs.

AXILE (*axilis*). Placed in the axis.

AXILLARY (*axillaris*). Placed in the axil of a leaf.

AXIS (*axis*). The line round which an organ is developed ; or the part of the plant on which other parts are attached, especially the stem.

BACCATE (*baccatus*). Berry-like.

BARBED (*glochidiatus*). Beset with hairs or spines directed backwards.

BASIFIXED (*basifixus*). Attached by the bottom.

591

BERRY (*bacca*).   A succulent indehiscent fruit with a thin and soft (membranous, parchment-like, or cartilaginous) endocarp.

BIENNIAL (*biennis*).   Fruiting the second year and then perishing.

BLADE (*lamina*).   The upper expanded part of a leaf or leaf-like organ.

BRACT (*bractea*).   A modified leaf, usually reduced in size, intermediate between the foliage-leaves and the flowers, especially those in the axil of which a flower or branch of inflorescence arises.

BRACTEOLE (*bracteola*).   A bract arising immediately below a flower or on the pedicel.

BULB (*bulbus*).   A usually underground part of the stem of certain plants, which is surrounded by numerous fleshy scales.

CADUCOUS (*caducus*).   Falling off very early.

CALYX (*calyx*).   The outer floral envelope, usually smaller and firmer than the inner and of green colour.

CAMPANULATE (*campanulatus*).   Bell-shaped.

CAPITATE (*capitatus*).   Head-like.

CAPSULE (*capsula*).   A dry dehiscent fruit, especially if formed of several carpels.

CARPEL (*carpellum*).   A modified leaf bearing the female reproductive organs (ovules).

CARUNCLE (*caruncula*).   An outgrowth near the hilum of certain seeds.

CATKIN (*amentum*).   A deciduous spike with a thin rachis and inconspicuous unisexual flowers.

CAULINE (*caulinus*).   Arising along the stem.

CELL (*cellula*).   One of the sack-like bodies of which the tissue of the plants is composed.

CELL (*loculus*).   One of the cavities into which the ovary, the fruit, and the anthers are usually divided.   The number of anther-cells refers to the time after their dehiscence, 2-celled anthers being 4-celled when young.

CENTRIFUGAL (*centrifugus*).   Developing from the centre outwards or from the apex towards the base.

CENTRIPETAL (*centripetus*).   Developing from without towards the centre or from the base towards the apex.

CIRCINNATE (*circinnatus*).   Coiled from the apex downwards.

CIRCUMSCISS (*circumscissus*).   Split circularly around.

CLAW (*unguis*).   The narrow base of perianth-leaves, especially petals.

CLEFT (*fissus, -fidus*).   Divided half-way down.

COHERENT (*cohaerens*).   Slightly united to an organ of the same kind.

COLLATERAL (*collateralis*).   Placed side by side.

COMPOUND LEAF (*folium compositum*).   A leaf formed of leaflets jointed with the rachis and usually falling off separately.

CONDUPLICATE (*conduplicatus*).   Doubled along the midrib.

CONE (*conus*).   A spike-like inflorescence flower or fruit with large bracts or scales usually becoming woody at maturity.

CONFLUENT (*confluens*).   Blended into one.

CONNATE (*connatus*).   United with an organ of the same kind by confluence of the margins or by elongation of the common base.

CONNECTIVE (*connectivum*).   The part of the stamen which connects the anther-halves.

CONNIVENT (*connivens*).   Converging.

CONTORTED (*contortus*).   Imbricate in bud, all segments overlapping on the same side (to the right or the left from the spectator).

CONVOLUTE (*convolutus*).   Rolled up from one margin.

CORDATE (*cordatus*).   Heart-shaped, i.e., with two rounded basal lobes.

CORM (*cormus*).   The thickened base of certain stems, enveloped by some large scales and usually underground.

COROLLA (*corolla*).   The inner floral envelope, usually larger than the outer, of soft texture, and bright coloured.

CORONA (*corona*).   A crown formed by scale- or thread-like appendages of the perianth or the stamens.

CORYMB (*corymbus*). A more or less flat-topped, raceme-like or compound inflorescence.

COTTONY (*tomentosus*). Covered with short matted hairs.

COTYLEDON (*cotyledo*). Seed-leaf, i.e., one of the first leaves of the embryo, which differ from the following.

CRENATE (*crenatus*). With rounded teeth at the margin.

CRUSTACEOUS (*crustaceus*). Crusty, i.e., thin and brittle.

CYME (*cyma*). An inflorescence of the centrifugal (cymose) type, especially when loose and equally-branched.

CYMOSE (*cymosus*). Consisting of a main axis, which ends in a flower, and several stronger lateral axes.

CYSTOLITH (*cystolithus*). Cell-stone, i.e., a hard outgrowth of the cell-wall, appearing as a point or short line on the surface of the leaves of certain plants.

DECIDUOUS (*deciduus*). Falling off after flowering or at the end of the season.

DECUMBENT (*decumbens*). Reclining.

DECURRENT (*decurrens*). Prolonged below the insertion.

DEHISCENT (*dehiscens*). Opening spontaneously when ripe to discharge the contents (seeds or pollen).

DENTATE (*dentatus*). Toothed, i.e., provided with small incisions and projections on the margin.

DESCENDING (*descendens*). Tending downwards ; or attached somewhat below the apex.

DICHOTOMOUS (*dichotomus*). Repeatedly divided in pairs, each branch dividing into two subequal branches.

DIDYMOUS (*didymus*). Bi-globose, i.e., divided into two roundish lobes.

DIDYNAMOUS (*didynamus*). In two pairs of unequal length.

DIGITATE (*digitatus*). Palmately compound.

DIOECIOUS (*dioicus*). Unisexual and the male and female flowers on different plants.

DISC (*discus*). A usually ring-, cushion-, or cup-shaped expansion of the receptacle.

DISSECTED (*dissectus*). Divided to the base, but not jointed with the rachis.

DISSEPIMENT (*septum*). A partition of the interior of the ovary, usually formed by the margins of the carpels. A partition not having that origin is called a false or spurious dissepiment.

DIVARICATE (*divaricatus*). Diverging at an angle approaching 180°.

DORSAL (*dorsalis*). Situated on the back, especially on the midrib of a folded leaf or leaf-like organ ; or turned away from the axis to which the organ in question is attached.

DORSIFIXED (*dorsifixus*). Attached by the back.

DRUPE (*drupa*). Stone-fruit, i.e., a fruit with a hard (bony, woody, or crusty) endocarp called the stone, a succulent, more or less fleshy mesocarp, and a thin (membranous or leathery) epicarp.

ELLIPTICAL (*ellipticus*). About twice as long as broad and narrowed towards both ends.

EMARGINATE (*emarginatus*). With a small, usually apical notch.

EMBRYO (*embryo*). The rudimentary plant formed in the seed.

ENDOCARP (*endocarpium*). The innermost layer of the pericarp.

ENTIRE (*integerrimus*). Without toothing or division.

EPICALYX (*epicalyx*). A whorl of bracts closely surrounding a flower and resembling an outer calyx.

EPICARP (*epicarpium*). The outermost layer of the pericarp.

EPIGYNOUS (*epigynus*). Inserted at the upper edge of a concave receptacle which is united with the ovary.

EPIPHYTE (*epiphyticus*). Growing upon other plants without deriving nourishment from them.

EX- (*ex-*). Without. Exalbuminous = without albumen. Exstipulate = without stipules.

EXOCARP (*exocarpium*). The outermost layer of the pericarp.

EXSERTED (*exsertus*). Projecting beyond the tube of the perianth or corolla.

EXTRORSE (*extrorsus*). Turned outwards.

FALCATE (*falcatus*).   Sickle-shaped.

FASCICLE (*fasciculus*).   A cluster, especially a short and dense cymose inflorescence of distinctly stalked or conspicuous flowers.

FEMALE FLOWER (*flos foemineus*).   A flower containing fertile (ovule-bearing) carpels, but no fertile (pollen-producing) stamens.

FERTILE (*fertilis*).   Capable of producing progeny, especially bearing pollen or ovules which develop into seeds.

FILAMENT (*filamentum*).   The lower narrow part (the stalk) of the stamen.

FILIFORM (*filiformis*).   Thread-shaped, i.e., cylindrical and very slender.

FLEXUOUS (*flexuosus*).   Bent alternately in opposite directions.

FOLIACEOUS (*foliaceus*).   Leaf-like, i.e., having the shape and texture of a foliage-leaf.

FOLIOLE (*foliolum*).   Leaflet, i.e., one of the leaf-like parts of a compound leaf, which are jointed to the rachis.

FOLLICLE (*folliculus*).   A one-celled fruit opening lengthwise (at the ventral suture).

FORKED (*furcatus*).   Divided into two subequal branches.

FREE (*liber*).   Not united, not even at the base.

FUNICLE (*funiculus*).   The stalk of the ovule.

GAMO- (*gamo-*).   With the parts more or less united, e.g., gamopetalous = with the petals united below into a ring, cup, or tube.

GLABROUS (*glaber*).   Without hairs.

GLAND (*glans*).   A thick, usually roundish outgrowth, generally secreting a liquid.

GLANDULAR (*glandulosus*).   Bearing a gland or glands.

GLOMERULE (*glomerulus*).   A short and dense cymose inflorescence of subsessile inconspicuous flowers.

GLUME (*gluma*).   A chaffy bract, especially in the inflorescence of grasses.

GYNOPHORE (*gynophorum*).   An elongation of the receptacle below the carpels.

HASTATE (*hastatus*).   Halbard-shaped, i.e., with two acute basal lobes turned outwards.

HEAD (*capitulum*).   A centripetal inflorescence with a short and usually thick axis and sessile or nearly sessile flowers.

HERMAPHRODITE (*hermaphroditus*).   Bisexual, i.e., containing both kinds of sexual organs (stamens and carpels) in complete development.

HILUM (*hilus*).   The point where the ovule or the seed is attached to the funicle or the placenta.

HIRSUTE (*hirsutus*).   Densely covered with erect, rather short and stiff hairs.

HISPID (*hispidus*).   Beset with long stiff hairs.

HYALINE (*hyalinus*).   Membranous and translucent.

HYPOGYNOUS (*hypogynus*).   Inserted at the base of the ovary or below it, upon a small and flat or an elevated receptacle.

IMBRICATE (*imbricatus*).   Overlapping at the edges, as the tiles of a roof, especially in the bud.

IMPARIPINNATE (*imparipinnatus*).   Unequally pinnate, i.e., pinnate with a terminal leaflet.

INCLUDED (*inclusus*).   Concealed within the tube of the perianth or corolla.

INCUMBENT (*incumbens*).   Placed upon the back, especially of the cotyledons.

INDEHISCENT (*indehiscens*).   Remaining closed at maturity.

INDUPLICATE (*induplicatus*).   Doubled along the midrib, with the margins turned inwards.

INFERIOR OVARY (*ovarium inferum*).   An ovary adnate to a concave receptacle or to the tube of the perianth or calyx.

INFLORESCENCE (*inflorescentia*).   The flowering part of a branch and the arrangement of the flowers upon it.   The flower-clusters constituting together a compound inflorescence are termed partial inflorescences.

INTRORSE (*introrsus*).   Turned inwards.

INVERTED OVULE (*ovulum anatropum*).   An ovule with the micropyle next to the hilum.

INVOLUCEL (*involucellum*).   The involucre of a partial inflorescence.

INVOLUCRE (*involucrum*).   A group of bracts surrounding an inflorescence.

INVOLUTE (*involutus*).   Rolled inward from the margins towards the midrib.

IRREGULAR FLOWER (*flos irregularis*).   A flower with unequally shaped or disposed perianth-leaves.

JOINTED (*articulatus*).   Divided into portions which subsequently separate ; or separating at the point of attachment.

LACINIATE (*laciniatus*).   Lacerated, i.e., slit into narrow and irregular segments.

LANCEOLATE (*lanceolatus*).   About 3—6 times as long as broad and ending in an angle or point.

LEGUME (*legumen*).   A one-celled fruit opening by two valves.

LIGULATE (*ligulatus*).   Strap-shaped, i.e., produced on one side into a long and narrow limb.

LIGULE (*ligula*).   A strap-shaped body, especially the scale-like appendage on the inner side of certain leaves, usually between the sheath and the blade.

LIMB (*limbus*).   The upper, more or less expanded part of a perianth.

LINEAR (*linearis*).   Very narrow (many times as long as broad) with almost parallel edges.

LIP (*labium*).   A part of a perianth formed of several united segments or of one large segment which is separated from the rest.

LOBE (*lobus*).   Division of a leaf or a perianth, especially when short.

LOBED (*lobatus*).   Shortly divided, the incisions not reaching to the middle.

LOCULICIDAL (*loculicidus*).   Opening along the median line of the outer wall of the ovary- or fruit-cells (along the dorsal suture of the carpels).

LYRATE (*lyratus*).   Lyre-shaped, i.e., pinnately divided with a large and rounded terminal lobe and small lateral ones.

MALE FLOWER (*flos masculus*).   A flower containing fertile (pollen-producing) stamens, but no fertile carpels.

MEDIAN (*medianus*).   Placed in the middle-line of a bilateral organ.

MERICARP (*mericarpium*).   Partial fruit, i.e., one of the parts into which a schizocarp separates.

MEROUS (*merus*).   With the parts of the flower consisting of a certain number of divisions or leaves, e.g., dimerous = with the parts in twos.

MESOCARP (*mesocarpium*).   The intermediate layer of the pericarp.

MICROPYLE (*micropyle*).   The aperture in the coats of the ovule.

MONOECIOUS (*monoicus*).   Unisexual and the flowers of both sexes on the same plant.

MUCRONATE (*mucronatus*).   Ending in a short bristle-like point (mucro).

MUTICOUS (*muticus*).   Without awns or spines.

NAKED (*nudus*).   Not enveloped by a perianth or by carpels.

NERVE (*nervus*).   A vascular bundle in a leaf or leaf-like organ, usually appearing as a dark or translucent line or a ridge projecting on the under surface.

NET-VEINED (*reticulatim venosus*).   With the lateral nerves irregularly connected by a network of small veins.

NEUTER (*neuter*).   Without perfect sexual organs.

NODE (*nodus*).   The usually knot-like part of the stem, where a leaf or a whorl of leaves are inserted.

NUT (*nux*).   A dry and indehiscent fruit, especially one with a thick and hard rind.

OB- (*ob-*).   Reversedly.   Thus obcordate or obovate = cordate or ovate, the upper part the broader.

OBLONG (*oblongus*).   About 3—6 times as long as broad and rounded at the top.

OBTUSE (*obtusus*).   Blunt, i.e., narrowed, but not pointed at the apex.

OPEN AESTIVATION (*aestivatio aperta*).   A form of aestivation in which the margins of the perianth-leaves do not touch one another.

OPPOSITE (*oppositus*).   Set against in pairs at the same level ; or placed one before another.

OVAL (*ovalis*).   About twice as long as broad and rounded at the top.

OVARY (*ovarium*). The lower part of the pistil, which encloses the ovules.

OVATE (*ovatus*). Shaped like the longitudinal section of an egg, i.e., oval and narrowed towards the top.

OVOID (*ovoideus*). Egg-shaped.

OVULE (*ovulum*). The grain-like body which contains the female reproductive cells and developes into the seed after fertilization.

PALMATE (*palmatus*). With the divisions or branches springing from one point.

PANICLE (*panicula*). A repeatedly branched inflorescence of more or less pyramidal or ovoid form.

PAPILLA (*papilla*). A soft superficial protuberance.

PARALLELNERVED (*parallelinervius*). With the principal nerves nearly parallel and connected almost at right angles by equally subparallel side-nerves.

PARASITE (*planta parasitica*). A plant growing upon an other plant and feeding from it.

PARIETAL (*parietalis*). Attached to the wall of the ovary, usually at the sutures of the carpels.

PARIPINNATE (*paripinnatus*). Equally or abruptly pinnate, i.e., pinnate without a terminal leaflet.

PARTED (*partitus*). Divided nearly to the base.

PEDATE (*pedatus*). With the larger branches or divisions springing from the lowest lateral ones.

PEDICEL (*pedicellus*). The stalk of a flower.

PEDUNCLE (*pedunculus*). The stalk of an inflorescence.

PELTATE (*peltatus*). Shield-shaped, i.e., roundish and attached by the middle of the under surface.

PENICILLATE (*penicillatus*). Shaped like a tuft of hairs or a painter's brush.

PENNINERVED (*penninervius*). With pinnate nervation.

PERENNIAL (*perennis*). Not perishing after maturity, the underground part of the stem at least remaining alive.

PERIANTH (*perianthium*). Floral envelope, i.e., the aggregate of the modified leaves surrounding the stamens and carpels and forming part of the flower.

PERICARP (*pericarpium*). The wall of the fruit enclosing the seeds.

PERIGYNOUS (*perigynus*). Inserted upon the margin of a more or less concave receptacle which is free from the ovary, at some distance from and usually higher than the ovary.

PERSISTENT (*persistens*). Remaining on the plant at the time of maturity.

PETAL (*petalum*). One of the inner perianth-leaves, usually differing from the outer in the larger size, the softer texture, and the bright colour.

PETALOID (*petaloideus*). Petal- or corolla-like.

PETIOLE (*petiolus*). The foot-stalk of a leaf.

PHYLLODE (*phyllodium*). A broadened, leaf-like branch.

PINNA (*pinna*). One of the lateral branches or divisions of a pinnate organ.

PINNATE (*pinnatus*). With the divisions, leaflets, or branches arranged along each side of the midrib or rachis. Unequally pinnate leaves have a terminal leaflet, equally (abruptly) pinnate ones have none.

PISTIL (*pistillum*). The aggregate of the carpels of a flower

PLACENTA (*placenta*). The part of the ovary or fruit which bears the ovules or seeds.

PLICATE (*plicatus*). Folded along the ribs.

PLUMULE (*plumula*). The upper part of the embryo (above the cotyledons).

POLLEN (*pollen*). The fertilizing cells produced in the anthers.

POLYGAMOUS (*polygamus*). Partly hermaphrodite and partly unisexual.

POSTERIOR (*posticus*). Directed towards the axis upon which the organ in question is inserted.

PRAEFLORATION (*praefloratio*). The arrangement of the perianth-leaves in the bud.

PRAEFOLIATION (*praefoliatio*). The mode in which a foliage-leaf is disposed before its expansion.

PROCUMBENT (*procumbens*). Spreading along the ground.

QUINCUNCIAL (*quincuncialis*). Imbricate in bud, so that one perianth-leaf is overlapped on one side only, the others on either or neither side.

RACEME (*racemus*). A centripetal (racemose) inflorescence with an elongated axis and distinctly stalked flowers.

RACEMOSE (*racemosus, botryosus*). Consisting of a main axis not ending in a flower and a number of weaker lateral axes.

RACHIS (*rhachis*). The main axis of an inflorescence or of a compound leaf.

RADIATING (*radians*). Spreading all round ; or bearing larger flowers or larger perianth-leaves at the circumference than in the centre.

RADICAL (*radicalis*). Arising from the base of the stem, apparently from the root.

RADICLE (*radicula*). The lower part of the embryo (below the cotyledons).

RAPHE (*raphe*). A cord of tissue forming a prolongation of the funicle along the coats of the ovule.

RECEPTACLE (*receptaculum*). The extremity of the flower-stalk bearing the floral envelopes and the sexual organs ; or the enlarged end of a branch upon which the flowers are seated.

REDUPLICATE (*reduplicatus*). Doubled along the midrib with the margins turned outwards.

REFLEXED (*reflexus*). Bent back.

REGULAR (*regularis*). With all parts of the same kind, especially all perianth leaves, equal in shape and arrangement.

RENIFORM (*reniformis*). Kidney-shaped.

REVOLUTE (*revolutus*). Rolled backwards from the margins.

RIB (*costa*). A strong, more or less projecting nerve.

ROOT-STOCK (*rhizoma*). The root-like, underground or prostrate lowest part of the stem of certain plants.

ROTATE (*rotatus*). Wheel-shaped, i.e., with a very short tube and a spreading limb.

RUDIMENTARY (*rudimentarius*). Very imperfectly developed.

RUMINATE (*ruminatus*). Marked with irregular fissures.

RUNCINATE (*runcinatus*). Pinnately cleft with pointed recurved lobes.

SACCATE (*saccatus*). Provided with a pouch-shaped appendage.

SAGITTATE (*sagittatus*). Arrow-shaped, i.e., with two acute basal lobes directed downwards.

SALVER-SHAPED (*hypocraterimorphus*). With a long and narrow tube and a spreading limb.

SAPROPHYTE (*saprophytum*). A plant living upon decaying organic matter.

SCALE (*squama*). A reduced leaf usually destitute of green colour, or a similar outgrowth of the skin of a plant.

SCAPE (*scapus*). A leafless stalk of an inflorescence rising from the ground.

SCARIOUS (*scariosus*). Dry and membranous.

SCHIZOCARP (*schizocarpium, fructus in coccos secedens*). A fruit separating into several usually nut-like mericarps.

SCORPIOID (*scorpioideus*). One-sided and coiled at the top.

SEGMENT (*segmentum*). A division of a deeply divided leaf, or a division of the perianth, especially when the latter is deeply divided.

SEPAL (*sepalum*). An outer perianth-leaf, usually small, green, and of a firm texture.

SEPALOID (*sepaloideus*). Sepal- or calyx-like.

SEPTATE (*septatus*). Chambered, i.e., divided into cells by dissepiments.

SEPTICIDAL (*septicidus*). Opening at the dissepiments or placentas.

SEPTIFRAGAL (*septifragus*). Opening so that the valves of the fruit break away from the dissepiments.

SERRATE (*serratus*). Cut at the margin into sharp teeth direct towards the apex.

SESSILE (*sessilis*). Without a stalk.

SHEATH (*vagina*). The dilated base of certain leaves.

SIMPLE (*simplex*). Without branches ; or without segments jointed to the rachis.

SMOOTH (*laevis*). With an even surface (without protuberances).

SPADIX (*spadix*). A spike with a thick axis and inconspicuous flowers, usually enveloped by a spathe.

SPATHE (*spatha*). A large bract more or less enveloping a flower or inflorescence.

SPATULATE (*spathulatus*). More or less rounded above and tapering towards the base.

SPIKE (*spica*). A centripetal (racemose) inflorescence with an elongated axis and sessile or nearly sessile flowers.

SPIKELET (*spicula*). A spike-like partial inflorescence.

STAMEN (*stamen*). A modified leaf bearing the male reproductive cells (the pollen)

STAMINODE (*staminodium*). A barren stamen (without anthers or with incompletely developed anthers).

STERILE (*sterilis*). Barren, i.e., without well developed ovules or pollen.

STIGMA (*stigma*). The uppermost, papillose part of the pistil, which receives the pollen.

STIPEL (*stipella*). A stipule at the base of a leaflet of a compound leaf.

STIPULE (*stipula*). A leaf-or scale-like appendage of the leaf-base.

STRIATE (*striatus*). Marked with longitudinal lines.

STROPHIOLE (*strophiolus*). Caruncle, i.e., an outgrowth near the hilum of certain seeds.

STYLE (*stylus*). The narrowed part of the pistil, intermediate between the ovary and the stigma.

SUB- (*sub-*). Under ; or almost, somewhat ; e.g., subsessile = almost sessile.

SUBTEND ((*subtendere*). Extend under ; especially : bear in its axil.

SUBULATE (*subulatus*). Awl-shaped, i.e., very narrow and pointed.

SUFFRUTICOSE (*suffruticosus*). Woody at the base, herbaceous above.

SUPERIOR OVARY (*ovarium superum*). An ovary free from the receptacle and the perianth.

SUTURE (*sutura*). Line of union, especially of the margins of carpels.

SYMMETRICAL (*symmetricus*). Divisible by one or several planes into two or more similar parts.

SYMPETALOUS (*sympetalus, gamopetalus*). With the petals more or less united.

TERETE (*teres*). Cylindrical and circular in transverse section.

TERNATE (*ternatus*). In threes ; especially with 3 leaflets or divisions.

TESTA (*testa*). The outer coat of the seed.

THROAT (*faux*). The mouth of the perianth-tube.

TOMENTOSE (*tomentosus*). Cottony, i.e., covered with short, soft, matted hairs.

TOOTHED (*dentatus*). Provided with short marginal incisions, especially when they are sharp and turned outwards.

TRIQUETROUS (*triqueter*). Three-edged (with 3 salient angles).

TRUNCATE (*truncatus*). Terminating abruptly as though cut off at the end

TUBE (*tubus*). A hollow, more or less elongated body, especially the lower undivided and more or less narrowed part of the perianth, or a concave receptacle bearing the perianth at the margin.

TUBER (*tuber*). A short and thick, more or less fleshy underground part of a stem, not surrounded by scales, or a similar root.

TUBERCLE (*tuberculum*). A wart-like swelling on the surface of an organ

UMBEL (*umbella*). A centripetal (racemose) inflorescence with a very short axis and stalked flowers arising apparently all from the same point.

UMBONATE (*umbonatus*). Bearing a boss in the centre of the surface

UNARMED (*inermis*). Without spines or bristles.

UNDERSHRUB (*suffrutex*). A plant woody in the lower part of the above-ground stem, herbaceous towards the top.

UNIFOLIOLATE (*unfoliolatus*). With a single leaflet, which is jointed to the leaf-stalk.

UNISEXUAL (*unisexualis*). Having only the organs of one sex completely developed ; or containing the flowers of one sex only.

URCEOLATE (*urceolatus*). Urn- or pitcher-shaped, i.e., with an inflated tube contracted at the mouth.

UTRICLE (*utriculus*). A bladder-shaped indehiscent or irregularly bursting fruit.

VALVATE (*valvatus*).   With the margins meeting in the bud without overlapping.

VASCULAR BUNDLES (*fasciae vasculares*).   Fibre-like bundles of vessels (confluent cells).

VEIN (*vena*).   A faint nerve.

VENTRAL (*ventralis*).   Placed at or directed towards the inner side of the carpel.

VENTRICOSE (*ventricosus*).   Swelling on one side.

VERNATION (*vernatio*).   Praefoliation, i.e., the disposition of a leaf in the bud.

VERSATILE (*versatilis*).   Attached by a point and turning freely on its support.

WINGED (*alatus*).   With a much projecting, thin and flat appendage.

WHORL (*verticillus*).   A group of similar organs arranged in a circle round an axis.

WHORLED (*verticillatus*).   Arranged in whorls of 3 or more parts.

ABBREVIATIONS OF AUTHORS' NAMES

Adans. ... Adanson
Afz....... Afzelius
Ait. ..... Aiton
All. ..... Allioni
Anders. .. Anderson
Andrz. ... Andrzeiowski
Ant. ..... Antoine
Arn. ..... Arnott
Aubl. .... Aublet

Baill. .... Baillon
Bak. ..... Baker
Balf. .... Balfour
Barckh. .. Barckhausen
Bartl. .... Bartling
Battand. . Battandier
Baumg. .. Baumgarten
Beauv. ... Palisot de Beau-
vois
Becc. .... Beccari
Benn. .... Bennett
Benth. ... Bentham
Berg. .... Berger
Bernh. ... Bernhardi
Berth..... Berthelot
Bertol. ... Bertoloni
Bisch. ... Bischoff
Bocq. .... Bocquillon
Boeck. ... Boeckeler
Boiss. .... Boissier
Boiv. .... Boivin
Boj. ..... Bojer
Bonpl. ... Bonpland
Br. ..... Brown, Browne
Briq. .... Briquet
Brongn. .. Brongniart
Brot...... Brotero
Bur. ..... Bureau
Burch. ... Burchell
Burm..... Burmann

Cambess. . Cambessèdes
Cass. .... Cassini
Cav. ..... Cavanilles
Celak. ... Celakovsky
Cerv...... Cervantes
Cham..... Chamisso
Chev. .... Chevalier

Chiov..... Chiovenda
Cogn. .... Cogniaux
Colebr. ... Colebrook
Comm. ... Commerson
Cord. .... Cordemoy
Coss. .... Cosson
Cost. .... Costantin
Coult. ... Coulter
Cuss. .... Cusson
Cyr. ..... Cyrillo

Dalech.... Dalechamps
Dalz...... Dalzell
Decne. ... Decaisne
DC. ..... De Candolle
Del....... Delile
Dennst. .. Dennstedt
De Not. .. De Notaris
Desf. .... Desfontaines
Desv. .... Desvaux
De Wild... De Wildeman
Didr...... Didrichsen
Dill. ..... Dillen
Dumort... Dumortier
Dun. .... Dunal
Dur. ..... Durand
Durazz. .. Durazzini
Duv. .... Duval

Eckl...... Ecklon
Ehrenb. .. Ehrenberg
Ehrh. .... Ehrhart
Endl. .... Endlicher
Engelm. .. Engelmann
Engl. .... Engler

f. (or fil.). filius (son)
Fisch. .... Fischer
Forsk..... Forskal
Forst. ... Forster
Foug. .... Fougeraux
Franch. .. Franchet
Frapp. ... Frappier
Fres. .... Fresenius

Gaertn.... Gaertner
Gall. ..... Gallaud
Gaud. ... Gaudin
Gaudich. . Gaudichaud

Gled. .... Gleditsch
Gmel. .... Gmelin
Godr. .... Godron
Grah. .... Graham
Gren. .... Grenier
Griff...... Griffith
Griseb. ... Grisebach
Gronov. .. Gronovius
Guill. .... Guillemin

Hack. ... Hackel
Hamilt. .. Hamilton
Harv. .... Harvey
Haw. .... Haworth
H. B. & K. Humboldt, Bon-
pland, & Kunth
Heist. ... Heister
Heldr..... Heldreich
Hemsl. ... Hemsley
Herb. .... Herbert
Hildebr... Hildebrand
Hochst. .. Hochstetter
Hoffm. ... Hoffmann
Hoffmsg. . Hoffmannsegg
Hook. ... Hooker
Horan. ... Horaninow
Houst. ... Houstoun
Humb. ... Humboldt

Jacks. ... Jackson
Jacq. .... Jacquin
Jaub. .... Jaubert
Jum. .... Jumelle
Juss. .... Jussieu

Kam. ... Kamienski
Kit....... Kitaibel
Koel. .... Koeler
Koen. ... Koenig
Koern. ... Koernicke
Korth. ... Korthals
Kraenzl... Kraenzlin
Ktze. .... Kuntze

Labill. ... Labillardière
Lag. ..... Lagasca
Lam..... Lamarck
Ledeb. ... Ledebour
Lehm..... Lehmann

600

Leschen... Leschenault
Less. .... Lessing
L'Hér. ... L'Héritier
Licht..... Lichtenstein
Lindb. ... Lindberg
Lindl. ... Lindley
L. .... Linné
Loefl. .... Loefling
Lopr. .... Lopriore
Loud. .... Loudon
Lour. .... Loureiro

Marcgr. .. Marcgraf
M. Bieb... Marschall von Bieberstein
Marsh. ... Marshal
Mart. .... Martius
Mast. .... Masters
Med. ..... Medikus
Meissn.... Meissner
Mey. .... Meyer
Mich. .... Micheli
Michx. ... Michaux
Mill. ..... Miller
Miq. ..... Miquel
Moehr. ... Moehring
Moq. .... Moquin-Tandon
Moris..... Morison
Muell..... Mueller
Muell. Arg. Mueller Argovensis

Naud. ... Naudin
Neck. .... Necker
Nied. .... Niedenzu
Nor. ..... Noronha
Nutt. .... Nuttall

Oerst..... Oersted
Oliv...... Oliver
Op. ...... Opiz

P. Beauv.. Palisot de Beauvois
Pall. ..... Pallas
Parl. .... Parlatore
Pauq. .... Pauquy

Pav. ..... Pavon
Perr. .... Perrotet
Pers. .... Persoon
Peyr. .... Peyritsch
Pfitz. .... Pfitzer
Pilg. ..... Pilger
Planch. .. Planchon
Plum. ... Plumier
Poepp. ... Poeppig
Pourr..... Pourret

Radlk. ... Radlkofer
Raf. ..... Rafinesque
Ram. .... Ramond
Reichb. .. Reichenbach
Rich. .... Richard
Ridl. .... Ridley
Roehl. ... Roehling
Roem. ... Roemer
Rohrb. ... Rohrbach
Rottb. ... Rottboell
Roxb. ... Roxburgh
Ruhl. .... Ruhland
Rumph. .. Rumphius
Rupr. .... Ruprecht

Salisb. ... Salisbury
Schimp. .. Schimper
Schlecht. . Schlechter
Schlechtd. Schlechtendal
Schleid. .. Schleiden
Schrad.... Schrader
Schreb. .. Schreber
Schult. ... Schultes
Schum. ... Schumann
Schweinf.. Schweinfurt
Scop. .... Scopoli
Seem. .... Seemann
Soland.... Solander
Sond. .... Sonder
Sonn. .... Sonnerat
Sparm.... Sparmann
Spenn. ... Spenner
Spreng.... Sprengel
Steinh.... Steinheil
Steud..... Steudel

Stev. .... Steven
St. Hil. .. St. Hilaire

Taub. .... Taubert
Targ. Tozz. Targioni-Tozzetti
Tausch. .. Tauscher
Ten. ..... Tenore
Thonn.... Thonning
Thou. .... Du Petit-Thouars
Thunb.... Thunberg
Thwait. .. Thwaites
Torr. .... Torrey
Tourn. ... Tournefort
Trin. .... Trinius
Tul....... Tulasne
Turcz..... Turczaninow

Urb. ..... Urban

Vaill...... Vaillant
Vand. .... Vandelli
Van Tiegh. Van Tieghem
Vell. ..... Velley
Vent. .... Ventenat
Vill. ..... Villars
Vis. ..... Visiani
Vog. ..... Vogel
Volk. .... Volkens

Wahlenb.. Wahlenberg
Waldst. .. Waldstein
Wall. .... Wallich
Walt. .... Walter
Warb. ... Warburg
Warm. ... Warming
Wedd. ... Weddell
Welw. ... Welwitsch
Wendl.... Wendland
Wettst.... Wettstein
Wikst. ... Wikstroem
Willd. ... Willdenow
Willk. ... Willkomm
Winckl. .. Winckler
Wuert. ... Wuertemberg

Zeyh. .... Zeyher
Zucc. .... Zuccarini

LIST OF POPULAR NAMES

OF AFRICAN PLANTS AND THEIR PRODUCTS

African ammoniacum — Ferula.
African mahogany — Khaya.
African sandal-wood — Osyris.
African teak — Oldfieldia.
African tulip-tree — Spathodea.
Akee — Blighia.
Alder — Alnus.
Alkanet — Anchusa.
Allseed — Radiola.
Allspice — Pimenta.
Almond — Prunus.
Ambatch — Aeschynomene.
Anise — Pimpinella.
Apple — Pirus.
Apricot — Prunus.
Arnatto — Bixa.
Arrow-root — Maranta, Tacca.
Artichoke — Cynara.
Ash — Fraxinus.
Avens — Geum.
Avocado-pear — Persea.

Balata — Mimusops.
Balm — Melissa.
Balsam — Impatiens.
Bamboo — Bambusa (and allies), Raphia.
Banana — Musa.
Baobab — Adansonia.
Barley — Hordeum.
Basil — Ocimum.
Bead-tree — Melia.
Bean — Phaseolus, Vicia.
Beef-wood — Casuarina, Mimusops.
Bent-grass — Agrostis.
Betel-palm — Areca.
Bindweed — Convolvulus.
Bird's-foot — Ornithopus.
Bitter cress — Cardamine.
Black mustard — Brassica.
Bladderwort — Utricularia.
Blood-plum — Haematostaphis.
Borage — Borrago.
Bottle-gourd — Lagenaria.
Box — Buxus.

Bowstring-hemp — Sansevieria.
Bramble — Rubus.
Breadfruit — Artocarpus.
Broomrape — Orobanche.
Buckthorn — Rhamnus.
Buckwheat — Fagopyrum.
Bugle — Ajuga.
Bugloss — Echium.
Burdock — Arctium.
Bur-reed — Sparganium.

Cabbage — Brassica.
Calabar-bean — Physostigma.
Calla — Zantedeschia.
Calumba-root — Iatrorrhiza.
Camellia — Thea.
Camomile — Anthemis, Matricaria.
Camphor — Blumea, Cinnamomum.
Cam-wood — Baphia.
Canary-seed — Phalaris.
Candlenut — Aleurites.
Candytuft — Iberis.
Cane — Calamus (and allies).
Caper — Capparis.
Caraway — Carum.
Cardamom — Elettaria.
Carob — Ceratonia.
Carrot — Daucus.
Cashew — Anacardium.
Cassava — Manihot.
Castor-oil — Ricinus.
Cayenne-pepper — Capsicum.
Ceara-rubber — Manihot.
Cedar — Cedrus.
Celandine — Chelidonium.
Celery — Apium.
Cherry — Prunus.
Chervil — Anthriscus.
Chestnut — Castanea.
Chick-pea — Cicer.
Chicory — Cichorium.
Chillies — Capsicum.
Chinese grasscloth-plant — Boehmeria
Clover — Trifolium.

Cloves — Jambosa.
Cock's foot — Dactylis.
Cocoa-plum — Chrysobalanus.
Coconut — Cocos.
Colt's foot — Tussilago.
Columbine — Aquilegia.
Comfrey — Symphytum.
Copal — Copaifera, Cynometra, Trachylobium.
Coracan — Eleusine.
Cork — Quercus.
Corn-cockle — Agrostemma.
Corn-salad — Valerianella.
Cotton — Gossypium.
Cotton-grass — Eriophorum.
Coutch-grass — Agropyrum.
Crab's eye — Abrus.
Cranes's bill — Geranium.
Crawberry — Empetrum.
Cucumber — Cucumis.
Cudweed — Gnaphalium.
Custard-apple — Anona.
Cypress — Cupressus.

Daisy — Bellis.
Dandelion — Taraxacum.
Darnel — Lolium.
Date-palm — Phoenix.
Date-plum — Diospyros.
Dattock — Detarium.
Day-lily — Hemerocallis
Dead-nettle — Lamium.
Dika — Irvingia.
Dill — Anethum.
Dinde — Colocasia.
Dock — Rumex.
Dodder — Cuscuta.
Dog's tail — Cynosurus.
Dog's tooth — Cynodon.
Double coconut — Lodoicea.
Dragons blood — Dracaena.
Duchn — Pennisetum.
Duckweed — Lemna.
Dum-palm — Hyphaene.
Dwale — Atropa.
Dwarf-palm — Chamaerops.

Ebony — Dalbergia, Diospyros, Euclea.
Egg-plant— Solanum.
Elder — Sambucus.
Elemi — Canarium.
Elm — Ulmus.
Esparto-grass — Ampelodesmos, Lygeum, Stipa.
Evening-primrose — Oenothera.

Everlasting — Helichrysum.
Eyebright — Euphrasia.

False bamboo — Raphia.
Feathergrass — Stipa.
Fennel — Foeniculum.
Fescue — Festuca.
Fig — Ficus.
Fir — Abies.
Flame-tree — Poinciana.
Flax — Linum.
Flowering rush — Butomus.
Fool's parsley — Aethusa.
Forget-me-not — Myosotis, Omphalodes.
Foxglove — Digitalis.
Foxtail — Alopecurus.
Frankincense — Boswellia.
Frogbit — Hydrocharis.
Fumitory — Fumaria.
Fundi — Paspalum.
Furze — Ulex.

Gambodge — Garcinia.
Garden-cress — Lepidium.
Garlic — Allium.
Germander — Teucrium.
Ginger — Zingiber.
Globe-thistle — Echinops.
Goldenrod — Solidago.
Gooseberry — Ribes.
Goosefoot — Chenopodium.
Grains of Paradise — Aframomum.
Grape-vine — Vitis.
Grasscloth-plant — Boehmeria.
Grasses — Gramineae.
Grasswrack — Zostera.
Gromwell — Lithospermum.
Groundnut — Arachis.
Guava — Psidium.
Guelder-rose — Viburnum.
Guinea-corn — Andropogon.
Guinea-pepper — Xylopia.
Gum-lac — Aleurites, Anona, Croton, Ficus, Zizyphus.
Guttapercha — Palaquium, Payena.

Hare's tail — Lagurus.
Hawkweed — Hieracium.
Hawthorn — Mespilus.
Hazel — Corylus.
Heartseed — Cardiospermum.
Heath — Erica.
Hemlock — Conium.
Hemp — Cannabis.
Henbane — Hyoscyamus.

Henna — Lawsonia.
Holly — Ilex.
Holygrass — Hierochloe.
Honeysuckle — Lonicera.
Hop — Humulus.
Horehound — Marrubium.
Horseradish-tree — Moringa.
Hound's tongue — Cynoglossum.
Houseleek — Sempervivum.

Indian corn — Zea.
Indian cress — Tropaeolum.
Indian plum — Flacourtia.
Indian shot — Canna.
Indigo — Indigofera.
Ireh — Funtumia.
Iron-wood — Acacia, Argania, Casuarina,
    Sideroxylon, Stadmannia.
Ivy — Hedera.

Jerusalem-artichoke — Helianthus.
Jessamine — Jasminum.
Job's tears — Coix.
Jujube — Zizyphus.
Jute — Corchorus.

Kino — Eucalyptus, Pterocarpus.

Ladanum — Cistus.
Lady's mantle — Alchimilla.
Lagos-rubber — Funtumia.
Larkspur — Delphinium.
Lattice-leaf — Aponogeton.
Laurustinus — Viburnum.
Lavender — Lavandula.
Leek — Allium.
Lemongrass — Andropogon.
Lentil — Lens.
Lettuce — Lattuca.
Ling — Calluna.
Liquorice — Glycyrrhiza.
Logwood — Haematoxylon.
Longan — Euphoria.
Loquat — Eriobotrya.
Lousewort — Pedicularis.
Lucern — Medicago.
Lymegrass — Elymus.

Mace — Myristica.
Madder — Rubia.
Mahogany — Khaya.
Maize — Zea.
Mallow — Malva.
Mandioc — Manihot.
Mandrake — Mandragora.
Mango — Mangifera.

Mangrove — Rhizophora.
Manila-hemp — Musa.
Manna — Alhagi, Astragalus, Cassia.
Maple — Acer.
Maram — Ammophila.
Marigold — Calendula.
Marjoram — Majorana.
Mastic — Pistacia.
Matgrass — Nardus.
Medlar — Mespilus.
Melon — Cucumis.
Mignonette — Reseda.
Milkwort — Polygala.
Millet — Panicum.
Mint — Mentha.
Mistletoe — Viscum.
Mousetail — Myosurus.
Mulberry — Morus.
Mullein — Verbascum.
Mustard — Brassica, Sinapis.
Myrrh — Commiphora.

Nettle — Urtica.
Nettle-tree — Celtis.
New Zealand flax — Phormium.
New Zealand spinach — Tetragonia.
Nitgrass — Gastridium.
Nitrebush — Nitraria.
Nutmeg — Myristica.

Oak—Quercus.
Oat — Avena.
Oil-palm — Elaeis.
Oleander — Nerium.
Oleaster — Elaeagnus.
Olive — Olea.
Onion — Allium.
Opium — Papaver.
Orange —Citrus.
Orris-root — Iris.
Ovala — Pentaclethra.

Palmiet — Prionium.
Palmyra-palm — Borassus.
Panama-rubber — Castilloa.
Pansy — Viola.
Papaw-tree — Carica.
Paper-mulberry — Broussonetia
Para-rubber — Hevea.
Parsley — Petroselinum.
Parsnip — Pastinaca.
Passion-flower — Passiflora.
Pea — Pisum.
Peach — Prunus.
Pear — Pirus.
Pearlwort— Sagina.

Pellitory — Parietaria.
Pennycress — Thlaspi.
Pepper — Capsicum, Piper.
Periwinkle — Vinca.
Persian lilac — Melia.
Persian manna — Alhagi.
Piassava — Borassus, Dictyosperma, Raphia.
Pigeon-pea — Cajanus.
Pimpernel — Anagallis.
Pine-apple — Ananas.
Pink — Dianthus.
Pistachio-nut — Pistacia.
Pitcher-plant — Nepenthes.
Plane — Platanus.
Plantain — Musa, Plantago.
Plum — Prunus.
Poke — Phytolacca.
Pomegranate — Punica.
Pondweed — Potamogeton.
Poplar — Populus.
Poppy — Papaver.
Potato — Ipomoea, Solanum.
Prickly pear — Opuntia.
Primrose — Primula.
Privet — Ligustrum.
Pumpkin — Cucurbita.
Purslane—Portulaca.

Quaking-grass — Briza.
Quince — Cydonia.
Quinine — Cinchona.
Quitch-grass — Agropyrum.

Radish — Rhaphanus.
Rambutan — Nephelium.
Ramie — Boehmeria.
Ramtil-oil — Guizotia.
Rapeseed — Brassica.
Rattan-palm — Calamus.
Ray-grass — Lolium.
Reed — Arundo, Phragmites.
Reedmace — Typha.
Rice — Oryza.
Rock-cress — Arabis.
Rock-rose — Cistus, Helianthemum.
Rose of Jericho — Anastatica, Odontospermum.
Rose-wood — Calophyllum, Pterocarpus, Thespesia.
Rosmary — Rosmarinus.
Rubber — Various Apocynaceae and Asclepiadaceae, Ficus, Manihot.
Rue — Ruta.
Rush — Juncus.

Rye — Secale.
Safflower — Carthamus.
Saffron — Crocus.
Safu — Pachylobus.
Sage — Salvia.
Sago — Cycas.
Sainfoin — Onobrychis.
Salep — Orchis (and allies).
Salsify — Tragopogon.
Saltwort — Salsola.
Samphire — Crithmum.
Sandal-wood — Pterocarpus, Osyris.
Sandarac — Callitris.
Sandbox-tree — Hura.
Sandwort — Arenaria.
Sapodilla-plum — Achras.
Sassy-tree — Erythrophloeum.
Savory — Satureia.
Sawwort — Serratula.
Screw-pine — Pandanus.
Scull-cap — Scutellaria.
Sedges — Cyperaceae.
Senegal-ebony — Dalbergia.
Senna-leaves — Cassia.
Shea-butter — Butyrospermum.
Shellac — Anona, Croton, Ficus, Zizyphus.
Shepherd's purse — Capsella.
Silver-fir — Abies.
Silver-tree — Leucadendron.
Snake-gourd — Trichosanthes.
Snapdragon — Antirrhinum.
Sneeze-wood — Pteroxylon.
Soapberry — Sapindus.
Soapwort — Saponaria.
Sorghum — Andropogon.
Soursop — Anona.
Sow-thistle — Sonchus.
Soy-bean — Glycine.
Spanish broom — Spartium.
Speedwell — Veronica.
Spinach — Spinacia, Tetragonia.
Spindle-tree — Evonymus.
Spurge — Euphorbia.
Spurry — Spergula.
Squill — Scilla.
Squirting cucumber — Ecballium
Stitchwort — Stellaria.
Stock — Matthiola.
Stork's bill — Erodium.
Strawberry — Fragaria.
Strawberry-tree — Arbutus.
Sugar-cane — Saccharum.
Sumac — Rhus.
Sundew — Drosera.

Sunflower — Helianthus.
Sweet basil — Ocimum.
Sweet flag — Acorus.
Sweet potato — Ipomoea.

Tallow-tree — Pentadesma.
Tapioca — Manihot.
Taro — Colocasia.
Tea — Thea.
Teak — Oldfieldia, Tectona.
Teasel — Dipsacus.
Tef — Eragrostis.
Teosinte — Euchlaena.
Thorn-apple — Datura.
Thrift — Armeria.
Thimothy-grass — Phleum.
Toad-flax — Linaria.
Tobacco — Nicotiana.
Tomato — Solanum.
Tragacanth — Astragalus.
Traveller's tree — Ravenala.
Tulip-tree — Spathodea.
Turmeric — Curcuma.
Turnip — Brassica.
Turnsole — Chrozophora.
Turpentine — Abies, Pinus, Pistacia.

Vegetable silk — Various Asclepiadaceae, Strophantus.
Venus' looking-glass — Specularia.

Verek — Acacia.
Vernal grass — Anthoxanthum.
Vervain — Verbena.
Vetch — Vicia.
Vetiver-root — Andropogon.
Violet — Viola.

Wallflower — Cheiranthus.
Walnut — Juglans.
Water-chestnut — Trapa.
Water-cress — Nasturtium.
Water-lily — Nymphaea.
Water-melon — Citrullus.
Water-plantain — Alisma.
Water-tree — Tetracera.
Wheat — Triticum.
White mustard — Sinapis.
Willow — Salix.
Willow-herb — Epilobium.
Winter-cherry — Physalis.
Winter-cress — Barbarea.
Woad — Isatis.
Woodruff — Asperula.
Woodrush — Luzula.
Wormwood — Artemisia.

Yams — Dioscorea.
Yew — Taxus.
Ylang-Ylang — Cananga.

Zachun-oil — Balanites.

ADDITIONS AND CORRECTIONS

(especially from the years 1911 and 1912).

Page VII., after line 21, insert : R. MUSCHLER, A manual flora of Egypt (Berlin, 1912).
„ VIII., after line 13, insert : E. DE WILDEMAN, Etudes sur la flore des districts des Bangala et de l'Ubangi (Bruxelles, 1910).
„ 10, No. 110, for " 83. **Monimiaceae,**" read : Leaves opposite, *Xymalos*, 83. **Monimiaceae.** Leaves alternate, *Plagiostyles*, 122. **Euphorbiaceae.**
„ 19, No. 202, for **"Prrteaceae,"** read : **Proteaceae.**
„ 20, No. 213, omit lines 1 and 2.
„ 35, No. 388, omit lines 1 and 2.
, 79, line 3, read : Genus 1, species 4. West Africa, Madagascar, and Seychelles.
„ 82, No. 21, line 3, add : (Including *Heteranthoecia* Stapf).
„ 84, No. 41, after line 4, insert : Outer glumes convex, without spines. Flowering glume awned. Stigmas feathery.—Species 2. East Africa . **Dignathia** Stapf
„ 85, No. 46, line 2, add : *Rytilix* Raf.
„ 89, No. 84, line 2, add : (Including *Lepturella* Stapf).
„ 92, No. 111, after line 3, insert : Spikes 2-3 together. Spikelets many-flowered. Fruit elliptical. Leaves narrow.—Species 1. Madagascar . **Sclerodactylon** Stapf
„ 100, No. 176, line 2, add : *Weingaertneria* Bernh.
„ 102, No. 195, line 5, add : *Trichoneura* Anders.
„ 104, No. 212, after line 3, insert : Spikelets in head-like panicles. Flowering glumes 5-nerved.—Species 1. East Africa . . . . . **Drake-Brockmania** Stapf
„ 105, No. 222, line 1, add : Axis of the spikelet jointed between and below the flowering glumes.
„ 105, No. 222, after line 1, insert : Flowering glumes 2-cleft, awned, 7-9-nerved, much exceeding the outer glumes. Axis of the spikelet jointed below the flowering glumes only. Spikelets in 1-3 spike-like racemes.—Species 1. East Africa. (Including *Negria* Chiov.) . . . . **Lintonia** Stapf
„ 117, No. 25, line 3, read : (*Hydrosme* Schott). (Plate 12). **Amorphophallus** Blume
„ 118, No. 32, line 4, add : Rudimentary flowers club-shaped. Appendage of the spadix long.
, 118, No. 32, after line 3, insert : Ovules 2. Leaves several, dissected. Rudimentary flowers awl-shaped. Appendage of the spadix short.—Species 1. Egypt.
Helicophyllum Schott
„ 123, No. 6, last line, insert : (Including *Baoutia* A. Chev.)
„ 128, No. 32, after line 3, insert : Capsule opening loculicidally. Flowers in spikes, with bracts. Ovary deeply lobed.—Species 1. South Africa (Cape Colony).
Neodregea C. H. Wright
129, No. 35, lines 2 and 3, omit : " (Including *Neodregea* Wright)."
136, No. 13, line 4, for " Perianth-tube long," read : Perianth-tube short or moderately long, not longer than the segments.
„ 136, No. 13, line 7, omit " (Including *Choananthus* Rendle)."
„ 136, No. 13, after line 7, add : Filaments longer than the anthers. Perianth-tube much longer than the segments. Leaves ovate.—Species 2. Equatorial Africa (Ruwenzori) . . . . **Choananthus** Rendle
„ 146, No. 4, line 3, insert : (Including *Siphonochilus* Wood & Franks).
„ 151, No. 11, line 4, after " *Penthea* Lindl." add : and *Orthopenthea* Rolfe.
„ 151, No. 15, line 3, for " Tropics," read : Tropical and South-east Africa.
„ 155, No. 52, line 3, for " Tropics," read : Tropical and South-east Africa.
„ 158, No. 78, line 4, after " including " insert : *Lemurorchis* Kraenzl.
„ 159, No. 89, omit lines 3 and 4.
„ 171, No. 8, line 2, after " Including " insert : *Diastella* Knight.
„ 176, No. 3, line 6, after " Islands " insert : (*Balaniella* Van Tiegh.).

607

Page 177, No. 1, line 4, for " Species 1 ; Southern West Africa," read : Species 2 ; Southern Central Africa.

„ 179, No. 5, line 5, add : Wings of the fruiting perianth equal.

„ 179, No. 5, at end add : Branches continuous. Disc lobed. Wings of the fruiting perianth unequal.—Species 1. Egypt . . . . . . **Seidlitzia** Bunge

„ 181, No. 18, at end add : Bracteoles united more than half-way up. Stigmas 2. Stem and leaves clothed with stellate hairs.—Species 1. Egypt. **Eurotia** Adans.

„ 184, No. 17, line 3, add : (Including *Centemopsis* Schinz and *Nelsia* Schinz).

„ 184, No. 18, line 3, add : Stigma entire.

„ 184, No. 18, after line 3, add : Stamens 4-5. Stigma 2-cleft. Perianth woolly at base. Undershrubs.—Species 1. East Africa . . . . . **Lopriorea** Schinz

„ 185, No. 20, line 2, add : Leaves opposite.

„ 185, No. 20, after line 2, add : Spurious staminodes none. Leaves alternate. Partial inflorescences consisting of 2-3 fertile and 2-4 spinous sterile flowers. Ovary glabrous.—Species 2. East Africa . . . . . **Neocentema** Schinz

„ 188, No. 4, line 7, for " Species 15," read : Species 25.

„ 189, No. 15, line 4, for " Species 1," read : Species 3.—In the same line omit " Cape Colony."

„ 191, No. 3, *Portulacaria* may be divided into two genera : **Portulacaria** Jacq. (Flowers hermaphrodite. Ovary turgid. Fruit with 3 wings, dry. Species 1.) and **Ceraria** Pearson & Stephens (Flowers polygamous. Ovary compressed. Fruit with 1 wing, finally berry-like. Species 3).

„ 193, No. 9, line 4, for " sepals obtuse " read : style very short.

„ 201, No. 11, line 6, add : including *Bricchettia* Pax.

„ 203, No. 31, line 4, add : (Including *Junodia* Pax).

„ 208, No. 3, omit *Chloropatane* Engl., which belongs to *Erythrococca* Benth. (Euphorbiaceae).

„ 233, No. 7, line 4, add : including *Geaya* Cost. & Poisson.

„ 236, No. 3, line 6, for " Species 1," read : Species 3.

„ 238, No. 11, line 5, add : *Nebelia* Neck.

„ 244, No. 6, line 3, add : (Including *Santaloides* Schellenb.).

„ 244, No. 7, line 2, for " Species 2," read : Species 4.

„ 244, No. 7, line 3, add : (Under *Byrsocarpus* Schum. & Thonn.)

„ 244, No. 7, after line 3, insert : Stem twining. Inflorescence fasciculate. Calyx herbaceous. Anther-halves approximate. Seeds with thick cotyledons.—Species 2. West Africa. . . . . **Roureopsis** Planch.

„ 244, No. 9, line 3, add : (Under *Manotes* Soland.).

„ 246, No. 18, line 4, read : Species 4. West Africa.

„ 249, No. 38, after line 3, insert : Receptacle saucer-shaped, thick. Calyx-lobes 2-3. Petals none. Stamens 16.—Species 1. Equatorial West Africa.

                                             Mildbraediodendron Harms

„ 249, No. 38, line 4, add : Calyx-lobes 4-5. Stamens very numerous.

„ 251, No. 54, line 1, for " Species 10," read : Species 25.

„ 251, No. 54, line 3, add : (Under *Dialium* L.)

„ 252, No. 61, line 2, read : Species 4. Central Africa.

„ 252, No. 61, line 3, add : including *Eriander* Winkl.

„ 253, No. 74, line 1, add : (Under *Cynometra* L.)

„ 253, No. 75, line 2, add : (Under *Cynometra* L.)

, 255, No. 89, last line, read : Species 1. Central Africa. Yields timber and aromatic resin. (Under *Daniella* Benn.) . . . . **Paradaniellia** Rolfe

„ 256, No. 95, line 4, after " pendulous," insert : oblong. Flowers in few-flowered racemes.

„ 256, No. 95, after line 4, add : Petals subequal. Seeds roundish. Flowers subsessile, paniculate.—Species 3. West Africa. (Under *Berlinia* Soland.)

                                             Isoberlinia Craib & Stapf

„ 256, No. 100, line 3, read : Species 8. Central Africa.

„ 256, No. 100, line 4, read : (Including *Cyanothyrsus* Harms) . . **Daniellia** Benn.

„ 256, No. 101, line 4, read : Species 6. Central Africa.

Page 258, No. 117, line 5, for "Species 2," read : Species 4.
 „ 259, No. 125, line 3, for "Species 2," read : Species 5.
 „ 263, No. 160, line 5, add : some are poisonous for cattle.
 „ 265, No. 175, line 1, add : Ovules few. Leaves distinctly stalked, stipulate.
 „ 265, No. 175, after line 3, insert : Keel and style straight. Bracteoles present. Ovules many. Fruit elongate. Leaves sessile or nearly so, exstipulate.—Species 10. South Africa. (Under *Lotononis* L.) . . . . . **Pearsonia** Duemmer
 „ 272, No. 239, line 5, add : other species yield dyes.
 „ 273, No. 242, line 4, after "Balf. f." add : and *Saldania* Sim.
 „ 278, No. 283, line 3, insert : One species has edible fruits and tubers.
 „ 287, No. 359, line 1, add : Standard broad.
 „ 287, No. 359, after line 2, add : Fruit winged. Standard narrow, boat-shaped. Calyx narrowly bell-shaped. Branches of the panicle nodose. — Species 17 Central Africa. (Under *Derris* Lour.) . . . . . . **Leptoderris** Dunn
 „ 288, No. 368, line 1, add : Leaflets without stipels.
 „ 288, No. 368, after line 1, insert : Wings adhering to the keel. Leaflets with stipels. Fruit flat, indehiscent.—Species 4. Central Africa . . . **Ostryoderris** Dunn
 „ 288, No. 374, after line 3, insert : Leaves alternate, not dotted. Fruit compressed.—Species 15. Central Africa. . . . . . **Craibia** Harms & Dunn
 „ 297, No. 21, omit lines 1-3, as *Eriander* Winkl. belongs to *Oxystigma* Harms (Leguminosae).
 „ 299, No. 32, add : Ovary with numerous ovules in each cell. Anthers oblong. Pericarp hard. Leaves with a single leaflet.—Species 1. West Africa.

Aeglopsis Swingle
 „ 300, No. 6, line 3, add : Filaments thread-like. Ovules laterally affixed. Leaflets few.
 „ 300, No. 6, after line 4, insert : Calyx 5-parted. Petals 5, with imbricate aestivation. Filaments broadened below, with a short scale. Style long. Ovules pendulous. Leaflets many, oblong.—Species 1. West Africa . . . **Simarubopsis** Engl.
 „ 300, No. 8, line 3, add : (Under *Mannia* Hook. fil.).
 „ 301, No. 15, *Irvingia* may be divided into two genera : **Irvingia** Hook. fil. (inflorescence axillary, seeds exalbuminous) and **Irvingella** Van Tiegh. (inflorescence terminal, seeds albuminous).
 „ 302, No. 4, line 3, add : Stamens inserted outside the cushion-shaped disc.
 „ 302, No. 4, line 9, add : Stamens inserted on the edge of the disc.
 ,, 302, No. 2, line 4, add : (Including *Katafa* Cost. & Poisson).
 „ 303, No. 4, omit lines 1-4, as *Pynaertia* De Wild. belongs to *Anopyxis* Pierre (Rhizophoraceae).
 „ 304, No. 13, last line, omit "*Bingeria* A. Chev."
 ,, 305, No. 20, for " **Tourraea** " read : **Turraea.**
 „ 305, No. 25, line 3, add : (Including *Bingeria* A. Chev.)
 „ 309, family 121, lines 7 and 13, for "species 75," read : species 120.—Line 7, add : one species has edible fruits.
 „ 309, family 122, line 6, omit " (Including *Daphniphyllaceae*)."
 „ 310, No. 8, line 5, for "Species 10," read : Species 20.
 „ 311 and 312, for No. 14—23 substitute the following :
   14. Calyx splitting into 5 equal segments. Disc indistinct or wanting. Herbs or undershrubs, rarely shrubs 15
     Calyx splitting into 2-4 more or less unequal segments. Shrubs or trees . 16
   15. Styles two-cleft. Rudimentary pistil absent in the male flowers. Plants with stellate hairs.—Species 7. Northern and tropical Africa. Some are poisonous or yield dyes and medicaments. "Turnsole." (*Tournesolia* Scop.)

Chrozophora Neck.
     Styles many-cleft. Rudimentary pistil present in the male flowers. Herbaceous plants with simple hairs.—Species 10. Tropics. Several species yield fibre. . . . . **Caperonia** St. Hil.
   16. Petals of the male flowers united below 17
     Petals of the male flowers free 18
   17. Styles two-cleft. Leaves palminerved. Climbing shrubs.—Species 1. West

Africa. Yields fibre. . . . . . .   **Manniophyton** Muell. Arg.
Styles 3-8-cleft. Leaves penninerved.—Species 12. West Africa. (Under
Crotonogyne Muell. Arg.) . . . . .   **Neomanniophyton** Pax & Hoffm.

18.   Young branches, leaves, and inflorescence clothed with scales 19
       Young branches, leaves, and inflorescence clothed with hairs or glabrous . 20

19.   Stamens 7-15. Receptacle of the male flowers with 5 glands, glabrous within
       them. Male inflorescence spicate.—Species 2. Equatorial West Africa.
                                                                  Crotonogyne Muell. Arg.
       Stamens 20-30. Receptacle of the male flowers with 10 glands, also glan-
       dular within them. Male inflorescence paniculate.—Species 1. Equatorial
       West Africa . . . .   **Cyrtogonone** Prain

20.   Fruit a drupe. Disc of the female flowers obscure or reduced to small glands.
       Stamens 8-20. Anthers attached by the base. Trees with stellate, rarely
       with simple hairs. Leaves palminerved. Flowers in terminal cymes or
       panicles.—Species 2. Cultivated and naturalized in the tropics. They
       yield timber, gum-lac, tanning bark, dye-stuffs, and edible oily seeds (candle-
       nuts) . . . .   **Aleurites** Forst.
       Fruit a capsule. Disc of the female flowers ring- or cup-shaped. Anthers
       attached by the tip or the back, sometimes near the base. Flowers in
       racemes, rarely in panicles, but then leaves penninerved. Glabrous or
       simple-haired shrubs or trees 21

21.   Receptacle of the male flowers glandular on the whole surface, but without
       separate glands. Stamens 20-30. Anther-halves pendulous from the
       connective. Flowers in axillary racemes.—Species 1. Islands of Fernando-
       Po and St. Thomas. (Under *Agrostistachys* Dalz.)
                                                        Pseudagrostistachys Pax & Hoffm.
       Receptacle of the male flowers with separate glands. Anther-halves attached
       by the back. Flowers in terminal racemes or panicles 22

22.   Stamens 20-30.—Species 3. West Africa. (Including *Fournaea* Pierre)
                                                                          Grossera Pax
       Stamens 8-12. Flowers in racemes 23

23.   Petals of the female flowers shorter than the calyx. Sepals of the female
       flowers free. Flowers dioecious.—Species 2. East Africa. (Under *Tannodia*
       Baill.) . . . .   **Holstia** Pax
       Petals of the female flowers exceeding the calyx. Sepals of the female
       flowers united at the base.—Species 2. East Africa . **Tannodia** Baill

Page 313, No. 30, line 7, add: (Including *Pseudotragia* Pax).
  „   313, No. 31, line 5, for " Species 20," read: Species 12.
  „   315, No. 48, omit lines 1-3, as *Pseudotragia* Pax belongs to *Plukenetia* L.
  „   316, No. 55, line 3, after " medicine " add: (Including *Discoclaoxylon* Pax & Hoffm.)
  „   316, No. 56, line 7, add: (Including *Chloropatane* Engl.).
  „   316, No. 57, after line 6, insert: Disc of the female flowers formed of 6-8 scales.
        Styles recurved, undivided. Stamens 7. Calyx 5-partite. Flowers in panicles.
        —Species 1. West Africa . . . .   **Discoglypremna** Prain
  „   316, No. 61, line 3, add: Bracts not forming an involucre. Petals membranous.
        Plants clothed with stellate hairs. (Under *Mildbraedia* Pax).
  „   316, No. 61, after line 3, insert: Flowers dioecious. Bracts forming an involucre.
        Petals leathery. Plants clothed with simple hairs.—Species 1. West Africa
        (Cameroons) . . . .   **Chlamydojatropha** Pax & Hoffm.
  „   317, No. 66, at end, add: Stamens numerous. Ovary 1-celled. Stigma 1, entire.
        Flowers in racemes, dioecious.—Species 1. West Africa. The seeds yield oil.
        (Under *Daphniphyllum* Blume) . . . .   **Plagiostyles** Pierre
        Stamens numerous. Ovary 3-celled. Stigmas 3, entire. Flowers in racemes,
        dioecious.—Species 1. West Africa. (Under *Plukenetia* L.) . **Hamilcoa** Prain
  „   317, No. 70, line 5, read: (*Excoecariopsis* Pax, under *Excoecaria* L.)
                                                              Spirostachys Sond.
  „   318, No. 72, line 7, add: (Under *Sapium* P. Browne or *Sebastiania* Spreng.)
  „   318, No. 74, line 3, for " Species 3," read: Species 6.

Page 318, No. 74, line 4, for " yields rubber," read : and three other species yield rubber.
  „ 318, No. 74, after line 7, insert : Flowers in panicles, which on the male plants are composed of fascicles, dioecious. Sepals 4-5, united half-way up in the male flowers. Disc present. Leaves undivided.—Species 1. Equatorial West Africa.

Klaineanthus Pierre

  „ 318, No. 75, line 5, add : (Including *Neochevaliera* Beille).
  „ 318, No. 76, line 3, add : (Tribe PHYLLANTHEAE).
  „ 319, omit No. 81, as *Junodia* Pax belongs to *Anisocycla* Baill. (Menispermaceae).
  „ 319, omit No. 82, as the African *Daphniphyllum* belongs to *Plagiostyles* Pierre.
  „ 319, omit No. 85, as *Bricchettia* Pax belongs to *Cocculus* L. (Menispermaceae).
  „ 319, No. 87, line 1, add : or nearly so.
  „ 320, No. 89, line 4, for " *Megabaria* Pierre," read : (Including *Megabaria* Pierre)

Spondianthus Engl.

  „ 320, omit No. 92, as *Neochevaliera* Beille belongs to *Chaetocarpus* Thwait.
  „ 321, No. 99, line 2, omit " Mosambic."
  „ 321, No. 104, omit lines 3-5.
  „ 322, No. 107, line 2, for " Species 4," read : Species 12.
  „ 322, No. 107, line 3, add : (Including *Staphysora* Pierre).
  „ 322, No. 109, line 2, add : (Under *Thecacoris* Juss.)
  „ 322, No. 109, after line 3, insert : Disc divided into 5 glands. Styles 4, short, entire. Flowers monoecious. Trees. Stipules lanceolate.—Species 1. West Africa.

Apodiscus Hutchinson

  „ 322, for No. 111, substitute the following :—

111. Bracts of the male flowers in 3 series, the intermediate in the shape of a cup. Disc of the female flowers adnate to the perianth.—Species 2. West Africa. (Under *Megabaria* Pierre) . . . . . **Protomegabaria** Hutchinson
Bracts of the male flowers solitary. Disc of the female flowers free from the perianth . . . . 111, b.
111, b. Fruit entire, 1-celled. (See 107) . . . . . **Maesobotrya** Benth.
Fruit lobed, 3-celled. (See 94) . . . .**Thecacoris** Juss.

  „ 322, No. 113, line 3, add : (Under *Drypetes* Vahl).
  „ 322, No. 114, line 4, add : (Under *Drypetes* Vahl).
  „ 323, No. 123, line 5, for " Species 2," read : Species 5.
  „ 324, No. 2, line 2, add : (Under *Notobuxus* Oliv.).
  „ 326, No. 5, omit line 5.
  „ 327, No. 12, line 6, for " Species 20," read : Species 30.
  „ 328, omit No. 20, as *Spondianthus* belongs to Euphorbiaceae.
  „ 329, No. 27, line 7, for " Species 30," read : Species 50.
  „ 341, No. 51, line 2, after " capsular," add : septicidal.
  „ 341, No. 51, after line 5, insert : Disc annular, with 10 teeth on the inside. Stamen. 8. Ovary 3-celled. Fruit capsular, loculicidal. Embryo spirally twisted. Leaves pinnate.—Species 1. West Africa . . . . **Anoumabia** A. Chevs
  „ 344, No. 6, line 4, add : including *Tzellemtinia* Chiov.
  „ 346, line 9, for " 200," read : 250.
  „ 346, No. 3, line 2, after " Inflorescences," add : nearly always.
  „ 346, No. 3 line 5, omit " mostly."
  „ 346, No. 4, line 6, for " 150," read : 200.
  „ 349, No. 3, line 1, omit " Ovules 2 in each ovary-cell."
  „ 349, No. 3, line 2, add : (Under *Christiania* DC.).
  „ 349, No. 9, line 6, add : (Under *Duboscia* Bocq.).
  „ 349, No. 10, line 4, add : under *Desplatzia* Bocq.
  „ 355, No. 11, line 4, add : (Tribe HUAEAE).
  „ 384, No. 5, for " **Ammania** " read : **Ammannia.**
  „ 386, at top, for " LECTYHIDACEAE " read : LECYTHIDACEAE.
  „ 388, No. 9, line 1, add : (Including *Pynaertia* De Wild.).
  „ 399, No. 9, last line, add : (*Raimannia* Rose).
  „ 403, No. 12, after line 4, insert : Secondary ribs thick, rounded, unarmed. Seeds slightly grooved on the inner face, somewhat compressed from front to back.— Species 1. Northern East Africa (Eritrea) . . . **Stephanorossia** Chiov.

Page 406, No. 37, after line 5, insert : Pericarp not much thickened. Ribs thread-shaped. Fruit with a broad commissure. Oil-channels 4-5 in each furrow.—Species 2. Central Africa . . . . **Afrosison** Wolff

,, 409, No. 53, line 2, after " furrows," insert : and sometimes under the ribs.

,, 409, No. 53, after line 2, insert : Marginal ribs of the mericarps thickened, corky. Oil-channels solitary under each dorsal rib, 3 under each marginal rib. Calyx indistinctly toothed. Petals straight or nearly so.—Species 1. Abyssinia. (Under *Peucedanum* L.) . . . . **Erythroselinum** Chiov.

,, 413, No. 92, after line 2, insert : Mericarps with 5 broad and thick ribs. Oil-channels solitary under each rib, none at the commissure. Calyx-teeth mucronate. Undershrubs.—Species 1. South-west Africa (Nama-land) **Marlothiella** Wolff

,, 413, No. 92, line 4, add : Oil-channels in the furrows and at the commissure.

,, 414, No. 93, at end, add : Petals yellow or brown, notched. Herbs.—Species 1. Equatorial East Africa . . . . **Volkensiella** Wolff

,, 418, No. 5, line 8, for " Species 10," read : Species 20.

,, 421, No. 3, after line 3, insert : Fertile stamens as many as the petals, 8. Calyx falling off very early, excepting the persistent base of the tube.—Species 1. West Africa. Yields timber . . . . **Dumoria** A. Chev.

,, 421, No. 3, line 4, add : Calyx persisting or falling off as a whole.

,, 421, No. 3, line 7, omit " *Dumoria* A. Chev."

,, 434, No. 15, after line 4, insert : Corolla-segments overlapping to the right. Disc wanting. Ovules numerous. Leaves with axillary glands.—Species 1. West Africa. . . . . **Farquharia** Stapf

,, 444, No. 22, line 6, insert : rarely shrubs.

,, 449, No. 59, last line, add : including *Folotsia* Cost. & Bois and *Voharanga* Cost. & Bois.

,, 454, No. 99, after line 1, insert : Corona simple, of 10 lobes. Calyx without glands. Corolla deeply divided, with spatulate segments.—Species 1. Northern East Africa. **Spathulopetalum** Chiov.

,, 463, No. 5, line 2, after " Shrubs," read : Species 2. Socotra and German South-west Africa. (Subfamily **WELLSTEDIOIDEAE**.)

,, 472, No. 8, line 6, for " 4-cleft," read : 4-5-cleft.

,, 472, No. 9, after line 3, insert : Lower lip of the corolla deeply 3-cleft, the median lobe slightly concave, the lateral ones narrow. Calyx 2-lipped ; the upper lip entire, the lower 4-toothed.—Species 1. South-east Africa. **Thorncroftia** N. E. Brown

,, 473, No. 15, line 2, insert : Including *Bouetia* A. Chev.

,, 473, No. 19, line 4, read : Species 2. Tropics.

,, 473, No. 19, line 5, omit " including *Iboza* N. E. Brown."

,, 480, No. 64, after line 5, insert : Corolla subequally 5-cleft ; tube exserted. Stamens 4, about equal in length. Flowers very small, indistinctly dioecious.—Species 12. Central and South-east Africa. (Under *Moschosma* Reichb.) **Iboza** N. E. Brown

,, 482, No. 10, line 2, for " Species 25 " read : Species 40.

,, 510, No. 66, after line 2, insert : Corolla-tube funnel-shaped. Flowers in lateral spikes. Bracts narrow; bracteoles broad. Leaves elliptical.—Species 1. Equatorial West Africa . . . . **Leiophaca** Lindau

,, 554, No. 93, line 2, for " Species 20," read : Species 30.

,, 556, No. 108, line 4, after " winged " add : Inner involucral bracts short, scale-like.

,, 556, No. 108, at end, add : Stem not winged. Inner involucral bracts long, bristle-like. Receptacle at first flat.—Species 1. North-west Africa. **Lifago** Schweinf. & Muschl.

,, 562, No. 186, after line 2, insert : Pappus wanting. Heads in corymbs.—Species 1. South-east Africa. . . . . **Humea** Sm.

,, 570, No. 258, line 2, for " Species 1," read : Species 4.

Plate 12, for *Hydrosme grata* Schott, read : *Amorphophallus gratus* (Schott) N. E. Brown.

,, 138, last line, for " plant " read : branch.

INDEX

OF LATIN NAMES OF FAMILIES AND GENERA

Synonyms are printed in *Italics*.

BRISTOL: BURLEIGH LTD., AT THE BURLEIGH PRESS.